Missile Design and System Engineering

Missile Design and System Engineering

Eugene L. Fleeman
Lilburn, Georgia

AIAA EDUCATION SERIES

Joseph A. Schetz, Editor-in-Chief
Virginia Polytechnic Institute and State University
Blacksburg, Virginia

Published by the
American Institute of Aeronautics and Astronautics, Inc.
1801 Alexander Bell Drive, Reston, Virginia 20191-4344

American Institute of Aeronautics and Astronautics, Inc., Reston, Virginia

1   2   3   4   5

Library of Congress Cataloging-in-Publication Data

Fleeman, Eugene L.
  Missile design and system engineering/Eugene L. Fleeman; Joseph A. Schetz,
editor-in-chief. – 1st ed.
    p. cm. – (AIAA education series)
    ISBN 978-1-60086-908-2
1. Tactical missiles – Design and construction. 2. Astronautics–Systems engineering. I.
Schetz, Joseph A. II. Title

UG1310.F578 2012
623.4'519 – dc23

2012011953

To Mary

CONTENTS

FOREWORD

We are delighted to present *Missile Design and System Engineering* by Eugene L. Fleeman, formerly of Georgia Tech. His previous books *Tactical Missile Design* (first and second editions) were very well received in the aerospace community. This new book has updated material and expanded coverage in missile design as well as new material in missile system engineering. We anticipate that it will be equally well received. The book has nine chapters and ten appendices in more than 800 pages covering all of the topics relevant to this subject. One appendix has homework problems and another contains multiple choice quizzes. In addition, there is a missile design spreadsheet and an aerospace engineering outreach project (Soda Straw Rocket Science) for middle school and high school students.

Eugene Fleeman is superbly qualified to write this book because of his long and productive career in the missile area. His command of the material is excellent, and he is able to organize and present it in a clear manner.

The AIAA Education Series aims to cover a very broad range of topics in the general aerospace field, including basic theory, applications, and design. The philosophy of the series is to develop textbooks that can be used in a university setting, instructional materials for continuing education and professional development courses, and also books that can serve as the basis for independent study. Suggestions for new topics or authors are always welcome.

Joseph A. Schetz
Editor-in-Chief
AIAA Education Series

PREFACE

The material in this book is oriented toward the needs of aerospace engineering students, engineering professors, system analysts, system engineers, and others working in the areas of missile systems and missile technology development. Readers will gain an understanding of missile design, missile technologies, launch platform integration, missile system measures of merit, and the missile system development process. One objective of writing this book is to provide a reference textbook for the aerospace engineering curriculum of universities. Although the missile community is large, receives a significant amount of funding, and has many technical and system problems to address, currently there are only a few universities that offer courses in missile design and system engineering. This introduction to missiles will hopefully spark the interest of young engineers to make a career in the missile community. A second objective is to provide a summary reference for the missile community.

What You Will Learn

- Key drivers in the missile design and system engineering process
- Critical tradeoffs, methods, and technologies in aerodynamic, propulsion, structure, seeker, warhead, fuzing, and subsystems sizing to meet flight performance and other requirements
- Launch platform-missile integration
- Robustness, lethality, guidance, navigation and control, accuracy, observables, survivability, reliability, and cost considerations
- Missile sizing examples for missile systems and missile technologies
- Missile system and missile technology development process

A system-level, integrated method is provided for the missile configuration design, development, and analysis activities in addressing requirements such as cost, performance, and risk. Configuration sizing examples are presented for rocket-powered, ramjet-powered, and turbojet-powered baseline missiles. System engineering considerations include launch platform integration constraints. Typical values of missile parameters and the characteristics of current operational missiles are discussed as well as the enabling subsystems and technologies for missiles and the current/projected state-of-the-art of missiles. Seventy videos illustrate missile development activities and missile performance.

The text is a summary of information that I have collected during my forty-seven years of experience in the development of missile systems and their technologies. It distills the knowledge that I have gathered into a method for the design and system engineering of missiles. Generally used are simple, closed-form, analytical, physics-based equations, to provide insight into the primary driving parameters. Closed-form analytical equations are a throwback to the way missile design and system engineering was conducted more than forty years ago. Although computers with modern numerical methods are more precise, they provide less insight into the underlying drivers. The more sophisticated computer-based methods are also often susceptible to modeling errors, software programming errors, and data input errors. The text also provides example calculations of rocket-powered, ramjet-powered, and turbojet-powered baseline missiles, typical values of missile parameters, examples of the characteristics of current operational missiles, discussion of the enabling subsystems and technologies of missiles, and the current/projected state-of-the-art of missiles. A verbal problem review of the material in each chapter is provided at the end of the chapter. When possible, the figures of this text have self-standing content. The objective is to reinforce the written text and to provide self-standing presentation slides for the course instructor. A disadvantage of this approach is that the figures are often cluttered and require a longer time to digest.

In recent years we have seen increased usage of missile systems for military operations. The accuracy of missiles compared to unguided weapons is a driver for their increased usage. Missiles are expected to have an even larger share of military operations in the future. A key contributor to the increased effectiveness is the advancement in technology. Examples of advancement in missile system effectiveness include improved accuracy, range, firepower, maneuverability, lethality, ease of use, and adverse weather capability.

A historical example of the value of guided weapons is the attack on the Thanh Hoa Bridge in Vietnam. For more than six years, a total of 871 aircraft sorties dropped unguided bombs but failed to close the bridge. However, the first operational application of laser-guided bombs on 13 May 1972 resulted in direct hits on the supporting piers, closing the bridge. Eleven aircraft had been lost in the 871 previous sorties. No aircraft were lost in the four sorties using precision-guided munitions. A more recent example is the use of precision-strike weapons in Desert Storm, Kosovo, and Enduring Freedom. In the 1991 Operation Desert Storm, 9% of the strike weapons were guided weapons. Eight years later in Kosovo 35% of the strike weapons were guided weapons. In the 2002 Operation Enduring Freedom, 69% of the strike weapons were guided weapons. Another example of the evolution of surface-to-air missiles: In the first combat demonstration of beyond visual range (BVR) kill, Sea Dart had seven kills in the 1982 Falkland Islands War, including BVR kills against long range, high-altitude aircraft. Twenty years later, during Operation Iraqi Freedom (2003), PAC-3 successfully demonstrated hit-to-kill missile defense capability by destroying threat ballistic missiles. Missile defense capability is also now provided by exo-atmospheric hit-to-kill missile defense systems such as SM-3 and THAAD.

The organization of the material in this text is as follows. Chapter 1 gives an overview of the missile design and system engineering process. Chapter 2 discusses aerodynamic design, aerodynamic system engineering considerations, and the aerodynamic technologies of low aspect ratio wing and wingless configurations. Conceptual design, system engineering considerations, and technologies for rocket, ramjet, and turbojet propulsion are included in Chapter 3. Chapter 4 addresses missile conceptual design, system engineering weight considerations, and technologies for missile weight reduction. Topics include weight prediction, aerodynamic heating prediction, technologies for light weight materials and subsystems, and low-cost manufacturing processes. Conceptual design prediction methods and system engineering considerations for missile flight trajectory range, velocity, time-to-target, maneuverability, and off boresight are given in Chapter 5. Chapter 6 provides measures of merit and launch platform integration/system engineering considerations. It includes conceptual design methods and technologies in the areas of robustness, warhead lethality, fuzing, miss distance, carriage and launch observables, other survivability considerations, reliability, cost, firepower, store separation and carriage, and storage/carriage environmental considerations. Conceptual design sizing examples and computer aided sizing tools are presented in Chapter 7. Sizing examples are for a rocket-powered missile, a ramjet-powered missile, turbojet-powered missile, and a soda straw rocket. The soda straw rocket sizing example illustrates the use of Pareto analysis, house of quality, and Design of Experiment (DOE) methods to facilitate the sizing process. An example of an electronic spreadsheet sizing tool is also presented. Chapter 8 discusses the missile system and technology development process. Finally, a summary of this text and lessons learned in missile development are given in Chapter 9.

The appendices in the back of the book have a set of homework problems/classroom exercises, an example of a request for proposal for a missile design study, a list of nomenclature, a list of acronyms, a table for conversion of English to metric units, an example of a syllabus for a graduate course curriculum in Missile Design and System Engineering, and multiple choice quizzes.

References of the data and methods used in this text and a bibliography of other reports and web sites that are related to missiles are provided in the back of the book.

Supporting materials for this book include the following:

- A Microsoft PowerPoint presentation of the Missile Design and System Engineering short course that is based on this book. The slides are in color. Embedded with the slides are seventy videos illustrating missile design considerations, development testing, manufacturing, and technologies.
- A Tactical Missile Design spreadsheet in Microsoft Excel format. The spreadsheet models the configuration sizing methods of this text.
- Six missile design case studies. These were conducted by Georgia Tech graduate students over the years 1999 to 2005.
- A presentation of projects entitled Soda Straw Rocket Science. It is an aerospace engineering outreach program for elementary and middle school students.

I would like to thank the faculty and students at the Georgia Institute of Technology for their support for the earlier *Tactical Missile Design* textbook that preceded this textbook. Special appreciation is expressed to Dr. Dimitri Mavris, Director of the Georgia Tech Aerospace Systems Design Laboratory.

I would like to also express my appreciation to the following persons who have supported my work in the areas of missile design, advanced weapon concepts, advanced weapons technologies, and missile system development: Bill Lamar, Charles Westbrook, and Don Hoak of the United States Air Force Research Laboratory, and Thad Sandford of the Boeing Company Phantom Works.

Finally, I would appreciate receiving your questions, comments and corrections on this text, as well as any data, photographs, drawings, videos, examples, or references that you may offer. Please e-mail these to: GeneFleeman@msn.com, or visit the web site: http://genefleeman.home.mindspring.com.

Eugene L. Fleeman
Lilburn, Georgia
June 2012

Chapter 1 | Introduction/Key Drivers in the Missile Design and System Engineering Process

- Overview of Missile Design and System Engineering Process
- Examples of System-of-Systems Integration
- Unique Characteristics of Missiles
- Key Aerodynamic Configuration Sizing Parameters
- Example of Pareto Analysis
- Examples of Processes to Establish Mission Requirements
- Benefits of Baseline Missile Data

1.1 Introduction

The primary emphasis of this text is physics-based methods and technologies for missile conceptual design and system engineering (Fig. 1.1). Aerodynamic configuration sizing is conducted to develop the configuration geometry and the dimensions of the missile. The output of aerodynamic configuration sizing includes the missile diameter, length, nose geometry, stabilizer size and geometry, and the control surface size and geometry. Most of the configuration sizing methods of this text are physics-based methods, to allow analytical sizing of the missile configuration. Areas that also receive primary emphasis because of their strong impact on aerodynamic configuration sizing are aerodynamic stability and control, aerodynamic flight performance, propulsion, structure, and weight. The primary area of emphasis in system engineering for this text is the integration of the missile with the launch platform, because of its strong impact on the missile aerodynamic configuration sizing. Other areas that receive secondary emphasis are warhead and fuzing; seeker, guidance, navigation, and control; miss distance; cost; power supply and actuators; and survivability, safety, and reliability.

Area	Emphasis
Aero configuration sizing	●
Aero stability and control	●
Aero flight performance	●
Propulsion	●
Structure	●
Weight	●
System engineering	●
Warhead and fuzing	○
Seeker, guidance, navigation, and control	○
Miss distance	○
Cost	○
Power supply and actuators	○
Survivability, safety, and reliability	○
Electronics	—
Software	—

● Primary emphasis   ○ Secondary emphasis   — Tertiary emphasis

Fig. 1.1 Emphasis of this text is on physics-based conceptual design and system engineering.

These are addressed to a level that is consistent with their impact on the aerodynamic configuration sizing and system engineering. Finally, tertiary emphasis is given to the areas of electronics and software. Although electronics and software are also important at the system level, they generally have lesser impact on the aerodynamic design configuration, which is the primary emphasis of this text.

1.2 Missile Characteristics Comparison

Missiles are different from other flight vehicles, such as combat aircraft (e.g., fighter aircraft). As a result, missiles are a technical specialty in their own right. Missiles are self-propelled guided weapons that can be characterized as either tactical or strategic. Distinctions between tactical and strategic missiles include the type of warhead (conventional warhead versus nuclear), flight range (relatively short range versus long), cost (relatively low-cost versus high), inventory (large inventory versus small), and frequency of use (often used in combat versus hopefully never required to be used).

Because tactical missiles are the subject of a larger design activity than strategic missiles, the focus of this text is on the design, development, and system engineering of tactical missiles.

Figure 1.2 is a state-of-the-art (SOTA) comparison of tactical missile characteristics with the current SOTA of strategic missiles. Examples are shown where each is driving technology. Note that the drivers are often different, requiring different design emphasis and technologies. The missile drawings are from Ref. [1].

Compared to other flight vehicles such as manned aircraft, missiles usually have higher maneuverability. Missile lateral maneuverability of 30g+ and longitudinal acceleration of 30g+ have been demonstrated. Notable examples of tactical missiles with high acceleration and maneuverability include the AGM-88 HARM and the AA-11 Archer missiles, respectively. In general, tactical missiles are somewhat more maneuverable than strategic missiles. As a comparison, the longitudinal acceleration and maneuverability of HARM and Archer are somewhat greater than that of Ground Based Interceptor (GBI). However, the old strategic Sprint missile demonstrated lateral maneuverability of 100g and longitudinal acceleration of 400g.

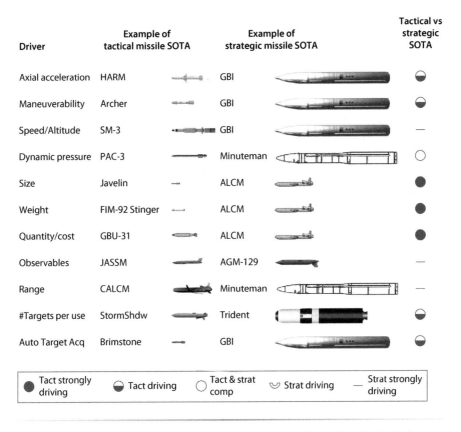

Driver	Example of tactical missile SOTA		Example of strategic missile SOTA		Tactical vs strategic SOTA
Axial acceleration	HARM		GBI		◒
Maneuverability	Archer		GBI		◒
Speed/Altitude	SM-3		GBI		—
Dynamic pressure	PAC-3		Minuteman		○
Size	Javelin		ALCM		●
Weight	FIM-92 Stinger		ALCM		●
Quantity/cost	GBU-31		ALCM		●
Observables	JASSM		AGM-129		—
Range	CALCM		Minuteman		—
#Targets per use	StormShdw		Trident		◒
Auto Target Acq	Brimstone		GBI		◒

● Tact strongly driving	◒ Tact driving	○ Tact & strat comp	◡ Strat driving	— Strat strongly driving

Fig. 1.2 Examples of tactical versus strategic missile drivers. Tactical missiles are often driven by cost while strategic missiles are often driven by range.

An example of a high speed exo-atmospheric missile for theater missile defense is the SM-3 Standard missile. The strategic GBI for US national missile defense has even higher speed and altitude, providing midcourse defense against threat intercontinental ballistic missiles (ICBMs).

The maximum dynamic pressure loading on a missile, which drives structure design, is often very high compared to that of other flight vehicles, such as manned aircraft. Examples of missiles with high dynamic pressure are the PAC-3 tactical missile and the Minuteman III ICBM reentry vehicle. As a comparison, they have comparable dynamic pressure.

Tactical missiles in general are smaller size and lighter weight than strategic missiles. As a comparison, the FIM-92 Stinger and Javelin man-portable tactical missiles are much smaller and lighter weight than the Air Launched Cruise Missile (ALCM), which is a relatively small strategic missile.

Related to quantity produced and cost, tactical missiles are produced in large numbers and are more cost-driven than strategic missiles. Development cost is lower for tactical missiles and the difference in unit production cost is even more dramatic. An example is the GBU-31 JDAM guided bomb, with a unit cost on the order of $20,000 compared to ALCM, with a unit cost on the order of $1,000,000.

Although many tactical cruise missiles such as JASSM have low radar cross section (RCS), strategic missiles may have lower RCS because of greater emphasis on survivability. Examples are SRAM, AGM-129, and ICBM reentry vehicles. A tactical cruise missile is often more limited by launch platform integration, which may limit the amount of low RCS configuration shaping and tailoring that is practical with a span constraint.

Strategic missiles by their nature are typically longer range than tactical missiles. Although the tactical version of the AGM-86 Conventional Air Launched Cruise Missile (CALCM) has a flight range that can exceed 700 nm, the strategic Minuteman III ICBM has much longer (intercontinental) range.

In the area of target kill capability, precision strike missiles have become more effective in recent years, with a single target kill probability approaching one and a capability for multiple target kills. The Storm Shadow/Scalp is an example of an efficient precision strike tactical missile. Precision strike missiles have high accuracy and are capable of dispensing submunitions, exhibiting high firepower. As a comparison, the Trident strategic missile has multiple independent target reentry vehicles (MIRVs), but it is operationally limited by treaties in the number of allowable MIRVs.

Finally, tactical precision strike missiles such as Brimstone and smart powered submunitions such as the Low Cost Autonomous Attack Submunition (LOCAAS) have demonstrated a capability for automatic target recognition (ATR). Autonomous target acquisition by precision strike missiles is a relatively immature technology that will improve in the future with new technologies such as multi-mode and multi-spectral seekers that may be aided by real time two-way data links. Because of operational constraints and a concern for countermeasures, strategic offense missiles (cruise missiles, intercontinental ballistic missiles) do not have automatic target acquisition. However, automatic target acquisition is used by the strategic defense GBI as well as tactical missile defense systems such as SM-3.

As a summary comparison of tactical missiles with strategic missiles, the state-of-the-art in maneuverability, size, weight, cost, and autonomous target acquisition is usually driven by tactical missiles while the SOTA in high altitude, high speed, and long range is usually driven by strategic missiles.

Because of the relatively large number of tactical targets, the largest number of missiles that are produced are tactical missiles. As shown in Fig. 1.3, based on the data of Ref. [2], the top twenty-three US currently operational missiles produced during the years 1973 to 2011 are tactical missiles, accounting for 99.6% of the US total missile production (1,051,731 of 1,055,629 total). Because of their relatively large production requirement, tactical missiles are more driven by production cost than strategic missiles such as cruise missiles and ICBMs.

As an illustration of the functions of the subsystems of a missile, Fig. 1.4 compares a missile to a human boxer. The statue of William Perry, a 19th century boxing champion from Tipton, England, illustrates the analogy of

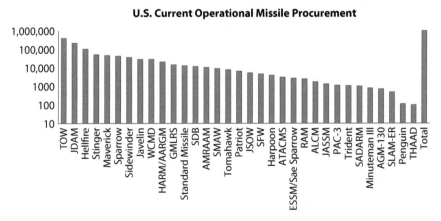

U.S. Current Operational Missile Procurement

Note: Top 23 US operational missile procurements are tactical missiles, with 99.6% of the US 1973–2011 total missile procurement (1,051,731 tactical missiles versus 3,898 strategic missile [ALCM, Trident, Minuteman III]).

Fig. 1.3 Tactical missiles are produced in relatively large quantity. (Source: Nicholas, T. and Rossi R., "U.S. Missile Data Book, 2011," Data Search Associates, Nov 2010.)

Fig. 1.4   Analogy of missile subsystems to a boxer.

the boxer with a typical missile (Python 4). As a comparison: the boxer's eyes (which track the target) correspond to the missile seeker, the boxer's brain (which provides commands to the muscles) corresponds to the missile electronics, the boxer's fist (which puts kinetic energy on the target) corresponds to the missile warhead, the boxer's forearm (which directs his fist) corresponds to the missile flight control, the boxer's upper arm (which propels his fist) corresponds to the missile propulsion, and the boxer's legs (which provide stabilization) correspond to the missile stabilizers.

Figure 1.5 illustrates the subsystems and packaging of another typical missile, the Javelin man-portable anti-armor missile. Note the high packaging density of the subsystems of this small-sized missile. As a comparison the typical density of a missile is about 60% that of concrete (0.05 lbm/in^3 versus 0.08 lbm/in^3). Compared to other flight vehicles, such as manned aircraft, missiles have much higher density. As a result, it is usually more important to minimize the volume of missile subsystems than to minimize the missile weight. This is especially true for rocket-propelled missiles, less so for air-breathing missiles such as turbojets and ramjets. The subsystems shown in the figure are the missile seeker dome, seeker, warhead, electronics, warhead (precursor, main), propulsion (rocket motor), and flight control. The subsystems are packaged longitudinally within the cylindrical section, with each subsystem behind another. Also shown are the airframe structure of the body, wing surfaces, and tail surface stabilizers/flight control.

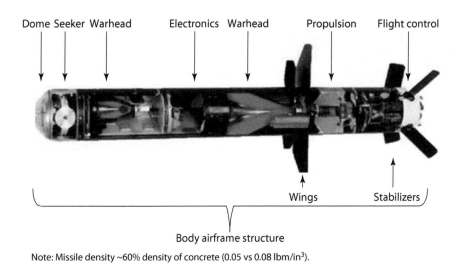

Note: Missile density ~60% density of concrete (0.05 vs 0.08 lbm/in³).

Fig. 1.5   Typical missile subsystem packaging is longitudinal with high density.

Figure 1.6 is a summary of the configuration sizing parameters empha-sized in this text. These are: flight conditions, nose fineness, diameter, pro-pulsion sizing of the propellant/fuel type and weight, wing geometry/size, stabilizer geometry/size, flight control geometry/size, missile length, and thrust profile. Flight condition parameters that are most important in the design and system engineering of missiles are angle of attack (α), Mach number (M), and altitude (h). For the aerodynamic configuration, the missile diameter (d) and length (l) have a first-order effect on characteristics

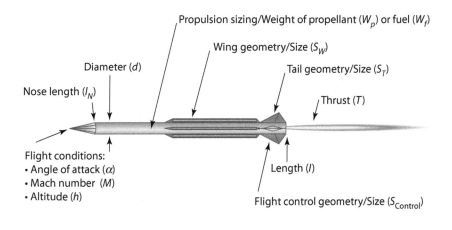

Fig. 1.6   Configuration sizing parameters emphasized in this text.

such as missile drag, subsystem packaging available volume, launch platform integration, seeker and warhead effectiveness, and body bending. Another configuration driver is nose fineness (l_N/d), an important contributor to the drag of supersonic missiles. Nose fineness also affects seeker performance, available propellant length, and missile observables. Another example is missile propellant/fuel type and weight (w_p, w_f), which drive flight performance range and velocity. The aerodynamic configuration wing geometry and size (S_W) are often set by maneuverability requirements and aerodynamic efficiency. Tail/stabilizer geometry and size (S_T) are often established by the static margin requirements for missile flight static stability. In the flight control area, the geometry and size of the flight control surfaces determine the maximum achievable angle of attack and the resulting maneuverability. Finally, the thrust profile determines the missile velocity time history.

1.3 Conceptual Design and System Engineering Process

Figure 1.7 shows the typical conceptual design and system engineering process that I have used for missiles. Conceptual design and system engineering is a fast, creative, and iterative process, requiring a number of design iterations to achieve a balance of emphasis from the diverse inputs and outputs. The conceptual design and system engineering team should ideally consist of unbiased individuals with open minds to the broad envelope of system design possibilities. The major tasks of conceptual design and system engineering are

1. Mission/scenario/system definition
2. Weapon system requirements, trade studies, and sensitivity analysis
3. Physical integration of the missile with the launch platform
4. Weapon concept design synthesis
5. Technology assessment and technology development roadmap

The initial design process begins with a general definition of the mission/scenario/system. The input is a "requirements pull" of the desired capability from the military customer. The customer's mission requirements are usually not changed during the design study. However, sometimes a customer may change a mission requirement if it is found to be too demanding, too expensive, or the "technology push" of potential technology availability shows that a new high payoff technology can be better utilized by changing the mission requirement. A house of quality may be used to relate the customer requirements and their relative weighting to the engineering design characteristics.

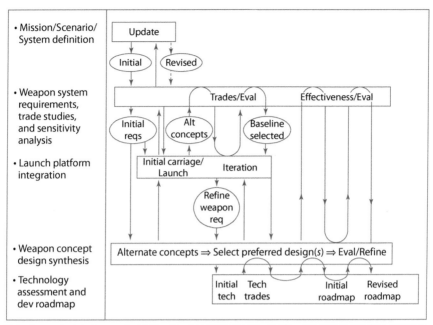

- Mission/Scenario/ System definition
- Weapon system requirements, trade studies, and sensitivity analysis
- Launch platform integration
- Weapon concept design synthesis
- Technology assessment and dev roadmap

Note: Conceptual design requires fast cycle, ~3 to 9 months. House of quality used to translate customer requirements to engineering characteristics. Design of experiments used to efficiently evaluate the broad range of design solutions.

Fig 1.7 Conceptual design and system engineering should be unbiased, creative, and iterative—with rapid evaluations.

The second task—weapon system requirements, trade studies, and sensitivity analysis task—provides better definition of the high level requirements on the missile such as range, time to target, and other measures of merit. This task is oriented toward an operations analysis of a system-of-systems, including system engineering considerations such as the command, control, and communication (C3) targeting. The high level requirements that were initially provided by the military customer are an input to a system-level computer modeling that provides higher definition and allocation of the requirements. The system-level computer models may be characterized as campaign, raid, or engagement models. In a campaign model many different types of systems are interacting over a relatively long simulated time interval (typically days to weeks). It includes complex system interactions such as the interaction of the missile with the other elements of the system and the system logistics. The next level model is typically a raid model, which has multiple platforms engaging multiple targets during a single raid. It includes combat tactics and doctrine. Finally, the third and most technically detailed model is an engagement model, which is an engineering model of a single launch platform and a single missile engaging a single target or threat. All of these models should be as transparent as possible, to minimize the possibility of "cooking the assumptions/input data" to support a preconceived desired output.

The third task, physical integration of the missile with the launch platform, provides constraints such as: length, span, and weight constraints, missile/launch platform physical and electrical (avionics/vetronics) interface; and the carriage environment (temperature, vibration, loads, etc.). This system engineering task is oriented toward system integration.

The fourth task, weapon concept design synthesis, is the most iterative and arguably the most creative. The missile is resized and reconfigured through an iterative process, in which the missile characteristics are evaluated. Characteristics include the aerodynamic shape, propellant or fuel type and weight, flight trajectory range, time to intercept, maneuverability, seeker detection range, accuracy, lethality, reliability, and cost. For example, the tail stabilizers and flight control surfaces may be resized for improved stability or maneuverability. Another example is adding propellant or fuel to match the flight range requirement. As the design matures and becomes better defined through iteration, the number of alternative solutions is reduced from a broad range of possibilities to a smaller set of preferred candidates that are more reasonable and cost effective. More in-depth information is provided for the design subsystems as the design matures.

Finally, the fifth task (technology assessment) further defines the subsystems and selects the best technologies from the candidate approaches. The technology trades lead to a set of preferred, enabling technologies that provide the "technology push" for the design. An output of this task is a technology roadmap that documents the development plan for maturing the enabling technologies.

Conceptual design and system engineering requires a fast cycle, with the duration for a conceptual design and system engineering activity typically about three to nine months. The products of the missile design and system engineering activity include: refined mission/scenario definitions, system-of-systems definition of the missile requirements, the interface of the missile with other system elements such as targeting, launch platform compatibility compliance, advanced missile concepts, identification of the enabling technologies, and a technology roadmap.

A good conceptual design and system engineering study should have about three design reviews that are attended by the customer and other experts from outside the conceptual design organization. For a typical six month conceptual design and system engineering design study, the recommended reviews are: 1) a kick-off system requirements review (SRR) conducted during the first month to ensure that the customer requirements are understood by the conceptual design and system engineering team, 2) a preliminary design review (PDR) conducted after about three months to obtain customer concurrence on a recommended baseline missile concept, and 3) a critical design review (CDR) to obtain customer approval of the final results of the study.

Figure 1.8 further illustrates the process that I have used for missile conceptual design synthesis and system engineering. Based on mission requirements, an initial baseline from an existing missile with similar propulsion is established. It is a starting point to expedite the design convergence. Advantages of a baseline missile include the prior consideration of balanced system engineering for the subsystems and the use of an accurate benchmark based on existing test data (e.g., wind tunnel data). Changes are made in the baseline missile aerodynamics, propulsion, subsystems, weight, and flight trajectory to reflect the new requirements of the new missile concept. The new conceptual design is evaluated against its flight performance requirements (e.g., range, time to target, maneuver footprint). The aerodynamics portion of the conceptual design process is an investigation

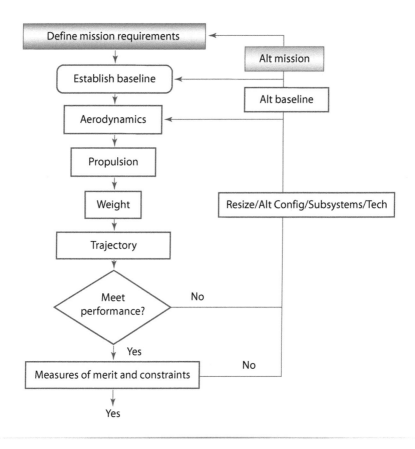

Fig 1.8 Conceptual design and system engineering require creative, rapid, and iterative evaluations.

of alternatives in configuration geometry. The output of the aerodynamics calculation is then inputted to the propulsion system design to begin the sizing of the propulsion system. Propulsion sizing includes providing sufficient propellant or fuel to meet the range and time-to-target requirements. The next step is to estimate the weight of the new missile with its modified aerodynamics and propulsion. Much of this activity is focused on structural design, which is sensitive to changes in flight performance. Following the weight sizing, flight trajectories are computed for the new missile. The range, terminal velocity, maneuverability, and other flight performance parameters are then compared with the mission flight performance requirements. If the missile does not meet the flight performance requirements, it is resized and reiterated. After completing a sufficient number of iterations to meet the flight performance requirements, the next step is evaluating the new missile against the other measures of merit and system engineering/constraint requirements. Other measures of merit and constraints include robustness (e.g., seeker performance in adverse weather), lethality, miss distance, observables, survivability, reliability, cost, and launch platform integration. If the missile does not meet the requirements, the design is changed (alternative configuration, alternative subsystems, alternative technologies) and resized for the next iteration and evaluation.

A synthesized missile will differ from the starting point baseline in several respects. For example, the wing area may have been resized to meet the maneuverability and/or cruise requirements. The tail area may have been resized to meet static margin and maximum trim angle of attack requirements. The rocket motor or the ramjet/turbojet engine may have been modified to improve its efficiency at the selected design altitude or Mach number. Additionally, the length of the propulsion system may have been changed to accommodate additional propellant/fuel necessary to satisfy flight range requirements. The design changes are reflected in revisions to the mass properties, configuration geometry, thrust profile, and flight trajectory for the missile. Typically, three-to-six design iterations are required before a synthesized missile converges to meet the flight performance requirements. These require rapid prediction/evaluation to achieve a robust, near-optimum design convergence within the limited time typically available for conceptual design and system engineering (e.g., 3–9 months).

Although a missile design may meet performance requirements and satisfy the other measures of merit and system engineering (e.g., launch platform constraints), it is not necessarily an optimum missile design. It is good design practice to evaluate as many design alternative concepts as possible within the time duration of the design study. Design of Experiment (DOE) is an efficient approach to evaluate the broad set of alternatives. DOE also expedites the follow-on process of design optimization.

Following conceptual design and system engineering, the missile is further refined in preliminary design. Preliminary design activities include parameter optimization and ground tests.

1.4 System-of-Systems Considerations

Examples of system-of-systems considerations in missile design and development are illustrated in Fig. 1.9. The first example (Fig. 1.9a) is a typical US carrier strike group consisting of an aircraft carrier (with combat aircraft launch platforms such as F-18 fighter aircraft and SH-60 Seahawk helicopters) and other missile launch platforms such as cruisers, destroyers, and submarines. Note the large number of air-to-surface (JASSM, SLAM, Harpoon, JSOW, JDAM, Maverick, HARM, GBU-10, GBU-5, Penguin, Hellfire), air-to-air (AMRAAM, Sparrow, Sidewinder), surface-to-air (SM-3, SM-6, SM-2, Sea Sparrow, RAM), and surface-to-surface missiles (Tomahawk, Harpoon). Because targets are different in their characteristics such as range, altitude, speed, signature, and hardness, many different types of missiles are required. To evaluate whether a new missile would be a beneficial asset to a carrier strike group requires a system-of-systems evaluation to determine the cost effectiveness of a new missile. In the bottom right section of Fig. 1.9a is a video illustrating

a) **Example: Typical US Carrier Strike Group, with Complementary Missile Launch Platforms/Load-out**

  • Air-to-surface: JASSM, SLAM, Harpoon, JSOW, JDAM, Maverick, HARM, GBU-10, GBU-5, Penguin, Hellfire

  • Air-to-air: AMRAAM, Sparrow, Sidewinder

  • Surface-to-air: SM-3, SM-6, SM-2, Sea Sparrow, RAM

  • Surface-to-surface: Tomahawk, Harpoon

Video

Fig 1.9a Missile development should be conducted in a system-of-systems context.

b)   **Example: US Missile Defense System**

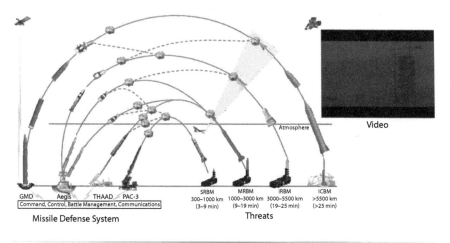

Fig 1.9b   Missile development should be conducted in a system-of-systems context. (Source: http://www.mda.mil/)

the large number of systems in a carrier strike group. This video may be viewed on the web site that is in support of this text.

The second example of system-of-systems consideration is shown in Fig. 1.9b. It illustrates the current system-of-systems considerations of the US missile defense system. Command, control, and battle management communications are drivers in the effectiveness of the missile defense interceptor. Overhead satellites and other early warning sensors (e.g., early warning ground radar, sea based X-band radar, Aegis, airborne infrared sensor) provide launch warning and a target track file for action within a multi-tier layered defense. For intercepting ICBMs, the GBI provides a long range/high altitude intercept. Midcourse intercept of IRBMs and MRBMs may be conducted exo-atmospherically by Aegis/SM-3 or THAAD. Finally, a relatively short range endo-atmospheric terminal defense is provided by PAC-3.

The system engineering emphasis of this text primarily addresses the following areas:

- Missile system requirements flow-down/specification
- Missile system integration
- Missile system modeling/system analysis
- Missile flight simulation

Missile system requirements flow-down/specification is a systematic, system level allocation of the missile system requirements to the missile subsystem requirements and finally to the missile component requirements. As an example, the system level flow-down of the missile kill probability requirement will impact the flow-down of requirements for missile miss distance, missile flight control bandwidth, and missile flight control actuator stall torque. Because kill probability may be achieved through either a larger warhead lethal range or a smaller missile miss distance, missile miss distance requirement is a tradeoff with warhead lethal range. Following the flow-down requirement for missile miss distance, the next step is to further flow-down the requirements to the factors that drive miss distance. Factors that drive miss distance include missile seeker bandwidth, missile radome error slope, and missile flight control bandwidth. Following a flow-down requirement for the flight control bandwidth that is consistent with the miss distance requirement, the next step is to further flow-down the requirements to the factors that drive flight control actuator bandwidth. As an example, high bandwidth for flight control may be achieved through factors such as lower hinge moment on the flight control surfaces and higher stall torque capability for the flight control actuators. This example illustrated a system requirements flow-down allocation of requirements from the high kill probability requirement to a lower level, individual component specification (flight control actuator stall torque).

Missile system integration is the primary system engineering activity that is addressed in this text. An example of system integration is defining the missile maximum length that is compatible with a length constraint of the missile launcher.

Missile system modeling/system analysis develops models and conducts system analysis of the dynamic subsystems, such as the guidance and control system, to improve their performance. An example is determining the best guidance gain for minimum miss distance.

Missile flight simulation is a sophisticated time-marching computer simulation that calculates the missile flight trajectory. The missile aerodynamics, propulsion, seeker, guidance, navigation, and flight control are modeled. Target modeling includes the target flight trajectory, target signature, background scene/clutter, and countermeasures by the target. Flight environment modeling includes the atmosphere and terrain. Missile flight simulation may be all digital (without hardware) or it may have selected hardware-in-loop (HWL) such as the missile seeker, autopilot, other electronics, gyros, accelerometers, and actuators for greater fidelity of the simulation.

As stated previously, the primary system engineering emphasis of this text is in the area of system integration. System integration considerations include a) environmental, b) launch platform constraints, and c) targeting. Figure 1.10 illustrates missile system integration considerations.

Environmental considerations (such as the maximum/minimum allowable temperature) include storage, transportation, and launch platform carriage.

* Environment
  * Storage ....
  * Transportation ....
  * Carriage ....
* Launch platform constraints
  * Geometry
  * Weight
  * Loading/Launcher/Launch
  * Safety/Observables/Survivability
  * Avionics/Vetronics
* Targeting
  * Command, Control, Communications, Computers, Intelligence, Surveillance, and Reconnaissance (C4ISR)
  * Fire control system

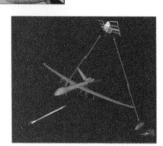

Fig. 1.10   Missile design and system engineering requires system integration.

Launch platform constraints include geometry constraints such as the maximum length and maximum span; maximum weight; loading the missile on the launch platform, launcher dynamics, and the launch separation dynamics; safety; survivability, including launch observables; and avionic/vetronics compatibility.

Targeting includes command, control, communications, computers, intelligence, surveillance, and reconnaissance (C4ISR) systems. C4ISR information is received by the launch platform and then acted upon, enabling missile launch.

1.5   Examples of State-of-the-Art Missiles

Figures 1.11 and 1.12 provide examples of current state-of-the-art missiles for the mission areas of air-to-air, air-to-surface, surface-to-surface, and surface-to-air. The missiles are drawn relative to a scale of 10 ft. Reference 1 was a source for missile drawings. Each mission area has examples of short, medium, and long/very long range missiles. Short range missiles operate within visual range engagements (less than about 3 nm), have rocket propulsion, and are usually guided by an electro-optical (e.g., infrared, laser) seeker, with seeker lock-on before launch. Medium range missiles can operate beyond visual range (BVR), with engagements out to the earth's horizon (about 20 nm), have rocket propulsion, and are usually

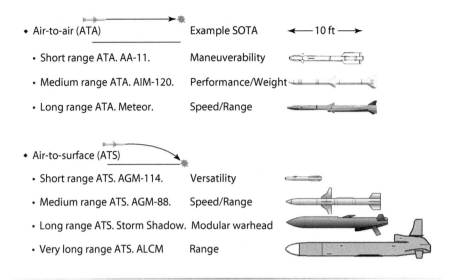

* Air-to-air (ATA)   Example SOTA   ←— 10 ft —→
  * Short range ATA. AA-11.   Maneuverability
  * Medium range ATA. AIM-120.   Performance/Weight
  * Long range ATA. Meteor.   Speed/Range

* Air-to-surface (ATS)
  * Short range ATS. AGM-114.   Versatility
  * Medium range ATS. AGM-88.   Speed/Range
  * Long range ATS. Storm Shadow.   Modular warhead
  * Very long range ATS. ALCM   Range

Fig. 1.11 Examples of air-launched missile missions/types/attributes. (Permission of Missile Index. Copyright 1997©Missile Index. All rights reserved.)

guided by a radar seeker. Most medium range missiles also have an inertial reference system and are capable of seeker lock-on after launch. Many also have a data link, for update commands after launch. Long range missiles have ranges greater than the earth's horizon. Long range tactical missiles

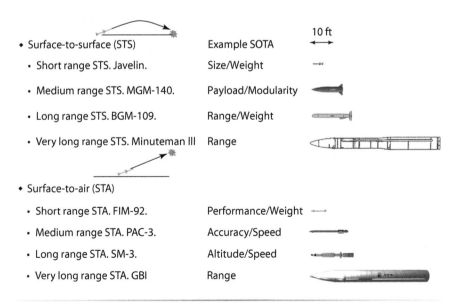

* Surface-to-surface (STS)   Example SOTA   10 ft
                                                            ←→
  * Short range STS. Javelin.   Size/Weight
  * Medium range STS. MGM-140.   Payload/Modularity
  * Long range STS. BGM-109.   Range/Weight
  * Very long range STS. Minuteman III Range

* Surface-to-air (STA)
  * Short range STA. FIM-92.   Performance/Weight
  * Medium range STA. PAC-3.   Accuracy/Speed
  * Long range STA. SM-3.   Altitude/Speed
  * Very long range STA. GBI   Range

Fig. 1.12 Examples of surface-launched missile missions/types/attributes. (Permission of Missile Index. Copyright 1997©Missile Index. All rights reserved.)

have combined inertial/seeker guidance, and are capable of seeker lock-on after an inertial midcourse fly-out to the vicinity of the target. Most also have a data link (one-way or two-way) for command inertial update and battle damage indication (BDI). Long range strategic strike missiles rely on inertial guidance while long range strategic missile defense missiles have multi-mode (inertial/command/seeker homing terminal) guidance. Long range missiles have rocket, ducted rocket, ramjet, or turbojet propulsion, depending upon their speed and range requirements. Ballistic missiles are rocket powered, while cruise missiles have air-breathing propulsion.

Three examples are shown in the top of Fig. 1.11 of the state-of-the-art drivers of air-to-air missiles. The selected drivers are short range air-to-air maneuverability, medium range air-to-air range performance with light weight, and long range air-to-air range. An example of a short range air-to-air missile is the highly maneuverable and large off boresight AA-11 Archer. An example of a medium range air-to-air missile is the high performance with relatively light weight AIM-120 AMRAAM. Finally, an example of a long range air-to-air missile that also has high average velocity/relatively short time to target is the ducted rocket Meteor.

Examples are shown in the bottom of Fig. 1.11 of the state-of-the-art drivers for air-to-surface missile types. The selected drivers are short range air-to-surface versatility, medium range air-to-surface speed, long range air-to-surface warhead modularity, and very long range air-to-surface range. The examples are a short range air-to-surface missile represented by the versatile AGM-114 Hellfire, a medium range missile represented by the high speed/short time to target radar defense suppression AGM-88 HARM, a long range tactical missile represented by the precision strike modular warhead Apache/Storm Shadow/Scalp and the very long range strategic ALCM.

Next, examples are shown in the top of Fig. 1.12 of surface-to-surface missiles that illustrate the state-of-the-art drivers. The selected drivers are short range surface-to-surface size/weight, medium range surface-to-surface payload/modularity, long range surface-to-surface range with relatively light weight, and very long range surface-to-surface range. The example missiles are: the man-portable Javelin anti-tank missile, the medium range modular payload (e.g., dumb submunitions, smart submunitions, unitary surface warhead, penetrator warhead) MGM-140 ATACMS, the long range standoff cruise missile BGM-109 Tomahawk, and the very long range intercontinental ballistic missile (ICBM) Minuteman III.

Finally, surface-to-air missile state-of-the art drivers are shown in the bottom of Fig. 1.12. The selected drivers are short range surface-to-air weight, medium range surface-to-air accuracy with high speed, long range surface-to-air altitude with high speed, and very long range surface-to-air range. The missiles shown are the short range high performance with light weight FIM-92 Stinger, medium range hit-to-kill with high speed PAC-3, the long range high altitude with high speed SM-3 Standard Missile, and the very long range GBI.

1.6 Aerodynamic Configuration Sizing and System Engineering Parameters

Aerodynamic configuration sizing and system engineering parameters have a high impact on missile requirements. Figure 1.13 is an assessment of the relative impact of aerodynamic configuration sizing and system engineering parameters on flight performance measures of merit (e.g., weight, range, maneuver footprint, time to target). Also shown is the impact of aerodynamic configuration sizing and system engineering parameters on other measures of merit (e.g., robustness, lethality, miss distance, observables, survivability, cost), as well as their impact on constraints (e.g., launch platform integration weight, length, and span constraints).

The aerodynamic configuration sizing and system engineering parameters that are addressed in this text are listed on the left side of the figure. These are: missile nose fineness, diameter, length, wing geometry/size, stabilizer geometry/size, flight control geometry/size, propellant/fuel, thrust profile, and flight conditions (angle of attack, Mach number,

Aero configuration Sizing/System Engineering parameter	Aero measures of merit			Other measures of merit						Constraint
	Weight	Range/Maneuver	Time to target	Robustness	Lethality	Miss distance	Observables	Survivability	Cost	Launch platform
Nose fineness	●	●	●	○	●	●	●	●	○	○
Diameter	●	●	●	○	●	◒	○	○	●	●
Length	●	●	◒	○	◒	◒	○	○	●	●
Wing geometry/Size	●	●	◒	○	●	●	◒	◒	—	●
Stabilizer geometry/Size	◒	●	○	○	●	●	◒	◒	—	●
Flight control geometry/Size	◒	●	○	○	●	●	◒	◒	○	●
Propellant/Fuel	●	●	●	○	◒	◒	◒	●	○	◒
Thrust profile	◒	◒	●	○	◒	◒	●	●	◒	○
Flight conditions (α, M, h)	●	●	●	●	●	●	●	●	●	○

● Very strong   ◒ Strong   ○ Moderate   — Relatively low

Fig. 1.13   Aero configuration sizing/system engineering has high impact on missile mission requirements.

altitude). Note from the figure that the above parameters have strong/very strong impact on missile requirements in the areas of weight, range, maneuverability, and time to target. The aerodynamic configuration sizing parameters also have a moderate-to-strong impact in the areas of lethality, miss distance, observables, survivability, and launch platform integration.

A Pareto analysis is useful in identifying the relative impact of design parameters. The example of Fig. 1.14 is the sensitivity of missile flight range to the primary parameters used in calculating flight range. The example is based on the rocket baseline (Sparrow-type) missile maximum flight range sensitivity for a nominal launch (Mach 0.7, 20k ft altitude) and end-of-flight termination (Mach 1.5). This is the first sizing example of Chapter 7.

Note that only four parameters (propulsion specific impulse, propellant weight, zero-lift drag coefficient, and drag-due-to-lift) contribute 85% of the sensitivity in maximum flight range. Based on this information, if the designer wishes to increase the maximum flight range of the rocket baseline missile, these are the parameters that should be emphasized. It is noted that some parameters may be easier to change than others. For example, it may be relatively easy to increase missile propellant weight to provide increased flight range if the missile is not constrained in either length or diameter. However, it is much more difficult to increase solid propellant specific impulse (I_{SP}) to provide an increase in flight range. Because of safety limitations, it is difficult to provide a meaningful increase in I_{SP} of solid propellant rockets.

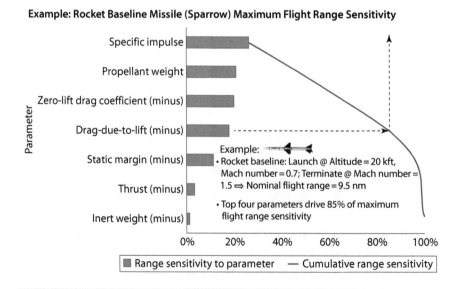

Example: Rocket Baseline Missile (Sparrow) Maximum Flight Range Sensitivity

Fig. 1.14 Pareto effect: only a few parameters are drivers for each measure of merit.

1.7   Example of Alternatives in Establishing Mission Requirements

Figure 1.15 is an example of alternative approaches in establishing future missile mission requirements. It illustrates an assessment of alternative approaches for precision strike of time critical targets. The assessment includes the approaches that are used today by current systems, as well as a projection of capabilities that may be used in the future for new missile systems. Three measures of merit are assumed in comparing future precision strike missiles with the current systems. These are cost per shot, number of launch platforms required, and the effectiveness against time-critical targets (TCTs). For the current systems, two approaches are used: 1) penetrating aircraft, with relatively short range subsonic precision guided munitions or short range missiles and 2) standoff platforms (ships, submarines, or aircraft) using subsonic cruise missiles. As shown, penetrating aircraft with subsonic precision guided munitions have an advantage of low cost per shot, about $20,000. However, the experience in Desert Storm showed that because of the limited number of available penetrating aircraft, there is a limited capability to counter TCTs such as theater ballistic missiles (TBMs). Another current approach, using standoff platforms such as ships, submarines, and large aircraft outside the threat borders requires fewer launch platforms, resulting in lower logistics costs. However, standoff platforms with subsonic cruise missiles (e.g., Tomahawk, CALCM, JASSM) are also ineffective against TCTs.

Alternatives for precision strike of time critical targets	Measures of merit		
	Cost per shot	Number of launch platforms required	Time critical target (TCT) effectiveness
Future systems			
• Standoff platforms/hypersonic missiles	○	●	◖
• Overhead loitering UCAVs/hypersonic missiles	◖	◖	●
• Overhead loitering UCAVs/light weight PGMs	●	○	◖
Current systems			
• Penetrating aircraft/subsonic PGMs	●	—	—
• Standoff platforms/subsonic missiles	○	●	—
● Superior ◖ Good ○ Average — Poor			

Note: C4ISR targeting state-of-the-art provides sensor-to-shooter/weapon connectivity time of less than 2 m and target location error (TLE) of less than 1 m for motion suspended target.

Fig. 1.15   Example of assessment of alternatives to establish requirements for a future mission.

Also shown in the figure are future missile system alternatives for precision strike of time critical targets. Technology development work is under way in all three of the areas; the best approach has yet to be demonstrated. One approach is based on a standoff platform, with an aircraft, ship, or submarine standing off outside the threat country border. Hypersonic long-range precision strike missiles would provide broad coverage, holding a large portion of the threat country at risk. This approach is attractive because only a small number of launch platforms are required and there is good effectiveness against TCTs. Based on current technology programs, the cost of future hypersonic missiles is projected to be comparable to that of current cruise missiles.

Another potential alternative approach is to use overhead loitering unmanned combat air vehicles (UCAVs) armed with smaller hypersonic missiles. The number of UCAVs required is dependent upon the speed and range of their on-board missiles and the loiter altitude. Although loitering at high altitude tends to improve UCAV survivability and increases the missile range, it has a disadvantage of reduced available payload weight/firepower. This approach would probably provide the fastest response time against TCTs, because of the shorter required flight range of the missile.

A third approach is overhead, loitering UCAVs with advanced light weight precision guided munitions such as the Small Diameter Bomb (SDB). Again, a design consideration is the loiter altitude required for survivability versus the weapon payload. This approach would have the lowest cost per shot, but would also require a larger number of UCAVs.

An enabling synergistic capability to counter TCTs is the application of near-real-time, accurate targeting from either overhead satellite or overhead unmanned air vehicle (UAV) sensors. A command, control, communication, computers, intelligence, surveillance, reconnaissance (C4ISR) network could support near-real-time and high accuracy targeting of time critical targets. The C4ISR network could be used by all types of launch platforms (e.g., fighter aircraft, bombers, helicopters, UCAVs, ships, submarines, ground vehicles). Illustrated in Fig. 1.16 are examples of a ground station, overhead satellite sensors and satellite relays, and the overhead UAV sensor platform elements of the assumed C4ISR architecture. The assumed C4ISR could have a capability for a target location error (TLE) of less than 1 m ($1\ \sigma$) of a motion suspended target and a sensor-to-shooter/weapon connectivity time of less than 2 min ($1\ \sigma$). A two-way data link from the launch platform to the missile will allow in-flight target updates and battle damage indication/battle damage assessment (BDI/BDA). An approach for a light weight/low volume missile-to-satellite or UAV data link is a phased array antenna. A phased array antenna can be configured for conformal mounting on the missile airframe.

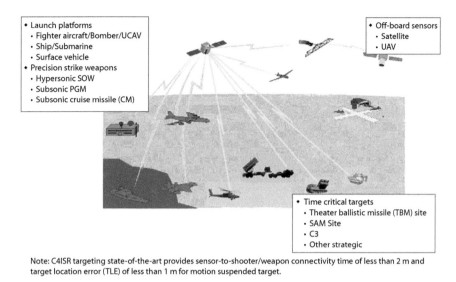

• Launch platforms
  • Fighter aircraft/Bomber/UCAV
  • Ship/Submarine
  • Surface vehicle
• Precision strike weapons
  • Hypersonic SOW
  • Subsonic PGM
  • Subsonic cruise missile (CM)

• Off-board sensors
  • Satellite
  • UAV

• Time critical targets
  • Theater ballistic missile (TBM) site
  • SAM Site
  • C3
  • Other strategic

Note: C4ISR targeting state-of-the-art provides sensor-to-shooter/weapon connectivity time of less than 2 m and target location error (TLE) of less than 1 m for motion suspended target.

Fig. 1.16 C4ISR satellites and UAVs have high effectiveness for time critical target cueing.

Figure 1.17 is an illustration of system-of-systems analysis. The example is a system analysis to develop mission requirements for precision strike. A comparison is made of a subsonic cruise missile (SCM) versus a high speed cruise missile (HSCM). In the initial activity, requirements are defined for the targeting time of the two types of missiles. In the example both missiles rely on C4ISR providing the target location in near real time, with a fast response capability for launch. The second system analysis activity (shown in the lower left section of the figure) develops a solution matrix of the missile time-to-target versus the missile average speed. Shown in the figure are three assumptions of a relatively short range R1 for standoff against a relatively small country (e.g., North Korea), medium range standoff R2, and long range standoff R3 against a relatively large country (e.g., Iran). Based on the knee of the curve of standoff range versus speed, an average speed and the type of propulsion system (turbojet versus ramjet) is selected. Note that an advantage of a turbojet missile is that for a target that is not time critical, it can cruise efficiently at subsonic Mach number. For a time critical target, a turbojet missile could also have the capability to cruise at supersonic Mach number. An advantage of a ramjet missile is the capability to cruise at even higher (hypersonic) Mach number against a time critical target. Because of treaty range limit of less than 500 km for a tactical ballistic missile, a long range ballistic missile with rocket propulsion is not an allowable option. Following this task, a third activity is initiated, involving tradeoffs of an efficient flight

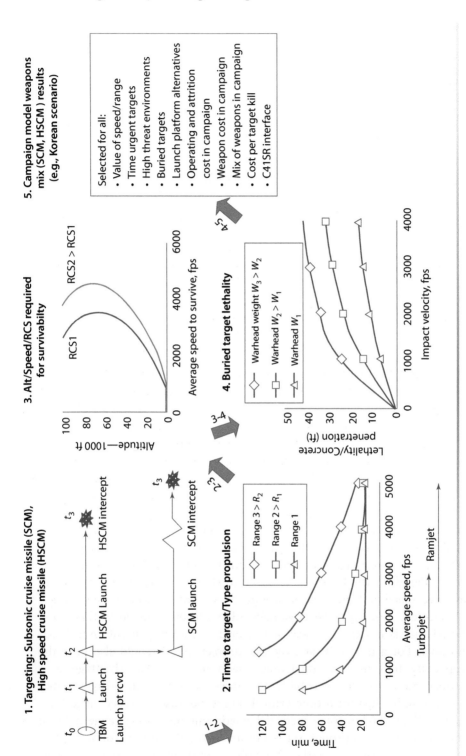

Fig. 1.17 Example of system-of-systems analysis to develop future cruise missile requirements.

attitude versus the level of reduced observables required for survivability. In the fourth activity (lower right section of the figure) a tradeoff is made of the missile lethality. In the example the impact velocity required for penetration of a buried target is evaluated as a function of warhead weight. Finally, a system-of-systems analysis campaign modeling activity is initiated (upper right section of the figure) to derive the weapon system-of-systems requirements such as the best mix of subsonic cruise missiles with high speed cruise missiles for a representative scenario (e.g., North Korean scenario). Measures of merit include the value of speed and range, capability against time-urgent targets, survivability in a high threat environment, effectiveness against buried targets, launch platform alternatives (e.g., ship, aircraft, submarine), operating and attrition cost during the assumed campaign, cost of the number of weapons used during the campaign, mix of weapons (e.g., high speed cruise missile, subsonic cruise missile, shorter range weapons), cost per target kill, and the requirements for the C4ISR interface.

Figure 1.18 is another illustration of the impact of mission requirements on missile design. It shows an example of technological surprise driving immediate mission requirements. The example is mission requirements for short range air-to-air missiles. A comparison is made of the older technology AIM-9L Sidewinder with the year 1987 technological surprise of the newer technology from the highly maneuverable Archer AA-11/ R-73 missile. As a result of the technological surprise of the AA-11, there was a sudden mission requirement for the US to develop the AIM-9X missile.

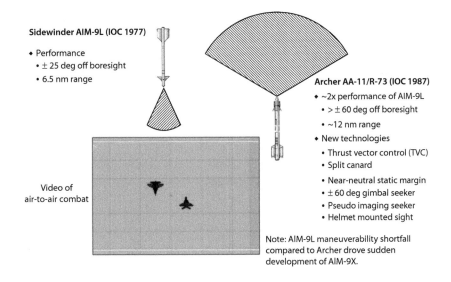

Fig. 1.18 Example of technological surprise driving immediate mission requirements.

Shown on the left side of Fig. 1.18 are the nominal off boresight and flight range capability of the AIM-9L Sidewinder. The initial operational capability (IOC) for AIM-9L was the year 1977. The performance of the AIM-9L is about $+/-25$ deg off boresight and approximately 6.5 nm range. Contrasting with AIM-9L is a more recent missile, the Archer AA-11/R-73. The Archer is described in the right section of the figure. The Archer has a more recent IOC, 1987. Its performance is about $+/-60$ deg off boresight and 12 nm range. New technologies developed for the Archer missile included thrust vector control (TVC), split canard, near-neutral static margin, $+/-60$ deg gimbaled seeker, a pseudo imaging seeker based on a rosette scan, and integration with a helmet mounted sight. Archer also has forward vanes that weathercock, providing information on the missile angle of attack. In summary, Archer has higher maneuverability, greater off boresight, and longer range than AIM-9L.

Also shown at the bottom of Fig. 1.18 is a video illustrating the off boresight advantage of a highly maneuverable missile such as Archer versus a relatively low maneuverable missile such as AIM-9L. In the video, large off boresight conditions and intensive pilot activities are required for short range air-to-air "dog fight" combat. A highly maneuverable missile such as Archer can be launched at much larger off boresight than a low maneuverable missile such as AIM-9L, allowing an earlier launch in a short range air-to-air engagement. Because an Archer-type missile has a superior short range air-to-air capability, an older, relatively low maneuverability aircraft that uses a highly maneuverable missile such as Archer may be able to defeat a more modern, highly maneuverability aircraft that has an older, lower technology missile such as AIM-9L. The shortfall of AIM-9L maneuverability compared to the Archer was an immediate driver in the sudden development of AIM-9X. Like the Archer AA-11/R-73, AIM-9X has high maneuverability (through TVC and near-neutral static margin) and large off boresight (through a large gimbal angle seeker and integration with a helmet mounted sight). In addition, AIM-9X has a high resolution imaging infrared seeker, for improved accuracy and resistance to countermeasures.

1.8 Use of a Baseline Missile

Missile conceptual design and system engineering is a creative and iterative process that requires a rapid evaluation of alternatives. Alternative configurations, alternative subsystems, and alternative technologies are evaluated in sizing the missile. As shown in Fig. 1.19, following the definition of mission requirement, a baseline missile is selected. For the purpose of this text, three alternative baselines are available for conceptual design, a rocket powered missile based on the AIM-7 Sparrow, a ramjet

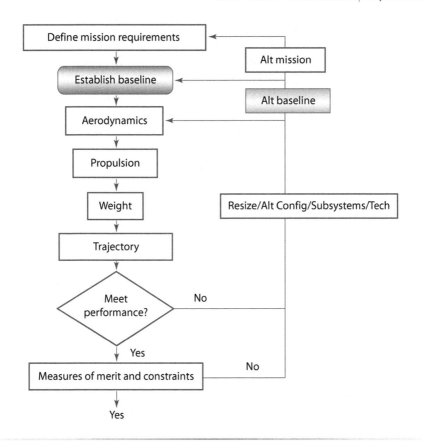

Fig. 1.19 Conceptual design and system engineering require creative, rapid, and iterative evaluations.

powered missile based on the Advanced Strategic Air Launched Missile (ASALM), and a turbojet powered missile based on Harpoon. Detailed information on the baseline missiles is provided in Chapter 7.

Using a baseline missile to initiate the design process has benefits that include a faster design process and a more accurate design. Because a baseline missile is a real missile that is anchored with test data, it allows corrections to simple conceptual design methods, such that they can be used with reasonable accuracy. Another benefit is the existing documentation and the configuration control of a baseline missile that provide traceability between cause and effect as the conceptual design and system engineering process is conducted. A third benefit is system engineering has already been applied to the baseline missile, providing a benchmark for balanced subsystems. A fourth benefit is the start-up time for conceptual design is greatly reduced by using a baseline missile. The default initial values for the conceptual design missile are the baseline missile. A fifth benefit is sensitivity trends for the baseline missile indicate changes that would provide an improved design. However, note that a single baseline missile may not cover all of the range of possible solutions. The more data that are available for missile baselines, the better. Typically the propulsion system of the new conceptual design missile should be the same type as that of the baseline missile. The baseline missile flight performance (e.g., range, Mach number, maneuverability) should also be comparable to that of the conceptual design missile. The baseline missile characteristics can usually be extrapolated about $+/-50\%$ with reasonable accuracy. As an example, the AIM-7 Sparrow missile would be a reasonable baseline missile in the initial designs of the Advanced Medium Range Air-to-Air Missile (AMRAAM) and the Evolved Sea Sparrow Missile (ESSM).

Note that, when using a baseline missile, it is important not to get locked in by the baseline but to be creative in exploring design alternatives. Also, because the baseline is an existing missile, whereas the conceptual design usually involves a missile projected for the future, the state-of-the-art must often be projected into the future, particularly for the electronic and sensor subsystems.

Shown in Fig. 1.20 is an example of baseline missile data for conceptual design sizing. The example is based on the chin inlet, integral rocket ramjet baseline described in Chapter 7. In the upper left of the figure is an illustration of a configuration drawing and the subsystems packaging of the baseline missile. The configuration drawing is a dimensioned layout, with an inboard profile showing the major subsystems (guidance, warhead, fuel, booster/engine, and flight control surfaces) and their packaging. In the upper center of the figure are examples of tables for a missile weight statement and geometry data. Missile weight and center-of-gravity location are provided for launch, booster burnout, and engine burnout flight conditions. Weight and geometry data are also provided for the subsystems. The upper right corner of the figure is an illustration of a description of the ramjet internal flow path geometry. The internal flow path geometry data includes the inlet design capture area and the internal areas of the inlet throat, diffuser exit, flame holder plane, combustor exit, nozzle throat, and nozzle exit. Examples of aerodynamic data plots are illustrated in the left center section of the figure. The aerodynamic data of the ramjet baseline covers angles of attack up to 16 deg and Mach numbers up to 4.0. Aerodynamic coefficients and derivatives include zero-lift drag coefficient C_{D_0}, normal force coefficient C_N, pitching moment coefficient C_m, pitching moment control effectiveness derivative C_{m_δ}, and normal force control effectiveness derivative C_{N_δ}. Examples of ramjet propulsion thrust T and the ramjet specific impulse I_{SP} are shown in the center of the figure. Thrust of the ramjet baseline is a function of Mach number, altitude, and fuel-to-air ratio. Specific impulse of the ramjet baseline is primarily a function of

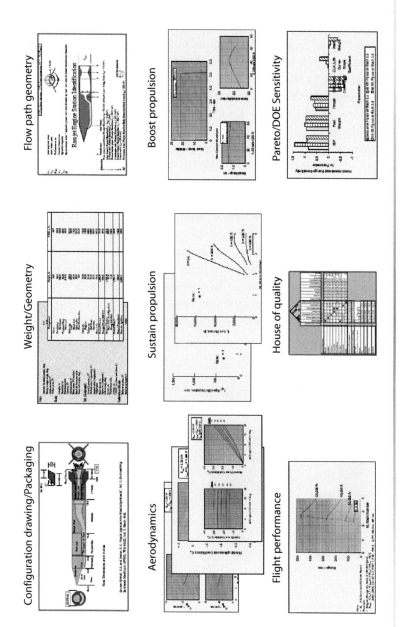

Fig. 1.20 Example of missile baseline data: Chapter 7 ramjet baseline missile.

Mach number for fuel-to-air ratios less than stoichiometric. Rocket booster propulsion thrust, boost range and burnout Mach number are illustrated in the right center of the figure as a function of launch Mach number and altitude. The left bottom section of the figure shows the maximum flight range of the ramjet baseline. Maximum flight range is a function of the launch Mach number, launch altitude, cruise Mach number, and the cruise altitude. In the bottom center section is an example of a "house of quality," which includes a most important requirements weighting. The house of quality is developed through a consensus with the customer on the most important requirements and their relative weighting. It is used to map the "voice of the customer" to the "voice of the engineer." The weighting from the house of quality is a tool for the down-select of the preferred concept alternative. Finally, the bottom right section of the figure is an example of Pareto (ranking) sensitivity of design parameters to a measure of merit (e.g., maximum flight range). The Pareto sensitivity study is used to define a Design of Experiment (DOE) set of alternative concepts for the design study.

Shown in Fig. 1.21 is the process of using baseline missile data to provide enhanced accuracy to conceptual design prediction methods. Conceptual design predicted values can be corrected through baseline test data. The process is as follows. First, an uncorrected prediction is made of a notional conceptual design parameter $P_{CD,U}$. Second, an uncorrected prediction is made of the baseline notional parameter $P_{B,U}$. The ratio

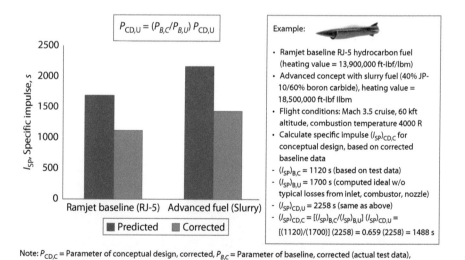

$$P_{CD,U} = (P_{B,C}/P_{B,U}) P_{CD,U}$$

Example:

- Ramjet baseline RJ-5 hydrocarbon fuel (heating value = 13,900,000 ft-lbf/lbm)
- Advanced concept with slurry fuel (40% JP-10/60% boron carbide), heating value = 18,500,000 ft-lbf llbm
- Flight conditions: Mach 3.5 cruise, 60 kft altitude, combustion temperature 4000 R
- Calculate specific impulse $(I_{SP})_{CD,C}$ for conceptual design, based on corrected baseline data
  - $(I_{SP})_{B,C} = 1120$ s (based on test data)
  - $(I_{SP})_{B,U} = 1700$ s (computed ideal w/o typical losses from inlet, combustor, nozzle)
  - $(I_{SP})_{CD,U} = 2258$ s (same as above)
  - $(I_{SP})_{CD,C} = [(I_{SP})_{B,C}/(I_{SP})_{B,U}] (I_{SP})_{CD,U} =$ [(1120)/(1700)] (2258) = 0.659 (2258) = 1488 s

Note: $P_{CD,C}$ = Parameter of conceptual design, corrected, $P_{B,C}$ = Parameter of baseline, corrected (actual test data), $P_{B,U}$ = Parameter of baseline, uncorrected (computed), $P_{CD,U}$ = Parameter of conceptual design, uncorrected (computed)

Fig. 1.21 Baseline design data allows correction of conceptual design computed parameters.

$P_{B,C}/P_{B,U}$ provides a correction to the prediction method. Finally, the conceptual design corrected parameter $P_{CD,C}$ is computed by

$$P_{CD,C} = (P_{B,C}/P_{B,U})P_{CD,U}$$

As an example, the ramjet baseline missile has a RJ-5 hydrocarbon fuel, which has a heating value $H_f = 13,900,000$ ft-lbf/lbm (17,900 BTU/lbm). Let us assume a conceptual design missile with an advanced fuel that is a high density slurry, consisting of 40% JP-10 and 60% boron carbide. It has a higher heating value, $H_f = 18,500,000$ ft-lbf/lbm (23,778 BTU/lbm). Also assume a cruise condition of Mach 3.5, 60k ft in altitude with a ramjet combustion temperature of 4000 R. Using the conceptual design prediction method of Chapter 3, the baseline missile uncorrected specific impulse is calculated to be $P_{B,U} = 1700$ s. The actual specific impulse of the ramjet baseline would be lower, because the Chapter 3 example does not include the effect of total pressure loss through the inlet, combustor, and nozzle. Using the same method, the computed conceptual design uncorrected specific impulse is $(I_{SP})_{CD,U} = 2258$ s. This can be corrected based on test data of the ramjet baseline. The ratio of baseline corrected (actual) specific impulse $[(I_{SP})_{B,C} = 1120$ s] to the baseline uncorrected predicted specific impulse $[(I_{SP})_{B,U} = 1700$ s] is 0.659. Finally, the conceptual design corrected specific impulse is

$$(I_{SP})_{CD,C} = [(I_{SP})_{B,C}/(I_{SP})_{B,U}](I_{SP})_{CD,U}$$
$$= (1120/1700)(2258) = 0.659(2258) = 1488 \text{ s}$$

1.9 Summary

This chapter provided an overview of the missile design and system engineering process. Examples were shown of how missiles are incorporated in a system-of-systems context. Elements of missile system engineering were presented. Also included were examples of air and surface-launched missile characteristics. A comparison was made of tactical missile and strategic missile capabilities. Each drives the state-of-the-art in different areas. The aerodynamic configuration sizing parameters of missiles were identified. It was shown most of the aerodynamic configuration sizing parameters have a strong impact on the missile system measures of merit and constraints. Also discussed was Pareto analysis. A Pareto analysis illustrated that typically only a few parameters are drivers for each measure of merit. The example showed that 85% of the flight range sensitivity of the rocket baseline missile is driven by only four parameters. The chapter also gave examples of the process and considerations for establishing mission requirements. Included was an example of defining the mission requirements for a hypersonic strike missile, based on an analysis of a mix of hypersonic strike missiles with subsonic cruise missiles. Another example was the sudden development of a mission requirement for a highly maneuverable air-to-air missile based on a "technology surprise" that pointed out the shortfall in the then-current capability. Finally, Chapter 1 presented a process for correcting design predictions using baseline missile data. The following chapters of this text will address the specific methods and technologies for missile design and system engineering.

1.10 Problem Review

1. The design team addresses the areas of mission/scenario definition, weapon requirements, launch platform integration, design synthesis, and t_____ a_____.

2. The steps to evaluate missile flight performance require computing the missile aerodynamics, propulsion, weight, and flight t_____.

3. Elements of missile system engineering include system requirements flow-down/specification, system integration, system analysis, and s_____.

4. Air-to-air missiles have light weight, high speed, and high m_____.

5. Air-to-surface missiles are often versatile and often have mo_____ warheads.

6. Surface-to-air missile measures of merit include accuracy and max al_____.

7. Four aeromechanics measures of merit are weight, range, maneuverability, and t___ to target.

8. The launch platform often constrains the missile span, length, and w_____.

9. An enabling capability for precision strike missiles is fast and accurate C____.

10. Unforeseen requirements may arrive from t_____ s_____.

11. A baseline design enhances design accuracy and gives fast s_____.

12. The Pareto effect states that the design is driven by a f__ parameters.

Chapter 2

Aerodynamic Considerations in the Missile Design and System Engineering Process

- Predicting Missile Aerodynamics
- Missile Configuration Layout (body, wing, tail)
- Selecting Flight Control Alternatives
- Maneuver Law Alternatives

2.1 Introduction

This chapter addresses aerodynamic considerations for missile design and system engineering. The conceptual design methods, design tradeoffs, design criteria, and technologies emphasize low aspect ratio wing and wingless configurations. Consideration is given to missile diameter tradeoffs; nose fineness tradeoffs; boattail considerations; lifting body versus axisymmetric body; calculation of body and planar surfaces (wings, tails, canards) normal force, lift-to-drag ratio, zero-lift drag coefficient, and center-of-pressure location; wings versus no wings; surface planform geometry alternatives; flight control alternatives; maneuver alternatives; roll orientation; static stability; tail area sizing; stability and control conceptual design criteria; and body buildup aerodynamics.

As shown in the Fig. 2.1, following the initial activities of defining mission requirements and establishing a baseline missile, the next activity is aerodynamic configuration synthesis and system engineering. Aerodynamic configuration and system engineering synthesis requires consideration of alternative configurations, aerodynamic technology, and the process for resizing the missile. One output is the missile body sizing

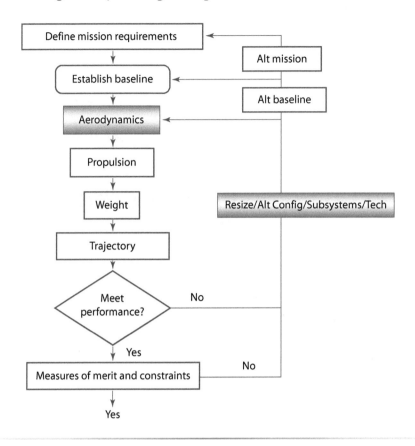

Fig. 2.1 Conceptual design and system engineering require creative, rapid, and iterative evaluations.

such as its diameter, length, and nose geometry. Another output is the missile surfaces sizing such as wing size/geometry, stabilizer surfaces size/geometry, and flight control surfaces size/geometry. A third output is the aerodynamic coefficients and derivatives of the complete missile configuration (body, wing, stabilizer, flight control). The output of the aerodynamic configuration synthesis and system engineering activity is an input to the next activity (propulsion system design and system engineering).

2.2 Missile Diameter Tradeoff

Missile diameter tradeoff has drivers toward a small diameter as well as other drivers toward a large diameter. These must be harmonized. The drivers toward a small diameter missile include lower drag and smaller lateral dimensions (for improved launch platform compatibility in lateral dimension constraint). However these must be harmonized with the other drivers toward a large diameter missile. These include 1) seeker increased range, higher resolution, better tracking, and higher signal-to-noise, 2) warhead increased effectiveness from higher fragment velocity and higher blast overpressure for a blast fragmentation warhead or a longer and faster jet for a shaped charge warhead, 3) body structure bending increased frequency, which reduces aeroelasticity and improves flight control feedback performance, 4) rocket motor decreased length, which increases the longitudinal combustion frequency (reducing the acoustic coupling peak load on the motor case), 5) subsystem packaging improved efficiency for diameter limited subsystems, and 6) shorter length for launch platform compatibility.

The typical range in missile body fineness ratio ($l/d =$ length-to-diameter ratio) is

$$5 < l/d < 25$$

An example of a low fineness missile is the Javelin anti-armor missile, which has an $l/d = 42.6$ in./5 in. $= 8.5$. The relatively large diameter and short length were selected to provide enhanced warhead and seeker effectiveness as well as improved ease of use as a man-portable weapon. Another example is the high fineness missile AIM-120 AMRAAM supersonic air-to-air missile, which has an $l/d = 144$ in./7 in. $= 20.5$. The relatively small diameter was selected to provide lower drag in supersonic flight. A relatively long length is required to package the propellant volume required for supersonic flight.

Drag is a major design parameter in satisfying flight range requirement, especially for a supersonic missile. It is a function of drag coefficient, dynamic pressure, and reference area, given by the equation

$$D = C_D q S_{\text{Ref}}$$

For a missile configuration, the reference area is the body cross sectional area. Substituting missile diameter for a typical circular cross section gives

$$D = C_D q (\pi/4) d^2 = 0.785 C_D q d^2$$

Shown in Fig. 2.2 is D/C_D as a function of diameter and dynamic pressure for a typical range in the values of these parameters for missiles.

As an example of missile drag, consider the rocket baseline missile. The rocket baseline missile has a reference area of 0.349 ft^2 and a reference length (diameter) of 8 in. At a typical flight condition of Mach 2 and flight altitude of 20,000 ft, the dynamic pressure $q = 2725$ psf. Also, from the Chapter 7 data, at Mach 2, the rocket baseline missile zero-lift drag coefficient for powered flight $C_{D_0} = 0.95$. Substituting into the drag equation, the zero-lift powered flight drag of the rocket 8-in. diameter baseline is $D_0 = 900$ lb, which 80% greater than the launch weight (500 lb).

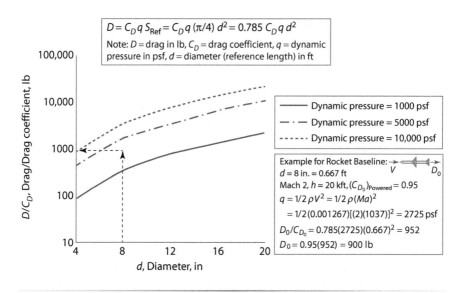

Fig. 2.2   A small diameter missile has lower drag.

A missile with configuration geometry similar to the rocket baseline missile, but with one-half the diameter (4 in.) would have one-fourth the drag (225 lb). A similar configuration with twice the diameter (16 in.) would have four times the drag (3600 lb).

Figure 2.3 shows the benefit of a large diameter in enhancing seeker detection range and resolution. Figure 2.3a is based on the two-way radar range equation for an active radar seeker, given by

$$(R_D)_{RF} = \left\{ \pi \sigma n^{3/4} / \left[64 \lambda^2 KTBFL(S/N)_{Detect} \right] \right\}^{1/4} P_T^{1/4} d$$

Assumptions are a uniformly illuminated circular aperture, non-coherent radar with integration of only the pulse signal amplitude, negligible clutter, negligible interference, negligible atmospheric attenuation, and thermal noise limited receiver sensitivity. In regard to pulse integration, the efficiency of integrating the number of pulses (n) can vary from $n^{1/2}$ to n. Coherent radar, which integrates both the signal amplitude and phase, can have an integration efficiency approaching an ideal value of n^1. For a non-coherent radar, which integrates only the signal amplitude, a typical value of the integration efficiency is $n^{3/4}$. Although a coherent radar seeker is usually more efficient, most radar missiles use non-coherent seekers, which integrate only the pulse amplitude. A non-coherent seeker is usually preferred because it is lower cost. Referring back to the radar range equation of the figure, the receiver threshold sensitivity P_r (in Watts) is given by the equation $P_r = KTBF$. Assumptions are a nominal receiver temperature $T = 290$ K, bandwidth $B = 10^6$ Hz (pulse width of about 10^{-6} s), and noise factor $F = 5$. Boltzmann's constant is the term $k = 1.38 \times 10^{-23}$ J/K. Substituting,

$$P_r = 1.38 \times 10^{-23}(290)(10^6)(5) = 2.0 \times 10^{-14} \text{ W}$$

Other assumptions for the example plotted in the figure are a target nominal radar cross section $\sigma = 10$ m^2, number of pulses integrated $n = 100$, transmitter frequency $f = 10$ GHz, transmitter loss factor $L = 5$, and target detection signal-to-noise ratio $(S/N)_{\text{Detect}} = 10$. The assumed value of $(S/N)_{\text{Detect}} = 10$ provides a false alarm of about 1% for a probability of detection of 90%. For a typical transmitter duty cycle of 20% and a loss factor of 5, the average output power is about 20% of the peak power and the input power is comparable to the peak power. The maximum allowable transmitted power by the seeker is limited by the transmitter technology, power available from the battery, maximum allowable temperature because of heating, and signal processing technology (such as pulse compression).

As an example, assume that the rocket baseline missile has an antenna diameter of about $d = 8$ in and a transmitted power $P_T = 1000$ W. Detection range is computed to be $(R_D)_{\text{RF}} = 13{,}070$ m or 7.1 nm.

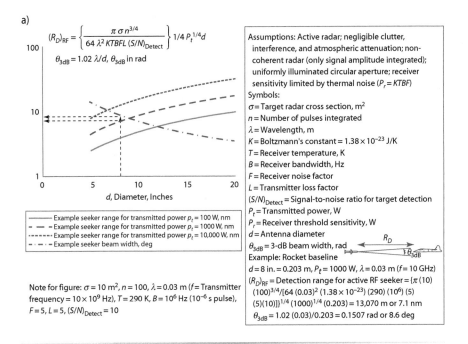

a)

$(R_D)_{\text{RF}} = \left\{ \dfrac{\pi\,\sigma\,n^{3/4}}{64\,\lambda^2\,KTBFL\,(S/N)_{\text{Detect}}} \right\}^{1/4} P_t^{1/4} d$

$\theta_{3dB} = 1.02\,\lambda/d,\ \theta_{3dB}$ in rad

x-axis: d, Diameter, Inches (0, 5, 10, 15, 20)
y-axis: (1, 10, 100)

—— Example seeker range for transmitted power $p_t = 100$ W, nm
— · — Example seeker range for transmitted power $p_t = 1000$ W, nm
········· Example seeker range for transmitted power $p_t = 10{,}000$ W, nm
— · · — Example seeker beam width, deg

Note for figure: $\sigma = 10$ m^2, $n = 100$, $\lambda = 0.03$ m (f = Transmitter frequency = 10×10^9 Hz), $T = 290$ K, $B = 10^6$ Hz (10^{-6} s pulse), $F = 5$, $L = 5$, $(S/N)_{\text{Detect}} = 10$

Assumptions: Active radar; negligible clutter, interference, and atmospheric attenuation; non-coherent radar (only signal amplitude integrated); uniformly illuminated circular aperture; receiver sensitivity limited by thermal noise ($P_r = KTBF$)
Symbols:
$\sigma =$ Target radar cross section, m^2
$n =$ Number of pulses integrated
$\lambda =$ Wavelength, m
$K =$ Boltzmann's constant $= 1.38 \times 10^{-23}$ J/K
$T =$ Receiver temperature, K
$B =$ Receiver bandwidth, Hz
$F =$ Receiver noise factor
$L =$ Transmitter loss factor
$(S/N)_{\text{Detect}} =$ Signal-to-noise ratio for target detection
$P_t =$ Transmitted power, W
$P_r =$ Receiver threshold sensitivity, W
$d =$ Antenna diameter
$\theta_{3dB} =$ 3-dB beam width, rad
Example: Rocket baseline
$d = 8$ in. $= 0.203$ m, $P_t = 1000$ W, $\lambda = 0.03$ m ($f = 10$ GHz)
$(R_D)_{\text{RF}} =$ Detection range for active RF seeker $= \{\pi\,(10)$
$(100)^{3/4}/[64\,(0.03)^2\,(1.38 \times 10^{-23})\,(290)\,(10^6)\,(5)$
$(5)(10)]\}^{1/4}\,(1000)^{1/4}\,(0.203) = 13{,}070$ m or 7.1 nm
$\theta_{3dB} = 1.02\,(0.03)/0.203 = 0.1507$ rad or 8.6 deg

Fig. 2.3a A large diameter seeker provides longer detection range and better resolution.

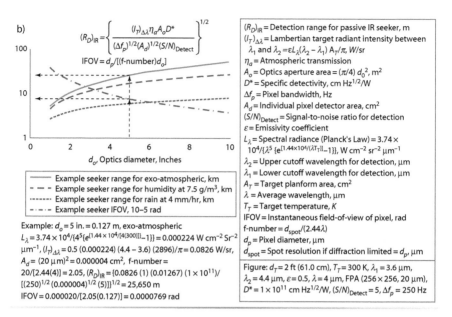

b)

$$(R_D)_{IR} = \left\{ \frac{(I_T)_{\Delta\lambda}\eta_a A_o D^*}{(\Delta f_p)^{1/2}(A_d)^{1/2}(S/N)_{Detect}} \right\}^{1/2}$$

IFOV $= d_p/[(\text{f-number})d_o]$

$(R_D)_{IR}$ = Detection range for passive IR seeker, m
$(I_T)_{\Delta\lambda}$ = Lambertian target radiant intensity between λ_1 and $\lambda_2 = \varepsilon L_\lambda(\lambda_2 - \lambda_1) A_T/\pi$, W/sr
η_a = Atmospheric transmission
A_o = Optics aperture area $= (\pi/4) d_o^2$, m^2
D^* = Specific detectivity, cm Hz$^{1/2}$/W
Δf_p = Pixel bandwidth, Hz
A_d = Individual pixel detector area, cm^2
$(S/N)_{Detect}$ = Signal-to-noise ratio for detection
ε = Emissivity coefficient
L_λ = Spectral radiance (Planck's Law) $= 3.74 \times 10^4/\{\lambda^5 \{e^{[1.44\times10^4/(\lambda T_T)]}-1\}\}$, W cm^{-2} sr^{-2} μm^{-1}
λ_2 = Upper cutoff wavelength for detection, μm
λ_1 = Lower cutoff wavelength for detection, μm
A_T = Target planform area, cm^2
λ = Average wavelength, μm
T_T = Target temperature, K
IFOV = Instantaneous field-of-view of pixel, rad
f-number $= d_{spot}/(2.44\lambda)$
d_p = Pixel diameter, μm
d_{spot} = Spot resolution if diffraction limited $= d_p$, μm

— Example seeker range for exo-atmospheric, km
– – – Example seeker range for humidity at 7.5 g/m^3, km
······· Example seeker range for rain at 4 mm/hr, km
–·–·– Example seeker IFOV, 10–5 rad

Example: $d_o = 5$ in. $= 0.127$ m, exo-atmospheric
$L_\lambda = 3.74 \times 10^4/\{4^5\{e^{[1.44 \times 10^4/[4(300)]]}-1\}\} = 0.000224$ W cm^{-2} Sr^{-2} μm^{-1}, $(I_T)_{\Delta\lambda} = 0.5$ (0.000224) $(4.4 - 3.6)$ $(2896)/\pi = 0.0826$ W/sr, $A_d = (20$ μm$)^2 = 0.000004$ cm^2, f-number $= 20/[2.44(4)] = 2.05$, $(R_D)_{IR} = \{0.0826$ (1) (0.01267) $(1 \times 10^{11})/[(250)^{1/2} (0.000004)^{1/2} (5)]\}^{1/2} = 25,650$ m
IFOV $= 0.000020/[2.05(0.127)] = 0.0000769$ rad

Figure: $d_T = 2$ ft (61.00 cm), $T_T = 300$ K, $\lambda_1 = 3.6$ μm, $\lambda_2 = 4.4$ μm, $\varepsilon = 0.5$, $\lambda = 4$ μm, FPA (256 × 256, 20 μm), $D^* = 1 \times 10^{11}$ cm Hz$^{1/2}$/W, $(S/N)_{Detect} = 5$, $\Delta f_p = 250$ Hz

Fig. 2.3b   A large diameter seeker provides longer detection range and better resolution.

Beam width of a radar seeker is given by the equation

$$\theta_{3dB} = 1.02\lambda/d$$

The 3-dB beam width for a frequency of 10 GHZ and an antenna diameter of 8 in is

$$\theta_{3dB} = 1.02\,(0.03)/0.203 = 0.151\,\text{rad} \quad \text{or} \quad 8.6\,\text{deg}$$

A larger antenna diameter provides longer range, more precise tracking, and finer resolution. For example, an increase of 100% in diameter (to 16 in.) provides an increase in the seeker range of 100% (to 14.1 nm) and a decrease in the seeker beam width of 50% (to 4.3 deg). Also, a longer pulse width would provide longer detection range, with disadvantages of degraded range measurement accuracy, higher false alarm rate, and potentially receiving overlapping pulses. Pulse modulation (e.g., chirp) can be used to avoid range ambiguity for a long duration pulse. Pulse compression is another approach to improve range. Processing provides the equivalence of an increase in the pulse width. Pulse compression has advantages of not degrading the range measurement accuracy, the pulse non-ambiguity, or the false alarm rate.

Signal processing for tracking allows the radar seeker to track with an accuracy that is much less than the beam width. Typically a radar seeker tracking accuracy is about 1/10-to-1/100 of the beam width, depending upon the target motion and acceleration. Advanced signal processing may allow tracking accuracy better than 1/100 of the beam width for a fixed target. An airborne high speed maneuvering target may limit the tracking accuracy to about 1/10 of the beam width.

Figure 2.3b shows a similar benefit of a large diameter in enhancing the detection range and resolution of a passive infrared (IR) seeker. It is based on the one-way IR range equation

$$(R_D)_{IR} = \left\{ (I_T)_{\Delta\lambda} \eta_a A_o D^* \Big/ \left[\Delta f_p^{1/2} A_d^{1/2} (S/N)_{\text{Detect}} \right] \right\}^{1/2}$$

Assumptions are negligible clutter, negligible solar reflection, isotropic emission from the target, and uniform pixel detectivity.

As shown in the equation, there are seven drivers for IR seeker range: radiant intensity of the target within the upper and lower wavelength cutoffs of the seeker $(I_T)_{\Delta\lambda}$, atmospheric transmission efficiency for the total distance from the target to the seeker η_a, seeker optics aperture area A_o, pixel specific detectivity D^*, pixel bandwidth Δf_p, detector total area A_d, and signal-to-noise ratio required for detection $(S/N)_{\text{Detect}}$.

Referring to the IR seeker range equation, the second term is atmospheric transmission efficiency η_a. It accounts for the attenuation over the total distance from the target to the seeker. The transmission can range from perfect transmission $(\eta_a = 1)$ for exo-atmospheric conditions to almost no transmission $(\eta_a \approx 0)$ through clouds. The effect of atmospheric transmission on detection range is shown in Fig. 2.3a. A typical value of atmospheric humidity of 7.5 g/m^3 results in an atmospheric attenuation of -0.2 dB per km for a 4μm IR signal, or an atmospheric transmission of 0.955 per km. Increasing the range reduces the received signal. As an example, an atmospheric attenuation of 0.955 per km results in 95% transmission at a range of 1 km but only 63% transmission at a range of 10 km $(0.955^{10} = 0.63)$. Adverse weather results in less transmission. As an example, moderate rainfall (4 mm/h) has an atmospheric attenuation of -2 dB per km for an IR signal, or an atmospheric transmission of 0.631 per km. It reduces the transmission to 63% at a range of 1 km. There is only 1% transmission at a range of 10 km.

The third term in the seeker range equation is seeker optics aperture area, which is a major configuration design parameter. A larger aperture captures more optical energy for the detectors, providing longer detection range. It also provides better resolution. For a strap-down seeker, the seeker optics diameter can be almost as large as the diameter of the missile. For a gimbaled seeker, the seeker optics diameter is typically limited to about one-half of the missile diameter. Shown in the figure is the effect of seeker optics diameter on detection range. A small optics diameter of 1 in, representative of a small diameter missile such as Stinger, has a typical detection range of only a few km and the detection range can be less than 1 km against a low signature target in adverse weather. A larger IR sensor diameter of 10 in, such as a FLIR on an aircraft or UAV, has ranges that can greatly exceed 10 km against moderate signature targets in favorable weather.

As an example, the seeker detection range will be calculated for a 5 in diameter aperture in an exo-atmospheric intercept of a relatively cold target. The seeker is assumed to operate over a wavelength range of 3.6 to 4.4 μm, with an average wavelength of $\lambda = 4$ μm. The target characteristics are assumed to be 2 ft diameter ($A_T = 2896$ cm^2), temperature $T_T = 300$ K, and emissivity $\varepsilon = 0.5$. The spectral radiance (Planck's Law) of the target is

$$L_\lambda = 3.74 \times 10^4 \Big/ \left\{ \lambda^5 \left\{ e^{[1.44 \times 10^4/(\lambda T_T)]} - 1 \right\} \right\}$$

$$= 3.74 \times 10^4 \Big/ \left\{ 4^5 \left\{ e^{\{1.44 \times 10^4/[4(300)]\}} - 1 \right\} \right\}$$

$$= 0.000224 \, \text{Wcm}^{-2}\text{sr}^{-2} \, \mu\text{m}^{-1}$$

Substituting into the equation for Lambertian target radiant intensity gives

$$(I_T)_{\Delta\lambda} = \varepsilon L_\lambda (\lambda_2 - \lambda_1) A_T / \pi = 0.5(0.000224)(4.4 - 3.6)(2896)/3.142$$

$$= 0.0826 \, \text{Wsr}^{-1}$$

The detector is assumed to be a diffraction limited 256 $\times$ 256 focal plane array with 20 μm pixels. Individual pixel detector area is therefore $A_d = 0.000004$ cm^2. A Hg$_{0.67}$Cd$_{0.33}$Te detector is assumed, which has a specific detectivity $D^* = 1 \times 10^{11}$ cmHz$^{1/2}$W^{-1} at a detector temperature of 77 K (liquid nitrogen) when it is optimized for the $\lambda = 4$ μm application. The pixel detector bandwidth for best signal-to-noise ratio (S/N) is assumed to be $\Delta f_p = 250$ Hz and the S/N for detection is assumed to be $(S/N)_{\text{Detect}} = 5$. Finally, substituting into the IR seeker range equation gives

$$(R_D)_{\text{IR}} = \left\{ (I_T)_{\Delta\lambda} \eta_a A_o \left\{ D^* \Big/ \left[\Delta f_p^{1/2} A_d^{1/2} (S/N)_{\text{Detect}} \right] \right\} \right\}^{1/2}$$

$$= \left\{ 0.0826(1)(0.01267) \left\{ 1 \times 10^{11} \Big/ \left[(250)^{1/2} (0.000004)^{1/2} (5) \right] \right\} \right\}^{1/2}$$

$$= 26{,}650 \, \text{m}$$

The figure also shows the benefit of optics diameter on instantaneous field of view (IFOV), which is the field of view of a single pixel. The equation is

$$\text{IFOV} = d_p/[(\text{f-number})d_o]$$

Note from the above equation that the IFOV becomes smaller (better resolution) as the diameter increases.

A typical tracking accuracy is comparable to the IFOV, about one pixel. Advanced processing can allow tracking within a fraction of the IFOV.

For a diffraction limited system, the minimum spot size is equal to the size of a single pixel detector. The Rayleigh criterion for the limiting angular resolution of the optics results in the equation

$$\text{f-number} = d_p/(2.44\lambda)$$

As an example, we will assume an optics aperture diameter $d_o = 5$ in (12.7 cm) diameter, a system that is diffraction limited, pixel size $d_p = 20$ μm, and wavelength $\lambda = 4$ μm. The f-number is given by the equation f-number $= 20$ μm$/[2.44(4$ μm$)] = 2.05$. Substituting into the equation for instantaneous field of view,

$$\text{IFOV} \approx 20 \times 10^{-6}/[2.05(0.127)] = 0.0000769 \text{ rad}$$

A high fineness ratio (l/d) missile may be limited by aeroelasticity problems from the body bending frequency. Shown in Fig. 2.4 is the first mode body bending frequency as a function of body fineness ratio. The equation is

$$\omega_{\text{BB}} = 276\left\{Et/\left[W(l/d)^3\right]\right\}^{1/2}, \quad \text{where } \omega_{\text{BB}} \text{ is in rad/s}$$

The equation is derived from Ref. 3. The assumptions are a thin wall cylinder structure with no stiffening from surfaces or bulkheads, uniform weight distribution, and free-free motion. Note that the body bending frequency is highest for a missile that has low fineness ratio, light weight, high modulus of elasticity, and large skin thickness of the airframe.

An example is given for the rocket baseline missile. The contribution from the wing is neglected. The rocket missile body is a combination of the pyroceram dome, aluminum airframe structure (including the aft body structure that shrouds the rocket nozzle), and the steel motor case. The modulus of elasticity of the steel motor case is 29.5×10^6 psi, the thickness of the case is 0.074 in, and the length of the case is 59.4 in. The modulus of elasticity of the aluminum body structure is 10.5×10^6 psi, thickness is 0.16 in, and the total length is 65.3 in. The contribution from the radome is neglected for this conceptual analysis, because of its relatively

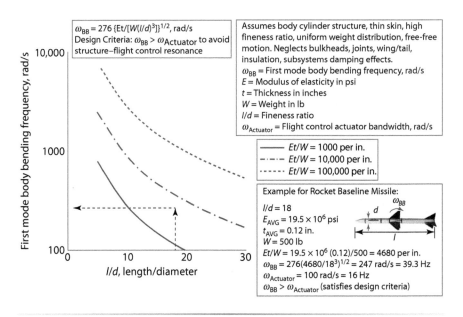

Fig. 2.4   Missile fineness ratio may be limited by the impact of body bending on flight control. (Derived from: AIAA *Aerospace Design Engineers Guide*, American Institute of Aeronautics and Astronautics, Inc., 1993.)

short length and the geometric stiffness of the tangent ogive radome. Using a weighted average based on length, the average modulus of elasticity is $E_{AVG} = 19.5 \times 10^6$ psi and the average thickness $t_{AVG} = 0.12$ in. The rocket baseline missile launch weight is 500 lb and the body fineness ratio is 18. Substituting into the equation, the first mode body bending frequency is computed to be

$$\omega_{BB} = 276\{19.5 \times 10^6 (0.12) / [500(18)^3]\}^{1/2} = 247 \text{ rad/s} \quad \text{or} \quad 39 \text{ Hz}$$

As a rule of thumb, the first mode body bending frequency should be greater than the actuator bandwidth of the flight control system. Actuators are typically the slowest component of the flight control system. A body bending frequency that is comparable to that of flight control system would be disruptive. For the rocket baseline missile, the flight control actuator frequency is 100 rad/s, providing a design margin in body bending frequency for the fineness ratio $l/d = 18$.

Adding a stiff bulkhead, such as a welded interface between the rocket motor case and the airframe, usually adds stiffness and usually increases the body bending frequency. However, a bulkhead interface using loose fittings or poor welding has poor mechanical attachment and decreased stiffness, resulting in lower body bending frequency.

2.3 Nose Fineness and Geometry Tradeoffs

Shown in Fig. 2.5 are the missile nose fineness and geometry tradeoffs and drivers. A high fineness nose, such as $l_N/d = 5$, is ideal for low supersonic drag and has low radar cross section (RCS). A low fineness nose, such as an $l_N/d = 0.5$ hemi-spherical nose, is ideal electromagnetically for the seeker and also allows more length for propellant and subsystems of a length limited missile. A nose spike is used on some supersonic missiles for reduced supersonic drag at low angle of attack, while also accommodating electromagnetic and optical requirements. The SA-16 IR guided missile has a fixed nose spike and the Trident ballistic missile has an extending nose spike. For most supersonic missiles, a moderate nose fineness compromise dome is a nose length-to-diameter ratio of about 2.

Alternative geometry for a high fineness nose includes a conventional dome, a faceted or pyramidal dome, a flat window dome, and a multi-lens dome. Conventional high fineness nose geometry alternatives include tangent ogive, parabolic, Sears-Haack, and von Karman. For conceptual design analysis, the differences in supersonic drag of the alternative nose geometries with the same fineness ratio is usually less than the accuracy of the conceptual design prediction methods (e.g., $+/-10\%$, 1σ). Supersonic drag is usually more sensitive to nose fineness than nose geometry. For this text, a representative high fineness conventional nose geometry is a tangent ogive nose, which has a circular arc surface. A tangent ogive nose

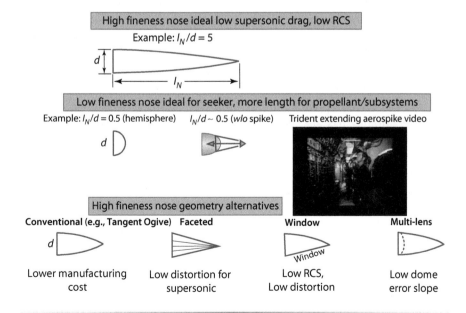

Fig. 2.5 Nose fineness and geometry tradeoff.

has relatively low supersonic drag, relatively low radar cross section, and relatively low manufacturing cost. A disadvantage of a tangent ogive dome is the curved surface results in a relatively high electromagnetic distortion and very high optical distortion, resulting in an error slope for the seeker tracking the target. Another (unconventional) alternative dome is a faceted dome. A faceted dome is typically composed of six-to-eight triangular surfaces that form a pyramid. A faceted dome has the advantage of low electromagnetic and optical distortion because of the flat surfaces. The bond line between the facets must be small to minimize distortion. A disadvantage of a faceted dome for an infrared seeker is the solar energy reflection off the facets into the seeker. Another unconventional dome is a window dome, composed of a single flat surface. The window dome also has an advantage of low optical distortion for an IR seeker and also has low RCS. A disadvantage of a window dome is that it limits the field of regard of the seeker, which may limit the ability of the seeker to acquire an off boresight target. Finally, a multi-lens dome is composed of two or more concentric domes, with a high fineness outer dome. A multi-lens dome can provide compensation that reduces the dome error slope that is seen by the seeker. The interior dome(s) provide correction to the dome error slope induced by the low drag/low RCS exterior dome.

Shown in Fig. 2.6 are current missiles with IR domes that are not hemi-spherical and also have low dome error slope. Faceted dome technology has been applied to supersonic surface-to-air and air-to-air missiles, to provide low drag combined with low dome error slope. Two supersonic missiles that have high fineness faceted IR domes are the United Kingdom Firestreak and the French Mistral. A concern with faceted domes is internal reflections off the facets. Background reflections into the detector increase the background clutter, reducing target contrast. Solar internal reflections off the facets can result in false "hot spots." A video of a sea-launched application of Mistral is in the upper right section of the figure. Faceted and window dome technology has also been applied to cruise missiles, to provide low radar cross section combined with low dome error slope. Cruise missiles that have high fineness IR domes are the US SLAM-ER missile, the US JASSM missile, the Norwegian Naval Strike Missile (NSM), and the South African TORGOS. SLAM-ER, NSM, and TORGOS domes have two facets (see photographs). JASSM has a single window dome. The JASSM seeker has a limited field of regard, and is biased downward to look through the window. Finally, the US THAAD missile defense missile dome is a high fineness window, for low drag and low dome error slope. Because the THAAD seeker is biased to look through the side window, there is a limited field of regard which increases the risk of an unsuccessful intercept. Shown in the bottom right section of the figure is a photograph of developmental hardware for a cooled window dome that is similar to THAAD.

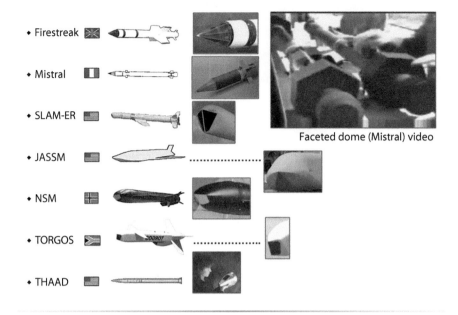

- Firestreak
- Mistral
- SLAM-ER
- JASSM
- NSM
- TORGOS
- THAAD

Faceted dome (Mistral) video

Fig. 2.6 Faceted and flat window domes can have low dome error slope, low drag, and low RCS.

2.4 Body Drag Prediction

The total zero-lift drag coefficient of a body is the combination of skin friction drag, base drag, and wave drag (if supersonic), given by the equation

$$(C_{D_0})_{\text{Body}} = (C_{D_0})_{\text{Body,Friction}} + (C_{D_0})_{\text{Base}} + (C_{D_0})_{\text{Body,Wave}}$$

Figure 2.7 shows $(C_{D_0})_{\text{Body}}$ of the rocket baseline missile as a function of Mach number. Note from the figure that the maximum value of $(C_{D_0})_{\text{Body}}$ occurs at Mach 1.

The equation for body wave drag coefficient based on Bonney [4] is

$$(C_{D_0})_{\text{Body,Wave}} = \left(1.586 + 1.834/\text{M}^2\right)\left\{\tan^{-1}[0.5/(l_N/d)]\right\}^{1.69}$$

In the equation the value of the inverse tangent is in radians. For supersonic missiles, the drag from the shock wave on the nose may be comparable to or even larger than skin friction drag and base drag.

The base drag for coasting flight at supersonic Mach number can be approximately correlated as

$$(C_D)_{\text{Base,Coast}} = 0.25/\text{M}$$

$$(C_{D_0})_{Body} = (C_{D_0})_{Body,Friction} + (C_{D_0})_{Base} + (C_{D_0})_{Body,Wave}$$

$(C_{D_0})_{Body,Friction} = 0.053\,(l/d)[M/(ql)]^{0.2}$ Based on Jerger reference, turbulent boundary layer, q in psf, l in ft.

$(C_{D_0})_{Body,Coast} = 0.25/M$, if $M > 1$ and $(C_{D_0})_{Base,Coast} = (0.12 + 0.13\,M^2)$, if $M < 1$

$(C_{D_0})_{Base,Powered} = (1 - A_e/S_{Ref})(0.25/M)$, if $M > 1$ and $(C_{D_0})_{Base,Powered} = (1 - A_e/S_{Ref})(0.12 + 0.13\,M^2)$, if $M < 1$

$(C_{D_0})_{Body,Wave} = (1.59 + 1.83/M^2)\{\tan^{-1}[0.5/(l_N/d)]\}^{1.69}$, for $M > 1$. Based on Bonney reference, $\tan^{-1}$ in rad.

Note: $(C_{D_0})_{Body,Wave}$ = body zero-lift wave drag coefficient, $(C_{D_0})_{Base}$ = body base drag coefficient, $(C_{D_0})_{Body,Friction}$ = body skin friction drag coefficient, $(C_{D_0})_{Body}$ = body zero-lift drag coefficient, l_N = nose length, d = body diameter, l = body length, A_e = nozzle exit area, S_{Ref} = reference area, q = dynamic pressure, $\tan^{-1}$ [0.5/(l_N/d)] in rad.

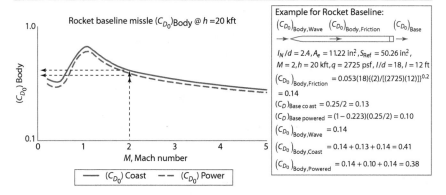

Example for Rocket Baseline:

$(C_{D_0})_{Body,Wave} \quad (C_{D_0})_{Body,Friction} \quad (C_{D_0})_{Base}$

$l_N/d = 2.4, A_e = 11.22$ in^2, $S_{Ref} = 50.26$ in^2,

$M = 2, h = 20$ kft, $q = 2725$ psf, $l/d = 18, l = 12$ ft

$(C_{D_0})_{Body,Friction} = 0.053(18)\{(2)/[(2725)(12)]\}^{0.2}$

$= 0.14$

$(C_D)_{Base\,coast} = 0.25/2 = 0.13$

$(C_D)_{Base\,powered} = (1 - 0.223)(0.25/2) = 0.10$

$(C_{D_0})_{Body,Wave} = 0.14$

$(C_{D_0})_{Body,Coast} = 0.14 + 0.13 + 0.14 = 0.41$

$(C_{D_0})_{Body,Powered} = 0.14 + 0.10 + 0.14 = 0.38$

Fig. 2.7 Maximum zero-lift drag coefficient occurs at Mach 1.

For coasting flight at subsonic Mach number,

$$(C_D)_{Base,Coast} = 0.12 + 0.13M^2$$

During powered flight the base drag is reduced by the factor $(1 - A_e/S_{Ref})$. If the nozzle exit area is nearly as large as the missile base area, the base drag may be negligible during powered flight. Body base drag can be a major contributor to the total drag during coasting flight, because of the low pressure in the base. Base drag is caused by flow separation at the base, which forms a low pressure wake.

Finally, skin friction drag is a major contributor to subsonic drag. $(C_{D_0})_{Body,Friction}$ is primarily driven by body fineness ratio. It is also a weak function of Mach number, dynamic pressure, and body length. The equation for the body skin friction drag coefficient, based on Jerger [5], is

$$(C_{D_0})_{Body,Friction} = 0.053(l/d)[M/(ql)]^{0.2}$$

Assumptions in the above equation are that the body wetted area of a noncircular lifting body can be approximated by the wetted area of an equivalent circular cross-section cylinder, the variation in the free stream speed of sound and viscosity with altitude is relatively small, the flow over the body has a turbulent boundary layer, and the body has no boattail.

The assumption of a turbulent boundary layer is least applicable for a short length missile at very low Mach number (e.g., $M < 0.2$) and for very high altitude (e.g., $h > 80,000$ ft). For the same flight conditions, a circular cross section body has less skin friction drag, because it has less wetted area than a lifting body.

As an example, we will calculate the body zero-lift drag coefficient of the rocket baseline missile, which has a nose fineness ratio of $l_N/d = 2.4$, body fineness $l/d = 18$, and body length $l = 12$ ft. At a nominal Mach number $M = 2$, the predicted zero-lift wave drag coefficient is $(C_{D_0})_{Body,Wave} = 0.14$. The base drag coefficient during coasting flight at Mach 2 is $(C_D)_{Base,Coast} = 0.13$, which is comparable to $(C_{D_0})_{Body,Wave}$. During powered flight at Mach 2, the base drag coefficient is smaller, $(C_D)_{Base,Powered} = 0.10$. The skin friction drag coefficient at Mach 2 and a nominal altitude of 20,000 ft (corresponding to a dynamic pressure of $q = 2725$ psf) is $(C_{D_0})_{Body,Friction} = 0.14$. Note that this is also comparable to the value of $(C_{D_0})_{Body,Wave}$. Finally, the body total power-off drag coefficient is computed as the sum of the contributions from the wave drag plus the base drag plus the skin friction drag. At Mach 2 and 20,000 ft in altitude, the predicted body drag coefficient during coasting flight is

$$(C_{D_0})_{Body,Coast} = 0.14 + 0.13 + 0.14 = 0.41$$

The body drag coefficient in powered flight is slightly lower

$$(C_{D_0})_{Body,Powered} = 0.14 + 0.10 + 0.14 = 0.38.$$

In the consideration of supersonic wave drag, Fig. 2.8 shows the benefit of nose fineness ratio (l_N/d) to reduce supersonic drag. For supersonic missiles, the drag due to the shock wave on the nose may be comparable to or even larger than skin friction drag and base drag. $(C_{D_0})_{Body,Wave}$ is driven by nose fineness and Mach number. The equation for body wave drag coefficient based on Bonney [4] is $(C_{D_0})_{Body,Wave} = (1.586 + 1.834/M^2)\{\tan^{-1}[0.5/(l_N/d)]\}^{1.69}$. In the equation the value of the inverse tangent is in radians. Note from the figure that $(C_{D_0})_{Body,Wave}$ greatly decreases with increasing nose fineness ratio. As an example, a high fineness nose with $l_N/d = 5$ has less than 10% of the supersonic drag of a hemispherical $(l_N/d = 0.5)$ nose.

As an example, we will calculate the body zero-lift wave drag coefficient of the rocket baseline missile, which has a nose fineness ratio of $l_N/d = 2.4$. At a nominal Mach number $M = 2$, the predicted zero-lift wave drag coefficient is

$$(C_{D_0})_{Body,Wave} = (1.59 + 1.83/2^2) \left[\tan^{-1}(0.5/2.4)\right]^{1.69} = 0.14$$

A small amount of nose tip bluntness is usually desirable for a missile. Nose tip bluntness alleviates problems of localized stress concentration and nose tip heating, usually with a relatively small increase in drag, seeker error, and radar cross section.

Fig. 2.9 illustrates the process of calculating the effect of nose tip bluntness on zero-lift wave drag. First, the blunted nose geometry is described as a spherical nose tip. Next, the zero-lift wave drag coefficient is calculated for a sharp nose, based on the equation [4]

$$(C_{D_0})_{\text{Wave,Sharp nose}} = \left(1.59 + 1.83/M^2\right)\left\{\tan^{-1}[0.5/(l_N/d)]\right\}^{1.69}$$

Next, the zero-lift drag wave coefficient of the hemispherical nose tip ($l_{\text{Nose tip}}/d_{\text{Nose tip}} = 0.5$) is calculated. The equation is

$$(C_{D_0})_{\text{Wave,Hemi}} = 0.665\left(1.59 + 1.83/M^2\right)$$

In the above equation $(C_{D_0})_{\text{Wave,Hemi}}$ is based on the nose tip cross sectional area. Finally, the zero lift wave drag coefficient of a missile with a blunt nose tip is the summation of the wave drag coefficient of the sharp nose plus the wave drag coefficient of the hemispherical nose tip, scaled by their areas. The equation is

$$(C_{D_0})_{\text{Wave,Blunt nose}} = (C_{D_0})_{\text{Wave,Sharp nose}}\left(S_{\text{Ref}} - S_{\text{Nose tip}}\right)/S_{\text{Ref}}$$
$$+ (C_{D_0})_{\text{Wave,Hemi}}S_{\text{Nose tip}}/S_{\text{Ref}}.$$

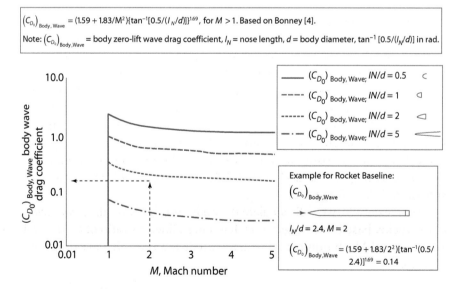

$(C_{D_0})_{\text{Body, Wave}} = (1.59 + 1.83/M^2)\{\tan^{-1}[0.5/(l_N/d)]\}^{1.69}$, for $M > 1$. Based on Bonney [4].

Note: $(C_{D_0})_{\text{Body,Wave}}$ = body zero-lift wave drag coefficient, l_N = nose length, d = body diameter, $\tan^{-1}[0.5/(l_N/d)]$ in rad.

Fig. 2.8   Supersonic body wave drag is driven by nose fineness.

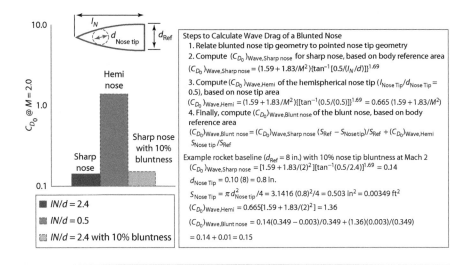

Fig. 2.9 Moderate nose tip bluntness causes a relatively small increase in supersonic drag.

As an example, the wave drag coefficient of the rocket baseline missile with a sharp nose of fineness ratio $l_N/d = 2.4$ and flying at Mach 2 has a nose zero-lift wave drag coefficient $(C_{D_0})_{\text{Wave,Sharp nose}} = 0.14$. The wave drag coefficient of a hemispherical nose tip is given by $(C_{D_0})_{\text{Wave,Hemi}} = 1.36$, where $(C_{D_0})_{\text{Wave,Hemi}}$ is based on the nose tip cross sectional area. Finally, the rocket baseline missile $(d = d_{\text{Ref}} = 8\ \text{in})$ with an assumed 10% nose tip bluntness at Mach 2 has a predicted zero-lift wave drag coefficient of $(C_{D_0})_{\text{Wave,Blunt nose}} = 0.14(0.349 - 0.003)/0.349 + 1.36(0.003)/0.349 = 0.14 + 0.01 = 0.15$, which is only slightly larger than that of a sharp nose.

2.5 Boattail

Boattailing has its best payoff for subsonic missiles; supersonic missiles are susceptible to aft flow separation from boattailing. Figure 2.10 from Chin[6] illustrates the benefit of boattailing. Without a boattail, during motor burn the base area that is outside the nozzle has a pressure less than that of the free stream, causing base drag. After motor burnout, the entire base area causes base drag. However, with boattailing the area occupied by the boattail has a larger base pressure, reducing the base drag in the area of the boattail. A design consideration if the missile has a boattail is that there is less volume available to package subsystems such as tail control actuators. Another design consideration is the maximum boattail angle that avoids flow separation over the boattail.

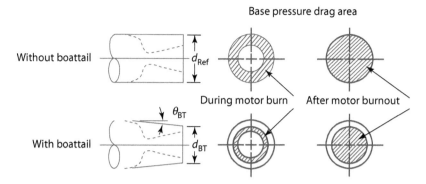

Base pressure drag area

Note: Boattail angle θ_{BT} and boattail diameter d_{BT} limited by propulsion nozzle packaging, tail flight control packaging, and flow separation

Fig. 2.10   A boattail decreases base pressure drag area. (Reference: Chin, S.S., *Missile Configuration Design*, McGraw-Hill Book Company, New York, 1961.)

Figure 2.11 from Ref. 7 shows that the payoff for a boattail is greatest for subsonic missiles. The example body has an overall fineness ratio of 10.5, a nose fineness ratio of 3.00, a center body fineness ratio of 6.00, and a boattail fineness ratio 1.50. Note that for subsonic Mach number, a boattail can

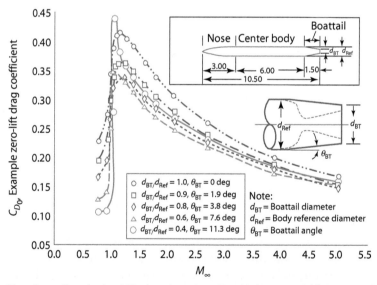

Note: Boattail angle should be less than about 7 to 10 deg, to avoid flow separation.

Fig. 2.11   Boattailing reduces drag for a subsonic missile. (Source: Mason, L.A., Devan, L. and Moore, F.G., "Aerodynamic Design Manual for Tactical Weapons," NSWC TR81-156, July 1981.)

reduce the drag by over 50%. However, at supersonic to hypersonic Mach number there is only a slight reduction in drag with a moderate boattail, and a large boattail angle actually causes an increase in drag. From the figure, note that at Mach 5.0 the C_{D_0} for $d_{BT}/d_{Ref} = 0.6$ (boattail angle = 7.6 deg) is larger than the C_{D_0} for $d_{BT}/d_{Ref} = 0.8$ (boattail angle = 3.8 deg). At high Mach number, a large boattail angle can cause flow separation over the boattail, resulting in increased drag. As a rule of thumb, the boattail angle should be less than about 7 to 10 deg. As an example from the figure, the largest boattailing evaluated ($d_{BT}/d_{Ref} = 0.4$, boattail angle = 11.3 deg) results in the highest transonic ($M_\infty \sim 1$) value of C_{D_0}.

2.6 Body Normal Force Prediction

As shown in Fig. 2.12, the maximum normal force of a lifting body (e.g., elliptical cross section) is higher than that of an axisymmetric body (circular cross section). The equation for normal force coefficient of a body is

$$|C_N| = [(a/b)\cos^2\phi + (b/a)\sin^2\phi][|\sin(2\alpha)\cos(\alpha/2)| + 1.3(l/d)\sin^2\alpha]$$

The normal force coefficient of a slender body is theoretically a function only of angle of attack and body geometry and is theoretically independent of Mach number and Reynolds number. The normal force prediction is

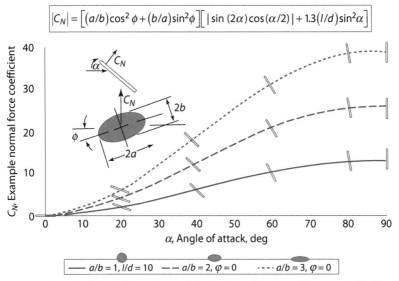

Note: Based on slender body theory (Pitts et al. [8]) and cross flow theory (Jorgensen [9]) references, Valid for $l/d > 5$, $d = 2 (ab)^{1/2}$

Fig. 2.12 A lifting body has higher normal force.

based on combining slender body theory (Ref. 8) and body cross flow theory (Ref. 9). At low angle of attack the normal force is driven by slender body theory. At very high angle of attack ($\alpha \rightarrow 90$ deg) it is driven by cross flow theory, represented by the cross flow drag of a cylinder. For a long circular cylinder (e.g., $l/d = 10$) at $\alpha = 90$ deg, the drag coefficient varies from about 1.2 to 1.5 times l/d, depending upon the Mach number. The cross flow drag coefficient is greatest ($C_{D_{\alpha=90°}} \approx 1.5 \, l/d$) for transonic Mach number ($0.8 < M < 1.2$). For subsonic ($M < 0.8$) and supersonic Mach number ($M > 1.2$) an average value of ($C_{N_{\alpha=90°}} = 1.3 \, l/d$) is usually of sufficient accuracy for conceptual design.

The normal force coefficient equation is valid for a body fineness ratio $l/d > 5$. For an elliptical cross section, an equivalent diameter is based on a circular cross section of the same area. The figure shows that normal force coefficient increases with α (up to $\alpha = 90$ deg) and a/b. As an example, at 90 deg angle of attack, the normal force coefficient for an elliptical cross section with a major-to-minor axis ratio of $a/b = 2$ is twice that of a circular cross section.

The body normal force curve slope from angle of attack is used in sizing the tail (or in some cases a flare) to meet the static stability requirement. $(C_{N_\alpha})_{\text{Body}}$ is the derivative of the body normal force coefficient. At low angle of attack,

$$(C_{N_\alpha})_{\text{Body}} = 2[(a/b)\cos^2\varphi + (b/a)\sin^2\varphi], \text{ with the units of per rad.}$$

2.7 Lifting Body Versus Axisymmetric Body

A measure of aerodynamic efficiency is the ratio of lift-to-drag (L/D). The equation for aerodynamic efficiency is

$$L/D = C_L/C_D = (C_N \cos\alpha - C_{D_0}\sin\alpha)/(C_N\sin\alpha + C_{D_0}\cos\alpha)$$

For a lifting body missile without wings, the equation for the normal force coefficient is

$$|C_N| = [(a/b)\cos^2\phi + (b/a)\sin^2\phi] \left[|\sin(2\alpha)\cos(\alpha/2)| + 1.3(l/d)\sin^2\alpha \right]$$

Again, C_N for a body is based on combining slender body theory[8] with cross flow theory[9]. As shown in Fig. 2.13, an increase in L/D is achievable by reducing the zero-lift drag coefficient, increasing the body fineness, or by providing a lifting body configuration ($a/b > 1$). Also shown is that as a higher L/D is achieved, the angle of attack in which $(L/D)_{\text{max}}$ is achieved is decreased. Note that other design considerations, such as launch platform lateral and length constraints, may limit the aerodynamic shaping that is practical. Also note that for 1-g, constant altitude flight the angle of

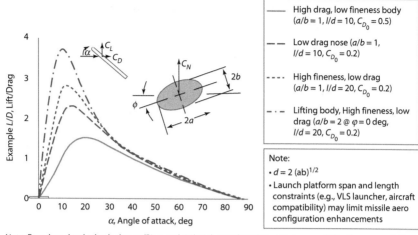

$$L/D = C_L/C_D = (C_N\cos\alpha - C_{D_0}\sin\alpha)/(C_N\sin\alpha + C_{D_0}\cos\alpha)$$

For lifting body, $|C_N| = \left[(a/b)\cos^2(\phi)+(b/a)\sin^2(\phi)\right]\left[|\sin(2\alpha)\cos(\alpha/2)|+1.3\,(l/d)\sin^2\alpha\right]$

High drag, low fineness body ($a/b = 1$, $l/d = 10$, $C_{D_0} = 0.5$)

Low drag nose ($a/b = 1$, $l/d = 10$, $C_{D_0} = 0.2$)

High fineness, low drag ($a/b = 1$, $l/d = 20$, $C_{D_0} = 0.2$)

Lifting body, High fineness, low drag ($a/b = 2$ @ $\varphi = 0$ deg, $l/d = 20$, $C_{D_0} = 0.2$)

Note:
• $d = 2\,(ab)^{1/2}$
• Launch platform span and length constraints (e.g., VLS launcher, aircraft compatibility) may limit missile aero configuration enhancements

Note: Based on slender body theory (Pitts et al. [8]) and cross flow theory (Jorgensen [9]) references, valid for $l/d > 5$, $d = 2\,(ab)^{1/2}$

Fig. 2.13 Body L/D is impacted by angle of attack, C_{D_0}, body fineness, and cross section geometry.

attack is usually much lower than the angle of attack for $(L/D)_{max}$. As a result, the L/D during the fly-out of most rocket powered missiles is usually much lower than $(L/D)_{max}$.

Although a lifting body configuration has a higher $(L/D)_{max}$ than a circular cross section configuration, for 1-g flight at low angles of attack/high dynamic pressure, a circular configuration can provide comparable L/D. Figure 2.14 compares the L/D of a lifting body configuration ($a/b = 2$) in symmetrical flight ($\varphi = 0$ deg) with that of a circular cross section ($a/b = 1$) configuration. Typical values are given for a precision strike missile configuration of 2 ft^2 cross sectional area and 2000 lb weight. As before, the L/D is based on combining slender body theory[8] with cross flow theory[9]. Maximum L/D for the lifting body configuration occurs at a dynamic pressure $q \approx 600$ psf while maximum L/D for the circular cross section body occurs at a dynamic pressure $q \approx 800$ psf. $(L/D)_{max}$ of the lifting body is about 40% higher than the circular cross section body ($L/D = 3.2$ versus 2.3). However, note that the circular body cross section configuration provides comparable L/D for flight at high dynamic pressure. At $q = 5000$ psf, the lifting body L/D is only about 5% higher than the circular cross section body ($L/D = 0.96$ versus 0.91).

Adding a surface (e.g., wing) also increases $(L/D)_{max}$, reduces $\alpha_{(L/D)max}$, and reduces $q_{(L/D)max}$. For example, the rocket baseline missile has a relatively high L/D, because of its wing. At Mach 0.8, $(L/D)_{max} = 6.2$, $\alpha_{(L/D)max} = 4.5$ deg, and $q_{(L/D)max} = 350$ psf. The rocket baseline missile during 1-g (lift = weight) $\gamma = 0$ deg supersonic flight has a much lower L/D. For example, its powered flight at Mach 2, 20 kft altitude has an $L/D = 0.41$.

Figure 2.15 compares weapon configurations that have conventional cylindrical bodies of circular cross-section to other weapons that are highly tailored, using aerodynamic shaping of their lifting body configurations. An indication of subsystems packaging efficiency is the ratio of body planform area to the 2/3 power of the body volume $(S_P/V^{2/3})$. For a circular cross section body, $S_P/V^{2/3}$ has a value of about 3. As shown in the figure, a highly tailored missile could have a value of the subsystems packaging efficiency parameter $S_P/V^{2/3} > 9$. An advantage of a tailored lifting body missile is higher aerodynamic efficiency L/D, for extended range cruise performance and enhanced maneuverability. Also shown is the synergy of tailored missiles with reduced radar cross section. Missiles with air-breathing propulsion (ramjets, turbojets) are usually amenable to configuration tailoring, because of their inlet and liquid hydrocarbon fuel packaging. Disadvantages of tailored missiles include relative their inefficiency for solid subsystems packaging, an adverse impact on launch platform integration because of a typically larger span, and the complexity of analysis of non-axisymmetric aerodynamics and structure. More

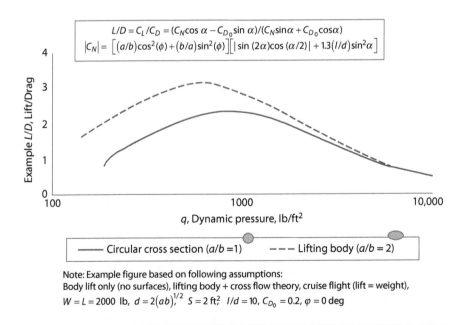

Note: Example figure based on following assumptions:
Body lift only (no surfaces), lifting body + cross flow theory, cruise flight (lift = weight),
$W = L = 2000$ lb, $d = 2(ab)^{1/2}$ $S = 2$ ft^2 $l/d = 10$, $C_{D_0} = 0.2$, $\varphi = 0$ deg

Fig. 2.14 A lifting body requires flight at low dynamic pressure to achieve high aerodynamic efficiency L/D.

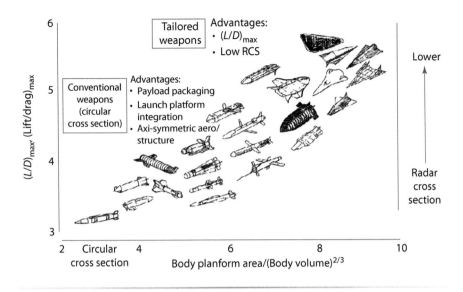

Fig. 2.15 Tradeoff of low observables and $(L/D)_{max}$ versus volumetric efficiency.

sophisticated methods and tests are required for the analysis of the aerodynamics and the structural loads of non-axisymmetric weapons. This includes more extensive wind tunnel tests, computational fluid dynamics (CFD) predictions, and finite element modeling (FEM) of structural integrity.

2.8 Forces, Moments, and Axes Sign Convention

Figure 2.16 shows typical definitions and sign conventions for the missile body axes coordinate system and the missile forces and moments. The body axes coordinate system is an inertial reference located at the missile center-of-gravity (cg). The coordinate system moves as the missile moves. The axes x, y, and z in the above sign convention are defined as positive x forward, positive y to the right, and positive z down. In the above assumed coordinate system, $\phi = 0$ deg is defined with the cruciform missile fins in the x orientation.

The forces on the missile are axial, side, and normal forces. Positive axial force is directed aft along the body centerline from the cg to the base of the missile. At zero angle of attack the axial force is equal to the zero lift drag coefficient. Looking forward from the base of the missile, positive side force is to the right. Positive normal force is up.

Rotations are defined as roll (ϕ), pitch (θ), and yaw (ψ). Positive roll, looking forward from the base of the missile, is right side down. Positive pitch is nose up. Positive yaw, looking forward from the base of the missile, is nose right.

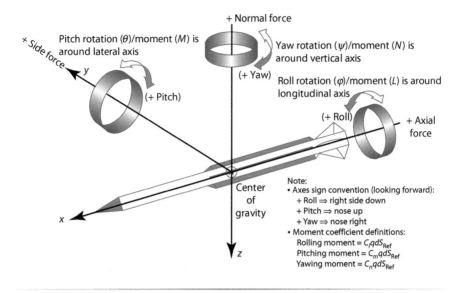

Fig. 2.16   Forces, moments, and axes sign convention of this text.

Aerodynamic force and moment scaling is provided by the reference area S_{Ref}, reference length d, and the free stream dynamic pressure q. As an example, for the missile roll moment L, the roll moment coefficient is defined by

$$C_l = L/(qdS_{\text{Ref}})$$

2.9 Static Stability

Static stability in pitch is defined by the slope of the pitching moment coefficient versus angle of attack $\Delta C_m/\Delta\alpha = C_{m_\alpha}$ and also by the difference between the location of the aerodynamic center x_{AC} and the center-of-gravity x_{CG}. Shown in the top left portion of Fig. 2.17 is an example of the pitching moment coefficient versus angle of attack curve for a statically stable missile. For a statically stable missile, the slope of the pitching moment coefficient versus angle of attack is negative, with the aerodynamic center aft of the center-of-gravity. An increase in angle of attack (nose up) causes a negative incremental pitching moment (nose down), which then tends to decrease the angle of attack. Control surface deflections allow the missile to trim ($C_m = 0$) at the desired angle of attack. The bottom left portion of the figure shows the decay of an incremental disturbance in the angle of attack as a function of time for a statically stable missile without an autopilot correction. For a highly stable, highly damped missile, the convergence is usually non-oscillatory. Most missiles

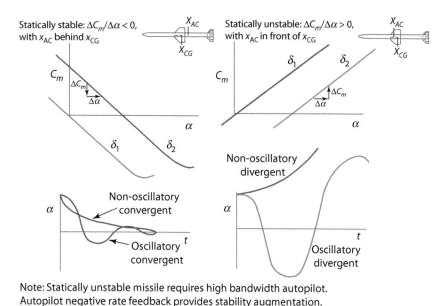

Note: Statically unstable missile requires high bandwidth autopilot. Autopilot negative rate feedback provides stability augmentation.

Fig. 2.17 Pitch moment stability $\Delta C_m/\Delta\alpha$ and static margin ($x_{AC} - x_{CG}$) define static stability.

have small tail surfaces, small static margin, and are lightly damped during free flight if there is no autopilot feedback (e.g., initially unguided flight trajectory during launch platform separation). The lightly damped missiles have an oscillatory convergence from a disturbance in angle of attack. The ideal damping is $\zeta \approx 0.7$.

As shown in the upper right of the figure, a statically unstable missile has the opposite trend. The slope of the pitching moment coefficient versus angle of attack is positive, with the aerodynamic center forward of the center-of-gravity. An increase in angle of attack causes an increase in pitching moment, which tends to cause a further increase in angle of attack. The rate of divergence is a function of dynamic pressure, with rapid divergence occurring at high dynamic pressure. If the autopilot has a high bandwidth and is sufficiently fast, it is possible to trim and control a statically unstable missile. Negative rate feedback from the gyros is an approach to provide the required stability augmentation. A statically unstable missile might be desirable, to improve the responsiveness and maneuverability. The bottom right portion of the figure shows the divergence of a statically unstable missile without an autopilot correction. A highly unstable missile will diverge monotonically. A statically unstable missile that is slightly unstable will tend to oscillate with increasing divergence.

2.10 Body Aerodynamic Center Prediction

Aerodynamic center is defined as the location that provides neutral static margin. If the center-of-gravity is located at the aerodynamic center, the pitching moment does not change with angle of attack. The aerodynamic center location for the body $(x_{AC})_B$ depends mostly on three parameters, angle of attack, nose length, and aft body length. For conceptual design, the effect of Mach number on $(x_{AC})_B$ may be neglected. As shown in Fig. 2.18, for a body without a flare at low angle of attack, $(x_{AC})_B$ is located at about 63% of the nose length. At angles of attack approaching $\alpha = 90$ deg, $(x_{AC})_B$ approaches the center of the body. Results in the figure are shown as a function of the body length-to-nose length ratio l_B/l_N and the angle of attack α. As before, results are based on combining slender body theory [8] with cross flow theory [9], giving the equation

$$(x_{AC})_B/l_N = 0.63(1 - \sin^2\alpha) + 0.5(l_B/l_N)\sin^2 \alpha$$

As an example from the data of Chapter 7, the rocket baseline missile has a nose length of 19.2 in and a total body length of 143.9 in. The ratio of body length to nose length is $l_B/l_N = 7.49$. For an angle of attack of $\alpha = 13$ deg, the center of pressure of the body $(x_{CP})_B$ is located at

$$(x_{AC})_B/l_N = 0.63(1 - \sin^2 13 \text{ deg}) + 0.5(7.49)\sin^2 13 \text{ deg} = 0.81$$

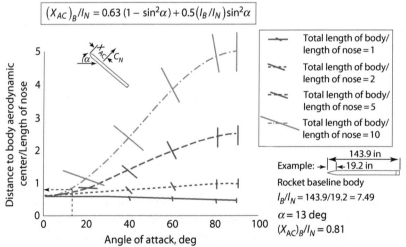

Fig. 2.18 Body aerodynamic center is driven by angle of attack, nose length, and body length.

Because the aerodynamic center of the body is located on the nose and the missile center-of-gravity is near the center of the body, the body is statically unstable. Tail stabilizers were added to rocket baseline body to compensate for the instability of the body.

2.11 Flare Stabilizer

A flare may be added to the aft end of a body to increase the static stability. Typically the flare half angle is less than about 10 deg, to avoid flow separation. Figure 2.19 illustrates a process to calculate the static margin of a body-flare configuration. It is based on the locations of the normal force coefficient derivative contributors to pitching moment. As shown previously, at low angle of attack, the normal force coefficient derivative contribution and its location for a circular cross-section body, based on slender body theory[8] are

$$(C_{N_\alpha})_B = 2 \text{ per rad}$$
$$(x_{ac})_B = 0.63 \, l_N$$

Also for low angle of attack, the flare normal force coefficient derivative contribution and its location, based on slender body theory are (Fig. 2.19a)

$$(C_{N_\alpha})_F = 2\left[(d_F/d)^2 - 1\right]$$
$$(x_{ac})_F = x_F + 0.33 l_F [2(d_F/d) + 1]/[(d_F/d) + 1]$$

The static margin of a body-flare missile, such as THAAD, is given by the equation

$$(x_{AC} - x_{CG})/d = -\left\{(C_{N_\alpha})_B\left\{\left[x_{CG} - (x_{AC})_B\right]/d\right\} + (C_{N_\alpha})_F\left\{\left[x_{CG} - (x_{AC})_F\right]/d\right\}\right\}/\left[(C_{N_\alpha})_B + (C_{N_\alpha})_F\right]$$

Figure 2.19b further illustrates the process of calculating static margin for a body-flare configuration, using the THAAD missile as an example. The THAAD flare somewhat compensates for the statically unstable body. As shown in the example, for a flare-to-body diameter ratio of $d_F/d = 18.7 \text{ in}/14.6 \text{ in} = 1.28$, THAAD is predicted to be statically unstable at launch, with a static margin of

$$(x_{AC} - x_{CG})/d = -0.41$$

The flare half-angle of THAAD is 9.7 deg, to avoid flow separation (and the separation pressure drag) in front of the flare.

Figure 2.20 is a comparison of a flare stabilizer with conventional tail stabilizers. A flare-stabilized missile, such as THAAD, has advantages of

a)

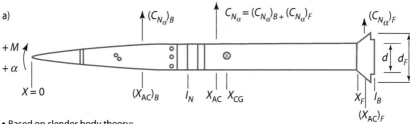

- Based on slender body theory:
  - $\left(C_{N_\alpha}\right)_F = 2\left[(d_F/d)^2 - 1\right]$
  - $\left(X_{ac}\right)_F = x_F + 0.33 l_F\left[2(d_F/d) + 1\right] / \left[(d_F/d) + 1\right]$
  - $\left(C_{N_\alpha}\right)_B = 2\,\text{per rad}$
  - $\left(X_{AC}\right)_B = 0.63\, l_N$
- $\Sigma M = 0$ at aerodynamic center. For a body-flare:
  - $\left(C_{N_\alpha}\right)_B\left\{\left[X_{CG} - (X_{AC})_B\right]/d\right\} + \left(C_{N_\alpha}\right)_F\left[X_{CG} - (X_{AC})_F\right]/d = -\left[\left(C_{N_\alpha}\right)_B + \left(C_{N_\alpha}\right)_F\right]$
  $\left[(X_{AC} - X_{CG})/d\right]$
- Static margin for a body-flare
  - $(X_{AC} - X_{CG})/d = -\left\{\left(C_{N_\alpha}\right)_B\left\{\left[X_{CG} - (X_{AC})_B\right]/d\right\} + \left(C_{N_\alpha}\right)_F\left\{\left[X_{CG} - (X_{AC})_F\right]/d\right\}\right\} /$
  $\left[\left(C_{N_\alpha}\right)_B + \left(C_{N_\alpha}\right)_F\right]$

Fig. 2.19a   An aft flare increases static stability.

b) **Example of Static Margin for THAAD**

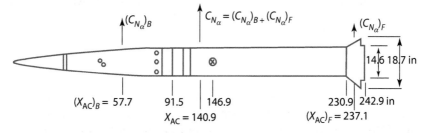

- $\left(C_{N_\alpha}\right)_F = 2\left[(18.7/14.6)^2 - 1\right] = 1.28\,\text{per rad}$
- $\left(X_{AC}\right)_F = 230.9 + 0.33(12.0)\left[2(18.7/14.6) + 1\right] / \left[(18.7/14.6) + 1\right] = 237.1\,\text{in}$
- $\left(X_{AC}\right)_B = 0.63\,(91.5) = 57.5\,\text{in}$
- $X_{CG\,Launch} = 146.9\,\text{in}$
- $(X_{AC} - X_{CG})_{Launch}/d = -\left\{2\left\{[146.9 - 57.7]/14.6\right\} + 1.28\left\{[146.9 - 237.1]/14.6\right\}\right\} / [2 + 1.28] = -0.41$
  (statically unstable)

Fig. 2.19b   An aft flare increases static stability.

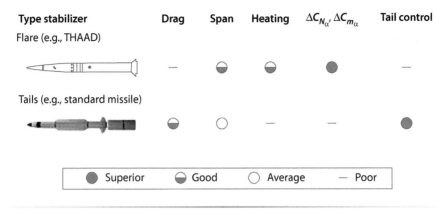

Type stabilizer	Drag	Span	Heating	$\Delta C_{N_\alpha}, \Delta C_{m_\alpha}$	Tail control
Flare (e.g., THAAD)	—	◒	◒	●	—
Tails (e.g., standard missile)	◒	○	—	—	◒

● Superior　　◒ Good　　○ Average　　— Poor

Fig. 2.20 Tail stabilizers have lower drag, while a flare stabilizer has lower aero heating and less change in stability.

lower required span for the stabilizer, lower aerodynamic heating, and less variation in its aerodynamics (e.g., ΔC_{N_α}, ΔC_{m_α}) with Mach number. Reduced aerodynamic heating is particularly beneficial for a hypersonic missile such as THAAD. Reentry vehicles also use flares to provide static stability while minimizing aerodynamic heating. An example of a missile that uses conventional tail surfaces for static stability is the Standard Missile. Compared to flares, conventional tails have benefits of lower drag and the availability of the tail surfaces for flight control in addition to stability. THAAD relies entirely on thrust vector control (TVC) and reaction jet control. Compared to aerodynamic control, a disadvantage of TVC and reaction jet control is a weight penalty, because of the additional weight of propellant.

2.12 Wings Versus No Wings

There are many considerations in the tradeoff of a small wing/strake/ no wing versus a larger wing (Fig. 2.21). A small wing, a strake, or no wing has advantages of range in high supersonic flight, range in high dynamic pressure, maximum angle of attack (stability and control at high angles of attack is better without a wing, with less induced roll and delayed stall compared to a missile with a large wing), launch platform compatibility, lower radar cross section, and the volume and weight available for propellant/fuel. Note that some of the disadvantages of a wingless missile can be alleviated by unconventional flight control (e.g., thrust vector control, reaction jet/jet interaction control). It is possible for a wingless missile to achieve small guidance time constant, high normal acceleration or maneuverability, and a high altitude intercept capability at low dynamic pressure through unconventional flight control.

a)

Measure of merit	No wing	Small wing/Strake	Large wing
Range in high supersonic flight/high dynamic pressure	●	○	—
Range in low supersonic flight/moderate dynamic pressure	○	●	—
Range in subsonic flight/low dynamic pressure	—	○	●
Max angle of attack	●	◒	—
Launch platform compatibility	●	○	—
Lower radar cross section	●	○	—
Volume and weight for propellant/fuel	●	◒	○

*Based on assumption of aero control

● Superior	◒ Good	○ Average	— Poor

Fig. 2.21a   Wing sizing is a tradeoff.

b)

Measure of merit	No wing	Small wing/Strake	Large wing
Lower guidance time constant*	—	○	●
Normal acceleration*	—	◒	●
High altitude intercept*	—	○	◒
Less body bending aeroelasticity (wing stiffens body)	—	○	◒
Less seeker error from dome error slope (lower angle of attack)	—	○	●
Less wipe velocity for warhead (lower angle of attack)	—	○	●
Lower gimbal requirement for seeker	—	○	●

*Based on assumption of aero control

● Superior	◒ Good	○ Average	— Poor

Fig. 2.21b   Wing sizing is a tradeoff.

A larger wing has advantages of range in subsonic flight, range in low dynamic pressure, lower guidance time constant, normal acceleration, high altitude intercept, body stiffness, seeker tracking (less dome error slope error from lower angle of attack), less wipe velocity for the warhead at impact (lower angle of attack), and a lower gimbal angle requirement for the seeker.

Because supersonic missiles generally operate at relatively high dynamic pressure, body lift may be sufficient for the required aerodynamic efficiency (L/D) and maneuverability. Shown in Fig. 2.22 are examples of supersonic missiles that do not have wings. Reference 1 was a source for the missile drawings. Many of these missiles are highly maneuverable, and are capable of operating at high angle of attack. The examples include canard, tail, and unconventional flight control. Unconventional flight control may be used if additional maneuverability is required to supplement the body lift. Examples of supersonic wingless missiles that use thrust vector control are THAAD, Archer AA-11 (thrust vector control combined with canard control), Sidewinder AIM-9X (TVC combined with tail control), Standard Missile (TVC combined with tail control), and GBI (TVC and reaction jet control). It is noted that most ballistic missiles (e.g., Minuteman, Trident) fly at nearly zero angle of attack and are wingless.

As a contrast, Fig. 2.23 shows examples of subsonic cruise missiles. Note that they have relatively large wings. Most cruise missiles have a single wing (two panels). The single wing may mounted low (JASSM, CALCM), mid-way (NSM, Tomahawk, Delilah), or high (Apache, Taurus) on the missile body. Examples of subsonic cruise missiles with cruciform

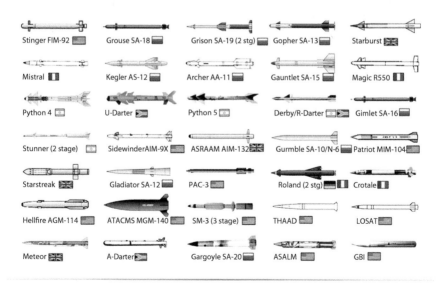

Fig. 2.22 Most supersonic missiles are wingless. (Permission of Missile Index. Copyright 1997©Missile Index. All rights reserved.)

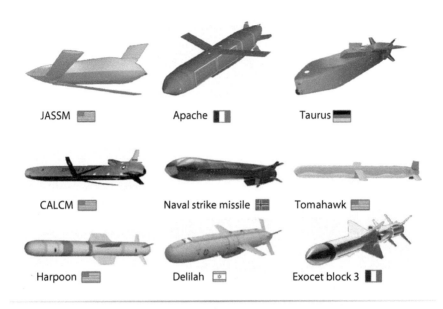

Fig. 2.23 Subsonic cruise missiles have relatively large wings and use tail flight control. Permission of Missile Index.

wings (four panels) are Harpoon and Exocet. Cruise missiles with cruciform wings (four panels) have somewhat smaller wings. A subsonic cruise missile with a large single wing has an advantage of longer range while a subsonic cruise missile with cruciform wings has an advantage of smaller span for launch platform compatibility. All of the above cruise missiles use tail flight control. Canard control is usually not appropriate for a subsonic cruise missile because of the large induced roll with the large wing.

2.13 Planar Aerodynamic Surface Geometry Parameters

Aerodynamic surface geometry parameters used in the missile conceptual design methods of this text are defined in Fig. 2.24. The conceptual design methods of this text treat each of the aerodynamic surfaces (e.g., body, wing, tail) independently and the interactions of the body-tail, body-wing, and wing-tail are neglected. Aerodynamic predictions are based on the exposed planform. The aerodynamic surface parameter definitions are:

c_{mac} = mean aerodynamic chord length

Λ_{LE} = leading edge sweep angle

δ_{LE} = leading edge section total angle

t_{mac} = maximum thickness of mean aerodynamic chord

b_e = span of exposed planform

S_e = area of exposed planform

$A_e = b_e^2/S_e$ = aspect ratio of exposed planform

2.14 Normal Force Prediction for Surfaces (e.g., Wing, Tail, Canard)

Wing, tail, and canard surfaces may be characterized by their location relative to the center-of-gravity, cg. Wing surfaces are located near the cg while tail surfaces are located aft of the cg and canard surfaces are located forward of the cg. Strake surfaces have very low aspect ratio ($A < 1$). Strakes may be located forward, aft, or near the center-of-gravity. Wing, tail, and canard surfaces may be fixed or movable (i.e., control surfaces). The Ref. 10 methodology for predicting the normal force on the wing is also applicable to other surfaces, such as tails and canards. The Ref. 10 respective equations for the normal force coefficient derivative based on linear wing theory and slender wing theory are respectively

$$dC_N/d\alpha \approx \left[4/\left(M^2 - 1\right)^{1/2}\right](S_{\text{Surface}}/S_{\text{Ref}}), \quad \text{if } \alpha <\approx 10 \deg,$$

$$M > \{1 + [8/(\pi A)]^2\}^{1/2}$$

$$dC_N/d\alpha \approx (\pi A/2)(S_{\text{Surface}}/S_{\text{Ref}}), \quad \text{if } \alpha <\approx 10 \deg, A < 3,$$

$$M < \{1 + [8/(\pi A)]^2\}^{1/2}$$

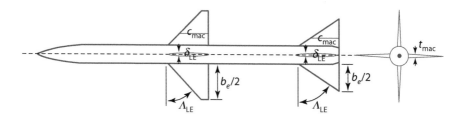

c_{mac} = mean aerodynamic chord length

Λ_{LE} = leading edge sweep angle

δ_{LE} = leading edge section total angle

t_{mac} = max thickness of mean aerodynamic chord

b_e = span of exposed planform

S_e = area of exposed planform

$A_e = b_e^2/S_e$ = aspect ratio of exposed planform

Fig. 2.24 Definition of planar aerodynamic surface geometry parameters.

Slender wing theory has excellent accuracy for low aspect ratio (e.g., $A = 1$) with incompressible flow (e.g., $M < 0.5$) and no wing sweep. At high aspect ratio (e.g., $A = 3$) with incompressible flow, slender wing theory equation over-predicts the effect of aspect ratio. At transonic Mach number the effect of compressibility tends to compensate for this error. Slender wing theory does not account for the effects of wing sweep and taper ratio. For $A > 2$, increasing wing sweep significantly decreases normal force.

Note from Fig. 2.25 that aerodynamic surfaces are more effective at subsonic Mach number if they are high aspect ratio. As a first order effect, doubling the aspect ratio doubles the normal force at a subsonic Mach number. However, an advantage of a low aspect ratio surface is there is less change in the aerodynamics with Mach number. For a high supersonic Mach number, there is a negligible effect of aspect ratio on normal force.

As an example, assume the rocket baseline missile wing, which has an exposed aspect ratio $A_e = 2.82$. Assume a Mach number $M = 0.8$. The test of the maximum Mach number to accurately use slender wing theory is $(M_{max})_{\text{Slender wing theory}} = \{1 + [8/(\pi A)]^2\}^{1/2} = 1.35$. Since $M = 0.8 < 1.35$, we can use slender wing theory.

Next compute the normal force coefficient derivative $dC_N/d\alpha \approx [\pi(2.82)/2](2.55/0.349) = 32.4$ per rad, based on the body cross section area (missile reference area).

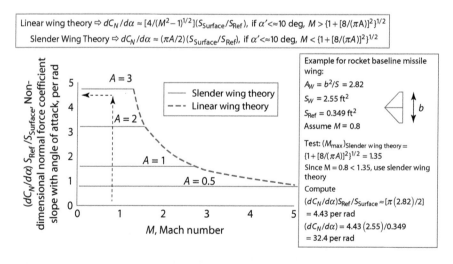

Linear wing theory $\Rightarrow dC_N/d\alpha \approx [4/(M^2-1)^{1/2}](S_{\text{Surface}}/S_{\text{Ref}})$, if $\alpha' < \approx 10$ deg, $M > \{1 + [8/(\pi A)]^2\}^{1/2}$

Slender Wing Theory $\Rightarrow dC_N/d\alpha \approx (\pi A/2)(S_{\text{Surface}}/S_{\text{Ref}})$, if $\alpha' < \approx 10$ deg, $M < \{1 + [8/(\pi A)]^2\}^{1/2}$

Example for rocket baseline missile wing:
$A_W = b^2/S = 2.82$
$S_W = 2.55$ ft^2
$S_{\text{Ref}} = 0.349$ ft^2
Assume $M = 0.8$

Test: $(M_{max})_{\text{Slender wing theory}} = \{1 + [8/(\pi A)]^2\}^{1/2} = 1.35$
Since $M = 0.8 < 1.35$, use slender wing theory
Compute
$(dC_N/d\alpha)S_{\text{Ref}}/S_{\text{Surface}} \approx [\pi(2.82)/2]$
$= 4.43$ per rad
$(dC_N/d\alpha) = 4.43 (2.55)/0.349$
$= 32.4$ per rad

Note: Linear wing theory and slender wing theory equations form USAF stability and control DATCOM. A = aspect ratio, S_{Surface} = surface planform area, S_{Ref} = reference area, α = angle of attack. Slender wing theory good accuracy limited to $A < \approx 2$ for small effects of compressibility, wing sweep, and taper ratio.

Fig. 2.25 Normal force coefficient of planar surfaces (Wings, Tails, Canards) is higher at low Mach number.

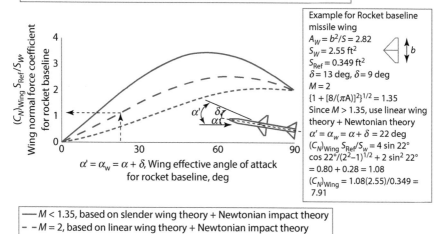

$$\left|(C_N)_{\text{Surface}}\right| = \left(\frac{4\left|\sin\alpha'\cos\alpha'\right| + 2\sin^2\alpha'}{(M^2-1)^{1/2}}\right)(S_{\text{Surface}}/S_{\text{Ref}}),\ \text{if } M > \{1+[8/(\pi A)]^2\}^{1/2}$$

$$\left|(C_N)_{\text{Surface}}\right| = [(\pi A/2)|\sin\alpha'\cos\alpha'| + 2\sin^2\alpha'](S_{\text{Surface}}/S_{\text{Ref}}),\ \text{if } M < \{1+[8/(\pi A)]^2\}^{1/2}$$

Note: Linear wing theory applicable if $M > \{1+[8/(\pi A)]^2\}^{1/2}$, slender win theory applicable if $M < \{1+[8/(\pi A)]^2\}^{1/2}$, A = Aspect ratlo, S_{Surface} = Surface planform area, S_{Ref} = Reference area, α' = Effective angle of attack, M = Mach number

Example for Rocket baseline missile wing
$A_W = b^2/S = 2.82$
$S_W = 2.55\ \text{ft}^2$
$S_{\text{Ref}} = 0.349\ \text{ft}^2$
$\delta = 13$ deg, $\delta = 9$ deg
$M = 2$
$\{1 + [8/(\pi A)]^2\}^{1/2} = 1.35$
Since $M > 1.35$, use linear wing theory + Newtonian theory
$\alpha' = \alpha_w = \alpha + \delta = 22$ deg
$(C_N)_{\text{Wing}}\ S_{\text{Ref}}/S_w = 4\sin 22°$
$\cos 22°/(2^2-1)^{1/2} + 2\sin^2 22°$
$= 0.80 + 0.28 = 1.08$
$(C_N)_{\text{Wing}} = 1.08(2.55)/0.349 = 7.91$

(vertical axis label) $(C_N)_{\text{Wing}}\ S_{\text{Ref}}/S_W$ Wing normal force coefficient for rocket baseline

(horizontal axis) $\alpha' = \alpha_w = \alpha + \delta$, Wing effective angle of attack for rocket baseline, deg

— $M < 1.35$, based on slender wing theory + Newtonian impact theory
– – $M = 2$, based on linear wing theory + Newtonian impact theory
--- $M = 5$, based on linear wing theory + Newtonian impact theory

Fig. 2.26 High normal force for planar surfaces occurs at high angle of attack.

Note that the normal force coefficient derivative of the rocket baseline missile wing is much greater than the normal force coefficient derivative of the body (32.4 versus 2 per rad).

As shown in the equations of Fig. 2.26, the surface normal force coefficient $(C_N)_{\text{Surface}}$ is a function of Mach number, local angle of attack, aspect ratio, and the surface planform area. $(C_N)_{\text{Surface}}$ decreases with increasing supersonic Mach number and increases with angle of attack and the surface area. In the figure, linear wing theory [10] plus Newtonian impact theory [9] are applied at supersonic Mach number, with the requirement that

$$M > \{1 + [8/(\pi A)]^2\}^{1/2}$$

The linear wing theory plus Newtonian impact theory equation is

$$\left|(C_N)_{\text{Surface}}\right| = \left[4|\sin\alpha'\cos\alpha'|/(M^2-1)^{1/2} + 2\sin^2\alpha'\right](S_{\text{Surface}}/S_{\text{Ref}})$$

Note that $(C_N)_{\text{Surface}}$ based on linear wing theory is independent of aspect ratio. For the rocket baseline missile wing with an aspect ratio of $A_W = 2.82$, linear wing theory is applicable for Mach numbers greater than 1.35. An alternative approach, slender wing theory [10] plus Newtonian impact theory [9] is more applicable at subsonic and low supersonic Mach number, with the requirement that

$$M < \{1 + [8/(\pi A)]^2\}^{1/2}$$

The slender wing theory plus Newtonian impact theory equation is

$$\left|(C_N)_{\text{Surface}}\right| = [(\pi A/2)|\sin \alpha' \cos \alpha'| + 2\sin^2 \alpha'] \, (S_{\text{Surface}}/S_{\text{Ref}})$$

Note that the above $(C_N)_{\text{Surface}}$, based on slender wing theory, is independent of Mach number. Slender wing theory is accurate for low aspect ratio wings (A $<\approx$ 3). As a comparison with lifting surface theory, which is most applicable to high aspect ratio surfaces, at an aspect ratio of A = 3, slender wing theory over-predicts normal force. For the rocket baseline missile wing (A_W = 2.82), slender wing theory is applicable for Mach numbers less than 1.35.

As an example, we shall evaluate the rocket baseline missile wing at Mach 2. Because the Mach number is greater than 1.35, the prediction is based on linear wing theory plus Newtonian impact theory. The rocket baseline missile wing is limited to a maximum local angle of attack of α' = 22 deg, because of stall of the wing. For a typical cg location, this results in an angle of attack of the body and tail of α = 9.4 deg for a maximum wing control deflection of δ = 12.6 deg. For this condition, the normal force coefficient of the wing, based on wing area S_W = 2.55 ft^2, is equal to

$$(C_N)_{\text{Wing}} S_{\text{Ref}}/S_W = 4\sin 22°\cos 22°/(2^2 - 1)^{1/2} + 2\sin^2 22° = 0.80 + 0.28$$
$$= 1.08$$

Note that even at the relatively high local angle of attack of α' = 22 deg, 74% of the normal force coefficient is due to the linear contribution from slender wing theory (0.80/1.08 = 0.74).

Finally, the normal coefficient of the wing, based on the body reference cross sectional area S_{Ref} = 0.349 ft^2, is computed to be

$$(C_N)_{\text{Wing}} = 1.08 \, (2.55)/0.349 = 7.91$$

Because the rocket baseline missile has a relatively large wing, most of the normal force of the missile comes from the wing. The following example shows the relative contributions to the total normal force coefficient of the rocket baseline missile. Contributors to the total normal force coefficient are the missile body, wing, and tail.

The rocket baseline missile has fixed tail surfaces with an exposed tail aspect ratio A_T = 2.59 and a tail planform area S_T = 1.54 ft^2. At Mach 2 and an angle of attack $\alpha = 9.4$ deg, the normal force coefficient of the tail is computed to be $(C_N)_{\text{Tail}} = 0.425$, based on the tail surface planform area. Based on the missile reference area, $(C_N)_{\text{Tail}} = 1.88$. Note that for the trimmed flight condition of Mach 2 and $\alpha = 9.4$ deg, the tail normal force is relatively small compared to that of the deflected wing $[(C_N)_{\text{Tail}}/(C_N)_{\text{Wing}} = 1.88/7.91 = 0.24]$. The total normal force coefficient of the wing-tail-body configuration is assumed to be the sum of the contributions from the wing plus the tail plus the body. As shown previously, the body normal force coefficient is a function of angle of attack, fineness ratio, and cross section geometry. The rocket baseline missile has a circular cross section $(a/b = 1)$ and a fineness ratio $l/d = 17.99$. At an angle of attack of $\alpha = 9.4$ deg, the body normal force coefficient is computed to be

$$(C_N)_{\text{Body}} = \sin(2\alpha)\cos(\alpha/2) + 1.3(l/d)\sin^2\alpha = 1.28$$

Note that the body normal force coefficient is only 16% of that provided by the deflected wing. Substituting, the total trimmed normal force coefficient at Mach 2, $\alpha = 9.4$ deg, and $\delta = 12.6$ deg is

$$C_N = (C_N)_{\text{Wing}} + (C_N)_{\text{Tail}} + (C_N)_{\text{Body}} = 7.91 + 1.88 + 1.28 = 11.1$$

A similar approach can be used to determine the wing normal force curve slope from angle of attack. $(C_{N_\alpha})_{\text{Surface}}$ is used in sizing the tail to meet the static stability requirement. It is the derivative of the equation for surface normal force coefficient. At low angle of attack, $(C_{N_\alpha})_{\text{Surface}} = 4/(M^2 - 1)^{1/2}$, if the parameter $M^2 > 1 + [8/(\pi A)]^2$. If the parameter $M^2 < 1 + [8/(\pi A)]^2$, then the appropriate equation is $(C_{N_\alpha})_{\text{Surface}} = \pi A/2$. Note that $(C_{N_\alpha})_{\text{Surface}}$ in these equations is based on the surface planform area and has the units per rad.

The total normal force curve slope from angle of attack is assumed to be the sum of the contributions from the wing plus the tail plus the body. As shown previously, the body normal force curve slope at low angle of attack is $(C_{N_\alpha})_{\text{Body}} = 2[(a/b)\cos^2\varphi + (b/a)\sin^2\varphi]$. For the rocket baseline missile with a circular cross section $(a/b = 1)$, $(C_{N_\alpha})_{\text{Body}} = 2$ per radian. At Mach 2, the total normal force curve slope at low angle of attack, based on body cross sectional reference area is

$$C_{N_\alpha} = (C_{N_\alpha})_{\text{Wing}}(S_W/S_{\text{Ref}}) + (C_{N_\alpha})_{\text{Tail}}(S_T/S_{\text{Ref}}) + (C_{N_\alpha})_{\text{Body}}$$
$$= 4/(2^2 - 1)^{1/2}(2.55/0.349) + 4/(2^2 - 1)^{1/2}(1.54/0.349) + 2$$
$$= 16.9 + 10.2 + 2 = 29.1 \text{ per rad}$$

As a comparison, the total normal force curve slope from angle of attack (Chapter 7), which is based on wind tunnel data, is $C_{N_\alpha} = 34.4$ per rad. The predicted value of C_{N_α} has an error of 14%.

The normal force prediction is likely to be optimistic for very low Mach number (e.g., $M < 0.2$) and for very high altitude (e.g., $h > 80{,}000$ ft). For these flight conditions, boundary layer transition from laminar to turbulent is delayed, resulting in a thicker boundary layer. The boundary layer thickness on the aft body may blanket a significant portion of the tails, reducing the stability and control effectiveness of the tails.

2.15 Aerodynamic Center Prediction for Planar Surfaces (e.g., Wing, Tail, Canard)

Shown in Fig. 2.27 is the variation of aerodynamic center $(x_{AC})_{Surface}$ of a planar surface (e.g., wings, tails, canards) with Mach number and aspect ratio. Results are applicable at low angles of attack ($\alpha < 10$ deg). At low Mach number, $(x_{AC})_{Surface}$ is located near 25% of the mean aerodynamic chord c_{mac}. At hypersonic Mach number, $(x_{AC})_{Surface}$ shifts to 50% of c_{mac}. Missiles with relatively long chord surfaces, such as AMRAAM AIM-120C, usually have large hinge moment at supersonic Mach number. The prediction of aerodynamic center at supersonic Mach number and low angle of attack, based on linear wing theory[5], is

$$(x_{AC}/c_{mac})_{Surface} = \left[A(M^2 - 1)^{1/2} - 0.67\right] / \left[2A(M^2 - 1)^{1/2} - 1\right]$$

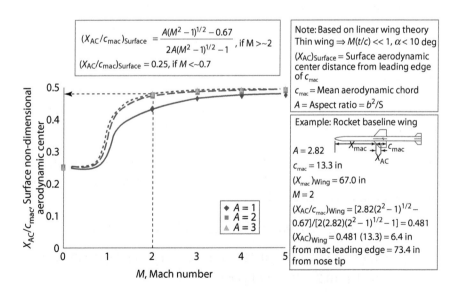

Fig. 2.27 Aerodynamic center of planar surfaces moves aft with Mach number. (Reference: Chin, S.S., *Missile Configuration Design*. McGraw-Hill Book Company, 1961.)

The following example calculation of $(x_{AC})_{Surface}$ is based on the wing of the rocket baseline missile. It has an exposed aspect ratio $A = 2.82$, a mean aerodynamic chord length $c_{mac} = 13.3$ in, and a location of the leading edge of the mean aerodynamic chord at 67.0 in from the nose tip. As shown in the figure, at Mach 2 the predicted aerodynamic center of the exposed wing is located at 48% of the length of the mean aerodynamic chord, providing a location of $(x_{AC})_{wing} = 73.4$ in from the nose tip. At subsonic Mach number, the wing aerodynamic center is located at approximately 25% of the mean aerodynamic chord, providing a location of $(x_{AC})_{wing} = 70.3$ in from the nose tip. The center-of-gravity location of the rocket baseline missile is 84.6 in from the nose tip at launch, and 76.2 in at burnout. Because the distance between the wing aerodynamic center and the missile center of gravity is always relatively small (less than 14.3 in) for all flight conditions, the deflection of the wing control causes a relatively small change in the rocket baseline missile angle of attack. If alternatives of tail control or canard control were used for the rocket baseline missile instead of wing control, the change in angle of attack with control surface deflection would be larger, because of the larger moment arm of a tail or canard control.

2.16 Hinge Moment Prediction

The hinge moment (HM) of an aerodynamic control surface is a function of the normal force $N_{Surface}$ on the surface times the moment arm between the aerodynamic center and the hinge line of the control surface $(x_{AC}-x_{HL})_{Surface}$. The equation is

$$HM = N_{Surface}(x_{AC} - x_{HL})_{Surface}$$

Shown in Fig. 2.28 is the variation of hinge moment with dynamic pressure and effective angle of attack for the rocket baseline missile. An assumed flight altitude is $h = 20,000$ ft altitude. As previously, the prediction of $N_{Surface}$ is based on the Ref. 10 linear wing theory at high supersonic Mach number and slender wing theory at subsonic and low supersonic Mach number. An assumption of slender wing and linear wing theories is that the surface section is thin $[M(t/c) \ll 1]$. From slender wing theory, at low subsonic Mach number, the aerodynamic center is located at the quarter chord of the mean aerodynamic center $(x_{AC} = 0.25c_{mac})$. For the example of the figure, the hinge line of the control surface of the rocket baseline missile is also assumed to be located at $x_{HL} = 0.25c_{mac}$. The hinge must be located either at or forward of the aerodynamic center, to avoid unstable feedback through the flight control system.

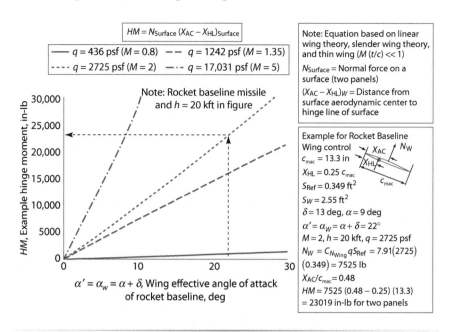

$HM = N_{\text{Surface}} (X_{AC} - X_{HL})_{\text{Surface}}$

— $q = 436$ psf ($M = 0.8$) — — $q = 1242$ psf ($M = 1.35$)
···· $q = 2725$ psf ($M = 2$) —·— $q = 17{,}031$ psf ($M = 5$)

Note: Equation based on linear wing theory, slender wing theory, and thin wing (M (t/c) << 1)
N_{Surface} = Normal force on a surface (two panels)
$(X_{AC} - X_{HL})_W$ = Distance from surface aerodynamic center to hinge line of surface

Note: Rocket baseline missile and $h = 20$ kft in figure

HM, Example hinge moment, in-lb

30,000
25,000
20,000
15,000
10,000
5000
0

0   10   20   30

$\alpha' = \alpha_w = \alpha + \delta$, Wing effective angle of attack of rocket baseline, deg

Example for Rocket Baseline
Wing control
$c_{mac} = 13.3$ in
$X_{HL} = 0.25\, c_{mac}$
$S_{Ref} = 0.349$ ft^2
$S_W = 2.55$ ft^2
$\delta = 13$ deg, $\alpha = 9$ deg
$\alpha' = \alpha_w = \alpha + \delta = 22°$
$M = 2$, $h = 20$ kft, $q = 2725$ psf
$N_W = C_{N_{Wing}} q S_{Ref} = 7.91(2725)$
$(0.349) = 7525$ lb
$X_{AC}/c_{mac} = 0.48$
$HM = 7525\,(0.48 - 0.25)\,(13.3)$
$= 23019$ in-lb for two panels

Fig. 2.28 Hinge moment increases with dynamic pressure and the effective angle of attack.

An example calculation is given for the rocket baseline missile wing control at Mach 2 and a maximum effective angle of attack $\alpha' = \alpha_W = 22$ deg. For this condition, the control deflection $\delta = 13$ deg and the body angle of attack $\alpha = 9$ deg. The total normal force on the two panels that comprise the wing is

$$N_{\text{Wing}} = [C_{N_{\text{Wing}}} q S_{\text{Ref}} = 7.91(2725)(0.349) = 7525\,\text{lb}$$

In the above equation, the value of $C_{N_{\text{Wing}}}$ is from a previous calculation of the rocket baseline missile wing and is based on the missile reference area (body cross section area $= 0.349$ in^2).

Also from a previous calculation, the aerodynamic center of the rocket baseline missile wing at Mach 2, is located at 48% of the mean aerodynamic center ($x_{AC} = 0.48\, c_{mac}$). Finally, calculating the hinge moment HM of the rocket baseline missile wing control at Mach 2, 20 kft altitude with maximum wing control deflection

$$HM = 7525(0.48 - 0.25)(13.3)$$

$$= 23{,}019\,\text{in-lb for the two panels that comprise the wing.}$$

Each actuator of the two panels has an individual hinge moment of 11, 510 in-lb. Control surface actuators are sized by the highest hinge moment flight condition, which usually occurs at the maximum maneuverability requirement for the highest dynamic pressure flight condition.

2.17 Planar Surface (e.g., Wing, Tail, Canard) Drag Prediction

For a subsonic planar surface, the dominant contributor to the total drag coefficient is skin friction. For a supersonic planar surface, the dominant contributors are skin friction and wave drag. A third potential contributor is base drag from flow separation on the trailing edge of the surface. However, for a surface with a sharp trailing edge, there is negligible flow separation. Base drag can usually be neglected in the aerodynamic analysis of most missile planar surfaces, which are usually thin.

The equation for predicting skin friction drag coefficient is shown in Fig. 2.29. The surface skin friction drag equation, based on Ref. 5, is

$$(C_{D_0})_{\text{Surface,Friction}} = n_{\text{Surface}} \left\{ 0.0133[M/(qc_{\text{mac}})]^{0.2} \right\} (2S_{\text{Surface}}/S_{\text{Ref}})$$

In the above equation the units of dynamic pressure q and mean aerodynamic chord c_{mac} are psf and ft respectively. Major contributors to the skin friction drag coefficient are the number of surface planforms

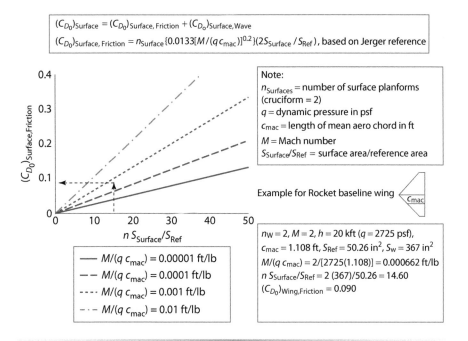

$(C_{D_0})_{\text{Surface}} = (C_{D_0})_{\text{Surface, Friction}} + (C_{D_0})_{\text{Surface,Wave}}$

$(C_{D_0})_{\text{Surface, Friction}} = n_{\text{Surface}} \{0.0133[M/(q\,c_{\text{mac}})]^{0.2}\}(2S_{\text{Surface}} / S_{\text{Ref}})$, based on Jerger reference

Note:
n_{Surfaces} = number of surface planforms (cruciform = 2)
q = dynamic pressure in psf
c_{mac} = length of mean aero chord in ft
M = Mach number
$S_{\text{Surface}}/S_{\text{Ref}}$ = surface area/reference area

Example for Rocket baseline wing

$n_W = 2$, $M = 2$, $h = 20$ kft ($q = 2725$ psf),
$c_{\text{mac}} = 1.108$ ft, $S_{\text{Ref}} = 50.26$ in^2, $S_W = 367$ in^2
$M/(q\,c_{\text{mac}}) = 2/[2725(1.108)] = 0.000662$ ft/lb
$n\,S_{\text{Surface}}/S_{\text{Ref}} = 2\,(367)/50.26 = 14.60$
$(C_{D_0})_{\text{Wing,Friction}} = 0.090$

— $M/(q\,c_{\text{mac}})$ = 0.00001 ft/lb
– – $M/(q\,c_{\text{mac}})$ = 0.0001 ft/lb
···· $M/(q\,c_{\text{mac}})$ = 0.001 ft/lb
–··– $M/(q\,c_{\text{mac}})$ = 0.01 ft/lb

Fig. 2.29 Skin friction drag is lower for a small surface area.

n_{Surface} and the planform surface area S_{Surface}. The total wetted surface area is equal to $2n_{\text{Surface}}S_{\text{Surface}}$. Note from the above equation for $(C_{D_0})_{\text{Surface,Friction}}$ that surface skin friction drag coefficient is a weak function of Mach number, dynamic pressure, and the length of the mean aerodynamic chord. The dominant contributor is the total wetted surface area $2n_{\text{Surface}}S_{\text{Surface}}$. Assumptions for the equation are that the variation in the free stream speed of sound and viscosity with altitude is relatively small, and a turbulent boundary layer.

As an example calculation of skin friction drag, the rocket baseline missile has cruciform wings ($n_W = 2$), an exposed planform area of each wing $S_W = 2.55$ ft², reference area based on the body cross sectional area of $S_{\text{Ref}} = 0.349$ ft², and length of the mean aerodynamic chord $c_{\text{mac}} = 1.108$ ft. At a typical flight condition of Mach 2/20,000 ft altitude, the wing skin friction contribution to zero-lift drag, based on two wings (four panels), is

$$(C_{D_0})_{\text{Wing,Friction}} = 2\{0.0133\{2/[(2725)(1.108)]\}^{0.2}\}[2(367)/(50.26)]$$

$$= 0.090$$

A second contributor to surface drag is wave drag. The wave drag prediction is based on modified Newtonian impact theory, described in Ref. 9, with the equation

$$(C_{D_0})_{\text{Surface,Wave}} = n_{\text{Surface}}\left[2/\left(\gamma M_{\text{ALE}}^2\right)\right]\left\{\left\{[(\gamma+1)M_{\text{ALE}}^2]/2\right\}^{\gamma/(\gamma-1)}\right.$$

$$\times \left\{(\gamma+1)/[2\gamma M_{\text{ALE}}^2 - (\gamma-1)]\right\}^{1/(\gamma-1)} - 1\}$$

$$\times \sin^2 \delta_{\text{LE}} \cos \Lambda_{\text{LE}} t_{\text{mac}} b/S_{\text{Ref}}$$

Newtonian theory is modified by calculating the pressure across the normal shock as a function of Mach number. Substituting $\gamma = 1.4$ for air gives

$$(C_{D_0})_{\text{Surface,Wave}} = n_{\text{Surface}}(1.429/M_{\text{ALE}}^2)\{(1.2M_{\text{ALE}}^2)^{3.5}[2.4/(2.8M_{\text{ALE}}^2$$

$$- 0.4)]^{2.5} - 1\} \sin^2 \delta_{\text{LE}} \cos \Lambda_{\text{LE}} t_{\text{mac}} b/S_{\text{Ref}}$$

Note from Fig. 2.30 that a small leading edge section angle (e.g., $\delta_{\text{LE}} = 5°$) has much smaller wave drag than a blunt leading edge ($\delta_{\text{LE}} = 90°$). Also, leading edge sweep reduces the effect of Mach number by the factor of $\cos\Lambda_{LE}$.

As an example, we will calculate the wave drag of the rocket baseline missile wing. It has cruciform wings ($n_W = 2$), wing leading edge sweep angle of $\Lambda_{\text{LE}} = 45$ deg, exposed planform area of each wing $S_W = 2.55$ square feet, leading edge section angle $\delta_{\text{LE}} = 10.01$ deg, maximum

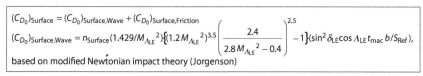

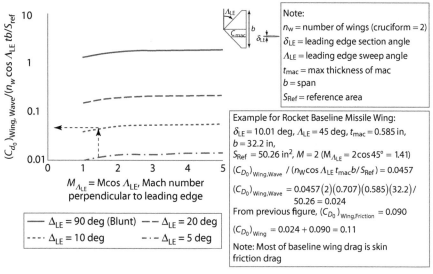

Fig. 2.30 Supersonic shock wave drag of a planar surface is smaller with a swept leading edge and a small section angle.

thickness of the mean aerodynamic chord $t_{mac} = 0.585$ inch, and exposed span $b = 32.2$ inches.

At Mach 2, $M_{ALE} = 2\cos 45° = 1.41$. The zero-lift wave drag coefficient of the cruciform wing (four panels), based on the reference area (body cross-sectional reference) is

$$(C_{D_0})_{\text{Wing,Wave}} = 2(1.429/1.41^2)$$
$$\times \left\{ \left[(1.2)(1.41^2)\right]^{3.5} \left\{ 2.4/\left[(2.8)(1.41^2 - 0.4)\right] \right\}^{2.5} - 1 \right\}$$
$$\times (\sin^2 10.01°)(\cos 45°)(0.585)(32.2)/(50.26)$$
$$= 0.024$$

Note from the previous figure, the wing skin friction drag coefficient for an assumed altitude of 20,000 feet is larger, with $(C_{D_0})_{\text{Wing,Friction}} = 0.090$. The total zero-lift drag coefficient is $(C_{D_0})_{\text{Wing}} = 0.02 + 0.09 = 0.11$. Note that 82% of the rocket baseline missile wing zero-lift drag is from skin friction.

Comparing with the previous calculation of body zero-lift drag coefficient, the rocket baseline missile wing has a zero-lift drag coefficient that is only 27% of the body coast zero-lift drag coefficient (0.11 versus 0.41). At supersonic Mach number, nose wave drag is the major contributor to the zero-lift drag.

The rocket baseline missile has cruciform tail surfaces ($n_T = 2$), tail leading edge sweep angle of $\Lambda_{LE} = 57$ deg, exposed tail planform area of $S_T = 1.54$ ft^2, leading edge section total angle $\delta_{LE} = 6.17$ deg, mean aerodynamic chord $c_{mac} = 1.025$ ft, maximum thickness of the mean aerodynamic chord $t_{mac} = 0.33$ in, and exposed span $b = 24.0$ in. At Mach 2/20,000 ft altitude, the zero-lift drag coefficient of the tail surfaces, based on the missile reference area, is computed to be

$$(C_{D_0})_{Tail} = (C_{D_0})_{Tail,Wave} + (C_{D_0})_{Tail,Friction} = 0.003 + 0.048 = 0.051$$

From above, the zero-lift drag of the tails is seen to be smaller than that of the wing. The tails have smaller leading edge section angle (6.17 versus 10.01 deg) and smaller planform area (1.54 versus 2.55 ft^2). Note that for the flight condition of Mach 2/20,000 ft altitude, the tail provides 12% of the zero-lift drag compared to that of the body.

Finally, the total zero-lift drag coefficient is assumed to be the sum of the contributions from the body plus the wings plus the tails. The assumption neglects wing-body, body-wing, tail-body, body-tail, and wing-tail interference[8]. Substituting, the total zero-lift drag coefficient of the rocket baseline missile during coasting flight at Mach 2 and 20,000 ft altitude is computed to be

$$C_{D_0} = (C_{D_0})_{Body} + (C_{D_0})_{Wing} + (C_{D_0})_{Tail} = 0.41 + 0.11 + 0.05 = 0.57$$

Figure 2.31 shows the drivers of wing aerodynamic efficiency lift-to-drag ratio L/D for typical values of missile wing aspect ratio and zero-lift drag coefficient. Maximum L/D is provided by a wing with high aspect ratio and low zero-lift drag coefficient, operating at a relatively low angle of attack of about 4 deg. Note that the L/D of a typical wing is much greater than the body L/D that was shown previously.

To calculate L/D, the body axes normal force coefficient C_N and zero-lift drag coefficient C_{D_0} are transferred to the stability axes coefficients C_L and C_D. L/D is then obtained from

$$L/D = C_L/C_D = (C_N \cos \alpha - C_{D_0} \sin \alpha)/(C_N \sin \alpha + C_{D_0} \cos \alpha)$$

If the wing satisfies the criteria for a slender wing ($M < \{1 + [8/(\pi A)]^2\}^{1/2}$), then from Ref. 10 the equation for normal

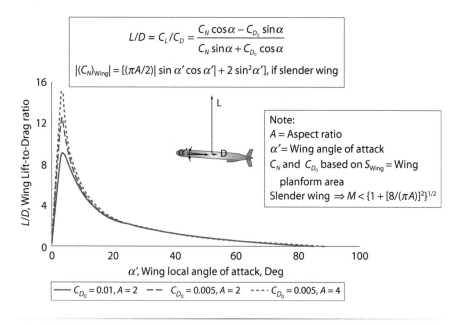

$$L/D = C_L/C_D = \frac{C_N \cos\alpha - C_{D_0} \sin\alpha}{C_N \sin\alpha + C_{D_0} \cos\alpha}$$

$|(C_N)_{\text{Wing}}| = [(\pi A/2)|\sin\alpha'\cos\alpha'| + 2\sin^2\alpha']$, if slender wing

Note:
A = Aspect ratio
α' = Wing angle of attack
C_N and C_{D_0} based on S_{Wing} = Wing
   planform area
Slender wing $\Rightarrow M < \{1 + [8/(\pi A)]^2\}^{1/2}$

α', Wing local angle of attack, Deg

L/D, Wing Lift-to-Drag ratio

— $C_{D_0} = 0.01, A = 2$ – – $C_{D_0} = 0.005, A = 2$ ···· $C_{D_0} = 0.005, A = 4$

Fig. 2.31 Wing subsonic aerodynamic efficiency L/D is driven by angle of attack, C_{D_0}, and aspect ratio.

force coefficient is

$$\left|(C_N)_{\text{Wing}}\right| = \left[(\pi A/2)|\sin\alpha'\cos\alpha'| + 2\sin^2\alpha'\right]$$

In the above equation, A = wing aspect ratio and α' = wing angle of attack. $(C_N)_{\text{Wing}}$ and C_{D_0} are based on S_{Wing} = wing planform area.

2.18 Surface Planform Geometry and Integration Alternatives

Shown in Fig. 2.32 are examples of alternative surface panel geometries for missile tails, canards, and wings. The figure compares 1) a triangular (delta), 2) a conventional trapezoidal with an aft swept leading edge, 3) a "bow tie" trapezoidal with a forward swept leading edge and an aft swept trailing edge, 4) a double swept leading edge, and 5) a rectangular surface planform geometry. The comparison is based on the same planform area, because roughly the same area is required to provide the same static stability and maneuverability. The comparison also considers that there may be a span constraint, which is often the case for launch platform compatibility.

Note from the figure that the triangular (delta) surface geometry has strengths of a low bending moment/less required thickness for structural

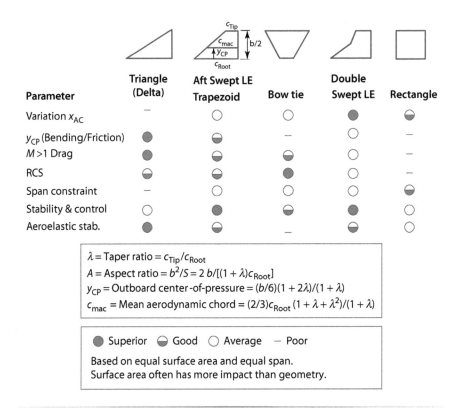

Parameter	Triangle (Delta)	Aft Swept LE Trapezoid	Bow tie	Double Swept LE	Rectangle
Variation x_{AC}	–	○	○	●	◐
y_{CP} (Bending/Friction)	●	◐	–	○	–
$M > 1$ Drag	●	◐	◐	○	–
RCS	◐	◐	●	○	–
Span constraint	–	○	○	○	◐
Stability & control	○	●	◐	●	○
Aeroelastic stab.	●	◐	–	◐	○

λ = Taper ratio = c_{Tip}/c_{Root}
A = Aspect ratio = $b^2/S = 2\,b/[(1+\lambda)c_{Root}]$
y_{CP} = Outboard center-of-pressure = $(b/6)(1+2\lambda)/(1+\lambda)$
c_{mac} = Mean aerodynamic chord = $(2/3)c_{Root}\,(1+\lambda+\lambda^2)/(1+\lambda)$

● Superior ◐ Good ○ Average – Poor
Based on equal surface area and equal span.
Surface area often has more impact than geometry.

Fig. 2.32 Planar surface (wing, tail, canard) panel geometry tradeoff.

integrity (which results in lighter weight), low supersonic drag (because of the larger sweep angle), relatively low frontal radar cross section, and a high structural stiffness. Disadvantages of delta geometry are the larger span, which may be a problem for launch platform integration, and a large variation in aerodynamic center. AGM-65 is an example of a missile with wing panels that have a triangular planform.

A second alternative, a trapezoidal surface with an aft swept leading edge, is often selected for missile wing, canard, and tail surfaces because it has high control effectiveness and does not have any serious weaknesses in the other attributes. Patriot and AIM-9X are examples.

Another example is the bow tie geometry, with a forward swept leading edge and an aft swept trailing edge. A bow tie geometry is beneficial for missiles that require low frontal and rear radar cross section (RCS). The swept leading and trailing edges reflect the specular, traveling wave, and creeping wave returns away from the threat and backscatter bouncing off the adjacent body is further attenuated. In addition to a low RCS, the bow tie geometry has low supersonic drag and good control effectiveness, especially roll control. An inherent disadvantage of a bow tie is the increased potential for aeroelastic instability. Composite structure is synergistic with a bow tie surface because the higher stiffness of composites mitigates aeroelastic instability and facilitates aeroelastic tailoring of the wing. Composite material may also be used in radar absorbing structure. Another disadvantage of a bow tie surface is the large outboard location of the lateral center-of-pressure y_{CP}. A large value of y_{CP} results in larger bending moment, which increases the flight control shaft friction and requires more actuator torque to maintain bandwidth. A larger bending moment also requires a thicker structure, which increases the structure weight. The US AGM-129 Advanced Cruise Missile and the Russia AA-10 are examples of missiles with forward swept wings.

A double swept leading edge geometry (double delta) has a major advantage of minimizing the shift in aerodynamic center. As a wing, the double delta has more nearly constant static margin. As a control surface, the double delta geometry has reduced hinge moment, allowing lighter weight, smaller size, and lower cost actuators. In addition to a low variation in the location of aerodynamic center, the double delta has superior control effectiveness (especially at subsonic Mach number), good aeroelastic stability, and no major weaknesses in the other design considerations. Standard Missile and HARM are examples of missiles with double delta wings. Both are high speed missiles that benefit from the reduced static margin shift of a double swept leading edge wing. Examples of missile that have control surfaces with double swept leading edges are Super 530, Standard Missile, Crotale, AIM-9L, Magic, SD-10, and U-Darter. All are high speed missiles that benefit from the reduced hinge moment and lighter weight actuators of a double swept leading edge. One reason that the double delta is not more popular is the additional development and manufacturing cost of the more complex planform.

Finally, rectangular surfaces have many disadvantages and are used less often. A superior characteristic of a rectangular surface is that it has the largest surface area that can be accommodated if there are launch platform constraints on the missile surface chord and span. A rectangular planform also has a relatively small shift in aerodynamic center, because of the relatively small required chord. Major disadvantages of a rectangular planform are larger control surface shaft bending moment/friction, large supersonic drag, and larger RCS. The AGM-130 and AGM-65 are examples of missiles with rectangular tails.

The surface planform geometry parameters shown in the figure include taper ratio, aspect ratio, outboard location of the center-of-pressure, and the mean aerodynamic chord. The planform geometry is based on two panels joined at the root chord. Taper ratio is the ratio of the tip chord to the root chord ($\lambda = c_{Tip}/c_{Root}$). Aspect ratio is defined as the square of the surface span divided by the surface area ($A = b^2/S$). For a conventional planform with straight leading and trailing edges

$$A = 2b/[(1 + \lambda)c_{Root}]$$

The outboard location of the mean aerodynamic chord, or center-of-pressure location, of a straight leading/trailing edge planform is given by

$$y_{CP} = (b/6)(1 + 2\lambda)/(1 + \lambda)$$

Note from the equation for y_{CP} that $\lambda = 0$ (delta wing) provides the benefit of a small value of the lateral center-of-pressure ($y_{CP} = b/6$), resulting in a lower flight control shaft bending moment, while $\lambda = 1$ (rectangular wing) gives the adverse effect of a larger value of the lateral center-of-pressure location ($y_{CP} = b/4$) and a larger bending moment.

The equation for the length of the mean aerodynamic chord of a trapezoidal planform is

$$c_{mac} = (2/3)c_{Root}(1 + \lambda + \lambda^2)/(1 + \lambda)$$

The aerodynamic center, which is the same as the center of pressure for a surface with a symmetrical non-cambered cross section, is located on the mean aerodynamic chord.

Surface area usually has a greater impact on aerodynamic stability, control, and performance than surface geometry. Because missiles are usually span limited, they usually cannot take advantage of high aspect ratio geometry.

Wing, stabilizer, and control surface integration alternatives are shown in Fig. 2.33 for a number of planar surfaces (two to eight), folding arrangements (folded, wraparound, extended), control surface deflection (balanced actuation control, flap control), and tandem surface orientation (interdigitated, inline).

At least three tail surfaces are required for static stability. An example of a missile with three tails is the AGM-69 SRAM missile. For most missiles, the wings, tails, and canards are comprised of four surfaces (cruciform). Most missiles have a cruciform, axisymmetic configuration and use skid-to-turn maneuvering. Most missiles that have an asymmetric configuration use bank-to-turn maneuvering. An example is a cruise missile with a mono-wing (two panel).

If a missile has more than four tail surfaces, the reasons are often either a span limit imposed by the launch platform or an attempt to reduce the rolling moment from vortices. A high angle of attack missile may have six or more tail surfaces, for lower induced roll. A ballistic weapon may have six or more tail surfaces to reduce the trajectory dispersal from induced roll. An example is the gun-launched XM982 Excalibur

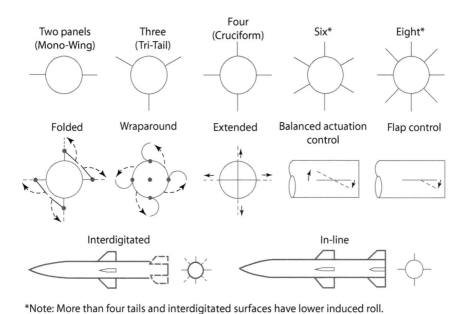

Fig. 2.33 Wing/stabilizer/control surface arrangements and alternatives.

GPS-guided weapon, which has four canard control surfaces and eight fixed stabilizer tail surfaces.

Planar surfaces may be folded to reduce the span requirement for compressed carriage on the launch platform. A folded surface usually has either a ballistic actuator or a spring that deploys the surface after separation from the launch platform. An example of a missile with folded tail surfaces is the AGM-86 cruise missile. Another approach to compressed carriage is wraparound surfaces. These are particularly suited for tube launch. A third approach is surfaces that are extended laterally after launch, such as switchblade wings and diamond back wings. The BGM-109 Tomahawk cruise missile has a switchblade wing. The enhanced range JDAM has a similar (diamond back) wing. Finally, reduced span surfaces may be used for compressed carriage on the launch platform. An example is compressed carriage AMRAAM.

Alternatives for the location of the hinge line/control shaft of flight control actuators are either near the aerodynamic center of an all movable surface (balanced actuation control) or a movable surface that is behind a fixed surface (flap control). Balanced actuation control, using an all movable surface, has advantages of lower hinge moment and lower drag. Flap control has advantages of a stable hinge moment and generally has a lower radar cross section.

Tandem surfaces include canard-tail and wing-tail planforms. Alternative orientation arrangements of the surfaces are either in-line or interdigitated. Interdigitated surfaces may have advantages of less induced roll (C_{l_ϕ}) and in some cases, better launch platform compatibility. However, in-line surfaces are usually preferred, because of lower drag and lower RCS.

2.19 Flight Control Alternatives

Most missiles have a cruciform configuration, use four aerodynamic control surfaces, and have combined integrated control of all three axes (pitch/yaw/roll). An example is the Adder AA-12. Figure 2.34 is a comparison of the control integration approaches. A few missiles have only two flight control surfaces. Advantages of missiles that use only two-axis flight control (pitch/yaw, pitch/roll) are lower cost (only two flight control actuators required) and ease of packaging (only two actuators). Stinger is a free-to-roll missile with two flight control surfaces for combined pitch/yaw control, but no active control of the roll axis. Another two-axis flight control missile is ALCM. It is a bank-to-turn missile with combined pitch/roll control, but no control of the yaw axis. A disadvantage of two-axis control is that it does not provide precision maneuvering.

Control integ	Control surfaces	Example	Control effect	Cost	Packaging
• Pitch/Yaw	2	Stinger FIM-92	Poor	Superior	Superior
• Pitch/Roll	2	ALCM AGM-86	Poor	Superior	Superior
• Pitch/Roll + Yaw	3	JASSM AGM-158	Poor	Good	Superior
• Pitch/Yaw/Roll	3	SRAM AGM-69	Poor	Good	Good
• Pitch/Yaw/Roll (Cruciform most commom type for missiles)	4	Adder AA-12	Average	Average	Average
• Pitch + Yaw + Roll	5	Kitchen AS-4	Superior	Poor	Poor
• Pitch/Yaw + Roll	6	Derby/R-Darter	Good	Poor	Poor
• Pitch/Yaw/Roll (Blended canard-Tail control)	8	Stunner	Superior	Poor	Poor

Legend: ● Superior   ◑ Good   ○ Average   — Poor

Fig. 2.34 Most aerodynamic control missiles use four flight control surfaces, with pitch/yaw/roll control integration.

Combined three-axis control requires at least three or four surfaces. The control effectiveness is typically less for a missile with three control surfaces. The JASSM cruise missile has three control surfaces. It is bank-to-turn, with combined pitch/roll control from elevons on the wings. JASSM also has independent yaw control from the vertical tail. Another missile with three flight control surfaces is SRAM. SRAM is a skid-to-turn missile with combined pitch/yaw/roll control from its three control surfaces. SRAM fits in the B-1 and B-52 rotary launchers without folding its surfaces. A disadvantage of three surfaces is a larger induced rolling moment. Also, it is more difficult to design an efficient autopilot. Another potential approach, to use independent control surfaces for each axis, is uncommon for a missile. In this case, the missile flight control is similar to that of an aircraft. The Russia Kitchen AS-4, which has five control surfaces (two for pitch, two for roll, one for yaw), is an example of independent axis control. Although independent axis control has high control effectiveness and a relatively simple autopilot, it is more expensive, because of the larger number of actuators, and it requires more volume for the actuators. Another example of flight control integration that is most appropriate for high angle of attack, highly maneuverable missiles, is the approach used by Derby/R-Darter. It has six control surfaces (four surfaces for combined pitch/yaw control plus two surfaces for dedicated roll control). Because vortex shedding and induced roll is a problem for high angle of attack missiles, dedicated roll control provides more roll control effectiveness at high angle of attack. Finally, the Stunner missile has eight control surfaces, with blended canard and tail control providing direct lift maneuverability at low angle of attack. The small required angle of attack reduces the missile time constant and radome error slope, resulting in low miss distance.

Exo-atmospheric interceptors such as GBI, SM-3, and THAAD have dedicated reaction jet control for each axis. Four divert thrusters (up, down, left, right) provide direct forces to change the flight trajectory, while eight attitude control thrusters (pitch up, pitch down, yaw right, yaw left, roll clockwise—two thrusters, roll counter-clockwise—two thrusters) provide independent stabilization in the three axes.

The types of flight control (tail, canard, wing, thrust vector/reaction jet control) and the alternative approaches for design and integration with fixed surfaces are shown in Fig. 2.35. For tail control, the control surface design alternatives include the number of tails (usually four) and the launch platform integration (no compressed carriage, folded, wraparound, extended). A tail control missile may also have fixed forward surfaces (fixed wings, strakes, canards). The forward surfaces may be either inline or inter-digitated with the tail controls. Fixed forward surfaces alternatives include two surfaces (mono-wing, usually used with bank-to-turn maneuvering), three surfaces (usually used with a tri-tail), or four (cruciform) surfaces.

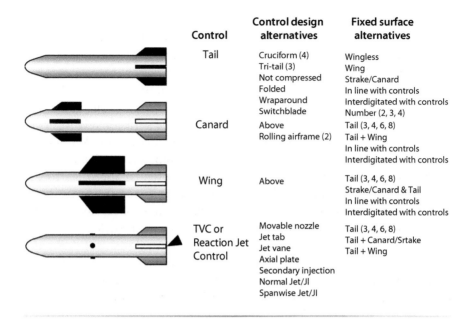

Control	Control design alternatives	Fixed surface alternatives
Tail	Cruciform (4) Tri-tail (3) Not compressed Folded Wraparound Switchblade	Wingless Wing Strake/Canard In line with controls Interdigitated with controls Number (2, 3, 4)
Canard	Above Rolling airframe (2)	Tail (3, 4, 6, 8) Tail + Wing In line with controls Interdigitated with controls
Wing	Above	Tail (3, 4, 6, 8) Strake/Canard & Tail In line with controls Interdigitated with controls
TVC or Reaction Jet Control	Movable nozzle Jet tab Jet vane Axial plate Secondary injection Normal Jet/JI Spanwise Jet/JI	Tail (3, 4, 6, 8) Tail + Canard/Srtake Tail + Wing

Fig. 2.35   There are many flight control aerodynamic configuration alternatives.

For canard control, there are similar control alternatives. Canard control has an additional design alternative of two control surfaces, for a rolling airframe missile. Two control surfaces reduces cost and subsystem volume. Examples of missiles with two control surfaces are the 5-in diameter Rolling Airframe Missile (RAM) and the 2.75-in diameter Stinger missile. The number of tail surfaces for a canard control missile may be tri-tail (three), cruciform (four), or more (six, eight) surfaces. Some missiles have free-to-roll tails, to minimize the rolling moment at high angle of attack. An example of a highly maneuverable canard control missile with free-to-roll tails is the Python 4.

Wing control requires three or more tail surfaces for static stability, similar to canard control. Although a wing control could potentially have fixed forward surfaces (fixed canards/strakes), it has not been used because of problems from induced roll at high angle of attack, from vortex shedding.

Finally, unconventional flight control includes thrust vector control (TVC) and jet interaction/reaction jet control. There are a number of approaches to unconventional flight control, with considerations including performance, cost, weight, packaging, and the capability for roll control. Thrust vector/reaction jet control is used when aerodynamic control has either insufficient control effectiveness or an excessive response time. An example of reaction jet control for exo-atmospheric intercept missiles is a divert and attitude control system (DACS). DACS controls the exo-atmospheric flight trajectory divert (up, down, left, right) and the missile attitude (pitch, yaw, roll) of GBI, SM-3 and THAAD.

Unconventional flight control for endo-atmospheric missiles is usually augmented by aerodynamic control for flight at higher dynamic pressure and longer duration. Fixed surfaces are also used with endo-atmospheric thrust vector/reaction jet control. Options include fixed tails (three or more), tails plus canards/strakes, and tails plus wings.

Figure 2.36 gives examples of missile flight control alternatives. TOW has tail control, located at the rear of the missile. The tails provide both flight control and stabilization. Another example is canard control. Canard control is located at the front of the missile. Python V has canard control. HARM has wing control. Wing control is located near the center-of-gravity of the missile. An example of thrust vector control (TVC), which is located at the rear rocket nozzle exhaust, is IRIS-T. The IRIS-T TVC is combined with tail control. PAC-3 has reaction jet control located at the front of the missile. The PAC-3 reaction jet control is used during the last few seconds of flight, to provide enhanced accuracy for hit-to-kill. Tail control is also used by PAC-3. Finally, the sophisticated three-stage SM-3 missile has a variety of controls. Reaction jet divert and attitude control are used for the third stage kill vehicle, tail control for the second stage, and TVC for the first stage.

Advantages and disadvantages of tail control are illustrated in Fig. 2.37. Typical advantages of tail control include 1) efficient packaging of the flight control components around the rocket nozzle blast tube, 2) low hinge moment and low actuator torque from the small local angle of attack,

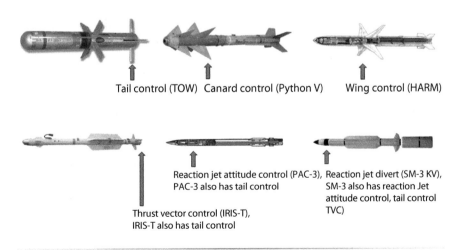

Fig. 2.36 Examples of missile flight control alternatives.

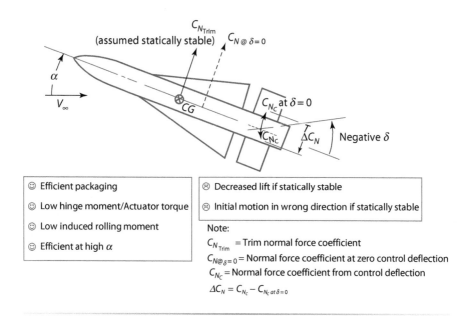

☺ Efficient packaging	⊗ Decreased lift if statically stable
☺ Low hinge moment/Actuator torque	⊗ Initial motion in wrong direction if statically stable
☺ Low induced rolling moment	Note:
☺ Efficient at high α	$C_{N_{Trim}}$ = Trim normal force coefficient
	$C_{N@\delta=0}$ = Normal force coefficient at zero control deflection
	C_{N_c} = Normal force coefficient from control deflection
	$\Delta C_N = C_{N_c} - C_{N_c \, at \, \delta=0}$

Fig. 2.37 Tail control is efficient at high angle of attack.

3) low induced rolling moment because the tail vortices are shed at the aft end, trailing behind the missile, and 4) good efficiency at high angle of attack. Note from the figure that for a statically stable missile, tail control surface deflection to trim the missile reduces the local angle of attack at the control surface. A disadvantage of tail control for a statically stable missile is the control deflection reduces the normal force/lift on the missile. Also, the control surface causes an initial rotation in the wrong direction. Conversely, for a statically unstable missile, the tail control deflection force adds to the total force on the missile.

Figure 2.38 compares the high angle of attack efficiency of tail control with conventional canard control. For a statically stable missile, tail control at high angle of attack is usually more effective than conventional canard control. As shown in the figure, the deflection of the tail to trim the missile reduces the local angle of attack at the tail. As a result the tail can be deflected to a high deflection angle without stall. In the case of conventional canard control of a statically stable missile, the deflection of the canard to trim the missile increases the local angle of attack at the canard. The canard can be deflected only to relatively small angles before stalling. Also, the vortices shed by the canard can interact with the tail, resulting in large induced roll and loss of roll control.

It is noted that a fixed forward surface in front of the movable canard (such as the split canards of Python 4) alleviates the problems of high angle of attack stall, induced roll, and loss of roll control. Also, free-to-roll tails (such as the free-to-roll tails of Python 4) alleviate the problems of induced roll and loss of roll control at high angle of attack. Finally, blended canard-tail control (such as Stunner) reduces the required canard control surface deflection.

About 70% of tail control missiles have low aspect ratio wings. Wings can provide greater aerodynamic efficiency (L/D) and higher maneuverability. Shown in Fig. 2.39 are examples of 28 subsonic and supersonic missiles that have wings and use tail control. The first 12 missiles (top three rows) are subsonic missiles. Subsonic missiles with wings, such as cruise missiles, generally have higher wing aspect ratio than supersonic missiles. The remaining 16 missiles in the figure are supersonic missiles. For supersonic missiles, the wing aspect ratio is generally less than 2.

An example of a new aeromechanics technology is lattice tail control. Figure 2.40 shows a comparison of lattice tail control with two conventional approaches to tail control, balanced actuation fin control and flap control. The example missiles are the lattice tail control Adder AA-12/R-77, the conventional balanced actuation fin control ASRAAM AIM-132, and the flap tail control Hellfire AGM-114.

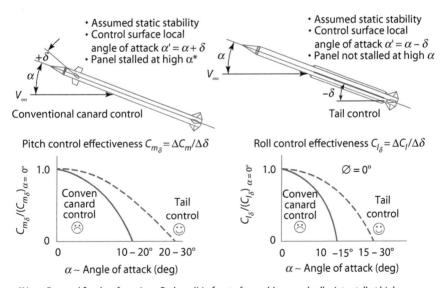

*Note: Forward fixed surfaces (e.g., Python 4) in front of movable canards alleviate stall at high α.
Free-to-roll tails (e.g., Python 4) and rollerons alleviate induced roll at high α.
Blended canard-tail control reduce canard deflection.

Fig. 2.38 Tail control can operate at higher angle of attack than conventional canard control.

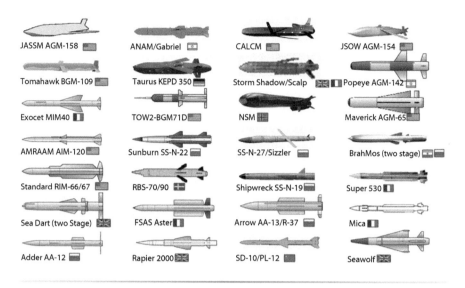

Fig. 2.39 About 70% of tail control missiles have wings. (Permission of Missile Index. Copyright 1997©Missile. Index All Rights Reserved.)

Lattice tail control is most appropriate at subsonic and high supersonic Mach number. Except for transonic Mach number, it has good performance in drag and superior control effectiveness and hinge moment. The vertical stacking of the surfaces and the smaller chord length results in greater

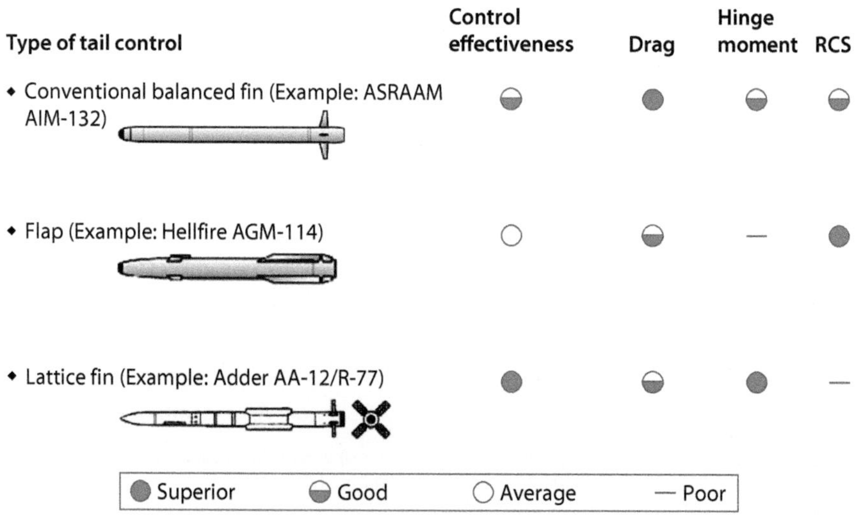

Type of tail control	Control effectiveness	Drag	Hinge moment	RCS
• Conventional balanced fin (Example: ASRAAM AIM-132)	◒	●	◒	◒
• Flap (Example: Hellfire AGM-114)	○	◒	—	●
• Lattice fin (Example: Adder AA-12/R-77)	●	◒	●	—

● Superior   ◒ Good   ○ Average   — Poor

Fig. 2.40 Tail control alternatives: conventional balanced actuation fin, flap, and lattice fin.

control effectiveness and less variation in the location of the center-of-pressure of the tail, leading to a lower hinge moment.

A disadvantage of lattice fins is high radar cross section. There are numerous cavities that can provide electromagnetic resonance. Also, the numerous leading edges are not swept, resulting in large backscatter. RCS is particularly high when there is a resonance of a lattice dimension with the radar wavelength. For example, a lattice with individual compartments of $1 \times 1 \times 1$ in will have high RCS if it is illuminated by an X-band (10 GHz frequency/1-in wavelength) radar.

The most popular type of tail control is a conventional balanced tail control. It has no serious weaknesses. For stability, the hinge line is typically located slightly aft of the aerodynamic center (25% mean aerodynamic chord for a subsonic missile, 50% mac for a high supersonic missile).

Because of its higher hinge moment, flap control is usually limited to subsonic and low supersonic missiles.

The bottom right section of Fig. 2.41 shows a schematic of the flow through a lattice fin at subsonic, transonic, a low supersonic, and a high supersonic Mach number. At subsonic Mach number the drag of lattice fins may be comparable to that of traditional fins. However, at transonic Mach number, lattice fins have higher drag and lower control effectiveness than traditional fins. At a low transonic free stream Mach number less than

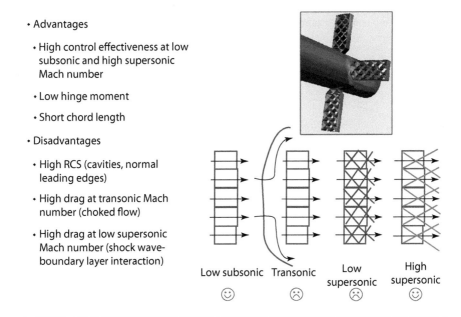

• Advantages

  • High control effectiveness at low subsonic and high supersonic Mach number

  • Low hinge moment

  • Short chord length

• Disadvantages

  • High RCS (cavities, normal leading edges)

  • High drag at transonic Mach number (choked flow)

  • High drag at low supersonic Mach number (shock wave-boundary layer interaction)

Low subsonic Transonic Low supersonic High supersonic

Fig. 2.41 Lattice fin control has advantages for low subsonic and high supersonic missiles.

1, the local flow through the lattice can accelerate to Mach 1, because of the thickness of the surface and the thickness of the boundary layer. For a transonic free stream Mach number slightly greater than 1, the flow through the lattice remains choked. A detached, normal shock wave in front of the lattice spills excess air flow around the lattice. The lattice remains choked until the Mach number is sufficiently high to allow the lattice to swallow the shock. An oblique shock is then formed on each leading edge of the surfaces of the lattice. At low supersonic Mach number the oblique shock angle of each leading edge is large and the oblique shocks are reflected downstream, off the lattice surfaces. The large number of reflected shocks results in a relatively high drag. At higher supersonic Mach number the oblique shock angle of each leading edge is smaller, passing through the lattice without intersecting a lattice surface, resulting in low drag. The thickness and the leading edge angles of the lattice can be a small, because of the efficiency of the box structure. The small thickness and small leading edge angle have low drag.

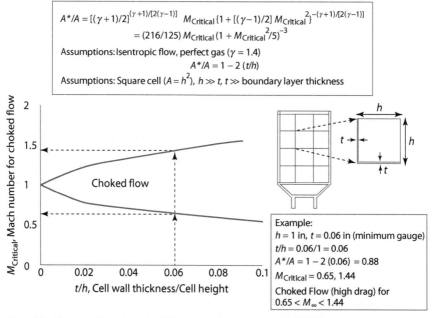

Note: A^* = Flow area through inside cell for choked flow (local Mach number = 1), A = Cell outside area, γ = Specific heat ratio = 1.4, $M_{Critical}$ = Critical free stream Mach number for choked flow, t = Cell wall thickness, h = Cell height

Fig. 2.42 Lattice fin choked flow is driven by lattice section thickness and transonic Mach number.

Figure 2.42 shows the flight Mach number region where lattice fins have choked flow, with high drag. Assuming isentropic flow of a perfect gas ($\gamma = 1.4$) through the lattice, $M_{Critical}$ can be obtained by solving the equation for the ratio A^*/A

$$A^*/A = [(\gamma+1)/2]^{(\gamma+1)/2[(\gamma-1)]}M_{Critical}\{1 + [(\gamma-1)/2]M_{Critical}^2\}^{-(\gamma+1)/[2(\gamma-1)]}$$

$$= (216/125)M_{Critical}\left(1 + M_{Critical}^2/5\right)^{-3}$$

In the above equation A^* = flow area through a lattice inside cell with choked flow (local Mach number inside cell = 1), A = cell outside area, $M_{Critical}$ = critical free stream Mach number for choked flow.

As an example, assume that the lattice has square cell sections of height h and section wall thickness t. For an individual cell, the outside area is $A = h^2$. Assume $h \gg t$ and $t \gg$ boundary layer thickness. Then

$$A^*/A \approx 1 - 2t/h$$

For this example, assume $h = 1$ in and $t = 0.06$ in (minimum gauge steel). Calculate

$$t/h = 0.06/1 = 0.06, \quad A^*/A = 1 - 2(0.06) = 0.88$$

The A^*/A equation for $M_{critical}$ values that provide $A^*/A = 0.88$ is satisfied for

$$M_{Critical} = 0.65, 1.44$$

Choked Flow (high drag) exists for this lattice over the flight number range $0.65 < M_\infty < 1.44$.

Lattice fins tend to be more expensive than conventional fins. One reason is the complexity of the lattice. Another reason is manufacturing to a precision minimum gauge thickness may require an expensive manufacturing process, such as electrical discharge machining (EDM). High strength steel, such as stainless steel, is often used for the lattice structure because it requires less thickness than aluminum to accommodate the lattice flight loads.

Figure 2.43 shows advantages and disadvantages of conventional canard control. Advantages of canard control include 1) efficient packaging of the guidance, navigation, and control subsystems in the same location, 2) simplified manufacturing and ease of integration of the guidance, navigation, and control subsystems, and for a statically stable missile 3) increased lift at low angle of attack, and 4) the initial rotational motion of the missile is in the desired direction. The figure illustrates that the incremental normal force from the canard to trim a statically stable missile provides additional lift. Disadvantages of conventional canard control include 1) a tendency to

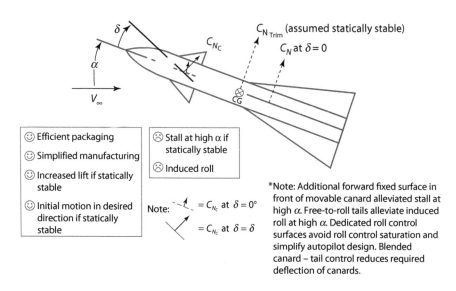

Fig. 2.43   Conventional canard control is efficient at low angle of attack, but stalls at high α with high induced roll.

stall at high angles of attack for a statically stable missile and 2) a large induced roll at high angles of attack. As noted previously, these problems are alleviated by the use of split canards, free-to-roll tails, dedicated roll control surfaces, blended canard-tail control, and a statically unstable missile.

Shown in Fig. 2.44 are examples of operational missiles that have canard control. Most canard control missiles do not have wings because the induced rolling moment from the vortex shedding from the canard makes it difficult to integrate a wing. Also, the additional surface area of the canard and the larger tail required for stability usually provide sufficient aerodynamic efficiency (L/D) and maneuverability. Because the location of the canard is forward of the center-of-gravity, the canard is destabilizing, requiring a larger tail for stability. Shown in the figure are twenty operational wingless guided weapons that use canard control. Fourteen of the twenty are air intercept missiles (SAM or AAM). Sixteen of the twenty, including the Kegler AS-12 and the Guided Multiple Launch Rocket System GMLRS, are supersonic missiles. A design consideration for the location of canards on a supersonic missile is that they should be located a sufficient aft distance behind the nose leading edge. At the highest Mach number the leading edge shock wave should pass in front of the canards, to minimize large changes in control effectiveness and stability. Subsonic canard guided weapons are shown at the bottom of the figure. The RBS-15, shown in the bottom left is a subsonic anti-ship cruise missile. The bottom row shows three examples of subsonic laser guided bombs (GBU-22, 27, and 28).

Examples of aerodynamic approaches to enhance the maneuverability and accuracy of canard control missiles are shown in Fig. 2.45. The top left is a photograph of Python 4. It has 1) split canards for pitch/yaw control, 2) dedicated roll control canards, and 3) free-to-roll tails. Split canards are comprised of a fixed surface in front of the deflected canard control. Split canards reduce the local angle of attack on the deflected control, allowing higher deflection without stall and lower hinge moment. Dedicated roll control surfaces avoid the problem of saturation of the pitch/yaw control surface deflection and simplify the autopilot design. Free-to-roll tails mounted on roll bearings that are decoupled from the airframe and weathercock into the local flow avoid the problem of induced roll from vortex shedding. The bottom left section is a video of a wind tunnel test of APKWS. APKWS has free-to-roll tails that are uncoupled from the airframe, to avoid induced roll. Note the high tail rotation rate induced by vortex shedding. The top right is a photograph of the AIM-9L Sidewinder. AIM-9L rollerons limit the missile roll rate, which improves the infrared seeker tracking accuracy. Rollerons are free-to-spin wheels on the tips of the tails that un-cage at a sufficiently high speed. The spinning rollerons (∼30,000 rpm) provide gyroscopic stability, which opposes roll and limits the missile roll rate. The bottom right section of the figure illustrates the blended canard-tail control of the Stunner missile. Blending the canard and tail control provides direct lift divert at low angle of attack. Because there is little rotation of the missile body,

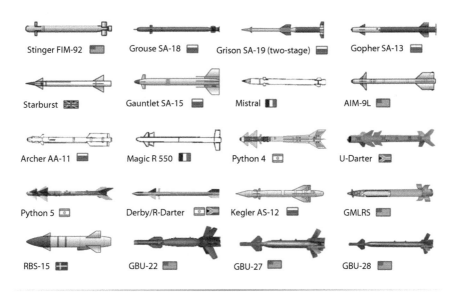

Fig. 2.44 Most canard control missiles are wingless and most are supersonic. (Permission of Missile Index. Copyright 1997©Missile Index. All Rights Reserved.)

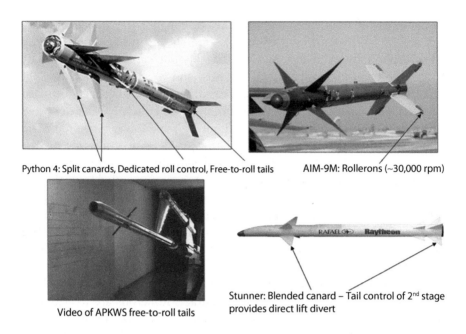

Python 4: Split canards, Dedicated roll control, Free-to-roll tails   AIM-9M: Rollerons (~30,000 rpm)

Video of APKWS free-to-roll tails

Stunner: Blended canard – Tail control of 2nd stage provides direct lift divert

Fig. 2.45   Aerodynamic approaches that enhance maneuverability and accuracy of canard control.

Stunner has accuracy benefits from low radome error slope and low missile time constant. Finally, a statically unstable missile alleviates the problem of canard stall. For a statically unstable missile, the required deflection of the canard to trim the missile is opposite the angle of attack, reducing the local angle of attack at the canard. A statically unstable missile requires careful analysis of its flight control dynamics and safety at launch.

As stated previously, a split canard control has a smaller local angle of attack, providing enhanced maneuverability at high angle of attack, with less induced roll and reduced hinge moment. Modern highly maneuverable missiles use split canards for flight control. Shown in Fig. 2.46 is a schematic of the local flow that illustrates the advantage of split canards. The incremental normal force coefficient (ΔC_N) in the figure is the difference between the normal force coefficient of the deflected control surface and the normal force coefficient of an undeflected control surface. Note that the forward surface reduces the local effective angle of attack α'. Because the trailing canard control deflection surface has a smaller local angle of attack, it is more effective at high control surface deflection δ and high angle of attack α, operating without stall. Also, the fixed forward surface provides enhanced normal force, reducing the required deflection of the control surface, resulting in lower hinge moment. Another benefit of a fixed forward surface is that the location of the vortex shedding is fixed, reducing the uncertainty in the aerodynamics and minimizing effects such as asymmetric vortex shedding. In addition to a fixed forward surface, AA-11 also has a weather-cocking forward surface to sense angle of attack. The measured angle of attack is fed into the autopilot, to improve the missile maneuverability. Most modern canard control missiles use split canard control, including the Kegler AS-12, Archer AA-11, Aphid AA-8, Magic R-550, Python 4, Python 5, and U-Darter.

Figure 2.47 illustrates the incremental control force from wing deflection and lists the advantages and disadvantages of wing control. The advantages of wing control are relatively few and the disadvantages are many. One advantage of wing control is that only a small body rotation is required to maneuver. This results in smaller seeker tracking error, because the small gimbal angle movement of the seeker results in a small variation in the dome error slope. The small angle of attack also results in a small field of view requirement if the missile has a strap-down seeker. Another advantage is fast response and lower time constant for a cruciform skid-to-turn missile. As shown in the figure, most of the missile lift is derived from deflecting the wing, resulting in a divert trajectory. The missile has small rotation and angle of attack. Because the wing can usually be deflected faster than body rotation, the time required to achieve maneuver g is shorter.

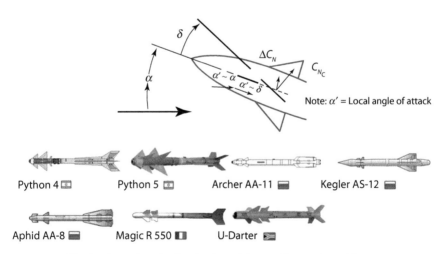

Note: Forward fixed surface reduces local angle-of-attack for movable canard, providing lower hinge moment and higher stall angle of attack. Forward surface also provides a fixed, symmetrical location for vortex shedding from the body.

Python 4 also has free-to-roll tails and dedicated roll control ailerons.

Fig. 2.46 Split canards provide enhanced maneuverability at high angle of attack with lower hinge moment.

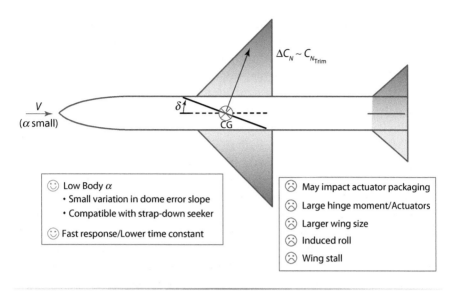

$\Delta C_N \sim C_{N_{Trim}}$

V
(α small)

δ

CG

☺ Low Body α
  • Small variation in dome error slope
  • Compatible with strap-down seeker
☺ Fast response/Lower time constant

☹ May impact actuator packaging
☹ Large hinge moment/Actuators
☹ Larger wing size
☹ Induced roll
☹ Wing stall

Fig. 2.47   Wing control has less body rotation, but has high hinge moment, induced roll, and stall concerns.

A major disadvantage of wing control is there may be limited space available for packaging of actuators. For some missiles, it may not be possible to place the wing aerodynamic center over the missile center-of-gravity. Other subsystems may overlap the cg, such as warhead or rocket motor. As a result, there may not be room to package the wing control actuators near the missile cg. Another disadvantage is the larger hinge moment required to deflect the wing. A third disadvantage is that the wing must be larger—it must be sized for maneuverability in addition to aerodynamic efficiency (L/D). A fourth disadvantage is the large induced roll produced by the wing. Finally, a wing-control missile usually has a higher aspect ratio, contributing to a wing stall at a relatively low angle of attack.

The strong vortex shedding for a wing control missile often has adverse effects on missile stability and control. The top right portion of Fig. 2.48 from Ref. 11 illustrates wing and body vortex shedding for a body-wing-tail configuration at high angle of attack. As shown in the figure, wing vortices are shed near the wing tips, trailing back with the free stream. The first set of body vortices are shed near the nose center-of-pressure, approximately 2/3 of the length of the nose. At high angles of attack, additional body vortices may be shed from the cylindrical body downstream of the nose. Surfaces aft of the wing, particularly aft surfaces with a span comparable to that of the wing, are susceptible to the strong vortices shed from the wing. As a result, and the missile may have large adverse induced roll, a loss in stability, and a loss in control effectiveness. Shown in the bottom left portion of the figure is a wind tunnel video of a highly swept wing pitching over an angle of attack range from 0 to 90 deg. The source of the video was the University of Notre Dame School of Aerospace and Mechanical Engineering. Note that the vortices are relatively weak at low angle of attack. As the angle of attack increases, the vortices increase in strength up to an angle of attack of about 60 deg. For angles of attack greater than about 60 deg, the flow detaches from the leading edge of the wing and there is a turbulent wake over the entire rear surface of the wing.

Examples of operational missiles that use wing control are shown in Fig. 2.49. Note that these missiles are supersonic and that the wings are generally large and located near the center-of-gravity. The configurations of Skyflash, HARM, and Aspide are similar to that of the Sparrow missile, which had its initial operational capability (IOC) in the year 1956. The AA-10/R-27 Alamo configuration is different from Sparrow. It has a fixed forward strake surface and a "bow tie" forward-swept movable wing. The Alamo geometry of a fixed, forward strake may have more predictable vortex shedding at high angle of attack because it tends to fix the location of vortex shedding. Also, the bow tie wing requires less wing span, which may enhance the missile fitment in launch platform carriage. The HARM missile wing is somewhat different from the Sparrow wing, because of a double swept leading edge. The double swept leading edge reduces the variation in aerodynamic center, providing a lower hinge moment.

Because of deficiencies such as actuator packaging, hinge moment, wing size, and angle of attack limitations from wing stall/induced roll, no wing

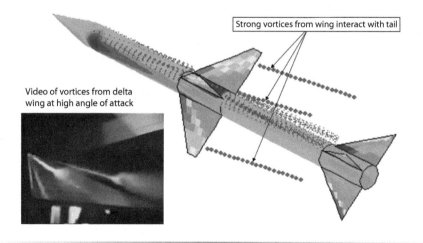

Fig. 2.48 Wings are susceptible to strong vortex shedding. (Source: University of Note Dame web site: http://www.nd.edu/~ame/facilities/SubsonicTunnels.html; Nielsen Engineering & Research (NEAR) web site: http://www.nearinc.com/near/project/MISDL.htm.)

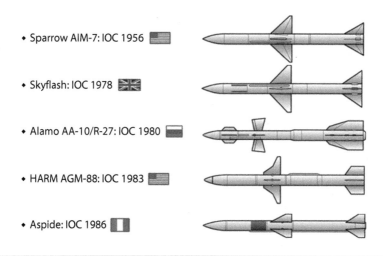

- Sparrow AIM-7: IOC 1956
- Skyflash: IOC 1978
- Alamo AA-10/R-27: IOC 1980
- HARM AGM-88: IOC 1983
- Aspide: IOC 1986

Fig. 2.49 Current wing control missiles are supersonic and are old technology. (Permission of Missile Index. Copyright 1997©Missile Index. All rights reserved.)

control missile has been developed in recent years. Modern missiles use tail, canard, or unconventional flight control. Although the wing control Sparrow has been largely replaced by the tail control AMRAAM as a preferred medium range air-to-air missile, the Sparrow was selected as a rocket baseline missile for this text, because of the availability of unclassified data for the Sparrow missile.

Unconventional flight control (thrust vector control, reaction jet control) provides higher maneuverability at low dynamic pressure than aerodynamic control. TVC and RJC also provide faster response than aerodynamic control. In general RJC has faster response and smaller miss distance than TVC, enabling hit-to-kill guidance. Unconventional flight control is especially suited for short duration operation, to enhance the missile maneuverability and responsiveness. Cost, weight, subsystem packaging, risk, and the capability for roll control are design considerations.

TVC is usually augmented by aerodynamic control. The physics of TVC and RJC are illustrated in Fig. 2.50 from Ref 12. The figure is a schematic of seven different types of unconventional flight control. It also shows the typical thrust angle for each of the flight control types. The first type of TVC is liquid injection. It uses a fluid such as freon, injected normal to the local stream, causing a bow shock wave inside the nozzle. Thrust deflection is of the order of $+/-7$ deg. Another type is hot gas injection TVC, which ducts hot gas products from the motor chamber into the nozzle. The injection of the hot gas into the nozzle causes a bow shock, similar to that of liquid injection TVC. Hot gas injection provides high deflection, although there may be problems for the high temperature valves, which must operate with gas products up to 5500°F. A third type of TVC is jet vanes, which are control surfaces inside the nozzle. Jet vanes have an advantage in that differential deflection also provides roll control. Jet vanes can also share common actuators with aerodynamic control. Jet vanes are continually exposed to the rocket exhaust plume, which results in about 3–5% loss in specific impulse even if they are not deflected. Axial plate thrust vector control is a fourth type of TVC, consisting of a plate that extends back and forth. When the plate is extended aft of the nozzle, the plume attaches the plate, because of the Coanda effect. A fifth type of TVC is jet tabs, which are simple devices that switch in and out of the plume. The jet tab sets up a bow shock inside the nozzle, similar to that of liquid injection TVC. A sixth type of TVC, movable nozzle, provides high deflection, about $+/-20$ deg. Movable nozzle TVC is often used with strategic ballistic missiles (Minuteman, Trident) and strategic defense missiles (GBI). Its application to tactical missiles, because of its high cost, is primarily limited to expensive, high performance missiles such as Standard Missile, Aster FSAF, and THAAD. Most movable nozzle TVC is based on a single vectored nozzle, providing pitch/yaw control but not roll control. Two or more vectored nozzles may be used for combined pitch/yaw/roll control, but it is expensive and usually not affordable for most missiles.

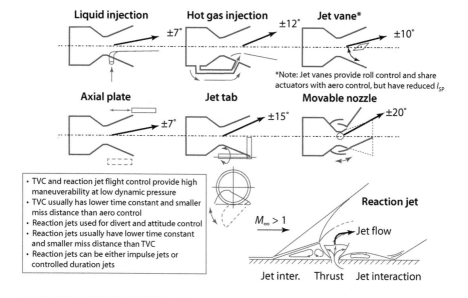

Fig. 2.50 TVC and reaction jet flight control provide high maneuverability at low dynamic pressure. (Source: Brebner, G.G., "The Control of Missiles," AGARD-LS-98, Feb 1979.)

Finally, the last type of unconventional flight control is reaction jet control. RJC that is located near the center-of-gravity directly provides flight trajectory divert (up, down, left, right). RJC that is located in either the forward or aft sections of the missile also provides flight attitude control (pitch, yaw, roll). Reaction jets can be based on either short-duration impulse, "shotgun shell-type" jets, similar to PAC-3 and Aster FSAF or longer duration controlled jets similar to GBI, SM-3 or THAAD. During endo-atmospheric flight, RJC interacts with the free stream air. The total force is a combination of the thrust force and the jet interaction force. The jet interaction force results from the change in the pressure distribution on the airframe surface. Jet interaction forces are greatest for a supersonic free stream, and can be comparable to the reaction jet thrust for aft mounted reaction jets with low values of jet chamber pressure-to-free stream pressure ratio (e.g., $p_{jet}/p_\infty < 20$). For aft-mounted reaction jets at very high values of jet chamber pressure-to-free stream pressure ratio (e.g., $p_{jet}/p_\infty > 1000$), the jet interaction force is much smaller than the reaction jet thrust. For a forward mounted jet, the jet inter-action force detracts from the reaction jet force and a low value of p_{jet}/p_∞ (e.g., <20) will result in a jet interaction force that is almost opposite that of the reaction jet force, resulting in very low control effectiveness. The bottom right figure illustrates jet interaction flow into a supersonic free stream. As illustrated, the free stream flow separates from the airframe surface, because of the obstruction of the jet. This causes a higher local pressure in the separated flow region in front of the nozzle and a lower local pressure in the separated flow region behind the nozzle. Although the jet interaction force usually augments the thrust force, there is relatively high uncertainty and risk in the magnitude of the jet interaction force.

Shown in Fig. 2.51 are examples of operational missiles that use either TVC or reaction jets for flight control. Jet vane is the most popular type of TVC. As mentioned previously, jet vanes can provide roll control and can also share actuators with aerodynamic control. Examples of missiles that use jet vane plus aerodynamic control include the French Mica; the US Sea Sparrow RIM-7, Sidewinder AIM-9X and Javelin; the UK Seawolf GWS 26; the German IRIS-T; and the South African A-Darter. A disadvantage of jet vanes is weight. Because jet vanes operate in the high temperature nozzle plume, they must be constructed from materials with high temperature capability, such as tungsten, rhenium, molybdenum, or carbon-carbon. For a missile flight control system that consists of jet vanes plus aerodynamic control, the jet vanes provide the large off boresight maneuvering that is often required after launch, while aerodynamic control provides the required trim and maneuvering after motor burnout.

Examples of missiles that use jet tab plus aerodynamic control are the Russian Archer AA-11, US Tomahawk, and French Exocet MIM40.

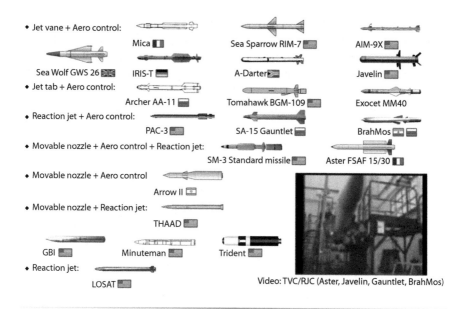

Fig. 2.51   Most missiles with TVC or reaction jet control also use aerodynamic control.

Archer uses jet tabs to provide high maneuverability following launch. Tomahawk and Exocet boosters use jet tabs. Jet tabs have advantages of higher pitch/yaw vectoring and lighter weight than jet vanes, but have a disadvantage in that they cannot provide roll control.

Examples of missiles that use reaction jet plus aerodynamic control are the US PAC-3, Russia SA-15 Gauntlet, and India/Russia BrahMos surface – to-air missiles. PAC-3 uses tail control during fly-out. Reaction jets are used by PAC-3 in the last few seconds before intercept, because their smaller time constant ($\sim$ ms) provides the smaller miss distance required for hit-to-kill. The SA-15 Gauntlet is a vertical launched missile that is cold-launched. It has a rolling airframe. Reaction jets provide the required pitch-over maneuver after launch. Conventional canards provide flight control during the fly-out. BrahMos is vertically launched using its rocket motor. Similarly to the Gauntlet, reaction jets provide the required pitch-over maneuver after launch. Conventional tail control is used for fly-out.

Examples of complex missiles that combine movable nozzle TVC, aerodynamic control, and reaction jet control are the US SM-3 Standard Missile and the French Aster FSAF 15/30. Movable nozzle TVC is used for launch stabilization and the initial off boresight maneuvering. Following launch, aerodynamic control provides midcourse trim and maneuvering. RJC provides terminal maneuvering during the hit-to-kill intercept. The SM-3 TVC has four movable nozzles for combined thrust vector control of pitch, yaw, and roll. SM-3 also has Divert and Attitude Control System (DACS) reaction jets for exo-atmospheric hit-to-kill intercept. SM-3 reaction jets use solid propellant (because of a concern for toxicity). The Aster TVC has two movable nozzles for combined control of pitch, yaw, and roll. Its RJC are impulse jets that are similar to PAC-3.

The Israeli Arrow II strategic defense missile has combined twin movable nozzle TVC plus aerodynamic control for its first stage. The second stage, an exo-atmospheric interceptor, also has twin movable nozzle TVC plus aerodynamic control.

The last five missiles in the figure are examples of missiles that do not have any aerodynamic control. THAAD and GBI have movable nozzle TVC for stabilization and off boresight maneuverability during launch and midcourse. THAAD and GBI also have divert and attitude control thruster reaction jets for the exo-atmospheric hit-to-kill intercept. The reaction jets use liquid propellant, which provides higher I_{SP}. Minuteman and Trident ICBMs have movable nozzle TVC for stabilization and maneuverability during motor burn. After exo-atmospheric burnout, divert and reaction jets are used in dispensing unguided ballistic reentry vehicles. Finally, shown at the bottom left of the figure is LOSAT. LOSAT has only reaction jet control. RJC provides the fast response time necessary for hit-to-kill accuracy of the hypersonic missile. The weight of the LOSAT reaction jet control system is relatively low, because of the short time of flight.

Shown in the bottom right of the figure is a video of Aster and Javelin. Aster has sophisticated dual TVC nozzles, which allow full axis control (roll control in addition to pitch/yaw control). Also note the firings of the Aster reaction jet control thrusters. A mission for Aster is defense against low altitude sea-skimming missiles. Because its active radar seeker is not effective at a low grazing angle, Aster has a lofted flight trajectory, impacting the target from above. Shown in the last section of the video of the Javelin missile. Javelin is a light weight, man-portable missile. Target acquisition is through a thermal imaging sight. Following a soft launch, using a low noise launch motor, the main motor kicks in. Thrust vector control can provide a rapid pitch-up and climb. Javelin can impact a tank target from the top, providing greater penetration and lethality.

2.20 Maneuver Law Alternatives

Figure 2.52 compares four missile maneuver law alternatives: skid-to-turn maneuvering, bank-to-turn maneuvering, rolling airframe maneuvering, and divert maneuvering.

Most missiles use skid-to-turn maneuvering. Skid-to-turn is particularly applicable to axisymmetric, cruciform missiles with low aspect ratio

a)

- Skid-To-Turn (STT)
  - Advantage: Fast response
  - Features
    - Usually small roll attitude/rate commands from autopilot
    - Best for axisymmetric cruciform missiles of low aspect ratio
- Bank-To-Turn (BTT)
  - Advantage: Provides higher maneuverability for mono-wing, noncircular/lifting bodies, and airbreathers
  - Disadvantages
    - Time to roll
    - Roll rate limited by gain for radome error slope stability
  - Features
    - Large roll attitude commands from autopilot
    - Small sideslip
- Rolling Airframe (RA)
  - Advantage: Requires fewer gyros/accelerometers/ actuators (packaging for small missile)
  - Disadvantages
    - Reduced maneuverability for aero control
    - Requires higher rate gyros/actuators/seeker tracking
    - Higher drag with coning flight trajectory
    - Requires precision geometry and thrust alignment
  - Features
    - Bias roll rate (~10 Hz) from bias roll moment
    - Can use "bang-bang"/impulse steering
    - Compensates for thrust offset

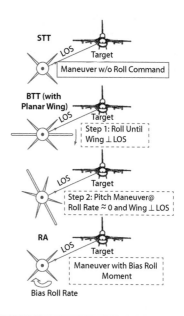

Fig. 2.52a Skid-to-turn is the most common maneuver law for missiles.

surfaces. A skid-to-turn maneuver is a commanded maneuver along the line-of-sight of the seeker. It usually requires relatively small roll attitude and roll rate commands from the autopilot. An advantage of skid-to-turn is fast response because the maneuver is immediately made along the line-of-sight without delay. Sea Sparrow is an example of a skid-to-turn missile.

Bank-to-turn maneuvering is a relatively new technology for missiles. It is most applicable to asymmetric missiles such as mono-wing, noncircular/

b)

- Divert
  - Advantages:
    - Lower time constant
    - Less effect of radome error slope
    - Smaller miss distance
  - Disadvantages:
    - Cost
    - May not provide sufficient maneuverability
  - Features
    - Direct lift/side force w/o rotation
    - Either wing, blended canard–tail, or divert reaction jet control

Fig. 2.52b Skid-to-turn is the most common maneuver law for missiles.

lifting body, and asymmetric inlet missiles. Missiles using bank-to-turn will first roll until the wings (or the major axis of a lifting body) are oriented perpendicular to the target line-of-sight. Following the roll maneuver, the missile then conducts a pitch maneuver, maintaining the preferred roll orientation. A benefit of bank-to-turn maneuvering is higher maneuverability for a lifting body, which has a non-circular (e.g., elliptical) cross section, or higher maneuverability for a missile with a mono-wing. Another benefit is a smaller sideslip angle for missiles with asymmetric inlets. Bank-to-turn is particularly suited for midcourse guidance maneuvers prior to seeker lock-on to the target. A disadvantage of bank-to-turn maneuvering is slower response in terminal maneuvers that could degrade guidance accuracy, increasing the missile miss distance. Alternative approaches to alleviate this problem include faster actuators for roll control; a hemi-spherical, faceted or multi-lens dome to decrease dome error slope; and switching from bank-to-turn maneuvering to skid-to-turn maneuvering for terminal flight. Bank-to-turn missiles often high greater miss distance because of dome error slope. The maximum allowable roll rate may be limited because of maximum allowable roll channel gain for stability from radome error slope. An example of a bank-to-turn guided weapon is JSOW.

A third type of maneuver is a rolling airframe maneuver. Rolling airframe maneuvering is similar to skid-to-turn, except the missile also has a rolling moment bias input to provide a bias roll rate. The rolling moment bias may be provided by thrust offset, tail incidence, canard incidence, or a combination of approaches. Advantages of rolling airframe missiles include lower cost because of fewer required flight control gyros, accelerometers, and actuators; lower volume to package less required flight control hardware; compensation for thrust misalignment; and compatibility with "bang-bang"/impulse control. The 5-in diameter Rolling Airframe Missile (RAM) and the 2.75-in diameter Stinger missile are examples of small diameter rolling airframe missiles. Stinger uses "bang-bang" single-axis flight control, requiring less flight control hardware packaging within the small diameter. The Stinger two canard panels share a single control shaft. Both canard panels are dithered to a maximum deflection (+/−15 deg) as a function of roll angle. Rolling moment bias is provided by a fixed roll deflection of the fins. PAC-3 and LOSAT are examples of larger diameter hypersonic rolling airframe missiles that use impulse reaction jet control. Disadvantages of rolling airframe missiles include reduced maneuverability if they use two axis flight control, a requirement for higher rate gyros and actuators, a requirement for higher rate seeker tracking, higher drag from the coning flight trajectory, and a requirement for precision geometry with precision thrust alignment. The maximum roll rate of a rolling airframe missile with "bang-bang" aerodynamic control is about 10 Hz, because most solenoids are limited to a maximum rate of about 4000 deg/s. For reaction jet control, the maximum roll rate is about 20 Hz. Another potential problem is susceptibility to roll-pitch-yaw cross-coupling instability. Roll-pitch-yaw cross-coupling tends to occur from roll resonance when the roll rate is comparable to the missile natural frequency in pitch or yaw. Another disadvantage of a rolling airframe missile is the steady roll rate typically induces a coning flight trajectory, resulting in higher drag. Designing a rolling airframe missile requires consideration of the precession and nutation modes of motion. Note that the miss distance from the seeker dome error slope may be reduced because of the averaging effect of roll rate. However, the miss distance may also be increased because of susceptibility to roll resonance.

Finally, the last maneuver law example is divert maneuvering. Divert maneuvering provides direct lift and direct side force without rotation. An advantage of divert control is faster response because the control response time to achieve high acceleration is much faster than the missile body rotation time to achieve an angle of attack. This results in a smaller time constant and smaller miss distance. Another advantage is the small body rotation reduces the miss distance from radome error slope. Disadvantages of divert control include a relatively large/expensive flight control and a potential for insufficient maneuverability. Small diameter missiles, which may be constrained to fit within the launch platform, are likely to be maneuverability limited. Types of control that allow divert maneuvers are wing control with the wing located at the center-of-gravity, blended canard-tail control, and reaction jet control with the divert thrusters located at the center-of-gravity. Sparrow, Stunner, and SM-3 upper stage are examples of missiles that use divert control.

The top portion of Fig. 2.53 shows examples of missiles that use skid-to-turn (Sea Sparrow), bank-to-turn (JSOW), rolling airframe (HOT), and divert (Multiple Kill Vehicle) maneuvering. The bottom portion of the figure is a video of Sea Sparrow, JSOW, HOT, and MKV with respective skid-to-turn, bank-to-turn, rolling airframe, and divert flight trajectories.

Air-breathing missiles with asymmetric inlet(s) usually require bank-to-turn maneuvering, to avoid loss of inlet efficiency from sideslip. Figure 2.54 shows examples of air-breathing missiles that use bank-to-turn maneuvering. The French ASMP and ANS and the Chinese C-101 and C-301 are examples of operational ramjet missiles, with twin side inlets that are separated by a radial angle of 180 deg. An example of a turbojet missile with twin side inlets is the German Taurus KEPD-350. Also shown are two developmental ducted rocket missiles, HSAD and Meteor, with twin cheek inlets. The cheek inlets are in tandem with the bottom cruciform tails, and are separated by a radial angle of 90 deg. A major difference between the US HSAD and the UK Meteor is the propulsion system. The HSAD has a variable flow solid hydrocarbon fuel ducted rocket. An

Skid-To-Turn (STT):   Bank-to-Turn (BTT)   Rolling Airframe (RA):   Divert:
Sea Sparrow   JSOW   HOT   MKV

Video of Sea Sparrow, JSOW, HOT, and MKV Flight Trajectories

Fig. 2.53 Most missiles use skid-to-turn maneuvering. The other options are bank-to-turn, rolling airframe, and divert maneuvering.

advantage of hydrocarbon fuel is a low observable plume. The Meteor engine is a variable flow boron fuel ducted rocket. Boron fuel provides longer range. Compared to liquid fuel ramjets, ducted rockets have simpler logistics and higher acceleration capability.

a)

Type inlet	Location	Propulsion	Example missile
Twin	Side	Ramjet	ASMP 　　　　　　ANS
"	"	"	C-101 　　　　　C-301
"	"	Turbojet	Taurus KEPD-350
"	Cheek	Ducted rocket	HSAD 　　　　　Meteor
Single	Bottom scoop	Scramjet	X-51 SED
"	"	Ramjet	ASALM
"	"	Turbojet	Tomahawk 　　　　RBS-15

Note: Bank-to-turn maneuvering maintains low sideslip for better inlet efficiency.

Fig. 2.54a Non-cruciform inlets require bank-to-turn maneuvering.

b)

Type inlet	Location	Propulsion	Example missile
Single	Bottom scoop (cont)	Turbojet	NSM Sizzler
"	"	"	Storm Shdw TORGOS
			Delilah Kh-35
"	"	"	Kh-55 Hyunmoo III
"	"	"	Babur Sea Eagle
"	Bottom flush	"	JASSM Harpoon
"	"	"	ANAM/Gabriel
"	Top	Turbofan	CALCM/ALCM

Note: Bank-to-turn maneuvering maintains low sideslip for better inlet efficiency.

Fig. 2.54b Non-cruciform inlets require bank-to-turn maneuvering.

The next set of missiles in the figure has a single inlet. The X-51 scramjet engine Demonstrator (SED) is a Mach 6.5 hydrocarbon fuel ramjet. Shown next in the figure is an example of a bank-to-turn ramjet missile with a single chin inlet. The US Advanced Strategic Air Launched Missile (ASALM) uses angle of attack α and angle of sideslip β feedback in the flight control system to provide a coordinated turn in bank-to-turn maneuvering. The ASALM was selected as a ramjet baseline missile for this text because of the availability of unclassified data and its high performance. The most popular type of inlet for a turbojet missile is a bottom scoop inlet. The US BGM-109 Tomahawk, Sweden RBS-15, Norway Naval Strike Missile (NSM), Russia Sizzler, UK/France Storm Shadow/Scalp, South Africa TORGOS, Israel Delilah, Russia Kh-35, Russia Kh-55, Republic of Korea Hyunmoo III, Pakistan Babur, and the UK Sea Eagle are examples of bank-to-turn turbojets with a single bottom inlet. Tomahawk is essentially a turbojet, although its engine has a small amount of air by-pass. NSM has a roll controlled dome—it can fly for most of its flight with the inlet on the bottom, for enhanced range, and switch to the inlet on top during terminal flight, for reduced RCS and enhanced survivability. A bottom flush inlet is used by the US JASSM and Harpoon/SLAM and the Israel ANAM. Finally, the US AGM-86 ALCM is an example of a single top inlet. An advantage of locating the inlet on top is reduced radar cross section against ground based radars because of the shielding of the body. A disadvantage is reduced specific impulse at high angle of attack because of inlet flow distortion. Inlet flow distortion occurs at high angle of attack because of cross flow, a thicker boundary, and a tendency for flow separation.

2.21 Roll Angle and Control Surface Sign Convention

A typical sign convention for missile roll angle and flight control surface deflection is assumed in Fig. 2.55. The axes x, y, and z in the assumed sign convention are defined as positive x forward, positive y to the right, and positive z down. The definition of roll angle $\phi = 0$ in this assumed sign convention is shown as $+$ orientation, with fin 1 on the top of the missile. Looking forward from the base of the missile, positive roll is clockwise. Looking forward from the base of the missile and proceeding clockwise, the sequence for the assumed sign convention is fin 1, 2, 3, and 4. If $\phi = 0$ deg, positive pitching moment (nose up) is provided by positive deflection of the trailing edges up for fins 2 and 4. Similarly if $\phi = 0$, positive yaw (nose right) is provided by positive deflection of the trailing edges right for fins 1 and 3.

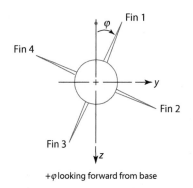

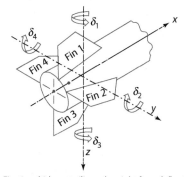

$+\varphi$ looking forward from base

Fins 1 and 3 have trailing edge right for + deflection
Fins 2 and 4 have trailing edge up for + deflection
In above figure Fins 1 and 2 have + deflection

δ_e = Equivalent elevator deflection ($+\delta_e$ produces + (up) pitching moment) = $[(\delta_2 + \delta_4)/2]\cos\varphi - [(\delta_1 + \delta_3)/2]\sin\varphi$
δ_r = Equivalent rudder deflection ($+\delta_r$ produces + (right) yawing moment) = $[(\delta_2 + \delta_4)/2]\sin\varphi + [(\delta_1 + \delta_3)/2]\cos\varphi$
δ_a = Equivalent aileron deflection ($+\delta_a$ produces + (clockwise) rolling moment) = $(\delta_2 + \delta_3 - \delta_1 - \delta_4)/4$

Note: For minimum total fin deflection ($\Rightarrow$ Lowest total hinge moment, Lowest drag, Highest control effectiveness): $\delta_1 = \delta_r - \delta_a, \ \delta_2 = \delta_e + \delta_a, \ \delta_3 = \delta_r + \delta_a, \ \delta_4 = \delta_e - \delta_a$

Fig. 2.55 Typical sign convention for cruciform missile roll angle and control surface deflection.

For a missile with cruciform flight control surfaces, the combined pitch, yaw, and roll control is provided by the combined deflections of four control surfaces. Typical definitions of δ_e equivalent elevator (pitch), δ_r rudder (yaw), and δ_a aileron (roll) deflection are

$$\delta_e = [(\delta_2 + \delta_4)/2]\cos\varphi - [(\delta_1 + \delta_3)/2]\sin\varphi$$
$$\delta_r = [(\delta_2 + \delta_4)/2]\sin\varphi + [(\delta_1 + \delta_3)/2]\cos\varphi$$
$$\delta_a = (\delta_2 + \delta_3 - \delta_1 - \delta_4)/4$$

For conceptual design of the missile autopilot, the missile control effectiveness and hinge moment are usually assumed to be linear with control surface deflection (e.g., twice the equivalent elevator deflection provides twice the pitching moment). For high angles of attack and high control surface deflection, a nonlinear analysis is required.

In providing the required pitch, yaw, and roll, it is desirable to minimize the total control surface deflection. This results in lower hinge moment and lower drag, and higher control effectiveness. The individual control surface deflections that result in the minimum total deflection are

$$\delta_1 = \delta_r - \delta_a$$
$$\delta_2 = \delta_e + \delta_a$$
$$\delta_3 = \delta_r + \delta_a$$
$$\delta_4 = \delta_e - \delta_a$$

2.22 Flight Roll Orientation

Figure 2.56 compares roll orientation and maneuver control deflection alternatives for a typical cruciform missile. Approaches to symmetric roll orientation during missile flight with no induced roll are + roll orientation and × roll orientation. Each has advantages and disadvantages. The + orientation aerodynamics are easier to predict for conceptual design analysis. For a positive pitch command using conventional control with four tail surfaces, the trailing edges of the two horizontal surfaces are deflected upward to cause a positive pitch-up moment. Similarly, for a positive yaw command using conventional tail control, the trailing edges of the two vertical surfaces are deflected to the right to cause a positive yaw right moment. For a positive roll command, the trailing edges of all four surfaces are deflected counter-clockwise to provide positive clockwise roll (roll right). The trailing edges are deflected clockwise to provide negative counter-clockwise roll (roll left).

The + orientation sometimes has an advantage of lower trim drag. A disadvantage is that it often has a statically unstable rolling moment

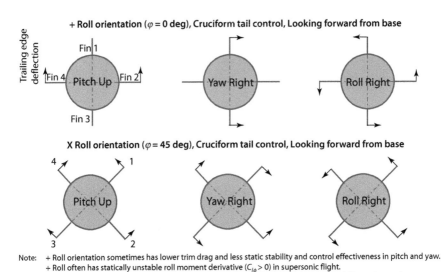

Note: + Roll orientation sometimes has lower trim drag and less static stability and control effectiveness in pitch and yaw.
+ Roll often has statically unstable roll moment derivative ($C_{l_\phi} > 0$) in supersonic flight.
X Roll orientation has better launch platform compatibility, higher L/D, higher static stability and control effectiveness in pitch and yaw. X Roll often has statically unstable roll moment derivative ($C_{l_\phi} > 0$) in subsonic flight.

Fig. 2.56 X roll orientation flight is usually better than + roll orientation flight.

derivative ($C_{l_\phi} > 0$) in supersonic flight. The + orientation has less static stability and less control effectiveness in pitch and yaw.

An alternative approach is × roll orientation. It is somewhat more difficult to predict the aerodynamic forces and moments. For a positive pitch command, the trailing edges of all four surfaces are deflected up, to provide a positive pitching moment without side force. For a positive yaw command, the trailing edges of all four surfaces are deflected to the right, to provide a yawing moment without normal force. The roll command is similar to that of the + orientation. For roll control, all four surfaces are deflected to provide either clockwise roll or counter-clockwise roll.

The × orientation usually has advantages of better fit for launch platform compatibility, higher aerodynamic efficiency (L/D), and higher static stability and control effectiveness in pitch and yaw. A disadvantage is that it often has a statically unstable rolling moment derivative ($C_{l_\phi} > 0$) in subsonic flight. The statically unstable roll moment is generally not a problem except for high angle of attack. Generally, the × orientation is preferred over the + orientation.

2.23 Trim and Static Stability Margin

Trim is defined at zero pitching/yawing moment. As shown in Fig. 2.57, the normal force in a trimmed flight condition is lower if a statically stable missile has tail control. Conversely, the normal force is higher for a statically stable missile with canard control. A rule of thumb for conceptual design is $|\alpha/\delta| > 1$ – the magnitude of the change in angle of attack from tail or canard control deflection should be greater than 1. A similar rule of thumb is $|C_{m_\delta}| > |C_{m_\alpha}|$ – the magnitude of missile pitching moment control effectiveness should be greater the magnitude of the static stability. Most control surfaces have deflection limits less than $+/-30$ deg. $|\alpha/\delta| > 1$ usually allows a trim angle of attack up to about 30 deg. The rule of thumb is applicable to skid-to-turn, bank-to-turn, and rolling airframe missiles but is not applicable to divert missiles.

Relaxed static stability margin allows the missile to trim at higher angle of attack, providing higher maneuverability. Shown in Fig. 2.58 is the normal force benefit of relaxed static stability for the rocket baseline missile, based on the data of Chapter 7. The rocket baseline missile has a large static margin (e.g., 0.88 diameter at Mach 2), resulting in a relatively low maximum angle of attack ($\alpha = 9.4$ deg) and a relatively low maximum trimmed normal force ($C_N = 9$). Reducing the static margin would increase the maximum angle of attack and the maximum trimmed normal force. In the example, a neutrally stable missile ($\alpha/\delta = \infty$, $C_{m_\alpha} = 0$, static margin $= 0$), has a 130% increase in maximum angle of attack ($\alpha = 21.8$ versus 9.4 deg) and an 80% increase in maximum available normal force ($C_N = 16$ versus 9). In general, reducing the static margin to provide an increase in missile maneuverability is desirable, especially for a skid-to-turn missile.

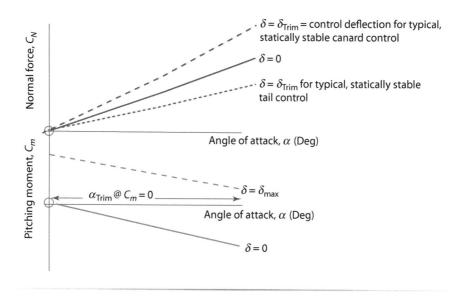

Fig. 2.57 Trimmed normal force is defined at zero pitching moment.

For the rocket baseline missile with high static margin, the higher angle of attack capability from reduced static may not necessarily be beneficial. The wing control baseline missile has a relatively low time constant, because the wing can be quickly deflected to provide maneuverability. The rocket baseline missile conducts more of a divert maneuver than a skid-to-turn maneuver. Analysis is required to determine whether reduced static margin would have a beneficial effect on miss distance for the rocket baseline wing control missile.

Relaxed static margin results in less required control deflection to achieve an angle of attack. A benefit is reduced trim drag and lower hinge moment. Figure 2.59 compares axial force of the rocket baseline missile for three cases: 1) its nominal static margin (0.88 diameter)/control effectiveness $(\alpha_{\text{Trim}}/\delta = 0.75)$, 2) reduced static margin (0.43 diameter)/increased control effectiveness $(\alpha_{\text{Trim}}/\delta = 1.5)$, and 3) neutral static margin (0 diameter)/maximum control effectiveness $(\alpha_{\text{Trim}}/\delta = \infty)$. Flight conditions are Mach 2 after motor burnout. The figure was derived from the data of Chapter 7. Note that there is a large increase in axial force with angle of attack for the nominal static margin case. As an

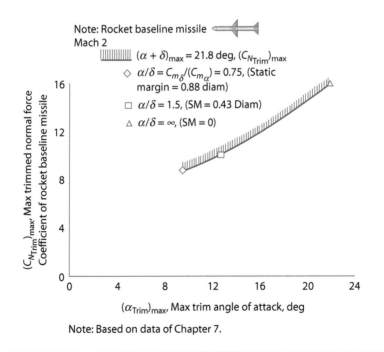

Fig. 2.58 Relaxed static stability margin allows higher trim angle of attack and higher normal force.

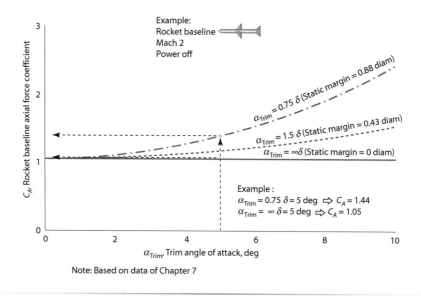

Fig. 2.59 Relaxed static stability margin reduces drag.

example calculation, assume $\alpha_{\text{Trim}} = 5$ deg. Comparing the nominal static margin ($\alpha_{\text{Trim}}/\delta = 0.75$) case with the neutrally stable missile ($\alpha_{\text{Trim}}/\delta = \infty$) case, the axial force with nominal static margin is 37% higher (1.44/1.05).

2.24 Tail Area Sizing

Much of the conceptual design configuration sizing process is oriented toward tail sizing. Because missiles are usually volume limited and the subsystems are of comparable density, the center-of-gravity location is usually near 50% of the length of the missile. Since the nose and any forward surfaces (strakes/canards) are destabilizing, tails must usually be added and sized to provide the required static stability. The tail contribution to pitching moment static stability is provided by the tail normal force effectiveness $(C_{N_\alpha})_T(S_T/S_{\text{Ref}})$ times its moment arm to the center-of-gravity $[(x_{\text{AC}})_T - x_{\text{CG}}]$. The tail contribution must balance the contributions to pitching moment from the nose and wing. Thus, $\Sigma M = 0$ at aerodynamic center gives

$$(C_{N_\alpha})_B\{[x_{\text{CG}} - (x_{\text{AC}})_B]/d\} + (C_{N_\alpha})_W\{[x_{\text{CG}} - (x_{\text{AC}})_W]/d\}S_W/S_{\text{Ref}}$$
$$+ (C_{N_\alpha})_T\{[x_{\text{CG}} - (x_{\text{AC}})_T]/d\}S_T/S_{\text{Ref}}$$
$$= -[(C_{N_\alpha})_B + (C_{N_\alpha})_W S_W/S_{\text{Ref}} + (C_{N_\alpha})_T S_T/S_{\text{Ref}}][(x_{\text{AC}} - x_{\text{CG}})/d]$$

Static stability margin for a specified tail area is

$$(x_{AC} - x_{CG})/d = -\{(C_{N_\alpha})_B\{[x_{CG} - (x_{AC})_B]/d\}$$
$$+ (C_{N_\alpha})_W\{[x_{CG} - (x_{AC})_W]/d\}S_W/S_{Ref}$$
$$+ (C_{N_\alpha})_T\{[x_{CG} - (x_{AC})_T]/d\}(S_T/S_{Ref})\}/[(C_{N_\alpha})_B$$
$$+ (C_{N_\alpha})_W S_W/S_{Ref} + (C_{N_\alpha})_T S_T/S_{Ref}]$$

The required tail area for a specified static margin is

$$S_T/S_{Ref} = (C_{N_\alpha})_B\{[x_{CG} - (x_{AC})_B]/d\}$$
$$+ (C_{N_\alpha})_W\{[x_{CG} - (x_{AC})_W]/d\}(S_W/S_{Ref}) + \{[(C_{N_\alpha})_B$$
$$+ (C_{N_\alpha})_W S_W/S_{Ref}][(x_{AC} - x_{CG})/d]\}/\{(C_{N_\alpha})_T[(x_{AC})_T - x_{CG}]/d$$
$$- (x_{AC} - x_{CG})/d\}$$

Of particular interest is the required tail area for neutral stability $[(x_{AC} - x_{CG})/d = 0]$. The equation is

$$S_T = \{(C_{N_\alpha})_B[x_{CG} - (x_{AC})_B]/d + (C_{N_\alpha})_W\{[x_{CG} - (x_{AC})_W]/d\}(S_W/S_{Ref})\}$$
$$\times \{d/[(x_{AC})_T - x_{CG}]\}S_{Ref}/(C_{N_\alpha})_T$$

Figure 2.60 shows the rocket baseline missile required tail area for neutral static margin as a function of Mach number and wing location. It is based on predicted aerodynamics from slender body theory [8], slender wing theory [10], and linear wing theory [10]. Note that the required tail area for neutral static stability must be larger as the Mach number increases from subsonic to supersonic. The tail loses aerodynamic efficiency as the supersonic Mach number increases. Also note that placing the wing such that its aerodynamic center is forward of the center-of-gravity location is destabilizing, requiring a larger tail area for compensation. The rocket baseline missile wing aerodynamic center is forward of the center of gravity, and therefore the rocket baseline requires a larger tail. Placing the wing aft of the center of gravity is stabilizing, allowing a smaller tail area to meet the static margin requirement. For a typical missile wing without camber, the location of the wing aerodynamic center is the same as the wing center-of-pressure location.

The prediction of body normal force coefficient derivative and location of the aerodynamic center, from slender body theory is $(C_{N_\alpha})_B = 2$ per rad and $(x_{AC})_B \approx d$ respectively. For the wing and tail, linear wing theory

$$(C_{N_\alpha})_W = (C_{N_\alpha})_T = 4/[M^2 - 1]^{1/2}$$

is used at high Mach number and slender wing theory $((C_{N_\alpha})_W = \pi A_W/2, (C_{N_\alpha})_T = \pi A_T/2)$ is used at subsonic and low supersonic Mach numbers. It is assumed that the moment arm from the tail aerodynamic

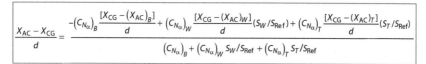

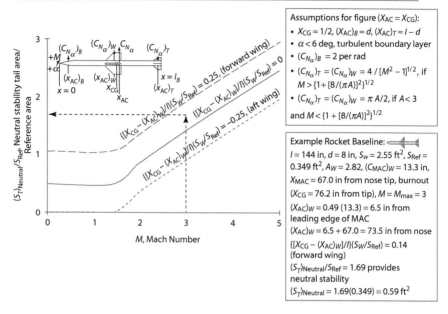

Assumptions for figure ($X_{AC} = X_{CG}$):
- $X_{CG} \approx 1/2$, $(X_{AC})_B \approx d$, $(X_{AC})_T \approx l - d$
- $\alpha < 6$ deg, turbulent boundary layer
- $(C_{N\alpha})_B = 2$ per rad
- $(C_{N\alpha})_T = (C_{N\alpha})_W = 4 / [M^2 - 1]^{1/2}$, if $M > \{1 + [8/(\pi A)]^2\}^{1/2}$
- $(C_{N\alpha})_T = (C_{N\alpha})_W = \pi A/2$, if $A < 3$ and $M < \{1 + [8/(\pi A)]^2\}^{1/2}$

Example Rocket Baseline:
$l = 144$ in, $d = 8$ in, $S_W = 2.55$ ft^2, $S_{Ref} = 0.349$ ft^2, $A_W = 2.82$, $(C_{MAC})_W = 13.3$ in, $X_{MAC} = 67.0$ in from nose tip, burnout $(X_{CG} = 76.2$ in from tip), $M = M_{max} = 3$
$(X_{AC})_W = 0.49 \, (13.3) = 6.5$ in from leading edge of MAC
$(X_{AC})_W = 6.5 + 67.0 = 73.5$ in from nose
$\{[X_{CG} - (X_{AC})_W]/l\}(S_W/S_{Ref}) = 0.14$ (forward wing)
$(S_T)_{Neutral}/S_{Ref} = 1.69$ provides neutral stability
$(S_T)_{Neutral} = 1.69(0.349) = 0.59$ ft^2

Fig. 2.60 A larger tail area is required for static stability at supersonic Mach number.

center to the missile center of gravity is approximately equal to the moment arm from the body (nose) aerodynamic center to the center-of-gravity. Another assumption is linear aerodynamics from low angle of attack ($\alpha < 6$ deg). Still another assumption is a turbulent boundary layer, with small boundary layer thickness. Note that for flight conditions with a laminar boundary layer over much of the body (e.g., $M < 0.2$ or $h > 80,000$ ft), the body boundary layer thickness at the tails may blanket a significant portion of the tails, reducing the tail effectiveness.

In the example for the rocket baseline missile at an assumed maximum Mach number $M = 3$, the predicted tail area must be 0.59 ft^2 for neutral static stability. The predicted tail area is 1.69 times the reference body cross sectional area. The actual rocket baseline missile has a tail area that is over four times the reference body cross sectional area. This is an indication that the rocket baseline missile has a large static margin from its relatively large tail. Also, the rocket baseline wing aerodynamic center location is forward of the missile center-of-gravity, requiring a larger tail area.

2.25 Stability and Control Conceptual Design Criteria

Stability and control has high impact on the aerodynamic configuration design, particularly tail sizing, and should be considered early in conceptual design. Because missiles tend to have near-neutral static stability and use combined pitch/yaw/roll controls, it may be difficult to accurately predict static margin and control effectiveness. Although the actual stability and control derivatives prediction may have large error, it is often possible to size the canard, wing, or tail surfaces with less than 10% error in the surface area. Predicting stability & control derivatives usually requires iteration as the surfaces are resized and the center-of-gravity location changes during the design convergence. It is helpful to start with a baseline missile, such as the rocket, ramjet, and turbojet baselines in this text, which have a balance of system engineering in their stability and control derivatives. It is useful to compare results from two different prediction methods and to try to rationalize the differences. It is also useful to compare stability & control derivatives with wind tunnel data to assess the accuracy of prediction methods. Conceptual design criteria are also useful, providing a "sanity check" and facilitating design convergence.

Figure 2.61 shows conceptual design typical criteria for roll cross coupling (rolling moment from rudder deflection $(C_{l_{\delta_r}})$, yaw cross coupling (yawing moment from aileron deflection $C_{n_{\delta_a}}$), roll control effectiveness

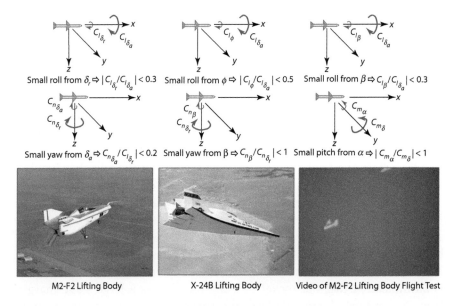

Small roll from $\delta_r \Rightarrow |C_{l_{\delta_r}}/C_{l_{\delta_a}}| < 0.3$ Small roll from $\phi \Rightarrow |C_{l_\phi}/C_{l_{\delta_a}}| < 0.5$ Small roll from $\beta \Rightarrow C_{l_\beta}/C_{l_{\delta_a}} | < 0.3$

Small yaw from $\delta_a \Rightarrow C_{n_{\delta_a}}/C_{l_{\delta_r}}| < 0.2$ Small yaw from $\beta \Rightarrow C_{n_\beta}/C_{n_{\delta_r}}| < 1$ Small pitch from $\alpha \Rightarrow |C_{m_\alpha}/C_{m_\delta}| < 1$

| M2-F2 Lifting Body | X-24B Lifting Body | Video of M2-F2 Lifting Body Flight Test |

Fig. 2.61 Stability & control cross coupling of a lifting body requires high flight control effectiveness.

C_{l_β} to compensate for the rolling moment from sideslip C_{l_β}, and roll control effectiveness $C_{l_{\delta a}}$ to compensate for induced roll from roll attitude C_{l_ϕ}. Also shown are pitch control effectiveness C_{m_δ}, and yaw control effectiveness $C_{n_{\delta r}}$ to compensate for static stability C_{m_α} and C_{n_β} respectively. Stability & control cross coupling or out-of-plane moments should generally be less than 30% of the "pure" in-plane moments, to maximize the control power and minimize the time constant for maneuvers. Examples of stability & control conceptual design typical criteria are:

- $\left| C_{l_{\delta r}} \right| < 0.3 \left| C_{l_{\delta a}} \right|$, rolling moment from rudder deflection should be less than 30% of the aileron control effectiveness, to have adequate control margin
- $\left| C_{n_{\delta a}} \right| < 0.2 \left| C_{n_{\delta r}} \right|$, yawing moment from aileron deflection should be less than 20% of the rudder control effectiveness, to have adequate control margin
- $\left| C_{l_\beta} \right| < 0.3 \left| C_{l_{\delta a}} \right|$, rolling moment from sideslip should be less than 30% of the aileron control effectiveness, to have adequate control margin
- $\left| C_{l_\phi} \right| < 0.5 \left| C_{l_{\delta a}} \right|$, rolling moment from roll orientation should be less than 50% of the aileron control effectiveness, to have adequate control margin
- $\left| C_{m_\alpha} \right| < \left| C_{m_\delta} \right|$, pitching moment from angle of attack should be less than the elevator control effectiveness, to have adequate control margin
- $\left| C_{n_\beta} \right| < \left| C_{n_{\delta r}} \right|$, yawing moment from sideslip should be less than the rudder control effectiveness, to have adequate control margin

Lifting body configurations are particularly susceptible to stability & control cross coupling because the roll, pitch, and yaw moments of inertia are of comparable magnitude, the flight control surfaces have short moment arms, and cross flow over the body often induces flow separation. Shown at the bottom of the figure are lifting body HL-10, M2-F2, and X-24B flight test photographs. All had problems from stability & control cross coupling. The bottom right of the figure is an M2-F2 flight test video, which ends in a crash that was caused by stability and control cross coupling.

2.26   Aerodynamic Configuration Buildup

A first-order estimate of total normal force, suitable for conceptual design, is to assume a build-up of the configuration, which consists of the contribution from the body plus the contribution from each surface. As an example, for a wing-body-tail conceptual design, it is assumed that the total normal force is the summation of the contribution from an isolated body plus the contribution from the wing (exposed) plus the contribution from the tail (exposed). For conceptual design, the effects of wing-body, body-wing, tail-body, body-tail, and wing-tail interference are typically assumed to be relatively small when compared to the contributions from the isolated configuration geometries. For a wing-body-tail configuration the equation is

$$(C_N)_{\text{Total}} = (C_N)_{\text{Wing-Body-Tail}} \approx (C_N)_{\text{Body}} + (C_N)_{\text{Wing}} + (C_N)_{\text{Tail}}$$

Figure 2.62 shows two examples of the buildup of the normal force coefficient of the rocket baseline missile at Mach 2. The left example is the normal force coefficient for a nominal static margin (0.88 diameter) and maximum angle of attack ($\alpha = 9.4$ deg). Note that for the rocket baseline missile most of the normal force is provided by the wing contribution. Deflecting the wing control provides the major contribution to normal force. The second largest contributor to normal force is from the tail. As mentioned previously, the rocket baseline missile has a large tail and a large static margin. The body provides a relatively small contribution to normal force. This has an implication in the design for maneuverability. The maneuverability requirements of the rocket baseline missile wing control missile are satisfied through sizing the wing. The right example is for neutral static margin (0 diameter) at maximum angle of attack

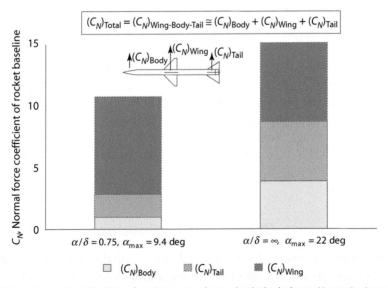

Note for figure: $M = 2$. Prediction from linear wing theory, slender body theory, Newtonian impact theory

Fig. 2.62 Conceptual design total aerodynamic force may be estimated by summing the individual contributors.

($\alpha = 22$ deg). The total normal force coefficient is much larger for this example because of the higher angle of attack on the body and tail.

The above buildup approach may be used in the conceptual design prediction of missile normal force, drag, and pitching moment. For preliminary design, more accurate methods based on including the effects from wing-body, body-wing, tail-body, body-tail, and wing-tail interaction[8] are used. Buildup wind tunnel tests are also normally conducted during preliminary design. For the conceptual design prediction methods of this text, the conceptual design predictions without interference effects can be corrected by the baseline missile aerodynamics, which include interference effects.

2.27 Summary

Chapter 2 provided conceptual design methods, design tradeoffs, design criteria, and technologies for the aerodynamics of missiles. The emphasis was on the aerodynamics of low aspect ratio wing and wingless missiles. The conceptual design methods of this text addressed the predictions of the normal force coefficient, the drag force coefficient, and the aerodynamic center/pitching moment coefficient of bodies and surfaces, and the hinge moment of surfaces. Design tradeoffs addressed missile diameter, nose fineness, boattail, lifting body versus axisymmetric body, wings versus no wings, tails versus flares, surface planform geometry, flight control alternatives, maneuver alternatives, roll orientation, and static margin. A process was given for tail area sizing. Stability and control design criteria were provided for static stability, control effectiveness, and cross coupling. A process to compute the total forces and moments based on the summation of the individual contributions (e.g., body, wing, tail) was demonstrated. New aerodynamic technologies were identified that have high payoff for missiles. These include faceted/window/multi-lens domes, bank-to-turn maneuvering, lifting body airframe, forward swept surfaces, neutral static margin, lattice tails, split canard control, and free-to-roll tails.

2.28 Problem Review

1. Missile diameter tradeoffs include consideration of seeker range, warhead lethality, subsystem packaging, structural mode frequency, and d___.

2. Benefits of a high fineness nose include lower supersonic drag and lower r____ c____ s_____.

3. Three contributors to drag are base drag, wave drag, and s___ f_____ drag.

4. A boattail or flare angle should be less than about 7 to 10 deg, to avoid flow s_____.

5. A lifting body is most efficient at about 700 psf d_____ p_____.

6. At low angle of attack the aerodynamic center of the body is on the n___.

7. Tail stabilizers have low drag, while lower aero heating and a relatively small shift in static stability are benefits of a f____ stabilizer.

8. Examples of simple physics-based methods for predicting body normal force and aerodynamic center are s_____ body theory and N_____ theory.

9. Subsonic missiles often have high aspect ratio wings, for enhanced r____.

10. Examples of simple physics-based methods for predicting wing normal force and aerodynamic center are l_____ wing, s_____ wing, and N_____ theory.

11. The aerodynamic center of the wing is between 25% and 50% of the m___ a_____ c____.

12. Hinge moment increases with the local flow angle due to control surface deflection and the a____ o_ a_____.

13. Increasing the surface area increases the s___ f_____ d___.

14. Leading edge sweep reduces drag and r____ c____ s_____.

15. A missile with six control surfaces, four surfaces providing combined pitch/yaw control plus two surfaces providing roll control, has an advantage of good c_____ e_____.

16. A missile with two control surfaces providing only combined pitch/yaw control has advantages of lower c___ and good pa_____.

17. A tail control missile has larger trim normal force if it is statically u_____.

18. Lattice fins have low h____ m_____.

19. Split canards allow higher maximum angle of attack and higher m_____.

20. Two types of unconventional flight control are thrust vector control and r_____ j__ control.

21. The most common type of TVC for missiles is j__ v___ control.

22. Four maneuver laws are skid to turn, bank to turn, rolling airframe, and d_____.

23. Bank to turn maneuvering is usually required for missiles with a single wing or with non-cr_____ inlets.

24. A missile is statically stable if the aero center is behind the c_____ o_ g_____.

25. If the moments on the missile are zero the missile is in tr__.

26. Total normal force on the missile is approximately the sum of the normal forces on the planar surfaces (e.g., wing, tail, canard) plus the normal force on the b___.

27. Increasing the tail area increases the missile static s_____.

Chapter 3

Propulsion Considerations in the Missile Design and System Engineering Process

- Alternative Propulsion Comparisons
- Turbojet Engine Design and System Engineering
- Ramjet Engine Design and System Engineering
- Rocket Motor Design and System Engineering

3.1 Introduction

Missile propulsion considerations that are addressed in this chapter emphasize conceptual design methods, design trades, and the technologies for rocket, ramjet, and turbojet propulsion. Consideration is given to propulsion system alternatives, limits on turbojet compressor and turbine temperature, turbojet specific impulse and thrust prediction, limits on ramjet Mach number and temperature, ramjet specific impulse and thrust prediction, ramjet engine/booster integration options, ramjet inlet options, inlet spillage prediction, inlet shock loss, ramjet inlet start Mach number, ramjet missile drag from booster integration, fuel alternatives, rocket propellant weight fraction required to achieve an incremental velocity, solid propellant burn area requirement, rocket throat area requirement, solid propellant rocket specific impulse and thrust prediction, solid propellant grain alternatives, solid propellant rocket thrust magnitude control, solid propellant composition tradeoffs, storage and propellant aging, motor case material alternatives, and rocket nozzle material alternatives.

Figure 3.1 again shows a typical sequence of the activity in missile conceptual design and system engineering. For the propulsion system, the design

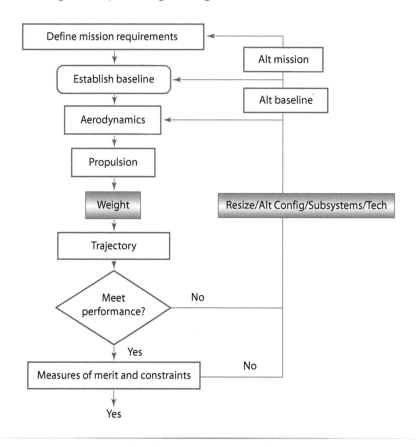

Fig. 3.1 Conceptual design and system engineering require creative, rapid, and iterative evaluations.

and system engineering activity typically follows the prior sequences of defining mission requirements, establishing a baseline missile, and sizing/ evaluating the aerodynamic configuration. Propulsion system design and system engineering is a creative and iterative process requiring rapid consideration of alternative propulsion systems, alternative propulsion subsystems, alternative technologies, and finally, the propulsion system sizing. The propulsion definition output includes the thrust, specific impulse, and the propellant/fuel weight. Propulsion definition establishes the propellant or fuel weight that is necessary to meet the range and time-to-target requirements.

3.2 Propulsion Alternatives Assessment

Figure 3.2 compares the efficiency of missile propulsion alternatives across the Mach number range of subsonic through hypersonic. Shown are a typical specific impulse envelope and typical constraints for the alternatives of liquid hydrocarbon fuel turbojet, liquid hydrocarbon or solid fuel ramjet, solid propellant ducted rocket, liquid hydrocarbon fuel scramjet, and solid propellant rocket propulsion.

Subsonic turbojet/turbofan propulsion is a relatively mature technology. It is most suited for subsonic cruise missiles, providing high efficiency against non-time-critical targets. Beyond Mach 2, there is a technology challenge of the maximum allowable temperature of the current turbine materials. Other problems for a supersonic turbojet include increasingly complex inlet systems to match the inlet airflow to the compressor, and the reliability of cooling systems to avoid exceeding the current material temperature limit of about 2500°F at the turbine.

A ramjet is efficient from about Mach 2.5 to 5. Below Mach 2.5 there is a risk in generating sufficient thrust to overcome drag. Above Mach 5, the combustor insulation material temperature limits the achievable exit velocity and thrust. Also, deceleration of the inlet airflow to subsonic velocity results in chemical dissociation of the air, which absorbs heat and negates a portion of the energy input of the combustor. For a subsonic launch platform, a rocket boost is required for ramjet thrust takeover at about Mach 2.5.

The maximum specific impulse of ducted rocket propulsion is about 800 to 1000 s, which is intermediate that of a solid propellant rocket and a ramjet. Ducted rockets are most efficient for a Mach number range

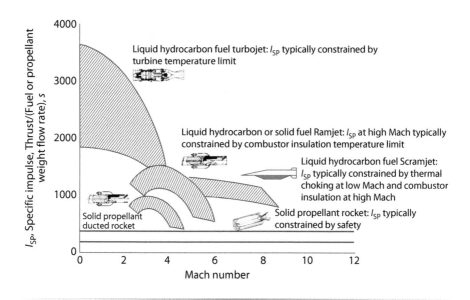

Fig. 3.2 Each type of air-breathing propulsion has an optimum Mach number for maximum specific impulse.

from about 2.5 to 4. Ducted rockets have higher acceleration capability (higher thrust) than ramjets and generally have longer range capability (higher specific impulse) than solid propellant rockets.

Scramjet propulsion has supersonic flow through the entire flow-path, including supersonic combustion. Efficient flight is from Mach 4.5 to 8, with a most efficient cruise at about Mach 6, 100 kft altitude. A typical limit in scramjet thrust/specific impulse at lower Mach number is thermal choking. A larger inlet is required to avoid thermal choking for Mach numbers less than Mach 6. Typical limits of maximum Mach number are the combustor insulation material maximum temperature and chemical dissociation of the air. Scramjet propulsion technology challenges include fuel/air mixing, efficient combustion, airframe integration, and sufficient thrust to overcome the drag. Compared to a ramjet, a longer combustion chamber is required, because of the mixing time/ length for supersonic combustion. An enabling technology to enhance supersonic combustion is endothermic fuels. Endothermic fuels decompose at high temperature into lighter weight molecular products that burn more readily, providing higher specific impulse and permitting shorter combustor length. An endothermic fuel also acts as a heat sink, cooling the adjacent structure. Because a scramjet has less thrust than the missile drag for a flight Mach number less than about 4, a scramjet requires a large rocket motor to boost it to a high takeover speed. Due to its relatively low thrust, a scramjet may not have sufficient thrust to accelerate or even maintain a cruise condition of thrust equal to drag.

A dual-combustion ramjet/scramjet (DCR) has some of the higher Mach number capability of a scramjet and some of the relatively higher thrust capability and lower take-over Mach number of a ramjet. DCR development is probably higher risk than a ramjet but lower risk than a scramjet. DCR propulsion separates the inlet airflow into two streams. The main airflow remains supersonic for scramjet combustion. The smaller airflow is decelerated to subsonic speed for fuel-rich combustion, after which it accelerates through a nozzle. Efficient flight is Mach 3 to Mach 7.

Rockets are capable of providing thrust across the entire Mach number range. Also, because a rocket can operate at any altitude, a boost-climb-glide trajectory can provide extended range by minimizing drag in high altitude flight. Rocket propellant can be either solid or liquid. However, concerns for logistics and toxicity limit most missile propellants to solid propellant. Concerns of explosive sensitivity and toxicity provide constraints on the practical specific impulse of solid propellants. Although the specific impulse of solid propellant rockets is relatively low, of the order of 250 s, solid propellant has an advantage of higher acceleration capability than either liquid propellant or air-breathing propulsion.

Figure 3.3 compares the flight range and time-to-target of four propulsion alternatives for long range precision strike. The alternatives are subsonic cruise turbojet, supersonic cruise liquid hydrocarbon fuel ramjet, hypersonic cruise liquid hydrocarbon fuel scramjet, and supersonic cruise solid propellant rocket. All four propulsion types are held to a missile launch weight of 2000 lb, a representative weight limit for carriage on a small fighter aircraft, such as the F-18C. The predicted cruise range is based on the Breguet range equation

$$R = (L/D)I_{SP}V \ln[W_L/(W_L - W_P)]$$

Note from the figure that subsonic cruise turbojet propulsion is the preferred approach for long-range strike against targets that are not time-critical. A disadvantage of a subsonic turbojet is poor effectiveness against time-critical targets. For example the time required for a subsonic turbojet to cruise 250 nm at a cruise velocity of 1000 fps is 25 m. The times required for a typical ramjet, scramjet, or endo-atmospheric rocket are much quicker (7 m, 4 m, and 8 m, respectively), less than a typical latency time of 15 m for a time-critical target.

Subsonic cruise turbojet propulsion has 120% greater range than the next best alternative, a supersonic cruise liquid hydrocarbon fuel ramjet (1800 versus 830 nm). An examination of the Breguet range equation explains

Breguet Range Equation: $R = (L/D) I_{SP} V \ln [W_L/ (W_L - W_P)]$

Parameter	Subsonic turbojet missile	Liquid fuel ramjet missile	Hydrocarbon fuel scramjet missile	Solid propellant rocket
L/D, Lift/Drag	10	5	3	5
I_{SP}, Specific impulse	3000 s	1300 s	1000 s	250 s
V_{AVG}, Average velocity	1000 ft/s	3500 ft/s	6000 ft/s	3000 ft/s
W_P/W_L, Cruise propellant or fuel weight/Launch weight	0.3	0.2	0.1	0.4
R, Max cruise range	1800 nm	830 nm	310 nm	250 nm
$t_{250 nm}$, Time to 250 nm range	25 m	7 m	4 m	8 m

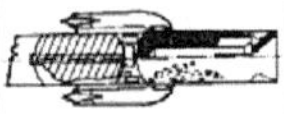

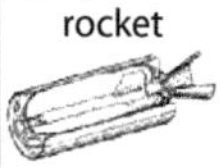

Note: Ramjet and scramjet missiles booster propellant for Mach 2.5 to 4 take-over speed not included in W_P for cruise. Rockets require thrust magnitude control (e.g., pintle, pulse, or gel motor) for effective cruise. Max range for a rocket is usually a semi-ballistic flight profile, instead of cruise flight. Multiple stages may be required for rocket range greater than 200 nm.

Fig. 3.3 Cruise range is driven by L/D, I_{SP}, velocity, and propellant or fuel weight fraction.

the difference in performance. The subsonic cruise turbojet has advantages compared to the supersonic cruise ramjet in the areas of maximum lift-to-drag ratio ($L/D = 10$ versus 5), specific impulse ($I_{SP} = 3000$ versus 1300 s), and available fuel for a specified launch weight of 2000 lb (600 versus 400 lb of fuel). The ramjet missile has less available weight for fuel because it requires a rocket to boost the missile up to about Mach 2.5, for transition to ramjet propulsion. However, a ramjet missile has an advantage of a shorter response time against time-critical targets. It may also have an advantage in survivability, because of the higher flight altitude and higher speed. If time-critical targets are of utmost importance, scramjet propulsion may be preferred. As shown in the figure, the scramjet missile example is 70% faster than the ramjet (6000 versus 3500 ft/s). However, the maximum range of a scramjet missile that is limited to 2000 lb launch weight is only 37% that of a liquid fuel ramjet (310 versus 830 nm). Again, examining the Breguet range equation is instructive. The liquid fuel ramjet has advantages compared to the scramjet in the areas of aerodynamic efficiency ($L/D = 5$ versus 3), specific impulse ($I_{SP} = 1300$ versus 1000 s), and available fuel for a missile limited to 2000 lb launch weight (400 versus 200 lb of fuel). The scramjet missile has less available weight for fuel because it requires a larger rocket booster for a higher takeover Mach number (Mach 4 versus 2.5), requires a longer combustor for efficient combustion, and requires more insulation. Finally, the supersonic cruise rocket has a maximum flight range of 250 nm. The most efficient cruise condition for the long range rocket was found to be Mach 3 cruise at high altitude. The solid propellant rocket example uses thrust magnitude control from a pintle motor, for more efficient acceleration and cruise. Although it is not shown, a semi-ballistic flight trajectory (e.g., launch, pitch-up, ballistic climb, glide) would have provided a more efficient flight trajectory for the rocket. For ranges greater than about 200 nm, a rocket may benefit from multiple stages. A consideration of the maximum allowable range of a ballistic missile is treaty limits.

Based on an examination of the Breguet range equation, new technology development has payoff in the areas of high cruise velocity, aerodynamic efficiency (lift/drag), specific impulse, light weight structure, light weight/low volume subsystems, and high density fuel/propellant.

Shown in Fig. 3.4 is a comparison of missile rocket, ramjet, and turbojet propulsion alternatives based on their acceleration capability. It is a typical envelope of the maximum thrust-to-weight ratio, based on the rocket motor or the engine weight. The comparison is shown as a function of Mach number.

Solid propellant rocket propulsion has the highest thrust-to-weight ratio. This is because of high exit velocity, the independence of the exit velocity from that of the free stream velocity, and the capability for high mass

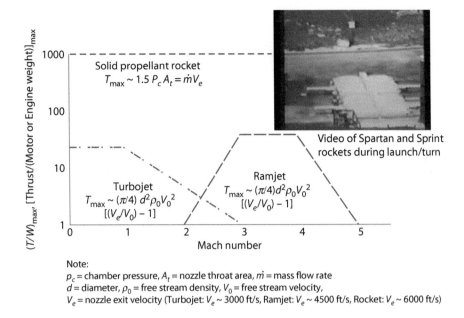

Fig. 3.4 Solid propellant rocket propulsion has higher thrust capability than air-breathing propulsion.

flow rate. A first order estimate of maximum thrust is $T_{max} \sim 1.5\, P_c\, A_t = \dot{m} V_e$. In the top right section of the figure is a video of the high thrust-weight Spartan and Sprint rockets in their initial launch and turn phase of flight. The video is circa 1970's. The acceleration of Sprint was 100+ g. Other flight demonstrations, such as the High-g Boost Experiment (HiBEX) have demonstrated 400+ g acceleration.

The exit velocity of a solid propellant rocket is about 6000 ft/s, much higher than that of a typical ramjet (exit velocity about 4500 ft/s) or a typical turbojet (exit velocity about 3000 ft/s). Note from the maximum thrust equation for air-breathing propulsion $T_{max} \sim (\pi/4) d^2 \rho_0 V_0^2 [(V_e/V_0) - 1]$ that turbojets and ramjets produce thrust only if the exit velocity is greater than the free stream velocity ($V_e > V_0$). The maximum velocity of an air-breathing missile is less than the exit velocity.

3.3 Turbine Propulsion Alternatives

It was previously shown that a turbine-based missile has longer range than a ramjet. Another advantage is a capability to loiter over the target area. Although a turbine-based missile is capable of subsonic through

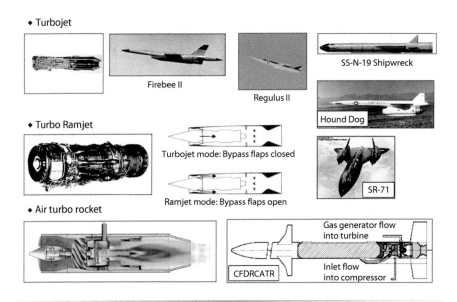

Fig. 3.5 A turbine-based missile is capable of subsonic to supersonic cruise.

supersonic cruise, to date there are few examples of supersonic turbojets. These are shown in Fig. 3.5. Examples of supersonic turbojets are the low supersonic Firebee II, the low supersonic Regulus II, and the higher supersonic SS-N-19 Shipwreck and Hound Dog. There are no examples of a turbo ramjet missile. Turbo ramjets are complicated, requiring variable by-pass air, and may be too expensive for missile applications. The high supersonic SR-71 has turbo ramjet propulsion. An air turbo rocket is a relatively new technology. The relatively low temperature gas from a fuel-rich gas generator drives the turbine, which drives the compressor. Free stream air is compressed by the compressor and then flows into the combustor, where it mixes with the fuel-rich gas from the gas generator. Secondary combustion occurs, followed by expansion through the nozzle. An advantage of an air turbo rocket is the turbine is not exposed to the high temperature of secondary combustion in the combustion chamber. An air turbo rocket has a higher I_{SP} than a ducted rocket, but a lower I_{SP} than an unconstrained turbojet.

A multi-mission strike missile using turbine-based propulsion has high potential. It could counter both conventional targets and time-critical targets. Benefits of a multi-mission turbine-based propulsion system could include 1) subsonic cruise efficiency against long range targets that are not time critical, 2) fast response (e.g., Mach 3+ cruise) against time-critical targets, 3) subsonic loiter capability over the target area, and 4) reduced logistics/cost of a multi-mission missile.

3.4 Turbojet Flow Path, Components, and Nomenclature

Shown in Fig. 3.6 is a schematic of the flow path through a turbojet engine. The flow path nomenclature consists of the initial free stream (station 0), inlet entrance (station 1), inlet exit/compressor entrance (station 2), compressor exit/combustor entrance (station 3), combustor exit/turbine entrance (station 4), and the turbine exit/nozzle entrance (station 5). For a theoretical (ideal) turbojet, the thermodynamic cycle consists of an isentropic compression of the flow by the inlet, isentropic compression by the compressor, constant pressure combustion in the combustor, isentropic expansion through the turbine, and finally, isentropic expansion through the nozzle to the free stream static pressure.

For an ideal turbojet engine, the work extracted from the flow by the rotating turbine is equal to the work that is required to drive the rotating compressor. The work is transmitted from the turbine to the compressor by a connecting spindle shaft. For a typical turbojet engine, with a moderate compression ratio, a single spindle connects the compressor with the turbine. The turbojet engine compressor has a maximum of about four stages using a single spindle. If there are more than four compression stages on a spindle, there is much more susceptibility to compressor stall. For a high compression ratio turbojet, such as a typical turbojet aircraft,

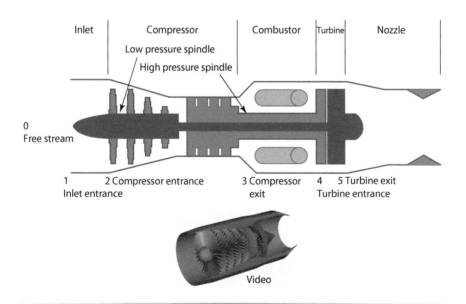

Fig. 3.6 Schematic of turbojet flow path, components, and nomenclature. (Source: http://www.lerc/nasa.gov.)

two spindle shafts are usually used (see top of figure). As shown at the top of the figure, the low pressure compressor is driven at its best speed by an inner spindle connected to a low pressure turbine. The high pressure compressor is located aft of the low pressure compressor. The high pressure compressor is driven at a higher speed by a concentric outer spindle connected to a high pressure turbine. Because of typical length and cost constraints, most missile turbojets have a only a single spindle, and are therefore limited to a moderate compressor pressure ratio (e.g., $p_3/p_2 < 10$). Note from the figure that the combustor is an annulus surrounding the spindle(s) connecting the compressor with the turbine.

For a subsonic turbojet, the nozzle is usually convergent. For a supersonic turbojet, the nozzle is usually a convergent-divergent nozzle, as shown in the figure.

The bottom of the figure has an animation of a subsonic turbojet engine. In the animation a four stage compressor (blue) is driven by a single stage turbine (purple). The annular combustor (red) is located between the compressor and the turbine. The convergent nozzle is aft of the turbine.

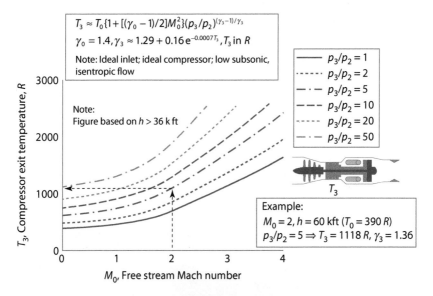

$T_3 = $ Compressor exit temperature in Rankine, $T_0 = $ Free stream temperature in Rankine, $\gamma = $ Specific heat ratio, $M_0 = $ Free stream Mach number, $p_3 = $ Compressor exit pressure, $p_2 = $ Compressor entrance pressure

Fig. 3.7 High temperature compressors are required to achieve high compressor pressure ratio at high Mach number.

Figure 3.7 shows the impact of the compressor pressure ratio and the flight Mach number on the compressor exit temperature T_3. Note from the figure that the compressor temperature increases with compressor pressure ratio and free stream Mach number. An assumption is low subsonic flow through the compressor, such that the static temperature is nearly equal to the total temperature ($T_3 \approx T_{3_t}$). For an ideal compressor, with isentropic flow, the compressor exit temperature is

$$T_3 \approx T_0\{1 + [(\gamma_0 - 1)/2]M_0^2\}(p_3/p_2)^{(\gamma_3-1)/\gamma_3}$$

If the temperature of air is less than about 800 R, it behaves as calorically perfect gas, with a constant specific heat ratio of $\gamma \approx 1.4$. It the temperature of air is greater than about 800 R but less than 5000 R, the vibration states of oxygen and nitrogen molecules affect the specific heat ratio. The air behaves as a thermally perfect gas with the specific heat ratio a function of temperature. If the temperature of air is greater than 5000 R, the oxygen molecules of the air chemically react to form dissociated atomic oxygen. An equation for γ for air temperatures between 500 and 5000 R is

$$\gamma \approx 1.29 + 0.16e^{-0.0007T}$$

As an example, assume a flight number of $M_0 = 2$, a flight altitude of $h = 60$ kft, and a compressor pressure ratio of $p_3/p_2 = 5$. Substituting into the equations for compressor exit temperature and specific heat ratio gives $T_3 = 1118$ R for a value of $\gamma_3 = 1.36$.

Figure 3.8 shows the impact of compressor exit temperature and fuel-to-air ratio on the turbine entrance temperature. The figure is based on JP-10 fuel, which has a heating value $H_f = 18,700$ BTU/lbm. It is assumed that the turbine entrance temperature is the same as the combustor exit temperature. Note from the figure that the turbine temperature is high for high values of compressor temperature and fuel-to-air ratio. An assumption is low subsonic flow from the combustor into the turbine, such that the static temperature is nearly equal to the total temperature ($T_4 \approx T_{4_t}$). For an ideal turbine, the turbine entrance temperature T_4 is equal to the sum of the compressor exit temperature T_3 plus the temperature rise from combustion. The equation is

$$T_4 \approx T_3 + (H_f/c_p)f/a$$

In the above equation $H_f =$ heating value of fuel, $c_p =$ specific heat at constant pressure, and $f/a =$ fuel-to-air ratio. The specific heat at constant pressure is a function of temperature, given by the equation

$$c_p \approx 0.122T^{0.109}$$

The units of c_p are BTU/lbm/R.

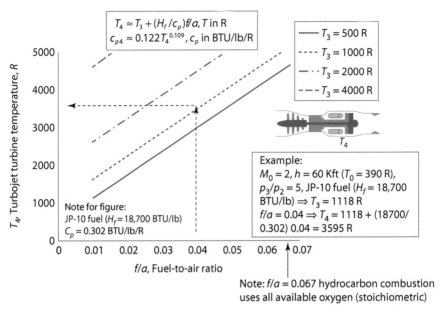

$$T_4 \approx T_3 + (H_f/c_p)f/a, T \text{ in R}$$
$$c_{p4} \approx 0.122 T_4^{0.109}, c_p \text{ in BTU/lb/R}$$

- — $T_3 = 500$ R
- ---- $T_3 = 1000$ R
- —·· $T_3 = 2000$ R
- --- $T_3 = 4000$ R

Example:
$M_0 = 2$, $h = 60$ Kft ($T_0 = 390$ R),
$p_3/p_2 = 5$, JP-10 fuel ($H_f = 18,700$
BTU/lb) $\Rightarrow T_3 = 1118$ R
$f/a = 0.04 \Rightarrow T_4 = 1118 + (18700/$
$0.302) 0.04 = 3595$ R

Note for figure:
JP-10 fuel ($H_f = 18,700$ BTU/lb)
$C_p = 0.302$ BTU/lb/R

y-axis: T_4, Turbojet turbine temperature, R

x-axis: f/a, Fuel-to-air ratio

Note: $f/a = 0.067$ hydrocarbon combustion uses all available oxygen (stoichiometric)

T_4 = Turbojet turbine entrance temperature in Rankine, T_3 = compressor exit temperature in Rankine, H_f = heating value of fuel, c_p = specific heat at constant pressure, f/a = fuel-to-air ratio

Fig. 3.8   A high temperature turbine is required for a high speed turbojet missile.

The range of fuel-to-air ratio shown in the figure is from $f/a = 0.01$, which is a lean typical lower limit of combustor blow out, to $f/a = 0.067$, which is stoichiometric combustion for a typical hydrocarbon fuel. Stoichiometric combustion uses all of the available oxygen in the air. Because of the high temperature of stoichiometric combustion, most missiles must operate at a low value of fuel-to-air ratio (e.g., $f/a < 0.04$).

As an example, let us calculate the turbine entrance temperature for flight at Mach 2 and $h = 60$ kft altitude. Assume a compressor pressure ratio $p_3/p_2 = 5$; JP-10 hydrocarbon fuel with a heating value of $H_f = 18,700$ BTU/lb; and a fuel-to-air ratio $f/a = 0.04$. Substituting into the previous equation for compressor exit temperature gives $T_3 = 1118$ R. Substituting into the equations for turbine entrance temperature and specific heat at constant pressure gives $T_4 = 3595$ R for a value of $c_p = 0.302$ BTU/lbm/R.

Missile turbojet engine thrust is usually limited by the turbine temperature and compressor pressure ratio. Also, for a specified turbine temperature, there is an optimum value of the compressor pressure ratio $(p_3/p_2)_{@T_{max}}$ that gives maximum thrust. For an ideal turbojet, from Ashley [14]

$$(p_3/p_2)_{@T_{max}} \approx \{(T_4/T_0)^{1/2}/\{1 + [(\gamma_0 - 1)/2]M_0^2\}\}^{\gamma_4/(\gamma_4-1)}$$

Symbols are:

T_{max} = Maximum thrust
T_0 = Free stream temperature
T_4 = Turbine entrance temperature
γ_0 = Free stream specific heat ratio
M_0 = Free stream Mach number
γ_4 = Turbine entrance specific heat ratio

The assumptions in the above equation are 1) isentropic flow through the inlet, compressor, turbine, and nozzle; 2) low subsonic flow through the compressor entrance and exit, with the static pressure approximately equal to the total pressure ($p_2 \approx p_{2_t}, p_3 \approx p_{3_t}$); 3) low subsonic flow and constant pressure combustion through the combustor; and 4) nozzle exit pressure equal to the free stream pressure.

Note from Fig. 3.9 that at subsonic Mach number, the ideal pressure ratio for maximum thrust is very high (e.g., $(p_3/p_2)_{@T_{max}} \gg 5$). A technology challenge for missiles is achieving a high compressor pressure ratio with a light weight/short length compressor. At the other extreme, the figure shows that at high supersonic Mach number with a technology limit on

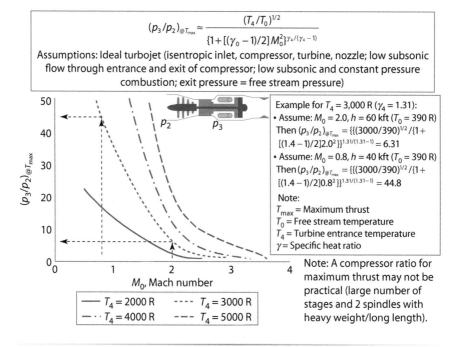

Fig. 3.9 Compressor pressure ratio and turbine temperature limit turbojet maximum thrust. (Source: Ashley, H., *Engineering Analysis of Flight Vehicles*, Dover Publications, Inc., New York, 1974.)

the turbine entrance temperature, low values of p_3/p_2 are optimum for maximum thrust. Considering the limit for the practical use of a turbojet, at very high supersonic Mach number the ideal compressor pressure ratio approaches $p_3/p_2 = 1$ (ramjet operation). Turbojet operation at high supersonic Mach number, with $p_3/p_2 > 1$, requires high temperature combustion, which requires a high temperature turbine. The turbine material temperature limit is usually a technology driver for a supersonic turbojet.

As an example calculation of $(p_3/p_2)_{@T_{max}}$, assume $T_4 = 3000$ R and $\gamma_4 = 1.31$. For a supersonic Mach number $M_0 = 2$ and altitude $h = 60$ kft ($T_0 = 390$ R), calculate

$$(p_3/p_2)_{@T_{max}} = \{\{(3000/390)^{1/2}/\{1 + [(1.4 - 1)/2]2^2\}\}^{1.31/(1.31-1)} = 6.31$$

As a comparison, for a subsonic Mach number $M_0 = 0.8$ and altitude $h = 40$ kft ($T_0 = 390$ R), the required compressor pressure ratio for maximum thrust is much higher,

$$(p_3/p_2)_{@T_{max}} = \{\{(3000/390)^{1/2}/\{1 + [(1.4 - 1)/2]0.8^2\}\}^{1.31/(1.31-1)} = 44.8$$

It is usually not be practical to design a subsonic turbojet missile engine with a compressor pressure ratio for maximum thrust because it would require a large number of compressor stages and two spindles, resulting in an excessively heavy weight/long length/expensive compressor.

Mach 4 turbojet propulsion for missiles not currently practical, because of un-cooled turbine material temperature limits. An assessment is given in Fig. 3.10 of the limitations of current and advanced materials. A low temperature turbine material requires a low fuel-to-air ratio. This results in reduced thrust and reduced specific impulse. The most popular turbine materials for the current subsonic turbojets are nickel-based super alloys. Nickel-based super alloys such as Inconel, Rene, Hastelloy, and Haynes have a maximum temperature limit of about 3000 R for short duration (e.g., less than 30 m) turbines. The turbine temperature limits the maximum Mach number. Maximum Mach number for a turbine temperature limit occurs at a minimum compressor pressure of $p_3/p_2 = 1$ (ramjet operation). For flight at an altitude $h > 36$ kft ($T_0 = 390$ R), the conceptual design equation for maximum Mach number M_{max} is

$$M_{max} = \{[2/(\gamma_0 - 1)][(T_4/T_0)^{1/2} - 1]\}^{1/2} = \{5[(T_4/390)^{1/2} - 1]\}^{1/2}$$

For nickel based alloys with $(T_4)_{max} = 3000$ R

$$M_{max} = \{5[(3000/390)^{1/2} - 1]\}^{1/2} = 2.98$$

An advanced material that is under development for turbine blades is titanium aluminide. Titanium aluminide is a more expensive but lighter

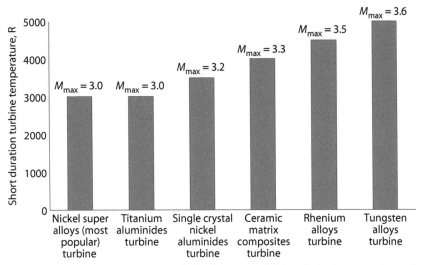

Note: Turbine maximum temperature limits the max available turbojet Mach number and thrust. M_{max} at $(p_3/p_2) = 1$, $h > 36$ kft ($T_0 = 390$ R), T_4 = Turbine temperature = Combustor temperature. $M_{max} = \{5[(T_4/390)^{1/2} - 1]\}^{1/2}$

Fig. 3.10 Advanced turbine materials allow a Mach 3 + turbojet.

weight alternative to nickel super alloys. However, the temperature limit of a titanium aluminide turbine is also about 3000 R, limiting the cruise Mach number to $M_{max} = 2.98$.

Another advanced material with a higher temperature capability is single crystal alloys. An advantage of a single crystal alloy is it does not have a grain boundary, eliminating a source of failure. The maximum short duration turbine temperature of single crystal nickel aluminide is about 3500 R. For a turbine temperature of 3500 R, this results in a maximum turbojet Mach number

$$M_{max} = \{5[(3500/390)^{1/2} - 1]\}^{1/2} = 3.16$$

A higher temperature, but higher risk, turbine material is ceramic matrix composite. A concern is fracture sensitivity. Short duration maximum turbine temperature is about 4000 R. For a turbine temperature of 4000 R, the maximum turbojet Mach number is

$$M_{max} = \{5[(4000/390)^{1/2} - 1]\}^{1/2} = 3.32$$

Rhenium would allow a short duration turbine temperature of about 4500 R and a turbojet cruise Mach number

$$M_{max} = \{5[(4500/390)^{1/2} - 1]\}^{1/2} = 3.46$$

Disadvantages of rhenium are high cost and heavy weight. However, rhenium has good potential for high temperature applications, and its cost should decrease in the future. The SM-3 Standard Missile Third Stage Rocket Motor (TSRM) is an example of an application of rhenium.

Finally, the highest temperature turbine material is tungsten, which has a maximum temperature of about 5000 R for a short duration application. The maximum cruise Mach number for an uncooled tungsten turbine is

$$M_{max} = \{5[(5000/390)^{1/2} - 1]\}^{1/2} = 3.59$$

Tungsten has disadvantages of a risk of fracture sensitivity, is difficult to fabricate to precision tolerance, and is very heavy.

For a turbojet missile at Mach 3.59 cruise at $h > 36$ kft with $p_3/p_2 = 1$ and a tungsten turbine temperature $T_4 = 5000$ R, the compressor temperature is

$$T_3 \approx T_0\{1 + [(\gamma_0 - 1)/2]M_0^2\}(p_3/p_2)^{(\gamma_3-1)/\gamma_3} = 390[1 + 0.2(3.59)^2(1)]$$
$$= 1395\,R$$

A compressor temperature of 1395 R allows the use of conventional materials such as nickel super alloy, steel, or titanium for the compressor.

Approaches to Mach 4 turbojet propulsion include a cooled turbine, an afterburner, and insulated turbine blades. These are compared in Fig. 3.11.

Approach for Mach 4 Turbojet	Measures of merit					
	Thrust	I_{SP}	Length	Weight	Cost	Risk
Actively cooled turbine[1]	○	○	○	○	○	—
Afterburner[2]	○	○	—	—	○	◐
Insulated turbine blades[3]	—	—	◐	◐	◐	—
● Superior ◐ Good ○ Average — Poor						

Note:
1. Max coolant rate is a risk for highly cooled turbine.
2. Afterburner adds length and weight
3. Insulation failure, char, and wall leakage are a risk for insulated turbine blades

Fig. 3.11   Alternative propulsion approaches for a Mach 4 missile turbojet.

For a turbojet missile at Mach 4 cruise at $h > 36$ kft with $p_3/p_2 = 1$, the combustion temperature is

$$T_4 = T_0\{[p_3/p_2)_{@T_{max}}]^{\gamma_4/(\gamma_4-1)}\{1 + [(\gamma_0 - 1)/2]M_0^2\}\}^2$$
$$= 390(1)[1 + 0.2(4)^2]^2 = 6879\,\text{R}$$

Active cooling, using as a hollow turbine, could use liquid coolant such as fuel.

For an actively cooled turbine, the compressor temperature for Mach 4 flight is

$$T_3 \approx T_0\{1 + [(\gamma_0 - 1)/2]M_0^2\}(p_3/p_2)^{(\gamma_3-1)/\gamma_3} = 390[1 + 0.2(4)^2(1)]$$
$$= 1638\,\text{R}$$

A compressor temperature of 1638 R allows the use of conventional materials for the compressor.

A risk of an actively cooled nickel super alloy turbine is the high cooling rate required to limit the temperature to $T = 3000$ R (material temperature limit). Higher temperature materials for the turbine would require less coolant but present another risk in new materials development. Tungsten, with a maximum temperature of 5000 R, would require the least coolant.

A second approach for a Mach 4 turbojet is an afterburner behind an un-cooled turbine. An un-cooled turbine must operate at low fuel-to-air ratio at Mach 4 cruise, to limit the temperature on the turbine. There is excess oxygen downstream of the turbine that is available for additional combustion. Although an afterburner for a Mach 4 turbojet is relatively low technology risk, it adds length/weight to the missile. The afterburner thrust and specific impulse would be comparable to that of the turbojet at $p_3/p_2 = 1$.

A third approach for a Mach 4 turbojet is insulated turbine blades. Insulated turbine blades have advantages of relatively low impact on the weight, cost, and length of the missile. High temperature insulation materials are discussed in Chapter 3. Graphite insulation is the current state-of-the art of high temperature insulation. However, since the maximum temperature of graphite is about 6000 R, less than the combustion temperature of 6879 R for a Mach 4 turbojet, turbine blade insulation failure is a high risk. The risk is dependent on the flight duration at high Mach number. For example, the insulation thickness required for Mach 4 flight duration of 10 m would be much larger than the insulation required for Mach 4 flight of 1 m duration. Another risk is erosion of the insulation could induce local heat transfer failure of the turbine blades. Also, erosion and wall leakage of the insulation would reduce the specific impulse and thrust.

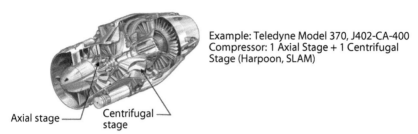

Example: Teledyne Model 370, J402-CA-400
Compressor: 1 Axial Stage + 1 Centrifugal
Stage (Harpoon, SLAM)

Axial stage —   Centrifugal —
                     stage

Type	Single stage pressure	Multi-stage pressure	Diameter	Cost
Axial	○	●	●	○
Centrifugal	●	—	—	●
Axial + Centrifugal	●	●	○	◒

● Superior   ◒ Good   ○ Average   — Poor

Fig. 3.12   Missile turbojet compressor alternatives: multi-stage axial, single stage centrifugal, multi-stage axial + centrifugal.

Figure 3.12 compares the advantages and disadvantages of three types of missile turbojet compressors: axial, centrifugal, and combined axial + centrifugal.

The compressor consists of a number of compression stages that increase the pressure and decrease the flow velocity prior to entering the combustor. The two types of compressor stages are axial stages and centrifugal.

Advantages of an axial compressor stage include a relatively low frontal area and better compatibility with multi-stage (higher) compression. An axial compressor stage has rotating and fixed blades, similar to airfoils. The rotor blades add work to the air, increasing the local velocity, stagnation temperature, and the stagnation pressure. Downstream of the rotor blades are the fixed, stationary stator blades. The fixed stator blades turn the flow back to the centerline, which decreases the velocity, increases the static temperature, and increases the static pressure. The typical stage pressure ratio for subsonic rotors is about 1.4. A higher stage pressure ratio is possible, with rotor blades operating at a local transonic Mach number. The maximum axial stage pressure ratio for high transonic (e.g., Mach 1.7) rotors is about 2.2. However, high transonic rotor blades are susceptible to flow separation and stall.

The increasing pressure and temperature across each stage of a multi-stage axial compressor requires decreasing the flow cross sectional area of each following stage. This results in decreasing efficiency across each stage.

A concern with axial compressors is flow separation because of flow deceleration in diffusion. As a result, a multi-stage axial compressor usually requires more stages than the turbine, because the accelerating flow through the turbine is less susceptible to flow separation.

Another concern for the compressor is high blade forces and vibration. Because of its relatively small blade size, an axial compressor requires close manufacturing clearance tolerances to achieve good efficiency. In recent years precision castings have achieved sufficient manufacturing tolerance accuracy to allow their application to axial compressors, resulting in cost savings.

A centrifugal compressor uses a different approach to compress the air. The centrifugal compressor has a radial blade impeller to accelerate the flow radially, followed by a diffuser that decelerates the flow (increasing pressure) and turns the flow 90 deg back to the centerline. The tip Mach number of the impeller is $M_{\text{Impeller tip}} \approx 1$.

Compared to an axial compressor, the advantages of a centrifugal compressor include higher single stage pressure ratio (typically about 3 to 4), fewer parts, relative ease of manufacturing, less concern for manufacturing tolerances, lower cost, higher reliability, better compatibility with small engines, less risk of boundary layer separation, and more robust operation over a wider envelope without surging or choking. Disadvantages of a centrifugal compressor include a limitation of only one centrifugal stage per compressor and a larger diameter.

Shown at the top of Fig. 3.12 is the turbojet missile baseline engine, the Teledyne Model 370, J402-CA-400. It has a multi-stage (one axial + one centrifugal) compressor.

Listed at the bottom of the figure is a tabular comparison of axial, centrifugal, and axial + centrifugal compressors. Most turbojet missiles use either a multi-stage axial compressor or a compressor with one or more axial stages followed by a single centrifugal stage. The selection is often driven by the combined attributes of multi-stage pressure, diameter, length, and cost.

Multi-stage compressors are required if it is necessary for the turbojet to have a high compressor pressure ratio. Neglecting inter-stage losses, an estimate of the compressor pressure ratio p_3/p_2 can be obtained by multiplying the pressure ratio of each stage. The equation for an n-stage compressor is

$$p_3/p_2 = (p_{\text{Exit}}/p_{\text{Entrance}})_1 (p_{\text{Exit}}/p_{\text{Entrance}})_2 \cdots (p_{\text{Exit}}/p_{\text{Entrance}})_n$$

For an axial stage, the stage pressure ratio is typically:

$$(p_{\text{Exit}}/p_{\text{Entrance}})_{\text{Axial}} = 1.605$$

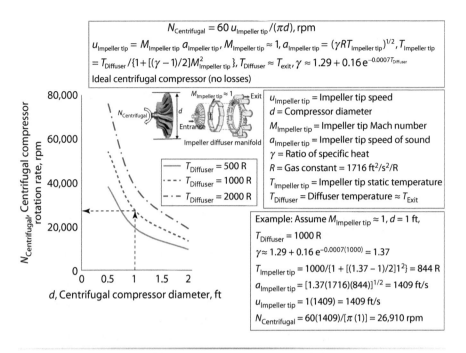

Fig. 3.13   A small diameter turbojet requires a high speed compressor. (Source: Durham, F. P., *Aircraft Jet Powerplants*, Prentice-Hall, 1961.)

The above axial stage pressure ratio prediction is based on a typical stator pressure coefficient $c_p = 0.6$ and a typical stator entrance Mach number $M_{Entrance} = 1.2$.

For a centrifugal stage, the pressure ratio is typically:

$$(p_{Exit}/p_{Entrance})_{Centrifugal} = 3.24$$

One of the differences between a cruise missile and a larger flight vehicle, such as a UAV or an aircraft, is a smaller diameter cruise missile has a larger rotational speed of its compressor. Figure 3.13 shows the rotation rate $N_{Centrifugal}$ of a centrifugal compressor as a function of compressor diameter d and diffuser temperature $T_{Diffuser}$. An assumption is an isentropic centrifugal compressor (no losses). The centrifugal compressor is driven by the missile turbine. A schematic of a centrifugal compressor is shown in the top center section of the figure. Elements are an impeller, a diffuser, and a manifold. First, the rotating impeller increases the flow velocity, resulting in a radial Mach number at the impeller tip of $M_{Impeller\ tip} \approx 1$. Next, the fixed diffuser decelerates the flow to low velocity, resulting in increased pressure. The compressor manifold then diverts the high pressure, low speed flow into the combustor.

The compressor rotation rate shown in the figure is based on the Ref. 13 equation

$$N_{\text{Centrifugal}} = 60 u_{\text{Impeller tip}}/(\pi d), \text{ rpm}$$

The impeller tip velocity $u_{\text{Impeller tip}}$ in the above equation is obtained from the local Mach number and speed of sound

$$u_{\text{Impeller tip}} = M_{\text{Impeller tip}} a_{\text{Impeller tip}}$$

The local speed of sound at the impeller tip is obtained from the local temperature

$$a_{\text{Impeller tip}} = (\gamma R T_{\text{Impeller tip}})^{1/2}$$

In the above equation, γ = ratio of specific heat $\approx 1.29 + 0.16\,e^{-0.0007 T_{\text{Diffuser}}}$ and R = gas constant = 1716 ft^2/s^2/R. The impeller tip temperature is given by

$$T_{\text{Impeller tip}} = T_{\text{Diffuser}}/\{1 + [(\gamma - 1)/2]M^2_{\text{Impeller tip}}\}$$

The diffuser temperature $T_{\text{Diffuser}} \approx T_{\text{Exit}}$ is obtained from the compressor isentropic pressure ratio $p_{\text{Exit}}/p_{\text{Entrance}}$.

As an example calculation of centrifugal compressor rotation rate, assume $M_{\text{Impeller tip}} = 1$, $d = 1$ ft, $T_{\text{Diffuser}} = 1000$ R

Compute

$$\gamma \approx 1.29 + 0.16\,e^{-0.0007(1000)} = 1.37$$

$$T_{\text{Impeller tip}} = 1000/\{1 + [(1.37 - 1)/2]1^2\} = 844\,\text{R}$$

$$a_{\text{Impeller tip}} = [1.37(1716)(844)]^{1/2} = 1409\,\text{ft/s}$$

$$u_{\text{Impeller tip}} = 1(1409) = 1409\,\text{ft/s}$$

$$N_{\text{Centrifugal}} = 60(1409)/[\pi(1)] = 26,910\,\text{rpm}$$

An animated schematic of a 4-stage axial compressor is shown in the top right section of Fig. 3.14. Note that each of the rotating rotors is followed by a fixed stator.

The typical stage total pressure efficiency of an axial compressor is $0.90 < \eta < 0.95$ per stage. The typical stage pressure ratio of an axial compressor is $1.2 < p_{\text{Exit}}/p_{\text{Entrance}} < 2$ per stage.

The pressure ratio of a single stage axial compressor is given by the equation

$$(p_{\text{Exit}}/p_{\text{Entrance}})_{\text{Axial}} = 1 + 0.5\gamma C_p M^2_{\text{Rotor}}$$

Typically, $\gamma \approx 1.4$, $0.4 < C_p < 0.8$, $1 < M_{\text{Rotor}} < 1.4$

In the above equation, p_{Exit} = exit pressure, $p_{Entrance}$ = entrance pressure, γ = ratio of specific heat, c_p = pressure coefficient, and M_{Rotor} = rotor maximum local Mach number.

Figure 3.14 shows the variation of $(p_{Exit}/p_{Entrance})_{Axial}$ with representative values of M_{Rotor} and C_p. Note the increasing $(p_{Exit}/p_{Entrance})_{Axial}$ with increasing M_{Rotor} and C_p. A problem achieving $M_{Rotor} > 1.5$ is shock wave—boundary layer interaction, which limits the maximum achievable Mach number. A problem with $C_p > 0.8$ is flow separation, which limits the maximum achievable pressure coefficient.

As an example, assume a single stage axial compressor with typical values of $\gamma = 1.4$, $C_p = 0.6$, $M_{Rotor} = 1.2$. Calculate:

$$(p_{Exit}/p_{Entrance})_{Axial} = 1 + 0.5(1.4)(0.6)(1.2)^2 = 1.605$$

For an ideal compressor, the total pressure ratio p_3/p_2 of n stages is the product of the individual pressure ratio $p_{Exit}/p_{Entrance}$ of each stage

$$p_3/p_2 = (p_{Exit}/p_{Entrance})_1 (p_{Exit}/p_{Entrance})_2 \cdots (p_{Exit}/p_{Entrance})_n$$

Figure 3.15 shows the typical range of p_3/p_2, based on typical values of an axial stage compression $(p_{Exit}/p_{Entrance} = 1.605)$ and centrifugal stage compression $(p_{Exit}/p_{Entrance} = 3.24)$. The solid red line is multi-stage, axial-only compression. The dashed pink line is multi-stage axial compression, followed by a single stage centrifugal compression. Note that

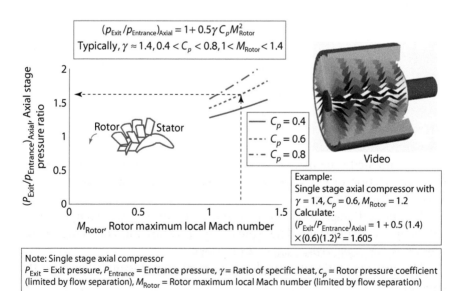

Fig. 3.14 Rotors of a high pressure axial compressor have high local Mach number. (Source: http://www.lerc/nasa.gov.)

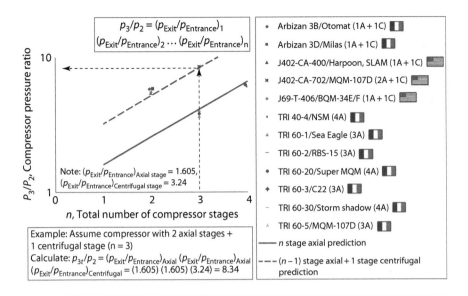

Fig. 3.15 Multi-stage compressors provide higher compressor pressure ratio. (Source of Compressor Data: Howell Instruments Web Site http://www.howellinst.com/Howell/Web/engine.jsp.)

for same number of stages, multi-stage axial compression followed by single stage centrifugal compression gives a higher pressure ratio.

The compressor pressure ratios for operational turbojet engines and their operational applications are also shown in the figure. Missile turbojet engine contractors include Turbomeca and Microturbo of France and Teledyne of the United States. Note that there is a good correlation of the predicted compressor pressure ratio with the data.

As an example of predicting compressor pressure ratio, assume a compressor with two stages of typical axial compression ($c_p = 0.6$, $M_{\text{Entrance}} = 1.2 \Rightarrow p_{\text{Exit}}/p_{\text{Entrance}} = 1.605$), followed by a single stage of typical centrifugal compression ($p_{\text{Exit}}/p_{\text{Entrance}} = 3.24$). For this example, the total number of stages is $n = 2 + 1 = 3$. Calculate:

$$p_3/p_2 = (1.605)^2(3.24) = 8.34$$

3.5 Turbojet Thrust Prediction

Shown in Fig. 3.16 is the non-dimensional maximum thrust of an ideal turbojet. Note from the figure that high thrust occurs for high atmospheric pressure p_0 (low altitude), large inlet flow area A_0, high free stream Mach number M_0, and high combustor exit/turbine entrance temperature T_4.

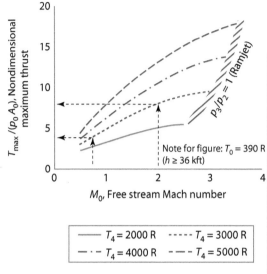

Fig. 3.16 Turbojet thrust is limited by inlet flow and turbine maximum allowable temperature.

Also note the boundary at the right side of the figure (ramjet operation), with a compressor pressure ratio $p_3/p_2 = 1$.

The equation for turbojet maximum thrust T_{max} is

$$T_{max}/(p_0 A_0) = (\gamma_0 M_0/a_0)(T/\dot{m})_{max}$$

In the above equation M_0 = free stream Mach number, p_0 = atmospheric static pressure, a_0 = atmospheric speed of sound, γ_0 = atmospheric specific heat ratio = 1.4, A_0 = free stream flow area, and $\dot{m}$ = mass flow rate.

Assumptions are isentropic flow through the inlet, compressor, turbine, and nozzle; low subsonic flow through the compressor; low subsonic flow and constant pressure through the combustor; and nozzle exit pressure equal to the free stream pressure. The thrust equation is derived from the momentum equation

$$T = \dot{m}(V_e - V_0)$$

The equation for the exit velocity of an ideal turbojet is

$$V_e = \{2c_p T_{5_t}[1 - (p_0/p_{5_t})^{(\gamma_5-1)/\gamma_5}]\}^{1/2}$$

The primary terms to be determined in the above equation are the turbine exit total temperature T_{5_t} and the turbine exit pressure p_{5_t}. The equation for the turbine exit total temperature of an ideal turbojet is $T_{5_t} \approx T_4 - T_3 + T_2$. The temperatures in this equation are the combustor temperature T_4, compressor exit temperature T_3, and the compressor entrance/inlet exit temperature T_2. In this analysis the combustor temperature T_4 is specified. For the ideal turbojet, the compressor exit temperature is

$$T_3 \approx T_2(p_3/p_2)^{(\gamma_3-1)/\gamma_3}$$

The compressor entrance temperature is

$$T_2 \approx T_0\{1 + [(\gamma_0 - 1)/2]M_0^2\}$$

Next, the term p_{5_t} in the exit velocity equation can be solved from

$$p_{5_t} \approx p_4(T_{5_t}/T_4)^{\gamma_4/(\gamma_4-1)}$$

We will assume constant pressure combustion ($p_4 = p_3$). This analysis is conducted for values of compressor pressure p_3/p_2 that provides maximum thrust,

$$p_3/p_2 \approx (p_3/p_2)_{@T_{\max}} \approx \{(T_4/T_0)^{1/2}/\{1 + [(\gamma_0 - 1)/2]M_0^2\}\}^{\gamma_4/(\gamma_4-1)}$$

The compressor entrance/inlet exit pressure p_2, for adiabatic flow through the inlet, is

$$p_2 \approx p_0\{1 + [(\gamma_0 - 1)/2]M_0^2\}^{\gamma_0/(\gamma_0-1)}$$

As an example, we shall calculate the maximum thrust of an ideal supersonic turbojet. Assume $A_0 = A_c = 114$ in^2, $T_4 = 3000$ R, $M_0 = 2$, and $h = 60$ kft altitude ($T_0 = 390$ R, $p_0 = 1.047$ psi, $a_0 = 968$ ft/s). From the previous example, $\gamma_4 = 1.31$ and $(p_3/p_2)_{@T_{\max}} = 6.31$. Calculate

$$p_2 = 1.047\{1 + [(1.4 - 1)/2]2^2\}^{1.4/(1.4-1)} = 8.19 \, \text{psi}$$

$$T_2 = 390\{1 + [(1.4 - 1)/2]2^2\} = 702 \, \text{R}$$

Solve for

$$p_3 = p_4 = 6.31(8.19) = 51.7 \, \text{psi}$$

$$T_3 = 702(6.31)^{(1.36-1)/1.36} = 1133 \, \text{R}$$

$$\gamma_3 = 1.29 + 0.1 \, e^{-0.0007(1133)} = 1.36$$

Substituting the values of the T_4, T_3, and T_2 temperatures gives

$$T_{5_t} = 3000 - 1133 + 702 = 2569 \, \text{R}$$

$$\gamma_5 = 1.29 + 0.16 \, e^{-0.0007(2569)} = 1.32$$

$$c_{p_5} = 0.122(3000)^{0.109} = 0.293 \, \text{BTU/lbm/R}$$

$$= 228 \, \text{lbf/lbm/R} = 7340 \, \text{ft}^2/\text{s}^2/\text{R}$$

Substituting the values of p_4, T_{5_t}, T_4, and γ_4 into the equation for the turbine exit total pressure gives

$$p_{5_t} = 51.7(2569/3000)^{1.31/(1.31-1)} = 23.0 \, \text{psi}$$

Also, substituting the values of c_{p_5}, T_{5_t}, p_{5_t}, p_0, and γ_5 in the exit velocity equation gives

$$V_e = \{2(7340)(2569)[1 - (1.047/23.0)^{(1.32-1)/1.32}]\}^{1/2} = 4524 \, \text{ft/s}$$

Thrust per unit mass flow rate (also the incremental velocity), is then

$$T/\dot{m} = 4524 - 1936 = 2588 \, \text{ft/s}$$

All of the required terms are now available to substitute in the non-dimensional thrust equation, giving

$$T_{max}/(p_0 A_0) = [1.4(2)/968](2588) = 7.49$$

Substituting the free stream static pressure p_0 and inlet capture area A_0 into the above equation gives the thrust

$$T_{max} = 7.49(1.047)(114) = 894 \, \text{lb}$$

As another example, let us calculate and compare the maximum thrust of the same turbojet [$T_4 = 3000 \, \text{R}$ ($\gamma_4 = 1.31$), $A_0 = 114 \, \text{in}^2$] at subsonic Mach number. Assume $M_0 = 0.8$, $h = 40 \, \text{kft}$ ($T_0 = 390 \, \text{R}$, $p_0 = 2.72 \, \text{psi}$, $a_0 = 968 \, \text{ft/s}$). For this case $(p_3/p_2)_{@T_{max}} = 44.8$, $p_2 = 4.15 \, \text{psi}$, $p_3 = 185.7 \, \text{psi}$, $T_2 = 440 \, \text{R}$, $T_3 = 1204 \, \text{R}$, $\gamma_3 = 1.36$, $T_{5_t} = 2236 \, \text{R}$, $\gamma_5 = 1.32$, $p_{5_t} = 53.6 \, \text{psi}$, $c_p = 0.283$ BTU/lbm/R = 220 lbf/lbm/R = 7315 $\text{ft}^2/\text{s}^2/\text{R}$, $V_e = 4173 \, \text{ft/s}$, $(T/\dot{m})_{max} = 3399 \, \text{ft/s}$, $T_{max}/(p_0 A_0) = 3.93 \Rightarrow T_{max} = 1219 \, \text{lb}$

Note that Mach 0.8/40 kft flight provides higher thrust than Mach 2/60 kft flight (1219 versus 894 lb).

In the theoretical limit of a flight Mach number $M = 0$, the above thrust equation is invalid, predicting zero thrust. The error in the equation for $M_0 = 0$ is because the equation does not account for the local lateral flow entrainment caused by the compressor. The minimum operating Mach number of a turbojet missile is typically greater than about Mach 0.5. Turbojet missiles are rocket boosted to a typical take-over of about Mach 0.5.

3.6 Turbojet Specific Impulse Prediction

Figure 3.17 shows the non-dimensional specific impulse of an ideal turbojet at maximum thrust. Note that turbojet specific impulse is highest at subsonic Mach number, decreasing with increasing Mach number. The specific impulse is based on the equation

$$(I_{SP})_{@T_{max}} g c_p T_0/(a_0 H_f) = T_{max} T_0/[(p_0 A_0 \gamma_0 M_0)(T_4 - T_3)]$$

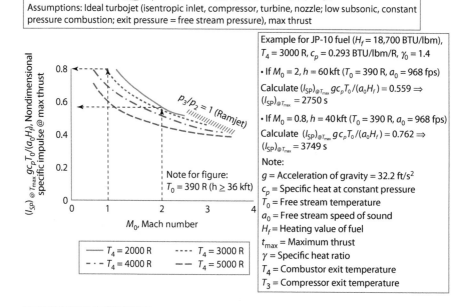

Fig. 3.17   Turbojet specific impulse decreases with Mach number and combustion temperature.

Assumptions are maximum thrust; isentropic flow through the inlet, compressor, turbine, and nozzle; low subsonic flow through the compressor $(T_3 \approx T_{3_t})$; combustor has low subsonic flow $(T_4 \approx T_{4_t})$ and constant pressure $(p_4 = p_3)$; and nozzle exit pressure equal to the free stream pressure.

The following is an example calculation of turbojet specific impulse at supersonic Mach number. It is based on the same conditions as the previous example calculation of turbojet thrust, which were $A_0 = 114$ in^2, $T_4 = 3000$ R, $M_0 = 2$, and $h = 60$ kft altitude $(T_0 = 390$ R, $p_0 = 1.047$ psi, $a = 968$ ft/s). Also, from the previous example, $T_3 = 1133$ R, $c_p = 0.293$ BTU/lbm/R, and $T_{max} = 894$ lb. We shall assume JP-10 fuel heating value $H_f = 18700$ BTU/lbm/R. Substituting, the non-dimensional specific impulse is

$$(I_{SP})_{@T_{max}} g c_p T_0/(a_0 H_f) = 894(390)/[1.047(114)(1.4)(2)(3000 - 1133)]$$
$$= 0.559$$

Substituting the values of the free stream speed of sound a_0, heating value of fuel H_f, acceleration of gravity $g = 32.2$ ft/s^2, specific heat at constant pressure c_p, and free stream temperature T_0 gives the specific impulse

$$(I_{SP})_{@T_{max}} = 0.559(968)(18700)/[32.2(0.293)(390)] = 2750 \text{ s}$$

As another example calculation, assume a subsonic flight at $M_0 = 0.8$, $h = 40$ kft $(T_0 = 390$ R, $a_0 = 968$ ft/s)
Calculate

$$(I_{SP})_{@T_{max}} g c_p T_0/(a_0 H_f) = 1219(390)/[2.72(114)(1.4)(0.8)(3000 - 1204)]$$
$$= 0.762$$
$$(I_{SP})_{@T_{max}} = 0.762(968)(18700)/\{32.2(0.293)(390)\} = 3749 \text{ s}$$

Note that Mach 0.8 flight has higher specific impulse than Mach 2 flight (3749 versus 2750 s).

While the previous figure showed that an increase in combustion temperature has the benefit of higher thrust, this figure shows that the opposite is true for specific impulse. A design tradeoff to achieve a required level of thrust (e.g., to overcome missile drag, provide acceleration to a higher Mach number) is designing for a high fuel-to-air ratio versus a low (lean) f/a. A high f/a design provides high temperature combustion with the benefit of high thrust with a small diameter inlet but it has reduced specific impulse and a potential materials temperature problem. A lean f/a design provides low temperature combustion with the benefit of high specific impulse and less material temperature risk, but it requires a larger diameter inlet to meet the thrust requirement, with adverse effects of a heavier inlet weight and higher drag.

For an ideal turbojet (isentropic inlet, compressor, turbine, nozzle; low subsonic inlet exit; low subsonic, constant pressure combustion; exit pressure = free stream pressure), the Ref. 14 ideal maximum thrust is given by

$$T_{max}/(p_0 A_0) = \gamma_0 M_0^2 \{\{1 + \{2/[(\gamma_0 - 1)M_0^2]\}[(T_4/T_0)^{1/2} - 1]^2\}^{1/2} - 1\},$$
$$\text{note: } \gamma = \gamma_0 = 1.4.$$

As a comparison, a more exact computation of thrust can be obtained by including real gas effects. Real gas effects include fuel mixing with the air and high temperature. To account for the effect of high temperature, the following equation is used for specific heat ratio γ

$$\gamma \approx 1.29 + 0.16 e^{-0.0007T}$$

The above equation is valid for 500 R < T < 5000 R with relatively low values of fuel-to-air ratio (e.g., $f/a < 0.04$). For T < 500 R, $\gamma = \gamma_0 = 1.4$.

The specific heat ratio γ is computed step-by-step for each component as $\gamma = \gamma$ (T) in the thrust equation

$$T/(p_0 A_0) = (\gamma_0 M_0/a_0)(T/\dot{m})$$

Figure 3.18 shows that the assumption $\gamma = \gamma_0 = 1.4$ has sufficient accuracy (e.g., <10% error) for predicting conceptual design thrust.

As an example, assume a typical value of turbine entrance temperature $T_4 = 3000$ R ($\gamma_4 = 1.31$), inlet free stream flow area = inlet capture area $A_0 \approx A_c = 114$ in^2 (same capture area as the Chapter 7 ramjet baseline), free stream Mach number $M_0 = 0.8$, flight altitude $h = 40$ kft ($T_0 = 390$ R, $a_0 = 968$ ft/s, $p_0 = 2.72$ psi).

The free stream velocity is

$$V_0 = M_0 a_0 = 774 \, \text{ft/s}.$$

For the Ashley [14] simple, closed-form analytical solution with $\gamma = \gamma_0 = 1.4$:

$$T_{max}/(p_0 A_0) = 1.4(0.8)^2 \{\{1 + \{2/[(1.4 - 1)(0.8)^2]\}$$
$$\times [(3000/390)^{1/2} - 1]^2\}^{1/2} - 1\} = 3.64$$
$$T_{max} = 3.64(2.72)(144) = 1129 \, \text{lb}$$

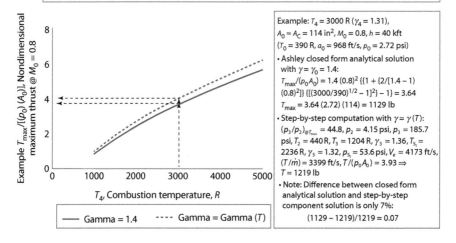

$$\frac{T_{max}}{p_0 A_0} = \gamma_0 M_0^2 \left\{\left[1 + \left(\frac{2}{(\gamma_0 - 1)M_0^2}\right)\left[(T_4/T_0)^{1/2} - 1\right]^2\right]^{1/2} - 1\right\}, \text{Note: } \gamma = \gamma_0 = 1.4, \text{Ref: Ashley [14]}$$

$T/(p_0 A_0) = (\gamma_0 M_0/a_0)(T/\dot{m})$, Note: γ computed step-by-step for each component as $\gamma = \gamma(T)$
Assumptions: Ideal turbojet (isentropic inlet, compressor, turbine, nozzle; low subsonic inlet exit; low subsonic, constant pressure combustion; exit pressure = free stream pressure)

Example axis label (y-axis): Example $T_{max}/[(p_0)(A_0)]$, Nondimensional maximum thrust @ $M_0 = 0.8$

x-axis: T_4, Combustion temperature, R (0, 1000, 2000, 3000, 4000, 5000)

— Gamma = 1.4   ---- Gamma = Gamma (T)

Example: $T_4 = 3000$ R ($\gamma_4 = 1.31$),
$A_0 \approx A_C = 114$ in^2, $M_0 = 0.8$, $h = 40$ kft
($T_0 = 390$ R, $a_0 = 968$ ft/s, $p_0 = 2.72$ psi)
• Ashley closed form analytical solution
  with $\gamma = \gamma_0 = 1.4$:
  $T_{max}/(p_0 A_0) = 1.4 (0.8)^2 \{\{1 + \{2/[1.4 - 1)$
  $(0.8)^2]\} \{[(3000/390)^{1/2} - 1]^2\} - 1\} = 3.64$
  $T_{max} = 3.64 (2.72) (114) = 1129$ lb
• Step-by-step computation with $\gamma = \gamma(T)$:
  $(p_3/p_2)_{@T_{max}} = 44.8, p_2 = 4.15$ psi, $p_3 = 185.7$
  psi, $T_2 = 440$ R, $T_3 = 1204$ R, $\gamma_3 = 1.36$, $T_{5_t} = $
  2236 R, $\gamma_5 = 1.32$, $p_{5_t} = 53.6$ psi, $V_e = 4173$ ft/s,
  $(T/\dot{m}) = 3399$ ft/s, $T/(p_0 A_0) = 3.93 \Rightarrow$
  $T = 1219$ lb
• Note: Difference between closed form
  analytical solution and step-by-step
  component solution is only 7%:
  $(1129 - 1219)/1219 = 0.07$

Fig. 3.18 Assumption $\gamma = \gamma_0 = 1.4$ has sufficient accuracy for turbojet conceptual design thrust. (Source: Ashley, H., *Engineering Analysis of Flight Vehicles*, Dover Publications, Inc., New York, 1974.)

Next, the more exact step-by-step computation with $\gamma = \gamma(T)$ gives:

$(p_3/p_2)_{@T_{max}} = 44.8$ (from prior example)
$p_2 = 2.72\{1 + [(1.4 - 1)/2]0.8^2\}^{1.4/(1.4-1)} = 4.15$ psi for an isentropic inlet with low subsonic exit
$p_3 = 44.8(4.15) = 185.7$ psi
$T_2 = 390\{1 + [(1.4-1)/2]0.8^2\} = 440$ R for an isentropic inlet with low subsonic exit
$T_3 = 440(44.8)^{(1.36-1)/1.36} = 1204$ R for an isentropic compressor with $\gamma_3 = 1.36$
$T_{5_t} = 3000 - 1204 + 440 = 2236$ R total temperature with $\gamma_5 = 1.32$
$p_4 = p_3 = 185.7$ psi for constant pressure combustion
$p_{5_t} = 185.7(2236/3000)^{1.31/(1.31-1)} = 53.6$ psi total pressure for an isentropic turbine with $\gamma_4 = 1.31$

For

$$c_{p_{T_4=3000\,R}} = 7315 \text{ lbf/slug/R}$$

$V_e = \{2(7315)(2236)[1-(2.72/53.6)]^{(1.32-1)/1.32}\}^{1/2} = 4173$ ft/s   exit velocity for an isentropic nozzle.

Thrust per unit mass flow rate is the difference between the turbojet engine exit velocity and the missile free stream velocity.

$$(T/\dot{m}) = V_e - V_0 = 4173 - 774 = 3399 \, \text{ft/s}$$

Note from the above equation that the exit velocity V_e must be greater than the free stream velocity V_0 for the engine to develop thrust. It is usually appropriate for conceptual design to assume that the air mass flow into the inlet is equal to the mass flow out of the nozzle (inlet air flow plus added fuel). This is because the fuel-to-air ratio is usually small (e.g., $f/a <$ 0.04). Substituting the previously computed values of γ_0, M_0, a_0, and $(T/\dot{m})$ gives the non-dimensional maximum ideal thrust with $\gamma = \gamma(T)$.

$$T/(p_0 A_0) = 1.4(0.8)(3399)/968 = 3.93$$

Finally, substituting for the values of p_0 and A_0 gives the maximum ideal thrust with $\gamma = \gamma(T)$.

$$T = 3.93(2.72)(114) = 1219 \, \text{lb}$$

Note that for this example the difference between the Ashley [14] simple closed form analytical solution with $\gamma = \gamma_0 = 1.4$ and the "more exact" step-by-step component solution with $\gamma = \gamma(T)$ is 7% [(1129 − 1219)/1219 = 0.07].

Figure 3.19 illustrates the tradeoff of the relatively high thrust from a moderate/relatively low value of compressor pressure ratio versus the higher specific impulse from a higher pressure ratio compressor. As stated earlier, most turbojet missiles operate at moderate/relatively low values of compressor pressure ratio because of limitations of length, weight, and cost. For most missiles, these limitations result in relatively low specific impulse compared to larger, more expensive systems such as UAVs, UCAVs, and aircraft. The Ref. 14 equation for ideal turbojet thrust with an assumption of perfect gas ($\gamma = \gamma_0$) is

$$T/(p_0 A_0) = \gamma_0 M_0^2 \{\{1 + \{2/[(\gamma_0 - 1)M_0^2]\}\}[(p_3/p_2)^{(\gamma_0-1)/\gamma_0} - 1]$$
$$\times \{(T_4/T_0)/\{[(p_3/p_2)^{(\gamma_0-1)/\gamma_0}]\{1 + (\gamma_0 - 1)/2]M_0^2\}\} - 1\}$$
$$+ \{(T_4/T_0)/\{[(p_3/p_2)^{(\gamma_0-1)/\gamma_0}]\{1 + (\gamma_0 - 1)/2]M_0^2\}\}^{1/2} - 1\}$$

The Ref. 14 equation for ideal turbojet specific impulse I_{SP} is

$$[gc_p T_0/(a_0 H_f)]I_{SP} = T/(p_0 A_0)/\{\gamma_0 M_0[(T_4/T_0) - (p_3/p_2)^{(\gamma_0-1)/\gamma_0}]\}$$

As an example, assume $T_4 = 3000$ R, JP-10 fuel ($H_f = 18{,}700$ BTU/ lbm), $A_0 \approx A_c = 114 \, \text{in}^2$, $M_0 = 0.8$, $\gamma = \gamma_0 = 1.4$, $h = 40$ kft ($T_0 = 390$ R, $a_0 = 968$ ft/s, $p_0 = 2.72$ psi).

$$T/(p_o A_o) = \gamma_o M_o^2 \{\{1 + \{2/[(\gamma_o - 1)M_o^2]\}\}[(p_3/p_2)^{(\gamma_o-1)/\gamma_o} - 1]\{(T_4/T_o)/\{[(p_3/p_2)^{(\gamma_o-1)/\gamma_o}]\{1 + (\gamma_o - 1)/2]M_o^2\}\} - 1\}$$
$$+ \{(T_4/T_o)/\{[(p_3/p_2)^{(\gamma_o-1)/\gamma_o}]\{1 + (\gamma_o - 1)/2]M_o^2\}\}\}^{1/2} - 1\}$$

$$[g\,c_p\,T_o/(a_o H_f)]I_{SP} = T/(p_o A_o)/\{\gamma_o M_o[(T_4/T_o) - (p_3/p_2)^{(\gamma_o-1)/\gamma_o}]\}$$

Assumptions: Ideal turbojet (isentropic inlet, compressor, turbine, nozzle; low subsonic inlet flow; low subsonic, constant pressure combustion; exit pressure = free stream pressure) with perfect gas ($\gamma = \gamma_o = 1.4$)

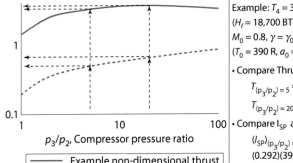

Example: $T_4 = 3000$ R, JP-10 fuel
($H_f = 18{,}700$ BTU/lbm), $A_o = A_c = 114$ in^2,
$M_0 = 0.8$, $\gamma = \gamma_o = 1.4$, $h = 40$ kft
($T_0 = 390$ R, $a_0 = 968$ ft/s, $p_0 = 2.72$ psi)

• Compare Thrust at $(p_3/p_2) = 5$ vs $(p_3/p_2) = 20$

$T_{(p_3/p_2) = 5} = 3.24\,(2.72)\,(114) = 1004$ lb

$T_{(p_3/p_2) = 20} = 3.63\,(2.72)\,(114) = 1126$ lb

• Compare I_{sp} at $(p_3/p_2) = 5$ vs $(p_3/p_2) = 20$

$(I_{SP})_{(p_3/p_2) = 5} = 0.490\,\{(968)\,(18700)/[(32.2)$
$(0.292)(390)]\} = 0.490\,(4936) = 2419$ s

$(I_{SP})_{(p_3/p_2) = 20} = 0.644\,(4936) = 3179$ s

x-axis: p_3/p_2, Compressor pressure ratio

—— Example non-dimensional thrust
------ Example non-dimensional ISP

Note: Short range (e.g., 50 nm) subsonic turbojet usually has relatively low compressor pressure ratio (e.g., $(p_3/p_2) \approx 5$). This provides near maximum thrust with relatively light weight, short length, low cost, high efficiency, and more reliable compressor.

Long range (e.g., 500 nm) subsonic turbojet usually has higher compressor pressure ratio ($(p_3/p_2) > 5$). This provides higher I_{SP} with enhanced range.

Fig. 3.19 Missile turbojet tradeoff: relatively high thrust at a relatively low compressor pressure ratio p_3/p_2 versus higher specific impulse at higher p_3/p_2. (Source: Ashley, H., *Engineering Analysis of Flight Vehicles*, Dover Publications, Inc., New York, 1974.)

First, compare thrust at a relatively low value of compressor pressure ratio ($p_3/p_2 = 5$) versus a relatively high value ($p_3/p_2 = 20$). Compute

$$T_{(p_3/p_2)=5} = 3.24(2.72)(114) = 1004\,\text{lb}$$

$$T_{(p_3/p_2)=20} = 3.63(2.72)(114) = 1126\,\text{lb}$$

Note from the example and the figure that a factor of four increase in p_3/p_2 from 5 to 20 provides only a relatively small increase in thrust (12% increase).

Next, compare I_{SP} at $p_3/p_2 = 5$ versus $p_3/p_2 = 20$. Compute

$$(I_{SP})_{(p_3/p_2)=5} = 0.490\{(968)(18700)/[(32.2)(0.292)(390)]\} = 0.490(4936)$$

$$= 2419\,\text{s}$$

$$(I_{SP})_{(p_3/p_2)=20} = 0.644(4936) = 3179\,\text{s}$$

Note from the example and the figure that increasing p_3/p_2 from 5 to 20 provides a relatively large increase in specific impulse (31% increase).

A typical short range (e.g., 50 nm) subsonic turbojet missile usually has a compressor with a relatively low pressure ratio (e.g., $p_3/p_2 \sim 5$), a single spool, and few stages (e.g., 2 to 4). This provides near maximum thrust with advantages of relatively light weight, short length, low cost, high efficiency, and high reliability.

A typical long range (e.g., 500 nm) subsonic turbojet missile usually has a compressor with higher pressure ratio ($p_3/p_2 \sim 10$), two spools, and more stages (e.g., 8). This provides higher I_{SP} with enhanced range.

Finally, a very long range (e.g., > 1000 nm) subsonic cruise missile usually has a turbofan engine instead of a turbojet engine, because of the higher I_{SP} of a turbofan compared to a turbojet. For this case, the very long range driving performance requirement allows the higher cost, greater complexity, and larger diameter of a turbofan engine.

3.7 Subsonic Turbojet Propulsion Efficiency

Figure 3.20 illustrates the contributions to the loss in total pressure efficiency and the inlet capture efficiency of subsonic turbojet missiles. Improved predictions of thrust and ideal specific impulse can be obtained by correcting the ideal thrust and the ideal specific impulse to account for total pressure efficiency and inlet capture efficiency. To compute

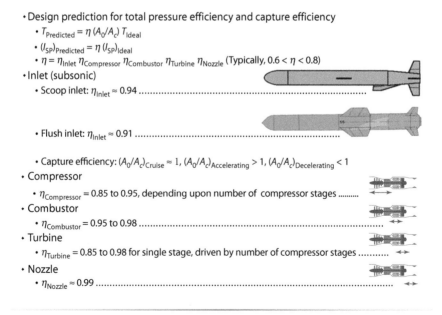

- Design prediction for total pressure efficiency and capture efficiency
  - $T_{Predicted} = \eta \, (A_0/A_c) \, T_{Ideal}$
  - $(I_{SP})_{Predicted} = \eta \, (I_{SP})_{Ideal}$
  - $\eta = \eta_{Inlet} \, \eta_{Compressor} \, \eta_{Combustor} \, \eta_{Turbine} \, \eta_{Nozzle}$ (Typically, $0.6 < \eta < 0.8$)
- Inlet (subsonic)
  - Scoop inlet: $\eta_{Inlet} \approx 0.94$ ....
  - Flush inlet: $\eta_{Inlet} \approx 0.91$ ....
  - Capture efficiency: $(A_0/A_c)_{Cruise} \approx 1$, $(A_0/A_c)_{Accelerating} > 1$, $(A_0/A_c)_{Decelerating} < 1$
- Compressor
  - $\eta_{Compressor} = 0.85$ to 0.95, depending upon number of compressor stages ....
- Combustor
  - $\eta_{Combustor} = 0.95$ to 0.98 ....
- Turbine
  - $\eta_{Turbine} = 0.85$ to 0.98 for single stage, driven by number of compressor stages ....
- Nozzle
  - $\eta_{Nozzle} \approx 0.99$ ....

Fig. 3.20 Typical values of subsonic turbojet propulsion efficiency.

predicted thrust, a correction may be applied to the Ashley [14] ideal thrust to account for the loss in total pressure and the inlet capture efficiency.

$$T_{\text{Predicted}} = \eta(A_0/A_c)T_{\text{Ideal}}$$

Similarly, to predict specific impulse, a correction is applied to the ideal specific impulse to account for the loss in total pressure.

$$(I_{\text{SP}})_{\text{Pedicted}} = \eta(I_{\text{SP}})_{\text{Ideal}}$$

For conceptual design, the total pressure efficiency is often assumed to be product of the efficiency of each component of the propulsion system (inlet, compressor, combustor, turbine, and nozzle).

$$\eta = \eta_{\text{Inlet}}\,\eta_{\text{Compressor}}\,\eta_{\text{Combustor}}\,\eta_{\text{Turbine}}\,\eta_{\text{Nozzle}}$$

For most turbojet missiles, $0.6 < \eta < 0.8$

The bottom right section of the figure shows the serial sequence locations of the turbojet inlet, compressor, combustor, turbine, and nozzle.

The inlet is a major contributor to the loss in total pressure. As shown in the figure, a scoop inlet (Tomahawk-type) usually has the highest subsonic total pressure efficiency ($\eta_{\text{Inlet}} \approx 0.94$), while a flush inlet (Harpoon-type) usually has the lowest subsonic total pressure efficiency ($\eta_{\text{Inlet}} \approx 0.91$). Total pressure efficiency is a function of angle of attack. A top inlet is more susceptible to a loss in total pressure at high angle of attack.

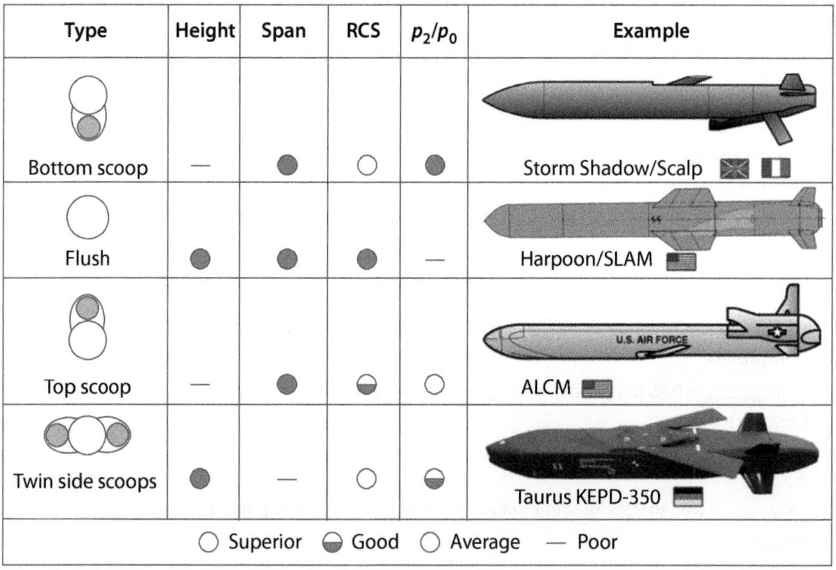

Type	Height	Span	RCS	p_2/p_0	Example
Bottom scoop	—	●	○	●	Storm Shadow/Scalp
Flush	●	●	●	—	Harpoon/SLAM
Top scoop	—	●	◑	○	ALCM
Twin side scoops	●	—	○	◑	Taurus KEPD-350
○ Superior ◑ Good ○ Average — Poor					

Fig. 3.21 Subsonic missile inlet design is driven by launch platform fitment, RCS, and pressure recovery.

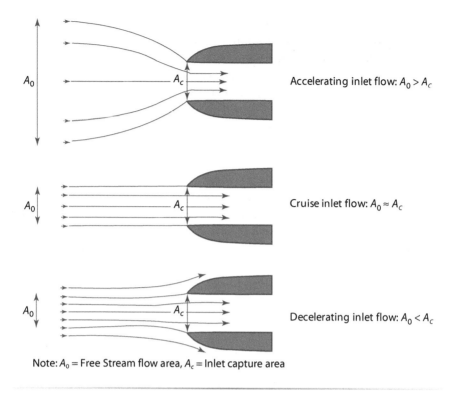

Note: A_0 = Free Stream flow area, A_c = Inlet capture area

Fig. 3.22 During subsonic cruise, the free stream flow into the inlet is approximately the same as the inlet capture geometry ($A_0 \approx A_c$).

As stated above, thrust is a function of the inlet capture efficiency. The subsonic turbojet inlet is typically designed for an inlet flow area-to-capture area efficiency of $A_0/A_c \approx 1$ during cruise. A top inlet is more susceptible to a loss in capture efficiency at high angle of attack.

The compressor is also a major contributor to the loss in total pressure. Compressor efficiency is typically $\eta_{Compressor} = 0.85$ to 0.95, depending upon number of compressor stages. A single stage compressor has relatively high efficiency (e.g., $\eta_{Compressor} \sim 0.95$), while a multi-stage compressor typically has lower efficiency (e.g., $\eta_{Compressor} \sim 0.85$).

Combustors usually have high efficiency, with $\eta_{Combustor} = 0.95$ to 0.98.

Turbine efficiency is typically $\eta_{Turbine} = 0.85$ to 0.98 for a single stage turbine, depending upon the number of compressor stages. More compressor stages require that the compressor receives more work from the turbine.

Finally, nozzle efficiency is usually very high. A typical value of turbojet nozzle efficiency is $\eta_{Nozzle} \approx 0.99$.

Figure 3.21 shows four types of subsonic turbojet missile inlets: a bottom scoop inlet represented by Storm Shadow/Scalp), a flush inlet represented by Harpoon/SLAM, a top scoop inlet represented by ALCM, and twin side scoop inlets represented by Taurus KEPD-350. Missile inlet tradeoffs include 1) height and span for launch platform integration/constraints (if fixed geometry), 2) radar cross section, and 3) inlet total pressure efficiency. Note from the figure that each inlet type has strengths and weaknesses. Selecting the best inlet type depends upon the specific missile application with the relative importance of launch platform integration/constraints, radar cross section, and inlet total pressure efficiency.

Figure 3.22 shows the free stream flow area A_0 into the inlet as a function of the missile flight acceleration/deceleration. The inlet is typically designed for a flow area-to-capture area efficiency of $A_0/A_c \approx 1$ during cruise. For accelerating flight the typical capture efficiency is greater ($A_0/A_c > 1$). For decelerating flight, the typical capture efficiency is lower ($A_0/A_c < 1$). Capture efficiency is also a function of angle of attack. A top inlet is more susceptible to a loss in capture efficiency at high angle of attack.

3.8 Ramjet Propulsion Alternatives

Figure 3.23 from Ref. 16 illustrates missile ramjet propulsion alternatives of a liquid fuel ramjet, a solid fuel ramjet, and a ducted rocket. The examples are based on an integral rocket-ramjet, with the rocket booster occupying the same volume as the ramjet engine combustor. Shown in the upper portion of each example is the rocket booster configuration during the initial boost phase of flight. The bottom portion of each example shows the ramjet engine configuration during the air-breathing sustain flight. Ramjet propulsion is relatively simple compared to turbojet propulsion; it has no moving parts. Air enters the inlet at supersonic velocity and is decelerated to low subsonic speed (e.g., Mach 0.2) at the combustor entrance. Downstream of the combustor is a convergent-divergent nozzle, which accelerates the airflow back to supersonic velocity.

The maximum specific impulse of a hydrocarbon liquid-fuel ramjet is about 1500 s, much higher than the specific impulse of a rocket. An efficient cruise condition for a liquid fuel ramjet is about Mach 4, 80 kft altitude. As mentioned previously, the maximum Mach number of a ramjet missile is about Mach 5. Because a ramjet is inefficient at low supersonic Mach number, a rocket is required to boost the missile to the ramjet thrust takeover (thrust > drag) at about Mach 2.5. One an advantage of a liquid-fuel ramjet compared to a solid fuel ramjet is liquid fuel can be stored in noncircular tanks, facilitating fuel packaging inside the missile airframe. Liquid-fuel ramjets can be throttled, for matching the fuel flow

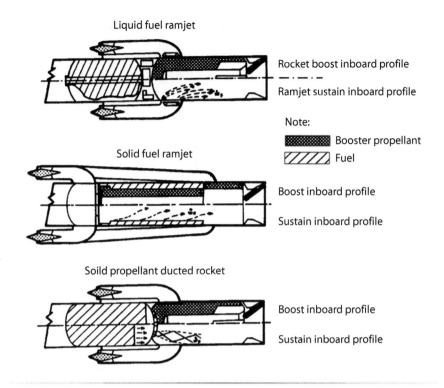

Liquid fuel ramjet

Rocket boost inboard profile

Ramjet sustain inboard profile

Note:

Booster propellant

Fuel

Solid fuel ramjet

Boost inboard profile

Sustain inboard profile

Soild propellant ducted rocket

Boost inboard profile

Sustain inboard profile

Fig. 3.23 Missile ramjet propulsion alternatives. (Source: Kinroth, G.D. and Anderson, W.R., *Ramjet Design Handbook*, CPIA Pub. 319, June 1980.)

rate with the inlet airflow over a flight envelope of Mach number and altitude.

A variation on the traditional liquid fuel ramjet is the solid fuel ramjet. The solid fuel ramjet has a fuel grain with a hollow center core for the inlet airflow. An advantage of the higher density solid fuel is its higher volumetric performance. Another advantage is the solid fuel provides an inherent insulation for the engine wall. Disadvantages are limited throttle capability, reduced volumetric loading of the fuel because of the hollow center grain, lower combustion efficiency, and lower maximum thrust capability. Some passive, but limited, fuel flow—inlet flow matching is provided from changing flight conditions. If a larger variation in fuel flow rate is required, shaping of the fuel grain is needed, at a loss in volumetric loading. Other means of thrust management, such as variable geometry inlets or nozzles, are probably not cost effective for missiles.

A third type of ramjet is a ducted rocket, which has elements of both a rocket and a ramjet. As mentioned previously, a ducted rocket has a typical specific impulse of about 500 – 800 s, intermediate that of a solid propellant rocket and a ramjet. Ducted rockets are most efficient for Mach 2.5 to 4.

A ducted rocket has higher acceleration (higher thrust) than a ramjet and longer range (higher specific impulse) than a rocket. Also, a ducted rocket has the logistical benefit of a solid propellant. Its gas generator provides fuel-rich products to the combustor. The gas generator flow rate can be controlled, providing a throttle capability for thrust magnitude control.

The integration of the ramjet booster impacts the missile compatibility for launch platform length and diameter constraints. Integral boosters that occupy the combustor case improve volumetric efficiency and reduce weight, enhancing integration with the launch platform. Another integration challenge for the booster is if there is a requirement to minimize fratricide by having no ejecta. A nozzleless booster with a common booster case/ramjet combustor avoids nozzle and booster ejecta. A nozzleless booster has a cast propellant grain that somewhat maintains the throat and divergence geometry of a nozzle during motor burn, however with some loss in specific impulse.

3.9 Ramjet Flow Path, Components, and Nomenclature

Shown in Fig. 3.24 is a schematic of the flow path through a liquid fuel ramjet engine. The flow path nomenclature consists of the initial free stream (station 0), inlet throat (station 1), inlet exit/combustor entrance (stations 2, 3), and the combustor exit (station 4). For a theoretical (ideal) ramjet, the thermodynamic cycle consists of an isentropic compression of the flow by the inlet, constant pressure combustion in the combustor, and isentropic expansion through a convergent-divergent nozzle to the free stream static pressure.

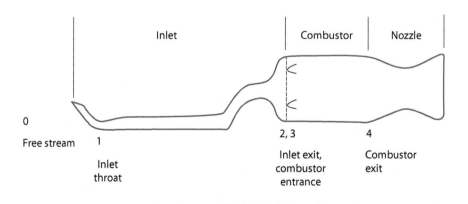

Fig. 3.24 Schematic of liquid fuel ramjet engine flow path, components, and nomenclature.

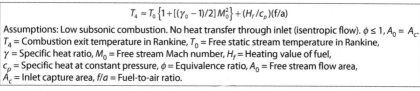

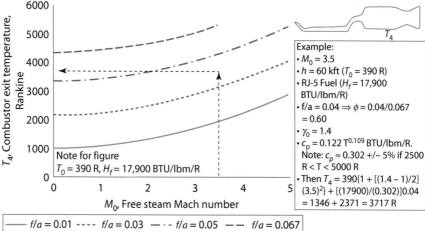

--- f/a = 0.01 ---- f/a = 0.03 —·· f/a = 0.05 —— f/a = 0.067

Note: $(f/a)_{\phi=1} \approx 0.067$ for stoichiometric combustion of liquid hydrocarbon fuel

Fig. 3.25 Ramjet combustion temperature increases with Mach number and fuel flow.

The liquid fuel is injected at the front of the combustor (station 3). Approaches to facilitate and stabilize combustion include spraying the fuel with small size droplets to maximize the fuel surface burning area, swirling the fuel spray to enhance mixing with the air, and possibly flame holders to fix the burning location. Flame holders provide turbulence and circulation, which enhance combustion but also cause a loss in total pressure. The ramjet baseline missile has a "Y" flame holder consisting of three struts, each with a thick base.

3.10 Ramjet Combustion Temperature

Figure 3.25 shows ramjet combustor flow exit temperature T_4 as a function of free stream Mach number M_0 and fuel-to-air ratio f/a. The equation used to develop the figure is

$$T_4 \approx T_0\{1 + [(\gamma_0 - 1)/2]M_0^2\} + (H_f/c_p)(f/a)$$

In the equation, T_0 is the free stream static temperature, γ_0 is the free stream specific heat ratio, H_f is the fuel heating value, and c_p is the specific heat at constant pressure of the air in the combustor. Assumptions are low subsonic combustion, no heat transfer through the inlet (isentropic flow), and fuel-to-air ratio less than stoichiometric. The figure is based on the RJ-5 heating value fuel $H_f = 17,900$ BTU/lbm/R.

Note from the figure that the ramjet combustion temperature exceeds 4000 R for flight conditions of high Mach number and fuel-to-air ratios approaching stoichiometric flow $((f/a)_{\phi=1} = 0.067$ for hydrocarbon fuel). Operation at less than stoichiometric $(\phi < 1)$, with excess inlet air, is usually required to avoid exceeding the temperature limit of the combustor and its insulation. The state-of-the art of ramjet combustor insulation technology is often a limiting factor in achieving the thrust that is required for efficient flight at hypersonic Mach number.

As an example, assume a subsonic combustion ramjet flying at a flight Mach number $M_0 = 3.5$ and an altitude $h = 60,000$ ft $(T_0 = 390$ R) with RJ-5 fuel (heating value $H_f = 17,900$ BTU/lbm) and a fuel-to-air ratio $f/a = 0.04$. It is also assumed that $\gamma_0 = 1.4$. A previous equation showed that c_p is a weak function of temperature

$$c_p = 0.122 \, T^{0.109} \text{ BTU/lbm/R.}$$

For the typical temperature range,

$$c_p = 0.302 \text{ BTU/lbm/R} +/- 5\% \quad \text{if } 2500 \text{ R } < T < 5000 \text{ R}$$

Substituting into the equation for combustion temperature gives

$$T_4 \approx T_0\{1 + [(\gamma_0 - 1)/2]M_0^2\} + (H_f/c_p)(f/a)$$
$$= 390\{1 + [(1.4 - 1)/2](3.5)^2\} + (17900/0.302)(0.055) = 3717 \text{ R.}$$

3.11 Ramjet Specific Impulse Prediction

Figure 3.26 is based on the Ashley [14] equation for the specific impulse of an ideal ramjet

$$I_{SP}g c_p T_0/(a_0 H_f) = M_0\{\{(T_4/T_0)/\{1 + [(\gamma_0 - 1)/2]M_0^2\}\}^{1/2} - 1\}$$
$$/\{\{1 + [(\gamma_0 - 1)/2]M_0^2\}\{(T_4/T_0)$$
$$/\{1 + [(\gamma_0 - 1)/2]M_0^2\}\} - 1\}$$

Note from the above equation that ideal specific impulse is a function of free stream Mach number M_0, heating value of fuel H_f, combustion temperature T_4, free stream temperature T_0, specific heat at constant pressure c_p, free stream speed of sound a_0, and the free stream specific heat ratio γ_0. The

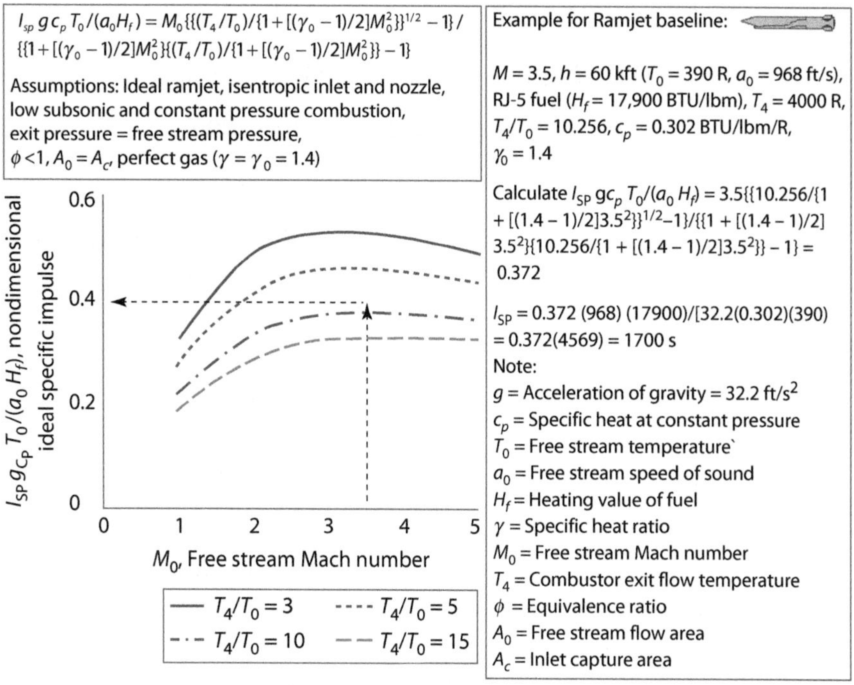

$I_{sp}\, g c_p T_0/(a_0 H_f) = M_0\{\{(T_4/T_0)/\{1+[(\gamma_0-1)/2]M_0^2\}\}^{1/2}-1\}/\{\{1+[(\gamma_0-1)/2]M_0^2\}\{(T_4/T_0)/\{1+[(\gamma_0-1)/2]M_0^2\}\}-1\}$
Assumptions: Ideal ramjet, isentropic inlet and nozzle, low subsonic and constant pressure combustion, exit pressure = free stream pressure, $\phi < 1$, $A_0 = A_c$, perfect gas ($\gamma = \gamma_0 = 1.4$)
$I_{SP}\, g c_P T_0/(a_0 H_f)$, nondimensional ideal specific impulse
0.6
0.4
0.2
0
0
1
2
3
4
5
M_0, Free stream Mach number
— $T_4/T_0 = 3$
---- $T_4/T_0 = 5$
-·- $T_4/T_0 = 10$
—— $T_4/T_0 = 15$
Example for Ramjet baseline:
$M = 3.5$, $h = 60$ kft ($T_0 = 390$ R, $a_0 = 968$ ft/s), RJ-5 fuel ($H_f = 17{,}900$ BTU/lbm), $T_4 = 4000$ R, $T_4/T_0 = 10.256$, $c_p = 0.302$ BTU/lbm/R, $\gamma_0 = 1.4$
Calculate $I_{SP}\, g c_p T_0/(a_0 H_f) = 3.5\{\{10.256/\{1+[(1.4-1)/2]3.5^2\}\}^{1/2}-1\}/\{\{1+[(1.4-1)/2]3.5^2\}\{10.256/\{1+[(1.4-1)/2]3.5^2\}\}-1\} = 0.372$
$I_{SP} = 0.372\,(968)\,(17900)/[32.2(0.302)(390)] = 0.372(4569) = 1700$ s
Note:
g = Acceleration of gravity = 32.2 ft/s^2
c_p = Specific heat at constant pressure
T_0 = Free stream temperature
a_0 = Free stream speed of sound
H_f = Heating value of fuel
γ = Specific heat ratio
M_0 = Free stream Mach number
T_4 = Combustor exit flow temperature
ϕ = Equivalence ratio
A_0 = Free stream flow area
A_c = Inlet capture area

Fig. 3.26 High specific impulse for a ramjet occurs with a high heating value fuel in Mach 3 to 4 flight. (Source: Ashley, H., *Engineering Analysis of Flight Vehicles*, Dover Publications, Inc., New York, 1974.)

equation is based on assumptions of isentropic inlet and nozzle, low subsonic combustion with the combustor static temperature approximately equal to the combustor total temperature, constant pressure combustion, ideal expansion to free stream pressure at the nozzle exit, an equivalence ratio less than one, and specific heat ratio $\gamma = \gamma_0 = 1.4$. It is also assumed that the ramjet combustor pressure is sufficiently high to provide complete combustion. This may be a problem for flight at a dynamic pressure less than 500 psf and an altitude above 60,000 ft. A design guideline for subsonic combustion is that the pressure inside the combustor should be greater than 5 psi, to ensure complete combustion.

An example will be calculated for the ramjet baseline at Mach 3.5 and an altitude $h = 60$ kft ($T_0 = 390$ R, $a_0 = 968$ ft/s). The baseline RJ-5 fuel heating value $H_f = 17{,}900$ BTU per lbm of fuel. The assumed combustion temperature is $T_4 = 4000$ R. The total temperature to free stream static temperature ratio is

$$T_4/T_0 = 4000/390 = 10.256$$

The non-dimensional specific impulse is calculated to be

$$I_{SP}gc_pT_0/(a_0H_f) = \{3.5\{\{(4000/390)/\{1 + [(1.4 - 1)/2]3.5^2\}\}^{1/2} - 1\}$$

$$/\{\{1 + [(1.4 - 1)/2]3.5^2\}\{(4000/390)$$

$$/\{1 + [(1.4 - 1)/2]3.5^2\}\} - 1\} = 0.372$$

The specific impulse, after substituting the values of free stream speed of sound $a_0 = 968$ ft/s, heating value of fuel $H_f = 17900$ BTU/lbm, acceleration of gravity $= 32.2$ ft/s^2, specific heat at constant pressure $c_p = 0.302$ BTU/lbm/R, and free stream temperature $T_0 = 390$ R, is

$$I_{SP} = 0.372(968)(17900)/[32.2(0.302)(390)] = 1700\text{ s}$$

From Chapter 7, the ramjet baseline specific impulse $I_{SP} = 1120$ s for flight at Mach 3.5, $h = 60$ kft. The predicted value is 52% higher than the Chapter 7 data ($1700/1120 = 1.52$). Most of this difference is from losses in total pressure in the flow through the inlet, combustor and nozzle. The ideal specific impulse may be corrected to account for losses in total pressure. A typical ramjet engine has an overall total pressure efficiency of about of 81% (not including the inlet total pressure efficiency). The typical efficiencies of the combustor and nozzle are about 0.86 and 0.96, respectively. The ramjet inlet total pressure efficiency is driven by shock wave losses, which vary greatly with the inlet design and flight conditions. Inlet shock wave total pressure efficiency may be estimated based on the methods of this chapter.

3.12 Ramjet Thrust Prediction

From Ashley [14], the non-dimensional thrust equation of an ideal ramjet is

$$T/(p_0A_0) = \gamma_0M_0^2\{\{[T_4/T_0]/\{1 + [(\gamma_0 - 1)/2]M_0^2\}\}^{1/2} - 1\}$$

Note that the ideal thrust is a function of the combustion temperature T_4, free stream flow area into the inlet A_0, free stream Mach number M_0, free stream static pressure p_0, free stream static temperature T_0, and ratio of specific heat γ_0. As previously, the assumptions are an isentropic inlet and nozzle, low subsonic combustion with the combustor static temperature approximately equal to the combustor total temperature, constant pressure combustion, ideal expansion to free stream pressure at the nozzle exit, an equivalence ratio less than one, specific heat ratio $\gamma = \gamma_0 = 1.4$, and the ramjet combustor pressure is sufficiently high to provide complete combustion.

Figure 3.27 is a plot of the above thrust equation for representative values of Mach number M_0 and combustion-to-free stream-temperature ratio T_4/T_0. Note that the maximum thrust occurs at a Mach number between Mach 3 to 5 and for high values of T_4/T_0. Also note that zero thrust occurs at a free stream Mach number $= 0$ and for low values of T_4/T_0.

As an example, assume that the ramjet baseline is at a flight condition of Mach 3.5/60 kft altitude ($T_0 = 390$ R, $p_0 = 1.047$ psi). Also assume a combustion temperature $T_4 = 4000$ R. The free stream flow area is assumed to be equal to the inlet capture area, $A_0 = 114$ in^2. Substituting in the non-dimensional thrust equation

$$T/(p_0 A_0) = 1.4(3.5)^2 \{\{[4000/390]/\{1 + [(1.4 - 1)/2](3.5)^2\}\}^{1/2} - 1\}$$
$$= 12.43$$

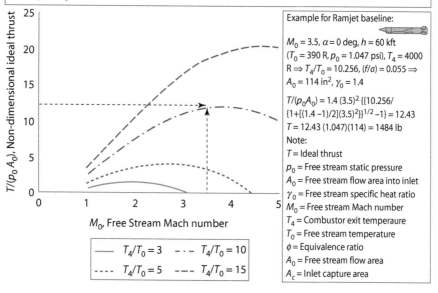

Fig. 3.27 High ramjet thrust occurs at Mach 3 to 5, high combustion temperature, and high inlet flow. (Source: Ashley, H., *Engineering Analysis of Flight Vehicles*, Dover Publications, Inc., New York, 1974.)

Substituting free stream pressure $p_0 = 1.047$ psi and free stream flow area $A_0 = 114$ in^2 in the thrust equation gives

$$T = 12.43(1.047)(114) = 1484 \text{ lb}$$

The actual thrust is lower than the above ideal thrust, because of combustor, nozzle, and inlet efficiency losses and because of the inlet capture efficiency.

Another way of presenting ideal ramjet thrust is shown in Fig. 3.28 as a function of fuel-to-air ratio and Mach number. The Ashley [14] thrust and the combustion temperature equations were shown previously

$$T/(p_0 A_0) = \gamma_0 M_0^2 \{\{[T_4/T_0]/\{1 + [(\gamma_0 - 1)/2]M_0^2\}\}^{1/2} - 1\}$$

$$T_4 \approx T_0\{1 + [(\gamma_0 - 1)/2]M_0^2\} + (H_f/c_p)(f/a)$$

Terms in the above equations are thrust T, atmospheric static pressure p_0, free stream flow area A_0, free stream specific heat ratio γ_0, free stream Mach number M_0, combustor exit temperature T_4, atmospheric static temperature T_0, fuel heating value H_f, specific heat of air at constant pressure in the combustor c_p, and fuel-to-air ratio f/a.

Note from the figure that zero thrust occurs at a free stream Mach number $= 0$ and for zero fuel flow (left and bottom sections of figure). Also note from the figure that high thrust occurs at high values of fuel-to-air ratio. Although increasing fuel-to-air ratio provides increasing thrust, the material temperature limit of the combustor insulation liner limits T_4 and usually limits f/a to less than stoichiometric.

As an example, we shall calculate the thrust of the ramjet baseline at a typical fuel-to-air ratio. Assume $M_0 = 3.5$, $\alpha = 0$ deg, $h = 60$ kft ($T_0 = 390$ R, $p_0 = 1.047$ psi), $f/a = 0.04$, RJ-5 fuel $H_f = 17,900$ BTU/lbm, $c_p = 0.302$ BTU/lbm/R, $A_0 = 114$ in^2, and $\gamma_0 = 1.4$. Calculate

$$T_4 = 390\{1 + [(1.4 - 1)/2]3.5^2\} + (17900/0.302)(0.04) = 3717 \text{ R}$$

Substituting $T_4/T_0 = 3717/390 = 9.53$ into the non-dimensional thrust equation

$$T/(p_0 A_0) = 1.4(3.5)^2\{\{9.53/\{1 + [(1.4 - 1)/2](3.5)^2\}\}^{1/2} - 1\} = 11.35$$

Finally, solving for thrust

$$T = 11.35(1.047)(114) = 1355 \text{ lb}$$

The fuel-to-air ratio that provides stoichiometric combustion is a function of the type of fuel. For typical liquid hydrocarbon fuels (e.g., RJ-4, RJ-5, RJ-6, JP-4, JP-7, JP-8, JP-10, kerosene), the fuel-to-air ratio for

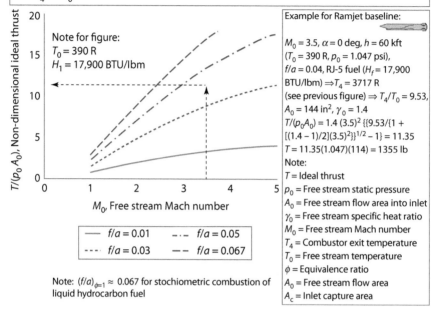

$$\frac{T}{p_oA_0} = \gamma_oM_o^2\left\{\left[\frac{T_4/T_0}{1+[(\gamma_0-1)/2]M_o^2}\right]^{1/2} -1\right\}, T_4 \approx T_0\{1+[(\gamma_0-1)/2]M_o^2\} + (H_f/c_p)(f/a)$$

Assumptions: Ideal ramjet, isentropic inlet and nozzle, low subsonic and constant pressure combustion, exit pressure = free stream pressure, $\phi \leq 1, A_0 = A_c, \gamma = \gamma_0 = 1.4$

Note: T_4 and T_0 in R

Note for figure:
$T_0 = 390$ R
$H_1 = 17,900$ BTU/lbm

T/($p_0 A_0$), Non-dimensional ideal thrust (y-axis, 0 to 20)

M_0, Free stream Mach number (x-axis, 0 to 5)

— $f/a = 0.01$ –·– $f/a = 0.05$
--- $f/a = 0.03$ – – $f/a = 0.067$

Note: $(f/a)_{\phi=1} \approx 0.067$ for stochiometric combustion of liquid hydrocarbon fuel

Example for Ramjet baseline:

$M_0 = 3.5, \alpha = 0$ deg, $h = 60$ kft
($T_0 = 390$ R, $p_0 = 1.047$ psi),
$f/a = 0.04$, RJ-5 fuel ($H_f = 17,900$
BTU/lbm) $\Rightarrow T_4 = 3717$ R
(see previous figure) $\Rightarrow T_4/T_0 = 9.53$,
$A_0 = 144$ in^2, $\gamma_0 = 1.4$
$T/(p_0A_0) = 1.4\ (3.5)^2\ \{\{9.53/\{1 + [(1.4-1)/2](3.5)^2\}\}^{1/2} - 1\} = 11.35$
$T = 11.35(1.047)(114) = 1355$ lb
Note:
T = Ideal thrust
p_0 = Free stream static pressure
A_0 = Free stream flow area into inlet
γ_0 = Free stream specific heat ratio
M_0 = Free stream Mach number
T_4 = Combustor exit temperature
T_0 = Free stream temperature
ϕ = Equivalence ratio
A_0 = Free stream flow area
A_c = Inlet capture area

Fig. 3.28 High ramjet thrust occurs at high Mach number, high fuel flow, and high inlet flow.

stoichiometric combustion is $f/a \approx 0.067$. For lighter weight hydrocarbon fuels, stoichiometric f/a values are somewhat lower. The general equation for combustion of a hydrocarbon fuel of composition C_xH_y with oxygen (O_2) is

$$C_xH_y + (x+y/4)O_2 \longrightarrow xCO_2 + (y/2)H_2O$$

Because air is approximately 21% oxygen and 79% nitrogen, the equation for combustion of a hydrocarbon fuel in air is

$$C_xH_y + (x+y/4)(0.21O_2 + 0.79N_2) \longrightarrow xCO_2 + (y/2)H_2O + [(x+y)/4](0.79/0.21)N_2$$

Substituting the molecular weight of Hydrogen (1), Carbon (12), Oxygen (16), and Nitrogen (14) gives a fuel-to-air ratio equation for stoichiometric combustion of a hydrocarbon fuel as

$$f/a = (12x + y)/\{(x + y/4)[32 + (0.79/0.21)28]\}$$

As an example calculation, octane (C_8H_{18}) has a stoichiometric fuel-to-air ratio

$$f/a = (96 + 18)/\{(8 + 18/4)[32 + (0.79/0.21)28]\} = 0.066$$

For methane (CH_4), which is a light weight gas, the stoichiometric fuel-to-air ratio is

$$f/a = (12 + 4)/\{(1 + 4/4)[32 + (0.79/0.21)28]\} = 0.058$$

3.13 Ramjet Combustor Design Considerations

In the conceptual design of a ramjet, a major consideration is the inlet throat. If the inlet throat area is relatively large, high velocity flow through the combustor may lead to low propulsion efficiency and lower specific impulse. At the other extreme, if the inlet throat area is relatively small, there may not be sufficient mass flow to provide the required thrust.

Downstream of the normal shock at the inlet throat, the inlet subsonic Mach number is a function of the ratio of the local cross sectional area to the inlet sonic throat area $A_{IT} = A_1$. From Ref. 15, the inlet exit/combustor entrance Mach number M_3 can be obtained from the equation

$$A_{IT}/A_3 = [(\gamma + 1)/2]^{(\gamma+1)/[2(\gamma-1)]} M_3[1 + (\gamma - 1)/2]M_3^2]^{-(\gamma+1)/[2(\gamma-1)]}$$

For $\gamma = 1.4$,

$$\frac{A_{IT}}{A_3} = \frac{1.728 M_3}{(1 + 0.2 M_3^2)^3}$$

Assumptions are an isentropic inlet, $M_{IT} = 1$, and $\gamma = 1.4$. Figure 3.29 shows the combustor entrance Mach number M_3 versus the ratio of the inlet throat cross sectional area to the combustor cross sectional area (A_{IT}/A_3). Note from the figure that a smaller throat has a lower entrance Mach number at the combustor (lower mass flow and lower thrust). A larger throat has a higher entrance Mach number at the combustor. However, as stated above, the higher thrust for a higher combustor Mach number must be balanced with combustion efficiency and specific impulse.

As an example, from the ramjet missile baseline data of Chapter 7, $A_{IT} = 41.9$ in^2 and $A_3 = 287$ in^2. Assume sonic flow ($M = 1$) at the inlet throat. Calculate

$$A_{IT}/A_3 = 41.9/287 = 0.1459$$

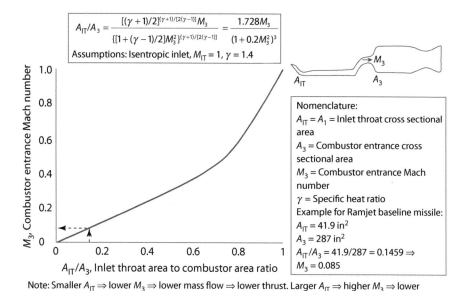

$$A_{IT}/A_3 = \frac{[(\gamma+1)/2]^{(\gamma+1)/[2(\gamma-1)]} M_3}{\{[1+(\gamma-1)/2]M_3^2\}^{(\gamma+1)/[2(\gamma-1)]}} = \frac{1.728 M_3}{(1+0.2M_3^2)^3}$$

Assumptions: Isentropic inlet, $M_{IT}=1$, $\gamma=1.4$

Nomenclature:
$A_{IT} = A_1$ = Inlet throat cross sectional area
A_3 = Combustor entrance cross sectional area
M_3 = Combustor entrance Mach number
γ = Specific heat ratio
Example for Ramjet baseline missile:
$A_{IT} = 41.9$ in^2
$A_3 = 287$ in^2
$A_{IT}/A_3 = 41.9/287 = 0.1459 \Rightarrow$
$M_3 = 0.085$

Note: Smaller $A_{IT} \Rightarrow$ lower $M_3 \Rightarrow$ lower mass flow $\Rightarrow$ lower thrust. Larger $A_{IT} \Rightarrow$ higher $M_3 \Rightarrow$ lower $\eta_{Combustor} \Rightarrow$ lower I_{SP}

Fig. 3.29 Ramjet inlet throat area is a tradeoff of specific impulse and thrust.

Substituting into the above equation gives

$$M_3 = 0.085$$

Combustion increases the Mach number of the flow through the ramjet combustor, which can lead to thermal choking. A limiting condition of maximum achievable thrust occurs when the local Mach number in the combustor is increased from the subsonic entrance Mach number M_3 to a thermally choked combustion Mach number $M_4 = 1$. Thermal choking limits the mass flow through the combustor. For a thermally choked combustor, increasing the fuel-to-air ratio does not increase the mass flow or the thrust and there is a resulting air spillage at the inlet entrance. Shown in Fig. 3.30 is the thermally choked combustor entrance Mach number $(M_3)_{TC}$ versus free stream Mach number M_0 and the ratio of the combustor total temperature to the free stream static temperature (T_{4_t}/T_0). The figure is based on the Anderson [15] Rayleigh flow equation for heat addition at a constant combustor cross sectional area and negligible friction

$$T_{4_t}/T_{3_t} = [(1+\gamma M_3^2)/(1+\gamma M_4^2)]^2 (M_4/M_3)^2 \{1 + [(\gamma-1)/2]M_4^2\}$$
$$/\{1+[(\gamma-1)/2]M_3^2\}$$

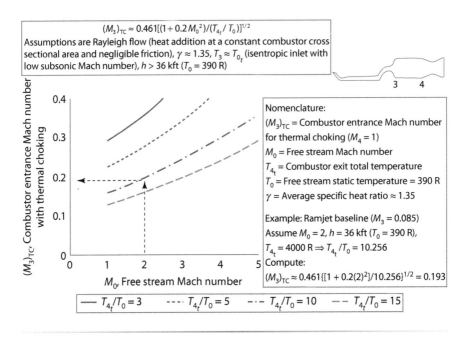

$$(M_3)_{TC} \approx 0.461[(1+0.2\,M_0{}^2)/(T_{4_t}/T_0)]^{1/2}$$

Assumptions are Rayleigh flow (heat addition at a constant combustor cross sectional area and negligible friction), $\gamma \approx 1.35$, $T_3 \approx T_{0_t}$ (isentropic inlet with low subsonic Mach number), $h > 36$ kft ($T_0 = 390$ R)

Nomenclature:
$(M_3)_{TC}$ = Combustor entrance Mach number for thermal choking ($M_4 = 1$)
M_0 = Free stream Mach number
T_{4_t} = Combustor exit total temperature
T_0 = Free stream static temperature = 390 R
γ = Average specific heat ratio ≈ 1.35

Example: Ramjet baseline ($M_3 = 0.085$)
Assume $M_0 = 2$, $h = 36$ kft ($T_0 = 390$ R),
$T_{4_t} = 4000$ R $\Rightarrow T_{4_t}/T_0 = 10.256$
Compute:
$(M_3)_{TC} \approx 0.461\{[1 + 0.2(2)^2]/10.256\}^{1/2} = 0.193$

y-axis: $(M_3)_{TC}$ Combustor entrance Mach number with thermal choking

x-axis: M_0, Free stream Mach number

— $T_{4_t}/T_0 = 3$ ---- $T_{4_t}/T_0 = 5$ --- $T_{4_t}/T_0 = 10$ -- $T_{4_t}/T_0 = 15$

Fig. 3.30   Ramjets in low supersonic flight with high temperature combustion are susceptible to thermal choking. (Reference: Anderson, *Modern Compressible Flow*, Second Edition, McGraw Hill, 1990).

Assume that the above term $\gamma M_3^2 \ll 1$, $\gamma \approx 1.35$ and $T_3 \approx T_{0t}$ (isentropic inlet with low subsonic flow). A simplified equation for the combustor entrance Mach number M_3 that causes thermal choking ($M_4 = 1$) is

$$(M_3)_{TC} \approx 0.461[(1 + 0.2M_0^2)/(T_4/T_0)]^{1/2}$$

Note from the figure that a low subsonic combustor entrance Mach number is required to avoid thermal choking, particularly for high values of combustor temperature ratio T_{4_t}/T_0 and low supersonic free stream Mach number M_0 (e.g., the low free stream Mach number for booster-to-ramjet transition).

As an example, assume the ramjet baseline missile at Mach 2, $h = 36$ kft altitude ft ($T_0 = 390$ R). This flight condition is shown in the Chapter 8 flight envelope requirement for thrust transition from the booster rocket to ramjet operation at the minimum flight Mach number. Also assume the highest combustion temperature of the ramjet baseline, $T_{4_t} = 4000$ R ($T_{4_t}/T_0 = 10.256$). The ramjet baseline is most susceptible to thermal choking for this "worst case" flight condition. The following calculation will compare the combustor entrance Mach number M_3 with $(M_3)_{TC}$.

Combustor and inlet environmental parameters are

$$\gamma_4 = 1.29 + 0.16\,e^{-0.0007(4000)} = 1.300$$

$$T_3 = [1 + 0.2(2)^2]390 = 702\,R$$

$$\gamma_3 = 1.29 + 0.16\,e^{-0.0007(702)} = 1.388$$

The above calculation of γ_4 is based on an assumption that the specific heat of the combustion gas is the same as that of air at the same temperature. The actual γ_4 is somewhat lower.

Next, calculate the combustor entrance Mach number for thermal choking

$$(M_3)_{TC} \approx 0.461\{[1 + 0.2(2)^2]/10.256\}^{1/2} = 0.193$$

Note that the combustor entrance Mach number $M_3 = 0.085$, which is less than the entrance Mach number for thermal choking [$(M_3)_{TC} = 0.195$]. The flow is not thermally choked.

Figure 3.31 shows that high combustion efficiency for a ramjet requires a low Mach number from the inlet into the combustor. From Anderson [15],

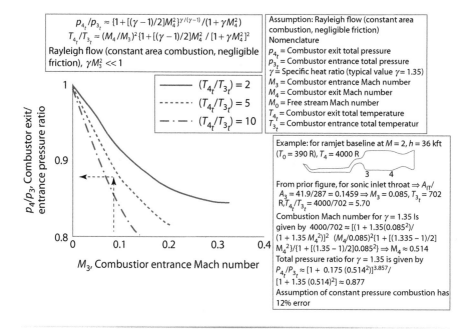

Fig. 3.31 A low Mach number into the combustor is desirable for high combustion efficiency. (Source: Anderson, *Modern Compressible Flow.*)

the total pressure ratio and temperature ratio in the combustor, assuming Rayleigh flow, is given by the equations

$$p_{4_t}/p_{3_t} = [(1 + \gamma M_3^2)/(1 + \gamma M_4^2)]\{\{1 + [(\gamma - 1)/2]M_4^2\}$$

$$/\{1 + [(\gamma - 1)/2]M_3^2\}\}^{\gamma/(\gamma-1)}$$

$$T_{4_t}/T_{3_t} = [(1 + \gamma M_3^2)/(1 + \gamma M_4^2)]^2 (M_4/M_3)^2 \{1 + [(\gamma - 1)/2]M_4^2\}$$

$$/\{1 + [(\gamma - 1)/2]M_3^2\}$$

Assumptions for Rayleigh flow are heat addition at a constant combustor cross sectional area and negligible friction. Assuming $\gamma M_3^2 \ll 1$, approximate equations are

$$p_{4_t}/p_{3_t} \approx \{1 + [(\gamma - 1)/2]M_4^2\}^{\gamma/(\gamma-1)}/(1 + \gamma M_4^2)$$

$$T_{4_t}/T_{3_t} \approx (M_4/M_3)^2 \{1 + [(\gamma - 1)/2]M_4^2/[1 + \gamma M_4^2]^2\}$$

From the equation for T_{4_t}/T_{3_t}, the Rayleigh flow combustion Mach number can be expressed as

$$M_4 \approx \{[-b - (b^2 - 4ac)^{1/2}]/(2a)\}^{1/2}$$

Substituting an approximate value of $\gamma \approx 1.35$, the terms in the above equation are

$$a = 1.822(T_{4_t}/T_{3_t})M_3^2 - 1.175$$

$$b = 2.70(T_{4_t}/T_{3_t})M_3^2$$

$$c = (T_{4_t}/T_{3_t})M_3^2$$

Assume the "worst case" flight conditions for the ramjet baseline from the prior example, $M_0 = 2$, $h = 36$ kft ($T_0 = 390$ R), $T_4 = 4000$ R, $\gamma_0 = 1.4$, $\gamma_4 = 1.300$, and $\gamma_3 = 1.388$. It was previously shown that for $A_{IT}/A_3 = 41.9/287 = 0.1459 \Rightarrow M_3 = 0.085$.

Solving for the terms in the combustion Mach number equation,

$$a = 1.822(5.70)(0.085)^2 - 1.175 = -1.010$$

$$b = 2.70(5.70)(0.085)^2 = 0.1112$$

$$c = 5.70(0.085)^2 = 0.04118$$

Substituting into the equation for combustion exit Mach number gives

$$M_4 \approx 0.514$$

Finally, solving for the Rayleigh flow total pressure ratio loss in the combustor for an assumed $\gamma \approx 1.35$

$$p_{4_t}/p_{3_t} \approx \{1 + [(1.35 - 1)/2]0.514^2\}^{1.35/(1.35-1)}/[1 + 1.35(0.514)^2]$$

$$= 0.877$$

Note that there is a 12% reduction in total pressure for this example, indicating that the typical assumption of constant pressure combustion is optimistic, with a maximum error of about 12%.

The integral rocket-ramjet engine is the most popular type of ramjet. After the rocket booster burnout, the rocket booster motor case is used as the ramjet engine. Typically the booster case length is sufficiently long to provide efficient ramjet combustion. Shown in Fig. 3.32 is the minimum length of the combustor for complete combustion as a function of time required for combustion and the velocity of the air flow through the combustor. The equation is

$$(I_{\text{Comb}})_{\text{min}} = t_{\text{Comb}} V_{\text{Comb}}$$

The time required for combustions is driven by the times required for fuel vaporization, ignition, and mixing. A subsonic combustion ramjet has a typical combustion time $t_{\text{Comb}} \approx 0.002$ s and a combustion velocity $V_{\text{Comb}} \approx 200$ ft/s. The minimum length of the combustor for efficient combustion is $(I_{\text{Comb}})_{\text{min}} \approx 0.4$ ft. For an integral rocket-ramjet, the typical

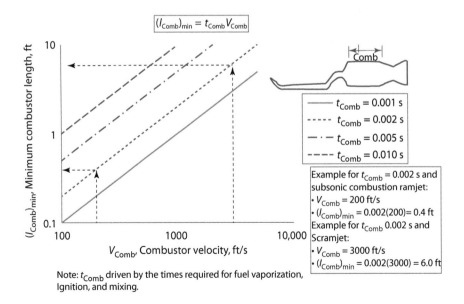

Note: t_{Comb} driven by the times required for fuel vaporization, Ignition, and mixing.

Fig. 3.32 Required length of the combustor is a function of combustor velocity.

booster length is much longer than the minimum combustor length, easily accommodating the required length of the combustor.

A supersonic combustion ramjet also has a typical combustion time $t_{Comb} \approx 0.002$ s. However, a typical combustion velocity is $V_{Comb} \approx 3000$ ft/s. The minimum length of the combustor for efficient combustion is $(l_{Comb})_{min} \approx 6$ ft. In the case of the scramjet, the impact of the minimum combustor length is large, requiring a much longer and heavier missile. However, the required combustor length of a scramjet is usually less than the booster length.

3.14 Ramjet Booster Integration

Figure 3.33 from Ref. 16 characterizes ramjet engine/booster integration options according to their cruise drag. Low cruise drag ramjet options are a tandem integral rocket-ramjet (IRR), an aft drop-off booster, a forward-located booster, and a podded drop-off booster. The high cruise drag historical ramjets shown in the bottom of the figure are the large diameters podded ramjet, podded integral-rocket ramjet, and the podded ramjet with a drop-off booster. Most modern ramjets have low cruise drag. The integral rocket-ramjet is particularly attractive. As noted previously, after booster burnout, an IRR uses the booster case as the combustion chamber for the ramjet. The IRR is often preferred because of advantages of low cruise

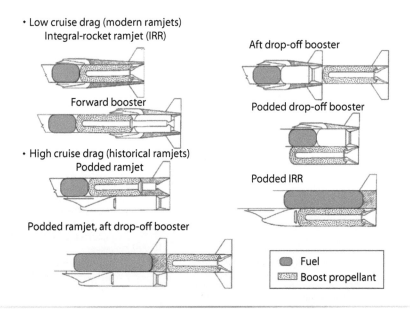

Fig. 3.33 Ramjet engine/booster integration options. (Source: Kinroth, G.D. and Anderson, W.R., "Ramjet Design Handbook," CPIA Pub. 319, June 1980.)

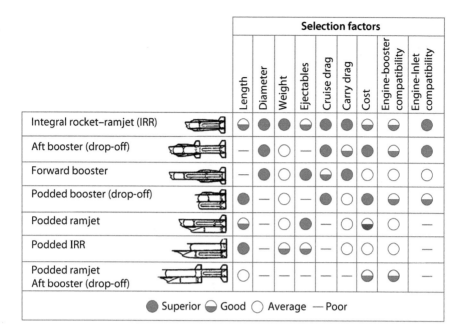

	Selection factors								
	Length	Diameter	Weight	Ejectables	Cruise drag	Carry drag	Cost	Engine-booster compatibility	Engine-Inlet compatibility
Integral rocket–ramjet (IRR)	◖	●	●	◖	●	●	◖	◖	●
Aft booster (drop-off)	—	●	○	—	●	◖	●	◖	●
Forward booster	—	●	○	●	◖	●	○	○	○
Podded booster (drop-off)	●	—	○	—	●	○	●	◖	◖
Podded ramjet	◖	—	○	●	—	○	◑	○	—
Podded IRR	●	—	◖	◖	—	○	○	○	—
Podded ramjet Aft booster (drop-off)	○	—	—	—	—	—	◖	◖	—

● Superior ◖ Good ○ Average — Poor

Fig. 3.34 Ramjet engine/booster/inlet integration trades. (Source: Kinroth, G.D. and Anderson, W.R., *Ramjet Design Handbook*, CPIA Pub. 319, June 1980.)

drag, low volume, light weight, and small diameter. A similar concept to the IRR is a slide-out booster ramjet such as BrahMos. A slide-out booster ramjet is short length and relatively easy to integrate. However compared to an IRR it has disadvantages of heavier weight (separate booster and combustor case) and the safety concern of the drop-off booster.

A further comparison of ramjet engine/booster integration options is given in Fig. 3.34 based on Ref. 16. Note that the integral rocket-ramjet engine has above-average-to-superior characteristics for the selection factors of length, diameter, weight, no ejecta, cruise drag, launch platform carriage drag, cost, compatibility of the ramjet engine with the booster, and compatibility of the ramjet engine with a broad range of inlets. The other candidate engines are below average in one or more of the selection factors. However, depending upon the weighting of the selection factors and the mission, one or more of the other candidate engines may be acceptable, or even preferable. The strengths and potential weaknesses of the other candidate ramjet engine alternatives to an IRR include the following:

1. Aft drop-off booster attractive features include small diameter, low cruise drag, low cost, and compatibility of the engine with a broad range of inlets. Disadvantages of an aft drop-off booster include long length and ejecta.

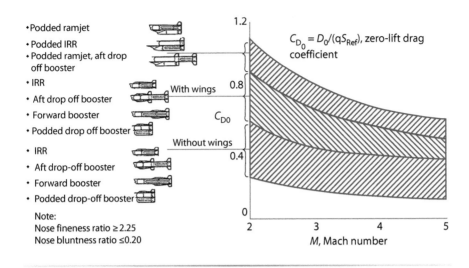

Fig. 3.35 Ramjets with internal boosters and no wings have lower drag. (Source: Kinroth, G.D. and Anderson, W.R., *Ramjet Design Handbook*, CPIA Pub. 319, June 1980.)

2. Forward booster has attractive features of small diameter, no ejecta, and low launch platform carriage drag. A disadvantage is the long length. Although it has good compatibility with an inlet behind the booster, it has poor compatibility with a nose or a chin inlet.
3. Podded drop-off booster has attractive features of short length, low cruise drag, and low cost. Disadvantages include a large diameter and ejecta.
4. Podded ramjet has an attractive feature of no ejecta. Disadvantages of a podded ramjet include a large diameter, high cruise drag, and poor compatibility with some inlets. The disadvantages make it unsuitable for most modern applications.
5. Podded IRR has attractive features of short length and relatively light weight. Disadvantages include large diameter, high cruise drag and poor inlet compatibility. The disadvantages make it unsuitable for most modern applications.
6. Podded ramjet with a drop-off booster has disadvantages of large diameter, heavy weight, ejecta, high cruise drag, high carriage drag, and poor inlet compatibility. The disadvantages make it unsuitable for most modern applications.

A first order estimate of ramjet zero-lift drag, based on Ref. 16, is given in Fig. 3.35. Results are applicable to ramjets that have a high fineness nose ($l_N/d \geq 2.25$) with small bluntness ($d_{\text{Nose tip}}/d \leq 0.2$). The examples of ramjets that have low cruise drag are at the bottom of the figure. They are wingless ramjets based on one of the following: an integral rocket-ramjet (IRR), an aft drop-off booster, a forward-located booster, or a podded drop-off booster. As an example, the wingless low drag ramjet missiles have a zero-lift drag coefficient at Mach 2 of $C_{D_0} \approx 0.3$ to 0.6. Adding wings to the low drag ramjets increases the drag (see middle portion of figure). At Mach 2, the value of the zero-lift drag coefficient is $C_{D_0} \approx 0.6$ to 0.9. Examples of the older high drag configurations are the podded ramjets shown at the top of the figure. The figure shows that at Mach 2, the zero-lift drag coefficient for podded ramjets is the highest, $C_{D_0} \approx 0.9$ to 1.1. As stated previously, the high drag podded ramjets are unsuitable for most modern applications.

3.15 Ramjet Inlet Options

Ramjet inlet design considerations include the type of opening, the location of the inlet on the body, and the number of inlets. Figure 3.36 from Ref. 16 shows the inlet placement and geometry of the following nine ramjet inlet options:

1. Annular nose inlet. The inlet surrounds the body. It may rely only on the cowl lip oblique shock for the initial compression, or it may also have a center spike for mixed (external plus internal) compression.
2. Chin inlet located forward underneath the nose. The nose compression angle provides an oblique shock in front of the inlet. The ramjet baseline missile of this textbook has a chin inlet.

Type inlet	Sketch	Placement
Nose		Annular nose inlet
Chin		Forward underside in nose compression field – partial annular
Forward cruciform annular	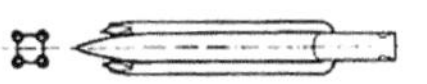	Forward in nose compression field – cruciform (four) annular inlets
Aft cruciform annular		Aft-cruciform (four) annular inlets
Under wing annular		In planar wing compression field – twin annular inlets
Twin two-dimensional		Aft – twin cheek-mounted two dimensional inlets
Underslung annular		Aft underside – full annular
Underslung two-dimensional		Aft underside – belly mounted two dimensional inlet
Aft cruciform two-dimensional		Aft – cruciform (four) two dimensional inlets

Fig. 3.36 Ramjet inlet options. (Source: Kinroth, G.D. and Anderson, W.R., *Ramjet Design Handbook*, CPIA Pub. 319, June 1980.)

3. Forward cruciform annular inlet. The nose compression angle provides an oblique shock in front of each inlet. The four inlets are usually in tandem with cruciform fins.
4. Aft cruciform annular inlet. There are four inlets located near the center of the missile. The inlets are usually in tandem with cruciform fins.
5. Under wing annular inlet. There are two inlets located near the center of the missile, under a planar wing. The wing provides an initial compression.
6. Twin two-dimensional inlet. This concept has two inlets near the center of the missile. They are usually located on the lower portion of the body, separated by a radial angle of about 90 deg. The inlets are usually in tandem with the bottom cruciform tails.
7. Underslung annular inlet. The underslung inlet is located near the center of the missile.
8. Underslung two-dimensional inlet. Similar to the above except two-dimensional cross section.
9. Aft cruciform two-dimensional inlet. Similar to the aft cruciform annular inlet.

Tradeoff considerations of ramjet inlet alternatives are shown in Fig. 3.37 from Ref. 16. The selection factors are:

Type inlet	Pressure recovery	Carriage envelope	Alpha capability	Weight	Drag	Warhead shrouding	Inlet cost	Preferred steering	Preferred control	Prime mission suitability
 1	◐	●	○	◐	●	—	◐	STT	W,C	ATS, STA
 2	●	●	●	○	●	○	○	BTT	T	ATS, ATA, STA
 3	○	○	◐	—	○	—	—	STT	T	ATS, ATA, STA
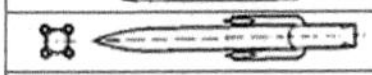 4	○	◐	○	◐	○	●	○	STT	T	ATS
 5	◐	—	●	●	○	●	◐	BTT	T	ATS, ATA, STA
 6	◐	○	◐	◐	◐	◐	○	BTT	T	ATS, ATA, STA
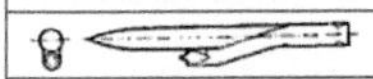 7	○	—	○	●	○	◐	●	BTT	T	ATS
 8	—	—	◐	◐	◐	◐	◐	BTT	T	ATS, ATA, STA
 9	○	◐	○	◐	◐	●	○	STT	T	ATS
	● Superior ◐ Good ○ Average — Poor									

Note: BTT = Bank to turn, STT = Skid to turn, W = Wing, C = Canard, T = Tail

Fig. 3.37 Ramjet inlet concept trades. (Source: Kinroth, G.D. and Anderson, W.R., *Ramjet Design Handbook*, CPIA Pub. 319, June 1980.)

1. High pressure recovery. The chin inlet and the forward cruciform annular inlet benefit from relatively high recovery pressure, provided by an oblique shock from the forebody in front of the inlet. Another benefit of the oblique shock is a lower Mach number at the inlet entrance, which allows the inlet to swallow the shock at a lower flight Mach number. Other inlets that also have relatively good pressure recovery are the nose inlet, under wing annular inlet, and the twin two-dimensional inlet. The under wing annular inlet benefits from the wing compression, whereas the twin two dimensional inlet benefits from the under body compression.
2. Small carriage envelope on the launch platform. The annular inlet and the chin inlet require only a small inlet height to capture airflow, because of the large wraparound angle.
3. High angle of attack capability. The chin inlet and the under wing annular inlets allow high positive angles of attack, providing a relatively high recovery pressure for bank-to-turn maneuvering.
4. Light weight. The under wing annular inlet and the underslung annular inlet, located aft on the missile body, require less material for structure.
5. Low drag. The annular nose inlet and the chin inlet have reduced drag on the nose.
6. Does not shroud the warhead. The aft cruciform annular inlet, aft twin annular inlet, and the aft cruciform two-dimensional inlet, as shown in the figure, are located aft of the warhead section of the missile.
7. Low cost. The lowest cost, simplest fabrication inlet is probably an underslung annular inlet.
8. Preferred steering approach (skid-to-turn, bank-to-turn). Cruciform inlets are consistent with skid-to-turn maneuvering, whereas chin, twin, or underslung inlets are consistent with bank-to-turn maneuvering.
9. Preferred flight control (tail, canard, wing). An annular inlet has volume available for the forward and mid-section packaging of the flight control actuators for canard or wing control. The other inlets are more compatible with tail control.
10. Preferred mission application (air-to-surface, air-to-air, or surface-to-air). The air intercept mission requires high maneuverability and high angle of attack, which is especially consistent with the capability of the chin inlet, the under wing annular, and the twin two-dimensional inlets. These inlets require bank-to-turn maneuvering.

There is no single inlet that is best for all missions. The selection factors must be weighted for the mission as part of the inlet selection.

The inlets of current supersonic/hypersonic air-breathing missiles are shown in Fig. 3.38. Except for the SS-N-19 Mach 2.5 turbojet, the missiles

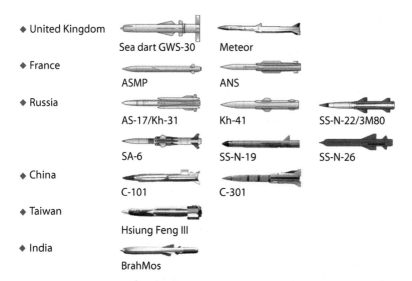

- United Kingdom — Sea dart GWS-30, Meteor
- France — ASMP, ANS
- Russia — AS-17/Kh-31, Kh-41, SS-N-22/3M80, SA-6, SS-N-19, SS-N-26
- China — C-101, C-301
- Taiwan — Hsiung Feng III
- India — BrahMos

♦ Aft inlets have lower inlet volume and do not degrade lethality of forward located warhead.

♦ Nose inlet may have higher flow capture, higher pressure recovery, smaller carriage envelope, and lower drag.

Fig. 3.38 Examples of inlets for current supersonic air-breathing missiles.

use ramjet propulsion. Missiles with a nose inlet are the United Kingdom Sea Dart, Russian SS-N-19 and SS-N-26, and India BrahMos. Missiles with aft inlets are the United Kingdom Meteor; French Anti Navire Supersonique (ANS) and Air Sol Moyenne Portee (ASMP); Russian AS-17/Kh-31, Kh-41, SS-N-22/3M80, and SA-6; Chinese C-101 and C-301; and the Taiwan Hsiung Feng III. A nose inlet has advantages of low drag, small carriage envelope, and may have higher flow capture and higher pressure recovery at low supersonic Mach number. Aft inlets have advantages of light weight, low volume, and they do not shroud/degrade the warhead. Note that the flight control for all of these missiles is based on tail control surfaces. The tail flight control actuators are efficiently packaged around the throat of the nozzle.

3.16 Supersonic Inlet/Airframe Integration

Inlet design and integration for a supersonic or hypersonic missile involves a host of considerations, including matching the flow delivered to the nozzle, swallowing capacity, inlet start, minimizing drag, and minimizing pressure oscillation. The inlet design considerations that are addressed in this text are those that are likely to have a relatively large effect on the aerodynamic configuration conceptual design.

Figure 3.39 shows the shock wave location of three types of supersonic inlet: external compression, internal compression, and mixed compression. In this example all of the inlets have 100% capture of the oncoming supersonic flow, with no spillage. An external compression inlet, shown in the top of the figure, has a body deflection angle in front of the inlet. The external compression may be either an annular spike or a 2-D compression ramp. An advantage of an external compression inlet is relatively low pressure oscillation inside the inlet. A disadvantage is the drag from the forebody inclination angle, the total pressure loss in a larger required turning angle before entering the combustor, and the thrust loss for off-design flight conditions. An inlet with internal compression, shown in the middle of the figure, has an advantage in that it swallows 100% of the oncoming air, with no spillage. A disadvantage is that it is more difficult to start, requiring a higher boost Mach number/larger booster. Another disadvantage is susceptibility to pressure oscillation, such as inlet buzz, for off-design flight conditions. Finally, the bottom section of the figure illustrates the shocks for a mixed compression inlet. A mixed compression inlet has external oblique shock(s) followed by internal oblique shock(s). A mixed compression inlet is most often selected for supersonic/hypersonic missiles because it is often a good compromise of relatively low forebody deflection drag, relatively low pressure oscillation, and relatively low inlet start Mach number.

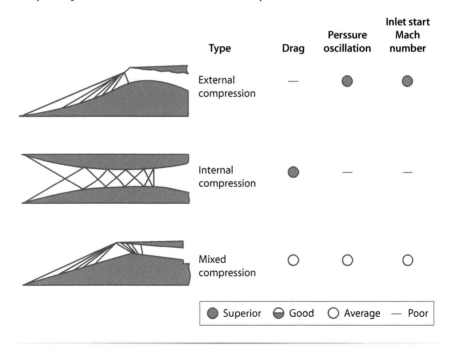

Fig. 3.39 Supersonic inlet/airframe integration tradeoffs include drag, pressure oscillation, and inlet start.

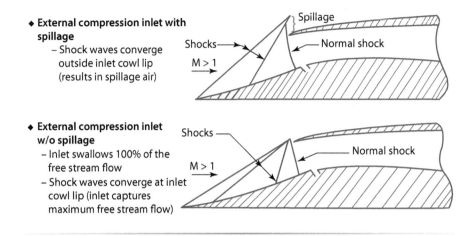

◆ **External compression inlet with spillage**
  – Shock waves converge outside inlet cowl lip (results in spillage air)

◆ **External compression inlet w/o spillage**
  – Inlet swallows 100% of the free stream flow
  – Shock waves converge at inlet cowl lip (inlet captures maximum free stream flow)

Fig. 3.40 A supersonic external compression inlet with shock wave(s) on the cowl lip prevents spillage.

Figure 3.40 shows the shock wave location with and without spillage of an external compression inlet. An external compression inlet has body deflection angles that produce oblique shock waves in front of the inlet. The external compression may be either an annular spike or a 2-D compression ramp.

Inlet spillage, shown at the top of the figure, occurs at a lower Mach number where the external shock waves have high shock wave angles, passing over the inlet. The inlet captures less of the free stream air and has spillage, which results in lower thrust and tends to increase the drag. Shown at the bottom of the figure is a higher Mach number condition with the shocks converging on the inlet lip. In this condition the external compression inlet swallows 100% of the oncoming air, providing higher thrust.

The forebody oblique shock wave angle provides a guideline for the inlet height that is required to achieve a shock-on-lip condition. Shown in Fig. 3.41 is the relationship of the oblique shock wave angle θ to the flow deflection angle $(\alpha + \delta)$ and Mach number M. The equation is

$$\tan(\alpha + \delta) = 2\cot\theta_{2D}(M^2\sin^2\theta_{2D} - 1)/[2 + M^2(\gamma + 1 - 2\sin^2\theta_{2D})]$$

The prediction is based on assumptions of two-dimensional flow of a perfect gas. Note that the shock wave angle increases with body deflection angle and decreases with Mach number. As a result, the inlet height to avoid air spillage must be larger for a missile with a low fineness nose at a low supersonic Mach number. Also, the maximum allowable flow deflection increases with Mach number. For example, at Mach 2 the maximum allowable flow deflection angle for an attached two-dimensional oblique shock with $\gamma = 1.4$ is $(\alpha + \delta)_{\max} = 23$ deg. At Mach 5, the maximum allowable flow deflection angle is greater, $(\alpha + \delta)_{\max} = 41$ deg.

A first order estimate of the two-dimensional shock wave angle, suitable for conceptual design, is to assume that the shock wave angle θ_{2D} is the sum of the Mach angle μ plus the flow deflection angle $\alpha + \delta$. The approximate equation is

$$\theta_{2D} \approx \mu + \alpha + \delta = \sin^{-1}(1/M) + \alpha + \delta$$

The approximate equation for θ_{2D} becomes inaccurate for lower supersonic Mach number and body deflection angle $\delta > 20$ deg.

For conical flow around a conical nose, the shock wave angle is

$$\theta_{\text{conical}} \approx 0.81\,\theta_{2D}$$

As an example for the ramjet baseline missile, which has a body deflection angle $\delta = 17.7$ deg (from its conical nose), assume Mach 3.5 and an angle of attack $\alpha = 0$ deg. The exact equation with $\gamma = 1.4$ gives a

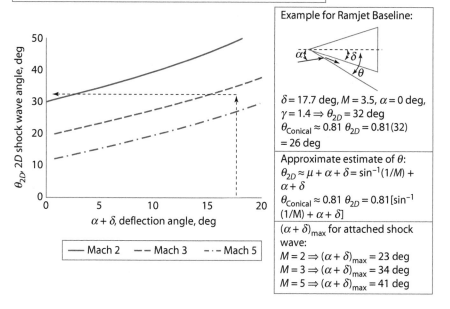

$$\tan(\alpha + \delta) = \frac{2\cot\theta_{2D}(M^2 \sin^2\theta_{2D} - 1)}{2 + M^2(\gamma + 1 - 2\sin^2\theta_{2D})} \text{ for 2D flow, perfect gas}$$

Note: θ_{2D} = 2D shock angle, M = Mach number, α = Angle of attack, δ = Body deflection angle, γ = Specific heat ratio

Example for Ramjet Baseline:

$\delta = 17.7$ deg, $M = 3.5$, $\alpha = 0$ deg, $\gamma = 1.4 \Rightarrow \theta_{2D} = 32$ deg
$\theta_{\text{Conical}} \approx 0.81\,\theta_{2D} = 0.81(32)$
$= 26$ deg

Approximate estimate of θ:
$\theta_{2D} \approx \mu + \alpha + \delta = \sin^{-1}(1/M) + \alpha + \delta$
$\theta_{\text{Conical}} \approx 0.81\,\theta_{2D} = 0.81[\sin^{-1}(1/M) + \alpha + \delta]$
$(\alpha + \delta)_{\max}$ for attached shock wave:
$M = 2 \Rightarrow (\alpha + \delta)_{\max} = 23$ deg
$M = 3 \Rightarrow (\alpha + \delta)_{\max} = 34$ deg
$M = 5 \Rightarrow (\alpha + \delta)_{\max} = 41$ deg

— Mach 2   — — Mach 3   — · — Mach 5

y-axis: θ_{2D} 2D shock wave angle, deg
x-axis: $\alpha + \delta$, deflection angle, deg

Fig. 3.41 Shock wave angle is driven by deflection angle and Mach number.

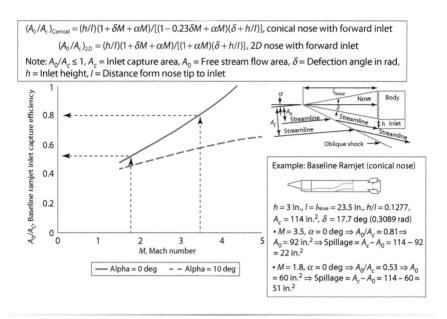

Fig. 3.42 Supersonic inlet capture efficiency increases with Mach number until the body shock wave converges on the inlet lip.

two-dimensional shock wave angle $\theta_{2D} = 32$ deg. The approximate equation gives $\theta_{2D} = 34.3$ deg, an error of 7%. The Mach 3.5 conical shock wave angle for the ramjet baseline missile is $\theta_{Conical} = 26$ deg (81% of a 2D shock wave angle).

Because of design constraints, supersonic missiles have fixed geometry inlets. The fixed geometry inlets are designed for shock-on-lip operation at the highest Mach number cruise condition. For a shock-on-lip design Mach number, a higher flight Mach number should be avoided. A higher Mach number would result in the shock wave entering the inlet, potentially causing shock-wave boundary layer interaction, flow separation, a loss in total pressure, a loss in thrust, and possibly inlet un-start. Operating at a lower Mach number results in a larger shock wave angle, streamlines spilling outside the inlet, a reduction in the captured air, a reduction in thrust, and spillage drag.

Inlet capture efficiency can be determined by tracing the shock wave and the streamlines back to the inlet lip. For a two-dimensional (wedge) nose, tracing the shock wave and streamlines shown in the right side of Fig. 3.42 results in the following 2D inlet capture efficiency equation

$$(A_0/A_c)_{2D} = (h/l)(1 + \delta M + \alpha M)/[(1 + \alpha M)(\delta + h/l)]$$

For a conical nose, a similar tracing gives the following conical inlet capture efficiency equation

$$(A_0/A_c)_{\text{Conical}} = (h/l)(1 + \delta M + \alpha M)/[(1 - 0.23\delta M + \alpha M)(\delta + h/l)]$$

At a given Mach number, a conical shock wave has a smaller shock angle $(\theta_{\text{Conical}} = 0.81\theta_{\text{2D}})$, resulting in higher capture efficiency for a given body deflection angle δ.

The ramjet baseline missile (Chapter 7) capture efficiency is shown in the figure as a function of Mach number $(2 < M < 5)$ and angle of attack $(\alpha = 0, 10 \deg)$. Note from the figure that the ramjet baseline has 100% capture efficiency (shock-on-lip operation) at the design maximum Mach number $M = 4$. Lower capture efficiency and spillage occur at lower Mach numbers, because of the larger value of the shock wave angle θ.

The ramjet baseline missile will be used as an example calculation of inlet capture efficiency. Its chin inlet has an inlet height $h = 3$ in, a distance from the nose tip to the inlet of $l = 23.5$ in, capture area $A_c = 114$ in^2, and a conical nose half angle $\delta = 17.7$ deg $= 0.309$ rad. For an assumed flight condition of $M = 3.5$ and an angle of attack $\alpha = 0$ deg, the ramjet baseline inlet capture efficiency is computed

$$(A_0/A_c) = (3/23.5)[1 + 0.309(3.5) + 0(3.5)]/$$
$$\{[1 - 0.23(0.309)(3.5) + 0(3.5)](0.309 + 3/23.5)\}$$
$$= 0.128(2.08)/[0.751(0.437)] = 0.81$$

For the ramjet baseline missile, a greater value of inlet height would be required for shock-on-lip operation if the maximum Mach number were reduced from Mach 4 to Mach 3.5.

As a comparison, we will also calculate the capture efficiency and air spillage at a lower Mach number $(M = 1.8)$ with the same angle of attack $(\alpha = 0$ deg$)$. Capture efficiency is

$$A_0/A_c = 0.128[1 + 0.309(1.8) + 0(1.8)]/[1 - 0.23(0.309)(1.8)$$
$$+ 0(1.8)](0.309 + 0.128)\} = 0.53$$

The free stream flow area is

$$A_0 = 0.53(114) = 60 \text{ in}^2$$

Finally, the air spillage is

$$A_c - A_0 = 114 - 60 = 51 \text{ in}^2$$

The equation for the non-dimensional inlet throat area that is required to start a 2-D supersonic inlet with ideal (isentropic) compression is

$$A_{IT}/A_0 = (M_{IE})_{Start}[(\gamma + 1)/2]^{(\gamma+1)/[2(\gamma-1)]}$$

$$\{[1 + (\gamma - 1)/2](M_{IE})^2_{Start}\}^{-(\gamma+1)/[2(\gamma-1)]}$$

The terms in the equation are A_{IT} = inlet throat area, A_0 = free stream flow area, $(M_{IE})_{Start}$ = inlet start Mach number, and γ = specific heat ratio. Substituting $\gamma = 1.4$ for air gives

$$A_{IT}/A_0 = 1.728(M_{IE})_{Start}[1 + 0.2(M_{IE})^2_{Start}]^{-3}$$

Another compression extreme is a 2-D supersonic inlet with a single, normal shock compression ($n = 1$). The equation for the non-dimensional inlet throat area that is required to start the single normal shock inlet is

$$A_{IT}/A_0 = (M_{IE})_{Start}\{[0.4(M_{IE})^2_{Start} + 2]/[2.4(M_{IE})^2_{Start}]^{3.5}\{[2.8(M_{IE})^2_{Start}$$
$$- 0.4]/2.4\}^{2.5}\{1.2/[1 + 0.2(M_{IE})^2_{Start}]\}\}^3$$

Figure 3.43 shows $(M_{IE})_{Start}$ versus A_{IT}/A_0 with the compression extremes. Note that $A_{IT} = A_0$ for $(M_{IE})_{Start}=1$ and that for values of $A_{IT} < A_0$, $(M_{IE})_{Start} > 1$. Also note that an inlet with a single, normal shock requires a larger Mach number to start the inlet. A tradeoff is a large inlet throat area that is desirable for a low value of supersonic inlet start Mach number versus a small inlet throat area that is desirable for a low combustion Mach number. The bottom section of the figure has a sketch of un-started and started inlets. Note the detached shock wave of the un-started inlet, which spills airflow around the inlet. The sketch of a started inlet shows an attached shock wave, with the captured air flow into the inlet.

As an example calculation, assume the ramjet baseline missile is at an angle of attack $\alpha = 0$ deg. The ramjet baseline inlet throat area is $A_{IT} = 0.29$ ft^2 and its inlet capture area is $A_c = 114$ in$^2 = 0.79$ ft^2. Compute $A_{IT}/A_c = 0.29/0.79 = 0.367$. The inlet start Mach number is obtained by iteration in the inlet start equation of A_{IT}/A_0. The process is to 1) assume a value of $(M_{IE})_{Start}$, 2) compute the capture efficiency A_{IT}/A_0, 3) compute $(M_{IE})_{Start}$ and compare with the assumed $(M_{IE})_{Start}$, and 4) iterate until convergence. For this example, assume an ideal isentropic inlet with $(M_{IE})_{Start} = 1.8$. From the previous figure, for $(M_{IE})_{Start} = 1.8$ and $\alpha = 0$ deg, the inlet capture efficiency is $A_0/A_c = 0.53$. Calculate

$$A_{IT}/A_0 = (A_{IT}/A_c)/(A_0/A_c) = 0.367/0.53 = 0.69$$

Substituting into the inlet start equation $A_{IT}/A_0 = 0.69 = 1.728(1.8)[1 + 0.2(1.8)^2]^{-3}$ verifies $(M_{IE})_{Start} = 1.8$.

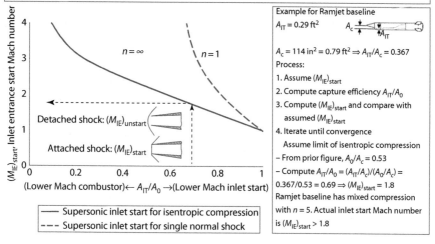

$A_{IT}/A_0 = 1.728(M_{IE})_{start}[1+0.2(M_{IE})_{start}^2]^{-3}$, Assumptions: 2-D inlet, isentropic flow through inlet ($n = \infty$), $\gamma = 1.4$

$A_{IT}/A_0 = (M_{IE})_{start}\{[0.4(M_{IE})_{start}^2 + 2]/[2.4(M_{IE})_{start}^2]^{3.5}\}\{[2.8(M_{IE})_{start}^2 - 0.4]/2.4\}^{2.5}\{[1.2/(1+0.2(M_{IE})_{start}^2]\}^3$, Assumptions: 2-D inlet, Single normal shock ($n = 1$), $\gamma = 1.4$

Note: A_{IT} = Inlet throat area, A_0 = Free stream flow area, $(M_{IE})_{start}$ = Inlet entrance start Mach number, γ = Specific heat ratio, n = Number of shocks

Example for Ramjet baseline

$A_{IT} = 0.29\ ft^2$

$A_c = 114\ in^2 = 0.79\ ft^2 \Rightarrow A_{IT}/A_c = 0.367$

Process:
1. Assume $(M_{IE})_{start}$
2. Compute capture efficiency A_{IT}/A_0
3. Compute $(M_{IE})_{start}$ and compare with assumed $(M_{IE})_{start}$
4. Iterate until convergence
   Assume limit of isentropic compression
   – From prior figure, $A_0/A_c = 0.53$
   – Compute $A_{IT}/A_0 = (A_{IT}/A_c)/(A_0/A_c) =$
   $0.367/0.53 = 0.69 \Rightarrow (M_{IE})_{start} = 1.8$
Ramjet baseline has mixed compression with $n = 5$. Actual inlet start Mach number is $(M_{IE})_{start} > 1.8$

Detached shock: $(M_{IE})_{unstart}$

Attached shock: $(M_{IE})_{start}$

(Lower Mach combustor) $\leftarrow A_{IT}/A_0 \rightarrow$ (Lower Mach inlet start)

—— Supersonic inlet start for isentropic compression
--- Supersonic inlet start for single normal shock

Fig. 3.43 Isentropic compression allows supersonic inlet start at a Lower Mach number.

The ramjet baseline has a mixed compression inlet, with a total of $n = 5$ shocks (four compressions prior to the normal shock inside the inlet). The actual inlet entrance start Mach number is greater than the isentropic inlet start Mach number of $(M_{IE})_{Start} = 1.8$. Also, a typical design criteria for a supersonic air-breathing missile is a minimum cruise Mach number of $(M_0)_{Min\ cruise} \approx 1.2 \times (M_0)_{InletStart}$, to overcome inlet buzz and to have sufficient design margin for the inlet to swallow the shock. Inlet buzz is caused by a transient start and un-start of the inlet. Also, a ramjet needs a thrust minus drag acceleration margin following inlet start, to accelerate under ramjet thrust to the cruise Mach number. A design criteria for the minimum Mach number for transition from booster to ramjet flight is $(M_0)_{Ramjet\ transition} \approx 1.2 \times (M_0)_{Inlet\ start}$.

It is noted that designing an inlet for the lower Mach number associated with near isentropic compression is higher risk. A larger design margin is recommended for a near isentropic inlet.

As discussed previously, it is usually desirable for a ramjet to have a low value of inlet entrance Mach number M_{IE}. A low value of M_{IE} reduces the required inlet start Mach number, allowing a smaller size/lighter weight booster. M_{IE} is driven by forebody shock wave compression and the free stream Mach number. The equation for the M_{IE} of a single oblique shock wave is

$$M_{IE} = \{\{36M_0^4 \sin^2 \theta_{2D} - 5[M_0^2 \sin^2 \theta_{2D} - 1][7M_0^2 \sin^2 \theta_{2D} + 5]\}/\{[7M_0^2 \sin^2 \theta_{2D} - 1][M_0^2 \sin^2 \theta_{2D} + 5]\}\}^{1/2}$$

The oblique shock wave angle θ_{2D} can be determined from the equation

$$\tan(\alpha + \delta) = 2\cot \theta_{2D}(M_0^2 \sin^2 \theta_{2D} - 1)/[2 + M_0^2(2.4 - 2\sin^2 \theta_{2D})]$$

Terms in the above equations are M_0 = free stream Mach number, α = angle of attack, and δ = body deflection angle. Assumptions are a single shock, 2-D flow, perfect gas, and specific heat ratio $\gamma = 1.4$.

Figure 3.44 shows M_{IE} for a flow deflection angle $\alpha + \delta$ up to the maximum value for attached flow. The free stream Mach number range shown in the figure is $2 < M_0 < 5$. Note the large effect of flow deflection on reducing M_{IE}.

As an example, assume that the ramjet baseline missile conical forebody can be approximated as a 2D deflection. Then for $\alpha = 0$ deg, $\alpha + \delta = 17.7$ deg. From the prior example, the inlet start Mach number is $(M_{IE})_{\text{Inletstart}} \approx 1.8$. Substituting into the above equations and neglecting the difference between a conical deflection versus a 2D deflection, the ramjet baseline missile booster should be sized for a ramjet transition Mach number of approximately $(M_0)_{\text{RamjetTransition}} \approx 2.55$.

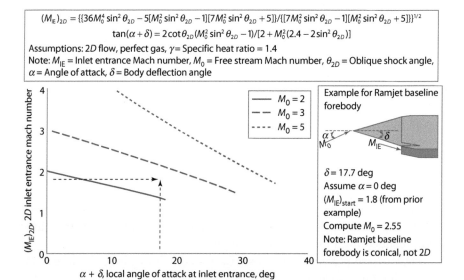

Fig. 3.44   Forebody shock wave compression reduces the inlet entrance Mach number.

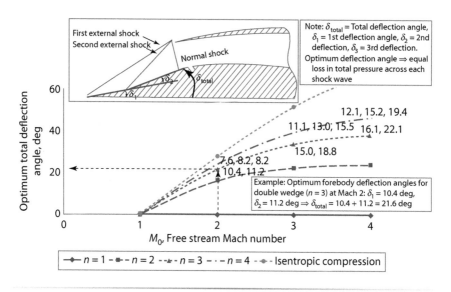

Fig. 3.45 Optimum forebody deflection angle(s) for best pressure recovery increases with Mach number. (Reference: "Technical Aerodynamics Manual", North American Rockwell Corporation, DTICAD 723823, June 1970).

Figure 3.45, derived from Ref. 17 presents the optimum deflection angles of wedge forebodies to give the highest value of the total pressure ratio following a normal shock. Oswatitsch [18] showed that the optimum forebody deflection angles for maximum total pressure behind a normal shock provide equal loss in total pressure across each shock wave. Note from the figure that the required deflection angle(s) for optimum pressure recovery increases with Mach number. For free stream Mach numbers greater than 4, the optimum deflection angle(s) increases slowly with increasing Mach number. The figure also shows that two external shocks have smaller optimum deflection angles than the optimum deflection angle of a single external shock. Also note that the sum of the deflections (total turning angle) for two optimum external shocks is greater than the deflection angle of a single optimum external shock. Similarly, three optimum external shocks have smaller deflection angles than two optimum external shocks. The total turning angle of three optimum external shocks is greater than the total turning angle of two optimum external shocks. The advantage of multiple shock waves over one shock wave is higher total pressure recovery. A disadvantage of multiple external shocks prior to the inlet normal shock is the flow is deflected more away from the centerline. As a rule of thumb, the total turning angle of the flow should typically be less than about 45 deg, to avoid flow separation inside the inlet.

As an example, at Mach 2, the forebody optimum total deflection angle for a double wedge forebody is 21.6 deg, with two oblique shock waves prior to a normal shock. The first deflection is 10.4 deg half-angle and the second deflection is 11.2 deg half-angle.

An example of a missile with a near-isentropic supersonic compression inlet is the Russia 3M80 (SS-N-22 Sunburn). A first-order estimate of its cruise Mach number can be derived by assuming a Prandtl-Meyer compression from its gradual turning inlet spike geometry. A Prandtl-Meyer compression is a gradual isentropic compression that turns a supersonic flow. From the photograph of Fig. 3.46, the total deflection angle of the inlet spike is $\delta_{\text{Total}} \approx 60$ deg. Assuming that the inlet spike is designed to provide Mach 1 at the inlet throat, the Prandtl-Meyer equation is

$$\delta_{\text{Total}} \approx 60° \approx \nu \approx [(\gamma+1)/(\gamma-1)]^{1/2}\tan^{-1}\{[(\gamma-1)/(\gamma+1)](M_0^2-1)\}^{1/2}$$

$$- \tan^{-1}(M_0^2-1)$$

$$= 2.45\tan^{-1}[0.408(M_0^2-1)] - \tan^{-1}(M_0^2-1)$$

Solving the above equation gives $M_0 \approx 3.6$

Because ramjet combustion is subsonic, there must be an inlet normal shock to provide subsonic flow into the combustor. Small oblique shocks

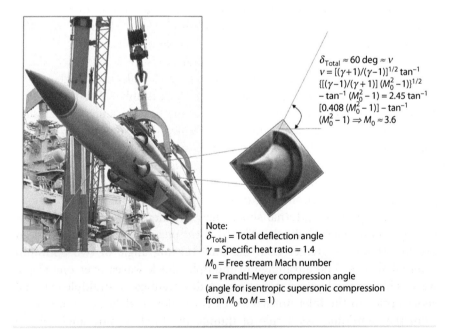

$\delta_{\text{Total}} \approx 60$ deg $\approx \nu$
$\nu = [(\gamma+1)/(\gamma-1)]^{1/2}\tan^{-1}$
$\{[(\gamma-1)/(\gamma+1)](M_0^2-1)\}^{1/2}$
$- \tan^{-1}(M_0^2-1) = 2.45\tan^{-1}$
$[0.408(M_0^2-1)] - \tan^{-1}$
$(M_0^2-1) \Rightarrow M_0 \approx 3.6$

Note:
δ_{Total} = Total deflection angle
γ = Specific heat ratio = 1.4
M_0 = Free stream Mach number
ν = Prandtl-Meyer compression angle
(angle for isentropic supersonic compression
from M_0 to $M = 1$)

Fig. 3.46   Example of a near-Isentropic supersonic compression inlet – 3M80 (SS-N-22 Sunburn).

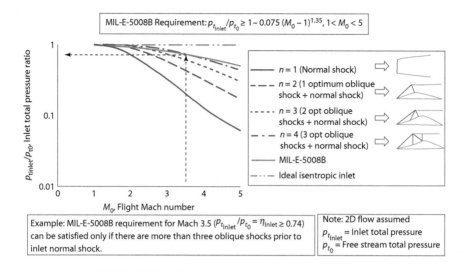

Fig. 3.47 Oblique shock waves prior to the inlet normal shock are required to satisfy MIL-E-5008B. (Source for Optimum 20 Shocks: Oswatitsch, K.L., "Pressure Recovery for Missiles with Reaction Propulsion at High Supersonic Speeds," NACA TM-1140, 1947.)

prior to the normal shock alleviate the problem of total (stagnation) pressure loss across the inlet normal shock. Figure 3.47, based on Ref. 17, compares the military specification MIL-E-5008B total pressure recovery requirement with that of the optimum pressure recoveries of $n = 1$ shocks (e.g., pitot inlet with a single normal shock, $n = 2$ (e.g., single wedge inlet with one oblique external shock plus normal shock), $n = 3$ (e.g., double wedge inlet with two oblique external shocks plus normal shock), $n = 4$ (e.g., mixed compression inlet with two oblique external shocks plus one oblique internal shock plus normal shock), and an ideal, theoretical, isentropic inlet. The requirement of MIL-E-5008B, which is a reasonable pressure recovery for a well designed inlet, is given by the equations

$$p_{\text{Tinlet}}/p_{t_0} \geq 1 - 0.075(M_0 - 1)^{1.35}, \, 1 < M_0 < 5$$

$$p_{\text{Tinlet}}/p_{t_0} \geq 800/(M_0^4 + 935), \, M_0 > 5$$

As stated previously, from Oswatitsch [18] we know that the maximum pressure recovery occurs for an equal loss in total pressure across each shock wave. Note from the figure that for hypersonic missiles, a mixed compression inlet requires three or more oblique shocks to satisfy MIL-E-5008B. The ramjet baseline missile (Chapter 7) inlet/airframe integration consists of 1) an external forebody compression (conical nose), 2) a ramp leading up to the cowl, 3) an inlet cowl lip angle, 4) internal turning, and 5) an internal normal shock. Compared to an external compression inlet, a mixed compression inlet reduces excessive flow turning away from the axial direction.

An example comparison is shown in the figure. The MIL-E-5008B Mach 3.5 requirement is compared with the Mach 3.5 total pressure recovery for three optimum oblique shocks plus a normal shock. From Ref. 17, at Mach 3.5 the optimum deflection angles are $\delta_1 = 11.9$ deg, $\delta_2 = 14.1$ deg, and $\delta_3 = 17.2$ deg. As shown in the figure, the total pressure recovery from three optimum oblique shocks at Mach 3.5 is $\eta_{\text{Inlet}} = 0.72$. The requirement from MIL-E-5008B, for Mach 3.5 is,

$$\eta_{\text{Inlet}} = p_{\text{Tinlet}}/p_{t0} \geq 1 - 0.075(3.5 - 1)^{1.35} = 0.74$$

Therefore, more than three oblique shocks are required to satisfy the military standard at Mach 3.5.

3.17 Fuel Alternatives

An area of high payoff for air-breathing missiles is that of high density fuels. As shown in Fig. 3.48, the high density fuels provide high volumetric performance, which is especially beneficial for volume-limited missiles.

Type	Fuel	Density, lbm/in^3	Volumetric performance, BTU/in^3	Low observables
Hydrocarbon	Turbine (JP-4, JP-5, JP-7, JP-8, JP-10)	~0.031	~559	●
	Liquid Ramjet (RJ-4, RJ-5, RJ-6, RJ-7)	~0.037	≈648	●
	HTPB	~0.034	606	○
	Slurry (40% JP-10/60% carbon)	~0.049	801	○
	Solid carbon (graphite)	~0.075	1132	—
Metal	Slurry (40% JP-10/60% aluminum)	~0.072	866	—
	Slurry (40% JP-10/60% boron cabide)	~0.050	1191	—
	Solid Mg	~0.068	1200	—
	Solid Al	~0.101	1300	—
	Solid boron	~0.082	2040	—
● Superior ◐ Good ○ Average — Poor				

Fig. 3.48   High density fuels provide higher volumetric performance, but have higher observables.

Conventional turbojet and ramjet fuels are a kerosene-type, with a complex mixture of different hydrocarbons that are combined with oxygen from the inlet air, which then produces carbon dioxide and water. An example of a combustion reaction is $C_xH_y + (x + y/4)\ (O_2) \rightarrow x\ CO_2 + y/2\ (H_2O)$. The fuel hydrocarbon compounds C_xH_y typically have a carbon distribution ranging from $8 < x < 16$.

The $C_{12}H_{24}$ compound is the most common compound of JP-7 fuel, $C_{12}H_{22}$ is the most common compound of JP-8 fuel, and $C_{10}H_{16}$ is the most common compound of JP-10 fuel. Considerations in fuel selection include safety, freezing point, density, volumetric performance, observables, and availability. Current turbojet fuels such as JP-4, JP-5, JP-7, JP-8, and JP-10 have relatively low density, ranging from 0.028 lbm/in^3 for JP-4 to 0.034 lbm/in^3 for JP-10, and relatively low volumetric performance, on the order of 559 BTU/in^3. JP-10 was selected as the baseline fuel for the turbojet baseline missile. Advantages of JP-10 compared to the other JP fuels include relatively high heating value ($H_f = 18{,}700$ BTU/lbm), relatively high density (0.034 lbm/in^3), low freezing temperature ($-79°C$), safety (flash point 54°C), and availability.

Compared to conventional turbojet fuels, liquid fuel ramjet hydrocarbon fuels such as RJ-4, RJ-5, RJ-6, and RJ-7 have higher density, ranging from 0.034 lbm/in^3 for RJ-4 to 0.040 lbm/in^3 for RJ-5. This provides higher volumetric performance (≈ 648 BTU/in^3). As an example of the heavier molecular weight of the RJ series of fuels compared to the JP series of fuels, $C_{14}H_{18}$ is the most common compound for RJ-5, the baseline ramjet fuel. RJ-5 fuel was selected for the ramjet baseline missile because of its high density (0.040 lbm/in^3), good heating value ($H_f = 17{,}900$ BTU/lbm), and high safety (flash point 104°C). However, RJ-5 has a disadvantage of a high freezing temperature ($-29°C$). Because it is unsuitable for a low temperature environment and its high cost, RJ-5 fuel is no longer available. The best currently available fuel for a ramjet is probably JP-10.

Unconventional fuels include binder, slurry, carbon, and metal fuels. Binder fuels, such as HTPB, have an advantage of the good logistical characteristics of a solid fuel. Compared to the conventional liquid hydrocarbon fuels, binder fuels volumetric performance (606 BTU/in^3) is somewhat higher than that of the JP series and somewhat lower than that of the RJ series. The density of HTPB (0.034 lbm/in^3) is intermediate that of the JP and RJ series. A disadvantage of binder fuels is increased visual observables compared to liquid hydrocarbon fuels. Liquid hydrocarbon fuels achieve near 100% combustion, with low observables at low altitude. There may be an ice crystal contrail at high altitude. Slurry fuels, such as JP-10 with carbon slurry, and solid carbon fuels, such as graphite have high volumetric performance, with a disadvantage of higher visual observables. High volumetric performance is also achievable with high density solid metal fuels such as magnesium, aluminum, and boron. Disadvantages of solid metal fuels include high observables from their metal oxide plumes and reduced volumetric loading/packaging efficiency. The highest theoretical volumetric performance fuel shown in the figure is boron. Boron fuel, if it has complete combustion with a solids loading of 100%, theoretically provides over three times the volumetric performance of a conventional liquid hydrocarbon fuel. Although it has high theoretical performance, boron fuel is technically immature with relatively high risk and has high observables.

3.18 Rocket Motor Performance Prediction

An objective of a rocket motor is to provide sufficient velocity to meet the missile range, time-to-target, and maneuverability requirements. For logistical and safety reasons, most modern missiles use solid propellant, instead of liquid propellant, rocket motors. This text does not address liquid propellant rocket motors.

The first order drivers of the incremental velocity (ΔV) provided by the rocket motor are the propellant weight-to-missile total weight fraction (W_p/W_i) and the propellant specific impulse (I_{SP}). Including the effect of missile drag would reduce the ΔV. The effect of missile drag on the missile incremental velocity will be considered later in Chapter 5. Figure 3.49 shows the relationship of the maximum incremental velocity of a rocket as a function of the propellant weight fraction and the specific impulse. From Newton's second law, the equation is

$$\Delta V = -gI_{SP} \ln (1 - W_p/W_i)$$

An assumption for the equation is a high thrust motor, with thrust much larger than drag. It is also assumed that the thrust is much greater than the component of the missile weight in the thrust direction, which is applicable for either a high thrust-to-weight ratio or horizontal flight. Also, the flight path angle is assumed to be constant. Note from the figure that a hypersonic Mach number can be achieved for a surface launched missile only if the propellant weight is more than one-half of the missile initial weight. Also note that higher specific impulse gives higher burnout velocity.

From the Chapter 7 data for the rocket baseline missile, the initial boost (launch) weight is $W_{i,boost} = W_L = 500$ lb, the boost propellant weight is $W_p = 84.8$ lb, and the specific impulse during boost is $I_{SP} = 250$ s. Computing the maximum theoretical incremental velocity from boost

$$\Delta V = -32.2(250) \ln (1 - 84.8/500) = 1496 \text{ ft/s}$$

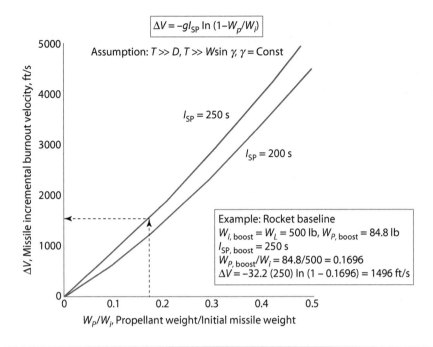

$$\Delta V = -gI_{SP} \ln (1-W_p/W_i)$$

Assumption: $T \gg D$, $T \gg W\sin \gamma$, $\gamma = $ Const

$I_{SP} = 250$ s

$I_{SP} = 200$ s

Example: Rocket baseline
$W_{i, boost} = W_L = 500$ lb, $W_{P, boost} = 84.8$ lb
$I_{SP, boost} = 250$ s
$W_{P, boost}/W_i = 84.8/500 = 0.1696$
$\Delta V = -32.2 \ (250) \ln (1 - 0.1696) = 1496$ ft/s

ΔV, Missile incremental burnout velocity, ft/s

W_p/W_i, Propellant weight/Initial missile weight

Fig. 3.49 High propellant weight fraction and high specific impulse increase rocket burnout velocity.

For a typical launch condition of Mach 0.8/20 kft altitude, the launch velocity is 820 ft/s, resulting in a theoretical end-of-boost velocity for horizontal flight of

$$V_{EB} = 820 + 1496 = 2316 \, \text{ft/s}$$

As mentioned previously, the actual end-of-boost velocity would be lower, because of drag.

The physics of a notional solid propellant rocket motor are illustrated in Fig. 3.50. The rocket motor consists of a combustion chamber and a nozzle. The top portion of the figure shows color-coded relative values of the static pressure and velocity in the combustion chamber and nozzle sections of the motor. Note the decreasing static pressure and increasing velocity as the gas flows travels from the high pressure, low subsonic combustion chamber (red) through the high subsonic aft dome to the sonic throat (yellow) through the supersonic expansion nozzle (yellow to green) and finally, the supersonic plume expansion aft of the nozzle exit to the local atmospheric pressure (blue). Most missiles have under-expanded nozzles, with the supersonic plume expanding outside the nozzle exit.

The physics of the rocket motor consist of high temperature/high pressure combustion of the propellant, which produces gas that flows out of the combustion chamber and exits through the nozzle into the atmosphere, producing thrust. It is a near-isentropic expansion process. Most missiles have a divergent nozzle to develop additional kinetic energy, which provides additional thrust. A notional sketch of the decreasing static pressure/increasing velocity is shown at the bottom of the figure.

A thrust performance Pareto sensitivity study was conducted of the baseline rocket motor to determine the most significant parameters. Note from Fig. 3.51 that the thrust is most sensitive to changes in the motor chamber pressure and the nozzle throat area. In the Pareto, these provide over 80% of the sensitivity. The sensitivity study was conducted at nominal values of altitude $h = 20$ kft ($p_0 = 6.75$ psi) and boost chamber pressure $p_c = 1769$ psi. The rocket baseline missile Chapter 7 values of nozzle throat area, specific heat ratio, and nozzle expansion ratio are $A_t = 1.81$ in^2, $\gamma = 1.18$ and $\varepsilon = 6.2$, respectively.

Based on the assumption of isentropic flow with an assumed discharge coefficient $c_d = 0.96$, the thrust equation is

$$T = c_d\, p_c\, A_t \{\{[2\gamma^2/(\gamma - 1)][2/(\gamma + 1)]^{(\gamma+1)/(\gamma-1)}[1 - (p_e/p_c)^{(\gamma-1)/\gamma}]\}^{1/2}$$
$$+ (p_e/p_c)\varepsilon - (p_0/p_c)\varepsilon\}$$

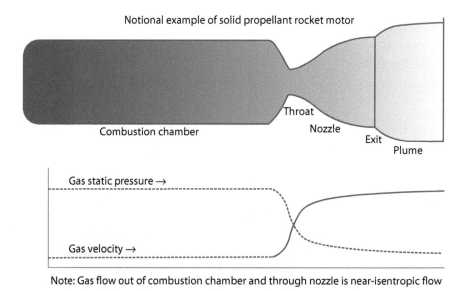

Notional example of solid propellant rocket motor

Combustion chamber   Throat   Nozzle   Exit   Plume

Gas static pressure →

Gas velocity →

Note: Gas flow out of combustion chamber and through nozzle is near-isentropic flow

Fig. 3.50 A rocket motor generates thrust by converting high pressure combustion gas into a high velocity exhaust.

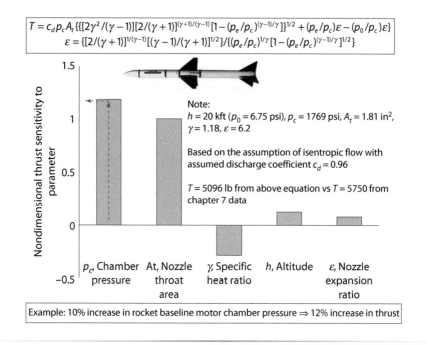

$$T = c_d p_c A_t \{\{[2\gamma^2/(\gamma-1)][2/(\gamma+1)]^{(\gamma+1)/(\gamma-1)}[1-(p_e/p_c)^{(\gamma-1)/\gamma}]\}^{1/2} + (p_e/p_c)\varepsilon - (p_0/p_c)\varepsilon\}$$
$$\varepsilon = \{[2/(\gamma+1)]^{1/(\gamma-1)}[(\gamma-1)/(\gamma+1)]^{1/2}\}/\{(p_e/p_c)^{1/\gamma}[1-(p_e/p_c)^{(\gamma-1)/\gamma}]^{1/2}\}$$

Note:
$h = 20$ kft ($p_0 = 6.75$ psi), $p_c = 1769$ psi, $A_t = 1.81$ in^2, $\gamma = 1.18$, $\varepsilon = 6.2$

Based on the assumption of isentropic flow with assumed discharge coefficient $c_d = 0.96$

$T = 5096$ lb from above equation vs $T = 5750$ from chapter 7 data

p_c, Chamber pressure   At, Nozzle throat area γ, Specific heat ratio h, Altitude ε, Nozzle expansion ratio

Example: 10% increase in rocket baseline motor chamber pressure $\Rightarrow$ 12% increase in thrust

Fig. 3.51 Rocket baseline thrust Pareto shows drivers are chamber pressure and nozzle throat area.

The nozzle expansion ratio equation is

$$\varepsilon = \{[2/(\gamma+1)]^{1/(\gamma-1)}[(\gamma-1)/(\gamma+1)]^{1/2}\}$$
$$/\{(p_e/p_c)^{1/\gamma}[1-(p_e/p_c)^{(\gamma-1)/\gamma}]^{1/2}\}$$

For the rocket baseline design, increased thrust would be provided for a new rocket motor design with increased chamber pressure, increased nozzle throat area, decreased combustion gas specific heat ratio (provided by higher combustion temperature), and increased nozzle expansion ratio. Also, operating at a higher altitude would provide higher thrust, with the highest thrust available for exo-atmospheric ($p_0 = 0$, vacuum) flight.

The predicted nominal boost thrust using the above equations is $T = 5096$ lb. The actual thrust from the rocket baseline missile data of Chapter 7 is 5750 lb. A possible contributor to the difference between prediction and data is the assumed value of specific heat ratio γ of the nozzle gases. Although the gases experience a large variation in temperature, the conceptual design prediction is based on an assumption of a constant $\gamma = 1.18$ during the expansion of the gases through the nozzle.

Specific impulse (I_{SP}), thrust (T), and nozzle expansion ratio (ε) are primary considerations in the rocket motor sizing process. Assuming isentropic flow, the equations are

$$I_{SP} = c_d\{\{[2\gamma^2/(\gamma-1)][2/(\gamma+1)]^{(\gamma+1)/(\gamma-1)}[1-(p_e/p_c)^{(\gamma-1)/\gamma}]\}^{1/2}$$
$$+ (p_e/p_c)\varepsilon - (p_0/p_c)\varepsilon\}c^*/g$$
$$T = \dot{w}_p I_{SP} = (g/c^*)p_c A_t I_{SP}$$

$$\varepsilon = \{[2/(\gamma+1)]^{1/(\gamma-1)}[(\gamma-1)/(\gamma+1)]^{1/2}\}/\{(p_e/p_c)^{1/\gamma}$$
$$\times [1-(p_e/p_c)^{(\gamma-1)/\gamma}]^{1/2}\}$$

Specific impulse of the rocket baseline is shown in Fig. 3.52 as a function of nozzle expansion ratio and chamber pressure. Results are based on typical values of specific heat ratio ($\gamma = 1.18$), discharge efficiency coefficient ($c_d = 0.96$), propellant characteristic velocity ($c^* = 5200$ ft/s), and altitude $h = 20$ kft ($p_0 = 6.75$ psi). The assumed characteristic velocity of 5200 ft/s is a representative value for a propellant. The c^* of a relatively low performance propellant, such as a minimum smoke propellant, may be less than 4800 ft/s. It may be greater than 5600 ft/s for a high performance, high smoke propellant. Referring again to the figure, note that a high

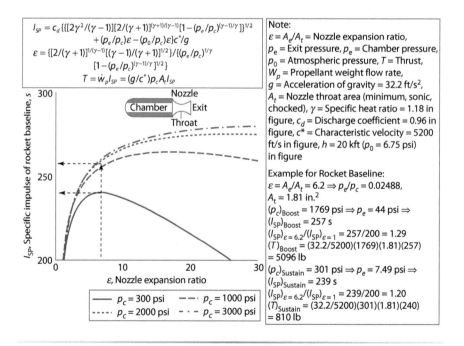

Fig. 3.52   A solid propellant rocket with high specific impulse has high chamber pressure and an optimum nozzle expansion.

chamber pressure requires a high nozzle expansion ratio for maximum specific impulse. Also note that for a low chamber pressure, a relatively small value of nozzle expansion provides maximum I_{SP}. A tradeoff is an optimum expansion nozzle with maximum I_{SP}, versus a lower expansion nozzle with shorter nozzle length/lighter weight. Although the lower expansion nozzle has lower I_{SP}, the shorter nozzle length allows more length for propellant for a length-limited missile. Another possible design approach for a length limited missile would be to use two or more adjacent nozzles instead of a single nozzle, such as the TOW missile. Multiple nozzles can be designed for optimum expansion and higher I_{SP} in a shorter length.

As an example calculation of specific impulse and thrust, the rocket baseline missile of Chapter 7 has a nozzle exit-area-to-throat-area expansion ratio of $\varepsilon = 6.2$ and a nozzle throat area (minimum flow area with sonic, choked flow) of $A_t = 1.81$ in^2. At an assumed altitude of $h = 20,000$ ft, the specific impulse and thrust during boost ($p_c = 1769$ psi) are computed to be $I_{SP} = 257$ s and $T = 5096$ lb, respectively. Following boost, the sustain flight phase has a sustain chamber pressure $p_c = 301$ psi. The computed sustain specific impulse and thrust from the above equations are $I_{SP} = 239$ s and $T = 810$ lb, respectively. Note from the figure that for the rocket baseline during sustain flight, its nozzle expansion ratio ($\varepsilon = 6.2$) provides maximum I_{SP}.

A purpose of using nozzle expansion is to provide increased specific impulse and thrust. Note from the figure that nozzle expansion of the rocket baseline increases the specific impulse by 29% during boost (257 s for $\varepsilon = 6.2$ versus 200 s for $\varepsilon = 1$). During sustain, the nozzle expansion increases the specific impulse by 20% (239 s with the nozzle versus 200 s if there were no nozzle expansion).

The actual specific impulse of the rocket baseline missile (Chapter 7) is about 3% lower than prediction (250 versus 257 s during boost and 230 versus 239 s during sustain). The actual thrust of the rocket baseline is about 20% higher than prediction (5750 versus 5096 lb during boost and 1018 versus 810 lb during sustain). The predicted burn time is about 20% longer than the actual burn time. As a result, the total impulse and incremental velocity of the prediction versus data are in near agreement.

3.19 Rocket Motor Sizing Process

Shown in Fig. 3.53 are the propellant weight flow rate $\dot{w}_p$ as a function of chamber pressure p_c, area of the nozzle throat A_t, and propellant characteristic velocity c^*. The equation is

$$\dot{w}_p = (g_c p_c A_t / c^*)$$

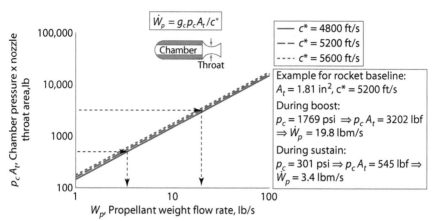

Note: A_t = Nozzle throat area, c^* = Characteristic velocity, $\dot{W}_p$ = Propellant weight flow rate, g_c = Gravitational constant = 32.2 lbm ft/lbf s^2), p_c = Chamber pressure

Fig. 3.53   High propellant weight flow rate is driven by high chamber pressure and a large nozzle throat area.

The range of values shown in the figure cover the typical range of values of A_t, $\dot{w}_p$, c^*, and p_c for missiles. The primary parameters that are used in conceptual design to define the propellant weight flow rate are chamber pressure and nozzle throat area. Propellant characteristic velocity, although it is an important parameter, is a usually a secondary consideration.

As an example, the propellant weight flow rate of the rocket baseline motor will be computed based on the above equation and data from Chapter 7. The rocket baseline motor has a nozzle throat area A_t= 1.81 in^2 and a propellant characteristic velocity of c^* = 5200 ft/s. At the boost condition the motor chamber pressure is p_c = 1769 psi. The propellant weight flow rate during boost is calculated to be

$$\dot{w}_p = 32.2(1769)(1.81)/5200 = 19.8 \text{ lbm/s}.$$

The actual propellant flow rate during boost is 16% greater, 23.0 lbm/s (Chapter 7).

During sustain, the motor chamber pressure is 301 psi, resulting in a calculated propellant flow rate

$$\dot{w}_p = 32.2(301)(1.81)/5200 = 3.4 \text{ lbm/s}.$$

The actual propellant flow rate during boost is 29% higher, 4.4 lbm/s (Chapter 7).

Figure 3.54 shows a relationship of the propellant burn area to the rocket motor chamber pressure and nozzle throat area. The equations are

$$A_b = g_c p_c A_t / (\rho c^* r)$$
$$r = r_{p_c = 1000\text{psi}} (p_c / 1000)^n$$

Note from the above equations that the required burn area A_b is a function of the chamber pressure, throat area, propellant density, characteristic velocity, and the propellant burn rate. To achieve a high chamber pressure, a large propellant burn area and a small nozzle throat are required. Burn rate r is a function of the propellant burn rate at a reference chamber pressure of 1000 psi ($r_{p_c = 1000\text{psi}}$), chamber pressure p_c, and the burn rate exponent n. For statically stable combustion, $0 < n < 1$. Typical values are $0.2 < n < 0.8$. For a boost-sustain motor or a pintle motor, it may be desirable for $n \rightarrow 1$. This allows a large change in burn rate, mass flow rate, and thrust with a small change in chamber pressure and burn area, resulting in a higher average value of specific impulse. For an all-boost motor, a low value of n is usually preferred because it results in less acoustic pressure instability.

In a solid propellant rocket, the oxidizer and fuel are all already mixed in the propellant. As a result, combustion occurs nearly instantaneously at the burning surface. Air-breathing and liquid propellant propulsion system

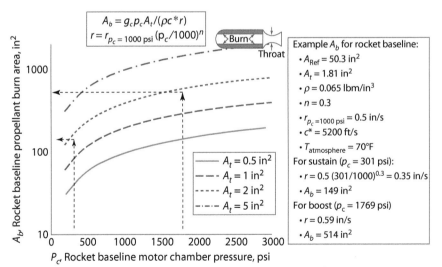

Note: A_b = Propellant burn area, g_c = Gravitational constant = 32.2 lbm ft/(lbf s²), A_t = Nozzle throat area, ρ = Density of propellant, c^* = Propellant characteristic velocity, r = Propellant burn rate, $r_{p_c=1000\text{ psi}}$ = Propellant burn rate at p_c=1000 psi, p_c = Chamber pressure, n = Propellant burn rate exponent

Fig. 3.54 Solid propellant rocket motor chamber pressure is driven by propellant burn area and nozzle throat area.

combustion occurs farther downstream, with mixing of the fuel and oxidizer. Air-breathing propulsion and liquid propellant rocket propulsion require additional length and volume to complete combustion compared to a solid propellant rocket.

From Chapter 7, the rocket baseline motor has a throat area $A_t = 1.81$ in^2, a propellant density $\rho = 0.065$ lbm/in^3, and a characteristic velocity $c^* = 5200$ ft/s. The burn rate exponent is $n = 0.3$, referenced to a nominal chamber pressure $p_c = 1000$ psi and a nominal atmospheric temperature $T = 70°$F. The nominal burn rate at standard conditions is $r = 0.5$ in/s. During sustain, with a chamber pressure of $p_c = 301$ psi, the burn rate is computed to be

$$r = 0.5(301/1000)^{0.3} = 0.35 \text{ in/s}$$

The required burn area for sustain is

$$A_b = 32.2(301)(1.81)/[0.065(5200)(0.35)] = 149 \text{ in}^2$$

For the 8-in diameter rocket baseline, the body cross sectional area is 50 in^2. An end-burning grain would not provide sufficient thrust for the rocket baseline missile. The constraint of an end-burning area, nozzle geometry, propellant burn rate exponent, and the propellant burn rate result in a limit in the chamber pressure to less than that required. Instead, a center cavity grain, with three radial slots, is used for the rocket baseline motor to obtain the required burn surface area for boost and sustain thrust. For the rocket baseline boost chamber pressure $p_c = 1769$ psi, the burn rate equation gives the boost burn rate as

$$r = 0.5(1769/1000)^{0.3} = 0.59 \text{ in/s}$$

The required burn area for boost is larger than the sustain burn area,

$$A_b = 32.2(1769)(1.81)/[0.065(5200)(0.59)] = 514 \text{ in}^2.$$

Figure 3.55 summarizes a conceptual design process for sizing a solid propellant rocket motor. It is a highly iterative process that harmonizes a large number of design parameters and constraints. The process begins by 1) specifying an altitude and assuming a desired thrust–time profile. In the next step, 2) assumptions are made for the type of propellant, the desired chamber pressure, the burn area(s), and the nozzle geometry. These are used in step 3) to calculate an initial estimate of the thrust and specific impulse. If the thrust and specific impulse are acceptable, the process continues to the next step. However, if the initial estimate of thrust and specific impulse are not acceptable, we go back to step 2) and try again, with a different combination of propellant, chamber pressure, burn area, and nozzle geometry. If we still cannot get an acceptable specific

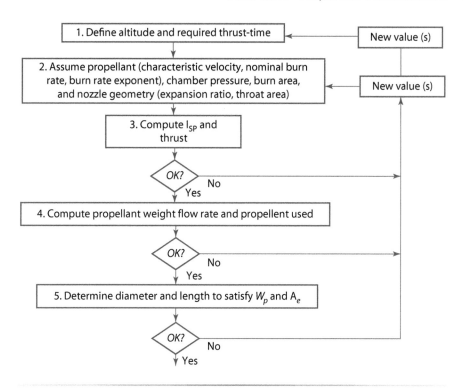

Fig. 3.55 Conceptual design sizing of a solid propellant rocket motor is an iterative process.

impulse and thrust after iterating in step 2), we may have to go back to step 1) and change the desired thrust-time profile. Assuming that the desired specific impulse and thrust are achievable, we next go to step 4) and calculate of the propellant weight flow rate and the weight of the propellant used. If this is acceptable, we go to the next step. If not, we go back and iterate step 2) until we reach a convergence. Again, if there is no convergence, we may have to go back to step 1) and change the desired thrust-time history. Assuming that there is a convergence, we next go to step 5), determining the diameter and length to satisfy the propellant weight and nozzle exit area. Considerations include the grain volumetric efficiency, insulation thickness, and the fore and aft dome geometry. If this is acceptable, we have completed *one* of the possible design solutions. If it is not acceptable, we have to go back and iterate until there is a solution.

For a specified nozzle geometry and altitude, the solid propellant rocket motor combustion pressure, propellant weight flow rate, and thrust are proportional to the propellant burn area. Shown in Fig. 3.56 is an example of the changes in the propellant grain cross sectional geometry of a five-spoke wagon wheel as a function of time. Burning of the propellant is in the

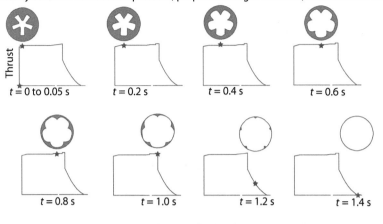

Example: Wagon wheel grain with nearly constant burn area vs. time
($\Rightarrow$ Nearly constant combustion pressure, propellant weight flow rate, and thrust vs. time)

Fig. 3.56   Solid propellant rocket motor chamber pressure, weight flow rate, and thrust are proportional to propellant burn area.

direction perpendicular to the grain surface. Note from the figure that the example grain has a nearly constant burn area over most of the burn time. The burn areas at time $t = 0.05$ s, 0.2 s, 0.4 s, 0.6 s, 0.8 s, and 1.0 s are nearly equal. As a result, there is nearly constant combustion chamber pressure, nearly constant propellant weight flow rate, and nearly constant thrust for $t < 1.0$ s. The rise time from ignition to quasi steady-state combustion for the example is about 0.05 s. For $t > 1.0$ s, the burn surface area is smaller, consisting of only five slivers from the inner web. Thrust is reduced rapidly during the final combustion of the five slivers, with burnout at $t = 1.4$ s. A propellant grain geometry that provides nearly constant pressure combustion, such as the example five-spoke wagon wheel, is often of interest because the nozzle can be more easily optimized for a single combustion pressure, providing higher specific impulse.

3.20 Solid Propellant Grain Alternatives

To define a varying thrust-time profile, a cavity through the center of the propellant grain can be used to provide the required burning surface area time profile. As shown in Fig. 3.57, a variety of internal shapes (e.g., wagon wheel, star, dendrite, end-burner, radial slotted tube) provide larger or smaller burn area and thus more or less hot gas, providing more or less thrust. The change in the burn area as a function of time provides the desired thrust-time profile. If the thrust increases with burn time, it is referred to as progressive burning. If the grain design produces a decrease in thrust with burn time, the rocket motor is said to have regressive burning characteristics. Shown in the right section of the figure are typical volumetric loadings for grain design. The volumetric efficiency of the propellant grain cavity loading for operational missiles typically varies from about 79 to 90%. High volumetric efficiency is desirable to maximize the amount of propellant and to minimize the weight of the motor case. A disadvantage of high volumetric loading of the propellant grain cavity is there may be problems of localized stress and cracks in the grain.

For a propellant grain with radial burn, the length of the radial-burn motor affects the thrust. A longer motor has more burn area, which provides higher thrust.

Shown in the top right section of the figure is an end-burner. An end-burner has no cavity, only the end of the grain burns. The end burning grain has nearly constant burning area, and if the throat area is constant, provides nearly constant thrust. Examples of long time duration end-burners are the rocket motors for Exocet and AGM-130, which provide nearly constant thrust for about 90 s and 60 s, respectively. An advantage of an end-burner is high volumetric loading. A disadvantage is that it requires thicker insulation, because the aft insulation is exposed to hot combustion gases for the entire burn duration. Another potential disadvantage is its relatively low thrust limits its application primarily to low speed missiles.

Another popular type of propellant grain cross section is a radial slotted tube, shown in the top right section of the figure. In this example, the

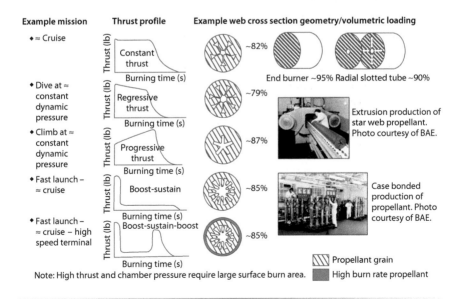

Fig. 3.57 Missile thrust-time requirements drive solid propellant rocket grain cross section geometry.

propellant grain cross section is primarily the simple center tube. Four radial slots are located mid-length of the motor case. Compared to the more complex web cross sections, a radial slotted motor has an advantage of high volumetric loading while also providing stress relief for a case-bonded propellant. A radial slotted tube has broad application, it can be designed to provide nearly constant, regressive, progressive, and boost-sustain thrust profiles. A common type of slotted tube provides a boost-sustain thrust profile. For boost-sustain, high burn rate propellant in the aft section of the motor provides an initial high thrust while a different, slower burn rate propellant in the forward section provides the follow-on sustain thrust.

A third popular type, shown in the middle of the figure is a five-point star cross-section. It provides progressive thrust. Volumetric loading is fairly high, about 87%.

The middle right section of the figure is a photograph of a three-point star grain cross section extrusion of a double base propellant. The propellant extrusion process is limited to propellant diameter less than about 10 in. Following extrusion, the propellant can be loaded into the motor case as a free-standing cartridge. A cartridge loaded grain has an advantage of less stress from thermal expansion/contraction of the propellant. A disadvantage is less volumetric loading and lower performance than a case-bonded propellant.

A second approach to loading propellant is to mix the propellant slurry and then pour it directly into the motor case. The bottom right section of the figure is a photograph of pouring composite propellant into a motor case. The loaded motor case is then placed in an oven for curing/bonding. Normal curing time typically ranges from three-to-seven days. Normal cure temperature typically ranges from 150 to 190°F. A high cure temperature requires less cure time and reduces manufacturing cost, but manufacturing safety limits the maximum cure temperature. Also, a high cure temperature puts additional strain on the propellant. Case bonded propellant is the most popular approach for missiles because it provides higher volumetric loading than a cartridge. A disadvantage of case-bonded propellant is greater stress from thermal expansion. Thermal stress/strain is of particular concern for a long length rocket motor that is case bonded with end-burning propellant (e.g. AGM-130).

3.21 Solid Propellant Rocket Thrust Magnitude Control

Shown in Fig. 3.58 are conventional solid propellant motor concepts, which have a single burn, compared to pulse motor concepts that have

Examples of conventional fixed burn intervel

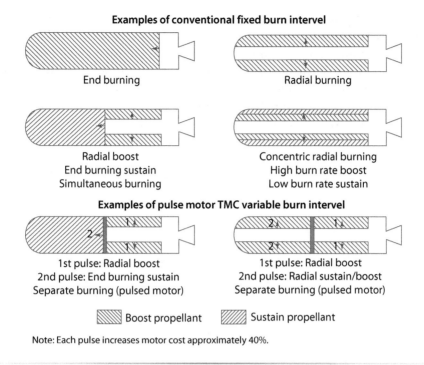

End burning

Radial burning

Radial boost
End burning sustain
Simultaneous burning

Concentric radial burning
High burn rate boost
Low burn rate sustain

Examples of pulse motor TMC variable burn intervel

1st pulse: Radial boost
2nd pulse: End burning sustain
Separate burning (pulsed motor)

1st pulse: Radial boost
2nd pulse: Radial sustain/boost
Separate burning (pulsed motor)

Boost propellant   Sustain propellant

Note: Each pulse increases motor cost approximately 40%.

Fig. 3.58 Thrust magnitude control provides flexibility of missile propulsion energy management.

thrust magnitude control (TMC). TMC provides the flexibility of propulsion energy management to better tailor the missile's velocity to a broader range of mission requirements. At the top of the figure are examples of single burn boost concepts, based on end-burning and radial-burning grain designs. The radial-burning grain has a larger burn area, providing higher thrust. In the center of the figure are two examples of single-burn concepts, capable of a boost-sustain-coast thrust profile. The left, middle concept has a radial-burn boost, using a high burn rate propellant, followed by an end-burning sustain, using a lower burn rate propellant. The right, middle concept has a concentric radial burn, with a high burn rate propellant for boost, followed by a low burn rate propellant for sustain.

The bottom concepts in the figure are examples of pulse motor TMC, which has a controlled time delay between pulses. The left, bottom concept is a pulse motor with a radial-burn boost using a high burn rate propellant. A barrier is provided (either mechanical or chemical) for a controlled time delay in initiating the second burn. High fineness pulse motors usually use a mechanical barrier because a mechanical barrier provides better stress relief. Low fineness pulse motors, which usually do not have a stress relief problem, usually have a chemical barrier. A chemical barrier requires less volume, allowing more propellant packaging. Following coast, the second burn in the example has a sustain thrust using an end-burning grain with a low burn rate propellant. The right bottom concept in the figure is another pulse motor concept, based on a radial grain for boost (with high burn rate propellant), followed by second radial grain with either sustain (with lower burn rate propellant) or a second boost (with a high burn rate propellant).

A design concern of layering a high burn rate propellant on top of a low burn rate propellant is the difference in the thermal expansion of the two different propellants. Localized stress and cracks can develop, because of differences in thermal expansion.

Potential advantages of a pulse motor include longer range, longer flight duration (if desired), and reduced aerodynamic heating (from the lower velocity at each pulse burnout). Pulse motors are more expensive than conventional single burn motors. Each pulse of a pulse motor increases the motor production cost by about 40%. Examples of missiles with a pulse motor are the AGM-69 SRAM two-pulse rocket motor, the SM-3 Standard Missile two-pulse third stage rocket motor (TSRM), the Stunner upper stage two-pulse motor, and the Javelin two-pulse rocket motor. The man-portable Javelin rocket motor provides a capability for a soft launch (low noise/low blast) even when the missile is launched from inside a building. After a time delay the flight motor is ignited at a safe distance away from the gunner.

Alternatives for missile rocket propulsion energy management include a liquid propellant engine, a pulse motor, a pintle motor, and a gel propellant engine. As previously noted, this text does not address liquid propellant rocket motors because of logistical and safety reasons. Most modern missiles do not use liquid propellant. Figure 3.59 compares the alternatives for thrust magnitude control using pulse, pintle, or gel TMC.

As mentioned previously, the solid propellant pulse motor uses thermal or mechanical barriers to provide separate motor pulses. It is usually limited to two or three pulses. Because the motor can be designed for an optimum combustion pressure, a pulse motor can be designed for maximum specific impulse. Another advantage is the time delay between pulses can be controlled to optimize the flight trajectory profile. As a result, a boost-coast-boost-coast pulse motor can have longer range and reduced aerodynamic heating compared to conventional single burn boost-coast and boost-sustain-coast motors.

The second approach to TMC, a solid propellant pintle motor, has a pintle plug that is moved in and out of the throat area. The pintle is constructed from a material with a very high temperature capability, such as tungsten, rhenium, or carbon-carbon. Moving the pintle into the throat area increases the chamber pressure, providing higher burn rate and

Solid propellant pulse

☺ High I_{SP}

☹ Limited pulse

Solid propellant pintle

☺ Continuously select up to 40:1 variation in thrust

☺ Can reduce MEOP for hot day

☺ Good I_{SP} at lowest thrust only if burn rate exponent $n \to 1$

Bi-propellant gel

☺ High I_{SP}

☺ Duty cycle thrust

☺ Insensitive munition

☹ Lower max thrust

☹ Toxicity

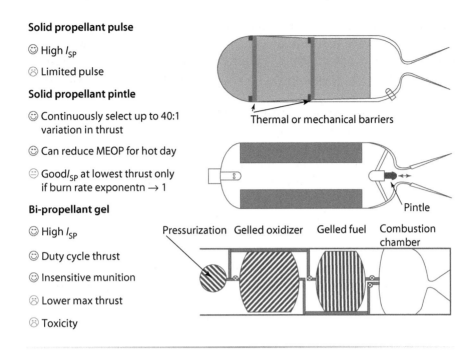

Thermal or mechanical barriers

Pintle

Pressurization Gelled oxidizer Gelled fuel Combustion chamber

Fig. 3.59 Missile solid propellant rocket motor thrust magnitude control alternatives and tradeoffs.

higher thrust. Moving the pintle out of the throat area decreases the chamber pressure, reducing the burn rate and thrust.

A potential benefit of a pintle motor is that it could be used to reduce the maximum effective operating pressure (MEOP) on a hot day, allowing a lower factor of safety and a lighter weight motor case. Another potential benefit of a high bandwidth pintle could be especially applicable to a long length motor, which has a large value of A_b/A_T. The pintle has the potential capability to reduce combustion pressure fluctuations. This capability could also allow a smaller factor of safety and a lighter weight motor case.

For a typical value of propellant burn rate exponent (e.g., $n = 0.3$), there is a large penalty in specific impulse for the pintle motor to operate over a wide range in chamber pressure. It is desirable for a pintle motor to use a propellant with a high burn rate exponent (e.g., $n \to 1$), which provides a large change in burn rate/mass flow rate/thrust with only a small change in chamber pressure. Pintle motors have demonstrated maximum-to-minimum thrust ratios of greater than to 40:1. Combustion can be sustained down to a chamber pressure that is the minimum for a sonic throat, allowing an "idle" mode similar to that of a pulse motor.

A technology opportunity for a pintle motor is the development of propellants with burn rate exponents that approach the value of one, allowing a large change in burn rate (and thrust) with a relatively small change in chamber pressure. Propellants with $n \rightarrow 1$ require high bandwidth and tight control of the position of the pintle, to avoid the hazard of combustion instability if $n > 1$. An example of a pintle motor is the divert thrusters of the SM-3 kill vehicle.

A third alternative for thrust magnitude control of a rocket is a gel propellant rocket engine using a low toxicity gelled fuel such as alcohol and a low toxicity gelled oxidizer such as hydrogen peroxide. The gelled propellant is nearly solid at atmospheric pressure, but flows like a liquid when it is pumped at high pressure. The thrust rise/shutdown time is controlled by the pulse width at which the fuel and oxidizer are pumped into the combustion chamber. A minimum pulse width of 0.002 s has been demonstrated. The specific impulse of a low toxicity gel propellant rocket can be higher than that of a solid propellant rocket. The specific impulse of a higher toxicity gel propellant could be comparable to that of a liquid propellant rocket. A disadvantage of a gel propellant rocket engine compared to a solid propellant rocket motor is lower maximum thrust. A second disadvantage is concern for toxicity, particularly for carriage on naval platforms. Although a gel propellant rocket is much less toxic than a liquid propellant rocket, it is probably unacceptable in a closed environment storage with humans, such as below deck of a ship. In regard to insensitive munitions, a gel propellant rocket engine is superior to a solid propellant rocket motor. The gelled fuel and gelled oxidizer are stored in separate tanks, reducing their sensitivity. The US Army has been a leader in the development of gel propellant rockets. For example, although the current THAAD divert and attitude control system (DACS) uses liquid propellants [monomethyl hydrazine (i.e., MMH or CH_3NHNH_2) fuel and nitrogen tetroxide (i.e., N_2O_4) oxidizer], development work has been conducted on a DACS based on gel propellant with less toxicity.

3.22 Solid Propellant Alternatives

Figure 3.60 is a comparison of missile solid propellant alternatives based on tradeoffs of rocket motor visual observable versus performance and safety. In high smoke and reduced smoke motors, the solid propellant is a composite consisting of a fuel and an oxidizer, blended together and mixed into a binder, or polymer. The mixture is then cast (poured) into the motor case and cured.

The highest performance solid propellants are composite propellants based on binding a metal fuel with an oxidizer such as ammonium perchlorate (ClO_4NH_4). Ammonium perchlorate is ground to sizes ranging

Type	I_{SP}, specific impulse, s	ρ, density lbm/in^3	Burn rate @ 1000 psi, in/s	Safety	Observables
• **Min smoke.** No Al fuel or AP xoidizer. Either composite with nitramine oxidizer (CL-20, ADN, HMX, RDX) or double base. Very low contrail (H$_2$O).	220–255	0.055–0.062	◒ 0.25–2.0	—	◒
• **Reduced smoke.** No Al (binder fuel). AP oxidizer. Low contrail (HCL).	○ 250–260	○ 0.062	◒ 0.1–1.5	○	○
• **High smoke.** Al fuel. AP oxidizer. High smoke (Al$_2$O$_3$).	◒ 260–265	◒ 0.065	● 0.1–3.0	◒	—
● Superior ◒ Good ○ Average — Poor					

Fig. 3.60 Solid propellant selection requires tradeoff of performance, safety, and observables.

from a few microns to about 100 μm. Although a finer grain provides higher performance, safety is more of a concern for a finer grain.

Powdered aluminum is the metallic fuel most widely used in solid rocket propellants. The metal fuel is typically ground to about the same size as the oxidizer. Benefits of a metal fuel include 1) increased combustion temperature, resulting in an increase in specific impulse, 2) increased density of the propellant, resulting in improved volumetric performance, and 3) improved combustion stability. Maximum specific impulse of a metal fuel is limited by the conversion of thermal energy to kinetic energy, to accelerate the metal fuel particles. For an aluminum fuel, about 20% aluminum loading provides maximum specific impulse. A disadvantage of metal fuels such as aluminum is high observable smoke particles (e.g., Al$_2$O$_3$), which leave an easily visible smoke trail.

Binders have been based on both natural and man-made materials. The organic prepolymers have rubbery properties following cure and form a strong binding within the inorganic fuels and chemical oxidizers. The most commonly used liquid polymers cure much like rubber. Prepolymers used as binders in composite propellants are initially liquid, so that the fuel and oxidizer can be blended more easily prior to the start of the polymerization cure. The most common binder used in missile rocket motors is hydroxyl terminated polybutadiene binder (HTPB).

An initial approach that was used to reduce the plume observables was reduced smoke propellant. Reduced smoke motors replace the metal fuel with a polyimide binder fuel, such as HTPB. The performance and insensitive munition capability of reduced smoke motors are somewhat lower than that of high smoke motors. Reduced smoke propellants can still have visual observables from a hydrogen chloride contrail, particularly at low atmospheric temperature, although it is much less observable than that of high smoke propellant.

A third category of propellant is minimum smoke propellant. Minimum smoke propellants eliminate the HCl contrail by eliminating ammonium perchlorate as an oxidizer, resulting in lower visual observables. However, the performance and safety of the current minimum smoke propellants are not as good as that of high smoke propellants. Current minimum smoke propellants are either composite propellants with a nitramine oxidizer or cross-linked double base (XLDB) propellants.

In the older minimum smoke double-base propellants, the propellant consists generally of cotton (cellulose) combined with nitric acid to form nitrocellulose (guncotton), which in turn is combined with nitroglycerin, another fuel-oxidizer. In double-base propellant, the nitrocellulose serves as the binder, and the nitroglycerin causes it to solidify.

A minimum smoke propellant based on nitramine oxidizer contains the radical group $NHNO_2$. Examples of the nitramine oxidizer of current minimum smoke composite propellants are HMX (Her Majesty's Explosive, cyclotetramethylene tetranitramine $C_4H_8N_8O_8$) and RDX (Royal Demolition Explosive, cyclotrimethylene trinitramine $C_3H_6N_6O_6$). An example of a relatively new minimum smoke propellant is the US Navy China Lake CL-20 propellant. CL-20 is a cyclic polynitramine, with a unique caged structure that provides higher crystal density, higher heat of formation, and higher oxidizer-to-fuel ratio. CL-20 propellant has 10-to-20% higher performance than HMX and RDX. CL-20 also has reduced shock sensitivity (Class 1.3 versus 1.1) and milder cook-off reaction than either HMX or RDX. A disadvantage of CL-20 propellant is high cost. The relatively high performance of CL-20 is primarily from its high flame temperature. As a first order estimate, to illustrate the benefit of high flame temperature, specific impulse can be calculated from the equation

$$I_{SP} \approx 25(T_f/MW)^{1/2}$$

In the above equation T_f is the flame temperature in Kelvin and MW is the molecular weight.

Another example of a relatively new minimum smoke propellant developed by Russia is ammonium dinitramine (ADN) $H_4N_4O_4$. ADN performance is superior to HMX and RDX. Its specific impulse is somewhat less than that of CL-20. ADN is lower density and has a lower flame temperature than CL-20.

Most short range missiles use minimum smoke propellant, to minimize launch detection by the threat. Most long range missiles use high smoke propellant, because it provides enhanced range and launch detection by the threat is of less concern. Most US Army and Air Force missiles use minimum smoke propellant, because of a concern for launch platform survivability. Most US Navy sea-launched missiles use high smoke propellant, because most threats to ships/submarines are at long range/over the horizon.

3.23 Solid Propellant Aging

Environmental factors that shorten the lifetime of solid propellant include elevated temperature, low temperature, temperature cycling, shock/vibration, and low/high humidity. The projected environmental conditions of a missile should be considered early, during conceptual design and system engineering. It is important to keep track of changing environmental conditions over the lifetime of the missile. For example, the Hellfire missile was originally designed for the Apache helicopter. Later it was qualified for the Tornado aircraft and the Predator UCAV. The differences in the lowest and maximum temperatures and the altitude/temperature cycling required an assessment of its suitability for the new launch platforms. Also, a missile that is later exported to a different region of the world with hotter or colder temperature and dryer/more humid environments should be reevaluated.

Elevated temperature is usually the greatest concern in solid propellant aging. Elevated temperature accelerates chemical reactions and migrations within the propellant. Because propellant formulations vary widely it is difficult to develop a generalized conceptual design prediction of the degradation in propellant lifetime from aging at elevated temperature. Elevated temperature aging causes many problems in the propellant characteristics, any one which could be the dominant limiter in the propellant lifetime. Problems from the chemical reactions and migrations include strain, loss of moisture, and oxidation. During missile development, accelerated aging tests are conducted and the results are extrapolated to the projected lifetime of the propellant in its anticipated temperature environment. As an example, the contractor may be required to provide a 20 year warranty for the missile, but the missile development program may be only 4 years. Extrapolation of the reduction in propellant lifetime from a nominal reference lifetime (e.g., 16 years @ 25°C) to a predicted lifetime from a 1 year accelerated aging at elevated temperature is risky. Test measurements following accelerated aging tests include measurement of the loss in weight (from moisture loss), chemistry composition, oxidation, strain, and brittleness. Motor firings are conducted to measure the thrust-time history performance of aged rocket motors. Many modern missiles are developed as wooden rounds that are housed in a sealed inert-gas container and stored in a temperature controlled environment, to minimize the effects of aging.

A first-order prediction of typical solid propellant lifetime at elevated temperature and the impact of accelerated aging is shown in Fig. 3.61. An equation for the missile lifetime L at an aging temperature T compared to its nominal lifetime at a nominal temperature of 25°C is

$$L = L_{T=25°C}\left(\frac{1}{2}\right)^{(T-25)/10}$$

As an example, let us assume that the rocket baseline propellant has a nominal lifetime of 16 years at a nominal temperature of 25°C ($L_{T=25°C} = 16$ yr). The projected lifetime if the missile environment is at an average temperature $T = 35°C$ is $L = 16(1/2)^{(35-25)/10} = 8$ years. Note that a 10°C increase in the average temperature environment reduced the lifetime of the propellant by 50%.

As an another example, assume that during the missile program development that only one year is available to conduct accelerated aging tests to

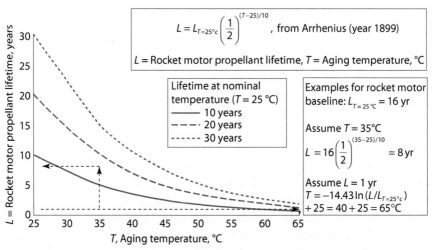

Note: Elevated temperature tests, with accelerated aging, are used to verify rocket motor propellant lifetime. Arrhenius equation also applicable to other energetic subsystems (e.g., Warhead, battery, squib).

Fig. 3.61 Solid propellant rocket motor lifetime is reduced by high temperature aging.

Type of storage	Typical min temp	Typical max temp	Typical max shock/vibration @ max/min temp
Depot (e.g., bunker) 	−9°F	120°F	100 g @ 10 ms (0.5 ft drop)
Transportation 	−20°F	130°F	100 g @ 10 ms (0.5 ft drop) 7g @ 300 Hz, 10 g @ 1000 Hz)
Field 	−60°F	160°F	100 g @ 10 ms (0.5 ft drop) 7g @ 300 Hz, 10 g @ 1000 Hz)

* Propellent failure from shock/vibration @ T_{min}
  * Grain cracking (from Δ thermal expansion: grain/case, fuel/oxidizer/binder; brittle propellant)
  * Insulation liner de-bond (from Δ thermal expansion of grain/case)
  * Voids (from Δ thermal expansion of fuel/oxidizer/binder)
* Propellant failure from shock/vibration @ T_{max}
  * Grain cracking (from low modulus of elasticity, propellant decomposition gas bubbles)
  * Does not satisfy IM requirements

Note:
* Propellant failure also caused by cycling at min/max temperature.
* Propellant failure also caused by low/high humidity.

Fig. 3.62 Solid propellant rocket motor lifetime may be driven by shock in a low temperature environment.

confirm a 16 warranty requirement. The required aging temperature for the accelerated aging test is

$$T = -14.43 \ln (L/L_{T=25°C}) + 25$$
$$= -14.43 \ln (1/16) + 25 = 40 + 25 = 65°C$$

The large extrapolation of the results from this highly elevated aging test has large uncertainty in satisfying the 16 year warranty. However, some data is better than none. Follow-on tests with longer duration aging at a lower elevated temperature would provide higher confidence in the results. This is an example of risk to the contractor in accepting a firm fixed price missile development program if the program requires a new rocket motor.

Figure 3.62 illustrates typical missile shock and vibration environmental requirements and the effect of shock/vibration on solid propellant failure. Typical shock and vibration loads are shown for depot storage, transportation, and field carriage on the launch platform. Depot storage may be in a bunker without heating or air-conditioning. A typical maximum/minimum temperature environment specification for depot storage is −9°F to 120°F. Vibration is usually not a factor in depot storage. A typical shock requirement is 100 g @ 10 ms, representing dropping the missile about 0.5 ft onto a concrete floor. Transportation may be aircraft, train, or truck. The transportation environmental specification for the missile is usually more severe than the storage environment. A typical temperature specification is $-20°F$ to $130°F$. Typical specifications for shock and vibration are 100 g @ 10 ms for shock and 7 g @ 300 Hz/10 g @ 100 Hz for vibration. Carriage of the missile on the launch platform is usually the most extreme environment. Typical temperature requirements are $-60°F$ to $160°F$. Launch platform shock and vibrations specifications are typically comparable to the transportation specification (100 g @ 10 ms for shock and 7 g @ 300 Hz/10 g @ 100 Hz for vibration), although some launch platform, such as tracked vehicles, may have a harsher environment.

Low temperature may lead to propellant failure, which may be aggravated by shock and vibration. Propellant failure includes grain cracking, insulation liner de-bond, and voids. Grain cracking is caused by thermal stress from the difference in the thermal expansion of the propellant grain to the motor case; difference in thermal expansion of the propellant, oxidizer, and binder; and the loss of elasticity of the brittle propellant. Insulation liner de-bond is caused by the difference in thermal expansion of the propellant grain and the motor case. Voids are caused by difference in thermal expansion of the fuel, oxidizer, and binder.

High temperature failure includes grain cracking and the failure to qualify as an insensitive munition. Grain cracking contributors include low modulus of elasticity and propellant decomposition at high temperature. It may not be possible to satisfy insensitive munition requirements in a high temperature environment.

Propellant failure is more likely to occur if there are by repeated cycles at minimum and maximum temperature. Each temperature cycle adds to the strain on the propellant. The temperature cycles from the low-to-high-to-low altitude cycles of aircraft external carriage are of particular concern.

Finally, propellant subjected to very low humidity loses its moisture. Propellant subjected to very high humidity causes propellant specie migration and softening.

3.24 Rocket Motor Case Material Alternatives

Primary design considerations in selecting the materials for the missile rocket motor case are shown in Fig. 3.63. These are high maximum temperature, high volumetric efficiency, light weight, insensitive munition (IM) safety, ease of attachment (e.g., bolt, weld, bond) of the motor case to the missile airframe, resistance to environment corrosion (e.g., sea salt corrosion in a naval environment), resistance to fatigue, and low cost. Other considerations include ease of manufacturing, handling, and storage.

The most common types of motor cases are conventional quench and temper steel (hardened by heating then plunging into liquid to cool

Type	Temperature	Volumetric efficiency	Weight	IM	Attachment to missile airframe	Corrosion	Fatigue	Cost
◆ Steel	●	●	○ ◒	○	●	○	◒	◒ ●
◆ Aluminum	—	— ○	○ ◒	○	◒	◒	—	◒ ●
◆ Strip steel/ epoxy laminate	○	●	○ ◒	●	—	○	◒	◒
◆ Graphite composite	○	○	●	●	—	●	●	—
◆ Titanium	◒	◒	◒	○	—	●	◒	—

● Superior ◒ Good ○ Average — Poor

Fig. 3.63 Steel and aluminum motor cases are low cost but a composite motor case is light weight.

suddenly) and nickel precipitation-hardening alloy steel. Other types include aluminum alloys, strip metal/epoxy laminate (e.g., steel/epoxy laminate), titanium alloys, and composite. If a combination of high performance and low cost is required, steel is often the best material. The cost of a steel motor case is a function of its strength/hardness and the amount of machining that is required. Steel is also relatively easy to weld. Although steel has high strength, it is susceptible to localized bucking and may require a thicker/heavier wall to avoid localized buckling.

If the rocket motor has relatively low heating (e.g., a small rocket motor usually has low heating), the manufacturing process requires significant machining, or a long fatigue lifetime is not required, aluminum may be the best material. Because the maximum allowable temperature of aluminum is lower than steel, aluminum requires more insulation.

A strip metal/epoxy laminate may be the best choice of balancing performance and cost. Another good feature of a strip metal/laminate motor case is it is often easier to qualify as an insensitive munition. Strip metal/ epoxy laminate has a mild cook-off reaction, venting gas through the laminate.

Composite and titanium motor cases have had relatively little application to date, because of their relatively high cost. However, the cost of a composite motor case is expected to decrease in the future, resulting in increased application of composite motor cases. To date the composite cases have been based in organic composites such as graphite polyimide. Current applications of composite cases include LOSAT, PAC-3, Arrow II, and the SM-3 third stage rocket motor. Future composite cases may also be based on higher temperature metal matrix composites such as carbon-silica carbide.

The fifth category material, titanium, is rarely used in missile rocket motor cases because of its higher cost. The molten titanium during manufacturing requires an expensive vacuum process to avoid oxidation.

For a volume-limited missile, such as a missile packaged inside a Vertical Launch System (VLS) canister which has a diameter limit, the volumetric efficiency of the motor case material may be as important as the weight efficiency. As an example, a graphite composite motor case may have the lightest weight, but the case may have a greater thickness and may also require greater thickness for the insulation, which may limit the available volume for propellant, possibly resulting in a reduction in flight range.

Internal insulation protects the motor case from the high flame temperature (e.g., 5200°F) of combustion. For a typical, case-bonded propellant, the internal insulator also provides the bonding of the propellant to the motor case, and must have sufficient strength to prevent the propellant from de-bonding. Most of the internal motor case insulators are rubber-based materials such as hydroxyl terminated polybutadiene (HTPB) or ethylene propylene dimethyl monomer (EPDM). Reinforcing erosion resistant fibers such as silica are usually added. Upon exposure to the combustion flame temperature, the insulator chars. A design consideration is the required insulation thickness to compensate for the recession and the change in thermal conductivity as a result of char. Another design consideration is the potential de-bonding from the motor case because of outgassing and stress/strain.

A case-bonded propellant has higher volumetric efficiency than a cartridge-loaded propellant and is the preferred approach for most missiles. However, a case-bonded propellant does require a greater concern for stress/strain. It is more susceptible to failure from the cumulative applications of the external loads and thermal stress. Events such as curing, transportation, handling, storage, carriage, launch, and maneuvering provide cumulative stress/strain (creep) on the bonding/propellant. A high fineness case-bonded propellant is particularly susceptible to failure. It is difficult to predict the failure conditions for a case-bonded propellant. Stress-strain analysis of the bonding and propellant requires consideration of not only the elastic characteristics but also the viscous characteristics, which are a function of the rate at which loads are applied.

3.25   Rocket Nozzle Material Alternatives

The rocket nozzle is an attachment at the end of the motor case. It is shaped to control the flow of gas and to convert the chemical energy released from combustion into kinetic energy, which provides higher specific impulse. Figure 3.64 shows material alternatives for missile rocket nozzle components (i.e., housing, dome closeout, blast tube, throat, and exit cone).

The housing is the overall structure of the nozzle. It may be made of high temperature steel for a high heating motor. A high heating motor has either a high chamber pressure and/or a long duration motor burn. A high heating nozzle is relatively high cost. Conversely, a low heating motor has a relatively low chamber pressure or a short duration burn. A low heating nozzle can use lower temperature materials such as cellulose/phenolic or aluminum alloy. Because it is subjected to the high velocity and high temperature erosive gas, the inside of the nozzle housing must usually be insulated to maintain structural integrity.

The dome closeout is a convergent section of the nozzle that is downstream of the motor case and upstream of the nozzle throat. In the dome closeout the flow area is reduced, and the speed of the subsonic exhaust gas is increased as it is channeled to the throat. For a high heating motor with a high chamber pressure and/or long burn duration, an insulation insert is usually required in the dome closeout structure housing. The

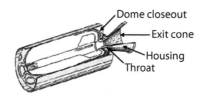

Rocket nozzle element	High heating (high chamber pressure or long burn) ⇒ high cost/heavy nozzle	Low heating (low chamber pressure or short burn) ⇒ low cost/light weight nozzle
• Housing material alternatives	• Steel	• Cellulose/phenolic • Aluminum
• Throat material alternatives	• Tungsten insert • Rhenium insert • Molybdenum insert	• Cellulose/phenolic insert • Silica/phenolic insert • Graphite insert • Carbon–carbon insert
• Exit cone, dome closeout, and blast tube material alternatives	• Silica/phenolic insert • Graphite/phenolic insert • Silicone elastomer insert	• No insert • Glass/phenolic insert

Fig. 3.64 Heat transfer drives rocket nozzle materials, weight, and cost.

candidate dome closeout insulation materials include silica/phenolic, graphite/phenolic, and silicone elastomer. For a relatively low heating motor, low-cost glass/phenolic is a candidate insulation material for the dome closeout. For a very low heating motor, it may not be necessary to have an insulation insert in the housing of the dome closeout.

A blast tube may be necessary to package subsystems, such as flight control actuators, around the nozzle. The blast tube is located between the dome close-out and the nozzle throat. Ideally, the blast tube should have a small diameter, to allow maximum packaging volume for the surrounding subsystems. However, as the blast tube diameter approaches the throat diameter, the local gas Mach number approaches Mach 1. Because of severe erosion from the hot gas at Mach 1, the blast tube diameter is usually significantly larger than the throat diameter, such that the local Mach number is less than about Mach 0.8. The material options for the above dome closeout materials are also applicable to the blast tube.

The nozzle throat is the smallest internal diameter of the nozzle assembly. At the nozzle throat the exhaust gas passes through the minimum flow area and reaches the speed of sound. Because of high heat transfer at the throat, it may be necessary to have a refractory metal insert in the throat of a high performance motor, to prevent erosion. Examples of low eroding refractory materials are tungsten, rhenium (used in SM-3 third stage rocket motor and the Harpoon booster), and molybdenum. The refractory materials are expensive. For a low heating motor, a lighter weight insert such as cellulose/phenolic, silica/phenolic, graphite, or carbon/carbon may be used. Most materials for a low heating throat are relatively inexpensive. An exception is carbon-carbon. Carbon-carbon is expensive, due to the long duration production process.

Downstream of the throat the gases expand in the exit cone to supersonic speed. The material selection for the exit cone is driven by heating and cost considerations (see figure). Materials used in the dome close-out and the blast tube are candidate materials. The exit cone may be contoured or conical. A contoured nozzle provides higher specific impulse, whereas a conical nozzle is shorter length, lighter weight, and lower cost. Most missiles use conical nozzles. Finally, the exit plane is at the end of the exit cone, where the static pressure of the gas is ideally nearly equal to the atmospheric pressure. However, because the nozzle exit diameter is usually constrained to be less than the missile diameter and the nozzle length is often constrained for a typical length-limited missile, the rocket exhaust at the nozzle exit is usually under-expanded, with an exhaust gas static pressure greater than the local atmospheric pressure. This results in a lower specific impulse compared to a fully expanded gas.

3.26 Ducted Rocket Design Considerations

The bottom portion of Fig. 3.65 compares the components of a ducted rocket propulsion system with the components of liquid fuel and solid fuel ramjet propulsion systems. Ducted rockets combine much of the higher specific impulse of a ramjet with some of the simplicity, acceleration capability, and logistics benefits of a solid propellant rocket. The figure shows a schematic with the elements of the ducted rocket propulsion system: a rocket propellant booster (shown in the top aft section of the schematic), a combustion chamber (shown in the bottom aft section of the schematic), a gas generator, and an inlet(s). Following boost, the gas generator is ignited, injecting fuel-rich gas into the combustion chamber, where it mixes with the inlet air, providing secondary combustion. Because the oxygen for the secondary combustion is provided by the atmosphere, ducted rocket propulsion has higher specific impulse than solid propellant rocket propulsion.

The oxidizer weight of a typical ducted rocket propellant is typically about 10% of the weight of oxidizer that would be required for stoichiometric combustion. Inlet air completes the combustion. If there is a relatively small amount of excess fuel from the gas generator (e.g., less than about 30% of the propellant weight), the ducted rocket behaves more like a rocket, with a higher burn rate and a higher combustion temperature but a lower specific impulse. Conversely, if the gas generator discharges a relatively large amount of excess fuel (e.g., greater than about 70% of the propellant weight), the ducted rocket behaves more like a ramjet, with a higher specific impulse and a lower burn rate/temperature. The fuel fraction of a ducted rocket propellant varies from about 30 to 80% of the propellant weight. Fuel fractions greater than 80% are not practical for ducted

- Gas generator propellant has small amount of oxidizer (~10% stoichiometric)
- Excess fuel from gas generator
    - <~30% propellant weight $\Rightarrow$ behaves more like a rocket (higher burn rate, higher burn temperature, lower I_{SP})
    - >~70% propellant weight $\Rightarrow$ behaves more like a Ramjet (higher I_{SP}, lower burn rate, lower burn temperature)

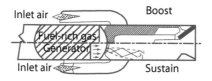

Fig. 3.65 Ducted rocket design considerations/tradeoffs.

rocket missile propulsion, because the reduced combustion temperature for a high fuel fraction severely reduces the fuel flow rate, resulting in an unacceptably low thrust.

A tradeoff of ducted rocket propellant is metal fuel versus carbon fuel. Metal fuels include boron, aluminum, and magnesium. Metal fuels have an advantage of higher specific impulse. Also, the higher density of metal fuels is beneficial for a volume-limited missile. Disadvantages of metal fuels include deposits and higher observables. A metal fuel may have deposits downstream of the gas generator. This is a particular problem for a high fuel fraction ducted rocket, because of the reduced combustion temperature. A particular problem for boron fuel is potentially inefficient combustion because of its high melting (3950°F) and boiling (6616°F) temperatures may be greater than the combustion temperature, resulting in reduced combustion efficiency. Approaches to alleviate this problem include coating the boron particles with an oxidizer such as ammonium perchlorate and injection transverse to the combustor (at the expense of axial thrust from the gas generator).

Carbon based fuels include graphite carbon and hydrocarbon hydroxy terminated polybudiene binder (HTPB). A carbon-based fuel has an advantage of lower observables and a higher reliability, from reduced deposits. A disadvantage of carbon fuel is lower maximum specific impulse compared to a metal fuel (e.g., 800 versus 1000 s).

Another consideration is the choice of oxidizer. The choice of oxidizer is a primary tradeoff of performance versus reduced observables. Ammonium perchlorate (AP) has advantages of higher burn rate and lower hazards. However AP provides an HCl contrail, particularly in a high altitude environment (low temperature). Minimum smoke oxidizers, such as HMX and RDX have reduced observables but have disadvantages of lower performance and are more hazardous.

A typical propellant mix for a boron fuel is 50% boron, 10% HTPB (binder/fuel), and 40% ammonium perchlorate. A typical propellant mix of a hydrocarbon fuel is 65% HTPB and 35% ammonium perchlorate.

The most popular approach for thrust magnitude control of a ducted rocket is to partially block the gas generator throat with a pintle or valve. Partially blocking the gas generator throat reduces the throat area, resulting in an increase in the chamber pressure. The increased chamber pressure increases the gas flow rate, which provides increased thrust. The thrust variation using this approach is about 10:1. A concern is deposits on the pintle or valve that may clog the gas generator throat. Another approach incorporates retractable wires in the gas generator propellant grain. The burn area of the gas generator propellant grain is a function of the retraction speed of the wires. A disadvantage of this approach is the maximum variation in thrust is only about 4:1.

3.27 Summary

Chapter 3 provided conceptual design methods, discussed design trades and system engineering considerations, and identified high payoff technologies for missile propulsion.

Conceptual design methods were provided for predicting the thrust and specific impulse of turbojet, ramjet, and rocket propulsion.

Design trades and system engineering considerations that were addressed for turbine-based propulsion include the turbine material, compressor pressure ratio, propulsion cycle, and inlet/launch platform integration. Design trades and system engineering considerations for ramjets include combustor material alternatives, ramjet engine/booster integration alternatives, ramjet inlet options, and ramjet fuel alternatives. Design trades and system engineering considerations for rockets include rocket propellant burn area required to provide the desired chamber pressure, nozzle throat area required to provide the desired mass flow rate, nozzle expansion ratio required for maximum specific impulse and maximum thrust, rocket motor grain alternatives, thrust magnitude control alternatives, solid propellant alternatives, aging, storage, motor case material alternatives, and nozzle material alternatives.

New propulsion technologies were identified that have high payoff for missiles. New technologies for turbojets include high temperature turbine materials and a high stage pressure axial compressor (e.g., using rotors with local supersonic un-separated flow). High payoff technologies for ramjets include high temperature insulation for the combustor and high density fuel. High payoff technologies for inlets include optimum oblique shock airframe compression, mixed compression inlet, and a low drag inlet. Finally, high payoff technologies for solid propellant rockets include thrust magnitude control, high burn exponent propellant, low observable propellant, and a composite light weight motor case.

3.28 Problem Review

1. An advantage of a turbojet compared to a ramjet is thrust at s_____ Mach number.
2. The thrust of a turbojet is often limited by the maximum allowable temperature of the t_____.
3. The specific impulse of a ramjet is often limited by the maximum allowable temperature of the combustor i_____.
4. Ducted rockets are based on a fuel-rich g__ g_____.
5. A safety advantage of solid propellant rocket propulsion over liquid propulsion is less t_____.

6. A rocket boost to a supersonic take-over Mach number is required by ramjets and s_____.

7. Parameters that enable the long range of subsonic cruise turbojet missiles are high lift, low drag, available fuel volume, and high s_____ i_____.

8. High thrust and high acceleration are achievable with s____ p_____ r_____ propulsion.

9. In a turbojet the power to drive the compressor is provided by the t_____.

10. The compressor exit temperature is a function of the flight Mach number and the compressor p_____ r____.

11. Compressor exit temperature, fuel heating value, and fuel-to-air ratio determine the turbojet t_____ temperature.

12. Three types of turbine based propulsion are turbojet, turbo ramjet, and a__ t____ r_____.

13. A turbojet axial compressor has advantages of smaller diameter and compatibility with multiple stages, while a centrifugal compressor has advantages of lower c___ and higher single stage p_____.

14. A high compressor pressure ratio requires a large number of axial s_____.

15. A long range subsonic turbojet usually has higher compressor pressure ratio, with higher s_____ i_____.

16. A scoop inlet has higher efficiency while a flush inlet has lower r____ c____ s_____.

17. Mach number, fuel heating value, and fuel-to-air ratio determine the ramjet c_____ temperature.

18. An example of a ramjet with low drag and light weight is an i_____ r_____ ramjet.

19. Russia, France, China, United Kingdom, Taiwan, and India are the only countries with currently operational r_____ missiles.

20. 100% inlet capture efficiency for a supersonic missile occurs when the forebody shock waves intercept the i____ l__.

21. Excess air that does not flow into the inlet is called s_____ air.

22. Starting a ramjet inlet at lower supersonic Mach number requires a larger area of the inlet t_____.

23. Optimum pressure recovery across shock waves is achieved when the total pressure loss across each shock wave is e____.

24. The specific impulse and thrust of a ramjet are a function of the efficiency of the combustor, nozzle, and i____.

25. A high density fuel has high payoff for a typical, v_____ limited missile.

26. The specific impulse of a ducted rocket with large excess fuel from the gas generator can approach that of a r_____.

27. A high speed rocket requires a large weight fraction of p_____.

28. At the rocket nozzle throat, the flow area is minimum, sonic, and ch_____ .

29. For an optimum nozzle expansion the nozzle exit pressure is equal to the at_____ pressure.

30. High thrust and high chamber pressure are achievable through a large propellant b___ area.

31. Three approaches to rocket thrust magnitude control are pulse motor, pintle motor, and g__ motor.

32. A high burn exponent propellant allows a large change in thrust with only a small change in chamber p_____.

33. Three tradeoffs in selecting a solid propellant are safety, observables, and s_____ i_____.

34. Increasing the rocket motor propellant environmental temperature by 10°C reduces the rocket motor lifetime by _____%.

35. A low cost motor case is usually based on steel or aluminum material while a light weight motor case is usually based on graphite c_____ material.

36. Rockets with high chamber pressure or long burn time may require a t_____ throat insert.

Chapter 4

Weight Considerations in the Missile Design and System Engineering Process

- How to Size Subsystems to Meet Flight Performance
- Structural Design
- Manufacturing Processes
- Airframe Materials
- Aerodynamic Heating Prediction and Insulation Trades
- Power Supply and Actuator Sizing

4.1 Introduction

Conceptual design methods, technologies, and system engineering considerations for missile weight are addressed in this chapter. Initial topics address the benefits of designing a light weight missile, subsystem weight sensitivity to flight performance, missile system and subsystem weight prediction based on typical densities, methodology for center-of-gravity and moment-of-inertia prediction, structure weight fraction, and guidelines for factors of safety. Topics in missile airframe structure design emphasize low cost, light weight, and high temperature/ short duration structure. Also addressed are missile airframe manufacturing processes/technology and airframe material alternatives. Aerodynamic heating topics include aerodynamic heating prediction, thermal stress concerns and areas of localized aerodynamic heating, airframe structure/ insulation trades and insulation material alternatives. Missile subsystem weight topics include seeker dome material trades and dome weight,

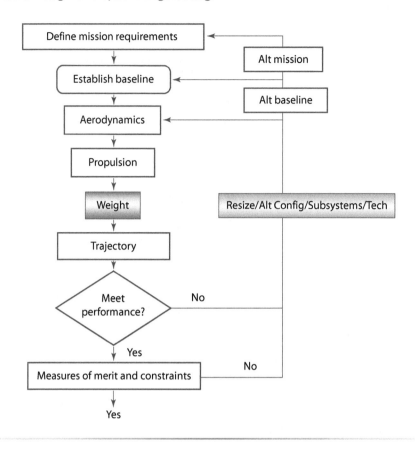

Fig. 4.1 Conceptual design and system engineering require creative, rapid, and iterative evaluations.

power supply alternatives and weight, and flight control actuation system alternatives and weight.

Figure 4.1 shows that the next step in the missile conceptual design and system engineering process following propulsion system definition is estimating and optimizing the missile weight. Weight estimation and optimization is an iterative process that includes alternative materials and subsystems, subsystem packaging, weight and balance bookkeeping, and structure weight prediction/optimization.

4.2 Benefits of a Light Weight Missile

Although missiles are more volume driven than weight driven, the benefits of light weight missiles are numerous. As illustrated in Fig. 4.2, they include lower production cost, lower logistics cost, smaller size, higher firepower for a weight/volume limited launch platform, reduced observables, better mission flexibility from the capability of carriage on multiple launch platforms, e.g., bombers, fighter aircraft, helicopters, UCAVs, ships, submarines, ground vehicles, and synergy with expeditionary warfare. The rapid force deployment requirement of expeditionary warfare requires light weight missiles.

4.3 Subsystem Weight Sensitivity to Flight Performance

As illustrated in Fig. 4.3, the required weights of most missile subsystems are sensitive to changes in flight performance requirements such as range, speed, and maneuverability. Missile subsystem weights that are usually highly impacted by changes in flight performance are the propulsion system, structure, and wing weight. Stabilizers, flight control, power supply, and insulation weights are usually moderately sensitive to changes in flight performance. Warhead required weight is usually relatively insensitive to flight performance for a precision strike missile but usually has moderate sensitivity for an air intercept missile. Finally subsystem weights that are usually relativity insensitive to changes in flight performance are the seeker dome, seeker, guidance and control, fuzing, and data link. In a

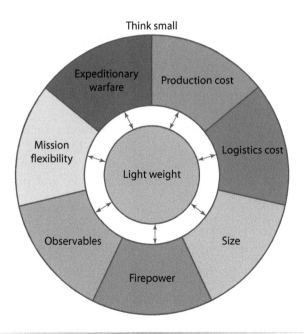

Fig. 4.2   A light weight missile has high payoff.

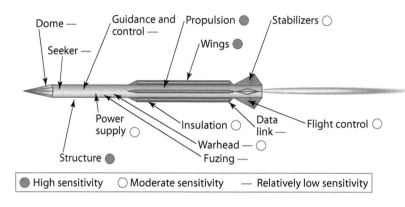

Fig. 4.3   Weights of missile subsystems are often sensitive to flight performance requirements (e.g., range, speed, maneuverability).

missile conceptual design study, the weights of the missile dome, seeker, guidance and control, fuzing, and data link are often considered to be a constant weight payload, to expedite the initial missile sizing process.

4.4 Missile Weight Prediction

A first-order approach to missile weight prediction can be based on the burnout incremental velocity equation from the previous chapter

$$V \approx -g I_{\mathrm{SP}} \ln(1 - W_P/W_L)$$

An assumption in the above equation is negligible drag, which provides an optimistic result.

The parameters that define the missile burnout velocity are the propellant weight W_P, the launch weight W_L, and the specific impulse I_{SP}. Integrating the velocity equation gives a first-order estimate of the respective ballistic flight range, maximum altitude, and maximum time of flight as

$$R \approx V^2 \sin(2\theta_i)/g$$
$$h_{\max} = V^2 \sin^2 \theta_i /(2g)$$
$$t_{\max} = 2V \sin\theta_i /g$$

Assuming an optimum launch angle $\theta_i = 45$ deg gives a first-order (optimistic) estimate of the maximum ballistic flight range

$$R \approx V^2/g$$

Note the same primary parameters of propellant weight W_P, launch weight W_L, and specific impulse I_{SP} also define the missile ballistic flight range. The above equations are based on the assumptions of negligible drag and a flat, non-rotating earth.

Figure 4.4 is based on the above equations. It shows launch weight versus missile ballistic maximum range, based on typical values of payload weight ($W_{Payload}$ = 5, 50, 500 lb), typical solid propellant specific impulse (I_{SP} = 250 s), and typical body structure weight-to-launch-weight fraction for a missile (W_{BS}/W_L = 0.2). It is noted that the structure weight fraction for a long range strategic intercontinental ballistic missile (ICBM) is usually much lower (e.g., W_{BS}/W_L = 0.1) and staging is required to achieve the longer required flight range. Payload weight is defined as the portion of the missile weight that is relatively insensitive to changes in flight range. Conceptual design modeling the payload of a ballistic missile typically includes the missile warhead, fuzing, seeker dome, seeker, guidance and control, and data link. Body structure is sensitive to flight range and is assumed to consist of the missile motor case and airframe structure.

As an example, consider a typical ballistic missile with a maximum flight range R_{max} = 50 nm = 303,800 ft, an initial (launch) angle θ_i = 45 deg, and a payload weight $W_{Payload}$ = 200 lb. Assume I_{SP} = 250 s and W_{BS} = 0.2 W_L.

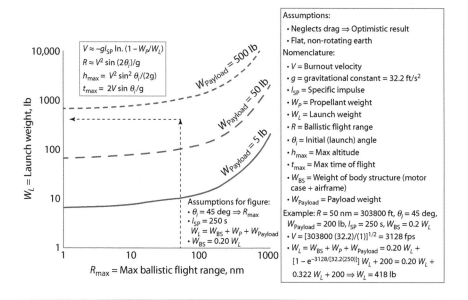

Fig. 4.4 Ballistic missile weight is driven by range, payload weight, propellant weight, and specific impulse.

Compute

$$V = \{Rg/\sin[2(45 \deg)]\}^{1/2} = [303800(32.2)/(1)]^{1/2} = 3128 \text{ fps}$$
$$W_L = W_{BS} + W_P + W_{\text{Payload}}$$

$$= 0.20 W_L + \left[1 - e^{-3128/[32.2(250)]}\right] W_L + 200 = 418 \text{ lb}$$

Similarly, the maximum altitude and time of flight for a 50 nm range ballistic missile with $\theta_i = 45$ deg are respectively

$$h_{\max} = (3128)^2(0.707)^2/[2(32.2)] = 75{,}943 \text{ ft}$$
$$t_{\max} = 2(3128)(0.707)/32.2 = 137 \text{ s}$$

In summary, for a typical ballistic missile using solid propellant rocket propulsion, an ideal (optimistic) launch weight $W_L = 418$ lb is required to achieve a flight range of 50 nm with a 200 lb payload. The above analysis also provides trajectory information for evaluating the missile stability and control.

The maximum ballistic range equation $R \approx V^2/g$ can also be used as a first-order tool to predict the maximum range of other types of missiles. For missiles other than ballistic missiles, the term V in the equation $R \approx V^2/g$ is not the actual burnout velocity, but instead represents the total energy available from the propulsion system. If a missile is dominated by propulsion and inertia forces with relatively low drag, such as a ballistic missile, the results may be sufficiently accurate for early conceptual design. The use of an existing baseline missile with launch weight, range, and payload similar to the conceptual design missile can provide a correction to the prediction. If a missile has good aerodynamic efficiency, such as a cruise missile, the results using the above equations will be highly conservative and corrections using an existing similar type of missile would be required.

Most missiles use single stage solid propellant rocket propulsion. However, multi-mode propulsion may be desirable for considerations such as to reduce launch acoustic noise (e.g., Javelin solid propellant launch motor/flight motor), provide rocket boost to the air-breathing propulsion minimum cruise Mach Number (e.g., Tomahawk booster/turbojet, Meteor booster/ducted rocket), provide high Mach number for terminal flight survivability and lethality (e.g., Sizzler SS-N-27 turbojet/rocket), or provide an endo-atmospheric axial rocket boost prior to separation of an exo-atmospheric divert rocket kill vehicle (e.g., THAAD). As stated previously, two or even three stages are required for a strategic missile to achieve intercontinental range. A solid propellant ICBM, such as Minuteman, requires three stages. A liquid propellant ICBM, such as Titan, may require only two stages because of the higher I_{SP} of liquid propellant.

The average subsystem density of a missile is about 0.05 lbm/in.^{3}. Except for the nose section, most missile bodies can be represented as a cylinder of diameter d and length l. Using the equation for the volume of a cylinder $[V = (\pi/4)d^2l]$, neglecting the geometry difference of the missile nose from that of a cylinder, and neglecting the weight of the surfaces, the missile launch weight can be correlated as the average density times the volume of a cylindrical body,

$$W_L = \rho_M V \approx 0.05(\pi/4)ld^2 \approx 0.04\,ld^2$$

Figure 4.5, which is based on the weight of 48 missiles, shows the correlation of the predicted weight with the actual weight. The scatter in the data includes the effects of differences in the launch environment, flight environment, maneuverability, subsystem density, nose fineness, body cross sectional geometry, boattailing, and the surface planform size/geometry. Note from the figure that the actual weights of the lightest weight missiles (FIM-92, SA-14, Javelin, RBS-70, Starstreak, Mistral) are less than the correlation the correlation equation $W_L \approx 0.04\,ld^2$. This could be explained by the relatively benign launch environment of these tube launched missiles and that the missiles have either small wings or no wings compared to the average missile of the correlation.

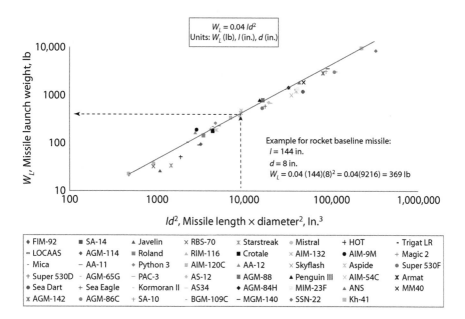

Fig. 4.5 A first-order estimate of missile weight can be derived from body geometry dimensions.

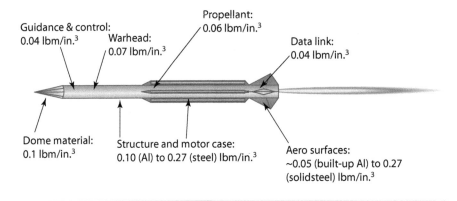

Guidance & control: 0.04 lbm/in.^{3}

Warhead: 0.07 lbm/in.^{3}

Propellant: 0.06 lbm/in.^{3}

Data link: 0.04 lbm/in.^{3}

Dome material: 0.1 lbm/in.^{3}

Structure and motor case: 0.10 (Al) to 0.27 (steel) lbm/in.^{3}

Aero surfaces: ~0.05 (built-up Al) to 0.27 (solid steel) lbm/in.^{3}

Fig. 4.6 Most subsystems for missiles have a weight density of about 0.05 lbm/in.^{3}.

As an example for the rocket baseline missile:

$$l = 144 \text{ in.}, \quad d = 8 \text{ in.}$$

Compute

$$W_L = 0.04(144)(8)^2 = 0.04(9216) = 369 \text{ lb}$$

Note that the actual launch weight $W_L = 500$ lb (from Chapter 7) is 36% higher than the predicted launch weight $W_L = 369$ lb. One explanation for the difference is the relatively large wings and tails of the rocket baseline missile, compared to the average missile of the correlation.

A more detailed correlation of missile weight at the subsystem level is shown in Fig. 4.6. Shown are typical values of subsystems density for rocket-powered missiles. Except for the monolithic (solid) components (dome material, structure, motor case, monolithic aerodynamic surfaces), the subsystems weight density variation is fairly small, from 0.04 to 0.07 lbm/in.^{3}, which supports the aggregate density $\rho_M \approx 0.05$ lbm/in.^{3} correlation of the previous figure. This also implies that the missile center-of-gravity at launch is near the center of the missile. As a follow-on to the previous system correlation equation $W_L \approx 0.04ld^2$, a more accurate estimate of missile weight and balance can be obtained by estimating the individual subsystems weights and locations through a detailed missile weight statement. Chapter 7 has examples of weight statements for the baseline missiles.

4.5 Center-of-Gravity and Moment-of-Inertia Prediction

The methodology for missile weight, balance, and moment-of-inertia prediction is shown in Fig. 4.7 from Ref. 19. Missile weight is the summation of the individual weights of the subsystems, structure, surfaces, and fuel/propellant. Estimates of missile launch weight and burnout weight are required for the analysis of missile flight performance. An estimate of the missile center-of-gravity is also important in determining missile stability and control and tail sizing. The moment-of-inertia is used to estimate the missile time constant and its effect on miss distance.

The longitudinal center-of-gravity is estimated by summing each subsystem weight times its distance from the nose tip, divided by the total weight.

$$x_{CG} = \sum (x_{subsystem1} W_{subsystem1} + x_{subsystem2} W_{subsystem2} + \cdots)/W_{total}$$

Again, x_{CG} should be calculated for launch and burnout conditions.

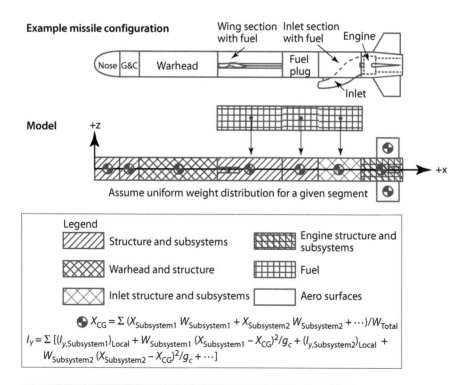

Fig. 4.7 Modeling missile weight, balance, and moment-of-inertia Is based on a build-up of subsystems.

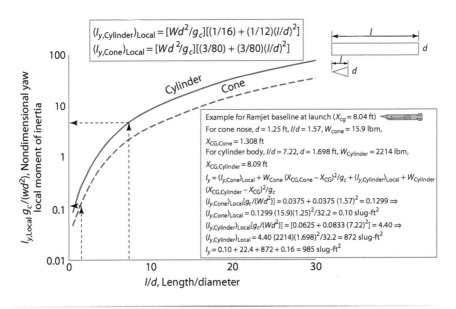

The figure contains:

$$(I_{y,\text{Cylinder}})_{\text{Local}} = [Wd^2/g_c][(1/16) + (1/12)(l/d)^2]$$
$$(I_{y,\text{Cone}})_{\text{Local}} = [Wd^2/g_c][(3/80) + (3/80)(l/d)^2]$$

y-axis: $I_{y,\text{Local}}\,g_c/(wd^2)$, Nondimensional yaw local moment of inertia

Curves labeled: Cylinder, Cone

Example for Ramjet baseline at launch ($X_{cg} = 8.04$ ft)
For cone nose, $d = 1.25$ ft, $l/d = 1.57$, $W_{\text{cone}} = 15.9$ lbm,
$X_{\text{CG,Cone}} = 1.308$ ft
For cylinder body, $l/d = 7.22$, $d = 1.698$ ft, $W_{\text{cylinder}} = 2214$ lbm,
$X_{\text{CG,Cylinder}} = 8.09$ ft
$I_y = (I_{y,\text{Cone}})_{\text{Local}} + W_{\text{Cone}} (X_{\text{CG,Cone}} - X_{\text{CG}})^2/g_c + (I_{y,\text{Cylinder}})_{\text{Local}} + W_{\text{Cylinder}}$
$(X_{\text{CG,Cylinder}} - X_{\text{CG}})^2/g_c$
$(I_{y,\text{Cone}})_{\text{Local}}[g_c/(Wd^2)] = 0.0375 + 0.0375\,(1.57)^2 = 0.1299 \Rightarrow$
$(I_{y,\text{Cone}})_{\text{Local}} = 0.1299\,(15.9)(1.25)^2/32.2 = 0.10$ slug-ft^2
$(I_{y,\text{Cylinder}})_{\text{Local}}[g_c/(Wd^2)] = [0.0625 + 0.0833\,(7.22)^2] = 4.40 \Rightarrow$
$(I_{y,\text{Cylinder}})_{\text{Local}} = 4.40\,(2214)(1.698)^2/32.2 = 872$ slug-ft^2
$I_y = 0.10 + 22.4 + 872 + 0.16 = 985$ slug-ft^2

x-axis: l/d, Length/diameter

Fig. 4.8 A high fineness body has a larger moment-of-inertia.

The moment-of-inertia about the missile center-of-gravity is calculated by summing the local moment-of-inertia of each subsystem about its local center-of-gravity, plus the weight of each subsystem times the square of the distance of the subsystem from the missile center-of-gravity. As an example, the moment-of-inertia about the y-axis is

$$I_y = \sum \left[(I_{y,\text{subsystem1}})_{\text{local}} + W_{\text{subsystem1}} (x_{\text{subsystem1}} - x_{\text{CG}})^2/g_c \right.$$
$$\left. + (I_{y,\text{subsystem2}})_{\text{local}} + W_{\text{subsystem2}} (x_{\text{subsystem2}} - x_{\text{CG}})^2/g_c + \cdots \right]$$

In the above equation the assumed units of weight are lbm and the assumed units of moment-of-inertia are slug-ft^2. The gravitational constant g_c converts lbm to slug ($g_c = 32.2$ lbm/slug). Moment-of-inertia should be calculated for both the launch and burnout conditions.

The yaw and pitch moments-of-inertia are factors in determining the missile maneuverability time constant and miss distance. For a typical missile with symmetric, circular cross section and cruciform surfaces, the yaw and pitch moments of inertia can be assumed to be equal ($I_y = I_z$). Figure 4.8 shows the yaw local moment-of-inertia $(I_y)_{\text{local}}$ variation with body fineness ratio l/d for cylindrical and conical bodies. The equation for the local moment-of-inertia of a cylinder is

$$(I_{y,\text{cylinder}})_{\text{local}} = [Wd^2/g_c][1/16 + (1/12)(l/d)^2]$$

For a cone, the equation for the local moment-of-inertia is

$$(I_{y,\text{cone}})_{\text{local}} = [Wd^2/g_c][3/80 + (3/80)(l/d)^2]$$

Note from the figure that there is a large increase in the body moment-of-inertia with increasing fineness ratio.

As an example, a first-order calculation of the moment-of-inertia of the ramjet baseline missile at launch can be based on the moment-of-inertia of a cone-cylinder configuration.

Based on the data of Chapter 7, $d_{\text{cone}} = 1.25$ ft, $(l/d)_{\text{cone}} = 1.57$, $W_{\text{cone}} = 15.9$ lbm, $x_{\text{cg,cone}} = 1.308$ ft. The yaw local moment-of-inertia of the conical nose about its center-of-gravity is

$$(I_{y,\text{cone}})_{\text{local}} = [15.9(1.25)^2/32.2][0.0375 + 0.0375(1.57)^2] = 0.10 \text{ slug-ft}^2$$

For the cylinder, $(l/d)_{\text{cylinder}} = 7.22$, $d_{\text{cylinder}} = 1.698$ ft, $W_{\text{cylinder}} = 2214$ lbm, $x_{\text{cg,cylinder}} = 8.09$ ft. The yaw local moment of the cylindrical body approximation about its center-of-gravity is

$$(I_{y,\text{cylinder}})_{\text{local}} = [2214(1.698)^2/32.2][0.0625 + 0.0833(7.22)^2]$$
$$= 872 \text{ slug-ft}^2$$

The total yaw moment-of-inertia about the missile center-of-gravity is given by

$$I_y = (I_{y,\text{cone}})_{\text{local}} + W_{\text{cone}}(x_{\text{cg,cone}} - x_{\text{CG}})^2/g_c$$
$$+ (I_{y,\text{cylinder}})_{\text{local}} + W_{\text{cylinder}}(x_{\text{cg,cylinder}} - x_{\text{CG}})^2/g_c$$

Substitution gives the total yaw moment-of-inertia of the ramjet baseline missile at launch as

$$I_y = 0.10 + 22.4 + 872 + 0.16 = 895 \text{ slug-ft}^2$$

Note that for this example, the nose section contributes only 3% to the total moment-of-inertia. For conceptual design, estimating the moment-of-inertia based only on the cylindrical body usually provides sufficient accuracy.

4.6 Missile Structure Factor of Safety

Typical structure factors of safety for missiles are shown in Fig. 4.9. The required factor of safety of a missile tends to be high where there is a danger

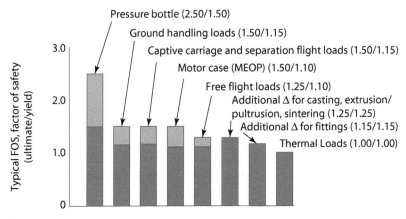

Pressure bottle (2.50/1.50)

Ground handling loads (1.50/1.15)

Captive carriage and separation flight loads (1.50/1.15)

Motor case (MEOP) (1.50/1.10)

Free flight loads (1.25/1.10)

Additional Δ for casting, extrusion/
pultrusion, sintering (1.25/1.25)

Additional Δ for fittings (1.15/1.15)

Thermal Loads (1.00/1.00)

Note:
- MIL STDs include environmental (HDBK-310, NATO STANAG 4370, 810G, 1670A), strength and rigidity (8856), and captive carriage (8591).
- The entire environment (e.g., manufacturing, transportation, storage, ground handling, captive carriage, launch separation, post-launch maneuvering, terminal maneuvering) must be examined for driving conditions in structure design.
- Additional Δ FOS for casting, extrusion/pultrusion, and sintering is expected to be reduced in future as technologies mature.
- Reduction in required factor of safety is expected as analysis accuracy improves will result in reduced missile weight/cost.

Fig. 4.9 Missile structure design factor of safety must be greater for hazardous subsystems and hazardous flight conditions.

of fratricide. As an example, pressure bottle ultimate and yield factors of safety are typically 2.5 and 1.5, respectively. Missile gas bottles are hazardous, with pressures up to 10,000 psi. Because gas bottles require periodic logistics maintenance and inspection by ground personnel, the required factor of safety is high. There has been a trend in recent years to minimize the use of high pressure bottles to improve safety and reduce logistics cost. Cryogenic coolers for seekers and electromechanical actuators for flight control are examples.

Another area where the required factor safety is high is ground handling, such as the handling that is required for cross-country transportation. Typical factors of safety for ground handling loads are about 1.5 for ultimate loads and 1.15 for yield loads.

Other examples of a high factor of safety are launch platform carriage and separation. During carriage or during separation, missile factors of safety are required to be about 1.5 for ultimate and 1.15 for yield.

The motor case is designed not only for conditions of environmental extremes, such as a hot day, but also for consideration of safety. The ultimate and yield factors of safety for the motor maximum effective operating pressure are about 1.5 and 1.1, respectively.

The required factors of safety are lower for flight conditions where the missile is safely away from the launch platform. For example, missile free-flight ultimate and yield loads factors of safety are about 1.25 and 1.1, respectively and the thermal loads, which occur near the end of flight, are just design considerations with a typical factor of safety of 1.0.

A distinguishing characteristic of missiles is a lower factor of safety compared with manned aircraft and unmanned air vehicles (UAVs). Because missiles are a one-way throwaway, the factor of safety can be reduced if there is little danger involved to friendly forces or neutrals. This contributes to lighter weight and lower cost.

An additional factor of safety is required for structural areas where there is a relatively large design uncertainty. Examples include casting, extrusion/pultrusion, sintering, and compression molding, which can have hidden voids. These typically require an additional factor of safety of about 1.25 in addition to the normal design factors of safety. Fittings also typically require an additional factor of safety, of about 1.15, because of the uncertainty in the analysis for attachment integrity.

The applicable military standards in the US that are considered in factors of safety include environmental (HDBK-310, NATO STANAG 4370, MIL-STD-810G, MIL-1670A), strength and rigidity (MIL-STD-8856), and captive carriage (MIL-STD-8591) military standards.

A broad range of environmental and load conditions must be examined to determine the driving conditions for missile structure design. As an example, the conditions to be considered for structure design could include manufacturing, transportation, storage, ground handling, launch platform carriage, launch, post-launch maneuvering, and terminal maneuvering.

A technology opportunity to reduce missile weight is to develop more accurate predictions of the missile environment, loads, and strength. This would allow a reduction in the required factor of safety (which is really a factor of ignorance). Another approach to reduce the required factor of safety is to conduct structural tests to the ultimate load conditions. A third approach is to heavily instrument the missile during development testing, to find the areas that are over-designed and under-designed. Small micro-machined electromechanical sensors (MEMS) that provide unobtrusive data at low cost are a high pay-off technology to reduce missile design uncertainty.

4.7 Missile Airframe Structure Manufacturing Processes

Shown in Fig. 4.10 are examples of manufacturing processes that are often used with missile metal and ceramic structure. The examples are metal casting, forming, sintering, machining, and welding.

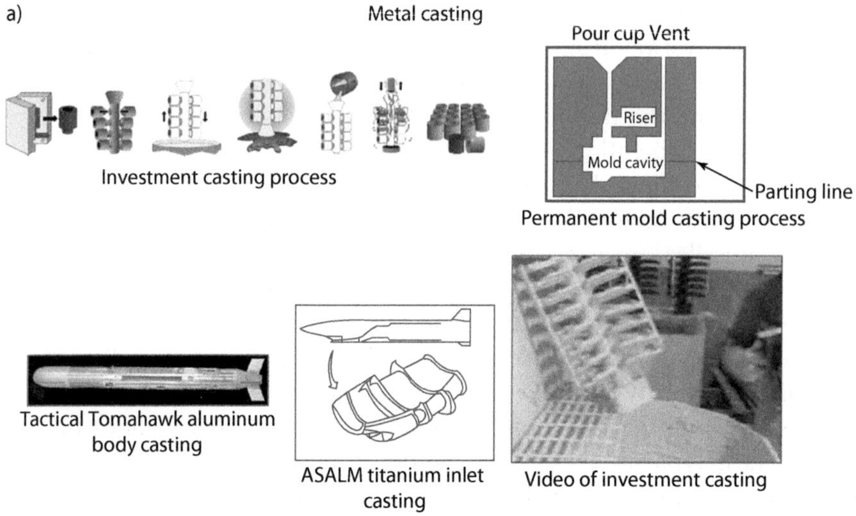

a)   Metal casting

Investment casting process

Permanent mold casting process

Tactical Tomahawk aluminum
body casting

ASALM titanium inlet
casting

Video of investment casting

Fig. 4.10a   Examples of missile metal and ceramic airframe structure
manufacturing processes.

The metal casting processes, shown in Fig. 4.10a, are particularly suited to reducing the parts count and cost of ramjets and turbojets, which typically have complex, non-axisymmetric airframe structure. Options for metal casting include investment casting and permanent mold casting.

The investment casting method that is most used for missile airframe structure is the lost wax process. The top left section of the figure summarizes this process. First, a wax model of the part(s) is produced by injection molding. The wax part(s) is then mounted on a sprue that includes vertical/horizontal passages that are required to mold the hollow portions of the part(s). The sprue is then immersed in a liquid ceramic slurry and covered with extremely fine sand. Several immersions and layers of sand may be required to build a sufficiently strong ceramic shell. After the ceramic shell is dry, the parts(s) is heated in a furnace to fire the ceramic shell and melt the wax. Next, the passages of the ceramic shell are filled with molten metal by gravity pouring. Upon solidification, the parts, gates, sprue, and pouring cup become one solid casting. After the metal solidifies, each part is separated from the sprue. Finally, the ceramic shell is broken off each part either by vibration or by a high pressure water jet. An advantage of investment casting is it provides a precision part with good dimensional tolerances that requires little or no touch-up machining.

Another method of precision casting is using a permanent non-reactive precision mold, such as a ceramic die. The permanent mold casting process is illustrated in the top right section of the figure. A ceramic die is preferred because it minimizes metal oxides at the die interface, which improves dimension tolerances. The process is as follows: First, the die cavity is filled with molten metal by gravity pouring. As the metal cools, the die cavity, riser, and pour cup become one solid casting. When the metal has cooled and solidified, the die is opened at the parting line and the part is removed by techniques such as vibration and water blasting.

Although it is more expensive, a hot isostatic press (HIP) process using an inert gas such as argon also can be used to improve the dimensional tolerances and mechanical properties (e.g., strength) of castings. HIP eliminates internal shrinkage and gas voids. An argon HIP process is often used for titanium casting, because hot titanium is reactive with the oxygen and nitrogen gases of the atmosphere.

Missile airframe castings include aluminum, steel, super alloys, and titanium. A disadvantage of aluminum and steel castings is generally lower strength compared to work hardened alloys. Titanium is an exception; it can be cast to relatively high strength.

Examples of missiles with a large metal casting, to reduce parts count and cost, are the aluminum cast structure of the Tactical Tomahawk missile (bottom left section of figure) and the titanium cast inlet of the ASALM missile (bottom center section of figure). The bottom right section of the figure is a video of the investment casting process.

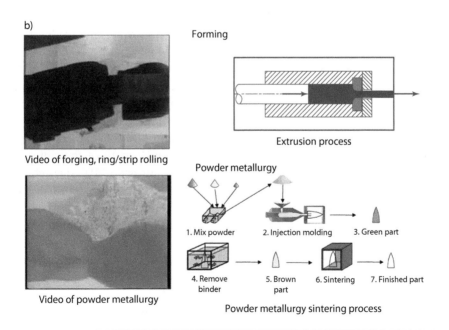

b)

Video of forging, ring/strip rolling

Forming

Extrusion process

Powder metallurgy

1. Mix powder   2. Injection molding   3. Green part

4. Remove binder   5. Brown part   6. Sintering   7. Finished part

Video of powder metallurgy

Powder metallurgy sintering process

Fig. 4.10b Examples of missile metal and ceramic airframe structure manufacturing processes.

Two other manufacturing processes for missile metal and ceramic structure are forming and sintering. Shown in Fig. 4.10b are examples of the forming and the sintering processes.

The forming process applies a high compression load to the metal material to deform it to a desired shape and thickness. The three most popular forming approaches for missile structure are hot forging, hot ring/strip rolling, and hot extrusion. Most formed missile structure is hot formed. Hot forming prevents the work hardening that would result from cold forming. Work hardening increases the difficulty of performing follow-up machining of the part. Also, if work hardening is desirable, other methods such as heat treating are generally more economical and more controllable. Most aluminum alloys are amenable to precipitation hardening and titanium can be hot formed, followed by hardening. The forming process is most applicable to high volume production missiles, because of the large investment in large, heavy duty mechanical equipment such as furnaces, cranes, and fork lifts. The top left video has examples of forging, ring rolling, and strip rolling. Another approach to metal forming, not shown in the video, is the extrusion process. It is illustrated in the top right section of the figure. The extrusion process applies a high longitudinal internal compression load on the material. The material is forced through a die opening to produce a shape of the desired cross sectional geometry.

Powder metallurgy (e.g., sintering) is most applicable to high temperature metal and ceramic materials, such as super alloy turbine blades and silicon nitride radomes. The bottom right section of the figure illustrates the sintering process. Sintering consists of mixing a fine metal powder with a solvent, compacting the mixture in a die to from a green part, and then sintering the part at high temperature to near theoretical, e.g., 90%, density. A disadvantage of sintering is the non-uniform shrinkage during sintering usually requires touch-up machining to satisfy dimensional tolerances. Another disadvantage is the relatively low strength of the sintered material, i.e., 90% theoretical density does not provide 90% theoretical strength. Additional treatment, such as hot isostatic press (HIP) may be required for improved strength. Because of the high cost of sintering equipment, sintering is most application to a high volume production of the missile.

Shown in Fig. 4.10c are examples of missile airframe structure manufacturing processes that are based on machining and welding.

The machining process achieves the desired shape and dimensions of the part by removing the excess material. Machining is an activity that follows another, primary manufacturing process that develops the overall part. Machining provides the final refinements and dimensional tolerances of the part.

c)

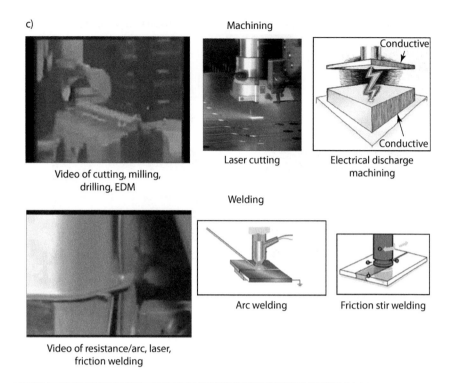

Fig. 4.10c Examples of missile metal and ceramic airframe structure manufacturing processes.

Machining methods that are applicable to missile airframe structure include cutting, drilling and electrical discharge machining (EDM). Approaches to cutting and drilling include conventional mechanical, high pressure water jet, and laser cutting techniques. EDM is most applicable to machining high precision parts that are very hard and electrically conductive, such as super alloys. The top left section of the figure is a video with examples of the cutting, drilling, and EDM processes. The top middle section of the figure is a photograph of a laser cutter. An advantage of laser cutting is the capability for narrow, precision cuts. The top right section illustrates the EDM process. The EDM alternating electrical current produces high frequency ($\sim$100,000 Hz) sparks that selectively removes material from the part.

The welding process joins solid materials by providing sufficient heat to soften or melt the materials at the joint. After cooling, a good weld has good strength. In the bottom left section is a video with examples of welding (electrical resistance/arc, laser, friction stir welding). The bottom middle section of the figure illustrates the arc welding process. Heat from the arc softens and melts the materials at their joint. The bottom right section

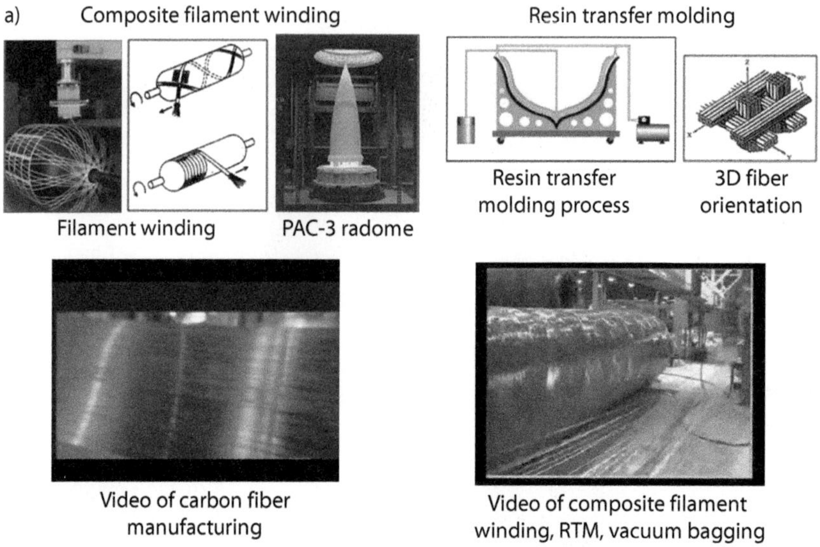

a)   Composite filament winding   Resin transfer molding

Filament winding   PAC-3 radome

Resin transfer   3D fiber
molding process   orientation

Video of carbon fiber   Video of composite filament
manufacturing   winding, RTM, vacuum bagging

Fig. 4.11a Examples of missile graphite composite airframe structure manufacturing processes.

illustrates the friction stir welding process. A cylindrical tool rotating at high speed is slowly plunged into the joint line between the two pieces, which are butted together. Friction heat causes the pieces to soften without reaching their melting point. The plasticised material is transferred from the leading edge to the trailing edge of the tool probe, leaving a solid phase bond between the two pieces. An advantage of friction stir welding is better quality control than arc welding, because there are fewer process variables.

Figure 4.11 provides examples of missile graphite composite structure manufacturing processes. The examples are filament winding, vacuum assisted resin transfer molding, compression molding, and pultrusion.

Filament winding, shown in top left section Fig. 4.11a, is an automated process that is most suited to circular and elliptical cross section shapes such as conventional geometry airframes and rocket motor cases. In this process, the filament fibers are pulled through a resin bath, and wound around a mandrel. The resin is usually worked into the fibers by roll coaters or by breaker bars in dip tanks. Cycle time is about 1 h for winding and an additional 3 h for oven curing. Because the winding action itself will compact the laminate, vacuum bagging or other compaction methods are not necessary. Filament winding is limited to a two-dimensional fiber orientation. Shown in the far left section of the figure is a photograph of filament winding. Next to the right is an illustration of a helical wind of a motor case. Helical winding deposits the fiber in a helical path in one direction, turns around at the end of the part, and the returns on a helical path in the opposite direction. An advantage of a helical wind is it provides both longitudinal and radial strength. Also shown is an illustration of a radial wind. Next, to the right is a photograph of the filament wound radome of the PAC-3 missile.

The vacuum assisted resin transfer molding (RTM) process is shown in the top right section of the figure. Vacuum assisted RTM is particularly suited to reducing the parts count and cost of ramjets and turbojets, which typically have complex, non-axisymmetric airframe structure. The process consists of inserting a fiber cloth into a mold, pulling a vacuum, injecting resin into the fibers, and then curing the part. The vacuum assisted RTM process has advantages of high production rate, good tolerances (e.g., $+/-0.005$ in.), the capability for a three-dimensional weave, and improved mechanical properties. The improved mechanical properties are because of the lower required injection pressure of a vacuum assisted RTM, which eliminates voids and blisters inside the part. Either a two-dimensional or three-dimensional fiber cloth may be used in the mold. A 3D fiber cloth provides more freedom to tailor the preform fiber type, direction, spacing, and volume fraction to the desired properties. Shown in the top far right section of the figure is an example of 3D orthogonal fiber orientation, which provides omni-directional strength. An example of a missile that uses vacuum assisted RTM with 3D fiber cloth is the AGM-158 JASSM.

The bottom left video shows the manufacturing process of carbon fiber that is used in composite structure. Graphite carbon fibers are made out of long, thin filaments that are transformed to graphite by heating to above $1500°C$ in an inert atmosphere. Finally, the bottom right video shows three examples of composite structure fabrication—filament winding, resin transfer molding, and vacuum bagging.

Shown in Fig. 4.11b are examples of the composite structure manufacturing processes that are based on compression molding and the pultrusion.

The compression molding process consists of inserting a charge (resin impregnated fiber sheet) into a cavity and molding the charge by subjecting it to a high compression force, e.g., 4000 psi. The compression force causes the charge to conform to the desired shape and dimensions of the part. Preheating the charge and the thermal management and moisture control of the compression cavity are required to provide a good bonding between the fiber and the matrix. The top left section of the figure illustrates the process. Shown in the top right section of the figure is a video of the compression molding process. Compression molding has advantages of precision tolerance with high production rate/low cost. A disadvantage is the variation in the quality of the bonding. Compression molding is most applicable to small, low cost, high production volume missiles.

Pultrusion is a continuous, automated closed-molding process that is cost-effective for high volume production of composite non-axisymmetric

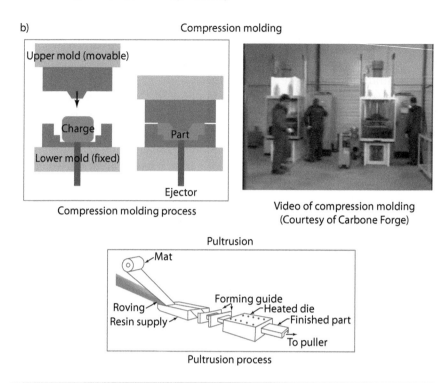

Fig. 4.11b Examples of missile graphite composite airframe structure manufacturing processes.

cross section shapes. The process is illustrated in the bottom section of the figure. Pultrusion pulls the fiber and resin continuously through a heated die that has the same cross sectional geometry as that of the desired part. The part cures into its shape as it passes through the die. After passing through the die, the part is then cut to the desired length. An advantage of pultrusion is high speed, low cost production. A disadvantage is that it is limited to parts with a constant cross section geometry that does not change with length.

Figure 4.12 illustrates the relationship of metal structure weight efficiency (strength-to-density) to its difficulty in machining (hardness). It is an example of a missile design tradeoff. The figure shows the structure weight efficiency and machining difficulty of the materials used for the rocket baseline missile aluminum alloy airframe and steel motor case. Note from the figure that strength increases with hardness. If the airframe manufacturing process requires a significant amount of machining, one of the design considerations is the airframe structure weight versus machining cost.

A popular approach to increase the strength of a metal is by heat treatment. Solid metals such as iron and aluminum are composed of crystals in a lattice. If a metal is heated to its melting point and then cooled, the lattice reforms with crystals in different grain orientations. The non-parallel boundaries between the grains help strengthen the metal, by resisting slippage between grains.

An alloy consists of a small amount of other elements in the metal, to improve properties such as strength, ductility, and corrosion resistance. For example, the strength of aluminum is improved by thermal treatment, mechanical working, and the addition of alloy elements such as copper, magnesium, zinc, and silicon.

The rocket baseline missile airframe is 2219-T81 aluminum alloy. Al 2219-T81 is an age-hardened aluminum alloy that contains a large amount of copper. It is noted for applications at high temperature. Al 2219-T81 consists of about 93% Al, 6.3% Cu, 0.3% Mn, a maximum of 0.3% Fe, and a maximum of 0.02% Mg. Significant material properties are ultimate tensile strength $\sigma_{ultimate,tensile} = 65{,}000$ psi, modulus of elasticity $E = 10.5 \times 10^6$ psi, density $\rho = 0.103$ lbm/in.^{3}, thermal capacitance $c = 0.21$ BTU/lbm/R, and thermal conductivity $k = 0.0194$ BTU/s/ft/R. 2219-T81 aluminum has relatively good attributes in machining, welding, and resistance to oxygen corrosion. However, because of 2219-T81 has a relatively high copper content (about 6%), it is susceptible to salt corrosion. A protective coating, such as chromium, is often applied to aluminum 2219.

Examples of the aluminum heat treatment processes shown in the figure are:

T31—Heat-treated, cold-work

T62—Heat treated, followed by cyclic heating.

T81, T851, T87—Heat treated, cold worked, followed by cyclic heating.

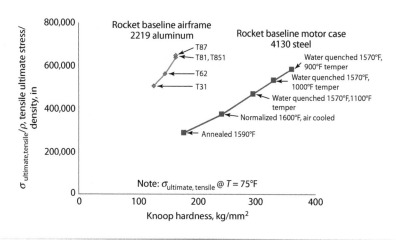

Fig. 4.12   Increasing metal hardness increases strength, but machining is more difficult/expensive.

The rocket baseline missile motor case is 4130 steel alloy that has been heat treated to high strength, with an ultimate tensile strength of $\sigma_{ultimate,tensile} = 190,000$ psi and a yield strength $\sigma_{ultimate,tensile} = 170,000$ psi. 4130 steel has a modulus of elasticity $E = 29.5 \times 10^6$ psi. Density is $\rho = 0.293$ lbm/in.^{3} 4130 steel consists of about 97.8% Fe, 1.0% Cr, 0.5% Mn, 0.3% C, 0.2% Mo, and 0.2% Si. Heat treatment can vary the strength of 4130 steel from a very ductile ultimate tensile strength of 70,000 psi to a very hard and brittle 225,000 psi.

Examples of 4130 steel heat treatments in the figure are:

Normalization—Uniform heat to a sufficiently high temperature that it produces a finer, more nearly uniform grain structure, followed by slow cooling.

Quenching—Heat to a temperature that produces a finer, more nearly uniform grain structure, followed by rapid cooling from water or oil quenching.

Tempering—Reheat after quenching, followed by air cooling.

Annealing—Heat and soak at a high temperature, followed by slow cooling.

Note from the figure, that for the same Knoop hardness, aluminum has a better structure weight efficiency ($\sigma_{ultimate,tensile}/\rho$) than 4130 steel. Yet, 4130 steel was selected for the baseline motor case instead of 2281 aluminum. Possible reasons for selecting high strength steel over high strength aluminum, in spite of the difficulty/cost of machining high strength steel include 1) aluminum requires a thicker motor case, which takes away propellant volume for the volume-limited missile, 2) aluminum requires more insulation, which also takes away propellant volume, 3) other tradeoff considerations that favor steel, such as lower cost, may be significant drivers for the design, and 4) the manufacturing process selected for the rocket motor case may not require a significant amount of machining. Tradeoffs of motor case material alternatives were previously discussed in Chapter 2.

The above discussion supports the thesis that the missile design process should include an evaluation of a broad range of alternatives. This requires finding the driving parameters (Pareto) and determining their relative weighting for system-level considerations such as cost, risk, and performance. As an example in selecting the best material for the rocket motor case, if a broad assessment of alternative materials finds that the design driver is have the highest performance (e.g., lightest weight), then a composite motor case probably would be selected over either the 4130 steel or 2219 aluminum alternatives.

Figure 4.13 shows examples of structure concepts and manufacturing processes that are used for missile airframe bodies and aerodynamic surfaces. Two types of body airframes are shown, a lifting body airframe

Missile airframe geometry alternatives	Missile structure concept alternatives	Structure manufacturing process alternatives									
		Graphite composites						Metals			
		Vacuum assist RTM	Compression mold	Filament wind	Pultrusion	Thermal form	Vacuum Bag/ autoclave	Cast	High speed machine	Forming	Strip laminate
Lifting body airframe	Monocoque	●	◐	●	●	◐	◐	●		◐	
	Integrally hoop stiffened	●	◐				◐	●	—		
	Integrally longitudinal stiffened	●	◐		●		◐	●	—		
Axisymmetric body airframe	Monocoque	●		●	●		●	●		●	●
	Integrally hoop stiffened	●					◐	●	◐		
	Integrally longitudinal stiffened	●			●		◐	●	◐		
Aerodynamic surface	Solid	●	●			●	●	●	●	●	
	Sandwich	◐	◐				◐			○	

● Very low parts count   ◐ Low parts count   ○ Moderate parts count   — High parts count

Note: Manufacturing process cost is a function of recurring cost (unit material, unit labor) and non-recurring cost (tooling).

Fig. 4.13 Missile airframe parts count is driven by the manufacturing process.

and an axisymmetric body airframe. A body airframe structure design concept may be a monocoque, integrally hoop stiffened (bulkhead), integrally longitudinally stiffened (stringer), or stiffened with both bulkheads and stringers. Also shown are the structure design and manufacturing alternatives for aerodynamic surfaces, such as wings, canards, and tails. Aerodynamic surfaces may be either a solid, monolithic structure or a lighter weight sandwich structure that is stiffened with ribs and spars.

A driving consideration for a low cost missile airframe is to minimize the parts count. Examples of manufacturing processes that reduce the parts count include vacuum assisted resin transfer molding (RTM), filament winding, pultrusion, casting, vacuum bag/autoclave forming, metal forming, strip laminate, and compression molding.

Examples of low cost manufacturing process that are particularly applicable to complex airframe shapes are precision casting, composite vacuum assisted RTM, and composite compression molding.

Precision casting is applicable to metal structure. It has high payoff for reducing the cost of air-breathing hypersonic missiles, which have high temperature metal airframes with complex shape. A historical limitation in applying castings to complex configurations is the tight manufacturing tolerances required for the complex configurations. However, new technology such as non-reactive ceramic tooling allows low cost precision castings suitable for complex airframe configurations such as ramjets and turbojets. Castings reduce the parts count, with a resulting cost savings. A one-piece cast airframe integrates all of the secondary structure. Precision casting

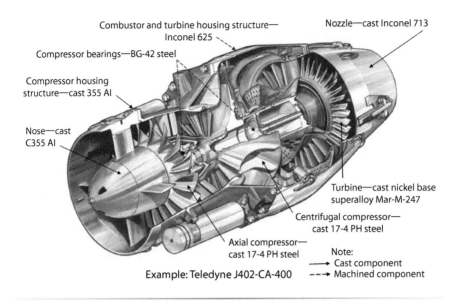

Combustor and turbine housing structure—
Inconel 625

Nozzle—cast Inconel 713

Compressor bearings—BG-42 steel

Compressor housing
structure—cast 355 Al

Nose—cast
C355 Al

Turbine—cast nickel base
superalloy Mar-M-247

Centrifugal compressor—
cast 17-4 PH steel

Axial compressor—
cast 17-4 PH steel

Note:
⟶ Cast component
---→ Machined component

Example: Teledyne J402-CA-400

Fig. 4.14 Missile turbojet engine parts are often metal castings, because castings provide lower parts count and lower cost.

minimizes subsequent machine and hand finishing of mating surfaces, by achieving a precision surface finish "as-cast." Fuel tanks can be an integral part of the structure and not require bladders. Structural attachment points (e.g., ejector attachments, payload supports, booster attachments) and self-indexing/aligning features can be integral to the structure. This minimizes or eliminates mating, alignment, and assembly tooling and test/inspection requirements. Aluminum, titanium, and steel precision castings have been demonstrated for missile airframes, motor cases, and combustors. A casting may or may not be heavier than a conventionally wrought metal. For a constant thickness casting, it is typically about 10% heavier and thicker than a conventionally wrought metal, because of its lower strength compared to that of a work hardened process. However, a variable thickness casting is typically about 20% lighter than a conventionally wrought metal structure with constant wall thickness.

Composite structure is also particularly suitable in providing a low parts count for complex airframe shapes such as ramjets and turbojets. An advantage of a graphite composite structure over a solid metal airframe structure is lighter weight. Note from the figure that vacuum assisted resin transfer molding has the attractive feature of its general applicability to most types of structure. Although the alternative of compression molding also reduces parts count, disadvantages include its limitation to smaller size, less complex structure. Pultrusion also provides low parts count. A disadvantage is its limitation to a less complex structure with a constant cross sectional area.

An example application of metal castings to missile propulsion systems is turbojet engines. Missile turbojet components are primarily precision castings of high temperature metals. An advantage of castings is a lower parts count, which results in lower cost. However, the castings must also be of precision quality because of close tolerances of the relatively small parts. Shown in Fig. 4.14 is the extensive use of castings in the baseline turbojet engine, Teledyne J402-CA-400, described in Chapter 7. Cast components are the nose (C355 aluminum), compressor housing structure (355 aluminum), axial compressor (17-4 PH steel), centrifugal compressor (17-4 PH steel), turbine (nickel base superalloy Mar-M-247), and the nozzle (Inconel 713). The compressor bearings and the housing structure of the combustor and turbine are machined components because of they require high strength and close tolerances that are not easily achievable through casting.

Aluminum casting is particularly attractive for low temperature structure, where the thickness is driven by minimum gauge ($\approx$0.06 in.) manufacturing considerations. An example of an aluminum alloy for casting is C555 (1–1.5% Cu, 4.5–5.5% Si, 0.4–0.6% Mg, 0.1% Zn, 0.2% Fe max) temper T6m which has an ultimate strength of 36k psi and a yield strength of 25k psi. Another example is 355 temper T6 cast aluminum, which has an ultimate strength of 32k psi and a yield strength of 20k psi.

4.8 Missile Airframe Material Alternatives

Examples of missile alternative airframe materials and their tradeoffs are shown in Fig. 4.15. Metallic airframe material alternatives of Aluminum 2219,

Fig. 4.15   Missile airframe material alternatives include aluminum, steel, titanium, and composite.

Steel PH 15-7Mo, and Titanium 6Al-4V are shown in order of increasing cost. Similarly, composite airframe material alternatives of S994 glass/epoxy and S994 glass/polyimide, glass or graphite reinforced molding, and graphite/epoxy and graphite/polyimide are shown in the order of increasing cost. Design considerations for airframe materials include maximum allowable stress, susceptibility to localized buckling, maximum temperature for the short-duration flight of missiles, sensitivity to thermal stress, ease of joining (e.g., weld, bond, bolt) to adjacent structure/subsystems, long lifetime from fatigue, low cost, and light weight. Corrosion resistance may also be a design condition, depending upon the environmental exposure.

For a light weight missile airframe at moderate temperature, graphite/epoxy and graphite/polyimide materials may be preferred. For a high temperature airframe, titanium or steel materials are often preferred. For a low cost airframe the preferred materials are usually aluminum, steel, S994 glass/epoxy, or S994 glass/polyimide.

However, aluminum alloy is the most popular missile airframe material within its temperature and fatigue lifetime limits. If the missile requires high Mach number flight, an external insulation over the aluminum structure is usually sufficient to maintain a low airframe temperature. Fatigue is not a problem for the one-way, relatively short flight time of a missile. However, fatigue may be a problem if there are many cycles of carriage on the launch platform. For example, a missile airframe exposed to 1000 hours of carriage is more like to suffer fatigue failure than a missile exposed to 100 hours of carriage.

Figure 4.16 compares the strength-elasticity of typical airframe materials. The relationship of tensile stress σ_t to strain ε is the equation

$$\sigma_t = P/A = E\varepsilon$$

In the above equation P is the tensile load, A is the loading area, and E is the modulus of elasticity. Shown in the figure are the tensile strength and the stress-strain curves of small diameter carbon, Kevlar, and S-glass fibers (without a composite matrix); high strength steel (such as precipitation hardening stainless steel); titanium alloy; and aluminum alloy material alternatives. Note that the strength capability of advanced small diameter fibers is very high. For example, as shown in the figure, the unidirectional tensile strength of a small diameter carbon fiber is more than 400,000 psi. Small diameter Kevlar and glass fibers may have comparable strength to graphite or carbon fiber. However, graphite fiber is usually preferred for missile structure because it also has a high modulus of elasticity and exhibits a low strain under load. A Kevlar structure could be preferred if there were a driving requirement to absorb energy from an impact without damage (toughness). However, toughness is usually not a driving requirement for missile structure. In addition to small diameter fibers, advanced composite structures have long, continuous fibers (e.g., longer than 4 in.)

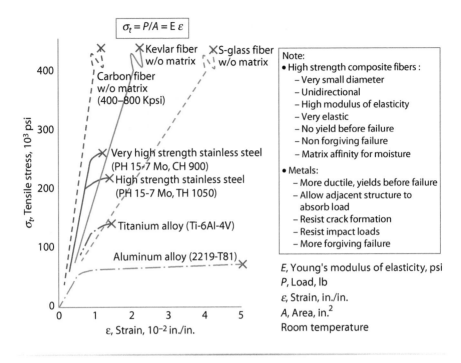

$$\sigma_t = P/A = E\,\varepsilon$$

Kevlar fiber w/o matrix

S-glass fiber w/o matrix

Carbon fiber w/o matrix (400–800 Kpsi)

Very high strength stainless steel (PH 15-7 Mo, CH 900)

High strength stainless steel (PH 15-7 Mo, TH 1050)

Titanium alloy (Ti-6Al-4V)

Aluminum alloy (2219-T81)

σ_{tr} Tensile stress, 10^3 psi

ε, Strain, 10^{-2} in./in.

Note:
• High strength composite fibers :
  – Very small diameter
  – Unidirectional
  – High modulus of elasticity
  – Very elastic
  – No yield before failure
  – Non forgiving failure
  – Matrix affinity for moisture
• Metals:
  – More ductile, yields before failure
  – Allow adjacent structure to absorb load
  – Resist crack formation
  – Resist impact loads
  – More forgiving failure

E, Young's modulus of elasticity, psi
P, Load, lb
ε, Strain, in./in.
A, Area, in.^{2}
Room temperature

Fig. 4.16 Strength—elasticity comparison of missile airframe example material alternatives.

and a fiber/matrix ratio that is greater than 50% fibers by volume. Fibers can be carbon, Kevlar, glass, boron, ceramic, silicon carbide, quartz, polyethylene, and others. As an example of strength at the structure level, a 50% volume carbon fiber composite structure can have strength in a tailored laminate that is above 200,000 psi, much greater than that of aluminum, or even most steels. Also, the low density of composites further reduces the weight compared to metals. An advantage of carbon fiber composite materials includes an extremely high modulus of elasticity, resulting in low strain and deflection compared to metals. Another advantage for a low observable missile is that carbon structure converts incident radar energy into thermal energy (increased temperature), resulting in reduced radar cross section. However, note with caution that composites are not fault-tolerant. The fiber has a nearly linear stress-strain curve out to the ultimate load, at which it suddenly fails. Unlike most metals that generally yield gracefully before ultimate failure, composite fibers generally fail suddenly without a graceful yield. Another disadvantage of composites is susceptibility to impact damage and the possibility that a failure of the structure may be hidden inside of the laminate. Micro-cracks can spread through the matrix, decreasing the ability of the fiber to transfer load. A third disadvantage is that the matrix usually has an affinity to absorb moisture.

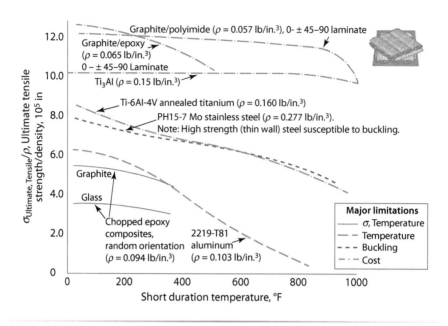

Fig. 4.17 Laminate graphite composite provides a high strength-to-weight airframe.

Figure 4.17 illustrates the structural efficiency advantage of laminate composites compared to conventional materials. The example is based on a typical $0 - \pm 45 - 90$ deg orientation tailoring of the laminate. For short-duration flight (e.g., less than 30 minutes) with temperatures up to about 500°F, laminate graphite/epoxy is a good candidate material, because of its characteristics of high strength and low density. A primary limitation of graphite/epoxy laminate is the relatively high cost compared to conventional metal structure, such as aluminum alloy. Examples of missiles with rocket motor cases that are graphite epoxy are PAC-3, LOSAT, THAAD, and SM-3 TSRM. Another graphite composite, with a high temperature capability, is graphite/polyimide. Graphite/polyimide can be used at temperatures up to about 1100°F, with short-duration (e.g., less than 30 m). A primary limitation of laminate graphite/polyimide is its relatively high cost. The polyimide resin is relatively high cost because of its higher processing temperature and pressure. Polyimide resin also has carcinogenic volatiles and is susceptible to moisture-induced damage. Another candidate resin is bismaleimide. The maximum short duration temperature of bismaleimide is about 700°F. Advantages of bismaleimide include its relatively low cost and it is nontoxic at room temperature. Another common high temperature resin is phenolic. Phenolics are based on phenol (carbolic acid) and formaldehydes. Epoxy, polyimide, bismaleimide, and phenolic matrices are thermo-set polymer matrices that require a chemical curing agent. Thermo-sets have relatively high temperature capability, good dimensional stability, and solvent resistance, but they require a relatively long cure time. An alternative low-cost polymer matrix with a shorter processing time is thermoplastic. Thermoplastics are most suitable to subsonic missiles because of a relatively low temperature capability. Examples of thermoplastic polymer matrices include polyetheretherketone (PEEK), polyphenylene (PPE), and polyetherketone (PEK).

A consideration in developing an airframe structure design based on laminate composites is complexity. In addition to the material itself having greater complexity, the structures are not as straightforward as metal or chopped epoxy composite structures. The designer of a metal or chopped epoxy composite structure has two primary design considerations: material choice and the geometric configuration. Laminate composites require another design consideration, the composite matrix orientation. Two structures of identical geometric configuration, weight and composite material, but with different lay-up, will have different stress-strain and failure modes as a function of orientation. Failure modes of laminate composites include exploding laminate, fibers pulling free from the matrix, first-ply-failure, matrix cracking, and de-lamination, which are difficult to predict.

A metal matrix composite that is filled with metallic or ceramic particles has a higher temperature capability. Metal matrix composites and ceramic matrix composites are in development for space system, UAV, and aircraft applications. An example is titanium matrix/silicon carbide. Although the performance is very high, the cost is very high. Metal matrix and ceramic matrix composites are not yet cost-effective for most missiles.

Above 1100°F, titanium and high strength steel alloys are the usually preferred materials, based on strength-to-weight ratio. A primary limitation of steel is its tendency to buckle for a thin wall structure. A primary limitation of titanium is its high cost.

The relatively low cost of aluminum makes it a primary choice for low temperature structure (less than 300°F). Although aluminum can be used at temperatures up to 600°F, note from the figure that at 600°F its strength is about 1/3 that of room temperature.

The strength of a material is a function of the number of cycles of operation and the duration of exposure to high temperature. An advantage of a missile compared to an aircraft or a UAV is that it can be operated at a higher temperature, because a missile has a one-way, relatively short duration flight. Because aircraft and UAVs operate over many cycles of longer duration flight, they must be operated at with a larger factor of safety and at a lower temperature.

The maximum Mach number for typical un-insulated missile airframe structure materials is shown in Fig. 4.18. An assumption is that the heat

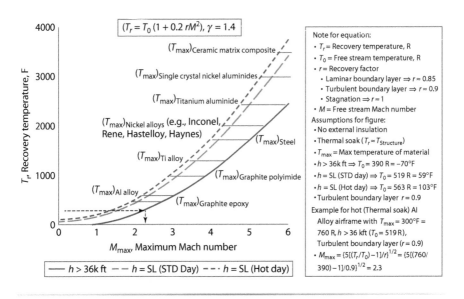

Fig. 4.18   A high speed missile without external insulation requires high temperature structure.

conducted to the airframe is large compared to the heat radiated by the airframe. This assumption is most applicable at low altitude/high atmospheric density. The airframe temperature would be slightly lower at high altitude, because of radiation from the airframe. A second assumption is the flight is of sufficient duration (typically $1-30$ m) that the structure is thermally soaked to the recovery temperature. The example airframe materials selected for the figure are based on the consideration of weight, cost, and maximum temperature capability.

The figure shows examples of the recovery (adiabatic wall) temperature T_r for a turbulent boundary layer (recovery factor r = 0.9). Assumed values of free stream temperature T_0 conditions are standard atmosphere stratospheric flight (altitude h > 36 kft, T_0 = 390 R), sea level flight for a nominal standard atmosphere (T_0 = 519 R), and sea level flight for a hot day standard atmosphere (T_0 = 563 R). The recovery temperature equation is

$$T_r = T_0\left(1 + 0.2rM^2\right)$$

As shown in the figure, at subsonic and supersonic Mach number, graphite epoxy and aluminum alloys are reasonable choices for a light-weight structure without external insulation. Graphite epoxy and aluminum alloys are easily fabricated and have good corrosion resistance. Graphite epoxy also has an advantage of high strength-to-weight ratio while aluminum has an advantage of low cost. Graphite epoxy maximum allowable temperature is $T_{max} \approx 500°F$. Un-insulated graphite epoxy structure may be used with maximum Mach numbers from $M = 2.0$ to 2.7, depending upon the free stream temperature. Similarly, un-insulated aluminum alloy has a maximum allowable temperature of $T_{max} \approx 300$ to 600°F. However, as mentioned previously, the strength at 600°F is only 1/3 of the room temperature strength. A thermally soaked aluminum alloy may be used up to a maximum Mach numbers from $M = 2.2$ to 3.0, depending upon the free stream temperature and the allowable thickness/weight penalty to accommodate the high temperature. For flight at higher Mach number, un-insulated graphite polyimide composite structure has an advantage of high structure efficiency temperatures up to $T_{max} \approx 1000°F$. Un-insulated graphite polyimide may be used for maximum Mach numbers from $M = 3$ to 4. For flight with a maximum Mach number from about $M = 3.5$ to 4.5 without external insulation, titanium alloy structure is preferred. A disadvantage of a titanium structure is higher material and machining cost. For example, the material cost of a titanium part can be up to 18 times that of a similar aluminum part and the machining cost can be up to 13 times that of aluminum. However, the cost to cast a part made of titanium is closer to the cost to cast an aluminum part. Small tolerance (e.g., +/− 0.001 in.) in casting is required to avoid expensive touch-up machining. For Mach 4 to 5 flight without external insulation, steel is usually the preferred structural material. Up to about Mach 5.5 without external insulation (about 2000°F), super nickel alloys such as Inconel, Rene, Hastelloy, and Haynes must be used. Precision castings can minimize the expensive machining and material cost associated with super alloys. Above Mach 5.5 the material alternatives for a hot structure require the use of highly immature and very expensive materials such as titanium aluminide ($T_{max} \approx 2500°F$), single crystal nickel aluminides ($T_{max} \approx 3000°F$), and ceramic matrix composites ($T_{max} \approx 3500°F$).

Alternatives to a hot structure include active cooling, thermal sink, and the use of external insulation. For the short-duration, one-way mission of missiles, external insulation is usually the best approach to minimize the temperature of the structure. Active cooling is usually not cost effective for missiles.

It was noted previously that the Mach number and temperature application relationships are dependent upon the recovery temperature T_r. Recovery temperature is the maximum temperature of a surface, after the temperature rises to an equilibrium temperature. At stagnation regions, such as the nose or leading edges, the recovery factor r is about 1, resulting in the highest (stagnation) temperature. A turbulent or laminar boundary layer downstream of the nose or leading edge will have temperature recovery factors of about $r \approx P_r^{1/3} \approx 0.88$ to 0.92 and $r \approx P_r^{1/2} \approx 0.84$ to 0.86 respectively, with the local temperatures less than stagnation. In addition to a higher recovery factor, a turbulent boundary has higher heat transfer than a laminar boundary layer, because of its turbulent mixing. The time required for the airframe structure to reach an equilibrium (thermal soak) condition is shorter for a turbulent boundary layer.

As an example calculation of the maximum Mach number of an airframe structure, consider a hot structure (thermal soak) using an aluminum alloy. Assume a flight altitude h > 36 kft ($T_0 = 390$ R), a maximum allowable temperature of the aluminum alloy of $T_{max} = 300°F = 760$ R, and a turbulent boundary layer ($r = 0.9$). Then since $T_r = T_0(1 + 0.2rM^2)$

$$M_{max} = \{5[(T_r/T_0) - 1]/r\}^{1/2} = \{5[(760/390) - 1]/0.9\}^{1/2} = 2.3$$

The above result is conservative for most missiles, which have short duration flight and do not reach a thermal soak flight condition. Most missiles do not fly long enough to reach a thermal soak because the thermal capacity of their structure delays the temperature rise. A transient heat transfer analysis is required for a more accurate estimate of the maximum Mach number of an un-insulated airframe structure.

4.9 Missile Structure/Insulation Trades

Thermal insulation provides short duration protection of structural materials from aerodynamic and propulsion heating. Missiles use passive thermal protection instead of active cooling because it is less expensive and requires less volume for the short duration flight. Airframe structure/insulation concepts/trades for missiles include 1) a hot metal structure with no external insulation, 2) a hot metal structure with internal insulation, 3) a one-piece self-insulating composite structure, and 4) external insulation over a "cold" metal structure. These are shown in Fig. 4.19. A consideration for a volume-limited missile is the total thickness of the structure with insulation. Large thickness means less volume for fuel or propellant, resulting in less range. An un-insulated structure (either metal or composite) is acceptable at low Mach number/low recovery temperature. However as discussed previously, at high Mach number the temperature of un-insulated structure may exceed the maximum allowable temperature of the structure material. The rise in temperature of an un-insulated is a function of the time of flight and the thermal capacity, thermal conductivity, and the density of the structure. This can be further delayed by the use of a thermal sink below the skin, such as a fuel tank for a ramjet missile. For short-duration flight at hypersonic Mach number, an external insulator/ablator over a "cold" metal airframe with internal insulation is usually the lightest weight approach, at the expense of large total thickness. The external insulation maintains the airframe below its maximum allowable temperature and the internal insulation maintains subsystems (e.g., warhead, electronics, sensors, batteries, propellant/fuel)

Example structure/Insulation concepts	Concept	T_{max}	k	c	ρ	α
Hot metal structure (e.g., Al) without Insulation	1	300–600	0.027	0.22	0.103	0.000722
Hot metal structure (e.g., Al)	2	300–600	0.027	0.22	0.103	0.000722
Internal insulation (e.g., Min-K)		2000	0.0000051	0.24	0.012	0.00000106
Self-insulating composite structure (e.g., Graphite polyimide)	3	1100	0.000109	0.27	0.057	0.00000410
Ext insulation (e.g., Micro-quartz paint)		1200	0.0000131	0.28	0.012	0.00000226
Cold metal structure (e.g., Al)	4	300–600	0.027	0.22	0.103	0.000722
Internal insulation (e.g., Min-K)		2000	0.0000051	0.24	0.012	0.00000106

Note:
• Missiles use passive thermal protection (no active cooling)
• Small thickness allows more propellant/fuel for diameter constrained missiles (e.g., VLS launcher)
• Weight and cost are application specific
• T_{max} = max temp capability, °F; k = thermal conductivity, BTU/s/ft/°F; c = specific heat or thermal capacity, BTU/lbm/°F; ρ = density, lbm/in.^{3}; α = thermal diffusivity = $k/(\rho c)$, ft^2/s

Fig. 4.19 Missile structure and insulation concepts and trades for short duration flight.

below their maximum allowable temperature. A typical maximum allowable temperature for subsystems is about 160°F. At intermediate (supersonic) Mach number the lightest weight approach for a relatively short duration flight is usually either an un-insulated metal airframe with internal insulation (to protect the subsystems) or a self-insulating composite structure, which has a relatively low thermal conductivity.

The figure also shows typical values of the insulation parameters for the alternative insulation approaches. Values of maximum allowable temperature T_{max}, thermal conductivity k, specific heat or thermal capacity c, density ρ, and diffusivity α for a typical metal structure (aluminum), composite structure (graphite/polyimide), internal insulation (Min-K), and external insulation (micro-quartz paint) are shown. As an external insulator, micro-quartz paint provides a high temperature capability (T_{max} = 2000°F). It protects a low temperature airframe such as aluminum (T_{max} = 300 to 600°F) in a short-term, high temperature environment. Similarly the low conductivity of Min-K (k = 0.0000051 BTU/s/ft/°F) as an internal insulator protects the warhead, electronics, and other subsystems. As a combined structure and insulator material, graphite/polyimide has good characteristics of a relatively high maximum temperature (T_{max} = 1100°F) and a relatively low thermal conductivity (k = 0.000109 BTU/s/ft/°F). The thickness that is required for insulation is a design consideration. Thermal diffusivity is an aggregate measure of the insulation

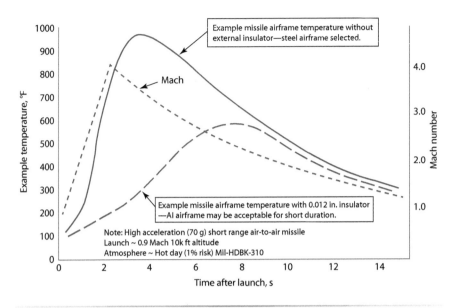

Fig. 4.20 External airframe insulation has high payoff for short duration flight at high Mach number.

thickness efficiency of a material. It is a function of the thermal conductivity, heat capacity, and the density of the material, given by the equation

$$\alpha = k/(\rho c)$$

As a comparison, the thermal diffusivity of Min-K is 0.1% that of aluminum. Micro-quartz paint and graphite/polyimide also have low thermal diffusivity compared to aluminum (0.3 and 0.6% respectively).

Mentioned previously, environmental control of a missile using an actively cooled (refrigerator) approach is usually not cost effective. Passive insulation using the thermal capacity of the structure, thermal inertia of an insulator, or a phase change material (e.g., wax, water) is usually the best approach for the short-duration flight of a missile. In the case of a ramjet, the fuel can provide a thermal sink that delays the rise in the structure temperature.

Figure 4.20 compares the temperature of an insulated airframe versus an un-insulated missile airframe in short-duration flight. The example is based on a high acceleration (70g longitudinal) short range air-to-air missile launched on a hot day at Mach 0.9 and 10,000 ft in altitude. The missile motor burnout is at 2.5 s, providing a burnout Mach number of 4.0. Note from the figure that for an un-insulated airframe, a steel structure was selected because of the high maximum temperature (950°F). An alternative is to use an aluminum airframe that is protected by a thin layer (0.012 in) of spray-on insulation. The combination of the thermal inertia of the external insulation plus the thermal capacity of the structure delays the temperature rise and reduces the peak temperature. The peak temperature on the insulated structure is reduced to 600°F, allowing the potential use of aluminum in the short-duration flight at high Mach number.

4.10 High Temperature Insulation Materials

Figure 4.21 shows tradeoffs in selecting high temperature insulation materials for high temperature structure and propulsion. Figure 4.21a has design considerations of medium density phenolic composites (e.g., nylon phenolic, silica phenolic, glass phenolic, carbon phenolic, graphite phenolic), low density composites (e.g., micro-quartz paint, glass-cork-epoxy, carbon-silicone rubber), plastics (e.g., teflon), porous ceramics (e.g., carbon-silicon carbide), bulk ceramics (e.g., zirconium ceramic, hafnium ceramic), and graphites (e.g., carbon/carbon). Design considerations include thermal conductivity, maximum temperature, maximum Mach number, density, maximum strain, tensile strength, out-gassing, and cost. For most missile propulsion systems and high temperature airframes, either medium density phenolic composites or low density composites are usually selected because of a good balance of cost, performance, and weight.

Figure 4.21b gives a graphical comparison of the maximum temperature capability and the short duration insulation efficiency of missile structure

a)

Type	Thermal conductivity	Max temp	Max Mach	Density	Max strain	Strength	Out-gassing	Cost
Phenolic composites	◐	◐	●	○	○	○ ●	◐	○
Low density composites	●	○	○ ◐	◐	●	○	○	○ ●
Plastics	○	—	—	●	●	—	—	●
Porous ceramics	—	○	◐	—	—	●	●	○
Bulk ceramics	—	◐	●	—	—	●	●	○ ●
Graphites	—	●	●	○	—	●	●	—
	● Superior ◐ Good ○ Average — Poor							

Fig. 4.21a Maximum temperature and insulation efficiency are considerations for high temperature insulation.

b)

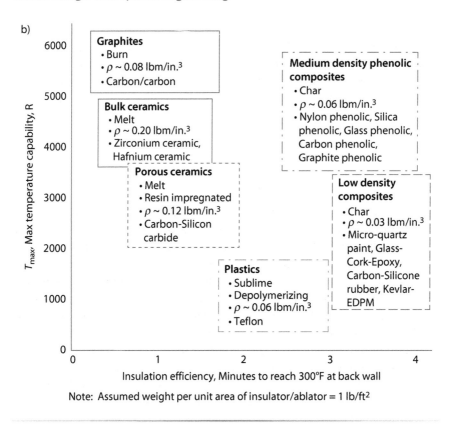

Note: Assumed weight per unit area of insulator/ablator = 1 lbm/ft²

Fig. 4.21b Maximum temperature and insulation efficiency are considerations for high temperature insulation.

insulation materials. The insulation efficiency of the figure is based on the time that is required to reach 300°F at the back wall of the insulator. The assumed surface area application of the insulator is 1 lb/ft².

High temperature composite materials are good light-weight insulators. For insulating high-temperature airframes, engines, and motor cases, the medium density plastic composites are often used. An example is reinforced phenolic resin containing nylon, silica, graphite, or carbon. Phenolics have good resistance to erosion, allow high surface temperatures over 5000 R and exhibit good insulation performance. These materials char at high temperature, but generally maintain their thickness and aerodynamic shape. Phenolic composites lose about 20% of their weight in charring. They are usually fabricated by wrapping tape over a metal form mandrel, so that the grain of the finished unit is tailored to a tradeoff of shear strength versus conductivity.

Another example of a good insulator at somewhat lower temperatures is low density composites. Low density composites such as micro-quartz paint, glass-cork-epoxy composite, or rubber polymers such as carbon-silicone rubber and Kevlar-Ethylene Propylene Diene Monomer (EPDM) may be used for temperatures up to about 3500 R. These also char at high temperature, losing up to 30–60% of their weight from out-gassing. Micro-quartz paint has an advantage of low cost and ease of application, but is limited in its flight duration at high Mach number because of the relatively low maximum thickness of the coating and a maximum temperature of about 2500 R. Micro-quartz paint consists of quartz bubbles of about 1 micron thickness and about 40 microns in diameter that are suspended in a phenolic resin. Rubber polymers are particularly good insulators for rocket motor cases because of their high rupture strain (e.g., 20%), which is consistent with that of solid propellant. Disadvantages of low density composites for airframe external insulation is a requirement for periodic maintenance touch-up and the relatively low strength of the char to velocity shear load.

A third approach based on subliming plastics such a teflon is rarely used for high speed missiles because of temperature limitations. Plastics decompose into gas at temperatures above about 1000 R, resulting in decreased thickness and changes in the aerodynamic shape.

Ceramic refractory materials and graphite materials are also candidate insulators for high speed airframes, engines, and motor cases. Ceramic refractory materials and graphites have high temperature capability, very small erosion, and can also be used for the structure. A disadvantage is the insulation efficiency is not as good as that of plastic composite materials. Another disadvantage of ceramics is their susceptibility to thermal shock and impact load failure. An example of a porous metal matrix composite ceramic, with a maximum temperature up to about 3500 R, is resin impregnated carbon-silicon carbide. At high temperatures the resin melts, providing convection cooling for the structure. Examples of bulk ceramics are zirconium ceramic and hafnium ceramic. Bulk ceramics are capable of withstanding temperatures up to 5000 R, but like porous ceramics, they have relatively poor insulation efficiency. Bulk ceramics are more often used as an external coating for erosion protection. Finally, graphite insulators such as carbon/carbon provide the highest temperature capability. A carbon/carbon composite consists of carbon fibers in a graphite matrix. Graphite is capable of withstanding temperatures up to about 6000 R. However, graphite has relatively poor insulation efficiency, is brittle, and is difficult/expensive to manufacture.

Because missiles have volume and weight constraints, higher density materials for convection heating insulation of the airframe, engine, and motor case structure are in development. High density insulation materials permit more fuel/propellant for a volume-limited missile, resulting in longer range.

4.11 Missile Aerodynamic Heating/Thermal Response Prediction

Figure 4.22 illustrates two types of thermal surfaces that will be modeled in our upcoming transient heat transfer discussion—thermally thin and thermally thick. The thermally thin surface shown in the left side of the figure is a good thermal conductor, with good transmission of heat. For a thermally thin surface, an approximation for conceptual design analysis is that the temperature is constant through the thickness of the surface—the inside temperature is approximately the same as the outside temperature. Metal structure is a good heat conductor and will be modeled as thermally thin. A criteria for a thermally thin surface is:

$$h(z/k)_{\text{surface}} < 0.1, \; T(0, t) \approx T(z, t)$$

In the above equation T = temperature, t = time, h = convection heat transfer coefficient, z = thickness; and k = conductivity.

A thermally thick surface is the opposite of thermally thin—it has a high resistance to heat transfer. A thermally thick surface has a large temperature gradient across the surface thickness. The missile insulation material and the radome will be modeled as thermally thick. A criteria for a thermally thick surface is

$$z/[2(\alpha t)^{1/2}] > 1$$

In the above equation α = thermal diffusivity.

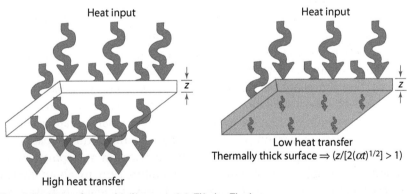

Heat input

Heat input

z

z

Low heat transfer
Thermally thick surface $\Rightarrow (z/[2(\alpha t)^{1/2}] > 1)$

High heat transfer
Thermally thin surface $\Rightarrow h(z/k)_{\text{surface}} < 0.1, \; T(0, t) \approx T(z, t)$

Note: T = Temperature, t = time, h = Convection heat transfer coefficient, z = Thickness; k = Conductivity, α = Diffusivity

Fig. 4.22 A thermally thin surface has a high heat transfer rate, while a thermally thick surface has a low heat transfer rate.

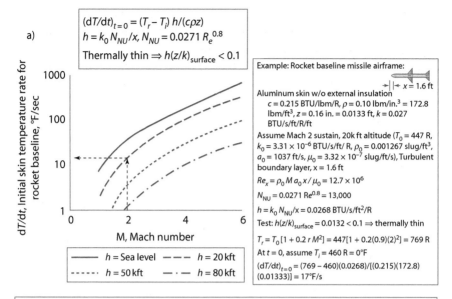

a)

$$(dT/dt)_{t=0} = (T_r - T_i)\,h/(c\rho z)$$
$$h = k_0\,N_{NU}/x,\; N_{NU} = 0.0271\,R_e^{0.8}$$
Thermally thin $\Rightarrow h(z/k)_{surface} < 0.1$

Example: Rocket baseline missile airframe:

$\leftarrow |+ x = 1.6\,\text{ft}$

Aluminum skin w/o external insulation
$c = 0.215$ BTU/lbm/R, $\rho = 0.10$ lbm/in.$^3 = 172.8$
lbm/ft^3, $z = 0.16$ in. $= 0.0133$ ft, $k = 0.027$
BTU/s/ft/R/ft
Assume Mach 2 sustain, 20k ft altitude ($T_0 = 447$ R,
$k_0 = 3.31 \times 10^{-6}$ BTU/s/ft/ R, $\rho_0 = 0.001267$ slug/ft^3,
$a_0 = 1037$ ft/s, $\mu_0 = 3.32 \times 10^{-7}$ slug/ft/s), Turbulent
boundary layer, x = 1.6 ft
$Re_x = \rho_0\,M\,a_0\,x/\mu_0 = 12.7 \times 10^6$
$N_{NU} = 0.0271\,Re^{0.8} = 13,000$
$h = k_0\,N_{NU}/x = 0.0268$ BTU/s/ft^2/R
Test: $h(z/k)_{surface} = 0.0132 < 0.1 \Rightarrow$ thermally thin
$T_r = T_0[1 + 0.2\,r\,M^2] = 447[1 + 0.2(0.9)(2)^2] = 769$ R
At t = 0, assume $T_i = 460$ R = 0°F
$(dT/dt)_{t=0} = (769 - 460)(0.0268)/[(0.215)(172.8)$
$(0.01333)] = 17$°F/s

y-axis: dT/dt, Initial skin temperature rate for rocket baseline, °F/sec

x-axis: M, Mach number

—— h = Sea level   – – – h = 20 kft
······ h = 50 kft   —·— h = 80 kft

Note: Aero heating; No external insulation; Thermally thin structure (uniform internal temperature); "Perfect" insulation behind airframe; 1-D heat transfer; Turbulent boundary layer; Radiation neglected; dT/dt = Temperature rate, R/s; T_r = Recovery (max) temperature, R; h = Convection heat transfer coefficient, BTU/s/ft^2/R; c = Specific heat, BTU/lbm/R; ρ = Density, lbm/ft^3; z = Thickness, ft; k_0 = Conductivity of air, BTU/s/ft/R; R_e = Reynolds number; N_{NU} = Nusselt number

Fig. 4.23a A "thermally thin" surface (e.g., exposed metal airframe) in aerodynamic heating has a rapid temperature rise. (Reference: Jerger, J. J., *Systems Preliminary Design Principles of Guided Missile Design*, D. Van Nostrand Company, Inc., Princeton, New Jersey, 1960).

Because most missiles have a relatively short time of flight, the airframe structure heat transfer is usually in a transient, not a steady-state, condition. Aerodynamic heating/thermal response prediction requires consideration of two different types of prediction methods applicable to two different types of thermal surfaces, thermally thin and thermally thick. We will first consider the aerodynamic heating/thermal response of a thermally thin surface, such as a high conductivity metal airframe without external insulation. A thermally thin surface can be approximated as one-dimensional heat transfer with nearly uniform internal temperature that increases with time, eventually approaching the recovery temperature.

Figure 4.23a shows the effect of flight Mach number and altitude on the initial temperature rate of the rocket baseline missile airframe. The figure is based on the method from Jerger [5], beginning with the equation

$$(dT/dt)_{t=0} = (T_r - T_i)h/(c\rho z)$$

In the above equation the initial temperature rate $(dT/dt)_{t=0}$ is a function of the recovery (maximum) temperature T_r, the initial temperature T_i, heat transfer coefficient h, and the airframe specific heat c, density ρ, and thickness z. Note from the figure that the airframe temperature rate is highest at high Mach number and low altitude. The rocket baseline missile has an aluminum alloy airframe ($c = 0.215$ BTU/lbm/R and $\rho = 0.10$ lbm/in.^{3} = 172.8 lb/ft^3), no external insulation, an airframe thickness $z = 0.16$ in. = 0.0133 ft, and "nearly perfect" (min-K) insulation behind the airframe (i.e., a near-adiabatic wall). It is also assumed that radiation from the airframe may be neglected.

As an example, we shall calculate the initial temperature rate of the aluminum airframe. Assume the rocket baseline missile is at a flight condition of Mach 2 and 20,000 ft altitude ($T_0 = 447$ R, $k_0 = 3.31 \times 10^{-6}$ BTU/s/ft/R, $\rho_0 = 0.001267$ slug/ft^3, $a_0 = 1037$ ft/s, $\mu_0 = 3.32 \times 10^{-7}$ slug/ft/s). We shall also assume a turbulent boundary at this location. The Reynolds number at the beginning of the aluminum airframe (aft of the radome), which is 1.6 ft aft of the nose tip, is $Re = \rho_0 V_0 x / \mu_0 = 0.001267(2)(1037)(1.6)/(3.32 \times 10^{-7}) = 12.7 \times 10^6$.

The heat transfer coefficient h of air is a function of the thermal conductivity k, Nusselt number N_{NU} and the boundary layer distance from the nose x, given by the equation

$$h = k N_{Nu} / x$$

The conductivity of air is a function of the free stream static temperature T_0, given by the equation from Jerger [5]

$$k_0 = 3.58 \times 10^{-6}[717/(T_0 + 225)](T_0/492)^{3/2}$$

For altitudes greater than 36 kft, $T_0 = 392$ R, giving

$$k_0 = 2.95 \times 10^{-6} \text{ BTU/s/ft/R}$$

For a standard atmosphere altitude of 20 kft, $T_0 = 447$ R and the conductivity of air is

$$k_0 = 3.31 \times 10^{-6} \text{ BTU/s/ft/R}.$$

Nusselt number is a dimensionless parameter that represents the heat transfer coefficient and the temperature gradient at the surface. It is a function of the type of boundary layer (laminar, transitional, turbulent) and the Reynolds number. Parameters that affect boundary layer transition from laminar flow to turbulent flow include Reynolds number, pressure gradient, surface temperature, Mach number, and surface roughness. Boundary layer transition usually occurs at a higher Reynolds number for a flight test than for a wind tunnel test, which typically has more turbulence. It also usually occurs at a higher Reynolds number for conditions of no pressure gradient, hypersonic Mach number, and a cold, smooth surface. For a missile body, the pressure gradient on the nose usually induces boundary layer transition prior to the end of the nose section [6]. Also from Chin [6], the transition Reynolds number for subsonic through supersonic ($M < 4$) Mach number is at Reynolds number of Re $\approx 1 \times 10^6$. For this example, Re $= 12.7 \times 10^6$, it is anticipated that the boundary layer is turbulent. Based on Jerger [5], the approximate Nusselt number of a turbulent boundary layer is given by the equation

$$N_{NU} \approx 0.0271\, Re^{0.8} = 13{,}000$$

Substituting the values of N_{NU} and x into the heat transfer coefficient equation gives,

$$h = 3.31 \times 10^{-6}(13000)/(1.6) = 0.0268\, BTU/s/ft^2/R$$

The testing of the assumption that the rocket baseline missile un-insulated airframe is a thermally thin surface is that

$$h(z/k)_{surface} < 0.1$$

The lumped parameter $h(z/k)_{surface}$ is the Biot number. It represents the relative importance of the surface internal thermal resistance compared to the boundary layer thermal resistance. If the Biot number $h(z/k)_{surface} \ll 1$, the conductance within the surface is much greater than the conductance within the boundary layer. If $h(z/k)_{surface} < 0.1$, for conceptual design we can assume a uniform temperature within the surface.

For our example, $h(z/k)_{surface} = 0.0268(0.0133)/0.027 = 0.0132 < 0.1$, which satisfies the test. The recovery temperature at Mach 2, 20 kft altitude for a turbulent boundary layer ($r = 0.9$) is

$$T_r = T_0(1 + 0.2rM^2) = 447\left[1 + 0.2(0.9)(2)^2\right] = 769\,R$$

Then for this flight condition, the airframe initial temperature rate is computed to be

$$(dT/dt)_{t=0} = (769 - 460)(0.0268)/[(0.215)(172.8)(0.01333)]$$
$$= 17\,R/s = 17°F/s$$

The 1D heat transfer equation for the aerodynamic heating temperature of a thermally thin airframe without external insulation is

$$T = T_r - [T_r - T_i]e^{-ht/(cpz)}$$

Figure 4.23b, based on the above equation, shows the non-dimensional temperature T/T_r as a function of the non-dimensional time of flight

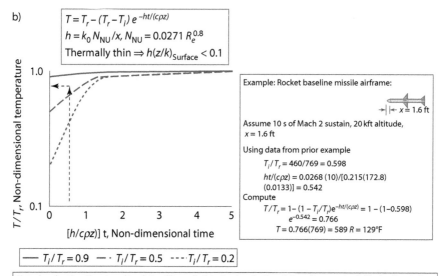

b)

$$T = T_r - (T_r - T_i) e^{-ht/(c\rho z)}$$
$$h = k_0 N_{NU}/x, \quad N_{NU} = 0.0271 R_e^{0.8}$$
Thermally thin $\Rightarrow h(z/k)_{Surface} < 0.1$

y-axis: T/T_r, Non-dimensional temperature

x-axis: $[h/c\rho z)]\,t$, Non-dimensional time

Example: Rocket baseline missile airframe:

$\rightarrow|\leftarrow x = 1.6$ ft

Assume 10 s of Mach 2 sustain, 20 kft altitude, $x = 1.6$ ft

Using data from prior example

$T_i/T_r = 460/769 = 0.598$

$ht/(c\rho z) = 0.0268\,(10)/[0.215(172.8)$
$(0.0133)] = 0.542$

Compute

$T/T_r = 1 - (1 - T_i/T_r)e^{-ht/(c\rho z)} = 1 - (1 - 0.598)$
$e^{-0.542} = 0.766$

$T = 0.766(769) = 589\ R = 129°F$

—— $T_i/T_r = 0.9$ —·— $T_i/T_r = 0.5$ ---- $T_i/T_r = 0.2$

Note: Aero heating; No external insulation; Thermally thin structure (uniform internal temperature); "Perfect" insulation behind airframe; 1-D heat transfer; Turbulent boundary layer; Radiation neglected; dT/dt = Temperature rate, R/s; T_r = Recovery (max) temperature, R; h = Convection heat transfer coefficient, BTU/s/ft²/R; c = Specific heat, BTU/lb/R; [ρ = Density, lbm/ft³; z = Thickness, ft; k_0 = Conductivity of air, BTU/s/ft/R; Re = Reynolds number; N_{NU} = Nusselt number

Fig. 4.23b A "thermally thin" surface (e.g., exposed metal airframe) in aerodynamic heating has a rapid temperature rise. (Reference: Jerger, J.J., *Systems Preliminary Design Principles of Guided Missile Design*, D. Van Nostrand Company, Princeston, New Jersey, 1960).

$ht/(c\rho z)$. Note that the airframe temperature approaches the recovery temperature ($T \Rightarrow T_r$) for a long duration flight. Also, the time to approach the recovery temperature is shortest for a large value of the convection heat transfer coefficient h, and for small values of surface specific heat c, density ρ, and thickness z, and an initial temperature that is near the recovery temperature ($T_i \approx T_r$).

As an example calculation, assume the rocket baseline missile has an airframe initial temperature of $T_i = 460$ R. Also assume missile launch at an altitude of 20 kft, followed by a rapid boost to Mach 2, with sustain Mach 2 flight for 10 s. Using data from the prior example,

$$T_i/T_r = 460/769 = 0.598$$
$$ht/(c\rho z) = 0.0268(10)/[0.215(172.8)(0.0133)] = 0.542$$

Computing the airframe temperature after 10 s exposure at Mach 2/20 kft altitude

$$T/T_r = 1 - (1 - 0.598)e^{-0.542} = 1 - (1 - 0.598)(0.582) = 0.766$$
$$T = 0.766(769) = 589\,R = 129°F$$

As another example, we will calculate the time required for the thermally thin surface temperature to reach 90% of the recovery temperature ($T = 0.9T_r$). The equation is

$$
\begin{aligned}
t_{T=90\%T_r} &= [(c\rho z)/h]\big[\ln(1 - T_i/T_r) - \ln(1 - T/T_r)\big] \\
&= 18.44[\ln(1 - 0.598) - \ln(1 - 0.9)] \\
&= 18.44(-0.911 + 2.303) = 25.7\,\text{s}
\end{aligned}
$$

The flight time of typical rocket-powered missiles is short enough that the airframe does not reach thermal equilibrium. However, turbojet and ramjet cruise missiles have a relatively long flight time, such that an un-insulated airframe will usually reach a thermal soak.

We will next consider the transient aerodynamic heating of a thermally thick surface, such as the rocket baseline missile radome, which has an internal temperature gradient. A thermally thick surface can be approximated as one-dimensional heat transfer through an infinite slab. As before, the temperature increases with time, eventually approaching the recovery temperature. From Jerger [5], the equation for the non-dimensional temperature of a thermally thick surface that is suddenly subjected to a free stream with a constant recovery temperature is

$$
\begin{aligned}
[T(z, t) - T_i]/[T_r - T_i] &= \text{erfc}\{z/[2(\alpha t)^{1/2}]\} \\
&\quad - e^{(hz/k)+h^2\alpha t/k^2}\,\text{erfc}\{z/[2(\alpha t)^{1/2}] + h(\alpha t)^{1/2}/k\}
\end{aligned}
$$

The surface temperature ($z = 0$) is

$$
[T(0, t) - T_i]/[T_r - T_i] = 1 - e^{h^2\alpha t/k^2}\,\text{erfc}[h(\alpha t)^{1/2}/k]
$$

In the above equations $T(z, t)$ is the temperature as a function of the internal distance z and the time t. T_i is the initial temperature, T_r is the recovery temperature, erfc is the complementary error function, α is thermal diffusivity, h is the convection heat transfer coefficient, and k is the thermal conductivity. The test for applicability of the thermally thick equation is

$$
z/[2(\alpha t)^{1/2}] > 1
$$

Figure 4.24a shows the non-dimensional temperature $[T(z, t) - T_i]/[T_r - T_i]$ versus non-dimensional time $h(\alpha t)^{1/2}/k$.

The complementary error function is defined as

$$
\text{erfc}(x) = (2/\pi^{1/2}) \int_x^\infty e^{-u^2}\,du
$$

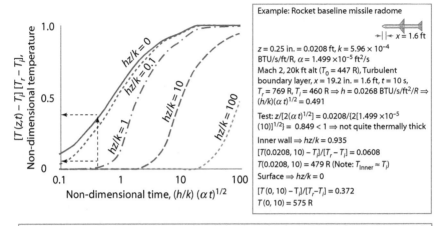

a)

$[T(z, t) - T_i]/[T_r - T_i] = \text{erfc}\{z/[2 (\alpha t)^{1/2}]\} - e^{(h z/k) + h^2 \alpha t / k^2} \text{erfc}\{z/[2 \alpha t)^{1/2}] + h(\alpha t)^{1/2}/k\}$

$[T(0, t) - T_i]/[T_r - T_i] = 1 - e^{h^2/\alpha t/k^2} \text{erfc}[h (\alpha t)^{1/2}/k]$

Thermally thick surface $(z/[2(\alpha t)^{1/2}] > 1)$, $T(z, 0) = T_i$

Example: Rocket baseline missile radome

$\dashv || \vdash x = 1.6$ ft

$z = 0.25$ in. $= 0.0208$ ft, $k = 5.96 \times 10^{-4}$
BTU/s/ft/R, $\alpha = 1.499 \times 10^{-5}$ ft^2/s
Mach 2, 20k ft alt $(T_0 = 447$ R), Turbulent
boundary layer, $x = 19.2$ in. $= 1.6$ ft, $t = 10$ s,
$T_r = 769$ R, $T_i = 460$ R $\Rightarrow h = 0.0268$ BTU/s/ft^2/R $\Rightarrow$
$(h/k)(\alpha t)^{1/2} = 0.491$

Test: $z/[2(\alpha t)^{1/2}] = 0.0208/\{2[1.499 \times 10^{-5}$
$(10)]^{1/2}\} = 0.849 < 1 \Rightarrow$ not quite thermally thick
Inner wall $\Rightarrow hz/k = 0.935$
$[T(0.0208, 10) - T_i]/[T_r - T_i] = 0.0608$
$T(0.0208, 10) = 479$ R (Note: $T_{inner} \approx T_i$)
Surface $\Rightarrow hz/k = 0$
$[T(0, 10) - T_i]/[T_r - T_i] = 0.372$
$T(0, 10) = 575$ R

Note: 1-D heat transfer; Radiation neglected; Turbulent boundary layer; T_r = Recovery temperature, R; h = Convection heat transfer coefficient, BTU/ft^2/s/R; k = Thermal conductivity of material, BTU/s/ft/R; α = Thermal diffusivity of material, ft^2/s; z_{max} = Thickness of material, ft; erfc = Complementary error function

Fig. 4.24a   A "thermally thick" surface (e.g., radome) in aerodynamic heating has a large internal temperature gradient. (Reference: Jerger, J.J., *Systems Preliminary Design Principles of Guided Missile Design*, D. Van Nostrand Company, Inc., Princeton, New Jersey, 1960).

Approximate solutions to the complementary error function are

$x < 0.1$, $\text{erfc}(x) \approx 1 - 1.128x$

$0.1 < x < 2$, $\text{erfc}(x) \approx (1 + 0.2784x + 0.2304x^2$

$+ 0.000972x^3 + 0.07811x^4)^{-4}$

$x > 2$, $\text{erfc}(x) = e^{-x^2}/(2\pi^{1/2})$

The time required for the surface to approach the recovery temperature is of interest. If the parameter $h(\alpha t)^{1/2}/k > 5$, a simplified equation for the non-dimensional surface temperature after a long duration, as the surface temperature approaches the recovery temperature, is

$$[T(0, t) - T_i]/[T_r - T_i] \approx 1 - k/[h(\alpha t)^{1/2}]$$

From the above equation, the time required for the non-dimensional surface temperature to achieve 90% of the recovery temperature is

$$t_{T=90\%T_r} \approx 100k^2/(\alpha h^2)[(T_r - T_i)/T_r)]^2$$

Note that the above are only first-order estimates. The flight time prediction from the above equation for the surface temperature to approach the recovery temperature likely violates the thermally thick test $z/[2(\alpha t)^{1/2}] > 1$.

A simplified equation gives the surface temperature for small values of the parameter $h(\alpha t)^{1/2}/k$. The simplified equation for the non-dimensional surface temperature at the beginning of the temperature rise is

$$[T(0, t) - T_i]/[T_r - T_i] \approx (2^{1/2}/\pi^{1/4})[h(\alpha t)^{1/2}/k] = 1.06[h(\alpha t)^{1/2}/k]$$

Note from the above equation that initially the surface temperature increases as $t^{1/2}$.

As an example, we will calculate the temperature of the rocket baseline missile radome. The assumed location is at the end of the radome, which is at a distance from the nose tip of $x = 19.2$ in. $= 1.6$ ft. The radome is made of pyroceram, which has a conductivity $k = 5.96 \times 10^{-4}$ BTU/s/ft and a thermal diffusivity $\alpha = 1.499 \times 10^{-5}$ ft^2/s. The radome thickness is $z = 0.25$ in. $= 0.0208$ ft. Assume a flight condition of $M = 2$, 20 kft altitude, and an initial temperature $T_i = 0°$F $= 460$ R, as before. From the previous example, the heat transfer coefficient $h = 0.0268$ BTU/s/ft^2/R and the recovery temperature $T_r = 769$ R. Testing for applicability to the thermally thick equation, $z/[2(\alpha t)^{1/2}] = 0.0208/\{2[1.499 \times 10^{-5}(10)]^{1/2}\} = 0.849$, which does not quite satisfy the criteria. As a second test, we will also calculate the inner wall temperature and compare it with the initial temperature. For a thermally thick surface, the inner wall temperature is approximately equal to the initial temperature. At the time $t = 10$ s, the inner wall non-dimensional temperature is

$$[T(0.0208, 10) - T_i]/[T_r - T_i]$$

$$= \text{erfc}\{0.0208/\{2[1.499 \times 10^{-5}(10)]^{1/2}\}\}$$

$$- e^{0.0268(0.0208)/(5.96\times10^{-4})+0.02682(1.499\times10^{-5})(10)/(5.96\times10^{-4})^2}$$

$$\times \text{erfc}\{0.0208/\{2[1.499 \times 10^{-5}(10)]^{1/2}\}$$

$$+ 0.0268[1.499 \times 10^{-5}(10)]^{1/2}/(5.96 \times 10^{-4})]\} = 0.0608$$

Substituting $T_r = 769$ R and $T_i = 460$ R in the above equation gives the radome internal temperature

$$T(0.0208, 10) = 479\,\text{R}$$

Note that $T_{inner} \approx T_i$, which is consistent with the assumption of a thermally thick surface.

Next, we will calculate the temperature near the surface. It is noted that this violates the test $z/[2(\alpha t)^{1/2}] > 1$. However, ignoring the test for the sake of an initial evaluation, at the same time $t = 10$ s, the non-dimensional surface temperature for the same location ($x = 19.2$ in. $= 1.6$ ft) is computed to be

$$[T(0, t) - T_i]/[T_r - T_i]$$

$$= 1 - e^{0.02682(1.499 \times 10^{-5})(10)/(5.96 \times 10^{-4})^2}$$

$$\times \text{erfc}\left\{0.0268\left[1.499 \times 10^{-5}(10)\right]^{1/2}/(5.96 \times 10^{-4})\right\}$$

$$= 0.372$$

The surface temperature is computed to be

$$T(0, 10) = (769 - 460)(0.372) + 460 = 575\,\text{R}$$

Note that the radome surface is predicted to have about the same rise in temperature as the aluminum airframe.

The time required for the radome surface temperature to achieve 90% of the recovery temperature is computed to be

$$t_{T=90\%T_r} \approx 100\left(5.96 \times 10^{-4}\right)^2/\left[1.499 \times 10^{-5}(0.0268)^2\right]$$

$$\times \left[(769 - 460)/769\right]^2$$

$$= 3300(0.402)^2 = 533\,\text{s}$$

The predicted time for the thermally thick radome surface to reach 90% saturation temperature is much longer than the prior example of the thermally thin metal airframe (533 versus 25.7 s).

An alternative (simpler) equation for predicting heat transfer of a thermally thick structure, based on Ref. 20, is

$$T(z, t) = T_r - (T_r - T_i)\text{erf}\{z/[2(\alpha t)^{1/2}]\}$$

Assumptions are the thermally thick surface satisfies the criteria $z/[2(\alpha t)^{1/2} > 1)$, 1D heat transfer, $T(z, 0) = T_i$, and $T(0, t) \approx T_r$.

Note from the above assumptions that there is a discontinuity at $T(0.0)$, with $T(0, 0) = T_i$, and $T(0, t) \approx T_r$. The surface outer wall ($z = 0$)

temperature will initially have large error. Also, for a small value of thickness z and a large value of time t the above criteria for a thermally thick structure will not be satisfied.

Figure 4.24b shows the non-dimensional temperature T/T_r versus non-dimensional time $z/[2(\alpha t)^{1/2}]$ for a typical range in the values of the non-dimensional initial temperature T_i/T_r. Note that the temperature approaches the final (recovery) temperature in a shorter time if the initial temperature is comparable to the recovery temperature $T_i \approx T_r$.

We will first compute the inner wall temperature and compare the results with results from the prior example. The data are: rocket baseline missile radome ($z = 0.25$ in. $= 0.0208$ ft, $\alpha = 1.499 \times 10^{-5}$ ft^2/s), Mach 2, 20 kft altitude ($T_0 = 447$ R), turbulent boundary layer, $x = 19.2$ in. $= 1.6$ ft, $t = 10$ s, $T_r = 769$ R, $T_i = 460$ R.

As before, the thermally thick test shows

$$z/[2(\alpha t)^{1/2}] = 0.0208/\{2[1.499 \times 10^{-5}(10)]^{1/2}\} = 0.849$$

Based on the test, the radome is not quite thermally thick. We will continue will the calculation, recognizing that the result will be in error.

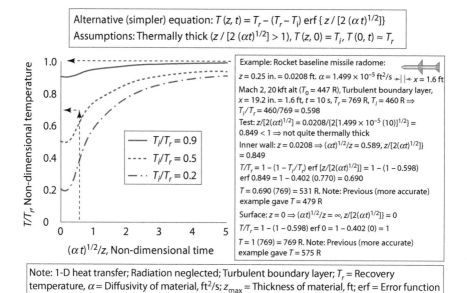

Fig. 4.24b A "thermally thick" surface (e.g., radome) in aerodynamic heating has a large internal temperature gradient. (Reference: Carslaw, H. S. and Jaeger, J. C., *Conduction of Heat in Solids*, Clarendon Press, 1989).

The radome inner wall temperature at time $t = 10$ s is

$$T(0.0208, 10) = 769 - (769 - 460)\ \text{erf}0.849 = 531\ \text{R}$$

It is noted that the previous (more accurate) method gave $T(0.0208, 10) = 479$ R, a difference of 10%.

Next, we will compute results for the outer wall ($z = 0$) temperature. For this case

$$z/[2(\alpha t)^{1/2}] = 0/\{2[1.499 \times 10^{-5}(10)]^{1/2}\} = 0$$

Although the above greatly violates the test for a thermally thick surface, we will continue with the calculation, recognizing that the result will be greatly in error. The radome outer wall temperature at time $t = 10$ s is computed

$$T(0, 10) = 769 - (769 - 460)\ \text{erf}\ 0 = 769\ \text{R}$$

The previous (more accurate) method gave $T(0, 10) = 575$ R, a difference of 25%.

Estimating the required thickness and weight of internal insulation is normally a part of the missile conceptual design process. The internal insulation thickness is usually sized to ensure that the maximum internal temperature is limited to an acceptable maximum value (e.g., $<160°$F) for the missile subsystems such as seeker, electronics, and warhead. From Ref. 20, an equation for the non-dimensional temperature of the insulation behind the airframe is

$$[T(z, t) - T_i]/[T(0, t) - T_i]$$
$$= e^{-z^2/(4\alpha t)} - [\pi/(\alpha t)]^{1/2}(z/2)\text{erfc}\{z/[2(\alpha t)^{1/2}]\}$$

The assumptions are 1-D conduction heat transfer, constant heat flux, negligible radiation, and a thermally thick insulation ($z/[2(\alpha t)^{1/2}] > 1$). Figure 4.25 shows the non-dimensional temperature $[T(z, t) - T_i]/[T(0, t) - T_i]$ versus the non-dimensional time $(\alpha t)^{1/2}/z$. As before the temperature increases with time, eventually approaching the recovery temperature.

As an example, the rocket baseline missile has $z = 0.10$ in. $= 0.0217$ ft of Min-K internal insulation ($\alpha = 0.00000106$ ft^2/s, $k = 0.0000051$ BTU/s/ft/R) behind its 0.16 in thick aluminum alloy airframe. As in the previous examples, assume $M = 2$, 20 kft altitude, $t = 10$ s, $x = 1.6$ ft, and $T_i = 460$ R. Also assume that the insulation is flush with the airframe, such that there is no temperature discontinuity gap between the airframe and the insulation, $(T_{inner})_{aluminum} = (T_{outer})_{min-K}$. From the previous example, the heat transfer coefficient $h = 0.0268$ BTU/s/ft^2/R and at

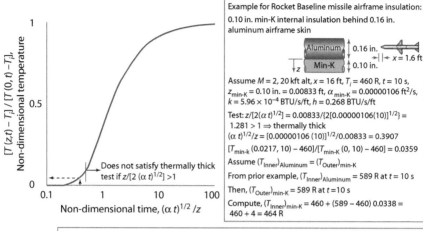

$$[T(z, t) - T_i] / [T(0, t) - T_i] = e^{-z^2/(4\alpha t)} - [\pi/(\alpha t)]^{1/2} (z/2) \, \text{erfc} \{z/[2 (\alpha t)^{1/2}]\}$$

Applicable for: thermally thick surface: $z/[2(\alpha t)^{1/2}] > 1$

Example for Rocket Baseline missile airframe insulation: 0.10 in. min-K internal insulation behind 0.16 in. aluminum airframe skin

Aluminum — 0.16 in. — $x = 1.6$ ft
Min-K — 0.10 in.

Assume $M = 2$, 20 kft alt, $x = 16$ ft, $T_i = 460$ R, $t = 10$ s, $z_{min-K} = 0.10$ in. $= 0.00833$ ft, $\alpha_{min-K} = 0.00000106$ ft^2/s, $k = 5.96 \times 10^{-4}$ BTU/s/ft, $h = 0.268$ BTU/s/ft

Test: $z/[2(\alpha t)^{1/2}] = 0.00833/\{2[0.00000106(10)]^{1/2}\} = 1.281 > 1 \Rightarrow$ thermally thick

$(\alpha t)^{1/2}/z = [0.00000106 (10)]^{1/2}/0.00833 = 0.3907$

$[T_{min-K} (0.0217, 10) - 460]/[T_{min-K} (0, 10) - 460] = 0.0359$

Assume $(T_{Inner})_{Aluminum} = (T_{Outer})_{min-K}$

From prior example, $(T_{Inner})_{Aluminum} = 589$ R at $t = 10$ s

Then, $(T_{Outer})_{min-K} = 589$ R at $t = 10$ s

Compute, $(T_{Inner})_{min-K} = 460 + (589 - 460) 0.0338 = 460 + 4 = 464$ R

Non-dimensional temperature $[T(z,t) - T_i]/[T(0,t) - T_i]$

Does not satisfy thermally thick test if $z/[2 (\alpha t)^{1/2}] > 1$

Non-dimensional time, $(\alpha t)^{1/2}/z$

Note: 1-D conduction heat transfer, Radiation neglected, Constant heat flux input, $T(z, t) =$ Inner temperature of insulation at time t, $T_i =$ Initial temperature, $T(0, t) =$ Outer temperature of insulation at time t, $\alpha =$ Diffusivity of insulation material, ft^2/s; $z_{max} =$ Thickness of insulation material, ft; erfc = Complementary error function

Fig. 4.25 Internal insulation temperature can be predicted assuming constant flux conduction. (Reference: Carslaw, H. S. and Jaeger, J. C., *Conduction of Heat in Solids*, Clarendon Press, 1989).

time $t = 10$ s the airframe temperature is $(T_{inner})_{aluminum} = 589$ R. Testing for a thermally thick insulator, $z/[2(\alpha t)^{1/2}] = 0.00833/\{2[0.00000106(10)]^{1/2}\} = 1.281 > 1$, which satisfies the criteria. Substituting $z/[2(\alpha t)^{1/2}] = 1.281$ into the non-dimensional temperature equation gives

$$[T(0.00833, 10) - 460]/[T(0, 10) - 460]$$

$$= e^{-1.638} - 1.281\pi^{1/2}\text{erfc}(1.281) = 0.1944 - 0.1585$$

$$= 0.0359$$

Substituting $T(0, 10) = 589$ R into the above equation gives

$$T = T(0.00833, 10) = 460 + (589 - 460)0.0359 = 460 + 4 = 464 \, \text{R}$$

Note that the internal insulation is highly effective, with only a 4°F increase in the temperature behind the insulation after 10 s of Mach 2 sustain flight.

Again, the test of $z/[2(\alpha t)^{1/2}] > 1$ would not be satisfied for a very large value of time t.

For a hypersonic missile, sizing the required thickness of external insulation over the airframe structure is also usually conducted during missile conceptual design. Based on the method of Ref. 21, a simplified model of the non-dimensional temperature of a thermally thin structure under a thermally thick insulation is

$$[T_r - T_{\text{structure}}]/[T_r - T_i] = e^{-k_{\text{insulation}}t/(\rho cz^2)_{\text{insulation}}/(0.406+0.981\mu)}$$

μ is an aggregate thermal resistance, given by

$$\mu = (k/z)_{\text{insulation}}/h + (c\rho z)_{\text{structure}}/(c\rho z)_{\text{insulation}}$$
$$+ [(k/z)_{\text{insulation}}/h](c\rho z)_{\text{structure}}/(c\rho z)_{\text{insulation}}$$

Assumptions are 1-D conduction, radiation neglected, constant heat input, constant temperature through the metal structure, and "perfect" insulation at the structure back face. Parameters are $T_{\text{structure}} =$ temperature of structure, R; $T_i =$ initial temperature, R; $T_r =$ recovery temperature, R; $t =$ time, s; $z =$ thickness, ft; $k =$ thermal conductivity, BTU/s/ft/R; $c =$ specific heat, BTU/lbm/R; $\rho =$ density, lbm/ft^3; and $h =$ convection heat transfer coefficient, BTU/ft^2/s/R.

Figure 4.26 shows the non-dimensional temperature of an externally insulated structure versus non-dimensional time. Note that the rise in temperature is delayed by large values of the aggregate thermal resistance μ.

An example calculation will be made for 0.10 in thickness of micro-quartz paint insulation over the rocket baseline missile aluminum airframe structure. We will assume the previous example flight conditions of $M = 2$, 20 kft alt, $x = 1.6$ ft, $h = 0.0268$ BTU/s/ft^2/R, $T_i = 460$ R, and $t = 10$ s.

For the micro-quartz paint insulation: $k = 1.31 \times 10^{-5}$ BTU/s/ft/R, $c = 0.28$ BTU/lbm/R, $\rho = 0.012$ lbm/in.$^3 = 20.74$ lbm/ft^3, and $z = 0.10$ in. $= 0.00833$ ft.

For the aluminum alloy airframe: $k = 0.027$ BTU/s/ft/R, $c = 0.22$ BTU/lbm/R, $\rho = 0.103$ lbm/in.$^3 = 180.0$ lbm/ft^3, and $z = 0.16$ in. $= 0.01333$ ft.

Calculate the values of the parameters:

$$\mu = (1.31 \times 10^{-5}/0.00833)/0.0268$$
$$+ [0.22(180.0)(0.01333)]/[0.28(20.74)(0.00833)]$$
$$+ [(1.31 \times 10^{-5}/0.00833)/0.0268]$$
$$\times [0.22(180.0)(0.01333)]/[0.28(20.74)(0.00833)]$$
$$= 10.92$$

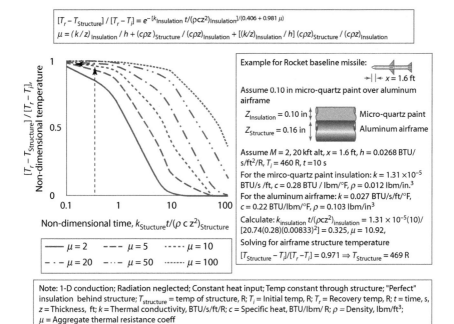

$$[T_r - T_{Structure}] / [T_r - T_i] = e^{-[k_{Insulation} t/(\rho cz^2)_{Insulation}]/(0.406 + 0.981 \mu)}$$

$$\mu = (k/z)_{Insulation} / h + (c\rho z)_{Structure} / (c\rho z)_{Insulation} + [(k/z)_{Insulation} / h] (c\rho z)_{Structure} / (c\rho z)_{Insulation}$$

Example for Rocket baseline missile:

$\leftarrow|\;|\leftarrow x = 1.6$ ft

Assume 0.10 in micro-quartz paint over aluminum airframe

$Z_{Insulation} = 0.10$ in   Micro-quartz paint
$Z_{Structure} = 0.16$ in   Aluminum airframe

Assume $M = 2$, 20 kft alt, $x = 1.6$ ft, $h = 0.0268$ BTU/s/ft²/R, $T_i = 460$ R, $t = 10$ s
For the mirco-quartz paint insulation: $k = 1.31 \times 10^{-5}$ BTU/s /ft, $c = 0.28$ BTU / lbm/°F, $\rho = 0.012$ lbm/in.³
For the aluminum airframe: $k = 0.027$ BTU/s/ft/°F, $c = 0.22$ BTU/lbm/°F, $\rho = 0.103$ lbm/in³
Calculate: $k_{insulation} t/(\rho cz^2)_{insulation} = 1.31 \times 10^{-5}(10)/[20.74(0.28)(0.00833)^2] = 0.325$, $\mu = 10.92$,
Solving for airframe structure temperature
$[T_{Structure} - T_i]/[T_r - T_i] = 0.971 \Rightarrow T_{Structure} = 469$ R

x-axis: Non-dimensional time, $k_{Stucture} t/(\rho \, c \, z^2)_{Structure}$

y-axis: $[T_r - T_{Structure}] / [T_r - T_i]$, Non-dimensional temperature

— $\mu = 2$ --- $\mu = 5$ ···· $\mu = 10$
-·- $\mu = 20$ -··- $\mu = 50$ ······ $\mu = 100$

Note: 1-D conduction; Radiation neglected; Constant heat input; Temp constant through structure; "Perfect" insulation behind structure; $T_{structure}$ = temp of structure, R; T_i = Initial temp, R; T_r = Recovery temp, R; t = time, s; z = Thickness, ft; k = Thermal conductivity, BTU/s/ft/R; c = Specific heat, BTU/lbm/ R; ρ = Density, lbm/ft³; μ = Aggregate thermal resistance coeff

Fig. 4.26 External insulation greatly reduces airframe structure temperature in short duration flight. (Reference: Grover, J. H. and Holter, W. H., Solution of the Transient Heat Conduction Equation for an Insulated, Infinite Metal Slab, *Journal of Jet Propulsion*, Number 27, 1957).

$$k_{insulation} t/(\rho cz^2)_{insulation} = 1.31 \times 10^{-5}(10)/\left[20.74(0.28)(0.00833)^2\right]$$
$$= 0.325$$

Solving for the structure temperature

$$[769 - T_{structure}]/[769 - 460] = e^{-0.325/[0.406+0.981(10.92)]} = e^{-0.0292}$$
$$= 0.971 \Rightarrow T_{structure} = 469\,\text{R}$$

The above external insulation ($z = 0.1$ in of min-K) was effective. It allowed only a $\Delta T = 6°F$ rise in the airframe structure temperature after 10 s of flight at Mach 2, 20 kft altitude. Note that in the previous example of an un-insulated airframe, the temperature rise was $\Delta T = 129°F$.

Selecting the missile nose tip bluntness or the wing/canard/tail surface leading edge bluntness requires considerations such as drag, localized stress, seeker performance, and the localized aerodynamic heating. A blunted nose/leading edge is usually required at high supersonic/hypersonic Mach numbers. Allen and Eggers [22] developed the following equation for the convection heat transfer coefficient of a blunt nose

$$h_r = N_{NU} k_{air,stagnation} / d_{NoseTip}$$

Based on Ref. 22, the equation for the Nusselt number of a laminar boundary layer over a blunt nose is

$$N_{NU} = 1.321 Re_{d,NoseTip}^{0.5} P_r^{0.4}$$

Prandtl number is given by

$$P_r = c_p \mu / k$$

The viscosity can be obtained from Sutherland's law [5]

$$\mu = 1.147 \times 10^{-5} [708/(T + 216)(T/492)^{3/2}]$$

Similarly, the conductivity of air[5] is

$$k = 3.58 \times 10^{-6} [717/(T + 225)](T/492)^{3/2}$$

Assumptions for the above equation are 1-D conduction heat transfer, a laminar boundary layer, stagnation heating, and negligible radiation.

Figure 4.27 shows the heat transfer coefficient of the rocket baseline missile for a Mach number range of M=1 to 6 and a nose bluntness range of $d_{NoseTip}/d_{Ref} = 0.01$ to 0.10. The assumed altitude is 20,000 ft. Note that a large value of bluntness is required to achieve low values of heat transfer.

The following is an example calculation of the heat transfer of the rocket baseline missile pyroceram nose tip, based on an assumed sustain ($M =$ constant, $T_r =$ constant) flight condition of $M = 2$, 20 kft altitude, $T_i = 460$ R, and $t = 10$ s. For an assumed nose tip with 1% bluntness, $d_{NoseTip}/d_{Ref} = 0.01$. The nose tip diameter is $d_{NoseTip} = 0.01 \times 8$ in. $= 0.08$ in. $= 0.00667$ ft. The stagnation recovery temperature ($r = 1$) is

$$T_r = T_0\{1 + r[(\gamma - 1)/2]M^2\} = 447\{1 + (1)[(1.4 - 1)/2](2)^2\} = 805 \text{ R}$$

Substituting into Sutherland's law gives

$$\mu = 1.147 \times 10^{-5} [708/(T_r + 216](T_r/492)^{3/2} = 1.665 \times 10^{-5} \text{ lb/s/ft}$$

The Reynolds number based on the nose tip diameter is $Re_{d,NoseTip} = \rho_0 V_0 d_{NoseTip}/\mu$. Substituting into the Reynolds number equation

$$Re_{d,NoseTip} = 32.2(0.001267)(2074)(0.00667)/1.665 \times 10^{-5} = 3.39 \times 10^4$$

The thermal conductivity of the air at the stagnation condition is

$$k = 3.58 \times 10^{-6} [717/(T_r + 225)](T_r/492)^{3/2} = 5.22 \times 10^{-6} \text{ BTU/s/ft/R}$$

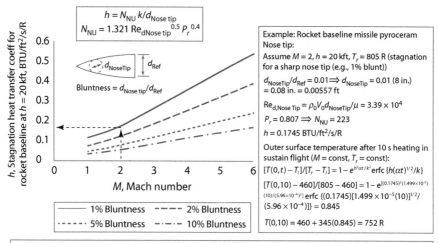

$h = N_{NU}\,k/d_{Nose\ tip}$
$N_{NU} = 1.321\ Re_{dNose\ tip}^{0.5}\,P_r^{\,0.4}$

Bluntness = $d_{Nose\ tip}/d_{Ref}$

Example: Rocket baseline missile pyroceram
Nose tip:

Assume $M = 2$, $h = 20$ kft, $T_r = 805$ R (stagnation
for a sharp nose tip (e.g., 1% blunt))

$d_{NoseTip}/d_{Ref} = 0.01 \Rightarrow d_{NoseTip} = 0.01$ (8 in.)
$= 0.08$ in. $= 0.00557$ ft

$Re_{d,Nose\ Tip} = \rho_0 V_0 d_{NoseTip}/\mu = 3.39 \times 10^4$

$P_r = 0.807 \Rightarrow N_{NU} = 223$

$h = 0.1745$ BTU/ft²/s/R

Outer surface temperature after 10 s heating in
sustain flight ($M = $ const, $T_r = $ const):

$[T(0,t) - T_i]/[T_r - T_i] = 1 - e^{h^2 \alpha t/k^2}\ \mathrm{erfc}\,\{h(\alpha t)^{1/2}/k\}$

$[T(0,10) - 460]/[805 - 460] = 1 - e^{[(0.1745)^2(1.499\times10^{-5})}$
$(10)/(5.96\times10^{-4})^2]}\ \mathrm{erfc}\,\{(0.1745)[1.499 \times 10^{-5}(10)]^{1/2}/$
$(5.96 \times 10^{-4})]\} = 0.845$

$T(0,10) = 460 + 345(0.845) = 752$ R

— 1% Bluntness   - - - - 2% Bluntness
· · · · · · 5% Bluntness   - · - · - 10% Bluntness

Note: 1-D conduction heat transfer; Laminar boundary layer; Stagnation heating; Radiation neglected; $h = $ Convection heat transfer coefficient for stagnation recovery, BTU/s/ft²/R; $N_{NU} = $ Nusselt number for stagnation recovery; $k = $ Air thermal conductivity at stagnation recovery (total) temperature, BTU/s/ft/R; $d_{Nose\ tip} = $ Nose tip diameter, ft; $Re_{dNose\ tip} = $ Reynolds number based on nose tip diameter, $P_r = $ Prandtl number

Fig. 4.27 A sharp nose tip/leading edge has high aerodynamic heating in hypersonic flight. (Reference: Allen, J. and Eggers, A. J., "A Study of the Motion and Aerodynamic Heating of Ballistic Missiles Entering the Earth's Atmosphere at High Supersonic Speeds", NACA Report 1381, April 1953).

Substituting into the Prandtl number equation

$$P_r = 0.253\left(1.665 \times 10^{-5}\right)/\left(5.22 \times 10^{-6}\right) = 0.807$$

Substituting the value of the Reynolds number and the value of the Prandtl number into the Nusselt number equation

$$N_{NU} = 1.321 Re_{d,NoseTip}^{1/2} P_r^{2/5} = 1.321\left(3.39 \times 10^4\right)^{1/2}(0.807)^{2/5} = 223$$

Finally, the heat transfer coefficient is

$$h = 223\left(5.22 \times 10^{-6}\right)/0.00667 = 0.1745\ \mathrm{BTU}/\mathrm{ft}^2/s/R$$

From the previous example calculations, note that the 1% bluntness nose tip heat transfer coefficient is $7.3x$ the heat transfer coefficient on the airframe at a location 1.6 ft downstream of the nose tip. For an assumed thermally thick surface, the nose tip non-dimensional outer surface temperature, after 10 s of heating is

$$[T(0, t) - T_i]/[T_r - T_i] = 1 - e^{h^2 \alpha t/k^2} \mathrm{erfc}\{h(\alpha t)^{1/2}/k\}$$

$$= 1 - e^{[(0.1745)^2(1.499 \times 10^{-5})(10)/(5.96 \times 10^{-4})^2]}$$

$$\times \mathrm{erfc}\left\{(0.1745)\left[1.499 \times 10^{-5}(10)\right]^{1/2}/\right.$$

$$\left.(5.96 \times 10^{-4})\right\} = 0.845$$

Substituting $T_i = 460$ R and $T_r = 805$ R gives

$$T(0, 10) = 460 + (805 - 460)(0.845) = 752 \, \mathrm{R}$$

Note that after 10 s of flight, the nose tip outer surface temperature is only 53 R less than the stagnation recovery temperature (752 versus 805 R). From the previous calculations, also note that at a location 1.6 ft downstream of the nose tip, the airframe outer surface temperature is 236 R less than the stagnation recovery temperature (569 versus 805 R). Again, the figure shows that a blunt nose (e.g., 10% bluntness) is preferable, with much lower heat transfer.

The previous methods for predicting aerodynamic heating/thermal response are based on a constant value of heat transfer coefficient, which is characteristic of sustain flight (e.g., constant Mach number, constant altitude, and constant recovery temperature). These conceptual design methods can be applied to missiles with varying Mach number and altitude by using a time-averaged value of the heat transfer coefficient of each flight phase. As an example for a boost-sustain-coast missile, the average heat transfer coefficient would be computed from the time-averaged values of the launch, end-of-boost, end-of-sustain, and end-of-coast heat transfer coefficients.

We will next consider radiation heat transfer. Figure 4.28 illustrates the drivers for thermal radiation from the missile airframe. Figure 4.28a shows the thermal radiation Q_{rad} versus temperature for the values of emissivity from $\varepsilon = 0.1$ to $\varepsilon = 1$. Assumptions for the figure are 1) steady-state, equilibrium heating, 2) equilibrium temperature approximately equal to the recovery temperature ($T \approx T_r$), 3) altitude h = 80 kft, with a free stream static temperature $T_0 = 398$ R, 4) ratio of specific heat $\gamma = 1.4$, and 5) a turbulent boundary layer, with a recovery factor $r = 0.9$. The equation for radiation heat loss is

$$Q_{\mathrm{rad}} = 4.76 \times 10^{-13} \varepsilon T^4$$

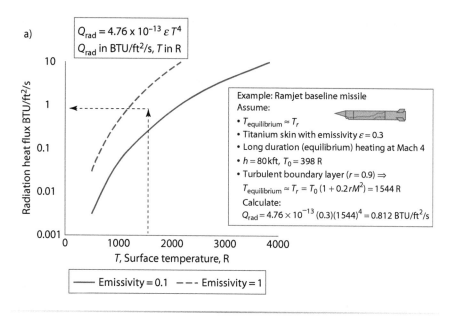

a)

$$Q_{rad} = 4.76 \times 10^{-13} \, \varepsilon \, T^4$$
Q_{rad} in BTU/ft^2/s, T in R

Example: Ramjet baseline missile
Assume:
• $T_{equilibrium} \approx T_r$
• Titanium skin with emissivity $\varepsilon = 0.3$
• Long duration (equilibrium) heating at Mach 4
• $h = 80$ kft, $T_0 = 398$ R
• Turbulent boundary layer ($r = 0.9$) $\Rightarrow$
$T_{equilibrium} \approx T_r = T_0 (1 + 0.2 r M^2) = 1544$ R
Calculate:
$Q_{rad} = 4.76 \times 10^{-13} (0.3)(1544)^4 = 0.812$ BTU/ft^2/s

Radiation heat flux BTU/ft^2/s

T, Surface temperature, R

—— Emissivity = 0.1   --- Emissivity = 1

Fig. 4.28a   Missiles have relatively low radiation heat loss at moderate temperature/Mach number.

The units of Q_{rad} are BTU/ft^2/s and the unit of T is R. The steady-state, equilibrium temperature is approximately

$$T_{equilibrium} \approx T_r = T_0 \left(1 + 0.2 r M^2\right)$$

Note from the figure that that the radiation heat flux is relatively low for a moderate temperature.

An example calculation for the ramjet baseline missile at Mach 4 and an altitude of 80 kft ($T_0 = 398$ R) gives $T_{equilibrium} \approx T_r = 398[1 + 0.2(0.9)(4)^2] = 1544$ R for a turbulent boundary layer ($r = 0.9$).

For the missile's titanium airframe, assume an emissivity $\varepsilon = 0.3$. Substituting $T_r = 1544$ R and $\varepsilon = 0.3$ in the radiation heat flux loss equation gives

$$Q_{rad} = 4.76 \times 10^{-13}(0.3)(1544)^4 = 0.812 \, \text{BTU/ft}^2/\text{s}.$$

Most missiles have short-duration flight, with transient heating. The transient surface temperature is usually much lower than the equilibrium, near recovery, temperature. As a result, the convection heat input is usually much larger than the radiation heat output.

Figure 4.28b relates the ramjet baseline missile radiation heat loss to its flight Mach number and altitude. For a long duration flight, with the airframe structure in a thermal soak/equilibrium temperature, the input from aerodynamic heating is equal to the radiation output

$$Q_{input} = Q_{output}$$

The equation for the aerodynamic heating input is

$$Q_{input} = h\left(T_r - T_{equilibrium}\right)$$

The radiation output for an equilibrium temperature is

$$Q_{output} = Q_{rad} = 4.76 \times 10^{-13}\varepsilon T_{equilibrium}^4, \ BTU/ft^2/s$$

Note from the figure that the effect of radiation can usually be neglected except for hypersonic flight at high altitude.

As an example calculation, assume the ramjet baseline missile is in a thermal soak flight condition at Mach 4, 80k altitude. The recovery temperature is

$$T_r = T_0\left(1 + 0.2rM^2\right) = 398\left[1 + 0.2(0.9)(4)^2\right] = 1544\,R$$

b)

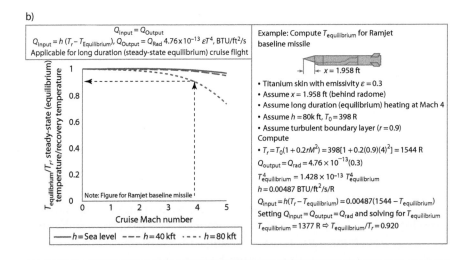

Fig. 4.28b   Missiles have relatively low radiation heat loss at moderate temperature/Mach number.

The convection heat coefficient at a location aft of the radome, at the beginning of the airframe ($x = 23.5$ in $= 1.958$ ft) is

$$h = kN_{\text{NU}}/x$$

$$N_{\text{NU}} = 0.0271R_e^{0.8}$$

$$Re = \rho Vx/\mu = 0.000084(978)(1.958)/2.96 \times 10^{-7} = 2.17 \times 10^6$$

$$N_{\text{NU}} = 0.0271(2.17 \times 10^6)^{0.8} = 3178$$

$$h = 3.00 \times 10^{-6}(3178)/1.96 = 0.00487\,\text{BTU/ft}^2/\text{s/R}$$

Solving for the convection heat input

$$Q_{\text{input}} = h(T_r - T_{\text{equilibrium}}) = 0.00487(1544 - T_{\text{equilibrium}})$$

The ramjet baseline missile titanium structure skin has an emissivity $\varepsilon = 0.3$. The output radiation is

$$Q_{\text{rad}} = 4.76 \times 10^{-13}(0.3)(T_{\text{equilibrium}})^4 = 1.428 \times 10^{-13}T_{\text{equilibrium}}^4$$

The airframe structure temperature $T_{\text{equilibrium}}$ is obtained from the equilibrium heat transfer balance

$$Q_{\text{input}} = 0.00487(1544 - T_{\text{equilibrium}}) = Q_{\text{output}} = Q_{\text{rad}}$$
$$= 1.428 \times 10^{-13}T_{\text{equilibrium}}^4 \Rightarrow T_{\text{equilibrium}} = 1420\,\text{R}$$

For this example, the ramjet baseline missile thermal equilibrium temperature at Mach 4/80 kft is 92% of the recovery temperature

$$T_{\text{equilibrium}}/T_r = 1420/1544 = 0.920$$

4.12 Localized Aerodynamic Heating and Thermal Stress

Figure 4.29 illustrates design concerns for localized aerodynamic heating trouble spots, such as the missile dome, structure joints, leading edges, and shock wave-boundary layer interaction.

Radomes and IR domes often have thermal stress problems at the attachment of the dome to the metal airframe, because of differences in temperature and thermal expansion (Fig. 4.29a). Domes usually have their material selection and thickness driven more by electromagnetic or electro-optical (EO) considerations than by structural design considerations. Because many dome materials have low strength, radomes and IR domes are susceptible to structural failure.

a)

IRdome/Radome
- Large temp gradients due to low thermal conduction
- Thermal stress at attachment
- Low tensile strength
- Dome fails in tension

Sharp leading edge/Nose tip
- Hot stagnation temperature on leading edge
- Small radius prevents use of external insulation
- Cold heat sink material as chord increases in thickness leads to leading edge warp
- Shock wave interaction with adjacent body structure

Body joint
- Hot missile shell
- Cold frames or bulkheads
- Causes premature buckling

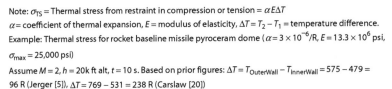

Note: σ_{TS} = Thermal stress from restraint in compression or tension = $\alpha E \Delta T$

α = coefficient of thermal expansion, E = modulus of elasticity, $\Delta T = T_2 - T_1$ = temperature difference.

Example: Thermal stress for rocket baseline missile pyroceram dome ($\alpha = 3 \times 10^{-6}$/R, $E = 13.3 \times 10^6$ psi,

$\sigma_{max} = 25,000$ psi)

Assume $M = 2$, $h = 20$k ft alt, $t = 10$ s. Based on prior figures: $\Delta T = T_{OuterWall} - T_{InnerWall} = 575 - 479 =$

96 R (Jerger [5]), $\Delta T = 769 - 531 = 238$ R (Carslaw [20])

Then $\sigma_{TS} = 3 \times 10^{-6}$ $(13.3 \times 10^6)(96) = 3830$ psi (Jerger), $\sigma_{TS} = 3 \times 10^{-6}$ $(13.3 \times 10^6)(238) = 9500$ psi (Carslaw)

Fig. 4.29a Missile design concerns for localized aerodynamic heating and thermal stress.

Another trouble spot is leading edges. Hypersonic leading edges are subjected to stagnation heating and could erode. Downstream of the hot leading edge, the additional thickness of the wing, canard, or tail surface provides a heat sink, and as a result the interior of the surface is relatively cold. The difference in temperature may cause the leading edge to warp.

Body joints are also susceptible to local stress concentration. For a supersonic or hypersonic missile, the difference in temperature of the hot outer airframe (from aerodynamic heating) and the relatively cold inner bulkhead (from the thermal heat sink of the interior bulkhead material) may lead to high local thermal stress at the body joint. This may cause premature buckling.

Thermal stress occurs if a structure is restrained. For a rigid restraint in compression or tension, a conceptual design equation for thermal stress is

$$\sigma_{TS} = \alpha E \Delta T$$

In the above equation σ_{TS} is the thermal stress, α is the coefficient of thermal expansion, E is the modulus of elasticity, and ΔT is the temperature difference.

As an example of thermal stress, consider the rocket baseline missile pyroceram radome, which has a maximum stress $\sigma_{max} = 25,000$ psi, a coefficient of thermal expansion $\alpha = 3 \times 10^{-6}$/R and a modulus of elasticity $E = 13 \times 10^6$ psi. For a typical flight condition of Mach 2, 20 kft altitude, and 10 s time of flight, a prior example based on the Jerger [5] method showed that the temperature difference between the radome outer and inner walls is

$$\Delta T = T_{\text{OuterWall}} - T_{\text{InnerWall}} = 575 - 479 = 96\,\text{R}$$

The thermal stress of the pyroceram radome if it is rigidly clamped to the airframe is approximately

$$\sigma_{TS} = 3 \times 10^{-6} (13.3 \times 10^6)(96) = 3830\,\text{psi}$$

A second (less accurate) prediction, based on the prior example using the method of Carslaw[20] is

$$\sigma_{TS} = 3 \times 10^{-6} (13.3 \times 10^6)(769 - 531) = 9500\,\text{psi}$$

Although the thermal stress for this example is less than the strength of pyroceram (25,000 psi), it does add to the other contributors to radome stress, such as maneuver load. Dome thermal stress is usually not a driving concern for missiles with a maximum Mach number less than 3. However for Mach 4 or greater missiles, radome and IR dome thermal stress can be a major concern.

Figure 4.29b shows examples of localized aerodynamic heating concerns from shock wave-boundary layer interaction. In addition to high

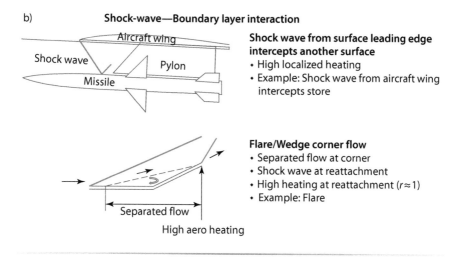

Fig. 4.29b Missile design concerns for localized aerodynamic heating and thermal stress.

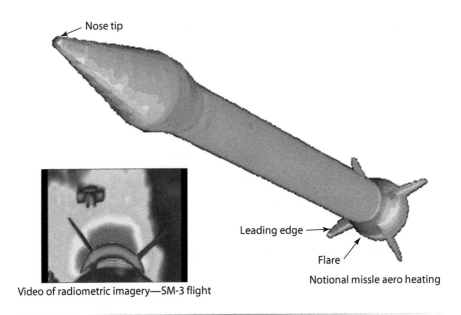

Nose tip

Leading edge →

Flare

Notional missle aero heating

Video of radiometric imagery—SM-3 flight

Fig. 4.30   Examples of aerodynamic hot spots.

localized aerodynamic heating, shock wave-boundary layer interaction may also cause flow separation. The top section of the figure shows an attached missile store in supersonic carriage. The shock wave from the leading edge of the aircraft wing is reflected off the missile store, causing localized aerodynamic heating. Another example of shock wave-wave boundary layer interaction is shown in the bottom section of the figure. Corner flow such as flares and wedges may also have localized aerodynamic heating because of shock wave–boundary layer interaction. The flow may separate upstream of the flare/wedge and then reattach downstream on the flare/wedge. High heating rates approaching stagnation heating ($r \approx 1$) occur at reattachment.

Shown in the Fig. 4.30 are examples of aerodynamic hot spots for supersonic/hypersonic missiles. Note the high aerodynamic heating that exists at the nose tip, leading edges of surfaces, corner flow at the cylinder-flare junction, and the reattachment of the separated boundary layer downstream of the cylinder-flare junction. Also note that the aerodynamic heating is somewhat higher on the bottom (windward) side of the missile, particularly on the bottom of the nose. The flow expansion region aft of the hammer-head bulge is a relatively cool region of low aerodynamic heating. Because of manufacturing cost considerations, most missiles use acreage insulation, with a constant thickness over the entire airframe. However, aerodynamic hot spots may require local treatment, such as additional local insulation or the local use of a high temperature airframe material.

In the bottom left section of the figure is a video of radiometric imagery of the tails section of the Standard Missile SM-3 during a flight test. In the video the plume diameter changes due to the decreasing atmospheric pressure with increasing altitude and changes in thrust. The leading edges of the tails are relatively hot (red) compared to the aft surfaces. Also note the ejection of insulation particles that follow after motor burnout.

4.13 Missile Structure Design

Missile structure weight estimation is major activity in conceptual design. A first-order estimate of the missile body structure weight can be based on a correlation of the body structure weight fraction of the missile launch weight. Shown in Fig. 4.31 is a correlation of 11 missiles. It covers a broad range in launch weight, from $W_L = 100$ to 2858 lb. Note that the average body structure weight W_{BS} is 22% of the launch weight W_L. Because of the emphasis on maximizing the flight range of most strategic missiles, such as an ICBMs, strategic missiles typically have more efficient, relatively light weight structure (with higher resulting cost).

The correlation of body structure weight is based on the load-carrying structure. If a rocket motor case, engine, or warhead case carries external loads, it is included in W_{BS}. W_{BS} does not include the weight of the tail, wing, or other planar surfaces. The body structures for the 11 missiles of this correlation are metal structures. A composite structure would be lighter, with a smaller structure weight fraction.

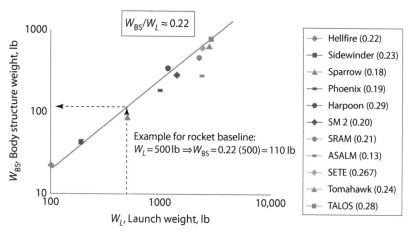

Note: W_{BS} includes all load carrying body structure. If motor case, engine, or warhead case carry external loads then they are included in W_{BS}. W_{BS} does not include tail, wing, or other surface weight.
Note: Above based on metal structure. Graphite composite structure would result in lower weight fraction.

Fig. 4.31   Missile metal body structure weight is about 22% of the launch weight.

Contributors to body structure thickness	Cylindrical body structure thickness equation
Min gauge for manufacturing	$t = 0.7d\,[p_{ext}/E)\,l/d]^{0.4}$, $t \approx 0.06$ in., if $p_{ext} \approx 10\,\text{psi}$
Localized buckling in bending	$t = 2.9\,r\sigma/E)$
Localized buckling in axial compression	$t = 4.0\,r\sigma/E)$
Thrust force	$t = T/(2\pi\sigma r)$
Maneuver bending moment	$t = M/(\pi\sigma r^2)$
Internal pressure	$t = pr/\sigma$

Note: Does not include factor of safety (FOS)

Fig. 4.32 Missile body structure required thickness is based on considering many design conditions.

As an example, the rocket baseline missile has a launch weight $W_L = 500$ lb. The predicted body structure weight is $W_{BS} = 0.22(500) = 110$ lb. From the data of Chapter 7, the actual body structure weight is 84 lb. The error in predicting body structure weight is 24%. Part of the reason for the error is the relatively large weight of the Sparrow missile wings and tails.

A number of conditions, from cradle to grave, may drive the missile airframe structure design. These include manufacturing, transportation, storage, carriage on the launch platform, launch, initial maneuvering, fly-out, and terminal maneuvering. For conceptual design and system engineering, the most important structure design considerations are usually the launch loads, rocket motor case buckling, rocket motor case internal pressure, initial maneuvering loads, and the terminal maneuvering loads.

For a conventional cylindrical body structure, there are simplified equations to estimate the required thickness for different design considerations. Figure 4.32 shows the required thickness equations for design considerations of 1) minimum gauge in manufacturing, 2) localized buckling in bending, 3) localized buckling in axial compression, 4) thrust force, 5) maneuver bending moment, and 6) internal pressure. Definitions of geometry parameters are given in the sketch at the bottom of the figure.

The first design condition, minimum gauge for manufacturing, requires sufficient thickness for the manufacturing operations such as drilling, machining, and bending. These operations can be represented as an equivalent external overpressure, typically about 10 psi. The equation for minimum gauge thickness is

$$t = 0.7\,d[(p_{ext}/E)l/d]^{0.4}$$

For an equivalent external overpressure $p_{ext} \approx 10$ psi, the minimum gauge of conventional metal airframe materials (e.g., aluminum, steel) is

$$t \approx 0.06\,\text{in.}$$

For the second design condition, the equation for the required thickness to counter localized buckling from bending is

$$t = 2.9r\sigma/E$$

For the third design condition, the equation for the required thickness to counter localized buckling from axial compression (e.g., thrust) is

$$t = 4.0r\sigma/E$$

For the fourth design condition, the required thickness to accommodate a thrust force load is

$$t = T/(2\pi\sigma r)$$

For the fifth design condition, the required thickness to accommodate a bending moment load is

$$t = M/(\pi\sigma r^2)$$

Finally, the required thickness of a cylindrical body to accommodate internal pressure loading (e.g., rocket motor chamber pressure) is

$$t = pr/\sigma$$

The critical design condition is usually a combination of the different types of structure loads. However, there may not be sufficient time in conceptual design to find the most critical combined loads condition, resulting in design uncertainty. Three simplified approaches may be used.

The first approach, which can be characterized as high-risk approach, has no consideration of combined loads. The thickness is the factor of safety (FOS) times the maximum value of the largest thickness considering each load condition

1. $t = \text{FOS} \times \text{Max}(t_{\text{Min gauge}}, t_{\text{Buckling, Bending}}, t_{\text{Buckling, Axial compression}},$
    $t_{\text{Axial load}}, t_{\text{Bending}}, t_{\text{Internal pressure}})$

The second approach is a moderate-risk approach, which uses a root-sum-of-the-squares (RSS) to select the airframe thickness

2. $t = \text{FOS} \times \left(t^2_{\text{Min gauge}} + t^2_{\text{Buckling, Bending}} + t^2_{\text{Buckling, Axial compression}} \right.$

$\left. + t^2_{\text{Axial load}} + t^2_{\text{Bending}} + t^2_{\text{Internal pressure}} \right)^{1/2}$

The third approach is a low-risk approach, but which usually results in an overdesigned/heavy airframe. It assumes that the required airframe thickness is the sum of the thicknesses for each of the loads

3. $t = \text{FOS} \times \left(t_{\text{Min gauge}} + t_{\text{Buckling, Bending}} + t_{\text{Buckling, Axial compression}} \right.$

$\left. + t_{\text{Axial load}} + t_{\text{Bending}} + t_{\text{Internal pressure}} \right)$

Approach 2 is often the approach used for conceptual design.

The most important structure design conditions for missiles are usually localized buckling, bending moment loads, and motor case internal pressure loads. The equation for localized buckling stress from bending of an un-stiffened, unpressurized circular cylinder is

$$\sigma_{\text{Buckling, Bending}}/E \approx 0.35(t/r)$$

Similarly, the equation for localized buckling stress from axial compression is

$$\sigma_{\text{Buckling, Axial compression}}/E \approx 0.25(t/r)$$

The accuracy of the above equations is limited to a typical, moderately thin wall structure, with a thickness-to-radius ratio from $0.003 < t/r > 0.03$. For a very thin wall structure ($t/r << 0.003$), the critical buckling stress would be significantly less than the prediction. Also, the actual buckling stress can vary as much as $+/-50\%$, 3σ because of typical imperfections in geometry and a slight asymmetry in the loading. Localized non-dimensional buckling stress $\sigma_{\text{Buckling}}/E$ in bending and compression are shown in Fig. 4.33 as a function of thickness ratio t/r. Note that for small thickness the allowable stress for localized buckling is very low. Localized buckling may occur in a thin wall structure prior to exceeding the yield stress.

An example is shown of the required rocket motor case wall thickness to avoid localized buckling. It is based on the Chapter 7 data of the rocket baseline missile. The rocket baseline motor case is 4130 steel, with a modulus of elasticity $E = 29.5 \times 10^6$ psi. The case thickness $t = 0.074$ in and the case radius $r = 4$ in. The value of $t/r = 0.074/4 = 0.0185$ satisfies the accuracy criteria $0.003 < (t/r) < 0.03$. From the above equation, the

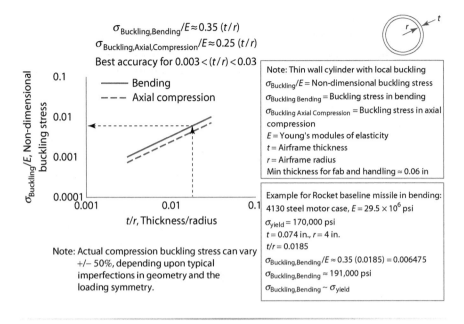

Fig. 4.33 Localized buckling may be a concern for a thin wall structure.

maximum allowable localized buckling stress from bending is

$$\sigma_{\text{Buckling,Bending}} \approx 29.5 \times 10^6 (0.35)(0.0185) = 191,000\,\text{psi}$$

The above localized buckling stress $\sigma_{\text{Buckling,Bending}} \approx 191,000$ psi is comparable to the yield stress $\sigma_{\text{yield}} = 170,000$ psi, and is within the typical uncertainty of buckling stress.

Considerations in selecting the type of steel for a rocket motor case include tradeoffs of strength, hardness (machining difficulty), buckling stability, joining/welding, and cost. An example is 4130 steel versus PH 15-7 Mo stainless steel for a rocket motor case. An advantage of 4130 steel is less susceptibility to buckling than PH 15-7 Mo steel, because it requires a thicker motor case. Other advantages of 4130 steel are that it is easier to machine, easier to weld, and it is lower cost. An advantage of PH 15-7 Mo steel is higher strength (yield strength of 200k to 265k psi, depending on the heat treatment) than 4130 steel. PH 15-7 Mo steel is more applicable to a very high chamber pressure motor case, where the required motor case thickness is set by strength and not set by buckling. For a very high chamber pressure motor case, the weight savings of very high strength steel would probably be worth the higher cost.

Noted previously, a consideration is the minimum gauge thickness for fabrication and handling loads. Manufacturing processes, such as vacuum molding and machining, exert loads on the missile section. Handling loads include consideration of the impact load of dropping tools on the structure. Based on the aluminum shell thickness of typical missiles that have shown good durability, such as the Harpoon missile, a minimum gauge thickness of 0.06 in is considered a reasonable value.

Considerations of missile captive flight carriage are illustrated in Fig. 4.34. A comparison is shown of a representative distribution of missile free flight maneuver loads versus launch platform carriage loads. The left section of the figure shows a typical missile free-flight maneuvering air load distribution and the weight load distribution on each bulkhead. The missile free flight loads are usually higher than the carriage loads because missile maximum maneuverability requirement is usually greater than that of aircraft (e.g., 30 versus 9 g). During conceptual design it is usually possible to get a fairly accurate prediction of the missile free flight loads. During follow-on preliminary design, wind tunnel tests are usually conducted to more accurately determine the missile free flight air loads. The top right section of the figure shows a notional maneuvering aircraft carriage air load distribution, carriage weight load distribution, and carriage suspension loads. The missile skin thickness is usually not sized by aircraft maneuver loads. As shown in the figure, carriage loads are taken out through a suspension system. It is difficult to accurately predict the two-body problem of a store in the flow field of the launch aircraft. Captive store wind tunnel data are usually not available in the conceptual design and system engineering phase of missile development. As a result,

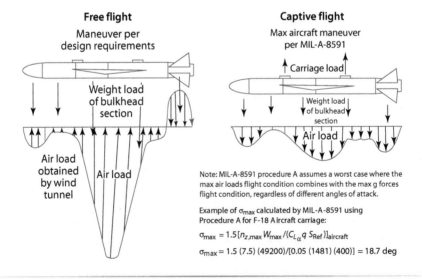

Free flight

Maneuver per design requirements

Weight load of bulkhead section

Air load obtained by wind tunnel

Air load

Captive flight

Max aircraft maneuver per MIL-A-8591

Carriage load

Weight load of bulkhead section

Air load

Note: MIL-A-8591 procedure A assumes a worst case where the max air loads flight condition combines with the max g forces flight condition, regardless of different angles of attack.

Example of σ_{max} calculated by MIL-A-8591 using Procedure A for F-18 Aircraft carriage:

$$\sigma_{max} = 1.5[n_{z,max} W_{max}/(C_{L_\alpha} q S_{Ref})]_{aircraft}$$

$$\sigma_{max} = 1.5 (7.5) (49200)/[0.05 (1481) (400)] = 18.7 \text{ deg}$$

Fig. 4.34   Conceptual design and system engineering procedure for captive flight carriage and free flight loads calculation.

the current conceptual design and system engineering approach to estimating carriage loads is often based on the usually conservative process of Military Standard (MIL STD) MIL-A-8591. As missile loads estimation becomes more accurate in the future, there is a potential for structure weight savings, based on improving the estimation accuracy for carriage loads.

MIL-A-8591 Procedure A assumes that the highest air loads flight condition combines with the highest inertial loads flight condition, regardless of the different angles of attack for each flight condition. The top right section of figure illustrates this assumption, with the captive carriage air loads and inertia loads combining in the same direction.

As an example of MIL-A-8591, the maximum missile angle of attack from an aircraft pitch maneuver, incremental missile angle of attack from aircraft roll rate, and the missile angle of sideslip from an aircraft sideslip maneuver, using Procedure A of MIL-A-8591, are given by the respective equations:

$$\alpha_{max} = [1.5 n_{z,max} W_{max}/(C_{L_\alpha} q S_{Ref})]_{aircraft}$$

$$\Delta \alpha_{\dot{\phi}_{max}} = [0.0345 \dot{\phi}_{max} y/(q)^{1/2}]_{aircraft}$$

$$\beta_{max} = [1.5 n_{y,max} W_{max}/(C_{y_\beta} q S_{Ref})]_{aircraft}$$

As an example, assume an F-18 aircraft with the following characteristics:

$n_{z,max}$ = maximum normal maneuverability = 7.5 g

$n_{y,max}$ = maximum side maneuverability = 1 g

W_{max} = maximum weight = 49,200 lb

S_{Ref} = 400 ft^2

C_{L_α} = lift curve slope at maximum dynamic pressure = 0.050 per deg

C_{y_β} = side force curve slope at maximum dynamic pressure

= 0.010 per deg

$\dot{\phi}_{max}$ = maximum roll rate at maximum dynamic pressure = 270 deg/s

y = lateral location of store from centerline of aircraft = 11.2 ft

q = dynamic pressure at store release

= 1481 psf (Mach 1 at sea level)

Using the above parameters, the store maximum angle of attack from an aircraft pitch maneuver, maximum incremental angle of attack from an aircraft roll maneuver, and the maximum angle of sideslip from an aircraft side maneuver are respectively:

$$\alpha_{max} = 1.5(7.5)(49200)/[0.050(1481)(400)] = 18.7\,\text{deg}$$

$$\Delta\alpha_{\dot{\phi}_{max}} = 0.0345(270)(11.2)/1481^{1/2} = 2.7\,\text{deg}$$

$$\beta_{max} = 1.5(1)(49200)/[0.010(1481)(400)] = 12.5\,\text{deg}$$

The above derived maximum angle of attack conditions are then used to compute the store loads.

Shown in Fig. 4.35 is a nomogram derived from Ref. 23 (my oldest college textbook). It calculates the bending moment M_B as a function of the applied load N, length l, and the type of loading c. The equation is

$$M_B = Nl/c$$

The scales of the nomogram cover the typical maximum/minimum ranges of the values of the parameters for missiles. An advantage of using a nomogram is insight into the design drivers.

Referring to the right section of the figure, note the shape of the typical load distributions, where w is the load per unit length. The load distributions shown are uniform loading ($c = 8$), linear loading increasing from the nose tip to the base ($c = 7.8$), linear loading increasing from the nose tip to the center of the missile and returning to zero at the base ($c = 6$), point

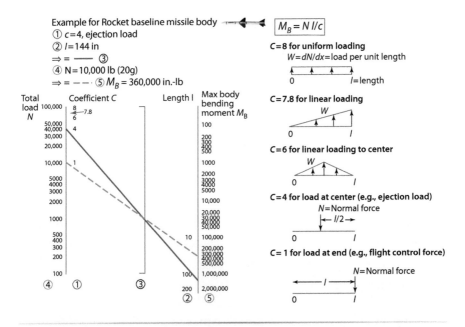

Fig. 4.35 Maximum body bending moment depends upon the load distribution. (Source: Levins, A.S., *Nomography*, Wiley, 1937.)

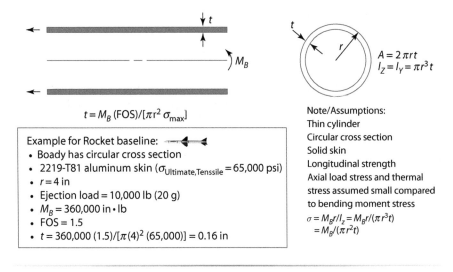

$$t = M_B \, (\text{FOS})/[\pi r^2 \, \sigma_{max}]$$

Example for Rocket baseline:
- Boady has circular cross section
- 2219-T81 aluminum skin ($\sigma_{\text{Ultimate,Tenssile}} = 65{,}000$ psi)
- $r = 4$ in
- Ejection load $= 10{,}000$ lb (20 g)
- $M_B = 360{,}000$ in·lb
- FOS $= 1.5$
- $t = 360{,}000 \, (1.5)/[\pi (4)^2 \, (65{,}000)] = 0.16$ in

$$A = 2\pi r t$$
$$I_z = I_y = \pi r^3 t$$

Note/Assumptions:
Thin cylinder
Circular cross section
Solid skin
Longitudinal strength
Axial load stress and thermal
stress assumed small compared
to bending moment stress
$\sigma = M_B r / I_z = M_B r / (\pi r^3 t)$
$\quad = M_B / (\pi r^2 t)$

Fig. 4.36 Body bending moment may drive body structure thickness/weight.

loading (e.g., ejection load) at the center ($c = 4$), and point loading (e.g., flight control force from a deflected tail surface) at the base ($c = 1$).

As an example for the 500-lb rocket baseline missile subjected to an ejection load of 20 g (10,000 lb load), the body bending moment is calculated as

$$M_B = Nl/c = 10{,}000(144)/4 = 360{,}000 \text{ in.-lb}$$

The body bending moment is estimated in the nomogram by drawing a straight line from line 1 ($c = 4$) to line 2 ($l = 144$), to determine a turning point on line 3. A second straight line is drawn from line 4 ($N = 10{,}000$) through the turning point on line 3 to intersect the value of the body bending moment on line 5 ($M_B = 360{,}000$ in.-lb).

The simple nomogram shown in the figure is a throwback to the way engineering estimates were made fifty years ago, before the wide-spread use of computers. Although nomograms are still in use in areas such as medicine, long ago they fell out of use in aerospace engineering. Up to about the year 1970, nomograms (including complex special slide rules with three or more sliders) were used in aerospace design and also as an aerospace engineering teaching tool in universities.

Figure 4.36 illustrates a conceptual design procedure to predict the required thickness of the missile body airframe structure. The objective is to ensure that the bending moment stress is below the maximum allowable stress. The required thickness is a function of the bending moment, airframe radius, maximum allowable stress, and the factor of safety. The equation is

$$t = M_B(\text{FOS})/[\pi r^2 \sigma_{max}]$$

Assumptions for the equation are a thin cylinder of circular cross section, solid skin, longitudinal bending moment, negligible axial (thrust and drag) stress, and negligible thermal stress.

As noted in the previous discussion, the rocket baseline missile subjected to an ejection load of 20 g will have a bending moment $M_B = 360,000$ in.-lb. Based on a factor of safety for an ultimate load of FOS $= 1.5$, a 2219-T81 aluminum airframe structure with ultimate tensile stress $\sigma_{\text{ultimate,tensile}} = 65,000$ psi and an airframe radius $r = 4$ in, the required airframe thickness is computed to be

$$t = 360000(1.5)/[\pi(4)^2(65000)] = 0.16 \, \text{in}$$

From the data of Chapter 7, the actual body structure thickness is also 0.16 in.

Figure 4.37 is a correlation of the propellant weight fraction of the rocket motors of eleven missiles. The solid propellant rocket motors range in weight from $W_M = 12.6$ to 4278 lb. The total motor weight includes the weight of the propellant, motor case, nozzle, and insulation.

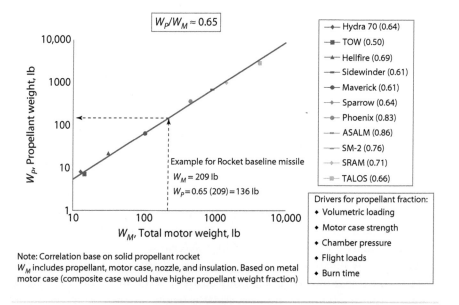

Note: Correlation base on solid propellant rocket
W_M includes propellant, motor case, nozzle, and insulation. Based on metal motor case (composite case would have higher propellant weight fraction)

Fig. 4.37 For a typical solid propellant rocket motor, about 65% of the weight is propellant.

Note that the average propellant weight fraction is

$$W_P/W_M \approx 0.65$$

Because a strategic missile has a greater emphasis on long range, a strategic missile typically has a more efficient, relatively light weight motor with a higher propellant weight fraction. Also, a liquid propellant motor is usually lighter weight with a higher propellant weight fraction.

A rocket motor with a high propellant weight fraction (i.e., greater than 65%) would tend to have high volumetric loading of propellant, a high strength motor case, low chamber pressure, low flight loads, and a short burn time. Correspondingly, drivers toward a low propellant fraction are a low volumetric loading, a low strength motor case, high chamber pressure, high flight loads, and a long burn time. It is noted that the correlation in the figure is based on rocket motors that have a metal (e.g., steel) motor case. A composite motor case would have a higher propellant weight fraction.

As an example, assume the rocket baseline missile, which has a motor weight $W_M = 209$ lb. The predicted propellant weight is $W_P = 0.65(209) = 136$ lb. This compares favorably with the Chapter 7 actual propellant weight (133 lb).

The rocket motor case is subjected to a variety of loads. The loads on the motor case include the internal pressure load produced during motor operation, thrust produced during motor operation, localized buckling, aerodynamic bending, thermal stress, and ground handling loads. Load conditions include handling, storage, launch platform carriage, ejection, and flight conditions.

The dominant load on the motor case is usually from the internal pressure. Figure 4.38 illustrates the motor case internal pressure and the resulting hoop stress and longitudinal stress. The stresses are a function of the internal pressure, case thickness, and the average radius. Hoop stress is the radial stress in the cylindrical section of the motor case. It is given by the equation

$$(\sigma_t)_{\text{Hoop stress}} = pr/t$$

The longitudinal stress is the tensile stress in the forward dome. For an ellipsoid dome, defined by the major axis radius a and the minor axis radius b, the tensile stress is

$$(\sigma_t)_{\text{Longitudinal stress}} = pa^2/(2bt)$$

For a hemispherical dome $(a = b = r)$, the equation for longitudinal stress is

$$(\sigma_t)_{\text{Longitudinal stress}} = pr/(2t)$$

• Assume motor case is axisymmetric, with a front ellipsoid dome and an aft cylinder body

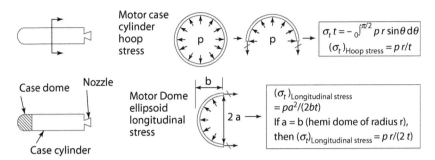

$$\sigma_t t = -\int_0^{\pi/2} p\, r \sin\theta\, d\theta$$

$$(\sigma_t)_{\text{Hoop stress}} = p\, r/t$$

Motor case cylinder hoop stress   p

Case dome   Nozzle

Motor Dome ellipsoid longitudinal stress   2 a

Case cylinder

$(\sigma_t)_{\text{Longitudinal stress}}$
$= pa^2/(2bt)$
If a = b (hemi dome of radius r),
then $(\sigma_t)_{\text{Longitudinal stress}} = p\, r/(2\, t)$

• With metals—the material also reacts body bending loads (e.g., maneuver loads)
• In composite motor designs, extra (longitudinal) fibers must usually be added to accommodate body bending loads

Fig. 4.38   Rocket motor case weight is usually driven by stress from internal pressure.

Because missiles are usually more volume limited than weight limited, many missiles have an ellipsoid forward dome with shorter length, to maximize the available volume for propellant. For a typical ellipsoid dome of $a/b = 3$, the thickness required for the dome longitudinal hoop stress is the same as the thickness required for the circular cylinder hoop stress.

A metal motor case has omni-directional strength to react both the radial (internal pressure) stress and the body bending stress. For a laminate composite motor case, the case thickness that is set by the radial fibers to react the internal pressure usually also requires additional (longitudinal) fibers to react the body bending loads. However, because motor cases are typically driven more by internal pressure than external loads, a laminate composite motor case is usually lighter than a metal motor case.

The following example illustrates a conceptual design process to predict the weight of a solid propellant rocket motor case. It compares the required thickness and weight of the steel motor case of the rocket baseline missile with that of a laminate graphite composite motor case of comparable size. The calculation shows the weight savings of a graphite composite motor case over a steel motor case.

First we will calculate the maximum effective operating pressure (MEOP). MEOP of a solid propellant rocket motor is a function of the propellant π_k, which relates the sensitivity of the combustion pressure to a change in ambient temperature

$$p_{\text{MEOP}} = p_{\text{Boost,Room temp}} \times e^{\pi_k \Delta T}$$

Using data from Chapter 7, the rocket baseline missile has a motor case diameter = 8 in.; case length = 55 in. (cylindrical section length = 53 in., forward dome section length = 2 in.); ellipsoid dome with $a/b = 2$; $p_{\text{Boost,Roomtemp}} = 1769$ psi; $\pi_k = (\Delta p/p)/\Delta T = 0.14\%/°\text{F}$

Assume a hot day ($T = 160°\text{F}$), calculate

$$e^{\pi_k \Delta T} = e^{0.0014(160 - 70)} = 1.134$$

The nominal MEOP is

$$p_{\text{MEOP}} \approx 1769 \times 1.134 = 2007 \, \text{psi}$$

Ignition spikes, poor welds, and other design uncertainty require that the design motor case burst pressure p_{Burst} be designed to a pressure higher than the nominal MEOP p_{MEOP}. Assume

$$p_{\text{Burst}} \approx p_{\text{Boost, Room temp}} \left(p_{\text{MEOP}}/p_{\text{Boost, Room temp}} \right)^n, \quad 1 < n < 3$$

Assume a conservative value of $n = 3$

$$p_{\text{Burst}} = 1769(2007/1769)^3 = 1769(1.135)^3 = 2582 \, \text{psi}$$

Figure 4.39 compares the required thickness of steel versus graphite composite for the rocket baseline motor case. Figure 4.39a shows the required thickness of the baseline steel motor case ($\rho = 0.283 \, \text{lb/in.}^3$, $(\sigma_t)_{\text{ult}} = 190{,}000$ psi) to satisfy the requirements of hoop internal pressure, forward dome internal pressure, maneuver load, buckling from bending,

a) Example for Rocket baseline missile steel motor case

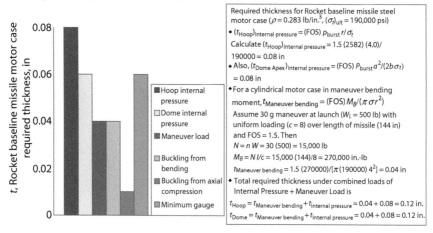

Fig. 4.39a Rocket baseline motor case thickness is driven by internal pressure.

buckling from axial compression, and the minimum gauge for manufacturing. For a combined loads condition of maneuvering with internal pressure, the thickness requirements of the cylindrical and the forward dome are

$$t_{\text{Hoop}} = t_{\text{Maneuver bending}} + t_{\text{Internal pressure}}$$

$$t_{\text{Dome}} = t_{\text{Maneuver bending}} + t_{\text{Internal pressure}}$$

The equation for the required cylindrical motor case structure thickness from bending is

$$t_{\text{maneuver bending}} = (\text{FOS})M_B/(\pi \sigma r^2).$$

We will next calculate the required thickness of the rocket baseline steel motor case. Assume that the missile is conducting a maximum g maneuver (30 g) at launch ($W_L = 500$ lb), with a uniform loading ($c = 8$) over the length of missile (144 in) and an ultimate factor of safety FOS $= 1.5$. Then

$$N = nW = 30(500) = 15{,}000\,\text{lb}$$

$$M_B = Nl/c = 15000(144)/8 = 270{,}000\,\text{in.-lb}$$

$$t_{\text{Maneuver bending}} = 1.5(270000)/[\pi(190000)4^2] = 0.04\,\text{in.}$$

For a motor case under internal pressure

$$(t_{\text{Hoop}})_{\text{Internal pressure}} = (\text{FOS})p_{\text{burst}}r/\sigma_t$$

Calculate

$$(t_{\text{Hoop}})_{\text{Internal pressure}} = 1.5(2582)(4.0)/190000 = 0.08\,\text{in.}$$

Also

$$(t_{\text{Dome}})_{\text{Internal pressure}} = (\text{FOS})p_{\text{burst}}\,a^2/(2b\sigma_t)$$

$$= 0.08\,\text{in.}$$

Then

$$t_{\text{Hoop}} = t_{\text{Maneuver bending}} + t_{\text{Internal pressure}} = 0.04 + 0.08 = 0.12\,\text{in}$$

The Chapter 7 data of the rocket baseline case thickness is $t = 0.074$ in. (conservative prediction of $t_{\text{Hoop}} = 0.12$ in.) Also

$$t_{\text{Dome}} = t_{\text{Maneuver bending}} + t_{\text{Internal pressure}} = 0.04 + 0.08 = 0.012\,\text{in.}$$

We will check to ensure that the dome thickness is greater than the thickness required to avoid bucking and to provide sufficient strength for manufacturing operations:

$$t_{Dome} > t_{Buckle}, t_{min\ gauge}$$

The buckling equation in bending is

$$t_{Buckling,Bending} = (FOS)(2.9)r\sigma_{Bending}/E$$

Solving for the buckling stress in bending

$$\sigma_{Bending} = (FOS)M_B/(\pi r^2 t_{Dome}) = 1.5(270000)/[\pi(4^2)(0.11)]$$
$$= 73{,}200\ psi$$

Solving for the required thickness to avoid localized buckling due to bending

$$t_{Buckling,Bending} = 1.5(2.9)(4)(73200)/29.5 \times 10^6 = 0.04\ in < 0.10 = t_{Dome}$$

Note that the dome thickness is greater than the thickness required to avoid localized buckling due to bending. Similarly, if $T = 5750(1.135)^3 = 8385\ lb$ the thickness required to avoid localized axial buckling

$$t_{Buckling,Axial\ compression} = (FOS)(4.0)r\sigma/E$$
$$\sigma_{Axial} = (FOS)T/(2\pi t_{Dome}) = 1.5(8385)/[2\pi(0.11)]$$
$$= 18{,}200\ psi$$

$$t_{Buckling,Axial\ compression} = 1.5(4.0)(4)(18200)/29.5 \times 10^6$$
$$= 0.01\ in < 0.10 = t_{Dome}$$

Note from above that the dome thickness is greater than the thickness that is required to avoid localized buckling due to axial compression. Finally, the minimum gauge for manufacturing steel is

$$t_{min\ gauge} = 0.06\ in < 0.10 = t_{Dome}$$

Note from above that the dome thickness is greater than the minimum thickness.

Figure 4.39b conducts a similar calculation of the required thickness of a 60% graphite fiber/40% polyimide matrix composite rocket motor case ($\rho = 0.057\ lb/in.^3$). For the graphite fiber alone, the ultimate tensile stress $(\sigma_t)_{ultimate} = 450{,}000$ psi. For 60% graphite/40% polyimide composite, we shall assume that all of the load is carried by the graphite fiber, giving

$$(\sigma_t)_{ultimate} \approx 0.6(450000) = 270{,}000\ psi.$$

b)

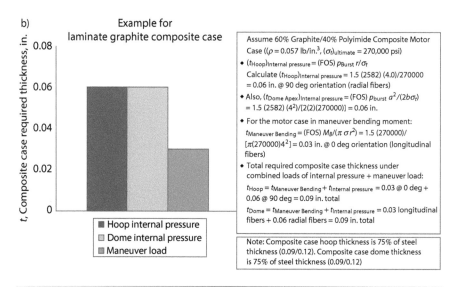

Example for laminate graphite composite case

Assume 60% Graphite/40% Polyimide Composite Motor Case (($\rho = 0.057$ lb/in.^{3}, (σ_t)$_{ultimate}$ = 270,000 psi)

- (t_{Hoop})$_{Internal pressure}$ = (FOS) p_{Burst} r/σ_t
  Calculate (t_{Hoop})$_{Internal pressure}$ = 1.5 (2582) (4.0)/270000
  = 0.06 in. @ 90 deg orientation (radial fibers)
- Also, ($t_{Dome Apex}$)$_{Internal pressure}$ = (FOS) p_{burst} $a^2/(2b\sigma_t)$
  = 1.5 (2582) (4^2)/[2(2)(270000)] = 0.06 in.
- For the motor case in maneuver bending moment:
  $t_{Maneuver Bending}$ = (FOS) $M_B/(\pi\ \sigma\ r^2)$ = 1.5 (270000)/
  [π(270000)4^2] = 0.03 in. @ 0 deg orientation (longitudinal fibers)
- Total required composite case thickness under combined loads of internal pressure + maneuver load:
  t_{Hoop} = $t_{Maneuver Bending}$ + $t_{Internal pressure}$ = 0.03 @ 0 deg + 0.06 @ 90 deg = 0.09 in. total
  t_{Dome} = $t_{Maneuver Bending}$ + $t_{Internal pressure}$ = 0.03 longitudinal fibers + 0.06 radial fibers = 0.09 in. total

■ Hoop internal pressure
□ Dome internal pressure
■ Maneuver load

Note: Composite case hoop thickness is 75% of steel thickness (0.09/0.12). Composite case dome thickness is 75% of steel thickness (0.09/0.12)

Fig. 4.39b Rocket baseline motor case thickness is driven by internal pressure.

As before, assume

$$t_{Hoop} = t_{Maneuver\ bending} + t_{Internal\ pressure}$$

Calculate

$$t_{Maneuver\ bending} = 1.5(270000)/[\pi(270000)4^2]$$
$$= 0.03 \text{ in. @ 0 deg orientation (longitudinal fibers)}$$
$$(t_{Hoop})_{Internal\ pressure} = 1.5(2582)(4.0)/(270000)$$
$$= 0.06 \text{ in. @ 90 deg orientation (radial fibers)}$$
$$t_{Hoop} = 0.03 @ 0 \deg + 0.06 @ 90 \deg = 0.09 \text{ in. total}$$
$$(t_{Dome})_{Internal\ pressure} = 1.5(2582)(4^2)/[2(2)(270000)] = 0.06 \text{ in.}$$
$$t_{Dome} = t_{Maneuver\ bending} + t_{Internal\ pressure}$$
$$= 0.03 \text{ longitudinal fibers} + 0.06 \text{ radial fibers}$$
$$= 0.09 \text{ in. total}$$

For the same loading, the laminate composite case cylindrical section thickness is thinner than the steel motor case (0.09 in. versus 0.12 in.). Also, the composite case dome is thinner than the steel dome (0.09 in. versus 0.12). For a typical volume limited missile, the reduced thickness of the composite motor case allows more propellant, allowing longer range.

Figure 4.40 compares the weight of a laminate graphite composite motor case with the rocket baseline steel motor case. Weight is computed from the density of the material times the volume of the case material ($W = \rho At$). The weight of the steel motor case is comprised of the weight of the cylindrical section plus the forward dome. Computing the weight of the steel motor case, without insulation, attachment, and the aft dome/nozzle

$$\text{Weight} = W_{\text{Cylinder}} + W_{\text{Dome}} = \rho \pi dt_{\text{Hoop}} l_{\text{Cylinder}} + \rho(2\pi ab)t_{\text{Dome}}$$
$$= 0.283(\pi)(8)(0.12)(53) + 0.283(2)(\pi)(2)(4)(0.10)$$
$$= 45 + 1.4 = 46\,\text{lb}$$

Also, the weight of the composite motor case without insulation, attachment, and aft dome/nozzle is

$$\text{Weight} = W_{\text{Cylinder}} + W_{\text{Dome}}$$
$$= 0.057(\pi)(8)(0.09)(53) + 0.057(2)(\pi)(2)(4)(0.07)$$
$$= 6.8 + 0.2 = 7.0\,\text{lb}$$

Note that the laminate graphite composite rocket motor case is only about 1/7 of the weight of the steel motor case ($7.0/46 = 0.15$). Because of their weight savings, composite motor cases should find increased application in the future as the cost of composites continues to decrease.

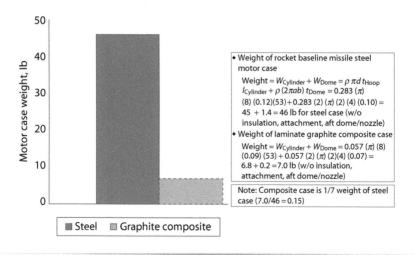

Fig. 4.40 A laminate graphite composite rocket motor case is lighter weight.

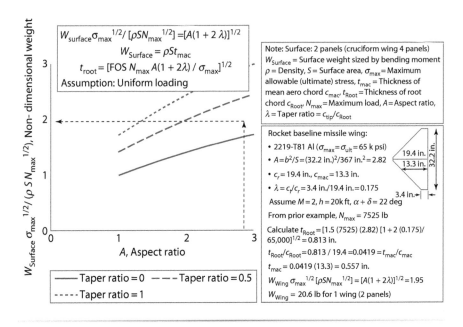

Fig. 4.41 A low aspect ratio delta planform is lighter weight.

Figure 4.41 shows the non-dimensional structure weight of planar surface (e.g., wing, canard, tail) planforms. The equation for the figure is

$$W_{\text{Surface}}\sigma_{\max}^{1/2}/[\rho S N_{\max}^{1/2}] = [A(1+2\lambda)]^{1/2}$$

Assumptions are that the planar surface is composed of two panels, it is monolithic (solid), has uniform loading, and its thickness is determined by bending moment stress. Note from the figure that a low aspect ratio surface with a delta ($\lambda = 0$) planform is the lightest weight.

Weight can be expressed as

$$W_{\text{Surface}} = \rho S t_{\text{mac}}$$

The terms in the above equation are $\rho =$ material density, $S =$ surface planform area, and $t_{\text{mac}} =$ thickness of the mean aerodynamic chord (average thickness).

The equation for surface root chord thickness is

$$t_{\text{root}} = (\text{FOS}) N_{\max} A[(1+2\lambda)/\sigma_{\max}]^{1/2}$$

The terms in the above equation are FOS = factor of safety, $N_{\max} =$ maximum load, $A =$ aspect ratio, $\lambda =$ taper ratio, and $\sigma_{\max} = \sigma_{\text{ult}} =$ maximum (ultimate) stress.

An example calculation will be based on the data of the rocket baseline missile wing of Chapter 7. The wing material is 2219-T81 aluminum, with a maximum allowable stress (ultimate stress) $\sigma_{max} = \sigma_{ultimate} = 65k$ psi and a density $\rho = 0.103$ lbm/in.^{3}. The wing geometry has a surface area $S = 2.55$ ft$^2 = 367$ in.^{2}, an aspect ratio $A = 2.82$, taper ratio $\lambda = 0.175$, root chord $c_{root} = 19.4$ in, and a mean aerodynamic chord $c_{mac} = 13.3$ in. Assume a typical intercept flight condition of $M = 2$, 20 kft altitude, and maximum local angle of attack on the wing of $\alpha + \delta = 22$ deg. From a prior example of Chapter 2, the maximum normal force on the wing for this flight condition is $N_{max} = 7525$ lb. Substitution gives

$$t_{root} = [1.5(7525)(2.82)[1 + 2(0.175)/65000]^{1/2} = 0.813 \text{ in}$$

Solving for the thickness ratio,

$$t_{root}/c_{root} = t_{mac}/c_{mac} = 0.813/19.4 = 0.0419$$

The predicted thickness ratio is comparable to the data of Chapter 7 (0.0419 versus 0.044).

The average predicted thickness of the mean aerodynamic chord is

$$t_{mac} = 0.0419(13.3) = 0.557 \text{ in}$$

Substituting into the wing weight equation, the predicted weight of one surface, a mono-wing with two panels, is

$$W_{wing} = \rho S t_{mac} = 0.103(367)(0.557) = 20.6 \text{ lb}$$

The rocket baseline missile has two wings (cruciform), with a predicted weight of $2 \times 20.6 = 41.2$ lb. The Chapter 7 data of the rocket baseline missile cruciform wing weight is 38.6 lb.

4.14 Seeker Dome

Shown in Figs. 4.42, 4.43, and 4.44 are comparisons of alternative dome materials for multi-mode (RF/IR), infrared (IR), and radar frequency (RF) seekers respectively.

Figure 4.42 lists multi-mode seeker dome material measures of merit of low dielectric constant, infrared bandpass for combined mid wave (3 to 5 μm)/long wave (8 to 14 μm), high transverse strength, low thermal expansion, high erosion resistance, and high maximum temperature capability for short duration flight. Dome materials that are suited for most combined radar and infrared seekers include zinc sulfide (Z_nS) and zinc selenide (Z_nSe). Zinc sulfide and zinc selenide are also suitable for IR-only seekers. Zinc selenide has an advantage of infrared broad bandpass, with a transmission of about 70% over the wavelength from 0.8 μm to greater than

Multi-mode seeker dome material	Density (g/cm³)	Dielectric constant	MWIR/LWIR bandpass		Transverse strength (10^3 psi)	Thermal expansion (10^{-6}/°F)	Erosion, Knoop (kg/mm²)	Max short-duration temp (°F)
Zinc Sulfide (ZnS)	4.05	8.4 (Average)	Superior	Good	18 (Average)	4 (Average)	350 (Average)	700 (Average)
Zinc Selenide (ZnSe)	5.16	9.0 (Poor)	Superior	Superior	8 (Poor)	4 (Average)	150 (Average)	600 (Average)
Sapphire (Al₂O₃)/ Spinel (MgAl₂O₄)	3.68	8.5 (Average)	Superior	Very poor	28 (Average)	3 (Average)	1650 (Superior)	1800 (Superior)
Quartz/fused Silica (SiO₂)	2.20	3.7 (Superior)	Average	Very poor	8 (Poor)	0.3 (Superior)	600 (Good)	2000 (Superior)
Silicon nitride (Si₃N₄)	3.18	6.1 (Good)	Poor	Very poor	90 (Superior)	2 (Good)	2200 (Superior)	2700 (Superior)
Diamond (C)	3.52	5.6 (Good)	Very poor	Poor	400 (Superior)	1 (Superior)	8800 (Superior)	3500 (Superior)
Pyroceram	2.55	5.8 (Good)	Poor	Very poor	25 (Average)	3 (Average)	700 (Good)	2200 (Superior)
Polyimide	1.54	3.2 (Superior)	Poor	Very poor	17 (Average)	40 (Poor)	70 (Poor)	700 (Average)
Mag. Fluoride (MgF₂)	3.18	5.5 (Good)	Superior	Poor	7 (Poor)	6 (Poor)	420 (Good)	1000 (Good)
Alon (Al₂₃O₂₇N₅)	3.67	9.3 (Poor)	Good	Very poor	44 (Good)	3 (Average)	1900 (Superior)	1800 (Superior)

● Superior ⊖ Good ○ Average ∽ Poor — Very poor

Fig. 4.42 Multi-mode seeker dome material is driven by *RF/IR* transmission and the flight environment.

14 μm. Zinc sulfide has advantages in its dielectric constant, transverse strength, and resistance to rain erosion. Ordinary zinc sulfide has a transmission of about 55% in the 3-to-5 μm range and about 65% in the 8-to-12 μm range. The infrared transmission of zinc sulfide can be enhanced by a post-deposition hot isostatic press, which removes the zinc hydrides from the crystal lattice. The transmission of zinc sulfide for a single crystal-like structure is about 70% from 0.8 to 10 μm. Zinc sulfide is generally the multi-mode dome material of choice for supersonic missiles with Mach numbers up to 3. Zinc selenide is often selected for subsonic missiles. For Mach number greater than 3, other materials are required for multi-mode seekers. Candidate high temperature capability materials for multi-mode seeker domes include sapphire/spinel (Al_2O_3/$MgAl_2O_4$), quartz/fused silicon (SiO_2), silicon nitride (Si_3N_4), and diamond (C). A disadvantage of the high temperature capability materials is their higher cost compared to zinc sulfide and zinc selenide. These high temperature materials may also be suitable for RF-only and mmW-only seekers.

Diamond dome material is under development for missile defense applications with RF/LWIR seekers. The material cost of a diamond dome is very high. In addition to high material cost, diamond dome assembly cost is high. Diamond domes must be assembled as a built-up mosaic because the present manufacturing processes produce relatively small diamonds. Diamond can also be used as a coating over a conventional dome, to provide erosion resistance. The coating can be deposited through a chemical vapor deposition (CVD) process.

In addition to quartz/fused silica and silicon nitride that can be used for multi-mode RF-MWIR seekers, other materials that are most suitable for RF-only seekers but may also be used for RF/MWIR seekers include pyroceram and polyimide.

Shown in Fig. 4.43 is a comparison of alternative dome materials for missile infrared (IR) seekers. Measures of merit are infrared bandpass for combined mid wave (3 to 5 μm)/long wave (8 to 14 μm), high transverse strength, low thermal expansion, high erosion resistance, and high maximum temperature capability for short duration flight. Dome materials that are suited for infrared seekers include zinc sulfide, zinc selenide, magnesium fluoride, germanium, spinel/sapphire, diamond, Alon, and quartz/fused silica. Zinc sulfide, zinc selenide, and germanium have good IR bandpass and are often used with multi-spectral (MWIR/LWIR) seekers. Germanium is most suitable for subsonic/low supersonic missiles with MWIR/LWIR seekers, such as SLAM-ER and AGM-130. Germanium has more than 50% transmission over the wavelength from 1.8 to 23 μm. For a high speed multi-spectral seeker, magnesium fluoride is often the choice. Spinel or sapphire domes are often used with MWIR-only seekers at high supersonic/low hypersonic Mach numbers. An example of a missile with a sapphire dome for its MWIR seeker is ASRAAM. For a very high Mach number LWIR seeker, a faceted diamond dome is a possibility. Other materials that are suitable for high Mach number MWIR-only seekers are Alon and quartz/fused silica.

Finally, shown in Fig. 4.44 is a comparison of alternative dome materials for RF-only seekers. Measures of merit are low dielectric constant, high

Infrared seeker dome material	Density (g/cm³)	MWIR/LWIR bandpass	Transverse strength (10³ psi)	Thermal expansion (10⁻⁶/°F)	Erosion, Knoop (kg/mm²)	Max short-duration temp (°F)
Zinc sulfide (ZnS)	4.05	● ◒	18 ○	4 ○	350 ○	700 ○
Zinc selenide (ZnSe)	5.16	● ●	8 ◡	4 ○	150 ○	600 ○
Mag. Fluoride (MgF₂)	3.18	● ◡	7 ◡	6 ◡	420 ◒	1000 ◒
Germanium (Ge)	5.33	● ●	15 ○	4 ○	780 ◒	200 ◡
Sapphire (Al₂O₃)/ Spinel (MgAl₂O₄)	3.68	● —	28 ○	3 ○	1650 ●	1800 ●
Diamond (C)	3.52	— ◡	400 ●	1 ●	8800 ●	3500 ●
Alon (Al₂₃O₂₇N₅)	3.67	◒ —	44 ◒	3 ○	1900 ●	1800 ●
Quartz/fused silica (SᵢO₂)	2.20	○ —	8 ◡	0.3 ●	600 ◒	2000 ●

● Superior   ◒ Good   ○ Average   ◡ Poor   — Very poor

Fig. 4.43 Infrared seeker dome material is driven by MWIR/LWIR transmission and the flight environment.

Radar seeker dome material	Density (g/cm³)	Dielectic constant	Transverse strength (10³ psi)	Thermal expansion (10⁻⁶/°F)	Erosion, Knoop (kg/mm²)	Max short-duration temp (°F)
Quartz/fused Silica (S_iO_2)	2.20	3.7 ●	8 ∪	0.3 ●	600 ◓	2000 ●
Silicon Nitride (Si_3N_4)	3.18	6.1 ◓	90 ●	2 ◓	2200 ●	2700 ●
Diamond (C)	3.52	5.6 ◓	400 ●	1 ●	8800 ●	3500 ●
Pyroceram	2.55	5.8 ◓	25 ○	3 ○	700 ◓	2200 ●
Polyimide	1.54	3.2 ●	17 ○	40 ∪	70 ∪	700 ○
Mag. Fluoride (MgF_2)	3.18	5.5 ◓	7 ∪	6 ∪	420 ◓	1000 ◓

● Superior   ◓ Good   ○ Average   ∪ Poor   — Very poor

Fig. 4.44   Radar seeker radome material is driven by RF transmission and the flight environment.

transverse strength, low thermal expansion, high erosion resistance, and high maximum temperature capability for short duration flight. Dome materials that are suited for RF seekers include quartz/fused silica, silicon nitride, diamond, pyroceram, polyimide, and magnesium fluoride. Pyroceram is the most common dome material in supersonic missiles, such as Sparrow and the Patriot PAC-2. For subsonic/low supersonic missiles, a polyimide radome is particularly applicable. The millimeter wave (mmW) Brimstone has a polyimide radome. Polyimide radomes have excellent dielectric characteristics. For hypersonic missiles, silicon nitride is the most popular material. PAC-3 has a silicon nitride radome.

The required weight of a radome is usually driven more by the optimum thickness that is required for efficient transmission of the radar signal, rather than by structural design or handling considerations.

The weight of a missile seeker dome is a function of the material density ρ, the wetted or surface area S_{wet}, and the thickness t. For a monolithic dome with constant thickness and neglecting the weight of the nose cap and aft attachment ring, the equation for dome weight for an optimum transmission thickness is

$$W_{Opt\ trans} = \rho S_{wet} t_{Opt\ trans}$$

Transmission efficiency of the radar signal through a radome is a function of the radome thickness t, the radar seeker wavelength in air λ_0, the dielectric constant ε, and the incidence angle of the radar signal with the radome surface θ_i. From Klein [24], the equation for radome thickness based on optimum transmission is

$$t_{Opt\ trans} = 0.5n\lambda_0/(\varepsilon - \sin^2\theta_i)^{1/2}$$

Figure 4.45 shows the non-dimensional thickness as a function of the dielectric constant ε of the radome material and the incidence angle θ_i. Note that a high value of dielectric constant requires a smaller value of the optimum thickness. Also, a shorter wavelength (e.g., millimeter wave) requires a smaller value of the optimum thickness.

There is a cyclic relationship ($n = 0, 1, 2, \ldots$) of good transmission efficiency with radome thickness. For $0 < n < 1$ with low values of n (e.g., $n < 0.3$) there is good transmission efficiency, but the thin wall radome usually does not have sufficient structural integrity. Except for very high dynamic pressure or very high bending moment, the $n = 1$ (thick wall) solution for the optimum thickness usually results in an over designed structure. Poor transmission efficiency occurs in the cyclic relationship of $n = 0.5, 1.5, \ldots$ A non-optimum thickness and a high value of the dielectric constant can result in a transmission loss of more than 60%.

Shown in top section of the figure is the geometric relationship of θ_i with seeker look angle δ and radome surface angle θ. The equation is

$$\theta_i = 90 \deg - \delta - \theta$$

From an electromagnetic point of view, a hemispheric radome would be ideal. Because a hemispherical radome provides a zero incidence angle to an

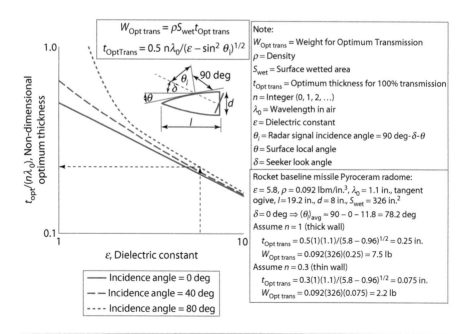

Fig. 4.45 A driver for radome weight is the optimum thickness required for efficient transmission.

incoming signal for all seeker look angles, its optimum thickness is constant. A hemispherical radome with an ideal dielectric constant of $\varepsilon = 1$ would have an ideal electromagnetic thickness of one-half of the radar wavelength.

The application of a hemispherical radome is usually limited to subsonic/low supersonic missiles, because of drag. At high supersonic Mach number, a high fineness radome is usually required. A disadvantage of a high fineness radome is the radar incidence angle changes with seeker look angle, resulting in a non-optimum thickness for a typical low cost missile radome, which is constant thickness. An optimized high fineness radome requires expensive prescription tailoring, with smaller thickness near the nose and a greater thickness near the airframe attachment.

As an example, the radome material of the rocket baseline missile is pyroceram. Pyroceram has a dielectric constant $\varepsilon = 5.8$ and a density $\rho = 0.092$ lbm/in.^{3}. The geometry of the baseline radome is a tangent ogive, with a length l, diameter d, and wetted area S_{wet} of 19.2 in., 8 in., and 326 in.^{2} respectively. The baseline seeker is an X-band radar seeker, with a frequency of $f = 10$ GHz and a wavelength in air of $\lambda_0 = 1.1$ in. For a seeker looking straight ahead ($\delta = 0$ deg), the average incidence angle is

$$(\theta_i)_{avg} = 90 - \delta - \theta \approx 90 - 0 - \tan^{-1}[(d/2)/l]$$
$$= 90 - 0 - \tan^{-1}[(8/2)/19.2] = 90 - 0 - 11.8 = 78.2 \, \text{deg}$$

Substituting into the optimum thickness equation

$$t_{\text{Opt trans}} = 0.5n\lambda_0/(\varepsilon - \sin^2\theta_i)^{1/2}$$

The smallest thickness with efficient thick wall ($n = 1$) transmission results in

$$t_{\text{Opt trans}} = 0.5(1)(1.1)/(5.8 - 0.96)^{1/2} = 0.25 \, \text{in}$$

Substituting into the weight equation, the weight of the optimum transmission thickness of a thick wall radome is

$$W_{\text{Opt trans}} = \rho S_{wet} t_{\text{Opt trans}} = 0.092(326)(0.25) = 7.5 \, \text{lb}$$

The thickness of a relatively efficient thin wall ($n = 0.3$) transmission results in

$$t_{\text{Opt trans}} = 0.5(0.3)(1.1)/(5.8 - 0.96)^{1/2} = 0.075 \, \text{in}$$

Substituting into the weight equation, the weight of the optimum transmission thickness of a thin wall radome is

$$W_{\text{Opt trans}} = \rho S_{wet} t_{\text{Opt trans}} = 0.092(326)(0.075) = 2.2 \, \text{lb}$$

From Chapter 7, the actual weight of the rocket baseline missile radome is 4.1 lb, which is intermediate the above predicted values of the thick wall and thin wall solutions. It appears that the Chapter 7 data may be for a thin wall radome that also includes the additional weight of a metal nose tip and the attachment joint fasteners.

The required radome thickness for high transmission efficiency should be checked to see if there is sufficient thickness for structural integrity, especially for a thin wall radome. If additional thickness is required for structural integrity, then the next largest multiple value of n should be used, to provide a good transmission efficiency that is combined with structural integrity.

4.15 Missile Power Supply and Flight Control Actuators

Missile electrical power supply provides the electrical energy required for the seeker, autopilot, navigation system, flight control system, initiators, and fuzes. Shown in Fig. 4.46 is a comparison of the alternative approaches of a generator, non-chargeable lithium battery, rechargeable lithium battery, and a thermal battery for electrical power supply. Measures of merit are the storage life (typically a maximum of about twenty years), cost, weight

$W = W_E E + W_P P$				
Measure of merit	Generator	Lithium battery (Non-rechargeable)	Lithium battery (Rechargeable)	Thermal battery
W_E, Weight/Energy (kg/kW-s)	0.0007 ●	0.0009 ●	0.0012 ◖	0.0125 ∨
W_P, Weight/Power (kg/kW)	1.4 ∨	0.6 ○	1.5 ∨	0.3 ●
Cost	∨	◖	○	●
Storage life	●	○◖	∨◖	●
Voltage stability	◖	●	●	∨
Temperature	○	∨	∨	○
Safety	●	○	○	○
	● Superior	◖ Good	○ Average	∨ Poor

Note: Generator provides highest energy with light weight for long time of flight (e.g., cruise missile). Lithium battery provides nearly constant voltage suitable for electronics. Relatively high energy with light weight. Thermal battery provides highest power with light weight (may be required for actuators). Example for thermal battery: If $E = 900$ kW-s, $P = 3$ kW $\Rightarrow W = W_E E + W_P P = 0.0125(900) + 0.3(3) = 12.2$ kg

Fig. 4.46 Missile electrical power supply alternatives and tradeoffs.

per energy in kg/kW-s, weight per power in kg/kW, voltage stability, maximum/minimum environmental temperature range, and safety. The weight per energy and weight per power are typical values based on the relatively small power supply that is appropriate for missile applications.

Power supply must accommodate both the total energy and the instantaneous power that are required. The weight of the power supply correlates with the equation

$$W = W_E E + W_P P$$

In the above equation W_E is the weight per energy and W_P is the weight per power. As an example, the predicted weight of a thermal battery for a missile requiring 3 kW of power for 300 s of flight time is

$$W = W_E E + W_P P = 0.0125(900) + 0.3(3) = 12.2\,\text{kg}$$

For a long range air-breathing cruise missile, a generator with a rechargeable battery is the usually the best approach for power supply. The generator can be efficiently powered by either the air flow through the inlet, or in the case of a turbojet engine, driven directly by the shaft of the turbojet.

For a shorter range missile (e.g., time of flight less than 10 m), the electrical power to the seeker and autopilot may be best provided by a lithium-ion battery. A lithium battery provides the nearly constant voltage required by electronics. A lithium battery is also efficient for energy storage—it provides relatively high power at light weight. For a shorter duration time of flight, a lithium battery would be lighter than a generator/battery. Also note that because the missile is used only once, the battery may not need to be rechargeable. However, a rechargeable battery may be desirable for periodic maintenance test surveillance. Rechargeable batteries tend to be less safe than non-rechargeable batteries. The rechargeable battery weight per energy and the weight per power values shown in the figure are based on the relatively safe with high performance lithium-ion polymer battery. This type of lithium battery is attractive for missile application because in addition to its relatively high performance and safety, the extrusion process adapted from the plastics industry results in a relatively low cost.

For a shorter range missile, the electrical power for electromechanical flight control actuators is usually best provided by a thermal battery. A thermal battery efficiently provides the power that is required by high power components such as actuators. Another advantage is that it can be stored almost indefinitely. An electrical energy impulse from a squib activates the thermal battery by igniting the pyrotechnic materials inside the battery, which melt the electrolyte. Most thermal batteries use an iron disulfide cathode and a lithium alloy anode (e.g., lithium/iron sulfide).

A typical short range missile may have two batteries—a lithium battery providing the nearly constant voltage required by the electronics and a thermal battery for high power subsystems such as the flight control actuators.

Flywheels, capacitors, fuel cells, lithium-air, and micro-miniature gas turbines are other potential sources of missile power supply. However, their technologies are relatively immature and they have not yet been applied to operational missiles.

A system integration tradeoff is the approach to the power supply of the missile during its captive carriage on the launch platform. During captive carriage the missile power could be provided by the launch platform, by the launcher, or by the missile.

Shown in Fig. 4.47 is a comparison of the missile flight control actuator alternatives of electromechanical (EM), warm gas pneumatic, cold gas pneumatic, and hydraulic. EM actuators are attractive because they have superior reliability, are light weight, and do not have any serious weaknesses. EM actuators are usually the best choice for most missiles. Warm gas pneumatic actuation is another possible choice. The "warm" gas is typically provided by an ammonium nitrate gas generator, with combustion temperature of 1000-to-1500°F. It has no serious weaknesses and is particularly applicable to high performance missiles that require high rate actuation, such as Sidewinder and the SM-3 third stage. A cold gas pneumatic actuation system is lowest cost but has disadvantages of high weight per

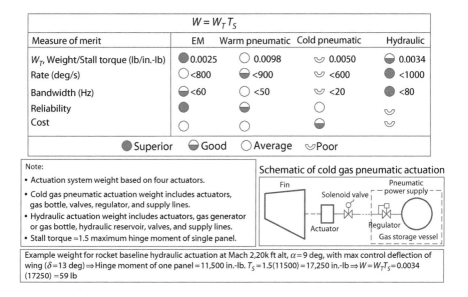

Fig. 4.47 Electromechanical flight control actuators are light weight and reliable.

torque (W_T), low rate, and low bandwidth. In the bottom right section of the figure is a schematic of the components of a cold gas pneumatic actuation system, which includes the actuators, gas bottle, valves, regulator, and supply lines. Cold gas pneumatic actuators are most applicable to small, low cost, and lower performance missiles. Higher performance hot gas (approximately 5000°F with aluminum fuel) pneumatic actuation systems have also been developed, but have seen much less application than warm and cold gas pneumatic because of their higher cost and lower reliability. Finally, a hydraulic actuation system has superior rate and bandwidth but is higher cost and has lower reliability. The components of a hydraulic actuation system include the actuators, gas generator or gas bottle pressurization, hydraulic reservoir, valves, and supply lines. Hydraulic actuators are most applicable to large, high cost, high performance missiles.

The weight of the flight control actuation system is given by the equation

$$W = W_T T_S$$

In the above equation W_T is the weight per stall torque and T_S is the stall torque. The equation is based on a typical missile flight control actuation system, consisting of four actuators. As a design practice, the stall torque should be about 50% larger than the maximum hinge moment, to allow sufficient design margin and bandwidth.

As an example, the rocket baseline missile has a hydraulic flight control actuation system with four actuators. As shown previously in Chapter 2, at a burnout condition of Mach 2 and 20,000 ft altitude, the maximum hinge moment for a maximum control surface deflection of $\delta = 13$ deg plus an angle of attack $\alpha = 9$ deg is a total of 23,000 in-lb for the two panels that comprise the wing. The hinge moment on a single panel is 23000/2 = 11,500 in.-lb. The design stall torque of the actuator is

$$T_S = 1.5(11500) = 17250 \text{ in.-lb}$$

Substituting into the weight equation for a hydraulic actuation system gives

$$W = W_T T_S = 0.0034(17250) = 59 \text{ lb}$$

From the rocket baseline missile data of Chapter 7, the actual weight of the flight control actuation system is 61 lb.

Figure 4.48 shows examples of the packaging of electromechanical actuators for flight control. The forward section and the aft (nozzle blast tube) section of the missile are the most efficient locations for packaging flight control actuators. In the top portion of the figure, note the inboard

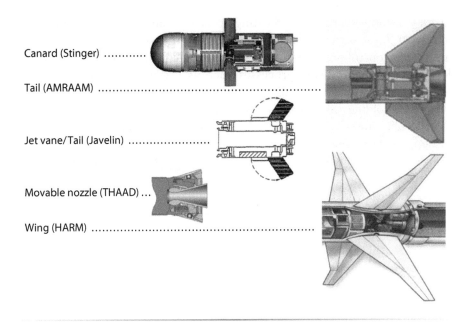

Canard (Stinger) ....

Tail (AMRAAM) ....

Jet vane/Tail (Javelin) ....

Movable nozzle (THAAD) ...

Wing (HARM) ....

Fig. 4.48 An electromechanical flight control actuator allows
efficient packaging.

profile of the single canard actuator packaging of Stinger. Shown in the
middle section of the figure are examples of tail control actuators. Shown
are the aft control actuator packaging for the four tail control actuators
of AMRAAM, four jet vane/tail control actuators of Javelin, and the two
movable nozzle TVC actuators of THAAD. Although the single canard
actuator packaging of the simple bang-bang control of Stinger is efficient,
it does increase the length of the missile. An advantage of the aft actuator
packaging around the blast tubes of AMRAAM, Javelin, and THAAD is it
may be accommodated with less impact on missile length. Also shown at
the bottom of the figure is the electromechanical actuator packaging of
the wing control HARM. Flight control actuators packaging of HARM
has a relatively large impact on missile volume because of the relatively
large hinge moments for wing control. Note from the figure that the
length of the HARM rocket motor is limited because the wing control
actuators are located near the center of the missile.

4.16 Summary

This chapter addressed weight design methods, manufacturing processes, subsystem design weight considerations, and the technologies for
light weight, low cost missiles. Design methods included missile system
weight prediction, center-of-gravity and moment-of-inertia prediction,

factors of safety, aerodynamic heating prediction, and the weight considerations for the structure, seeker dome, propulsion, insulation, power supply,
and flight control actuation. Airframe manufacturing processes included
low parts count/low cost processes such as precision castings, vacuum
assisted resin transfer molding, sintering, pultrusion, extrusion, compression molding, and filament winding. Design considerations for a
light-weight missile included airframe material alternatives, load distribution, insulation material alternatives, seeker dome material alternatives,
power supply and actuator alternatives, thermal stress, and aerodynamic
heating. Finally, new technologies were identified for light-weight missiles.
These include MEMS diagnostic technology, composites, titanium alloys,
high density insulation, high energy and power density power supply, and
high torque flight control actuators.

4.17 Problem Review

1. Light weight missiles tend to be lower c____.
2. Ballistic missile launch weight is driven by maximum range, payload
   weight, propellant weight, and s_____ i_____.
3. Missile weight is proportional to its v_____.
4. Missile subsystems d_____ is about 0.05 lbm/in.^{3}
5. Modeling missile weight, balance, and moment-of-inertia is based on a
   build-up of s_____.
6. Missile structure factor of safety for free flight is usually about 1.25 for
   ultimate loads and about 1.10 for y____ loads.
7. Airframe manufacturing processes with low parts count include
   vacuum assisted resin transfer molding of composites and c_____
   of metals.
8. Other examples of composite airframe fabrication include vacuum
   bagging, pultrusion, thermal forming, compression molding, and
   fi_____ wi_____.
9. Other missile airframe manufacturing processes of metals include
   forming, sintering, welding, and ma_____.
10. Aluminum has lower hardness than steel, which makes it easier to
    m_____.
11. Increasing metal hardness increases its s_____.
12. Low cost missile airframe materials are usually based on metal (e.g.,
    aluminum) while light weight airframe materials are usually based
    laminate c_____ materials.
13. Carbon fiber has high strength and high m_____ o_ e_____.
14. The recovery factors of 1.0, 0.9, and 0.85 are appropriate respectively
    for stagnation, turbulent boundary layer, and l_____ boundary layer.

15. The most popular types of missile insulation for temperatures greater than 4000 R are charring insulators based on ph_____ composites.
16. Missiles experience transient heating, and with increasing time the temperature approaches the r_____ temperature.
17. The inner wall temperature is nearly the same as the surface temperature for a t_____ t___ structure.
18. A thermally thick surface is a good i_____.
19. A low conductivity structure is susceptible to thermal st____.
20. The minimum airframe gauge thickness is often set by the m_____ process.
21. A very thin wall structure is susceptible to localized b_____.
22. Ejection loads and flight control loads often result in large b_____ moment.
23. An approach to increase the missile propellant/motor weight fraction over the typical value of 65% would be a g_____ c_____ motor case.
24. The required rocket motor case thickness is often driven by the combustion chamber p_____.
25. A low aspect ratio delta wing has reduced w_____.
26. For low speed missiles, a popular infrared dome material is z___ su_____.
27. A thermal battery provides high p____.
28. The most popular type of flight control actuator for missiles is an e_____ actuator.

Chapter 5

Flight Performance Considerations in Missile Design and System Engineering

- Missile Flight Envelope Limitations
- Aerodynamic Design Implications from Equations of Motion
- Maximizing Missile Flight Performance
- Missile Flight Performance Prediction

5.1 Introduction

This chapter provides conceptual design modeling prediction and system engineering considerations for missile flight performance. It addresses the missile flight range, velocity, time to target, and off boresight maneuvering capability. Flight performance considerations include the flight envelope, equations of motion modeling, driving parameters, trajectory shaping, intercept lead angle and velocity, and comparison with requirements. Analytical prediction methods are developed for alternative modes of missile flight, including cruise (Breguet range equation), other steady-state flight, turning (turn radius and turn rate prediction), coast, ballistic, boost, divert, and intercept.

Figure 5.1 illustrates the next step in the missile conceptual design synthesis and system engineering process—flight trajectory evaluation. Evaluations of the forward and off boresight flight trajectories are conducted to determine maximum/minimum range envelopes, velocity, time-to-target, off boresight envelope, and maneuverability limits. Alternative flight trajectories are compared with the flight performance requirements, to develop an effective flight trajectory.

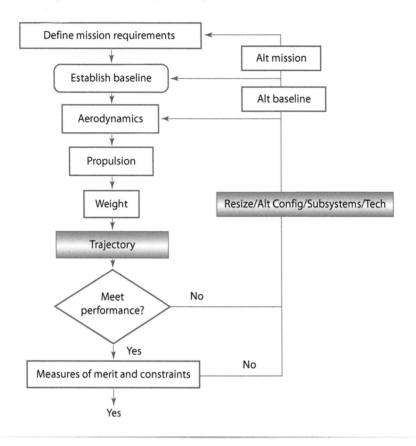

Fig. 5.1   Conceptual design and system engineering require creative, rapid, and iterative evaluations.

5.2 Missile Flight Performance Envelope

The missile flight envelope may be characterized by the maximum and the minimum flight ranges in straight-ahead (forward) and in maneuvering (off boresight) flight with a heading change. In the example shown in Fig. 5.2, the missile has a large off boresight capability, up to $+/-180$ deg off boresight.

Illustrated in the figure are the drivers for the maximum and minimum ranges in straight-ahead flight and for off boresight flight. The maximum coast range in straight-ahead flight may be driven by the zero-lift drag coefficient C_{D_0}. For example, a supersonic missile in 1 g flight and at low altitude is at near zero angle of attack, with its flight range driven by C_{D_0}. The maximum effective range of a missile may also be established by the speed and maneuverability required to successfully intercept the target. It was discussed previously that higher missile speed and higher maneuverability are required against a maneuvering target. The maximum effective range may also be set by miss distance. For example, the maximum effective range is degraded by the miss distance from a maneuvering target. Another consideration for the maximum effective range is the intercept altitude. For example, a boost-coast rocket usually has lower velocity and maneuverability for a high altitude intercept than for a low altitude intercept. Other constraints on the maximum range include the fire control system maximum range, fire control system off boresight capability, time of flight limits for the missile (e.g., battery duration, gas generator duration), and the minimum closing velocity that is required to arm the warhead and to capture an evading target. As a rule of thumb, the launch platform fire control system range should usually be at least twice the missile range.

For the off boresight envelope, the maximum off boresight capability may be set by the fire control system and any launch platform obscuration of the missile seeker. The off boresight minimum range may also be established by the missile maneuverability required to correct an initial heading error. For a beam flight trajectory to the side of the launch platform, the missile must operate at high angle of attack, to rapidly turn the velocity vector to 90 deg off boresight. The time to arm the warhead, based on establishing a safe standoff from the launch platform, may also set the minimum range. Another limitation is the seeker gimbal angle and tracking rate, which may set the minimum range in off-boresight maneuvers. The maximum/minimum range for a beam intercept may be driven by a combination of parameters, such as the seeker gimbal angle and tracking limits, maneuverability, stability, and the drag due to lift. For flight to the rear of the launch platform, the missile must make a heading change of 180 deg.

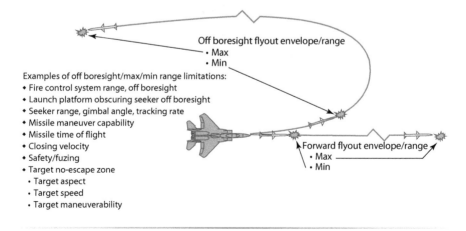

Fig. 5.2 The missile flight envelope should have a large maximum range, a small minimum range, and a large off boresight capability.

The flight performance drivers for a rear intercept may be a combination of parameters such as zero-lift drag and the drag due to lift.

The target may try to escape if it detects a missile launch. Ideally, the launch platform fire control system will dynamically display the target no-escape zone as a launch decision aid. The no-escape zone is a dynamic function of the target aspect, speed, and maneuverability.

If practical, the missile should have a large maximum range, a small minimum range, and a large off boresight capability. This provides robustness for long range, short range, and off boresight targets.

Based on Newton's second law, the external forces on the missile provide the time-rate-of-change in the missile's momentum. Newton's equation is

$$F = \mathrm{d}(mV)/\mathrm{d}t$$

For missile conceptual design, we will neglect the gas momentum differences within the propulsion system $\Rightarrow F \approx \dot{m}V + ma$

Also, assuming $ma \gg \dot{m}V \Rightarrow F \approx ma$

The video of Fig. 5.3 illustrates aerodynamic lift magnitude/orientation for cruise, climb, dive, and turn trajectories.

Figure 5.4 shows examples of targets that require special consideration of the intercept trajectory flight path and the flight trajectory shaping that may be required.

Sir Isaac Newton (Philosophiae Naturalis Principia Mathematica, July 5, 1687):
$$F = d\,(mV)/dt \approx \dot{m}\,V + ma \approx ma$$

Fig. 5.3   Forces drive the flight trajectory. Source of video: Penn State Schuylkill http://phys23p.sl.psu.edu/phys_anim/Phys_anim.htm.

Vertical impact trajectory

Deeply buried target

Horizontal impact trajectory

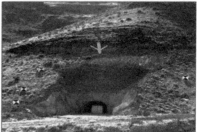

Cave target

Urban target between bulidings

Submarine base target

Fig. 5.4   Examples of targets that require extreme terminal flight trajectory shaping (vertical/horizontal).

Examples of targets that require a vertical impact trajectory include deeply buried targets and targets that are located in an urban environment. The top left section is an example of a deeply buried target. A vertical impact at near zero angle of attack is desired to maximize the vertical penetration and to reduce the lateral penetration error. The bottom left section illustrates the problem of attacking a target in an urban environment with minimum collateral damage. An advantage of a vertical impact on the target is reduced probability of impacting adjacent buildings.

The right section of the figure illustrates targets that require a horizontal flight trajectory at impact. The examples are entrances to a cave target and a submarine base target that are located at the bottom of a mountain. A horizontal flight trajectory is desirable to maximize the damage at the entrance.

5.3   Equations of Motion Modeling

The flight trajectory evaluation activity during missile concept synthesis requires consideration of the degrees of freedom (DOF) to be simulated. Figure 5.5 compares the simulation modeling degrees of freedom that are

◆ Conceptual Design Force and Moment Modeling

• 1 DOF [axial force (C_{D_0}), thrust, weight]

• 2 DOF [normal force (C_N), axial force, thrust, weight]

• 2 DOF [lift force (C_L), drag (C_D), thrust, weight]

• 3 DOF point mass [3 aero forces (normal, axial, side), thrust, weight]

• 3 DOF pitching [2 aero forces (normal, axial), 1 aero moment (pitching), thrust, weight]

• 4 DOF [2 aero forces (normal, axial), 2 aero moments (pitching, rolling), thrust, weight]

◆ Preliminary Design Force and Moment Modeling

• 5 DOF [3 aero forces (normal, axial, side), 2 aero moments (pitching, yawing), thrust, weight]

• 6 DOF [3 aero forces (normal, axial, side), 3 aero moments [pitching, rolling, yawing], thrust, weight]

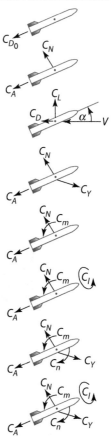

Aero Forces & Moments

Fig. 5.5 A comparison of conceptual design flight trajectory models versus preliminary design models, based on modeling their degrees of freedom (DOF).

usually used in conceptual design with the degrees of freedom that are appropriate for preliminary design.

As discussed previously, conceptual design is the rapid evaluation of a large range of alternatives. It requires that the design methods be fast, be easy to use, and have a broad range of applicability. The simplest flight trajectory model, often acceptable for the conceptual design of high-speed missiles, is one degree of freedom (1-DOF). The 1-DOF flight trajectory requires modeling only the forces of zero-lift drag, thrust, and weight. Analytical equations can be used to model a 1-DOF trajectory. Other modeling used for conceptual design are two-degrees-of-freedom (2-DOF) point-mass modeling with trim normal force, trim axial force, thrust, and weight; 2-DOF point mass modeling with trim lift force, trim drag force, thrust, and weight; three-degrees-of-freedom (3-DOF) point-mass modeling with trim normal, axial, and side forces, thrust, and weight; 3-DOF with trim normal force, trim axial force, and pitching moment modeling (out-of-trim), thrust, and weight; and four-degrees-of-freedom (4-DOF), with trim normal force, trim axial force, pitching moment modeling (untrimmed pitch), uncoupled rolling moment modeling (un-trimmed roll), thrust, and weight. The 3-DOF point mass simulation is a standard for conceptual design evaluation of the flight envelope of a missile. Based on the missile flight envelope, it can provide first-order requirements for the launch platform fire control system. The 3-DOF pitching moment modeling includes the pitch stability and control derivatives C_{m_α} and C_{m_δ}. It is most applicable to skid-to-turn missiles with no/small wings. The 3-DOF pitching moment modeling allows conceptual design sizing of the tail stabilizers. It also allows an initial modeling of the pitching motion of an unguided flight trajectory. The 4-DOF simulation is often used for conceptual design evaluation of a rolling airframe missile. Roll damping C_{l_p}, induced roll C_{l_ϕ}, and roll control effectiveness $C_{l_{\delta_a}}$ are included in the 4-DOF simulation.

Finally, more sophisticated missile simulation during preliminary design is usually modeled in either five-degrees-of-freedom (5-DOF) or six-degrees-of-freedom (6-DOF). A 5-DOF simulation includes three aerodynamic forces (normal force, axial force, side force), two aerodynamic moments (pitching moment, yawing moment), thrust, and weight. It includes modeling of pitch static stability and control effectiveness C_{m_α} and C_{m_δ}, and yaw static stability and control effectiveness C_{n_β} and $C_{n_{\delta_r}}$. A 5-DOF simulation does not include rolling moment (roll rate is assumed to be near zero). It is most applicable to a cruciform missile with small surfaces. A 6-DOF simulation is a standard for missile development. It includes the autopilot modeling of all axes. The 6-DOF simulation models all rigid body translational and rotational motion. It includes three aerodynamic forces (normal force, axial force, side force), three aerodynamic moments (pitching moment, rolling moment, yawing moment), thrust, and weight. Cross coupling derivates (e.g., rolling moment from rudder deflection $C_{l_{\delta_r}}$, yawing moment from aileron deflection $C_{n_{\delta_a}}$, roll control effectiveness $C_{l_{\delta_a}}$ to compensate for the rolling moment from sideslip C_{l_β}, and roll control effectiveness $C_{l_{\delta_a}}$ to compensate for induced roll from roll attitude C_{l_ϕ}) are usually modeled in the 6-DOF simulation. Non-cruciform missiles that use bank-to-turn maneuvering require a 6-DOF simulation. For a thrust vector control or a reaction jet control missile, the propulsion vector forces and moments must be included.

Missile simulation with degrees of freedom greater than 6-DOF describe the missile airframe structure bending modes. Because most missiles are relatively stiff, modeling at greater than 6-DOF is usually not

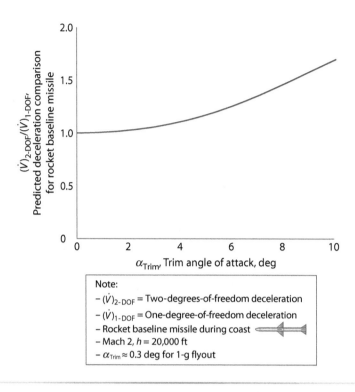

Fig. 5.6 The 1-DOF coast equation has good accuracy if the missile fly-out is at low angle of attack.

required for aerodynamic control missiles but may be required for impulse reaction jet control missiles.

The 1-DOF coast equation is compared in Fig. 5.6 with the more accurate 2-DOF coast equation. Results are for the rocket baseline missile coasting in horizontal flight at Mach 2 and 20,000 ft altitude, following motor burnout. Note that the 1-DOF coast equation has less than 10% error in the missile deceleration $\dot{V}$ for angles of attack up to about 3 deg. For the rocket baseline missile, the angle of attack for the example 1-g flight is only 0.3 deg. The 1-DOF coast equation usually provides sufficient accuracy for an initial conceptual design assessment of the 1-g flight trajectory of a rocket powered missile.

5.4 Driving Parameters for Missile Flight Performance

It is instructive to examine the equations of motion for missile design drivers. Figure 5.7 shows the simplified equations of motion for three degrees of freedom with pitching moment modeling.

In Fig. 5.7a, aerodynamic control is assumed. The equations describe the missile angular acceleration $\ddot{\theta}$, rate of change in the flight path angle $\dot{\gamma}$, and the rate of change in the velocity $\dot{V}$. Assuming $\ddot{\theta} \approx \ddot{\alpha}$ (second time derivative of the angle of attack), the configuration sizing implication from examining the angular acceleration equation shows the importance of control effectiveness in providing the missile with high agility/fast body rotation

$$I_y \ddot{\theta} \approx I_y \ddot{\alpha} \approx q S_{Ref} dC_{m_\alpha} \alpha + q S_{Ref} dC_{m_\delta} \delta$$

Note that fast body rotation is provided by high pitching moment control effectiveness C_{m_δ}, low static stability C_{m_α}, small moment-of-inertia I_y, and large dynamic pressure q. A small moment-of-inertia is a characteristic of a light-weight missile.

The second equation shows the design drivers for the maneuver capability to rapidly change the flight path heading ($\dot{\gamma} = \Delta\gamma/\Delta t$)

$$(W/g_c)\dot{\gamma} \approx S_{Ref}\rho V C_{N_\alpha}\alpha/2 + S_{Ref}\rho V C_{N_\delta}\delta/2 + (T\sin\alpha)/V - (W/V)\cos\gamma$$

High maneuverability provides the capability to make large and rapid changes in the flight path angle. This occurs for large normal force coefficient C_N, light weight W, high atmospheric density ρ (low altitude flight), high velocity V, and high values of T/V. Large C_N is achievable through large values of C_{N_α}, α, C_{N_δ}, and δ. For example, a missile with relatively low C_{N_α} (such as the wing-less ASRAAM) may achieve high maneuverability through the capability to fly at high angle of attack. Another missile, with a relatively low angle of attack capability (such as the wing control Sparrow missile baseline), may achieve high maneuverability through a large value

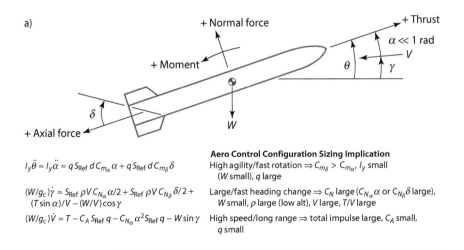

Aero Control Configuration Sizing Implication

$I_y\ddot{\theta} \approx I_y\ddot{\alpha} \approx q S_{Ref} dC_{m_\alpha}\alpha + q S_{Ref} dC_{m_\delta}\delta$ High agility/fast rotation $\Rightarrow C_{m_\delta} > C_{m_\alpha}$, I_y small (W small), q large

$(W/g_c)\dot{\gamma} \approx S_{Ref}\rho V C_{N_\alpha}\alpha/2 + S_{Ref}\rho V C_{N_\delta}\delta/2 + (T\sin\alpha)/V - (W/V)\cos\gamma$ Large/fast heading change $\Rightarrow C_N$ large ($C_{N_\alpha}\alpha$ or $C_{N_\delta}\delta$ large), W small, ρ large (low alt), V large, T/V large

$(W/g_c)\dot{V} \approx T - C_A S_{Ref} q - C_{N_\alpha}\alpha^2 S_{Ref} q - W\sin\gamma$ High speed/long range $\Rightarrow$ total impulse large, C_A small, q small

Fig. 5.7a   3-DOF simplified equations of motion show drivers for missile configuration sizing.

of C_{N_δ}. The above equation describes vertical climb maneuvers. The term $W \cos\gamma$ is the weight component in the vertical plane. For horizontal plane maneuvers, the term $(W/V)\cos\gamma$ is not included.

Implications of the third equation are the drivers of missile speed and range

$$(W/g_c)\dot{V} \approx T - C_A S_{\text{Ref}}q - C_{N_\alpha}\alpha^2 S_{\text{Ref}}q - W \sin\gamma$$

Note that high speed and long range are provided by a large total impulse, which is the integral of propulsion system thrust for the burn time duration ($\int T \, dt$). There is a payoff for flight range in using high density propellant/fuel to maximize the total energy available within the available volume. High density propellant/fuel increases the total impulse of a volume-limited propulsion system. The third equation also shows that a low axial force coefficient C_A and a low dynamic pressure q provide longer range. Axial force coefficient is approximately equal to the zero-lift drag coefficient C_{D_0}. The term $W \sin\gamma$ in the above equation is the weight component in the horizontal plane. For horizontal flight, $\gamma = 0$ and $W \sin\gamma = 0$.

Note from equations 1) and 3) that there is a conflicting requirement on the value of dynamic pressure q that provides both rapid rotation and long flight range. High q is desirable to provide the capability for rapid body rotation (first equation) using aerodynamic flight control, while low q is desirable to provide the capability for long range (3rd equation). However, if aerodynamic flight control does not provide sufficient maneuverability at low q, an alternative approach is to use thrust vector control (next paragraph).

A similar assessment can be made of the driving parameters of a thrust vector control (TVC) missile. Assuming that the TVC has the capability to provide a much larger moment that overwhelms the smaller aerodynamic moments (see Fig. 5.7b), the equations of motion are

$$I_y\ddot{\theta} \approx I_y\ddot{\alpha} \approx Tl \sin\delta$$
$$(W/g_c)\dot{\gamma} \approx (T \sin\alpha)/V + S_{\text{Ref}}\rho V C_L/2 - (W/V)\cos\gamma$$
$$(W/g_c)\dot{V} \approx T \cos\alpha - C_D S_{\text{Ref}}q - W \sin\gamma$$

Examining the above equations, the TVC sizing implications are

1. For high control effectiveness: T, l, and δ should be large and I_y should be small (W small).
2. For a large or fast heading change: $(T \sin\alpha)/V$ should be large.
3. For high speed or long range flight: Total impulse ($\int T \, dt$) should be large, C_D should be small, and q should be small.

b)

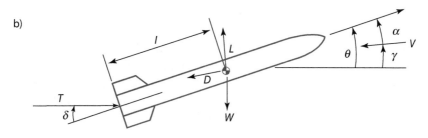

$I_y \ddot{\theta} \approx I_y \ddot{\alpha} \approx T I \sin \delta$

$(W/g_c)\dot{\gamma} \approx (T \sin \alpha)/V + S_{Ref}\, \rho\, V C_L/2 - (W/V)\cos\gamma$

$(W/g_c)\dot{V} \approx T \cos\alpha - C_D\, S_{Ref}\, q - W \sin\gamma$

Thrust Vector Control Sizing Implication*
High agility/fast rotation $\Rightarrow T, I, \delta$ large, I_y
small (W small)

Large/fast heading change $\Rightarrow T \sin \alpha/V$ large

High speed/long range $\Rightarrow$ total impulse large,
C_D small, q small

*Assumption: Aero moment small compared to
TVC moment

Fig. 5.7b 3-DOF simplified equations of motion show drivers for missile configuration sizing.

5.5 Cruise Flight Performance

The Breguet range equation provides a conceptual design prediction of the missile flight range during cruise flight. Assumptions in the derivation of the Breguet range equation are constant velocity, constant lift-to-drag ratio, and constant specific impulse. The derivation is as follows:

The missile flight range is the time integral of the missile velocity

$$R = \int V \, dt$$

Incremental time dt is related to the fuel flow rate, thrust, and specific impulse by

$$dW/dt = T/I_{SP}$$

For non-accelerating flight, lift equals weight and thrust equals drag (noted in the sketch in the top right section of Fig. 5.8). Therefore

$$L/D = W/T$$

Substitution and integration gives the Breguet cruise range equation

$$R = (VI_{SP})(L/D)\ln[W_{BC}/(W_{BC} - W_{f/p})]$$

Note that the Breguet cruise range equation is a function of the missile weight at the beginning of cruise W_{BC}, fuel or propellant weight $W_{f/p}$, aerodynamic efficiency L/D, specific impulse I_{SP}, and the velocity V. Figure 5.8 compares the maximum cruise range for a typical solid propellant rocket, a typical axisymmetric ramjet, and a typical subsonic turbojet that has a wing. The bottom curve in the figure is the range for rocket propulsion. It is based on a typical maximum value of the solid propellant rocket parameter of

$$VI_{SP}(L/D) = 2 \times 10^6 \text{ ft}$$

The middle curve is the range for ramjet propulsion. It is based on a typical maximum value of the ramjet propulsion parameter for an axisymmetric, low L/D airframe of

$$VI_{SP}(L/D) = 10 \times 10^6 \text{ ft}$$

Finally, the top curve is the range for turbojet propulsion. It is based on a typical maximum value of $VI_{SP}(L/D)$ for a subsonic turbojet with a wing:

$$VI_{SP}(L/D) = 25 \times 10^6 \text{ ft}$$

The curves are shown as a function of the fuel or propellant fraction of the missile weight at the beginning of cruise ($W_{f/p}/W_{BC}$). Note from the figure that for the same fuel/propellant weight fraction the subsonic turbojet with a wing has the longest cruise range, while the rocket has the shortest

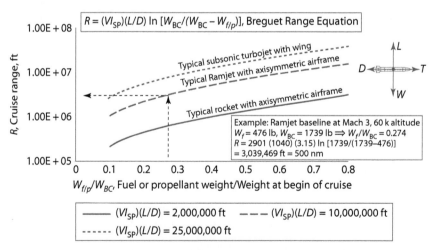

Note: R = cruise range, V = cruise velocity, I_{SP} = specific impulse, L = lift, D = drag, W_{BC} = weight at begin of cruise, $W_{f/p}$ = weight of fuel or propellant

Fig. 5.8   For a long range cruise - maximize VI_{SP}, L/D, and the weight fraction of the fuel or propellant.

cruise range. However as mentioned previously, a rocket in ballistic or semi-ballistic flight trajectory would probably have a longer range than a cruise flight trajectory. Also, for the same total missile weight the rocket would probably have a larger propellant weight fraction than that of a ramjet or a turbojet.

For supersonic missiles in low altitude flight, the dynamic pressure is high. One-g flight (lift equals weight) at high dynamic pressure results in a cruise L/D that is usually much lower than $(L/D)_{\text{Max}}$. The lower L/D results in shorter range.

As an example of the Breguet range equation, the ramjet baseline missile will be evaluated at a typical flight condition of Mach 3, 60 kft altitude $(V = 2901 \text{ ft/s})$. From the data of Chapter 7, the ramjet baseline missile has a specific impulse $I_{\text{SP}} = 1040$ s and an aerodynamic efficiency $L/D = 3.15$ for this flight condition. At the beginning of cruise the missile weight $W_{\text{BC}} = 1739$ lb and the fuel weight $W_f = 476$ lb. Computing the range for Mach 3 cruise at 60 kft altitude gives

$$R = 2901(1040)(3.15)\ln[1739/(1739 - 476)] = 3.0 \times 10^6 \text{ ft or } 500 \text{ nm.}$$

Comparing this result with the data of Chapter 7, the Breguet range equation prediction (500 nm) is 10% higher than the actual range (450 nm).

5.6 Steady-State Flight

The steady-state flight conditions of steady level flight, steady climb, and steady dive are illustrated in Fig. 5.9 from Chin [6].

In steady-state level flight (cruise) at low angle of attack, the lift L is approximately equal to the weight W and the thrust T is approximately equal to the drag D. Note that the thrust required for steady-state level flight is the missile weight divided by the aerodynamic efficiency

$$T = W/(L/D)$$

High L/D and light weight have the benefit of reducing the required thrust, resulting in a lower fuel flow rate, providing longer range.

Note from the steady climb equation in the figure, the flight path angle γ_c and climb velocity V_c are proportional to the excess thrust $(T - D)$. High thrust and low drag provide a higher climb angle and higher climb velocity. The horizontal flight range in a steady climb is given by the equation

$$R_c = \Delta h/\tan \gamma_c = \Delta h(L/D)$$

Similarly, in a steady dive (glide) the flight path angle γ_D and dive velocity V_D are proportional to the excess drag $(D - T)$. Low drag allows a shallow glide angle after burnout $(T = 0)$, providing an extended glide

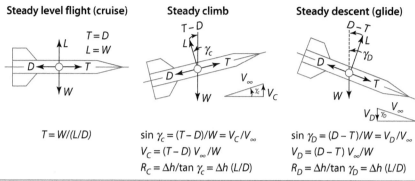

Steady level flight (cruise)	Steady climb	Steady descent (glide)

$$T = W/(L/D)$$

$$\sin \gamma_c = (T - D)/W = V_C/V_\infty$$
$$V_C = (T - D)\, V_\infty/W$$
$$R_C = \Delta h/\tan \gamma_c = \Delta h\, (L/D)$$

$$\sin \gamma_D = (D - T)/W = V_D/V_\infty$$
$$V_D = (D - T)\, V_\infty/W$$
$$R_D = \Delta h/\tan \gamma_D = \Delta h\, (L/D)$$

Note:
- Small angle of attack
- Equilibrium flight
- V_C = Velocity of climb
- V_D = Velocity of descent
- γ_c = Flight path angle during climb

- γ_D = Flight path angle during descent
- V_∞ = Total velocity
- Δh = Incremental altitude
- R_C = Horizontal range in steady climb
- R_D = Horizontal range in steady dive (glide)

Fig. 5.9   Flight range in steady flight is enhanced by high L/D and light weight. (Reference: Chin, S. S., *Missile Configuration Design*, McGraw Hill Book Company, New York, 1961).

range. The horizontal flight range in a steady dive is

$$R_D = \Delta h/\tan \gamma_D = \Delta h(L/D)$$

5.7 Flight Trajectory Shaping for Maximum Range

Figure 5.10 illustrates the extended range advantage of boost-loft-glide missiles that use flight trajectory shaping. Flight trajectory shaping is particularly beneficial for high performance supersonic missiles, which have large propellant or fuel weight fraction. It can double or even triple the range compared to a straight line-of-sight trajectory. To take advantage of flight trajectory shaping for maximum range, the missile must rapidly pitch up to about 45 deg flight path angle and then climb to an efficient flight altitude. The missile initial thrust-to-weight ratio should be high ($T/W \approx 10$) for safe separation, followed by a relatively low (≈ 2) thrust-to-weight during the climb. A thrust-to-weight ratio greater than about 2–3 will result in a high dynamic pressure, which increases missile drag. After reaching higher altitude, the missile benefits from an improved lift-to-drag ratio, such as $(L/D)_{max}$. Dynamic pressure for efficient flight of a high performance supersonic missile is of the order of $q = 500$ to 1000 psf. Following burnout, the missile can have extended range through glide at a dynamic pressure of about 700 psf, providing an aerodynamic efficiency approximately equal to $(L/D)_{max}$.

5.8 Turn Performance

Figure 5.11 shows an example of missile instantaneous turn radius using aerodynamic control of the flight path. The turn radius of the missile should be less than the turn radius of a maneuvering target, for small miss distance. The equation of motion for a vertical maneuver turn, relating the time rate of change in the flight path angle $\dot{\gamma}$ to the forces on the missile, is

$$(W/g_c)V\dot{\gamma} = qS_{\text{Ref}}C_N + (T\sin\alpha)/V - W\cos\gamma$$

Also, the instantaneous turn radius R_T is a function of $\dot{\gamma}$ and velocity V, by the equation

$$R_T = V/\dot{\gamma}$$

If the missile is maneuvering in a horizontal turn or is in a vertical turn such that the aerodynamic normal force ($N = qS_{\text{Ref}}C_N$) is much larger than the missile weight W and the thrust component $T\sin\alpha$, then

$$R_T \approx 2W/(g_c C_N S_{\text{Ref}}\rho)$$

Note that the instantaneous turn radius is a function of missile weight W, normal force coefficient C_N, reference area S_{Ref}, and the atmospheric density ρ. The term g_c in the equation is the gravitational constant for English units ($g_c = 32.2$ lbm/slug).

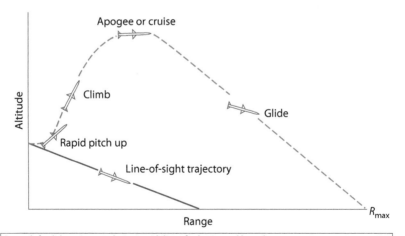

Boost-loft-glide trajectory design guidelines for horizontal launch:
  – High thrust-to-weight ≈ 10 for safe separation
  – Rapid pitch up minimizes time/propellant to reach efficient altitude
  – Climb at $\gamma \approx 45$ deg, thrust-to-weight $T/W \approx 2$, and $q \approx 700$ psf to minimize drag/propellant
  – Apogee at $q \approx 700$ psf, followed by either $(L/D)_{\text{max}}$ cruise or $(L/D)_{\text{max}}$ glide

Fig. 5.10 Flight trajectory boost-loft-glide shaping provides extended range for high performance missiles.

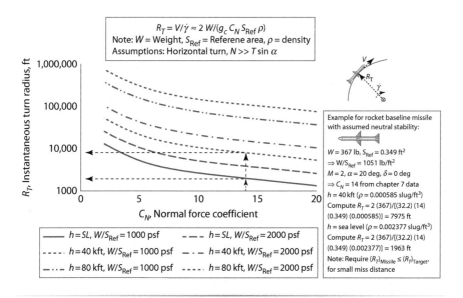

Fig. 5.11 A small turn radius using aerodynamic flight control requires a high normal force coefficient, light weight, and low altitude flight.

An example is shown in the figure for the rocket baseline missile at burnout, with an assumed neutral stability. Using data from Chapter 7, the rocket baseline missile burnout weight and reference area are $W = 367$ lb and $S_{\text{Ref}} = 0.349$ ft^2. Compute

$$W/S_{\text{Ref}} = 1051\ \text{lb/ft}^2$$

Assume $M = 2$, $\alpha = 20$ deg, and $\delta = 0$ deg. Then from Chapter 7

$$C_N = 14$$

Assume an altitude $h = 40$ kft ($\rho = 0.000585$ slug/ft^3)
Compute

$$R_T = 2(367)/[(32.2)(14)(0.349)(0.000585)] = 7975\ \text{ft}$$

As a comparison, we will also compute the turn radius at $h =$ sea level ($\rho = 0.002377$ slug/ft^3)

$$R_T = 2(367)/[(32.2)(14)(0.349)(0.002377)] = 1963\ \text{ft}$$

Note that the aerodynamic control rocket baseline missile has a tighter turn radius at sea level than at high altitude. Because the missile has a large turn radius at high altitude, it is more susceptible at high altitude to a maneuvering target countermeasure.

The capability to rapidly make a heading change in the flight path angle γ is a consideration in defining the required maneuverability of a missile. The approximate equation shown previously, which is based on using aerodynamic control in a horizontal turn with $N \gg T \sin \alpha$, is

$$\dot{\gamma} = g_c C_N \rho V S_{\text{Ref}} / (2W)$$

In the above equation, the units of $\dot{\gamma}$ are rad/s.

Figure 5.12 shows an example of the time rate of change in flight path angle $\dot{\gamma}$ for the aerodynamically controlled rocket baseline missile after rocket motor burnout, as a function of its normal force coefficient C_N for combinations of the flight altitude (h = sea level, 40 kft) and velocity (V = 1000, 2000 ft/s). The weight is W = 367 lbm and the reference area is S_{Ref} = 0.349 ft². Note from the figure that high turn rate occurs for a high value of normal force coefficient, a high velocity, light weight, and a low altitude.

We shall first compute an example of the turn rate with the assumption of a neutrally stable missile. Assume

$$M = 2, \quad \alpha = 20 \, \text{deg}, \quad \delta = 0 \, \text{deg}$$

From the Chapter 7 data, $C_N = 14$.

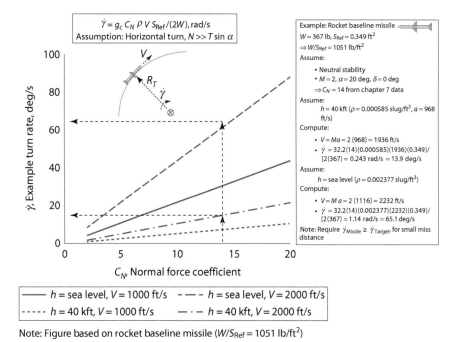

Fig. 5.12 A high turn rate with aerodynamic flight control requires high normal force, high velocity, low altitude, and light weight.

Also assume

$$h = 40\,\text{kft} \,(\rho = 0.000585\,\text{slug/ft}^3, \quad a = 968\,\text{ft/s})$$

Compute

$$V = Ma = 2(968) = 1936\,\text{ft/s}$$
$$\dot\gamma = 32.2(14)(0.000585)(1936)(0.349)/2(367) = 0.243\,\text{rad/s} = 13.9\,\text{deg/s}$$

As a comparison to evaluate the effect of altitude, assume

$$h = \text{sea level} \,(\rho = 0.002377\,\text{slug/ft}^3)$$

Compute

$$V = Ma = 2(1116) = 2232\,\text{ft/s}$$
$$\dot\gamma = 32.2(14)(0.002377)(2232)(0.349)/2(367) = 1.14\,\text{rad/s} = 65.1\,\text{deg/s}$$

Note that the turn rate is much higher at sea level than at 40 kft altitude. A requirement for small miss distance is the missile turn rate should be greater than that of the target ($\dot\gamma_{\text{Missile}} \geq \dot\gamma_{\text{Target}}$). An aerodynamically controlled missile usually has a higher turn rate, with higher lethality, at low altitude than at high altitude.

As another example of a requirement for turn rate performance, we shall compare the capability of an anti-aircraft missile to least match the turn rate of the target, for a successful intercept. For manned combat aircraft, typical air-to-air combat maneuvering conditions are a maximum normal acceleration of about $n = 9$ g (pilot limit) and a velocity of about $V = 1000$ ft/s. Substitution into the turn rate equation gives a typical maximum turn rate of a manned aircraft of about

$$\dot\gamma = 32.2(9)/1000 = 0.290\,\text{rad/s or }16.6\,\text{deg/s}$$

Because the missile must have a speed advantage to intercept the aircraft, it must also have higher maneuverability than the aircraft target, to match the turn rate of the aircraft. For example, a missile with a velocity $V = 3000$ ft/s must have 27-g maneuverability to achieve a turn rate of $\dot\gamma = 16.6$ deg/s.

The rocket baseline missile and its data from Chapter 7 will be used to illustrate these drivers for turn rate performance. Assume that a climb maneuver is commanded for a launch condition of Mach 0.8 and 20 kft altitude. At this flight condition the velocity $V = 830$ ft/s, dynamic pressure $q = 436$ psf, launch weight $W_L = 500$ lb, and the launch center of gravity $x_{cg} = 84.6$ in from the nose tip. The trim angle of attack and the control surface deflection based on the launch cg are derived from the wind tunnel data of Chapter 7. Based on the reference cg for the wind tunnel data of 75.7 in, the maximum trimmed angle of attack α and control surface deflection δ for the launch center of gravity are computed from

$$(C_{m_\alpha})_{x_{cg}=84.6} = (C_{m_\alpha})_{x_{cg}=75.7} + C_{N_\alpha}(84.6 - 75.7)/d$$

$$= -0.40 + 0.68(8.9)/8 = 0.36 \text{ per deg}$$

$$(C_{m_\delta})_{x_{cg}=84.6} = (C_{m_\delta})_{x_{cg}=75.7} + C_{N_\delta}(84.6-75.7)/d$$

$$= -0.60 + 0.27(8.9)/8 = 0.90 \text{ per deg}$$

Note that the missile is statically unstable at launch ($C_{m_\alpha} > 0$), with safe store separation a concern for this launch condition. The control effectiveness is given by

$$\alpha/\delta = -C_{m_\delta}/C_{m_\alpha} = -0.90/0.36 = -2.5$$

The maximum wing local angle of attack $|\alpha'| = |\alpha + \delta| < 22$ deg. For a maximum angle of attack of the body of $\alpha = 30$ deg, the trim control deflection is $\delta = -12$ deg. Compute

$$\dot{\gamma} = gn/V = [qSC_{N_\alpha}\alpha + qSC_{N_\delta}\delta - W \cos \gamma]/[(W/g_c)V]$$

$$= [436(0.349)(0.68)(30) + 436(0.349)(0.27)(-12)$$

$$- 500(1)]/[(500/32.2)(830)]$$

$$= 0.164 \text{ rad/s or } 9.4 \text{ deg/s}$$

For a post-burnout flight condition of Mach 2 at 20 kft altitude, the missile has a higher turn rate. The missile is statically stable, with $\alpha/\delta = 0.75$. The turn rate

$$\dot{\gamma} = [2725(0.349)(0.60)(9.4) + 2725(0.349)(0.19)(12.6)$$

$$- 367(1)]/[(367/32.2)(2074)]$$

$$= 0.31 \text{ rad/s or } 18 \text{ deg/s}$$

The faster turn rate after burnout is from the higher velocity $V = 2075$ ft/s, positive wing control deflection to trim the missile, and lighter weight.

A metric for missile response time is the angle of attack sensitivity to turn rate, or $\alpha/\dot{\gamma}$. For the aerodynamically controlled rocket baseline missile at Mach 0.8 launch and 20 kft altitude

$$\alpha/\dot{\gamma} = 30/9.4 = 3.2 \text{ s}$$

As a comparison, the response time metric for Mach 2 at 20,000 ft altitude is better

$$\alpha/\dot{\gamma} = 9.4/18 = 0.52 \text{ s}$$

It will be shown in Chapter 6 that values of $\alpha/\dot{\gamma} < 0.5$ s is required for a small miss distance.

An advantage of thrust vector control (TVC) over aerodynamic flight control is a small turn radius at low velocity, such as the missile launch flight condition or the minimum range intercept flight condition. Figure 5.13 shows missile turn radius as a function of velocity, thrust-to-weight ratio, and angle of attack. It is based on the equation

$$R_T = V/\dot{\gamma} \approx V^2/[g(T/W)\sin\alpha]$$

Assumptions are a horizontal turn, $T\sin\alpha \gg N$, $T \gg W\sin\gamma$, and $\alpha/\delta \gg 1$.

Note from the figure that a small turn radius is achieved with low velocity V, high thrust T, light weight W, and high angle of attack α.

As an example, assume that the rocket baseline missile has thrust vector control, similar to Sea Sparrow. Based on the data of Chapter 7

$$W \approx W_{\text{Launch}} = 500\,\text{lb}$$
$$T = T_{\text{Boost}} = 5750\,\text{lb}$$
$$T/W = 5750/500 = 11.5$$

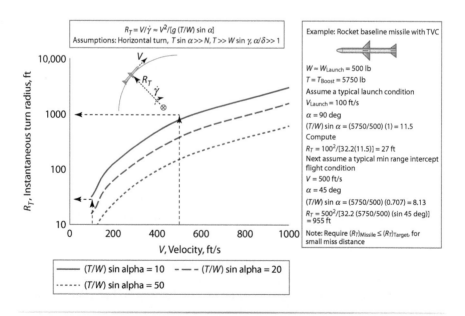

Fig. 5.13   A small turn radius with TVC requires high thrust-to-weight, high angle of attack, and low velocity.

Assume a vertical launch (surface-to-air missile) with a high angle of attack

$$V_{\text{Launch}} = 100\,\text{ft/s}$$
$$\alpha = 90\,\text{deg}$$

Compute

$$R_T = 100^2/[32.2(5750/500)(\sin 90\,\text{deg}] = 27\,\text{ft}$$

Next assume a typical minimum range intercept flight condition

$$V = 500\,\text{ft/s}$$
$$\alpha = 45\,\text{deg}$$

Compute

$$R_T = 500^2/[32.2(5750/500)(\sin 45\,\text{deg}] = 955\,\text{ft}$$

One reason the turn radius of the TVC missile for the above conditions is less than that of an aerodynamically controlled missile is because it can achieve a higher angle of attack. It is noted that the turn radius of the missile should be less than the turn radius of the target $(R_T)_{\text{Missile}} \leq (R_T)_{\text{Target}}$, for a small miss distance.

TVC provides the capability the turn faster at low velocity/dynamic pressure, when aerodynamic flight control does not provide sufficient maneuverability. The equation for missile turn rate $\dot{\gamma}$ with TVC is

$$\dot{\gamma} = g[(T/W)\sin \alpha]/V, \text{rad/s}$$

Assumptions are a horizontal turn, $T \sin \alpha \gg N$, $T \gg W \sin \gamma$, and $\alpha/\delta \gg 1$.

Note from Fig. 5.14 that contributors to a high turn rate using TVC are low velocity V, high thrust T, light weight W, and high angle of attack α.

As an example, we will evaluate the rocket baseline missile turn rate with thrust vector control, using the same flight conditions as the previous example for turn radius. Based on the data of Chapter 7

$$W \approx W_{\text{Launch}} = 500\,\text{lb}$$
$$T = T_{\text{Boost}} = 5750\,\text{lb}$$
$$T/W = 5750/500 = 11.5$$

Assume a typical vertical launch condition

$$V_{\text{Launch}} = 100\,\text{ft/s}$$
$$\alpha = 90\,\text{deg}$$

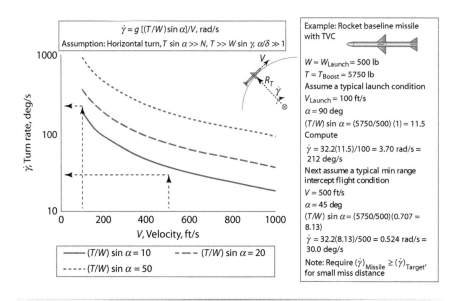

Fig. 5.14 A high turn rate with TVC requires high thrust-to-weight, high angle of attack, and low velocity.

Compute

$$\dot{\gamma} = 32.2(11.5)(1)/100 = 3.70\,\text{rad/s} = 212\,\text{deg/s}$$

Next assume a typical minimum range intercept flight condition

$$V = 500\,\text{ft/s}$$
$$\alpha = 45\,\text{deg}$$

Compute

$$\dot{\gamma} = 32.2(11.5)(0.707)/500 = 0.524\ \text{rad/s} = 30.0\,\text{deg/s}$$

The turn rate of $\dot{\gamma} = 30.0$ deg/s for a TVC missile is greater than the turn rate of an aerodynamically controlled missile at the same velocity. As before, a reason the aerodynamically controlled missile has a lower turn rate is because its maximum angle of attack is lower than the TVC missile. It is noted that the turn rate of the missile should be greater than the turn rate of the target $(\dot{\gamma})_{\text{Missile}} > (\dot{\gamma})_{\text{Target}}$, for a small miss distance.

An approach to achieve a rapid heading change using TVC is a constant attitude ($\theta =$ constant) turn law. Another approach is a constant angle of attack ($\alpha =$ constant) turn law. Figure 5.15 compares the flight performance of each approach.

In a constant attitude turn, the missile uses TVC to quickly slew its body to a prescribed attitude θ and maintains the attitude until the flight path angle γ is changed to the desired intercept direction. The missile then quickly slews to approximately zero angle of attack ($\alpha \approx 0$ deg) for the fly-out to intercept. An advantage of a constant attitude turn is a relatively simple autopilot. The inertial reference system on the missile provides the required autopilot feedback. A disadvantage of a constant attitude turn is it requires a high angle of attack at the beginning of the turn. The equations for a constant attitude turn are

$$\alpha = \cot^{-1}\{\cot\theta + [Tt/(mV_0)]\}$$
$$\gamma = \theta - \alpha$$

Assumptions for the above equation are the thrust is much larger than the aerodynamic lift, drag, and the vertical component of weight ($T \gg L, D, W\sin\gamma$); thrust is much larger than the product of propellant mass flow rate and the missile initial velocity ($T \gg \dot{m}V_0$); and near-neutral static stability ($\alpha/\delta \gg 1$).

Figure 5.15a illustrates the constant attitude turn and its flight performance. The flight path angle γ is shown as a function of non-dimensional time $Tt/(mV_0)$ and attitude θ. Note that a large heading change is consistent

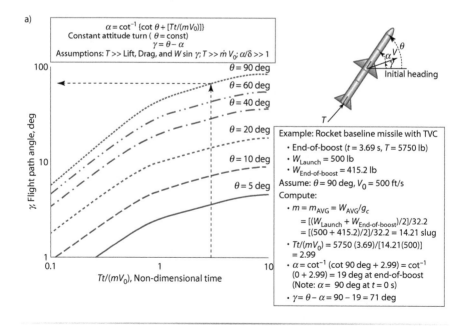

a)

$\alpha = \cot^{-1}\{\cot\theta + [Tt/(mV_0)]\}$
Constant attitude turn (θ = const)
$\gamma = \theta - \alpha$
Assumptions: $T \gg$ Lift, Drag, and $W\sin\gamma$; $T \gg \dot{m}V_0$; $\alpha/\delta \gg 1$

γ, Flight path angle, deg

$Tt/(mV_0)$, Non-dimensional time

θ = 90 deg
θ = 60 deg
θ = 40 deg
θ = 20 deg
θ = 10 deg
θ = 5 deg

Initial heading

Example: Rocket baseline missile with TVC
• End-of-boost (t = 3.69 s, T = 5750 lb)
• W_{Launch} = 500 lb
• $W_{End\text{-}of\text{-}boost}$ = 415.2 lb
Assume: θ = 90 deg, V_0 = 500 ft/s
Compute:
• $m = m_{AVG} = W_{AVG}/g_c$
   $= [(W_{Launch} + W_{End\text{-}of\text{-}boost})/2]/32.2$
   $= [(500 + 415.2)/2]/32.2 = 14.21$ slug
• $Tt/(mV_0) = 5750\ (3.69)/[14.21(500)]$
   $= 2.99$
• $\alpha = \cot^{-1}\ (\cot 90\ \text{deg} + 2.99) = \cot^{-1}$
   $(0 + 2.99) = 19$ deg at end-of-boost
   (Note: α = 90 deg at t = 0 s)
• $\gamma = \theta - \alpha = 90 - 19 = 71$ deg

Fig. 5.15a A large/rapid heading change with TVC requires high thrust-to-weight, high angle of attack, and low velocity.

with a large slew attitude, high thrust, long slew time, light weight, and a low velocity.

We shall give an example of the result from a constant attitude turn law, again using the rocket baseline missile with TVC. Assume an end-of-boost flight condition ($t = 3.69$ s, $T = 5750$ lb). The missile weight during boost is

$$W_{\text{Launch}} = 500\,\text{lb}$$

$$W_{\text{End-of-Boost}} = 415.2\,\text{lb}$$

Assume $\theta = 90$ deg and $V_0 = 500$ ft/s
  Compute:

$$m = m_{\text{AVG}} = W_{\text{AVG}}/g_c = [(W_{\text{Launch}} + W_{\text{End-of-Boost}})/2]/32.2$$
$$= [(500 + 415.2)/2]/32.2 = 14.21\,\text{slug}$$
$$Tt/(mV_0) = 5750(3.69)/[14.21(500)] = 2.99$$

$$\alpha = \cot^{-1}(\cot 90\,\text{deg} + 2.99) = \cot^{-1}(0 + 2.99)$$
$$= 19\,\text{deg at end-of-boost}\quad (\text{Note: } \alpha = 90\,\text{deg at } t = 0\,\text{s})$$
$$\gamma = \theta - \alpha = 90 - 19 = 71\,\text{deg}$$

Using TVC with a constant attitude turn law, the missile achieves a 71 deg heading change with 3.69 s of boost.

In a constant angle of attack turn, the missile uses TVC to quickly slew its body to a prescribed angle of attack α and maintains the angle of attack until the flight path angle γ is changed to the desired intercept direction. The missile then quickly slews to approximately zero angle of attack ($\alpha \approx 0$ deg) for the fly-out to intercept. An advantage of a constant angle of attack turn is that for the same maximum angle of attack it provides a larger heading change. A disadvantage is it requires a more complex autopilot. The inertial reference system on the missile has to derive the angle of attack from additional sensor measurements, such as velocity and acceleration. The missile autopilot provides feedback of constant angle of attack during the turn. The equation for a constant angle of attack turn is

$$\gamma = \tan \alpha \ln\{1 + [Tt/(mV_0)]\cos \alpha\}, \quad \text{where } \gamma \text{ is in rad}$$

As before, assumptions are the thrust is much larger than the aerodynamic lift, drag, and the vertical component of weight ($T \gg L, D, W \sin \gamma$); thrust is much larger than the product of propellant mass flow rate and the missile initial velocity ($T \gg \dot{m}V_0$); and near-neutral static stability ($\alpha/\delta \gg 1$).

Figure 5.15b illustrates the constant angle of attack turn and its flight performance. The flight path angle γ is shown as a function of non-dimensional time $Tt/(mV_0)$ and angle of attack α. Note that a large

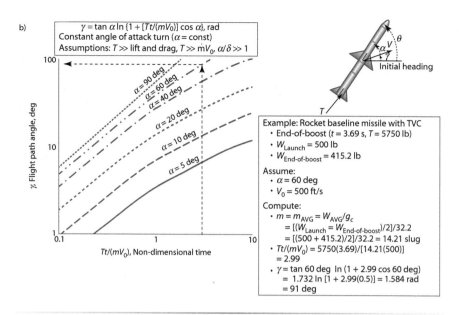

b)

$\gamma = \tan\alpha\ln\{1 + [Tt/(mV_0)]\cos\alpha\}$, rad
Constant angle of attack turn (α = const)
Assumptions: $T \gg$ lift and drag, $T \gg \dot{m}V_0$, $\alpha/\delta \gg 1$

Initial heading

Example: Rocket baseline missile with TVC
• End-of-boost ($t = 3.69$ s, $T = 5750$ lb)
• $W_{Launch} = 500$ lb
• $W_{End\text{-}of\text{-}boost} = 415.2$ lb

Assume:
• $\alpha = 60$ deg
• $V_0 = 500$ ft/s

Compute:
• $m = m_{AVG} = W_{AVG}/g_c$
  $= [(W_{Launch} = W_{End\text{-}of\text{-}boost})/2]/32.2$
  $= [(500 + 415.2)/2]/32.2 = 14.21$ slug
• $Tt/(mV_0) = 5750(3.69)/[14.21(500)]$
  $= 2.99$
• $\gamma = \tan 60$ deg In $(1 + 2.99\cos 60$ deg$)$
  $= 1.732$ In $[1 + 2.99(0.5)] = 1.584$ rad
  $= 91$ deg

Fig. 5.15b A large/rapid heading change with TVC requires high thrust-to-weight, high angle of attack, and low velocity.

heading change is consistent with a large slew angle of attack, high thrust, long slew time, light weight, and a low velocity.

The following example calculation is for a constant attitude turn law, again using the rocket baseline missile with TVC. Assume an end-of-boost flight condition ($t = 3.69$ s, $T = 5750$ lb). The missile weight during boost is

$$W_{Launch} = 500\,lb$$
$$W_{End\text{-}of\text{-}Boost} = 415.2\,lb$$

Assume $\alpha = 60$ deg and $V_0 = 500$ ft/s.
   Compute:

$$m = m_{AVG} = W_{AVG}/g_c = [(W_{Launch} + W_{End\text{-}of\text{-}Boost})/2]/32.2$$
$$= [(500 + 415.2)/2]/32.2 = 14.21\text{ slug}$$
$$Tt/(mV_0) = 5750(3.69)/[14.21(500)] = 2.99$$
$$\gamma = \tan 60\text{ deg }\ln(1 + 2.99\cos 60\text{ deg})$$
$$= 1.732\ \ln[1 + 2.99(0.5)] = 1.584\,\text{rad} = 91\,\text{deg}$$

Using TVC with a constant angle of attack turn law, the missile achieves a 91 deg heading change with 3.69 s of boost.

5.9   Coast Flight Performance

Conceptual design predictions of missile coast velocity and the coast range are shown in Fig. 5.16. Coast velocity and range are functions of the missile coast time, weight, atmospheric density, reference area, zero-lift drag coefficient, and the initial velocity. It is based on the one-degree-of-freedom (1-DOF) equation of motion with the assumptions of constant flight path angle ($\gamma =$ constant) and low angle of attack ($\alpha \approx 0$ deg), which implies $C_D \approx C_{D_0}$. The simplified equation of motion is

$$dV/dt = -gC_{D_0}S_{\text{Ref}}q/W - g\sin\gamma$$

Integrating, the equation for missile coast velocity is

$$V = V_i\{1 - [(g\sin\gamma)/V_i]t\}/\{1 + \{[g_c\rho_{\text{AVG}}S_{\text{Ref}}(C_{D_0})_{\text{AVG}}V_i]/(2W)\}t\}$$

Integrating again, the incremental flight range during coast is given by

$$R = \{2W/[g_c\rho_{\text{AVG}}S_{\text{Ref}}(C_{D_0})_{\text{AVG}}]\}\ln\{1 - [g_c^2\rho_{\text{AVG}}S_{\text{Ref}}(C_{D_0})_{\text{AVG}}/(2W)]$$
$$\times [\sin\gamma]t^2 + \{[g_c\rho_{\text{AVG}}S_{\text{Ref}}(C_{D_0})_{\text{AVG}}V_i]/(2W)\}t\}$$

Examining the equations shows that the contributors to a long-range coast include a high initial velocity, a low zero-lift drag coefficient and high altitude (low atmospheric density) flight.

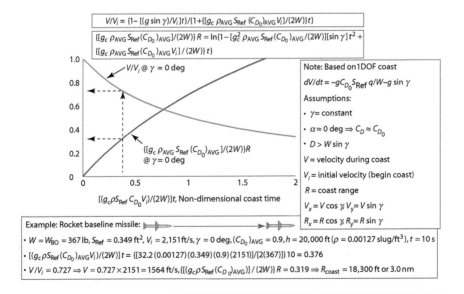

Fig. 5.16   Missile coast range is driven by its initial velocity, altitude, drag, and weight.

The zero-lift drag coefficient C_{D_0} will vary during the coast flight trajectory, because of the variation in Mach number. An approach to estimate the average value of the zero-lift drag coefficient $(C_{D_0})_{AVG}$ is to first compute the end-of-coast condition based on the initial value of C_{D_0}. $(C_{D_0})_{AVG}$ is the average of the initial and the end-of-coast estimate of C_{D_0}. Similarly, the atmospheric density ρ will vary for changes in altitude. The average density ρ_{AVG} is assumed to be the average of the initial and the end-of-coast estimate of density.

The computed coast velocity can be resolved into horizontal and vertical components by the equations

$$V_x = V \cos\gamma$$
$$V_y = V \sin\gamma$$

Similarly, coast range can be resolved into

$$R_x = R \cos\gamma$$
$$R_y = R \sin\gamma.$$

As an example for the rocket baseline missile, the coast (burnout) weight $W = W_{BO} = 367$ lb and the reference area $S_{Ref} = 0.349$ ft^2. Assume that the coast flight is at a constant altitude ($\gamma = 0$ deg). For a burnout flight condition of Mach 2.1 at 20,000 ft altitude ($\rho = 0.00127$ slug/ft^3), the zero-lift drag coefficient $C_{D_0} = 0.9$ and the beginning of coast velocity $V_i = 2151$ ft/s. The end-of-coast velocity after 10 s of coast is computed to be

$$V = 2151\{1 - [(32.2 \sin 0)/2151]10\}/$$
$$\{1 + \{[32.2(0.00127)(0.349)(0.9)(2151)]/[2(367)]\}10\}$$
$$= 1564 \, \text{ft/s}$$

The incremental range during coast is

$$R_{coast} = \{2(367)/[32.2(0.00127)(0.349)(0.9)]\}$$
$$\times \ln\{1 - \{32.2^2(0.00127)(0.349)(0.9)/[2(367)]\}[\sin 0]10^2$$
$$+\{[32.2(0.00127)(0.349)(0.9)(2151)]/[2(367)]\}10\}$$
$$= 18,300 \, \text{ft or } 3.0 \, \text{nm.}$$

5.10 Ballistic Flight Performance

Conceptual design prediction of missile ballistic flight velocity and range are shown in Fig. 5.17. These are functions of the missile time of flight, weight, atmospheric density, reference area, zero-lift drag coefficient,

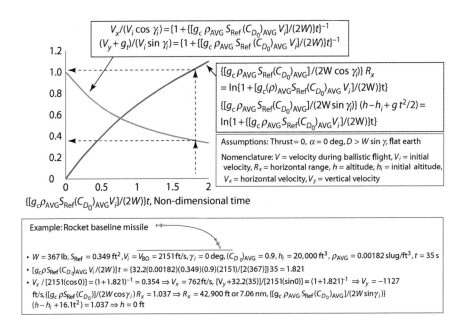

Fig. 5.17 Missile ballistic range is driven by its initial velocity, launch angle, drag, and weight.

initial velocity, and the initial flight path angle. The figure is based on the one-degree-of-freedom (1-DOF) equation of motion with the assumptions of no thrust ($T = 0$), zero angle of attack ($\alpha = 0$ deg), drag force greater than the component of weight along the drag axis ($D > W \sin \gamma$), and negligible error from the curvature of the earth. The simplified equation for the horizontal component of velocity is

$$V_x = V_i \cos \gamma_i / \left\{ 1 + \left\{ \left[g_c \rho_{\text{AVG}} S_{\text{Ref}} (C_{D_0})_{\text{AVG}} V_i \right] / (2W) \right\} t \right\}$$

The vertical component of velocity is

$$V_y = V_i \sin \gamma_i / \left\{ 1 + \left\{ \left[g_c \rho_{\text{AVG}} S_{\text{Ref}} (C_{D_0})_{\text{AVG}} V_i \right] / (2W) \right\} t \right\} - gt$$

Horizontal flight distance traveled (range) during ballistic flight is given by

$$R_x = \left\{ 2W \cos g_i / \left[g_c \rho_{\text{AVG}} S_{\text{Ref}} (C_{D_0})_{\text{AVG}} \right] \right\} \\ \times \ln \left\{ 1 + \left\{ \left[g_c \rho_{\text{AVG}} S_{\text{Ref}} (C_{D_0})_{\text{AVG}} V_i \right] / (2W) \right\} t \right\}$$

The vertical location (altitude) during ballistic flight is given by

$$h = h_i + \{(2W \sin \gamma_i)/[g_c \rho_{AVG} S_{Ref}(C_{D_0})_{AVG}]\}$$
$$\times \ln\{1 + \{[g_c \rho_{AVG} S_{Ref}(C_{D_0})_{AVG} V_i]/(2W)\}t - gt^2/2\}$$

Examining the above equations shows that the contributors to a long-range ballistic flight include a high initial (burnout) velocity, a low value of the zero-lift drag coefficient, an optimum launch angle, and a high altitude (low atmospheric density) flight.

The zero-lift drag coefficient C_{D_0} will vary during ballistic flight, because of the variation in Mach number. An approach to estimate the average value of the zero-lift drag coefficient $(C_{D_0})_{AVG}$ is to first compute the end-of-flight condition based on the initial value of C_{D_0}. $(C_{D_0})_{AVG}$ is the average of the C_{D_0} at the initial Mach number and the C_{D_0} at the end-of-flight Mach number. Similarly, the atmospheric density ρ will vary because of changes in altitude. The average density ρ_{AVG} is assumed to be the average of the density at the initial altitude and the density at the end-of-flight altitude. For a large change in altitude, a more accurate approach would be a calculation based on summing the incremental changes in the above equations for smaller changes in altitude.

As an example, we will calculate ballistic flight velocity, altitude, and range for the rocket baseline missile, which has a burnout weight $W = 367$ lb and a reference area $S_{Ref} = 0.349$ ft². Assume an initial horizontal flight path angle ($\gamma_i = 0$ deg). For a burnout flight condition of Mach 2.1 at 20,000 ft altitude ($\rho = 0.00127$ slug/ft³), the zero-lift drag coefficient $C_{D_0} = 0.9$ and the beginning-of-coast velocity $V_i = 2151$ ft/s. An initial estimate of the missile impact time is obtained by neglecting drag, solving the equation

$$t = (2h/g)^{1/2} + (2V_i/g) \sin \theta_i = 30 \text{ s}$$

Iteration of the altitude equation gives that the missile impacts the ground ($h = 0$) at a time $t = 35$ s. The average atmospheric density is the average of the atmospheric densities at the launch ($h = 20$ kft) and impact (sea level) altitudes

$$\rho_{AVG} = (0.00127 + 0.00238)/2 = 0.00182 \text{ slug/ft}^3$$

The horizontal component of velocity V_x after 35 s of ballistic flight is computed to be

$$V_x = 2151 \cos 0/\{1 + \{[32.2(0.00182)(0.349)(0.9)(2151)]/[2(367\ W)]\}35\}$$
$$= 762 \text{ ft/s}$$

The vertical component of velocity V_y at impact after 35 s of flight is

$$V_y = 2151 \sin 0 / \{1 + \{[32.2(0.00182)(0.349)(0.9)(2151)]/[2(367)]\}35\}$$
$$- 32.2(35) = 0 - 1127 = -1127 \, \text{ft/s}$$

The impact angle γ is

$$\gamma = \tan^{-1}(V_y/V_x) = \tan^{-1}(-1127/762) = \tan^{-1}(-1.479) = -55.9 \, \text{deg}$$

Finally, the horizontal range R_x for 35 s of ballistic flight is

$$R_x = \{[2(367) \cos 0]/[32.2(0.00182)(0.349)(0.9)]\}$$
$$\times \ln\{1 + \{[32.2(0.00182)(0.349)(0.9)(2151)]/[2(367)]\}35\}$$
$$= 42,886 \, \text{ft or 7.1 nm.}$$

5.11 Boost Flight Performance

Based on assumptions of low angle of attack ($\alpha \approx 0$ deg), constant flight path angle (γ = constant), and the thrust larger than the weight component along the thrust axis ($T > W \sin \gamma$), the incremental velocity from rocket motor burn is

$$\Delta V / (gI_{SP}) = -[1 - (D_{AVG}/T) - (W_{AVG} \sin \gamma / T)]\ln(1 - W_p/W_i)$$

High incremental velocity from the motor burn is provided if there is a high propellant weight fraction of the missile initial weight (W_P/W_i), a low average drag D_{AVG}, high thrust T, high specific impulse I_{SP}, and a diving flight trajectory ($\gamma < 0$).

The incremental range during boost is given by the equation

$$R = (V_i + \Delta V/2)t_B$$

In the above equation V_i is the initial velocity and t_B is the boost time.

Figure 5.18 shows the non-dimensional incremental velocity $\Delta V/(gI_{SP})$ for $\gamma = 0$ deg flight. The parameter D_{AVG}/T varies from $D_{AVG}/T = 0$ for high acceleration boost, with thrust much larger than drag, to $D_{AVG}/T = 1$ for sustain, with thrust equal to drag.

As an example, the incremental velocity at the end of boost is calculated for the rocket baseline missile, which has an initial (launch) weight $W_i = 500$ lb, boost propellant weight $W_P = 84.8$ lb, boost specific impulse $I_{SP} = 250$ s, and a boost thrust $T = 5750$ lb. The assumed launch condition of Mach 0.8, 20 kft altitude is at an initial (launch) velocity of $V_i = 820$ ft/s. We will also assume that the missile is flying at a constant altitude ($\gamma = 0$ deg). After iterating, using an initial estimate of end-of-boost drag based on the theoretical end-of-boost velocity with no

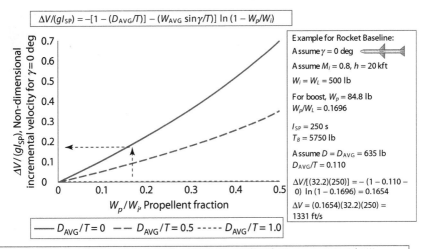

$$\Delta V/(gI_{SP}) = -[1 - (D_{AVG}/T)] - (W_{AVG}\sin\gamma/T)]\ln(1 - W_p/W_i)$$

Example for Rocket Baseline:
Assume $\gamma = 0$ deg
Assume $M_i = 0.8$, $h = 20$ kft
$W_i = W_L = 500$ lb
For boost, $W_p = 84.8$ lb
$W_p/W_L = 0.1696$
$I_{SP} = 250$ s
$T_B = 5750$ lb
Assume $D = D_{AVG} = 635$ lb
$D_{AVG}/T = 0.110$
$\Delta V/[(32.2)(250)] = -(1 - 0.110 - 0)\ln(1 - 0.1696) = 0.1654$
$\Delta V = (0.1654)(32.2)(250) = 1331$ ft/s

Axis labels: $\Delta V/(gI_{SP})$, Non-dimensional incremental velocity for $\gamma = 0$ deg (vertical); W_p/W_i, Propellent fraction (horizontal)

Legend: —— $D_{AVG}/T=0$ –– $D_{AVG}/T=0.5$ ····· $D_{AVG}/T=1.0$

Note: 1DOF Equation of Motion with $\alpha \approx 0$ deg, $\gamma =$ constant, $W_i =$ initial weight, $W_{AVG} =$ average weight, $W_p =$ propellant weight, $I_{SP} =$ specific impulse, $T =$ thrust, $M_i =$ initial Mach number, $h =$ altitude, $D_{AVG} =$ average drag, $\Delta V =$ incremental velocity, $g =$ acceleration of gravity $= 32.2$ ft/s², $V_x = V\cos\gamma$, $V_y = V\sin\gamma$, $R_x = R\cos\gamma$, $R_y = R\sin\gamma$
Note: $R = (V_i + \Delta V/2)\, t_B$, where $R =$ boost range, $V_i =$ initial velocity, $t_B =$ boost time

Fig. 5.18 High propellant weight, high specific impulse, and low drag provide high incremental velocity at the end of boost.

drag, the average drag between launch and the end of boost is found to be $D_{AVG} = 635$ lb. The incremental velocity from boost is computed to be

$$\Delta V = -32.2(250)[1 - (635/5750) - 457.6(\sin 0)/5750)]\ln(1 - 84.8/500)$$
$$= 1331 \text{ ft/s}$$

The end-of-boost velocity is

$$V_{\text{EOB}} = V_i + \Delta V = 820 + 1331 = 2151 \text{ ft/s}$$

Including the effect of drag results in an end-of-boost velocity that is 93% of the theoretical maximum (no drag) velocity (2316 versus 2151 ft/s).

Finally, the incremental range for horizontal flight during boost is computed to be

$$R = (V_i + \Delta V/2)t_B = (820 + 1331/2)3.69 = 5481 \text{ ft}.$$

5.12 Divert Flight Performance

A divert trajectory is a change in the missile heading without body rotation. Most exo-atmospheric intercept missiles use a divert flight trajectory. Divert thrusters, which are located near the missile center-of-gravity, correct the midcourse guidance error at seeker lock-on to the target.

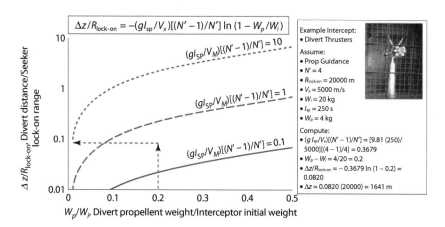

Fig. 5.19   Maximum divert capability is driven by the divert thruster propellant weight, axial velocity, and seeker lock-on range. (Source: Jerger, J.J., *Systems Preliminary Design, Principles of Guided Missile Design*, D. Van Nostrand, Inc., 1960.)

The non-dimensional divert at seeker lock-on Δz is a function of the seeker lock-on range $R_{\text{lock-on}}$, divert thruster specific impulse I_{SP}, interceptor axial velocity V_x, effective navigation ratio N', weight of divert propellant W_p, and the initial weight of the interceptor W_i. From Jerger [5], a conceptual design equation for the lateral divert distance after initiating seeker homing guidance is

$$\Delta z/R_{\text{lock-on}} = -(gI_{\text{SP}}/V_x)[(N'-1)/N']\ln\left(1 - W_p/W_i\right)$$

Assumptions for the above equation are the divert thrust is much larger than the interceptor weight, negligible drag, and proportional homing guidance.

Figure 5.19 shows the non-dimensional divert $\Delta z/R_{\text{lock-on}}$ for a divert propellant fraction up to $W_p/W_i = 0.5$. Note the benefit of a high propellant fraction, a high specific impulse, and a high value of N'. In the top right section of the figure is a photograph of a hover test demonstration of interceptor divert and attitude control thrusters. The large divert thruster is firing downward to counter gravity while the attitude control thrusters are providing roll, pitch, and yaw stabilization.

As an example of a divert intercept using solid propellant, with typical values of parameters, assume a proportional guidance effective navigation ratio $N' = 4$, seeker lock-on range $R_{\text{lock-on}} = 20000$ m, axial velocity $V_x = 5000$ m/s, interceptor initial weight $W_i = 20$ kg, specific impulse $I_{\text{SP}} = 250$ s, and a divert propellant weight $W_p = 4$ kg.

Compute:

$$(gI_{SP}/V_x)[(N' - 1)/N'] = [9.81(250)/5000][(4 - 1)/4] = 0.3679$$
$$W_p/W_i = 4/20 = 0.2$$
$$\Delta z/R_{\text{lock-on}} = -0.3679\ln(1 - 0.2) = 0.0820$$
$$\Delta z = 0.0820(20000) = 1641 \text{ m}$$

Because most exo-atmospheric interceptor seekers have relatively short range, consistent with typical light weight interceptors, it is important that the interceptor have sufficient divert capability to correct the midcourse guidance error at seeker lock-on.

5.13 Intercept Lead Angle and Velocity

The average missile velocity and the lead angle required for intercept are shown in Fig. 5.20 as a function of target aspect and velocity. The equation is

$$V_M \sin L = V_T \sin A$$

The above equation is based on constant bearing (L = constant) homing guidance.

An assumption is that the seeker look angle is approximately equal to the missile lead angle. The assumption is most applicable for constant altitude intercepts at a low angle of attack flight trajectory.

Note from the figure that high average missile velocity is required to intercept a target at an aspect angle $A = 90$ deg (beam shot). Increasing

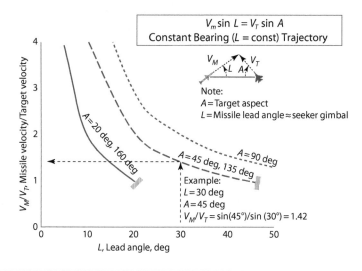

Fig. 5.20 High missile velocity and target lead are required to intercept a high speed crossing target.

the maximum lead angle/seeker gimbal angle reduces the required missile velocity for intercept.

As an example, assume a target with an aspect angle $A = 45$ deg. Also assume that the maximum allowable lead angle is $L = 30$ deg, a typical gimbal limit for a seeker. Compute

$$V_M/V_T = \sin 45°/\sin 30° = 1.42$$

For these assumptions, the missile must have an average velocity that is 42% greater than the velocity of the target to achieve a homing intercept without exceeding the gimbal limit of the seeker. Also as a rule of thumb, the missile velocity should be at least 1.5 times the target velocity, for a good capture capability, especially for a tail chase intercept.

5.14 Comparison of Missile Design with Performance Requirements

As shown in Fig. 5.21, after completing the missile flight performance computation, the next step in the missile configuration synthesis and system engineering process is to compare the candidate missile design flight performance (e.g., range, velocity, time-to-target, off-boresight) with the mission requirements for flight performance. If the candidate missile has insufficient flight performance, changes are made in the aerodynamic configuration, propulsion, structure, subsystems, and/or flight trajectory to improve the flight performance. The refined/resized missile is then sent through another cycle of evaluation. The iteration continues until there is a convergence that meets the flight performance requirements.

During the typical conceptual design and system engineering study there is usually more emphasis on meeting flight performance requirements than on design optimization. Because of the limited time for conceptual design, missile design refinement and optimization often has to wait until the follow-on preliminary design activity.

5.15 Summary

Flight performance consideration in missile design and system engineering is oriented toward flight trajectory computation and comparison with the missile flight performance requirements. Missile flight performance requirements include range, velocity, time-to-target, and off-boresight capability. Much of the impact of changes in the missile aerodynamics, propulsion, and weight is in the area of flight performance. Converging to a design that harmonizes the aerodynamics, propulsion, and weight, while also satisfying the flight performance requirements is a primary activity in missile configuration design and system engineering.

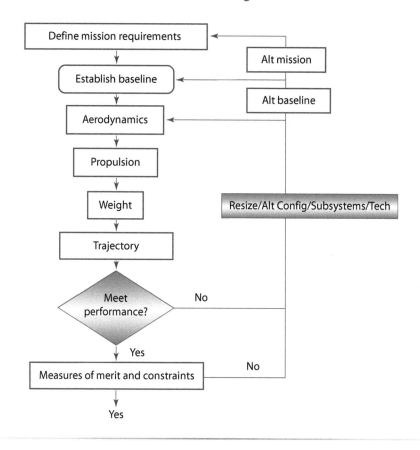

Fig. 5.21 Conceptual design and system engineering require creative, rapid, and iterative evaluations.

This chapter presented equations of motion modeling, examples of missile flight performance drivers, typical flight performance for missile propulsion alternatives, steady state flight relationships, and the proportional homing lead angle requirement. It also provided equations for predicting the missile flight trajectories of steady climb, steady glide, cruise, boost, coast, turn, ballistic, and divert flight. The analytical equations are most suitable for missile conceptual design and system engineering. The missile flight phases (e.g., boost-cruise-glide) can be patched together to compute a complete flight trajectory.

5.16 Problem Review

1. Flight trajectory calculation requires input from aerodynamics, propulsion, and w_____.

2. A robust missile flight envelope can be characterized by the maximum effective range, minimum effective range, and a large o___ b_____ capability.

3. Limitations to the missile effective range include the launch platform fire control system, seeker, time of flight, closing velocity, and the missile ma_____ capability.

4. 1-DOF simulation requires modeling only the thrust, weight, and a____ f____.

5. A 3-DOF simulation that models 3 aero forces is called a p____ m___ simulation.

6. A simulation that includes 3 aerodynamic forces (normal, axial, side), 3 aerodynamic moments (pitch, roll, yaw), thrust, and weight is called a ____DOF simulation.

7. The pitch angular acceleration $\ddot{\theta}$ is approximately equal to the second time derivative of the a____ o_ a_____.

8. Cruise range is a function of the velocity, specific impulse, L/D, and the fu__ fraction.

9. If thrust is equal to drag and lift is equal to weight, the missile is in s_____ l____ flight.

10. Turn rate using aero control is a function of the normal force, weight, altitude, and v_____.

11. Turn rate with TVC is a function of thrust, weight, angle of attack, and v_____.

12. Coast range is a function of the initial velocity, weight, drag, and the t___ of flight.

13. Incremental velocity due to boost is a function of I_{SP}, drag, and the p_____ weight fraction.

14. To intercept a high speed crossing target requires a high speed missile with a high g_____ angle seeker.

15. An analytical model of a rocket in co-altitude, non-maneuvering flight can be developed by patching together the flight phases of boost, followed by co___.

16. An analytical model of a rocket in a short range, off-boresight intercept can be developed by patching the flight phases of boost and tu__.

17. An analytical model of a guided bomb in non-maneuvering flight can be developed from the flight phase of a steady de_____ or g____.

18. An analytical model of an unguided ($\alpha = 0$ deg) weapon can be developed from the ba_____ flight phase.

19. An analytical model of a ramjet/turbojet in co-altitude, non-maneuvering flight can be developed by patching the flight phases of boost followed by cr____.

Chapter 6

Measures of Merit and Launch Platform Integration/System Engineering

- Robustness in Adverse Weather, Uncertainty, and Countermeasures
- High Warhead Lethality and Low Collateral Damage
- Drivers for Small Miss Distance
- Minimizing Carriage and Launch Observables
- Low Radar Cross Section and Other Survivability Considerations
- Approaches for High Reliability
- Minimizing Development, Production, and Logistics Cost
- Launch Platform Integration/Firepower

6.1 Introduction

Measures of merit and launch platform integration/system engineering considerations in missile design include robustness, warhead lethality, miss distance, carriage and launch observables, other survivability considerations, reliability, cost, and launch platform integration/firepower. Examples of measures of merit, launch platform integration/system engineering considerations, and conceptual design prediction methods are given in this chapter.

As shown in Fig. 6.1, following the missile configuration sizing to meet flight performance requirements, the next step in missile design and system engineering is satisfying the other measures of merit requirements and system engineering constraints. These include system-of-systems command, control, and communication (C^3) and physical compatibility with the launch platform. If the missile design satisfies the measures of merit and constraints, the design has converged. If not, the designer selects alternative configurations, subsystems, technologies, baseline missiles, or mission requirements and the design is reiterated until it satisfies the measures of merit and constraints. Again, simply satisfying the mission requirements does not necessarily make it an optimum design. Because a relatively short time constraint is typical for a conceptual design and system engineering study, the activity is usually focused on developing a balanced design(s) that meets the mission requirements. Refinement of the design is usually conducted later, in a follow-on preliminary design activity.

Figure 6.2 illustrates the considerations of typical measures of merit for a balanced missile design and system engineering activity. The aeromechanics

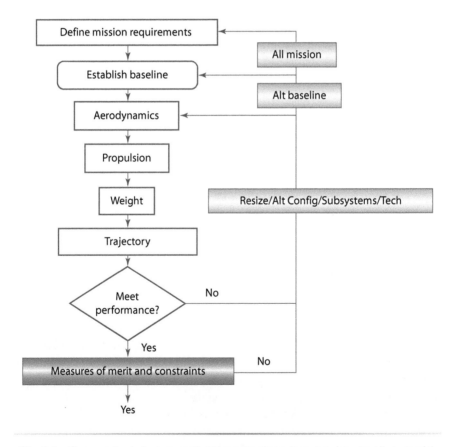

Fig. 6.1 Conceptual design and system engineering require creative, rapid, and iterative evaluations.

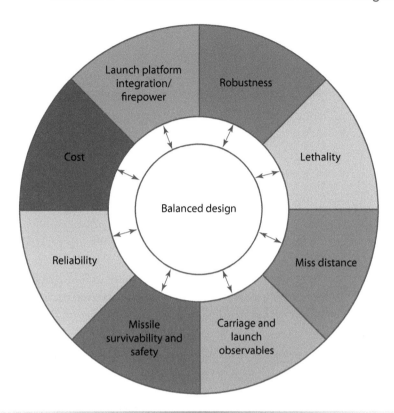

Fig. 6.2 Measures of merit and launch platform integration/system engineering should be harmonized.

performance of the missile should be harmonized with other measures of merit such as robustness, warhead lethality, miss distance, carriage and launch observables, missile survivability and safety, reliability, and cost, as well as system engineering constraints/requirements such as launch platform integration/firepower.

6.2 Robustness

The first measure of merit to be discussed is robustness. Missiles must have sufficient robustness to handle effects such as adverse weather, ground clutter, local climate, flight environment variations, uncertainty, countermeasures, and electromagnetic compatibility (EMC). This section of the text provides examples of requirements and technologies for robustness.

Adverse weather capability is a driving concern for most missiles, especially missiles with seekers. Cloud cover is a particular concern for the missile seeker/target sensors because clouds are pervasive worldwide.

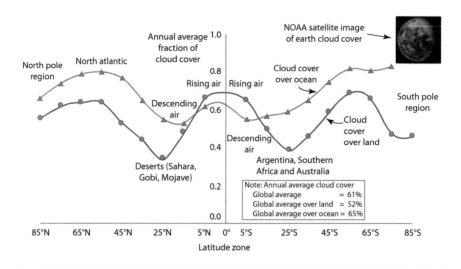

Fig. 6.3 Cloud cover is pervasive. (Reference: Schneider, Stephen H. *Encyclopedia of Climate and Weather.* Oxford University Press, 1996.)

As shown in the National Oceanic and Atmospheric Administration (NOAA) typical satellite image in Fig. 6.3, clouds cover a large portion of the earth. The figure shows that the global average annual cloud cover is about 61%. The average cloud cover over land is about 52% and the average cloud cover over the oceans is about 65%. The figure is based on Ref. 25. Clouds tend to occur between 3000 and 20,000 ft elevation. Clouds may be thick, in some cases the thickness may be greater than 6000 ft. The average annual cloud cover shown in the figure is based on weather observers around the world. It is a composite of averages that vary widely with geographical location, season, and time of day.

An example of a geographical cloud system that changes regularly with the season and the time of day is the low-level, layered stratus cloud cover that occurs over much of the world's oceans. Stratus clouds are more frequent during the summer months of the Eastern Pacific and the Eastern Atlantic and in the hours before sunrise.

Another example of a geographical cloud system that changes regularly with the season and the time of day is cumulonimbus. Cumulonimbus clouds are large columnar clouds that can extend to high altitude, even up to the stratosphere. These clouds are concentrated where surface temperatures are high and there is a general upward movement of the air. An example is a zone known as the Inter-Tropical Convergence Zone (ITCZ). In the ITCZ the trade winds of the Northern Hemisphere converge with those of the Southern Hemisphere. Cumulonimbus clouds have high concentrations of droplets and ice crystals, which can grow to a large size. Cumulonimbus clouds are often responsible for the frequent summer afternoon rainfall of South East Asia, North America, and Europe, and the rainfall of the Amazon basin during the months of December, January, and February.

For the purpose of conceptual design, typical environmental requirements for missile sensors are an assumed cloud base height of 1 to 5 km, cloud thickness up to 2 km, cloud water density of about 0.1 g/m^3, rain rate of about 4 mm/h, and humidity of about 7.5 g/m^3. These typical requirements should be examined at the beginning of the design study, especially if the missile is to be used in an extreme environment. For example, in a wet tropical climate the probability that the rain rate is currently exceeding 4 mm/h is less than 1%. In a desert environment the probability is less than 0.1%. It would be unnecessarily restrictive to require missile target sensors to operate in 100% weather conditions, such as severe thunderstorms.

The relative locations of the missile and its target have an effect on the target signal attenuation. For example, a high altitude seeker looking downward at a ground target would have a relatively short path length through fog. It would have less attenuation of the target signal than a low altitude seeker looking horizontally at the ground target through the fog. The low altitude horizontal seeker would have a longer path length through the fog and greater attenuation of the target signal.

Shown in Fig. 6.4, based on Ref. 24, is the signal attenuation versus wavelength for a representative atmospheric environment of cloud droplet density, rain rate, and humidity level. The solid curve is the

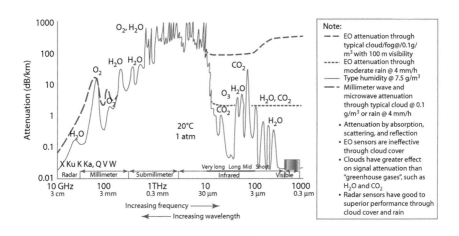

Fig. 6.4 A radar seeker/sensor is more robust in adverse weather. (Source: Klien, L.A., *Millimeter-Wave and Infrared Multisensor Design and Signal Processing*, Artech House, Boston, 1997.)

attenuation from "greenhouse" gases (water vapor, carbon dioxide, ozone) for a nominal humidity of 7.5 g/m^3. Greenhouse gas molecules absorb and scatter energy at discrete frequencies and wavelengths. This is a driving factor in selecting a sensor frequency or wavelength window that allows good transmission without high molecular absorption and scattering. From the narrow-dash and long-dash curves of the figure, note that although passive electro-optical (EO) sensors have one-way transmission through rain of about 50% per km, there is almost no transmission of an EO signal through clouds. Cloud droplets are small, about 5 to 20 μm in diameter, with dimensions comparable to the EO wavelength. The concentration is high, about 50 to 500 droplets per cm^3. EO wavelengths are strongly diffracted around cloud droplets because of Mie electromagnetic scattering, which provides a concentration of the scatter in the forward direction. However, raindrops are about 2 to 6 mm in diameter (much larger than EO wavelengths) and cause less attenuation of an EO signal. Rain rate attenuation is primarily from optical scattering. EO transmission through rain is a function of the size of the raindrops, rain rate, and the path length through the rain. A typical EO transmission limit through rain is about 2 to 5 km of path length. EO array sensors for missiles cover the wavelength range from ultraviolet (UV) through long wave infrared (LWIR).

The best sensors for looking through cloud cover and rain are radar sensors. Radar sensors have negligible atmospheric attenuation at frequencies below 10 GHz. At higher frequencies, millimeter wave (mmW) sensors operating in cloud cover and rain are limited to about 2 to 5 km of path length through the clouds and rain, with the same implications as those discussed in the previous paragraph. Cloud droplets, which are much smaller than mmW wavelengths, absorb mmW radiation (much like a microwave oven). A different mechanism is responsible for the attenuation of a mmW signal through rain or snow. Raindrops and snowflakes are comparable in size to mmW wavelengths and cause Rayleigh and Mie electromagnetic scattering attenuation. Lower frequency radars, such as Ku-band radars, are less affected by cloud cover and rain rate.

As shown in Fig. 6.5, most clouds occupy elevation heights between 3000 and 20,000 ft, which is an altitude envelope of interest for many missiles. Also, as shown previously, cloud cover is a frequent occurrence. Clouds vary in thickness from a few meters (e.g., fog) to more than a km. Because of the extent and frequency of cloud cover, EO sensors are often limited in their applications. The Low Cost Autonomous Attack System (LOCAAS) and the Brilliant Anti-armor Technology (BAT) submunitions were designed to minimize the problem of cloud cover by operating at low altitude under most clouds. LOCAAS and BAT were also designed to fly at low velocity, to maximize the time available for target lock-on and homing under the constraint of a shallow look-down angle. The "under

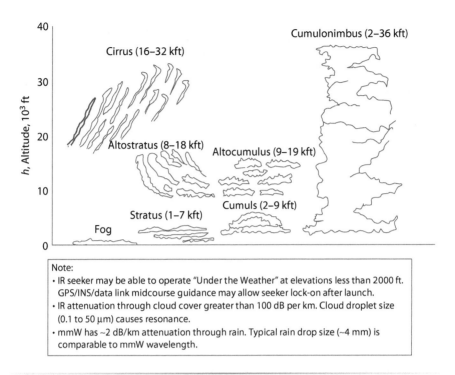

Note:
- IR seeker may be able to operate "Under the Weather" at elevations less than 2000 ft. GPS/INS/data link midcourse guidance may allow seeker lock-on after launch.
- IR attenuation through cloud cover greater than 100 dB per km. Cloud droplet size (0.1 to 50 µm) causes resonance.
- mmW has ~2 dB/km attenuation through rain. Typical rain drop size (~4 mm) is comparable to mmW wavelength.

Fig. 6.5 A radar seeker/sensor has an advantage of more robust operation through clouds.

the weather" operation is effective for most battlefield EO missiles, such as Hellfire. Exceptions include the occurrence of dense/thick fog, heavy rain, and heavy obscurants. For an EO missile that must lock-on after launch in adverse weather, the search capability at low altitude can be improved by adding an additional wide field of view (FOV) sensor, such as passive imaging IR. For example, a wide FOV sensor could cue a narrow FOV sensor, such as a laser detection and ranging (LADAR) sensor, which is then used for target recognition, acquisition, and fine tracking. Also, GPS/INS/data link midcourse guidance may allow an EO seeker lock-on after launch. However, as stated previously, for most missiles operating in adverse weather, especially SAMs and AAMs, the most robust target sensor is a radar sensor.

The prevailing climate of the country developing a missile is a cultural factor in selecting an EO seeker versus a radar seeker. A country that has a high annual precipitation is more likely to select a radar seeker than a country that has a low annual precipitation. Other cultural considerations include the country's emphasis on worldwide export and its emphasis on expeditionary warfare.

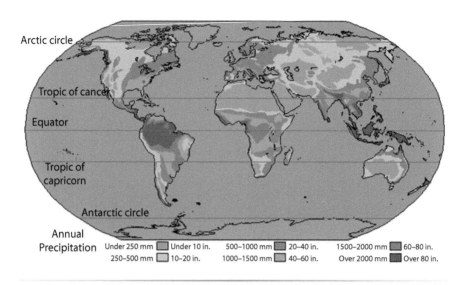

Fig. 6.6   A consideration in missile seeker/sensor selection is the probability of precipitation. (Source: Microsoft Encarta.)

The average annual precipitation of the world is 41.3 in. However, it varies widely, depending upon the region of the world. Figure 6.6 shows the worldwide regions where the annual precipitation is very low (less than 10 in.), low (10 to 20 in.), average (20 to 40 in.), above average (40 to 60 in.), high (60 to 80 in.), and very high (above 80 in.). Countries that have low annual precipitation tend to be in the desert, mid-continental, or the polar regions of the world. Countries that have high annual precipitation tend to be in either the equatorial or the mountain range regions of the world.

Aerosol particles that have a dimension d that is comparable to the missile seeker/sensor wavelength λ ($0.1 < d/\lambda < 10$) have Mie resonance, which results in a large attenuation of the signal. Figure 6.7, based on Ref. 26, shows the particle size of typical aerosols. Note from the figure that for a visible or short wave IR seeker/sensor, the wavelength is comparable to the physical dimensions of haze (up to 1 μm), smoke (0.2 to 2 μm), and fume (up to 100 μm) particles, causing signal attenuation from Mie resonance. An MWIR (3 to 5 μm) seeker/sensor is susceptible to Mie resonance from fumes and also dust particles (1 to 10 μm). LWIR (8 to 12 μm) generally performs better in dust than MWIR. However, an LWIR seeker/sensor is more susceptible to Mie resonance from fumes and also fog/cloud droplets (5 to 50 μm). MWIR generally performs better than LWIR in fog/clouds, but it still has large attenuation from the concentration of the particles. A mmW seeker/sensor is usually more susceptible to Mie resonance from rain (~0.5 to 5 mm diameter) than an IR sensor.

Aerosol particles that are much larger than the missile seeker/sensor wavelength attenuate the signal by reflecting it in a random direction. The attenuation is a function of the concentration of the particles. Clouds and fog cause large attenuation of all EO signals because of the large concentration of particles.

Meteorological visibility R is shown in Fig. 6.8 as a function of the atmospheric attenuation coefficient σ from Ref. 26 for the visibility definitions from the 1982 International Visibility Code. The maximum attenuation and the shortest range is in dense fog ($\sigma = 160/km$). The theoretical maximum range is for pure air without humidity ($\sigma = 0.014/km$). Range is based on the Koschmieder formula

$$R = \sigma^{-1} \ln C_{\text{Threshold}}^{-1}$$

For a nominal value of $C_{\text{Threshold}} = 0.02$

$$R = 3.91/\sigma$$

σ is the atmospheric attenuation coefficient at a nominal visible wavelength of $\lambda = 0.55\ \mu m$. These results may be optimistic for infrared sensors, which may be strongly attenuated by H_2O and CO_2 molecular interaction (Fig. 6.4). A 2% threshold contrast criteria for detection may be optimistic,

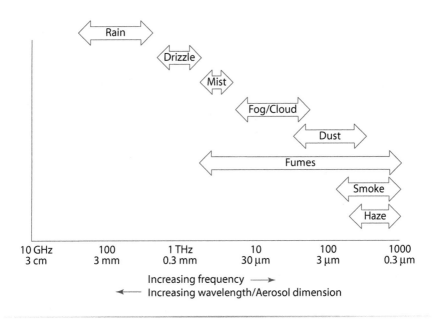

Fig. 6.7 Aerosols drive seeker/sensor atmospheric attenuation if the aerosol dimension is comparable to the wavelength. (Source: Richardson, M.A., et al, *Surveillance and Target Acquisition Systems*, Brassey's, London, Boston, 2000.)

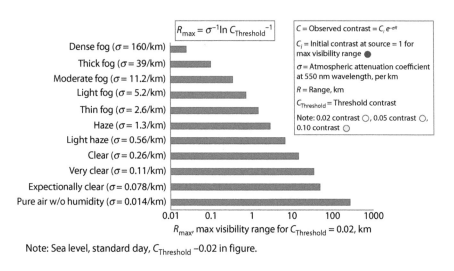

Fig. 6.8 A lock-on before launch EO missile is limited to about 4 km range in typical weather. (Reference: Richardson, M.A., et al, *Surveillance and Target Acquisition Systems*, Brassey's, London, Boston, 2000.)

depending upon the quality/sensitivity of the missile seeker/sensor. For a low cost seeker/sensor, a larger value of threshold contrast (e.g., 5%, 10%) may be more realistic. The right section of the figure illustrates the 2%, 5%, and 10% contrast levels. Compared to a 2% contrast threshold criteria for detection, a 5% threshold results in 73% of the range of the 2% criteria, while a 10% threshold results in 59% of the range of the 2% criteria.

The relative importance of fog/cloud, haze, and humidity (7.5 g/m^3) that was previously shown in Fig. 6.4 is consistent with their relative ranking of Fig. 6.8. Many battlefield EO lock-on before launch missiles (e.g., TOW) have up to 4 km of range. However, 4 km range is not possible in fog and it may not be achievable in haze. For a battlefield EO missile with a required range longer than 4 km (e.g. Hellfire), a lock-on after launch capability is probably required.

A comparison of seeker and navigation sensor alternatives for missiles is shown in the Fig. 6.9. The selected measures of merit are: 1) performance in an adverse weather environment such as cloud cover, rain, snow, or dust, 2) automatic target recognition (ATR)/automatic target acquisition (ATA) performance in ground clutter, 3) sensor range, 4) performance against moving targets, 5) volume search cycle time to cover the required field of view/field of regard, 6) compatibility with a dome suitable for hypersonic application, such as an endo-atmospheric missile defense interceptor, 7) diameter required, 8) weight/cost, and 9) technology maturity.

Synthetic aperture radar (SAR) is a potential seeker with many performance advantages for a precision strike missile. SAR has the flexibility required to cover an area search for single-cell target detection, and then switch to high resolution for target identification and targeting. SAR sensors can also provide high-accuracy profiling of the terrain features around the target to provide a reference for deriving global positioning system (GPS) coordinates of the target. Polarization provides a SAR sensor with the capability to extract information on the physical shape characteristics of the target, enhancing ATR. Other discriminates that improve the ATR performance of SAR include motion detection and three-dimensional imagery. The weight and cost of SAR sensors have been reduced in recent years. However, SAR technology is relatively immature for missiles. It is also limited to relatively slow moving ground targets. There are no current SAR missiles.

Active imaging mm wave (mmW) is another potential sensor. Cost and technology maturity are limitations. PAC-3 has a pseudo-imaging capability based on range profiling of the target aim-point selection, providing higher lethality against the target warhead. Phased array is an enabling technology.

A passive imaging mmW sensor is another sensor with potential application to future precision strike missiles. Passive imaging mmW has an

Sensor	Adverse weather impact	ATR/ATA in clutter	Range	Moving target	Volume search time	Hypersonic dome compact.	Diameter required	Weight and cost	Maturity
• SAR	●	◐	●	—○	◐	●	○	—	—
• Active imaging mmW	◐	○	◐	○●	○	●	○	—	—
• Passive imaging mmW	◐	●	—	℧○	○	●	—	○	—
• Active imaging IR (LADAR)	—	●	○	◐	—	○	●	◐	◐
• Active Non-image IR (LADAR)	—	○	○	◐	◐	○	◐	●	●
• Active Non-image RF	◐	—	◐	◐	●	●	●	○	●
• Passive imaging IR	—	◐	◐	℧○	◐	—	●	◐	◐
• Acoustic	●	◐	—	—○	●	—	—	●	◐
• GPS/INS/ data link	●	●	●	—℧	●	●	●	●	◐

● Superior ◐ Good ○ Average ℧ Poor — Probably unacceptable

Fig. 6.9 Missile seekers are complemented by GPS/INS/data link sensors.

advantage over EO in the capability to see through cloud cover and its high contrast of metal objects in the mmW spectrum. Advantages over active radar sensors include lower observables (passive), lower noise, and avoidance of radar glint. The cold sky temperature is about 35 K, and is reflected by metal objects at mmW frequencies, enhancing detection in clutter against many targets. The temperature of terrestrial object clutter is about 300 K, and is not reflected. There are no current passive imaging mmW missiles.

Other, more mature missile seeker alternatives include active imaging IR based on LADAR, passive imaging staring or scanning IR, active non-imaging mmW or centimeter wave (cmW) radar, active non-imaging LADAR, passive non-imaging IR, visible, and acoustic/seismic. Seekers cover the range of acoustic-to-visible. Because seekers have limitations in one or more areas, multi-mode seekers using sensor data fusion will be developed for future missiles. Multidimensional orthogonal discriminants that are likely to be used in sensor data fusion include angular resolution, range resolution, contrast, polarization, temporal, multi-spectral, and gas composition signatures of the target. Because of the importance of operating in adverse weather, radar seekers are projected to have increased usage for future missiles.

The approach to navigation by most of the US modern long range missiles involves the use of the satellite Global Positioning System (GPS), an inertial navigation system (INS), and a data link. GPS/INS/data link guidance is an enabling capability for precision navigation and the fusion of target sensor data in a clutter environment. GPS/INS accuracy for a tightly coupled system in the Wide Area GPS Enhancement (WAGE), differential or relative modes has sensor hand-off error less than 3 m, allowing precision guidance against a fixed target without having to use a seeker. Also, the enhanced accuracy from GPS facilitates seeker lock-on in clutter, adverse weather, and long range target intercept with lock-on after launch. GPS performance in clutter is particularly beneficial for a ground urban target.

Advanced GPS/INS receivers are based on a centralized Kalman filter that processes the raw data from all of the sensors (e.g., seeker, GPS receiver, INS). Tightly coupled GPS/INS is able to make pseudo-range measurements from three, two, or even one satellite if one or more of the satellites are lost. A tightly coupled GPS/INS system corrects the navigation error through Kalman filtering. A typical Kalman filter has about 23 states, correcting measurements such as the missile position error (3 states for x, y, and z location), velocity error (3 states), attitude error (3 states), accelerometer bias (3 states), gyro bias (3 states), GPS receiver clock bias (1 state), GPS receiver clock drift (1 state), data link radar misalignment (3 states), and launch position error (3 states). Benefits of tightly coupled integration of the INS with the GPS for navigation include high-precision position and velocity measurement and reduced susceptibility to jamming. The availability of GPS to continuously update the inertial system allows the design trades to consider a lower cost and less expensive INS, while maintaining good navigation and anti-jam (A/J) performance.

An in-flight data link allows a target location update during missile flight, which is particularly useful against a movable target. A real-time data link has the potential to eliminate the seeker, reducing missile cost. In the case of a data link with sufficient bandwidth (approximately 100 Mb/s) to provide target image data, transmitting an image of the target prior to impact reduces the possibility of collateral damage and provides battle damage indication (BDI) information. At the present time a limitation for data links is their bandwidth capability against moving targets. Real-time data links that could replace seekers are currently limited to slowly moving targets, such as surface moving targets.

Shown in Fig. 6.10 are examples of the resolution of missile imaging seekers.

An example of the resolution of a LADAR seeker is shown in the upper left corner of the figure. A LADAR seeker has the best resolution for target discrimination in clutter. It can also provide contrast, three-dimensional imagery, polarization information, and temporal information on the target, enhancing ATR. Because of its narrow field of view (FOV) and the relatively long time required to search, a LADAR seeker is best used as a multi-mode seeker, complemented by a wide FOV sensor such as passive

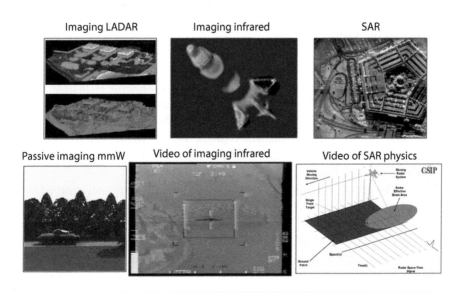

Fig. 6.10 An imaging seeker enhances target acquisition/discrimination.

imaging IR. The laser transmitter is usually boresighted to a passive imaging IR sensor that acquires the target.

The next best resolution is a passive imaging infrared seeker. The top middle image shows the resolution of the SM-3 Standard Missile 256 × 256 imaging infrared seeker against a Lance missile target. Imaging IR seekers are in development with resolution up to 1000 × 1000 pixels. Passive imaging IR seekers have advantages of angular resolution, clutter rejection, and low noise. A limitation in the production of large size high performance (cryogenic cooled) arrays is the mismatch in the coefficient of the thermal expansion of the detector and the silicon readout base. High performance FPA detectors that are appropriate for missile applications include InSb, HgCdTe, and QWIP.

The upper right image is from a SAR sensor. SAR has a resolution of about 0.3 m, and depending upon the computational and inertial reference capability, it is almost independent of range. At very long range a SAR sensor can have higher resolution than the other sensor alternatives. A cmW SAR seeker performance is almost independent of adverse weather.

The bottom left image is from a passive imaging mmW seeker. Advantages of passive imaging mmW include an adverse weather capability, high contrast of metal targets, and low noise. A disadvantage of passive imaging mmW is relatively low resolution compared to imaging IR. Sizes have been produced up to 60 × 75 elements for focal plane arrays and 128 elements for linear scanning arrays, with apertures sizes down to 0.4 meter in diameter. The frequency and frame rate demonstrated to date for missile applications are 89 GHz and 30 Hz respectively. Passive imaging mmW is a relatively immature technology, and the resolution is expected to improve in the future.

The bottom center section of the figure is a video from a 256 × 256 imaging infrared seeker. The AGM-130 missile is attacking a bridge in Kosovo. The initial phase of flight before seeker lock-on is provided by GPS/INS. Note that the initially low contrast and high clutter is not a problem for the GPS/INS guided portion of the flight. Seeker lock-on would not be possible in this early phase of the flight. As the missile closes on the target in the final (seeker guided) portion of the flight there is higher contrast, less clutter, and higher resolution.

The bottom right section of the figure is a video demonstration of the physics of SAR. The video is courtesy of the Georgia Tech Center for Signal and Image Processing (CSIP). Shown is a flight vehicle with a fixed side-looking SAR sensor operating in a strip map mode. Along the flight path, the SAR sensor and SAR computer measure and process the amplitude, phase, and frequency of the backscattered signal. The SAR computer stores the received signals at each point in time and files them as to position, amplitude, and phase. As an example, at time zero in the video the target is at the edge of the effective beam area of the SAR sensor. There is a relatively long time delay in receiving the return from the target, from the large down-range and lateral offset distances. At the next time the time delay is smaller, because the distances are smaller. This continues until the target is in the center of the radar effective beam area, with a minimum time delay in the return signal. As the vehicle continues in flight, the target moves out of the center of the radar effective beam area, and the time delay increases. Summing up the radar space-time signals provides the location of the target. An alternative approach to strip map SAR, which has a relatively long dwell time because of the time for a point on the ground to travel through the antenna beam, is scanning SAR. For scanning SAR, the dwell time is the time required to scan one beam width. Although scanning SAR has less resolution than strip map SAR, scanning SAR is more often used because it provides a relatively high search rate. SAR requires accurate velocity measurement and motion compensation to support the signal processing. A precision inertial navigation system is required, which is one reason why SAR is relatively expensive.

An option to an imaging seeker that also provides high accuracy is a semi-active laser (SAL) seeker. A SAL seeker homes on laser energy that is reflected off the target. A laser designator, either on the launch platform or provided by another platform, provides a laser spot on the target. The laser beam has a coherent wavelength with low divergence, which provides a laser spot that is relatively small and with a high signal-to-noise ratio. The laser designator frequency modulation coding can be changed, for countermeasure resistance.

The top left corner of Fig. 6.11 illustrates the laser designator, its laser beam reflecting off the target, and the missile SAL seeker optics receiving the reflected laser energy. The radiation received by the SAL seeker first passes through a narrow-band optical filter in front of the detector array. This reduces the background radiation noise. Next, the seeker optics defocus the received spot energy onto the detector array. The objective of defocusing the laser spot is to cover a larger portion of the detector array, for improved tracking accuracy.

The top right portion of the figure illustrates the laser seeker detector array, which has four detectors. The detector array senses the laser energy in each of its quadrants.

The bottom left portion of the figure illustrates the signal processing of the laser energy that is detected by each quadrant. These are summed to provide the elevation and azimuth errors in tracking the target, which are then used by the seeker to provide flight control homing commands. The missile maneuvers to balance the signals coming from the four detectors.

Finally, the bottom right portion of the figure is a video illustrating semi-active laser designation and homing for SAL JDAM.

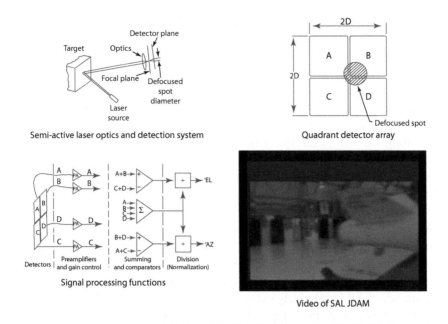

Fig. 6.11 SAL seeker quadrant detector resolution and a small laser spot provide high accuracy.

Most missile seekers have a gimbal system that mechanically tracks the target and stabilizes the seeker in inertial space. The gimbal stabilization facilitates target tracking by minimizing the interference from the motion of the missile body. Other advantages of a gimbaled seeker include a large field of regard, compensation for missile body bending, and a longer detection range. Most missile seekers have two gimbals (yaw, pitch), relying on the missile roll autopilot for roll stabilization. A few missiles have three gimbals (pitch, yaw, roll), which also allows roll stabilization of the seeker. The top left portion of Fig. 6.12 shows an example of a seeker that has three gimbals, the IRIS-T large field of regard imaging infrared seeker.

An alternative approach to a gimbal seeker is a strapdown seeker, such as the SM-3 imaging infrared seeker shown in the bottom left portion of the figure. Instead of mechanical tracking, a strapdown seeker electronically tracks the target within its field of view. Advantages of a strapdown seeker include lower cost, lighter weight, and less sensitivity to dome error slope. A tradeoff for a strapdown seeker is the size of the array, its field of view, and the resolution/homing error/detection range. A large field of view with good resolution, small homing error, and diffraction limited detection range requires a large size array. A large field of view with a small size array would have less resolution, a larger homing error,

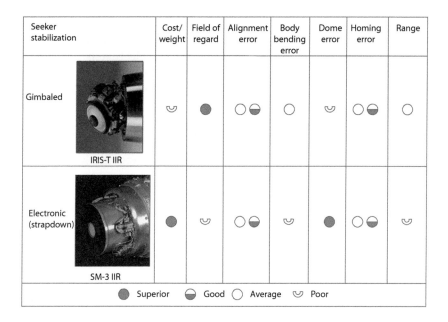

Seeker stabilization		Cost/weight	Field of regard	Alignment error	Body bending error	Dome error	Homing error	Range
Gimbaled	IRIS-T IIR	☡ Poor	● Superior	○◔ Average/Good	○ Average	☡ Poor	○◔ Average/Good	○ Average
Electronic (strapdown)	SM-3 IIR	● Superior	☡ Poor	○◔ Average/Good	☡ Poor	● Superior	○◔ Average/Good	☡ Poor

● Superior   ◔ Good   ○ Average   ☡ Poor

Fig. 6.12 A strapdown seeker is lower cost and lighter weight. A gimbaled seeker has longer range and a wider field of regard.

and shorter detection range. Most exo-atmospheric missile defense interceptors (e.g., GBI, SM-3, THADD) have strapdown imaging IR seekers, because of the emphasis on a light weight interceptor. An exception is the Arrow II, which has a gimbaled seeker.

The advantage of the large field of regard of a gimbaled seeker to provide a large off-boresight intercept is illustrated in Fig. 6.13. A notional

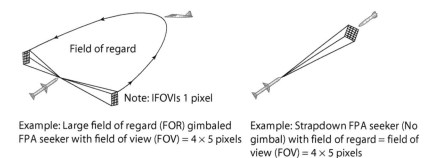

Example: Large field of regard (FOR) gimbaled FPA seeker with field of view (FOV) = 4 × 5 pixels

Example: Strapdown FPA seeker (No gimbal) with field of regard = field of view (FOV) = 4 × 5 pixels

Fig. 6.13 The field of regard of a gimbaled seeker is usually larger than the field of view of a strapdown seeker.

gimbaled seeker is shown in the left portion of the figure. Note the definitions of field of regard, field of view, and instantaneous field of view. The field of regard (FOR) is the total gimbal angle that is available to the seeker. For the example gimbal seeker, the FOR of $\pm$ 90 deg allows lock-on before launch with a large off-boresight capability. Field of view (FOV) is the total view that is available at a specified gimbal angle. The example FOV is the total view angle of a small (4×5 pixel) focal plane array (FPA). The FOV of most gimbal IR seekers is typically about 1 to 3 deg, depending the target tracking requirement and the seeker optics design. The instantaneous field of view (IFOV) of an FPA is the single field of view of an individual pixel. FOV is approximately equal to $n^{1/2} \times$ IFOV, where n is the total number of pixels of the two-dimensional FPA. An advantage of a large FPA, e.g., 256×256, is that it is possible to focus a small, diffraction limited spot that is comparable to the size of an individual pixel, while also allowing a fairly large FOV that is consistent with good tracking.

The right portion of the figure illustrates a strapdown seeker, which has no gimbals. For a strapdown seeker, the FOR is the same as the FOV. In the example the seeker also has a small 4×5 pixel FPA, with the same IFOV as that of the gimbal example. A problem with the strapdown seeker is its limited FOV limits its off-boresight capability. Also, a large size FPA is required to have good resolution (small IFOV) as well as a good tracking capability (large FOV). Most strapdown seekers are lock-on after launch and require an accurate inertial guidance system (e.g., GPS/INS).

In summary, a lock-on before launch missile with a large off-boresight capability requires a gimbal seeker. A defensive missile may have a strapdown seeker, because it requires less off-boresight capability. Also, a lock-on after launch missile that has a relatively low terminal maneuvering requirement, such as a cruise missile, may have a strapdown seeker.

Figure 6.14 compares imaging infrared seeker alternatives of staring focal plane array (FPA), scanning array, and pseudo imaging.

The top left portion of the figure illustrates a small (16×16) notional staring FPA. A staring FPA consists of detector elements (pixels) with the processing electronics on the same surface of a computer chip. The seeker optics focus the IR image onto the array of detector elements. Each detector element receives a portion of the scene. Missile staring FPA seeker sizes typically range from 64×64 to 256×256. As an example, the AIM-9x and ASRAAM seeker has a 128×128 pixel FPA. Advantages of a staring FPA include light weight, longer detection range, less sensitivity to clutter, and better accuracy. The staring array is lighter weight because it has fewer parts. The functions of detection, integration, filtering, and multiplexing are carried out directly on the FPA. This reduces the number of interconnects and the amount of outside signal

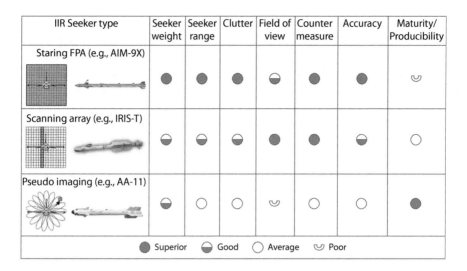

IIR Seeker type	Seeker weight	Seeker range	Clutter	Field of view	Counter measure	Accuracy	Maturity/ Producibility
Staring FPA (e.g., AIM-9X)	●	●	●	◐	●	●	◡
Scanning array (e.g., IRIS-T)	◐	◐	◐	●	●	◐	○
Pseudo imaging (e.g., AA-11)	◐	○	○	◡	○	○	●
	● Superior	◐ Good	○ Average	◡ Poor			

Fig. 6.14 Imaging infrared seeker trades: staring focal plane array versus scanning array versus pseudo image.

processing. It also has no moving parts. Longer detection range is achieved because more integration time is available to fill the pixel wells, providing greater sensitivity. It is less sensitive to clutter and is more accurate because the pixels remain focused on the target scene. The greatest disadvantages of a staring FPA seeker are its immaturity and producibility. Producibility is of particular concern for a large size FPA (e.g., $> 256 \times 256$). An MWIR staring array is more producible than an LWIR array of the same size.

The left middle section of the figure illustrates a small (1×16) notional scanning array. A scanning array consists of a linear array of detector elements. Scanning arrays for missile seekers typically vary in size from 2×64 to 4×240 pixels. Missiles with scanning array seekers include IRIS-T, Python 4, and Mica. A scanning array is based on mirrors that mechanically scan across the target scene field of view (FOV). The mirrors scan the FOV within a few milliseconds, briefing focusing a portion of the scene on each detector. The output from each detector is fed to amplifiers for signal processing. A modern scanning array has the readout circuit mounted directly to each detector of the array. An advantage of a scanning array is its capability for a wide FOV. Also, compared to a staring FPA, the scanning array usually has more uniform pixels. It is easier to provide electronic non-uniformity compensation for a scanning array because a staring FPA typically has a larger number of pixels with a greater range in sensitivity and also has more dead pixels.

Finally, the bottom left section of the figure illustrates a pseudo imaging seeker with a 16 petal rosette. An example of a missile with a pseudo imaging seeker is the AA-11 Archer. A pseudo imaging seeker uses a rosette scan of a fixed detector with rotating optics to derive an image of the scene. The rosette scan makes many loops to cover the FOV. The target location is determined by the timing of detections. Advantages of pseudo imaging seeker include its technical maturity, high producibility, and low cost. A disadvantage is its relatively small FOV. Compared to higher technology alternatives such as staring FPA and scanning array seekers, a pseudo imaging seeker has lower performance. Also, a pseudo imaging seeker does not work well against an extended target or a target that is in clutter.

Design considerations in the passive infrared seeker include trades of optics diameter and wavelength (e.g., mid wave infrared detector versus long wave infrared detector). This will be illustrated by examining the detection range equation. The equation for IR detection range is

$$(R_D)_{IR} = \{(I_T)_{\Delta\lambda}\eta_a A_o\{D^*/(\Delta f_p^{1/2} A_d^{1/2})\}(S/N)_{\text{Detect}}^{-1}\}^{1/2}$$

As shown in the equation, there are seven drivers for IR seeker range: radiant intensity of the target within the upper and lower wavelength cutoffs of the seeker $(I_T)_{\Delta\lambda}$, atmospheric transmission efficiency for the total distance from the target to the seeker η_a, seeker optics aperture area A_o, pixel specific detectivity D^*, pixel detector bandwidth Δf_p, detector total area A_d, and signal-to-noise ratio required for detection $(S/N)_{\text{Detect}}$.

Referring to the first term in the above equation for seeker range, the radiant intensity of a Lambertian (hemispherical emission) target with gray body radiation is given by the equation

$$(I_T)_{\Delta\lambda} = \varepsilon L_\lambda(\lambda_2 - \lambda_1)A_T/\pi$$

In the above equation ε is the emissivity of the target, L_λ is the spectral radiance at a given wavelength, λ_2 is the upper wavelength cutoff of the seeker, λ_1 is the lower wavelength cutoff of the seeker, and A_T is the target planform area viewed by the seeker (typically assumed to be a Lambertian source at long distance). Radiant intensity is the power emitted per unit solid angle from an isotropic radiator, a theoretical point source that radiates equally in all directions in three-dimensional space. The units of radiant intensity are W sr^{-1}.

Inspecting the first term of the equation for $(I_T)_{\Delta\lambda}$, the value of ε is between 0 (perfect polished mirror) and 1 (blackbody radiator/absorber). Emissivity is a function of the target material, surface roughness, and temperature. As an example, the emissivity of aluminum is less than 0.3 while the emissivity of carbon is greater than 0.7.

The second term in the $(I_T)_{\Delta\lambda}$ equation is the spectral radiance L_λ. Spectral radiance is given by Planck's Law, which states

$$L_\lambda = 3.74 \times 10^4 / \{\lambda^5 \{e^{[1.44 \times 10^4/(\lambda T_T)]} - 1\}\}$$

Units are $Wcm^{-2}sr^{-1}\mu m^{-1}$. It can be seen from Planck's Law that higher spectral radiance occurs at shorter wavelength and higher temperature.

The third term in the $(I_T)_{\Delta\lambda}$ equation is the upper wavelength cutoff λ_2 of the seeker. It is a design consideration that includes tradeoffs such as maximizing the energy collected at longer wavelengths, maximizing the atmospheric transmission, maximizing the quality of the optics design, and minimizing background clutter. The lower wavelength cutoff λ_1 has similar tradeoffs, including minimizing stray solar radiation.

Finally, the area of the target A_T is an obvious design driver for the missile seeker, a smaller target has less radiant intensity and is more difficult to detect.

Referring back to the IR seeker range equation, the second term is atmospheric transmission efficiency η_a. It accounts for the attenuation over the total distance from the target to the seeker. The transmission can range from perfect transmission ($\eta_a = 1$) for exo-atmospheric conditions to almost no transmission ($\eta_a \approx 0$) through clouds. The effect of atmospheric transmission on detection range was discussed previously.

The third term in the IR seeker range equation is the seeker optics aperture area. As discussed in Chapter 2, optics diameter is a design consideration in selecting the missile diameter. A larger aperture delivers more optical energy to the detectors, providing longer detection range. It also provides better resolution.

The fourth term in the IR seeker range equation is specific detectivity D^*, which is the sensitivity performance of the detector material. D^* allows a comparison of different detector materials on a material basis only. The units are $cmHz^{1/2}W^{-1}$. D^* represents the signal-to-noise ratio when 1 W of radiation is incident upon a detector with a sensitive area of $1\ cm^2$ and the noise is measured at an electrical bandwidth of 1 Hz. D^* for an IR detector varies widely, with values ranging from as low as 10^9 to greater than 10^{12}, depending upon the detector material, detector cooling temperature, and wavelength. As a reference, the human eye has a $D^* = 10^{14}$ in the visible wavelengths. A low cost, uncooled detector such as bolometer thermal detector has a relatively low value of D^*, about 10^9. A high performance detector such as $Hg_{0.67}Cd_{0.33}Te$ has a value of D^* of about 8×10^{11} at a detector temperature of 77 K (liquid nitrogen cooling) when it is optimized for a mid wave IR (e.g., 4 μm) application. The strong impact of detector cooling on D^* can seen from the theoretical D^* equation for a bolometer thermal detector as

$$D^* = (8\pi\sigma kT^5)^{-1/2}$$

Substituting for the Stephan-Boltzmann constant $\sigma = 5.67 \times 10^{-12}$ $\mathrm{Wcm^{-2}K^{-4}}$ and Boltzmann's constant $k = 1.3807 \times 10^{-23}$ $\mathrm{WsK^{-1}}$ gives a theoretical maximum

$$D^* = 7.02 \times 10^4 \ T^{-5/2}$$

As an example, for an un-cooled bolometer at room temperature (e.g., $T = 300$ K), the theoretical $D^* = 1.44 \times 10^{10}$ is lower than that of a bolometer detector cooled to liquid nitrogen temperature ($T = 77$ K), which has a theoretical $D^* = 4.32 \times 10^{11}$.

Referring back to the IR seeker range equation, the fifth term is the pixel detector bandwidth Δf_p. Selecting the pixel detector bandwidth and integration time is a tradeoff of signal versus noise. The pixel detector signal increases approximately linearly with the integration time, while random noise increases with the square root of time. Pixel detector bandwidth is related to integration time by the equation

$$\Delta f_p = 2\pi t_{\text{Integ}}$$

The pixel integration time, also called dwell time, can be selected to optimize the detector signal-to-noise ratio. For HgCdTe detectors, the optimum integration time typically varies from about 0.5 to about 8 ms. A background with high temperature/noise requires a shorter dwell time for an optimum signal-to-noise ratio. A low noise detector with low noise electronics in a low background temperature/noise environment provides a higher signal-to-noise ratio with longer dwell time. Note that either the pixel detector electron well capacity of a HgCdTe detector or the guidance update rate, or frame rate, may set an upper limit on the pixel dwell time. As an example, for a fast guidance update rate of 100 Hz (10 ms), the pixel dwell time is usually less than 10 ms.

The sixth term in the IR seeker range equation is the active area of the detector A_d. For a focal plane array it is the active area of a single pixel multiplied by the total number of pixels in the FPA. A small size pixel (e.g., 12 μm) has advantages of longer detection range and better resolution while a large size pixel (e.g., 60 μm) has an advantage of lower manufacturing cost. A large focal plane array (e.g., 1024 × 1024) has an advantage of a large field of view while a smaller FPA (e.g., 128 × 128) has advantages of lower manufacturing cost and higher reliability.

The final term in the IR seeker range equation is the signal-to-noise ratio (S/N) that is required for detection. The signal-to-noise ratio required for detection of a noise limited system can be as low as $(S/N)_{\text{Detect}} = 1$ or as high as $(S/N)_{\text{Detect}} = 5$, depending upon the sophistication of the signal processing and the background noise. For a target in a background where the temperature of the background is comparable to the temperature of the target, detection may be background limited rather than detector noise limited. A higher value of signal-to-noise ratio (e.g., $S/N > 10$) is required for a low signature target in clutter.

As an example, the detection range will be compared for 5-in. aperture mid wave and long wave seekers in an exo-atmospheric intercept.

The mid wave seeker is assumed to operate over a wavelength range of 3.6 to 4.4 µm, with an average wavelength of $\lambda = 4$ µm. The assumed target characteristics are 2 ft diameter ($A_T = 2919$ cm^2), temperature $T_T = 300$ K, and emissivity $\varepsilon = 0.5$. The spectral radiance of the target is computed to be

$$L_\lambda = 3.74 \times 10^4 / \{\lambda^5 \{e^{[1.44 \times 10^4/(\lambda T_T)]} - 1\}\}$$

$$= 3.74 \times 10^4 / \{4^5 \{e^{\{1.44 \times 10^4/[4(300)]\}} - 1\}\}$$

$$= 0.000224 \ \text{Wcm}^{-2}\text{sr}^{-1}\mu\text{m}^{-1}$$

Substituting into the equation for a Lambertian target radiant intensity gives

$$(I_T)_{\Delta\lambda} = \varepsilon L_\lambda(\lambda_2 - \lambda_1)A_T/\pi = 0.5(0.000224)(4.4 - 3.6)(2919)/\pi$$

$$= 0.0826 \ \text{Wsr}^{-1}$$

The detector is assumed to be a diffraction limited 256×256 focal plane array with 40 µm pixels. Individual pixel detector area is $A_d = 0.004^2 = 0.000016$ cm^2. A Hg$_{0.67}$Cd$_{0.33}$Te detector is assumed, which has a value of D^* of about 1×10^{11} at a detector temperature of 77 K (liquid nitrogen) when it is optimized for mid wave IR (e.g., 4 µm) application. The pixel detector bandwidth for best signal-to-noise ratio (S/N) is assumed to be $\Delta f_p = 50$ Hz and the S/N for detection is assumed to be $(S/N)_{\text{Detect}} = 5$. Substituting into the IR seeker range equation gives

$$(R_D)_{\text{IR}} = \{(I_T)_{\Delta\lambda}\eta_a A_o\{D^*/(\Delta f_p^{1/2} A_d^{1/2})\}(S/N)_{\text{Detect}}^{-1}\}^{1/2}$$

$$= \{0.0826(4.4 - 3.6)(0.01267)$$

$$\times \{1 \times 10^{11}/[(50)^{1/2}(0.000016)^{1/2}]\}(5)^{-1}\}^{1/2}$$

$$= 27{,}200 \ \text{m}$$

Next, the detection range will be calculated for a long wave IR seeker with consistent assumptions that were applicable to the mid wave IR seeker. The unique assumptions for the LWIR seeker are a nominal wavelength of $\lambda = 10$ µm, an upper cutoff wavelength $\lambda_2 = 11$ µm, a lower cutoff wavelength $\lambda_1 = 9$ µm, and an Hg$_{0.80}$Cd$_{0.20}$Te detector that is optimized for best performance at $\lambda = 10$ µm with 77 K detector cooling. The specific detectivity $D^* = 3 \times 10^{10}\ \mathrm{cm}^{1/2}\,\mathrm{Hz}^{1/2}\mathrm{W}^{-1}$. Solving for the spectral radiance

$$L_\lambda = 3.74 \times 10^4 / \{\lambda^5 \{e^{[1.44 \times 10^4 / (\lambda T_T)]} - 1\}\}$$

$$= 3.74 \times 10^4 / \{10^5 \{e^{\{1.44 \times 10^4 / [10(300)]\}} - 1\}\} = 0.00310\ \mathrm{Wcm}^{-2}\mathrm{sr}^{-1}\mathrm{\mu m}^{-1}$$

Solving for radiant intensity

$$(I_T)_{\Delta\lambda} = \varepsilon L\lambda(\lambda_2 - \lambda_1)A_T / \pi = 0.5(0.00310)(11 - 9)(2919)/\pi$$

$$= 2.86\ \mathrm{Wsr}^{-1}$$

Finally, the detection range is

$$(R_D)_{\mathrm{IR}} = \{(I_T)_{\Delta\lambda}\eta_a A_0 \{D^* / (\Delta f_p^{1/2} A_d^{1/2})\}(S/N)_{\mathrm{Detect}}^{-1}\}^{1/2}$$

$$= \{(2.86)(1)(0.01267)\{(3 \times 10^{10})/[(50)^{1/2}(0.000016)^{1/2}]\}(5)^{-1}\}^{1/2}$$

$$= 87{,}700\ \mathrm{m}$$

Note that the LWIR seeker has over 3× the range of the MWIR seeker for the example against a low temperature target. This illustrates that target

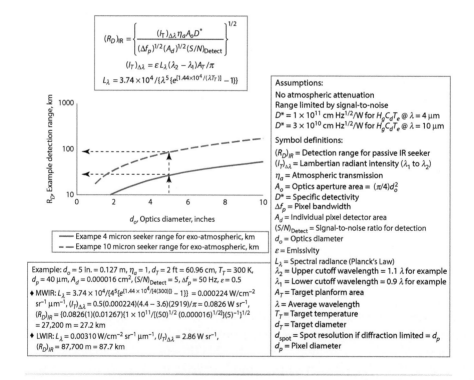

Fig. 6.15 A long wave infrared seeker has longer detection range against a cold target.

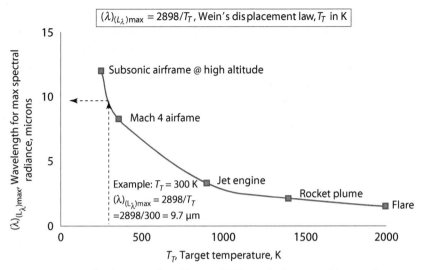

Fig. 6.16 Most of a cold target energy is at long wavelength—most warm target energy is at shorter wavelength.

temperature is often a driving consideration in selecting the best seeker wavelength. Most of the spectral radiance of low temperature targets is in the long wave region (e.g., 8 to 12 μm) while for high temperature targets most of the spectral radiance is at mid wave (e.g., 3 to 5 μm).

The range benefit of an LWIR seeker in detecting a cold target is shown in Fig. 6.15. The figure also shows the benefit of a large optics diameter. Seeker optics diameter was discussed in Chapter 2 as a tradeoff in selecting the missile diameter.

Figure 6.16 shows the wavelength for maximum spectral radiance $\lambda_{(L\lambda)\mathrm{max}}$ at a given target temperature T_T. The equation is based on Wien's Displacement Law, which states

$$\lambda_{(L_\lambda)\mathrm{max}} = 2898/T_T$$

In the above equation T_T is the target temperature in K. Note from the figure that an LWIR seeker is best suited for a relatively cold airframe target while an MWIR seeker is best suited for a relatively hot signature, such as a jet engine or a rocket plume. As an example, assume a cold target with $T_T = 300$ K. The wavelength for maximum spectral radiance is

$$\lambda_{(L_\lambda)\mathrm{max}} = 2898/T_T = 2898/300 = 9.7 \mu\mathrm{m}$$

For targets in clutter, contrast may be a driver for detection and acquisition. An MWIR seeker may be preferable against targets in clutter, because it provides higher contrast. Another consideration is that an MWIR seeker has better resolution, compatibility with the small diameter optics of small missiles, and is lower cost. Examples of US missiles with MWIR staring FPA seekers include JASSM, GBU-15/AGM-130, AIM-9x, THAAD, and SM-3. An example of a US missile with an LWIR staring FPA seeker is Javelin. Because cost is often a driving consideration, most IR missiles have MWIR seekers.

Figure 6.17 lists advantages and disadvantages of a millimeter wave (mmW) seeker compared to a conventional centimeter wave (cmW) seeker. The atmospheric transmission window, discussed previously, allows efficient mmW transmission at frequencies of about 35 and 94 GHz. Because of its relatively short wavelength, an mmW seeker has an advantage of higher resolution and better clutter performance than a cmW seeker, which operates at a frequency of about 10 GHz. It is also smaller size and lighter weight than a cmW seeker. Bandwidth is also greater than cmW, because of its higher frequency and the mmW spectrum is less populated/crowded than the cmW spectrum.

A disadvantage of mmW is its short range/limited available power. Another disadvantage is the atmospheric attenuation discussed previously.

- ◆ Advantages of mmW (e.g., 35 GHz, 94 GHz) seeker compared to cmW (e.g., X-Band):
  - ◆ Resolution
  - ◆ Performance in clutter
  - ◆ Size/weight
  - ◆ Bandwidth
- ◆ Disadvantages of mmW seeker
  - ◆ Limited range/max transmitted power
  - ◆ Atmospheric attenuation
- ◆ Examples of mmW seekers
  - ◆ Surfaced-to-air:
    - ◆ PAC-3
  - ◆ Air-to-surface:
    - ◆ Brimstone
    - ◆ Longbow
  - ◆ AARGM

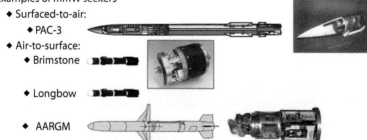

Fig. 6.17 A mmW seeker has higher resolution than cmW, but mmW is limited to short range lock-on.

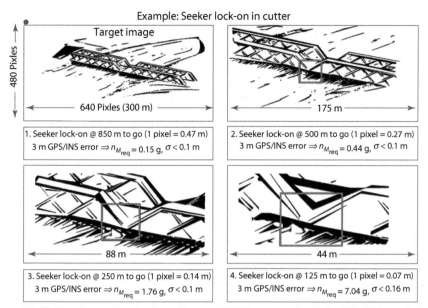

Fig. 6.18 GPS/INS guidance allows robust seeker lock-on in adverse weather and clutter.

Its atmospheric attenuation is especially high at low altitude and at a frequency of 60 GHz, where O_2 molecular interaction results in an attenuation of 16 dB/km.

The bottom portion of the figure shows examples of missiles with mmW seekers. The examples are the PAC-3 endo-atmospheric interceptor, Brimstone precision strike missile, Longbow precision strike missile, and the AARGM radar defense suppression missile.

Figure 6.18 illustrates the benefit of precision GPS/INS guidance as an aid for seeker acquisition of the target in adverse weather and clutter. GPS/INS precision accuracy (3 m) is independent of adverse weather and clutter. It allows a delay of the seeker lock-on and terminal guidance until the missile is closer to the target. The notional example in the figure is a bridge target in a high clutter environment consisting of a river and rolling terrain. In this example a relatively high-resolution (640 pixels × 480 pixels) strapdown IIR seeker provides terminal homing. The aim point is the center pier of the bridge. Note that even for a relatively large target such as the bridge in the figure, at the initial range of 850 m there is a large amount of clutter in the seeker field of view (FOV). Also, adverse weather may reduce the target contrast and signal to a low value, such that the seeker may not be able to lock-on the target at 850 m. At a range of 850 m the 20-deg FOV seeker provides a 300 m × 230 m scene. As the missile closes to the ranges of 500 m and 250 m, note that there is less and less clutter. Finally, at a range-to-go of 125 m, note that there is almost no clutter within the seeker FOV. The GPS/INS accuracy of 3 m is comparable to the tracking gate accuracy of the seeker, allowing a smooth transition from GPS/INS midcourse guidance to seeker terminal guidance. For a typical closing velocity of 300 m/s and a guidance update rate of 60 Hz, there are up to 25 guidance updates available to conduct ATR when the weapon is at a range-to-go of 125 m. At this point the terminal accuracy is driven more by the airframe response than by the seeker tracking error. As a result of the GPS/INS precision guidance, the missile has a high probability of hitting the center pier aim point and dropping the center span of the bridge. A GPS/INS guided missile can be treated almost like an artillery projectile, with a high probability of impacting in the target area and a low probability of collateral damage.

Also, shown in the figure is the missile maneuverability requirement to correct the heading error at seeker lock-on. Because of the accuracy of GPS/INS the maneuverability required is very low at long range, and becomes significant (e.g., greater than 2 g) only if the seeker lock-on range is less than 200 m.

A data link can provide an updated location of a moving target during the missile fly-out, facilitating seeker lock-on. The target error (TE) at seeker lock-on is a function of the target location error (TLE) at an update, target velocity V_T, and the target latency time $t_{Latency}$. Target latency is the time between the last update and seeker lock-on, given by the equation

$$t_{Latency} = t_{Seeker \ lock-on} - t_{Update}$$

In the above equation $t_{Seeker \ lock-on} =$ seeker lock-on time and $t_{Update} =$ data link update time. It is noted that this does not include the missile inertial navigation system (INS) drift. For a conceptual design assessment of a GPS/INS guided missile, the INS drift is usually considered to be negligible at seeker lock-on.

Assuming that the errors in TLE and TE are uniformly random, the RSS equation is

$$TE_{Seeker \ lock-on} = \left[TLE^2 + \left(V_T t_{Latency} \right)^2 \right]^{1/2}$$

Figure 6.19 shows the rapid growth in target error at seeker lock-on if the target latency is large or if the target has high velocity. A high bandwidth data link is required to minimize the error growth from the last update to

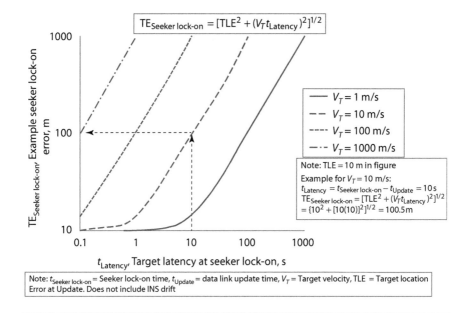

Fig. 6.19 A high bandwidth data link reduces moving target location error.

seeker lock-on. For a relatively low speed target, the data link bandwidth may be sufficient to allow a seeker-less missile. However, as shown in the figure a seeker-less missile that is used against a high speed target would require a data link with very high bandwidth/very small update time that is probably not practical.

As an example, assume

$$TLE = 10\,\text{m},\ V_T = 10\,\text{m/s, and } t_{\text{Latency}} = t_{\text{Seeker lock-on}} - t_{\text{Update}} = 10\,\text{s}$$

Substituting into the target error equation gives

$$TE_{\text{Seeker lock-on}} = \left[TLE^2 + \left(V_T t_{\text{Latency}}\right)^2\right]^{1/2} = \{10^2 + [10(10)]^2\}^{1/2}$$
$$= 100.5\,\text{m}$$

From the above result, note that a target update latency of 10 s prior to seeker lock-on results in a large target error. A near real-time (e.g., $t_{\text{Latency}} \sim$ 1 s) data link would be required to have a target error at seeker lock-on that would be comparable to the target location error (TLE).

Most modern precision strike standoff missiles (e.g., JASSM, SLAM-ER, Tomahawk, JSOW, AGM-130, NSM, Delilah, TORGOS) have combined GPS/INS/data link guidance. The addition of a data link to GPS/INS guidance is especially effective in facilitating seeker acquisition of a moving

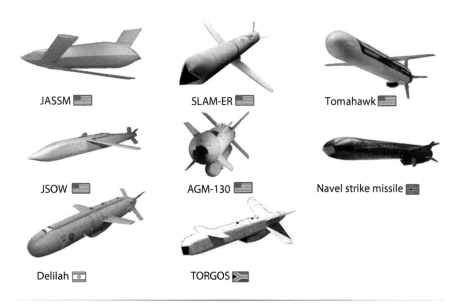

Fig. 6.20 Modern precision strike standoff missiles have combined GPS/INS/ data link guidance.

target in ground clutter. All of the examples shown in Fig. 6.20 have EO staring FPA seekers.

Figure 6.21 shows the optimum cruise flight environment for missiles. Note that there is a large variation in dynamic pressure over the Mach number and altitude envelope. Also note that for a given Mach number the dynamic pressure decreases rapidly with altitude. The figure shows the flight conditions for the optimum dynamic pressure for a typical wing-less subsonic turbojet, a typical subsonic turbojet missile with a wing, a typical ramjet, and a typical scramjet. Most wingless cruise missiles have their best aerodynamic efficiency $(L/D)_{max}$ at a dynamic pressure of about 700 psf. A cruise missile with a wing has a lower value of the optimum dynamic pressure. For a wingless turbojet flying at about Mach 0.8 (e.g., subsonic wingless cruise missile), the optimum flight altitude is sea level. Adding a wing to a subsonic cruise missile results in an altitude for optimum aerodynamic efficiency that is higher, about 30k ft altitude. As shown in the figure, for a wingless ramjet missile flying at Mach 4, the optimum cruise altitude is about 80,000 ft. For a wingless scramjet missile flying at Mach 6.5, the optimum cruise altitude is about 100,000 ft.

There is a minimum value of dynamic pressure (approximately 200 psf) that is required for sufficient aerodynamic control effectiveness to provide flight control stabilization and maneuverability. For $q < \approx 200\text{psf}$, either thrust vector control or reaction jet control are required.

Shown in Fig. 6.22 is an example of the broad range in the flight environment that can be encountered by a high performance missile, such as a precision strike ramjet. Shown are examples of the typical flight phases of an air-launched and a surface-launched ramjet. The air launched example is ejection launched at a subsonic Mach number. It is subjected to high angles of attack during ejection. The missile has compressed carriage surfaces that are deployed as soon as possible, to minimize the angle of attack divergence from the static instability. After safe separation from the launch platform, the missile then conducts a pitch-up maneuver at high angle of attack. It then begins a climb at an efficient flight path angle (e.g., $\gamma \approx 45$ deg), for maximum range and for a minimum fuel that is required to reach an efficient cruise altitude. The surface launched ramjet example is vertically launched in a cross wind, which also results in a high angle of attack during launch platform separation. Its compressed carriage surfaces are also deployed as soon as possible. Following launch, the surface launched ramjet pitches over at a high angle of attack. It then begins a climb at an efficient flight path angle (e.g., $\gamma \approx 45$ deg). Both the air launched and the surface launched ramjets are boosted to a supersonic Mach number while climbing. Following booster shutdown during the climb, the ramjet is ignited, and each missile continues to climb under ramjet propulsion. As each missile approaches the optimum altitude for

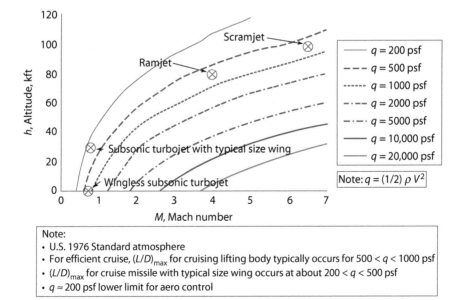

Fig. 6.21 Optimum cruise is a function of the missile Mach number, altitude, and planform geometry.

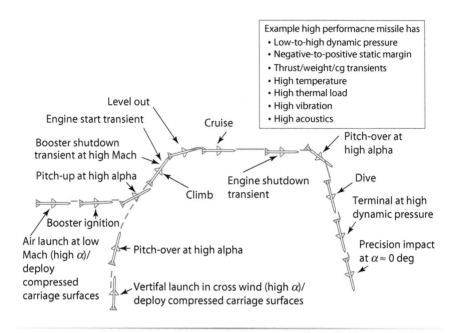

Example high performacne missile has
- Low-to-high dynamic pressure
- Negative-to-positive static margin
- Thrust/weight/cg transients
- High temperature
- High thermal load
- High vibration
- High acoustics

Level out

Engine start transient

Cruise

Pitch-over at high alpha

Booster shutdown transient at high Mach

Pitch-up at high alpha

Engine shutdown transient

Dive

Climb

Terminal at high dynamic pressure

Booster ignition

Air launch at low Mach (high α)/ deploy compressed carriage surfaces

Pitch-over at high alpha

Precision impact at $\alpha \approx 0$ deg

Vertifal launch in cross wind (high α)/ deploy compressed carriage surfaces

Fig. 6.22 Missile guidance and control must be robust for changing events, flight environment, and uncertainty.

ramjet cruise, a pitch-over maneuver is conducted to level off for cruise flight. Each missile cruises at an optimum altitude until it approaches the target area. The engine may be shut down at the end of cruise, or if there is sufficient fuel, the engine may continue to operate to maximize its speed during the dive to the target. At the end of cruise a pitch-over maneuver at high angle of attack is initiated, and the missile dives toward the target. During the dive through the lower atmosphere the dynamic pressure reaches a maximum. For a deeply buried target, the angle of attack at ground impact must be tightly controlled, usually to less than one deg, to avoid breaking up the warhead during ground penetration.

A modern flight control autopilot is required to handle the broad range of events, flight phases, flight environment, and uncertainty of a high performance missile, such as the notional missiles described in the previous paragraph. The autopilot is the brain of the missile. It provides flight control commands based on input data from the seeker, navigation, and stabilization sensors. Gains are multidimensional functions of complex parameters and are selected to maintain stable gain and phase margins. Special attention is given to the different flight phases. The autopilot design allows for sequencing between flight phases and fading in the different control gains for each phase. The flight phases may have low-to-high dynamic pressure, negative-to-positive static margin, and thrust/weight/center-of-gravity transients. Another consideration is designing robust subsystem hardware to handle a severe thermal, vibration, and acoustic environment.

Design robustness is impacted by the variation in the flight environment design parameters with flight altitude. Figure 6.23 shows the variation of atmospheric temperature, pressure, density, and speed of sound as a function of altitude. Within the troposphere, the temperature and speed of sound decrease with increasing altitude up to about 36,000 ft. Based on the US 1976 Standard Atmosphere, an equation for the troposphere temperature T at an altitude h compared to the sea level temperature T_{SL} is

$$T/T_{SL} = 1 - 6.875 \times 10^{-6}\,h$$

Note from the figure that atmospheric pressure and density decrease rapidly with altitude. The standard atmosphere ratios of the troposphere pressure p and density ρ to their sea level values are given by

$$p/p_{SL} = (T/T_{SL})^{5.2561}$$

$$\rho/\rho_{SL} = (T/T_{SL})^{4.2561}$$

For a given velocity, there is a slight increase in Mach number with increasing altitude for flight within the troposphere, resulting from the slight decrease in the speed of sound with altitude. Because weather and clouds are driven by changes in temperature, the troposphere has active

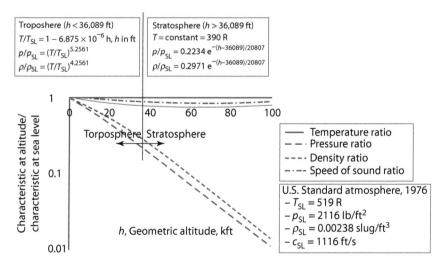

Note: T_{SL} = Temperature at sea level, p_{SL} = Pressure at sea level, ρ_{SL} = Density at sea level, c_{SL} = Speed of sound at sea level, h = Altitude in ft.

Fig. 6.23 Missile design robustness requires consideration of the variation of atmospheric properties with altitude.

weather and clouds. Above the troposphere is the stratosphere. For flight within the stratosphere, above about 36,089 ft, the temperature and the speed of sound are nearly constant. From the US 1976 Standard Atmosphere, the temperature at $h = 36$ kft is $T = 390$ R and the temperature at $h = 80$ kft is almost the same, $T = 398$ R. Above $h = 80$ kft the temperature begins to rise.

Similar to the troposphere, the atmospheric pressure and density decrease rapidly with altitude in the stratosphere. The standard atmosphere ratios of the stratosphere pressure and density to their sea level values are given by the equations

$$p/p_{SL} = 0.2234e^{-(h-36089)/20807}$$

$$\rho/\rho_{SL} = 0.2971e^{-(h-36089)/20807}$$

Note from the figure that for an altitude of 36,089 ft, the pressure is only 22% of the sea level value and the density is only 30% of the sea level value. Because dynamic pressure, aerodynamic heating, and air-breathing propulsion thrust are a function of atmospheric density, for a given velocity they also decrease rapidly with an increase in altitude. However, rocket motor thrust for a typical (under expanded) nozzle increases with altitude, because of the decreasing atmospheric pressure.

The values of the atmospheric properties vary with the different atmospheric models. The traditional standard atmospheric model used for many design activities is the US 1976 Standard Atmosphere. However, the worldwide weather and climate can provide significant differences in the atmospheric temperature, density, and speed of sound. Shown in Fig. 6.24 are comparisons of cold, hot, polar, and tropic atmospheric models with the US 1976 Standard Atmospheric model. Note that the values of the parameters can differ by up to 30% compared to the US 1976 Standard Atmospheric model. The design of subsystems such as the rocket motor requires consideration of off-nominal design conditions, such as extreme hot and extreme cold atmospheric temperatures. Also, the design evaluation of flight performance may require consideration of other atmospheric conditions, such as the wind velocity and its direction (head, tail, cross wind).

Examples of typical design uncertainties of missiles are illustrated in the probability density functions of Fig. 6.25. A probability density function that is often used to represent design uncertainties is the normal distribution, which is symmetrical. The normal distribution function is given by the equation

$$\text{PDF} = \{1/[\sigma(2\pi)^{1/2}]\}e^{\{[(x-\mu)/\sigma]^2/2\}}$$

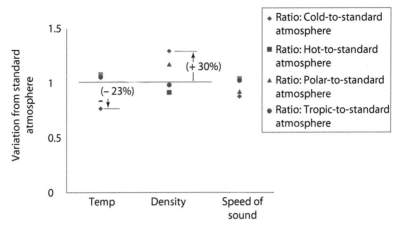

Note:
- Based on properties at sea level
- US 1976 Standard Atmosphere: Temperature = 519 R, Density = 0.002377 slug/ft^3, Speed of sound = 1116 ft/s

Fig. 6.24 Design robustness requires consideration of standard atmospheric modeling differences.

The design uncertainty in engineering and manufacturing development (EMD), should ideally be small, for a low risk in meeting the mission requirements. Design uncertainty in EMD flight performance is usually a

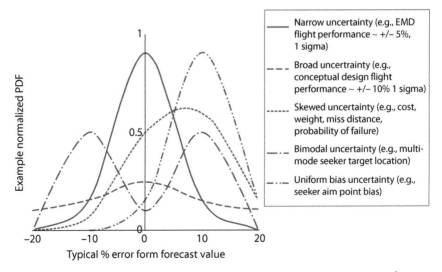

Note for normal distribution: PDF = $\{1/[\sigma(2\pi)^{1/2}]\}e^{\{[(x-\mu)/\sigma]^2/2\}}$

Fig. 6.25 Design robustness requires consideration of uncertainty.

symmetrical, normal distribution of uncertainty, with a relatively small deviation (e.g., $\pm 5\%$, 1σ). Usually there is a single set of technologies for EMD, based on a prior down-select of the technology alternatives. Note that the typical design uncertainty in conceptual design flight performance is much larger (e.g., $\pm 10\%$, 1σ). The elements that contribute to conceptual design flight performance can have even larger uncertainty. For example, the uncertainty in the static margin of a nearly neutrally stable missile may be more than 100%. As a result of the larger uncertainty in conceptual design, alternative technology solutions should be explored and developed. Different technologies have the potential to satisfy the mission requirements, but some have higher probability of success than others. The benefit of investment in the technology alternatives to quantify their performance and reduce their uncertainty through activities such as ground test is to reduce the missile system design uncertainty and to mature the design. Prior to entering EMD there is usually sufficient confidence to select a preferred technology from the set of alternatives.

Because of the large design uncertainty in conceptual design, it is important to evaluate the robustness of the conceptual design and the associated technology alternatives. Insufficient design robustness may be a factor in not selecting a technology that may have higher potential performance or lower potential cost. A high potential payoff technology may be too sensitive to uncertainty and there may not be sufficient funding or time available to reduce the uncertainty.

The most important requirements (MIRs) may have design values that are specified as a threshold, a standard, and a goal. The threshold value represents marginal utility, with less capability than the standard (e.g., -3σ). The standard value is the nominal, expected utility. The goal is typically represented as an enhancement over the standard (e.g., $+3\sigma$).

Some uncertainty distributions are not a normal distribution. The third curve in the figure is a skewed uncertainty distribution. Examples of skewed distributions are the cost, weight, and miss distance uncertainties. Usually the actual cost, the actual weight, and the actual miss distance after the completion of EMD tend to be higher than the original predictions. The design maturation process, such as testing, usually shows that the initial conceptual design predictions are optimistic. An approach used during conceptual design to compensate for the usually optimistic prediction methods is to provide a design margin for robustness. For example, during conceptual design the warhead lethal radius may be sized for a large (e.g., 3σ) miss distance. The fourth curve in the figure is a bimodal distribution. As an example of a bimodal distribution, a dual mode seeker (e.g., mmW/IR) could measure two different locations of the target, with uncertainty in the target location from each sensor. The final curve in the figure is a distribution that is similar to a normal distribution, except for a bias. An example is a seeker that has an aim point bias, such as IR or UV seeker of an air intercept missile that homes on the hot plume aft of the target aircraft instead of the airframe centroid of the target.

Another consideration for missile design robustness is the robustness against threat countermeasures. Threat countermeasures include

1. electro-optical countermeasures (EOCM) against an IR missile seeker, such as directed energy lasers, flares, and smoke/oil fog to blind the missile seeker;
2. radar frequency countermeasures (RFCM) against a radar missile seeker or GPS, such as active radar deception (e.g., velocity gate and range gate stealers, automatic gain capture control, crosseye/angle track error) ECM, noise jammers (e.g., spot noise, barrage noise, swept noise), and chaff to cause the missile seeker to break lock;
3. decoys (e.g., vertical/horizontal powered decoys, towed decoys, free flight decoys) that mimic the flight trajectory and the signature of the launch platform, to induce homing on the decoy false target;
4. low observables, including reduction in the threat contrail, RCS, and IR signature and reduced power emission from the threat fire control system (through approaches such as pulse integration and broad band) to prevent the missile seeker from acquiring the target;
5. high speed flight, to defeat the missile seeker tracking and warhead fuzing;
6. high altitude flight, to prevent missile seeker lock-on and exceed the flight altitude capability of the missile;
7. high maneuverability, to induce missile miss distance; and
8. lethal defense, to destroy the missile in flight.

Robust counter-countermeasures (CCM) by the missile may use new technology that was not envisioned when the countermeasure was originally developed by the threat. Robust CCM include

1. An imaging seeker, to provide the resolution required to separate the target from ejected or towed countermeasures;
2. multi-spectral/multi-mode/multi-band seeker, to provide broad band discrimination of the target signature;
3. temporal processing, to identify the time varying unique characteristics of the target;
4. home-on-jam, similar to an anti-radiation homing missile;
5. RF seeker design with increased signal-to-noise ratio (such as pulse compression (chirping) to increase the signal), frequency agility (to avoid the countermeasure frequency), and polarization (to filter out jamming);

6. hardened GPS/INS, to maintain a high signal-to-noise in a jamming environment, through approaches such as P(Y) lock-on at a standoff range and altitude (this forces the jammer to break GPS P(Y) code track, which requires more jammer power), an integrated GPS/INS, which allows seeker lock-on at shorter range in a jamming environment and against a low observable target, a directional antenna aimed toward the satellites/away from the threat jammer, pseudolites/differential GPS consisting of high power transponders with corrected accuracy and high signal-to-jam ratio, and high altitude flight to reduce the line-of-sight effective range of surface-based jammers;

7. automatic target recognition/automatic target acquisition (ATR/ATA), to pull the target out of the countermeasures;

8. high speed, to minimize the exposure time and the probability of exposure to countermeasures;

9. high altitude flight, to avoid detection and exceed the threat envelope capability;

10. high maneuverability, to minimize miss distance from countermeasures;

11. low observable missile RCS, IR, and plume visual signatures and delayed lock-on by an active seeker power emission, to avoid detection by the threat;

12. increased hardness to protect against laser threats such as a quick reacting shield to protect the seeker and thermal insulation coating over the structure; and

13. saturation, to overwhelm the threat by the simultaneous attack of the threat by more than one missile and to destroy the threat decoys.

Shown in the top middle section of Fig. 6.26 is a photograph of an AC-130 Gunship dispensing flares. Below it is a video of countermeasures to missiles. In the first portion of the video are an AC-130 Gunship, helicopters, and fighter aircraft dispensing flares. In the last portion of the video is a fighter aircraft using an RF cross-eye phase front distortion/angle deception countermeasure against RF guided missiles. Counter-countermeasures that are used by missiles against the countermeasures of the video include 1) a high resolution imaging seeker with a sufficient number of pixels to maintain tracking of the larger target compared to the smaller flare(s), 2) a multi-spectral/multi-mode/multi-band seeker to provide signal robustness across a wide electromagnetic spectrum, and 3) temporal processing of successive frames of the seeker to separate the target frequency from the countermeasure frequency, 4) frequency agility to avoid the countermeasure frequency, and 5) GPS/INS to maintain a target heading if the seeker is jammed.

Counter-countermeasures is like a chess game. It requires early planning, timely development, and quick reaction to the changes in the threat. Early and frequent intelligence information on the threat should drive the approach.

Figure 6.27 shows examples of missiles that have countermeasure resistant seekers. Examples in the photographs are imaging IR (AGM-130), two color imaging IR (Python 5), acoustic/imaging IR (BAT), imaging IR/LADAR (LOCAAS), anti-radiation homing/active mmW (AARGM), and tri-mode semi-active laser/imaging IR/mmW (JAGM). Other missiles that also have countermeasure resistant seekers are RAM (ARH-imaging IR), Stinger (IR-UV), SM-6 (2 color imaging IR), MRM (SAL-imaging IR), A-Darter (2 color imaging IR), SDBII (SAL-imaging IR-mmW), and Harop (ARH-imaging IR-TV).

In the bottom right corner of the figure is a video of Harop, which is a ground launched missile that can loiter over the battlefield, seeking out radar emitting targets. It can also be directed to the target by a data link. When a threat radar turns on, Harop homes on the target using its ARH seeker. In the event of target shut-down, Harop switches to its imaging IR/TV homing.

Examples of concern for electromagnetic compatibility (EMC) of missiles are shown in Fig. 6.28. The examples are ship radar sources of electromagnetic interference (EMI), lightning strike of a Sidewinder mounted on an F-18 aircraft, electromagnetic pulse from a nuclear artillery shell

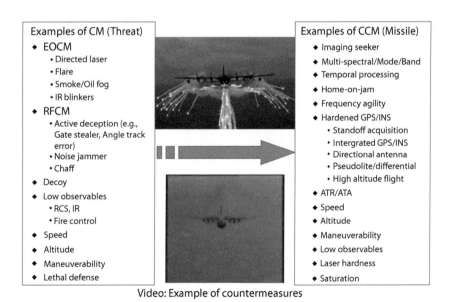

Examples of CM (Threat)	Examples of CCM (Missile)
◆ EOCM	◆ Imaging seeker
• Directed laser	◆ Multi-spectral/Mode/Band
• Flare	◆ Temporal processing
• Smoke/Oil fog	◆ Home-on-jam
• IR blinkers	◆ Frequency agility
◆ RFCM	◆ Hardened GPS/INS
• Active deception (e.g., Gate stealer, Angle track error)	• Standoff acquisition
	• Intergrated GPS/INS
• Noise jammer	• Directional antenna
• Chaff	• Pseudolite/differential
◆ Decoy	• High altitude flight
◆ Low observables	◆ ATR/ATA
• RCS, IR	◆ Speed
• Fire control	◆ Altitude
◆ Speed	◆ Maneuverability
◆ Altitude	◆ Low observables
◆ Maneuverability	◆ Laser hardness
◆ Lethal defense	◆ Saturation

Video: Example of countermeasures

Fig. 6.26 Design robustness requires consideration of countermeasures/counter-countermeasures.

IIR (I²R AGM-130) ....

Two color IIR (Python 5)

Acoustic— IIR (BAT) ....

IIR—LADAR (LOCAAS)

ARH—mmW (AARGM) ....

SAL-IIR—mmW (JAGM)

ARH–IIR—TV (Harop) video ....

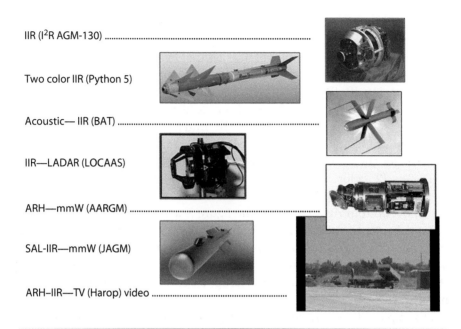

Fig. 6.27 Examples of countermeasure resistant seekers.

impacting at 10 km range (note the lightning discharge), and a Pershing II rocket motor that was destroyed by an electrostatic discharge (ESD).

The energetic components of a missile (rocket motor, warhead, power supply) receive special attention for EMC analysis. Also, the missile electronics receive special attenuation because integrated circuits (ICs) and commercial-of-the-shelf (COTS) electronics do not have the hardening that is required for military systems (e.g., nuclear EMP hardening). Specifications applicable to EMC include MIL-STD-1795A, 461E, 464, 469A, 1512, 1857 and MIL-A-17161D.

Radars are often the greatest concern for EMI because of their proliferation, high power, and broad range in frequency. Shipboard missiles require special analysis of ship radar induced EMI.

The voltages and currents generated by lightning strike are higher than the other non-nuclear sources. Prior to the actual lightning strike on a missile, a corona and streamers form around the missile. When the field strength reaches about 5000 volts/cm a breakdown will occur that allows the lightning to pass through the most vulnerable section of the missile. Two areas that are particularly susceptible to lightning strike entry are the missile radome and non-conducting composite structure materials (e.g., graphite composite rocket motor case/missile airframe). A lightning strike typically has a strength of about 100,000 amperes, which may be enough to explode the missile rocket motor and warhead. The typical rise time and duration are about 0.5 μs and 20 μs respectively.

A missile exposed to EMP acts as a half-wavelength dipole antenna. The strength of the EMP is related to the length of the missile. A rule of thumb is the EMP voltage is approximately

$$V_{\text{EMP}} = 8000 \times l_{\text{Missile}}$$

In the above equation V_{EMP} units are Volts and l_{Missile} units are ft.

For a typical missile length of 12 ft, the strength of EMP is about 100,000 Volts. The rise time and duration of EMP are about 5 ns and 50 ns respectively.

ESD is typically created when two insulating surfaces are ungrounded and are rubbed together or pulled apart. This results in a static charge. If the static charge is of sufficient strength it can as like a miniature lightning bolt, jumping between the two surfaces. The typical strength of ESD is about 5 amperes. The typical rise time and duration are about 1 ns and 150 ns respectively. The bottom right portion of the figure is a post-explosion photograph of a Pershing II rocket motor that killed three soldiers on January 11, 1985 in Heilbronn, Germany. An investigation revealed that the rocket motor had accumulated a static charge in the cold dry weather.

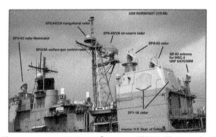

Electromagnetic interference (EMI): Ship radars

Lightning strike

Electromagnetic pulse (EMP)

Electrostatic discharge (ESD)

Fig. 6.28 Electromagnetic compatibility (EMC) considers EMI, lightning strike, EMP, and ESD hardening.

An ESD between the Kevlar composite motor case and the plastic shipping container caused the rocket motor to explode when it was pulled out of the shipping container. Another example of an ESD-induced explosion is the MX rocket motor explosion on December 27, 1987 in Brigham City, Utah that killed 5 people. The explosion occurred during rocket motor production while pulling the mandrel from the propellant casting.

The EMC-induced explosion and fire on the Forrestal aircraft carrier will be described later in this chapter.

6.3 Warhead Lethality

The next measure of merit of this chapter is warhead lethality. The warhead types that are emphasized in this text are blast fragmentation and kinetic energy warheads, because of their relatively high impact on missile configuration design and the availability of unclassified information. Warheads that receive less emphasis include shaped charge, continuous expanding rod, thermobaric, and directed energy warheads (such as electromagnetic pulse (EMP) and high power microwave (HPM) warheads).

A driving consideration for warhead design is the target size and hardness. For example, a small size, hard target such as a tank is best defeated by either a shaped charge warhead, an explosively formed penetrator warhead, or a kinetic energy warhead. A deeply buried target, such as a bunker, requires a two stage warhead: a long-length kinetic energy penetration warhead, followed by a blast fragmentation warhead. A ship target is also usually best defeated by a kinetic energy penetrator followed by a blast fragmentation warhead. Another example target is a large size surface target, such as a building, which requires a large blast fragmentation warhead. A fourth target example is a group of relatively soft targets covering a fairly large area, such as the components of a large SAM site, which may be best defeated by dispensing either combined effects bomblets (CEBs) or sensor fuzed weapons (SFWs).

Shown in Fig. 6.29 is a general war typical surface target set for a standoff precision strike missile. Armor targets and transportation choke points are usually the largest number of targets. New precision strike missiles should ideally have a capability against more than one type of target. An example is a combined capability to engage and defeat hardened buried targets in addition to fixed and mobile surface targets. Benefits of producing a multipurpose missile that is effective against a broad range of targets include reduced unit production cost from a larger production run and reduced logistic cost because of a more simplified logistics organization. A disadvantage of a multipurpose warhead is that it may lack the effectiveness of a dedicated warhead that is optimized for a specific target.

Shown in the video are examples of different standoff precision strike missiles that are used against different targets. The missions are

1. *Cutting airfield runways*: The first example is an Apache missile dispensing runway cutting submunitions at a low altitude.
2. *Destroying aircraft shelters*: In the second example, a Diameter Back Small Diameter Bomb penetrates an aircraft shelter.
3. *Destroying deeply buried targets*: The third example is defeating a deeply buried target bunker using a GBU-24 laser guided bomb with the BLU-109 penetrator warhead.
4. *Destroying buildings*: In the fourth example, a laser-guided bomb attacks a large building target of concrete/steel construction.
5. *Destroying general purpose targets such as parked aircraft, bunkers, shallow caves, and tanks*: The fifth example is a Maverick general purpose missile attacking a within-visual-range airfield aircraft, bunker, shallow cave, and tank targets.
6. *Fixed SAM sites*: A sixth example is a HARM anti-radiation homing missile attacking a fixed SAM site.

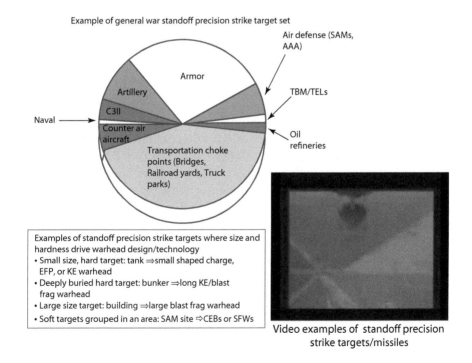

Example of general war standoff precision strike target set

Air defense (SAMs, AAA)

Armor

Artillery

TBM/TELs

C3II

Naval

Counter air aircraft

Oil refineries

Transportation choke points (Bridges, Railroad yards, Truck parks)

Examples of standoff precision strike targets where size and hardness drive warhead design/technology
• Small size, hard target: tank ⇒small shaped charge, EFP, or KE warhead
• Deeply buried hard target: bunker ⇒long KE/blast frag warhead
• Large size target: building ⇒large blast frag warhead
• Soft targets grouped in an area: SAM site ⇨CEBs or SFWs

Video examples of standoff precision strike targets/missiles

Fig. 6.29 The target set size and hardness drive the missile warhead design/technology.

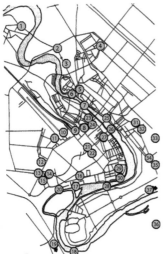

Targets: **1**. Directorate of military intelligence; **2**, **5**, **8**, **13**, **34**. Telephone switching stations; **3**. Ministry of defense national computer complex; **4**. Electrical transfer station; **6**. Ministry of defense headquarters; 7. Ashudad highway bridge; 9. Railroad yard; 10. Muthena airfield (Militray section); **11**. Air force headquarters; **12**. Iraqi intelligence service; **14**. Secret police complex; 15. Army storage depot; **16**. Republican guard headquarters; **17**. New presidential palace; **18**. Electrical power station; 19. SRBM assembly factory (Scud); **20**. Baath party headquarters; **21**. Government conference center; 22. Minisitry of industry and military production; **23**. Ministry of propaganda; **24**. TV transmitter; **25**, **31**. Communications relay stations; 26. Jumhuriya highway bridge; **27**. Government control center south; 28. Karada highway bridge (14th july bridge); **29**. Presidential palace command center; **30**. Presidential palace command bunker; **32**. Secret police headquarters; **33**. Iraqi intelligence service regional headquarters; **35**. National air defense operation center; 36. Ad Dawrah oil refinery; **37**. Electrical power plant

Fig. 6.30 76% of the Baghdad targets that were struck during the first night of Desert Storm were C^3 time critical targets. (Source: *Air Force Magazine*, 1 April 1998.)

7. *Mobile SAMs*: A seventh example is a Diamond Back Small Diameter Bomb using a standoff warhead against a mobile SAM site.
8. *Ships*: Finally, the eighth example is a Harpoon missile attacking a ship target.

There is an emphasis to reduce the unit production cost and the logistics cost by producing multipurpose missiles that can cover a broad range of targets. An example is the Joint Standoff Weapon (JSOW). JSOW is a neckdown replacement of Walleye, Skipper, Rockeye, and some of the laser guided bomb, Maverick and other precision strike weapon missions. A multipurpose weapon system for the standoff precision strike mission should consider a broad target set (see figure). Challenges include targets with low signature (e.g., command and control bunkers), small size (e.g., trucks), small vulnerable area (e.g., armor), mobility (e.g., artillery), time urgency (e.g., ballistic missile transporter/erector/launcher), and weapon cost effectiveness (e.g., cost per target kill versus the target value). As an example, a multi-mode seeker may be a good technical solution for a broad target set, but it may not be a cost effective approach against the numerous low value targets.

Time critical targets are the highest priority targets in the opening round of a war. Taking out the threat command, control, and communication (C^3) is particularly important. An example is shown in Fig. 6.30

derived from Air Force magazine, dated 1 April 1998. It shows the Baghdad targets that were struck on the first night of Desert Storm. Time critical targets are noted with a bold font. Note that the greatest emphasis (76%) was on time critical targets, particularly C^3 targets such as telephone systems, electricity, computers, and military headquarters.

Figure 6.31 is an example of surface target types and the characteristics of current precision strike missiles for the target types. The specific missions for precision strike missiles cover a broad range of targets, including fixed targets, radar sites, ships, armor, and buried targets. Most of the missile configurations shown in the figure are from Ref 1.

In the case of **fixed targets** (which usually are of large size with hardness ranging from soft to hard), a blast fragmentation warhead or dispensed cluster submunitions are usually used. The current missiles for use against fixed targets are mostly relatively large standoff missiles, with wings for efficient subsonic flight. Many rely on low observables for survivability. Current missiles in this category include AGM-158 JASSM, Storm Shadow/Scalp/Apache, KEPD-350 Taurus, BGM-109 Tomahawk, and AGM-142 Popeye/Have Nap.

The second target category is **radar sites**. Radar sites are relatively soft, and can usually be defeated by either a relatively small blast fragmentation

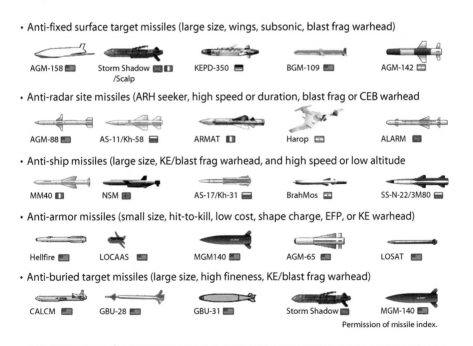

• Anti-fixed surface target missiles (large size, wings, subsonic, blast frag warhead)

AGM-158   Storm Shadow /Scalp   KEPD-350   BGM-109   AGM-142

• Anti-radar site missiles (ARH seeker, high speed or duration, blast frag or CEB warhead

AGM-88   AS-11/Kh-58   ARMAT   Harop   ALARM

• Anti-ship missiles (large size, KE/blast frag warhead, and high speed or low altitude

MM40   NSM   AS-17/Kh-31   BrahMos   SS-N-22/3M80

• Anti-armor missiles (small size, hit-to-kill, low cost, shape charge, EFP, or KE warhead)

Hellfire   LOCAAS   MGM140   AGM-65   LOSAT

• Anti-buried target missiles (large size, high fineness, KE/blast frag warhead)

CALCM   GBU-28   GBU-31   Storm Shadow   MGM-140

Permission of missile index.

Fig. 6.31 The type of target drives precision strike missile size, speed, cost, seeker, and warhead.

warhead for a unitary radar site or dispensed combined effects bomblets for a large area complex radar site. Most anti-radar site missiles have an anti-radiation homing (ARH) seeker. Most fly at high supersonic Mach number, for launch aircraft survivability in a SAM engagement and to minimize the likelihood of the threat radar shutdown before missile impact. Missiles in this category include AGM-88 HARM, AS-11 Kilter/Kh-58, and ARMAT. In the event that the threat radar shuts down prior to impact, a modern missile such as AARGM may use GPS/INS to maintain the heading course toward the target. AARGM also has multi-mode seeker guidance, switching to active mmW homing if the threat radar shuts down. Another approach for an ARH-guided missile to counter threat radar shutdown is to go into a loiter mode. This approach is used by Harop and ALARM. Harop is a propeller driven cruise missile that is easily compatible with loiter. If the threat radar comes back on-line during loiter, the Harop can reacquire the target and reinitiate homing. ALARM has boost-coast rocket propulsion. If the target shuts down, ALARM continues a high altitude flight trajectory into the stratosphere until it is directly above the target. It then deploys a parachute while slowly descending onto the target. Since it is directly above the target, it is probably outside of the scan angle of the target radar. If the target radar turn on, ALARM jettisons the parachute and reinitiates homing guidance. Finally, a cruise missile that does not have an ARH seeker can also be used against a radar site, if it is provided the site target coordinates.

A third target category is **ship targets**. Ships are relatively hard targets and usually require a kinetic energy penetrating warhead, followed by blast fragmentation after penetration of the hull. Anti-ship missiles are generally large in size and have a large warhead. Anti-ship missiles are designed to survive ship defenses, relying on high speed, low observables, high altitude, or low altitude/sea clutter to survive. Current anti-ship missiles include MM40 Exocet, NSM Naval Strike Missile, AS-17 Krypton/Kh-34, BrahMos, and SS-N-22 Sunburn/3M80. Anti-ship missiles may also be adapted for use against fixed targets, such as buildings.

A fourth category is **armor targets**. This includes tanks, armored personnel carriers, and other armored combat vehicles. Armor targets are relatively small in size, are mobile, and are hard. Typical anti-armor warheads include shaped charge, explosively formed projectile (EFP), and kinetic energy penetrator warheads. Most anti-armor missiles are small size, have hit-to-kill accuracy, and are low cost. Examples are Hellfire/Brimstone, LOCAAS, AGM-65 Maverick, and LOSAT. An exception is MGM-140 ATACMS, which is a relatively large ballistic missile that uses submunitions to defeat an array of armor targets. Anti-armor warheads may also be effective against larger area, relatively soft targets. For example, the Hellfire shaped charge warhead has a natural fragmenting case that may also be effective against targets such as radar sites, bunkers, small buildings, and small ships.

A final category is **buried targets**. The current penetration capability against buried targets is typically about 5 to 20 ft of concrete, depending upon the warhead characteristics and the impact velocity. Most missiles used against buried targets have a two stage warhead - high fineness kinetic energy penetration followed by blast fragmentation. Some missiles have a forward shape charge warhead that is followed by a kinetic energy/blast fragmentation warhead. Buried targets include underground command posts and bunkers. The current missiles in this category (CALCM, GBU-28, GBU-31 JDAM, Storm Shadow, MGM-140) are large and heavy. A concern for the missile flight control system design is the maneuverability precision at impact, to avoid breaking up the warhead. Design considerations for the warhead include the nose shape, weight, case material, and diameter. A challenge for explosives and fuzes is survival at high deceleration. Another challenge for fuzing is the ability to sense changes in deceleration during passage through earth, concrete, and the target rooms, in order to detonate the warhead at the proper time in the correct room.

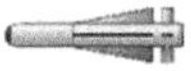

Weapon	Fixed surface targets[1]	Moving targets[2]	Time critical targets[3]	Buried targets[4]	Adverse weather[5]	Firepower[6]
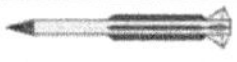 National new missile	●	●	●	●	●	◒
AGM-65	●	○	○	○	—	○
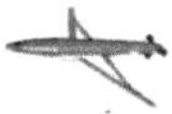 Small diameter bomb	●	—	—	○	●	◒
AGM-88	◒	—	◒	—	●	—
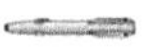 Hellfire/Brimstone/ Longbow	○	●	○	—	—●	◒
LOCAAS	○	●	◒	—	○	●
APKWS	○	●	○	—	—	●

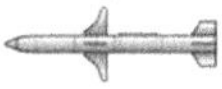

● Superior	◒ Good	○ Average	— Poor

(1) - Large multi-mode warhead desired. GPS/INS provides precision (3 m) accuracy.
(2) - Seeker or high bandwidth data link required for terminal homing.
(3) - High speed with duration required ⇒ High payoff of high speed with loiter or with powered submunition.
(4) - KE penetration warhead required ⇒ High impact speed, low drag, high density, long length.
(5) - GPS/INS, SAR seeker, imaging mmW seeker, and data link have high payoff.
(6) - Light weight required. Light weight also provides low cost.

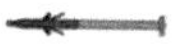

Fig. 6.32 Example of light weight air launched multi-purpose precision strike weapon tradeoffs.

Examples of light weight, air-launched multi-purpose precision strike weapons and their system considerations are shown in Fig. 6.32. An advantage of a light weight missile is enhanced firepower. Firepower is especially important for light weight fighter aircraft, helicopters, and UCAVs, which may have a firepower limitation because of a store weight or size limit. Current air-launched precision strike missiles that are relatively light weight include AGM-65 Maverick, Small Diameter Bomb, AGM-88 HARM, Brimstone/Longbow/Hellfire, LOCAAS, and APKWS. Measures of merit shown are the effectiveness against the broad range of fixed surface targets, effectiveness against moving targets, effectiveness against time critical targets, effectiveness against buried targets, effectiveness in adverse weather, and the firepower load-out on the air launch platform. Note that no one operational missile is superior in all areas. The Small Diameter Bomb (SDB) is a small GPS/INS guided bomb that has good effectiveness against fixed surface targets; has moderate effectiveness against buried targets; is capable of operation in adverse weather; and is relatively light weight (about 250 lb), providing high firepower. In addition to GPS/INS, new technologies for SDB include compressed carriage lattice fins for higher control effectiveness and a compressed carriage diamond back wing for longer range. However, since the SDB is subsonic and the current SDB does not have a seeker, it is relatively ineffective against moving targets and time critical targets. A new light weight precision strike missile that combines the attributes of a small smart bomb with the capability to handle moving targets and time critical targets would be more robust. Examples of technologies that could provide more robustness to handle a broad range of targets include GPS/INS precision guidance, SAR seeker, millimeter wave seeker, and a high bandwidth data link for adverse weather homing and moving targets; ducted rocket propulsion for time critical targets; turbine propulsion and a powered submunition for loiter duration and targeting flexibility; multi-mode kinetic energy/blast fragmentation warhead for deeply buried and surface targets; and light weight subsystems for a lighter weight missile that allows higher firepower.

Examples of UCAVs with their weapons are shown in Fig. 6.33. The examples are an MQ-1 Predator with a 100 lb Hellfire missiles, an MQ-9 Reaper launching a 500 lb GBU-12, an X-45 launching a 250 lb GBU-39 Small Diameter Bomb, and an MQ-5B Hunter launching a 40 lb Viper Strike guided munition. Compared to fixed wing aircraft, UCAVs are more limited in the weight and size of their weapons. UCAVs have limited payload because they are not only smaller than fixed wing aircraft but also most require a higher fuel fraction for a longer flight duration and a higher avionics weight fraction for surveillance and target acquisition.

UCAV sensor suites may consist of a combination of forward looking infrared (FLIR), television (TV) CCD camera, data link, SAR, LADAR, and EW sensors. Benefits of a combination of sensors include a broader range of missions, wider area coverage, real time ATR, reduced false alarm rate (FAR), real time precision targeting, and enhanced survivability. An example of a typical UCAV sensor suite is that of Predator. Predator has a SAR, FLIR, TV, laser rangefinder, Ku-band and UHF-band satellite communication (SATCOM), C-band line-of-sight data link, and GPS/INS navigation sensors.

The bottom right portion of the figure is a video of X-45 with an ejection launch of an SDB and Predator with a rail launch of Hellfire.

Figure 6.34 shows the overpressure Δp of the rocket baseline missile warhead as a function of the distance r from the charge to the target. Two predictions are shown for the blast overpressure. The first prediction is based on the blast wave scaling correlation of Ref. 27. Blast overpressure is given by the equation

$$\Delta p / p_0 = 37.95/(z p_0^{1/3}) + 154.9/(z p_0^{1/3})^2 + 203.4/(z p_0^{1/3})^3$$
$$+ 403.9/(z p_0^{1/3})^4$$

In the above equation $p_0 =$ undisturbed atmospheric pressure in psi and $z =$ scaling parameter $= r/W_c^{1/3}$, $r =$ distance from the warhead in ft, and $W_c =$ warhead charge weight in lb. The correlation is for a bare pentolite sphere charge. Pentolite consists of 50% TNT ($C_7H_5N_3O_6$) and 50% PETN ($C_5H_8N_4O_{12}$) and has a Gurney constant $(2E_c)^{1/2} = 8500$ ft/s.

MQ-1 Predator: Hellfire (~100 lb)

MQ-9 Reaper: GBU-12 laser guided bomb (~500 lb)

X-45: GBU-39 SDB (~250 lb)

MQ-5B Hunter: Viper Strike (~40 lb)

Video–X-45 ejection launch: SDB, Predator rail launch: Hellfire

Fig. 6.33 UCAVs require light weight weapons.

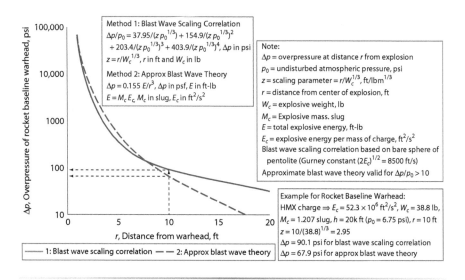

Fig. 6.34   Warhead blast kill requires a small miss distance.

The second prediction is based on Taylor [28] approximate blast wave theory. Taylor assumed that an intense explosion provides a similarity solution of blast wave parameters. Using only publicly-available photographs of a nuclear explosion, Taylor was able to predict the yield of an atomic bomb. The approximate analytical solution is

$$\Delta p = 0.155\, E/r^3$$

with $E = M_c\, E_c$.

In the above equation E = total explosive energy in ft-lb, E_c = explosive energy per mass of charge in ft^2/s^2, and M_c = explosive mass in slug.

The rocket baseline missile warhead will be used as an example to demonstrate the two methods of predicting blast overpressure. The rocket baseline missile warhead has a charge weight of $W_c = 38.8$ lb. Assume a standoff distance of $r = 10$ ft and an altitude $h = 20$ kft ($p_0 = 6.75$ psi). The scaling parameter z is computed to be

$$z = 10/38.8^{1/3} = 2.95$$

Substituting into the above blast overpressure equation provides a maximum overpressure at $r = 10$ ft

$$\Delta p/p_o = 37.95/[2.95(6.75)^{1/3}] + 154.9/[2.95(6.75)^{1/3}]^2$$

$$+203.4/[2.95(6.75)^{1/3}]^3 + 403.9/[2.95(6.75)^{1/3}]^4$$

$$\Delta p = 90.1\,\text{psi}$$

Comparing a smaller (10-lb) charge for the same value of z, the distance is $r = 6.4$ ft to achieve the same overpressure of 90.1 psi. A 36% reduction in miss distance has the same effect as a 290% increase in warhead weight! Because decreasing miss distance is more important to enhance lethality than increasing warhead weight, more accurate missile guidance with a small warhead can often provide the same lethality as a much larger missile with a much larger warhead that has somewhat less accurate guidance. In addition to a lighter weight missile, other benefits of a lighter warhead from more accurate guidance include higher firepower, less collateral damage, and perhaps lower cost.

The Taylor [28] method, based on approximate blast wave theory, has an advantage that it models the charge energy of different types of explosives. For example, the rocket baseline warhead explosive (HMX) has more energy than the pentolite charge assumed for the blast wave scaling correlation method (HMX Gurney constant $(2E_c)^{1/2} = 10,230$ ft/s versus pentolite Gurney constant $(2E_c)^{1/2} = 8500$ ft/s). Another advantage of approximate blast wave theory is a simpler computation. Disadvantages of approximate blast wave theory compared to blast wave scaling correlation are approximate blast wave theory does not include the effect of undisturbed atmospheric pressure p_0 and it is accurate only for overpressures greater than 10 atmospheres. Calculating the overpressure for the rocket baseline missile warhead with an HMX explosive charge ($E_c = 52.3 \times 10^6$ ft^2/s^2, warhead charge weight $W_c = 38.8$ lb, warhead charge mass $M_c = 1.207$ slug, and radius $r = 10$ ft)

$$E = M_c E_c = 1.207(52.3 \times 10^6) = 63.1 \times 10^6 \text{ ft-lb}$$

$$\Delta p = 0.155(63.1 \times 10^6)/10^3 = 9.79 \times 10^3 \text{ psf} = 67.9 \text{ psi}$$

At an assumed altitude $h = 20$ kft ($p_0 = 6.75$ psi), $\Delta p = 10$ atmospheres (the accuracy limit of approximate blast wave theory).

For most missiles, blast wave scaling correlation gives a more accurate prediction for typical charge materials (e.g., pentolite-type charges), typical (relatively low) overpressure, and typical (relatively low) altitude. However, approximate blast wave theory may provide a more accurate prediction for a warhead charge if it is much more energetic than pentolite or if it is detonated at a very high altitude (e.g., exo-atmospheric).

The primary type of missile warhead that is discussed in the text is blast/fragmentation. A blast/fragmentation warhead has an explosive charge that breaks up the warhead case, accelerating fragments to a high velocity. The size and the angular distribution of the fragments is a function of the warhead design. Figure 6.35 illustrates a portion of the fragment radial spray of a notional cylindrical warhead. A cylindrical warhead is usually designed for a full circumferential radial spray ($0 < \phi < 360$ deg).

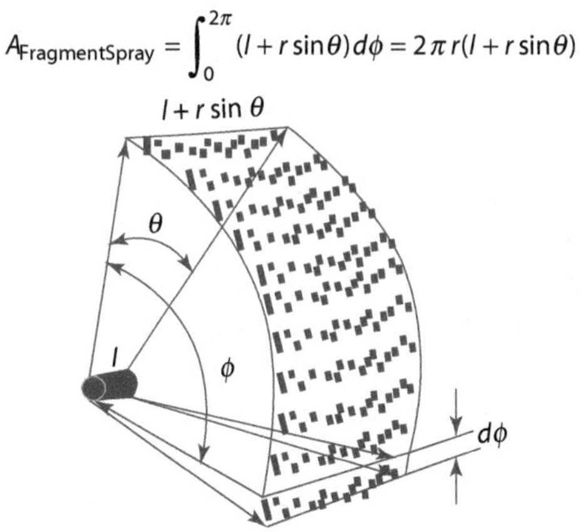

$$A_{\text{FragmentSpray}} = \int_0^{2\pi} (l + r\sin\theta)\,d\phi = 2\pi r(l + r\sin\theta)$$

Note:

$A_{\text{FragmentSpray}}$ = Fragmentation spray surface area, l = Warhead case length, r = Distance from center explosion, θ = Vertical spray angle, ϕ = Radial spray angle

Fig. 6.35   The primary kill mechanism of a typical blast/fragmentation warhead is the warhead fragments.

The vertical spray typically varies from $2 < \theta < 50$ deg. Later in the section will discuss the advantages and disadvantages of more advanced warheads that provide a more focused spray pattern.

From the figure, we can see that the warhead fragmentation spray area is

$$A_{\text{Fragment spray}} = \int_0^{2\pi} (l + r\sin\theta)\,d\phi = 2\pi r(l + r\sin\theta)$$

In the above equation l = warhead case length, r = distance from the center of the explosion, θ = vertical spray angle, and ϕ = radial spray angle.

The types of target kill include catastrophic kill, firepower kill, and mobility kill. A catastrophic kill destroys the target, a firepower kill prevents the target from using its weapons, and a mobility kill prevents the target from moving. For a catastrophic kill (k-kill), the fragments from the blast/fragmentation warhead must usually penetrate the skin of the target structure to have a reasonable probability of kill. Following structure penetration, the kill probability depends upon destroying a vulnerable component. As an example, for an aircraft target the most vulnerable components include the pilot, flight control system, fuel tank, and ordnance. For a fire power kill (F-kill), the most vulnerable components are usually the external sensors. It is usually easier to achieve an F-kill than a K-kill. A mobility kill (M-kill) also usually requires less damage than a K-kill. The vulnerable component for an M-kill kill could be the propulsion system (e.g., the engine of a tank). The design of the warhead fragment size and weight is based on the type of desired kill. K-kill fragments are usually larger and heavier than F or M-kill fragments. Also, a K-kill warhead is usually larger and heavier. Although a K-kill is often preferred, an F or M-kill may be sufficient if there is a long time required for repair (e.g., more than the duration of the war).

During the preliminary design activity, a Monte Carlo analysis may be conducted of fragment shot lines through the target to obtain an estimate of the probability of kill. For conceptual design, the assessment is usually based on a simple aggregate assessment of the target hardness. Aggregate measures of merit of fragment warhead effectiveness include the kinetic energy density, the kinetic energy power, and the total kinetic energy provided by the warhead on the target. Kinetic energy density and power are usually better indications of K-kill than the total kinetic energy on the target. Total kinetic energy on the target may be a better indication of an F or an M-kill. Kinetic energy density is the primary measure of merit that we will use in this text to assess the conceptual design fragmentation effectiveness of a blast/fragmentation warhead. For conceptual design, the blast overpressure is usually the primary measure of the blast effectiveness. However, the time duration of the blast overpressure ($\int \Delta p\, dt$) is also a factor in warhead effectiveness and the target structure failure. Another consideration is the target natural frequency. If the overpressure time duration is comparable to the target structure natural frequency, the target structure resonance enhances failure. A relatively long duration blast from a thermobaric warhead may excite the target structural resonance.

The total kinetic energy of a cylindrical blast/fragmentation warhead is given by the Gurney equation [29]

$$KE = (1/2)M_m V_f^2 = E_c M_c / (1.5 + 0.5\, M_c/M_m)$$

The Gurney equation predicts the warhead case fragment velocity that is produced by a linear velocity gradient of the gas from the explosive charge. Figure 6.36 shows the non-dimensional total kinetic energy of a blast fragmentation warhead $KE/(E_c M_{wh})$ as a function of charge-to-metal case ratio (M_c/M_m). It is based on the equation

$$KE/E_c M_{wh} = \left[1.5 + 0.5\, M_c/M_m + (M_c/M_m)^{-1}\right]^{-1}$$

Maximizing the total kinetic energy of the fragments is an optimization of the warhead M_c/M_m. A small value of charge-to-metal ratio has low kinetic energy because the small charge cannot accelerate the metal fragments to a high velocity. A large charge-to-metal ratio ($M_c/M_m \gg 1$) provides high individual fragment kinetic energy, because fragments are accelerated to high velocity. However, there is less total fragment kinetic energy because fewer fragments are available. The optimum value of

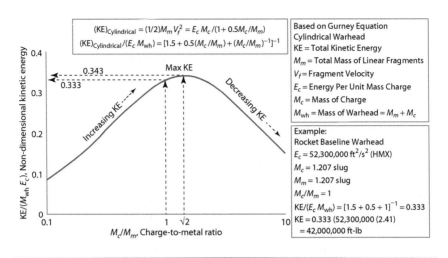

Fig. 6.36 Maximum total fragment kinetic energy requires $M_c/M_m \sim 1$ while maximum blast overpressure requires $M_c/M_m \gg 1$. (Reference: Carleone, Joseph (Editor), "Tactical Missile Warheads", *Progress in Astronautics and Aeronautics*, Vol 155, AIAA, 1993.)

M_c/M_m that maximizes $\mathrm{KE}/E_c M_{wh}$ of a cylindrical warhead is

$$M_c/M_m = 2^{1/2} = 1.414$$

A very large value of charge-to-metal ratio implies that blast is the primary kill mechanism, with a higher blast overpressure. An advantage of a warhead with $M_c/M_m \gg 1$ is fewer fragments, resulting in lower collateral damage.

As an example, the rocket baseline warhead has a total weight $M_{wh} = M_m + M_c = 77.7$ lb $= 2.41$ slug and a charge-to-metal mass ratio $M_c/M_m = 1$. The Her Majesty's Explosive (HMX) explosive charge has an energy per unit mass of $E_c = 52{,}300{,}000$ ft^2/s^2. The total charge energy is

$$E = E_c M_c = 52.3 \times 10^6 (1.207) = 63.1 \times 10^6 \text{ ft-lb.}$$

Computing the non-dimensional kinetic energy

$$\mathrm{KE}/(E_c M_{wh}) = \left[1.5 + 0.5(M_c/M_m) + (M_c/M_m)^{-1}\right]^{-1} = [1.5 + 0.5 + 1]^{-1}$$
$$= 0.333.$$

The total kinetic energy of the fragments is therefore

$$\mathrm{KE} = 0.333\, E_c M_{wh} = 0.333\left(52.3 \times 10^6\right)(2.41) = 42 \times 10^6 \text{ ft-lb.}$$

Approximately 67% of the charge energy is converted into kinetic energy. Again, note from the figure that the rocket baseline missile warhead charge-to-metal ratio $M_c/M_m = 1$ provides near-maximum total kinetic energy.

Fragment initial velocity is a function of the warhead charge energy and the charge-to-metal-ratio (M_c/M_m). Figure 6.37, based on the Gurney equation for a cylindrical warhead [29], shows the fragment initial velocity of a relatively modern explosive (HMX, $C_4H_8N_8O_8$) compared to that of TNT ($C_7H_5N_3O_6$). The Gurney equation for the fragment velocity of a cylindrical warhead is

$$V_f = (2E_c)^{1/2}[(M_c/M_m)/(1 + 0.5\,M_c/M_m)]^{1/2}$$

HMX provides higher fragment velocity because it has 35% more explosive energy than TNT [$(2E_c)^{1/2}$ = 10,230 versus 7600 ft/s]. Note from the figure that very high fragment velocity V_f requires $M_c/M_m > 1$.

As an example, the rocket baseline missile has a cylindrical warhead with HMX explosive and $M_c/M_m = 1$. The fragment velocity is computed

$$V_f = 10230[1/(1 + 0.5(1)]^{1/2} = 8353\,\text{ft/s}.$$

A more general form of the Gurney equation [29] may be used to predict the fragment velocity of more general warhead configurations.

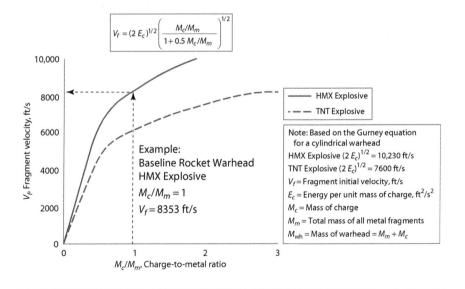

Fig. 6.37 High fragment velocity requires high charge-to-metal ratio.

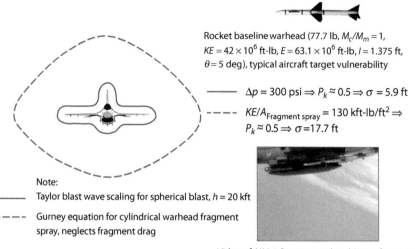

Rocket baseline warhead (77.7 lb, $M_c/M_m = 1$,
$KE = 42 \times 10^6$ ft-lb, $E = 63.1 \times 10^6$ ft-lb, $l = 1.375$ ft,
$\theta = 5$ deg), typical aircraft target vulnerability

—— $\Delta p = 300$ psi $\Rightarrow P_k \approx 0.5 \Rightarrow \sigma = 5.9$ ft

---- $KE/A_{\text{Fragment spray}} = 130$ kft-lb/ft^2 $\Rightarrow$
$P_k \approx 0.5 \Rightarrow \sigma = 17.7$ ft

Note:
—— Taylor blast wave scaling for spherical blast, $h = 20$ kft

---- Gurney equation for cylindrical warhead fragment
spray, neglects fragment drag

Video of AIM-7 Sparrow warhead (Aircraft targets)

Fig. 6.38   Warhead fragment kinetic energy usually provides a larger lethal radius than blast overpressure.

The equation is

$$V_f = (2E_c)^{1/2}\{(M_c/M_m)/\{1 + [n/(n+2)]M_c/M_m\}\}^{1/2}$$

In the above equation $n = 1$ for a flat sandwich of explosive between two flat plates, $n = 2$ for a cylindrical warhead, and $n = 3$ for a spherical warhead. For the same value of M_c/M_m and $2E_c$, a flat plate warhead provides the highest fragment velocity while a spherical warhead provides the lowest fragment velocity.

The kill envelope from a blast/fragmentation warhead against a typical aircraft target is shown in Fig. 6.38. The kill envelope is based on the rocket baseline missile warhead weight $W_{wh} = 77.7$ lb, length $l = 1.375$ ft, charge-to-metal ratio of 1 (warhead total kinetic energy KE $= 42 \times 10^6$ ft-lb, warhead charge $E = 63.1 \times 10^6$ ft-lb), an assumed spherical blast, and an assumed cylindrical fragment spray with $\theta = 5$ deg. The altitude is assumed to be 20,000 ft. Other assumptions are that the blast overpressure and the fragments impact kinetic energy density that are required for a probability of kill $P_K = 0.5$ of a typical aircraft target are $\Delta p = 330$ psi and 130,000 ft-lb/ft^2, respectively. Based on the Taylor [28] blast wave approximation, the $P_K = 0.5$ overpressure of $\Delta p = 330$ psi occurs at a distance of

$$r = \{0.155(63.1 \times 10^6)/[330(144)]\}^{1/3} = 5.9\,\text{ft}$$

Based on the Gurney [29] equation and the $P_K = 0.5$ fragment kinetic energy density of $KE/A_{Fragment\ spray} = 130{,}000$ ft-lb/ft^2 the lethal radius r is obtained by solving the equation

$$KE/A_{Fragment\ spray} = 130k\ \text{ft-lb/ft}^2 = KE/[2\pi r(l + r\sin\theta)]$$
$$= 42 \times 10^6/[2\pi r(1.375 + r\sin 5\deg)]$$

Solving the above quadratic equation gives

$$r = 17.7\ \text{ft}$$

The warhead fragment kinetic energy density provides 3 × the lethal distance compared to the blast lethal radius (17.7 versus 5.9 ft).

Shown at the bottom right of the figure is a video of the lethality of AIM-7 Sparrow flight test missiles launched against drone aircraft. The Sparrow missile flight trajectory results in a relatively small miss distance, with the missile impacting the target in some cases.

Most cylindrical blast/fragmentation warheads have a fragment distribution kinetic energy density distribution that is intermediate the pure spherical ($\theta = 360$ deg) and the pure cylindrical ($\theta = 0$ deg) fragment distributions. A typical cylindrical warhead has a vertical spray angle of about $2 < \theta < 50$ deg. Figure 6.39 compares the $P_K = 0.5$ lethality of the rocket baseline missile warhead for $2 < \theta < 50$ deg. Note the larger lethal radius for the small vertical spray angle. The $P_K = 0.5$ is based on a fragment kinetic energy density of $130{,}000$ ft-lb/ft^2 for a typical aircraft

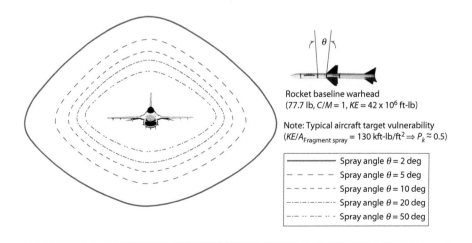

Rocket baseline warhead
(77.7 lb, C/M = 1, KE = 42 x 10⁶ ft-lb)

Note: Typical aircraft target vulnerability
(KE/A$_{Fragment\ spray}$ = 130 kft-lb/ft² ⟹ P_k ≈ 0.5)

——————— Spray angle θ = 2 deg
– – – – – Spray angle θ = 5 deg
– · – · – · Spray angle θ = 10 deg
– · · – · · – Spray angle θ = 20 deg
– · · – · · – · · Spray angle θ = 50 deg

Fig. 6.39 A blast/fragment warhead with a small spray angle has a larger lethal radius.

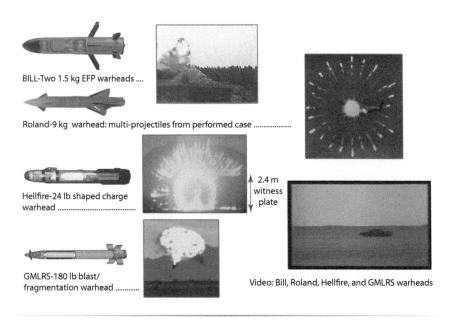

BILL-Two 1.5 kg EFP warheads ....

Roland-9 kg warhead: multi-projectiles from performed case ....

Hellfire-24 lb shaped charge warhead ....

2.4 m witness plate

GMLRS-180 lb blast/ fragmentation warhead ....

Video: Bill, Roland, Hellfire, and GMLRS warheads

Fig. 6.40 Accurate guidance enhances lethality.

target. The lethal radius of each spray angle is

$$r = 23.4 \text{ ft} \quad \text{if } \theta = 2 \deg$$
$$r = 17.7 \text{ ft} \quad \text{if } \theta = 5 \deg$$
$$r = 13.7 \text{ ft} \quad \text{if } \theta = 10 \deg$$
$$r = 10.4 \text{ ft} \quad \text{if } \theta = 20 \deg$$
$$r = 7.4 \text{ ft} \quad \text{if } \theta = 50 \deg$$

An assumption is that entire area of the target aircraft is uniformly impacted by fragments. This would be true for a sufficiently large miss distance but not at a small miss distance. For a small miss distance, for example, a near hit, only a portion of the target is impacted by fragments. Also, only a portion of the target would be impacted for a highly directional warhead, such as an aimed cylindrical or a rod warhead. Fragment impacts over the entire target may provide a higher lethality. A highly directional warhead would likely require more attention to target vulnerability analysis, such as a shot line analysis, to better determine the probability that the warhead fragments impact a vulnerable subsystem of the target.

The photographs in Fig. 6.40 show the fireball and fragments from the detonations of four different warheads. The top section of the figure illustrates the BILL warhead. BILL has two light weight (1.5 kg each) explosively formed penetrators that fire from the bottom of the missile as it passes over the target. The second, next heavier example is the Roland warhead (9 kg weight). Roland has a multi-projectile warhead. Dimples in the side of the warhead case provide explosively formed projectiles. In the top right section of the figure is a detonation of the Roland warhead against a helicopter drone target. Note the tight distribution of the projectiles that extends beyond the target. The third next heavier example is the Hellfire shaped charge warhead, which weighs 24 lb. Hellfire has a naturally fragmenting case. Note that the fireball and fragment coverage is larger than the 8 ft (2.4 m) witness plate. Finally, the bottom left example is an airburst of the relatively heavy Guided Multiple Launch Rocket System (GMLRS), which has a 180 lb blast/fragmentation warhead.

The bottom right section of the figure is a video illustrating the BILL, Roland, Hellfire, and MLRS warheads. BILL detonates its warhead when it is over the top (most vulnerable area) of the tank target. Although BILL has a small warhead, it is sufficiently energetic to penetrate the top of the tank and initiate post-detonation effects on the target. Interior spall, blast, and heat set off sympathetic detonations of the tank ordnance and fuel. The next portion of the video illustrates the accuracy of Roland against maneuvering targets and the effectiveness of the warhead. For a target impact, the relatively small Roland warhead provides catastrophic kill. The third portion of the video illustrates the accuracy and lethality of Hellfire. Hellfire is a fly-to-buy missile. A portion of each month's production is selected for accuracy, reliability, and effectiveness demonstration flights at Eglin Air Force Base. Hellfire is conditioned to either $-40\ °F$ or $140\ °F$ and then launched at a 4 ft $\times$ 4 ft target board at 8 km range. A high reliability has been demonstrated, with 200+ consecutive successful intercepts. The last portion of the video is a GMLRS impacting a SAM at White Sands Missile Range. The 180 lb warhead initiates collateral debris over a long time duration and over a large area.

The number of fragment hits on the target from a cylindrical warhead is shown in Fig. 6.41 as a function of the missile miss distance and the warhead weight. It is based on the equation

$$n_{\text{Hits}} = n_{\text{Fragments}}\{[A_p/2\pi(\sin\theta)\sigma^2]\}$$

The assumptions in the above equation are a cylindrical fragment distribution and a miss distance much larger than the warhead length ($\sigma \gg l$), such that $A_{\text{Fragment spray}} \approx 2\pi \sin\theta\, \sigma^2$. Other assumptions in the figure are a vertical spray angle $\theta = 5$ deg, warhead charge mass equal to metal case mass ($M_c/M_m = 1$), an average fragment weight that is typically required for an aircraft target (50 grains or 3.2 g), and a target presented area that is typical for an aircraft target ($A_p = 20\ \text{ft}^2$).

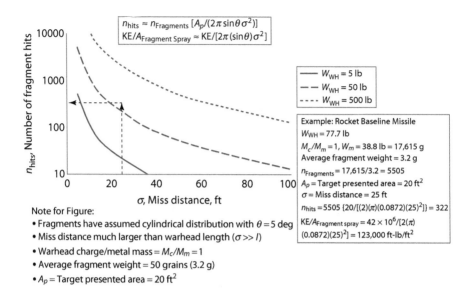

$$n_{hits} \approx n_{Fragments}\,[A_p/(2\pi\sin\theta\,\sigma^2)]$$
$$KE/A_{Fragment\ Spray} \approx KE/[2\pi\,(\sin\theta)\,\sigma^2]$$

— $W_{WH} = 5$ lb
-- $W_{WH} = 50$ lb
···· $W_{WH} = 500$ lb

Example: Rocket Baseline Missile
$W_{WH} = 77.7$ lb
$M_c/M_m = 1$, $W_m = 38.8$ lb $= 17,615$ g
Average fragment weight $= 3.2$ g
$n_{Fragments} = 17,615/3.2 = 5505$
$A_p =$ Target presented area $= 20$ ft^2
$\sigma =$ Miss distance $= 25$ ft
$n_{hits} = 5505\ \{20/[(2)(\pi)(0.0872)(25)^2]\} = 322$
$KE/A_{Fragment\ spray} = 42 \times 10^6/[2(\pi)$
$(0.0872)(25)^2] = 123,000$ ft-lb/ft^2

Note for Figure:
- Fragments have assumed cylindrical distribution with $\theta = 5$ deg
- Miss distance much larger than warhead length ($\sigma \gg l$)
- Warhead charge/metal mass $= M_c/M_m = 1$
- Average fragment weight $= 50$ grains (3.2 g)
- $A_p =$ Target presented area $= 20$ ft^2

Fig. 6.41   A small miss distance improves the number of warhead fragment hits.

Note the value of guidance accuracy in increasing the number of fragment hits on target. At a small miss distance less than 10 ft, even a small 5-lb warhead has multiple fragment hits on the target.

Technology may be used to focus the warhead kinetic energy to provide a greater density of fragments compared to that available from a conventional cylindrical distribution. Examples are aimed cylindrical warheads and mass focus warheads. Disadvantages are the requirement for more sophisticated fuzing and the increased risk that the warhead kinetic energy may not be accurately focused toward the target.

As an example of warhead fragment impacts, the rocket baseline missile 77.7 lb warhead has a charge-to-metal ratio of one, providing a total fragment weight of 38.8 lb or 17,615 g. For an average fragment weight of 3.2 g there are $n_{Fragments} = 17615/3.2 = 5505$ fragments. For an assumed cylindrical distribution with a vertical spray angle $\theta = 5$ deg, and a miss distance $\sigma = 25$ ft, the number of fragment hits against a target with a presented area $A_p = 20$ ft^2 is

$$n_{Hits} = 5505\{20/[2\pi(\sin 5\ \text{deg})(25^2)]\} = 322$$

The kinetic energy density of the fragments impacting on the target is

$$KE/A_{Fragment\ spray} \approx KE/[2\pi(\sin\theta)\sigma^2] = 42 \times 10^6/[2\pi(0.0872)(25)^2]$$
$$= 123,000\ \text{ft-lb/ft}^2$$

A warhead design tradeoff is the number of fragment hits versus the kinetic energy density. A catastrophic kill requirement usually puts more emphasis on a high value of kinetic energy density while a firepower or mobility kill requirement usually puts more emphasis on a high value of fragment hits.

Penetration of the fragments from a blast/fragmentation warhead is shown in Fig. 6.42 as a function of the miss distance and the fragment weight. Again, the value of small miss distance is apparent: fragments have much greater penetration at small miss distance. Warhead fragments have high drag, and the fragment velocity decays rapidly with distance. In the example, a fragment that travels 10 ft has about four times the penetration compared to a fragment that travels 100 ft. The data for the figure is based on a fragment initial velocity of 5000 ft/s, sea level test, average fragment weight of 50 grains (3.2 g), and maximum fragment weight of 150 grains (9.7 g). The average fragment weight of a typical air blast/fragmentation warhead that uses preformed fragments is about 50 grains. Less than 0.3% of the fragments that are nominally preformed to 50 grains will weigh more than 150 grains. Preformed and multi-projectile blast fragmentation warheads for air intercept targets have been developed

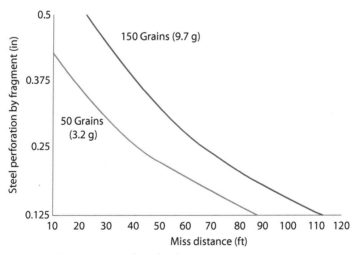

Note: Typical air intercept missile warhead
• Fragments initial velocity 5000 ft/s
• Sea level
• Average fragment weight 3.2 g
• Fewer than 0.3% of the fragments weigh more than 9.7 g for nominal 3.2 g preformed warhead fragments
• Small miss distance gives less reduction in fragment velocity, enhancing penetration

Fig. 6.42 A small miss distance improves fragment penetration.

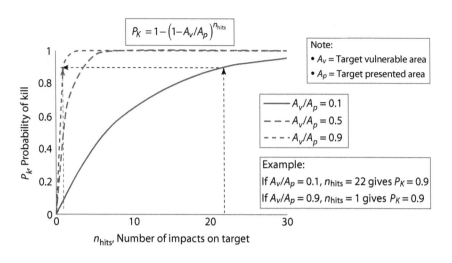

$$P_K = 1 - \left(1 - A_v/A_p\right)^{n_{hits}}$$

Note:
- A_v = Target vulnerable area
- A_p = Target presented area

——— $A_v/A_p = 0.1$
- - - $A_v/A_p = 0.5$
···· $A_v/A_p = 0.9$

Example:
If $A_v/A_p = 0.1$, $n_{hits} = 22$ gives $P_K = 0.9$
If $A_v/A_p = 0.9$, $n_{hits} = 1$ gives $P_K = 0.9$

P_K, Probability of kill

n_{hits}, Number of impacts on target

Fig. 6.43 Multiple impacts enhance the effectiveness against the target vulnerable area subsystems.

with a broad range of fragment weight, ranging from 4 to 200 grains. The optimum fragment weight is a function of the missile accuracy, target size, target hardness, and the type of kill (e.g., K-kill, F-Kill, M-kill).

For a target kill by warhead fragments, the probability of kill P_K is a function of the number of hits on the target and the fractional area of the target that is vulnerable. For a single hit, the probability of kill is

$$P_K = A_V/A_p$$

If the kill probability of a second hit is independent of the first hit, then the probability of kill for two hits is

$$P_K = 1 - \left(1 - A_V/A_p\right)^2$$

For n hits, the general equation is

$$P_K = 1 - \left(1 - A_V/A_p\right)^{n_{Hits}}$$

Figure 6.43 shows the probability of kill from fragments impacting a target with low vulnerable area ($A_V/A_p = 0.1$), a target with a moderate vulnerable area ($A_V/A_p = 0.5$), and a target with a large vulnerable area ($A_V/A_p = 0.9$). Note that only a few warhead fragments are required to kill a soft target with a large vulnerable area, while many fragment impacts are required to kill a hard target with a relatively small vulnerable area.

As an example for a kill probability of kill $P_K = 0.9$, the number of hits that are required on a hard target with a vulnerable area that is 10% of the presented area is

$$n_{\text{Hits}} = -\ln(1 - P_K)/\ln(1 - A_v/A_p) = -\ln(1 - 0.9)/\ln(1 - 0.1) = 22$$

However, only 1 hit is required against a soft target with a vulnerable area that is 90% of the presented area.

Figure 6.44 illustrates the advantages and disadvantages of different types of kinetic energy density distributions. Shown are examples of spherical, cylindrical, conical, and linear kinetic energy distributions.

A spherical distribution has isotropic coverage (full 360 deg) from the fragments. Because of its full coverage, it is relatively low risk. The effectiveness is relatively insensitive to errors in fuzing and in guidance and control. However, a spherical warhead is uncommon because its low kinetic energy density requires a larger, heavier warhead.

A cylindrical warhead is the most popular type of fragmentation warhead. It provides a more focused, directional warhead. The radial distribution of kinetic energy has a higher kinetic energy density, providing a larger lethal radius than a spherical warhead. There is a somewhat greater risk in fuzing and in guidance and control.

An even more directional warhead has a conical distribution of the fragments, similar to a shotgun. This warhead requires precision aiming at the

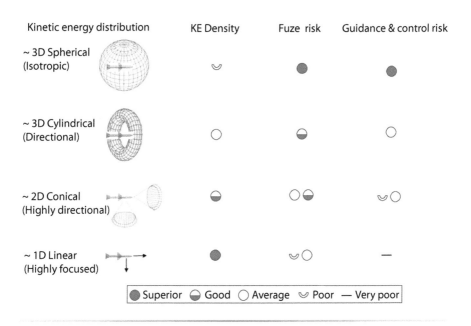

Fig. 6.44 A directional warhead has high kinetic energy density but it also has higher risk fuzing and higher risk guidance and control.

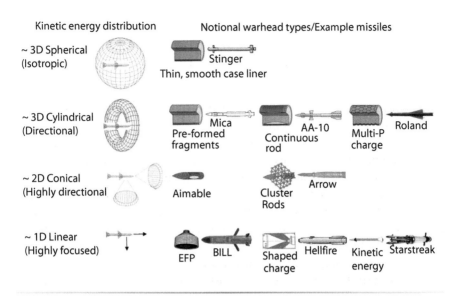

Kinetic energy distribution

Notional warhead types/Example missiles

~ 3D Spherical (Isotropic) — Stinger — Thin, smooth case liner

~ 3D Cylindrical (Directional) — Mica / Pre-formed fragments — AA-10 / Continuous rod — Multi-P charge — Roland

~ 2D Conical (Highly directional) — Aimable — Cluster Rods — Arrow

~ 1D Linear (Highly focused) — EFP — BILL — Shaped charge — Hellfire — Kinetic energy — Starstreak

Fig. 6.45   Kinetic energy directional distribution drives the type of warhead design. (Reference: Carleone, Joseph (Editor), "Tactical Missile Warheads", *Progress in Astronautics and Aeronautics*, Vol 155, AIAA, 1993.)

target. Aiming may be either laterally or forward. Lateral aiming is the most common.

Finally, the most focused warhead has all of its kinetic energy focused in a line that deposits all of the energy on the target. Examples of linear kinetic energy warheads include explosively formed projectile and shaped charge warheads. Although the linear kinetic energy type has the highest kinetic energy density, it also has the highest risk in fuzing and in guidance and control.

Figure 6.45 gives examples of notional warheads. The warhead sketches are from Ref. 29. Also shown are examples of operational missiles for each type of warhead.

An example of a warhead that approximates an isotopic (spherical) fragment distribution is a low fineness (length $\approx$ diameter) blast/fragmentation warhead with a high charge-to-metal ratio ($M_c/M_m \gg 1$). The notional warhead in the figure has a $\frac{1}{4}$ section removed to show the warhead case detail. An example of an operational missile which has the characteristics of a spherical warhead is Stinger. Stinger has a thin-wall, short-length case.

Examples of cylindrical warheads include pre-formed fragment, continuous rod, and multi-p charge warheads. The warheads shown in the figure have a $\frac{1}{4}$ section removed to show the case detail. A pre-formed fragment warhead has a scored pattern that separates along the scoring upon detonation. This produces cubical fragments of nearly uniform weight. An example of a missile with a pre-formed warhead is Mica. A continuous rod warhead consists of folded rods that are linked around the circumference. Upon detonation the rods unfold as an expanding ring. A continuous rod warhead works best on a subsonic target. An example of a missile with a continuous rod warhead is the AA-10. A multi-P charge warhead produces explosively formed projectiles. Conical or hemispherical dimple depressions in the case act as multiple shaped charges. Multi-P charges provides very fast, heavy fragments. A disadvantage is there are relatively few fragments. Roland is an example of a missile with a multi-P warhead.

Examples of warheads that provide a conical kinetic energy distribution are aimable and cluster rod warheads. Based on the fuzing information on the location of the target, an aimable warhead can selectively aim the direction of the fragments toward the target. It typically has about eight detonators that are radially spaced around the circumference. Selected radial detonators are initiated prior to the main detonator. Based on a desired radial angle bias that is provided by fuzing, the case is selectively deformed by the radial detonators. Next, the main detonator is initiated and the fragments are accelerated in the desired direction. The aimable warhead has much more focused kinetic energy in the desired direction. Although there have been a number of technology demonstrations, there are no current operational missiles that have an aimable warhead. The fuzing and the guidance and control are high risk. A cluster rod warhead releases a cloud of rods prior to intercept. These effectively increase the diameter of the missile, allowing hit-to-kill. This type of warhead is most applicable to exo-atmospheric intercept missiles. Arrow is an example of a missile with a cluster rod warhead.

Finally, examples of warheads that have strictly linear kinetic energy are explosively formed penetrator (EFP), shaped charge, and kinetic energy warheads. An EFP is explosively formed by the explosive charge, shaping the liner into a projectile. Compared to a fragmenting warhead, the EFP projectile is much larger, much heavier, and has much greater penetration of the target. An EFP warhead requires accurate pointing toward the target. EFP warheads are often used against armor targets. An example of a missile with an EFP warhead is BILL. Like an EFP warhead, a shaped charge uses an explosive charge to shape the liner. However, the shaped charge subjects the liner to much higher pressure, causing the liner to collapse into a high speed metal stream. A tradeoff for shaped charge liner materials includes ductility versus density. For example, a ductile copper liner can form a long, high velocity jet without breaking up. However, a depleted uranium liner has higher density, which also enhances penetration. Other liner materials include molybdenum, tantalum, and tungsten. A shaped charge warhead requires fuzing at an optimum short range standoff distance and highly accurate guidance to impact the target. The shaped charge also requires a relatively low angle of attack and a low rotation rate for good effectiveness. Most shaped

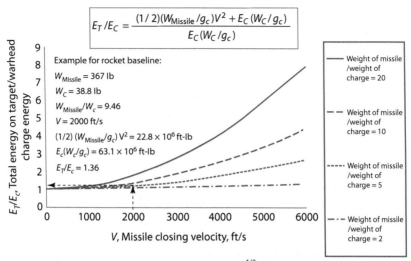

$$E_T/E_C = \frac{(1/2)(W_{Missile}/g_c)V^2 + E_C(W_C/g_c)}{E_C(W_C/g_c)}$$

Example for rocket baseline:

$W_{Missile} = 367$ lb

$W_C = 38.8$ lb

$W_{Missile}/W_C = 9.46$

$V = 2000$ ft/s

$(1/2)(W_{Missile}/g_c)V^2 = 22.8 \times 10^6$ ft-lb

$E_C(W_C/g_c) = 63.1 \times 10^6$ ft-lb

$E_T/E_C = 1.36$

Legend:
— Weight of missile/weight of charge = 20
-- Weight of missile/weight of charge = 10
···· Weight of missile/weight of charge = 5
-·- Weight of missile/weight of charge = 2

x-axis: V, Missile closing velocity, ft/s

y-axis: E_T/E_{C_T} Total energy on target/warhead charge energy

Note: Warhead explosive charge energy based on HMX, $(2 E_c)^{1/2} = 10,230$ ft/s.
1 kg weight at Mach 3 closing velocity has kinetic energy of 391,000 J $\Rightarrow$ equivalent chemical energy of 0.4 lb TNT.

Fig. 6.46 Hypersonic hit-to-kill enhances energy on target.

charge warheads are anti-armor warheads. Hellfire is an example of a missile with a shaped charge warhead. Finally, a kinetic energy warhead has no explosive charge. It defeats the target by the kinetic energy from the missile. A kinetic energy warhead requires hit-to-kill guidance accuracy—it must impact the target to have any effectiveness. Shown in the figure is Starstreak, an endo-atmospheric missile. Although Starstreak has small explosive charges on each its dart interceptors, it relies primarily on the kinetic energy of its darts for kill. Another example of a kinetic energy warhead is the endo-atmospheric hit-to-kill PAC-3. Examples of exo-atmospheric hit-to-kill interceptors are the kill vehicles for THAAD, SM-3, and GBI.

If the total energy E_T of a missile is the sum of the warhead charge energy $E_C(W_C/g_c)$ plus the missile kinetic energy $(1/2)(W_{Missile}/g_c)V^2$, the ratio of the total energy to the warhead charge energy is

$$E_T/E_C = \left[(1/2)\left(W_{Missile}/g_c\right)V^2 + E_C\left(W_C/g_c\right)\right]/\left[E_C\left(W_C/g_c\right)\right]$$

Note from Fig. 6.46 that for a supersonic missile with a missile weight much larger than the warhead charge weight (e.g., $W_{missile}/W_c > 20$), most of the total energy is from the missile kinetic energy. The warhead charge energy in the figure is based on HMX explosive. At a hypersonic closing velocity the missile kinetic energy is sufficiently large so that if the missile impacts the target, a warhead charge may not be required.

As an example, consider a direct hit intercept by the rocket baseline missile. It has a burnout weight of 367 lb and a warhead charge weight of 38.8 lb. The missile weight is 9.46 times the warhead charge weight. At a relatively slow closing velocity of 2000 ft/s (e.g., 1200 ft/s missile velocity + 800 ft/s target velocity), the kinetic energy is

$$(1/2)(367/32.2)(2000)^2 = 22.8 \times 10^6 \text{ ft-lb}$$

The warhead explosive charge energy is based on HMX, with a unit energy $E_C = 52.3 \times 10^6$ ft^2/s^2. For a warhead charge weight $W_C = 38.8$ lb, the warhead charge energy is

$$E_C(W_C/g_c) = 52.3 \times 10^6 (38.8/32.2) = 63.1 \times 10^6 \text{ ft-lb}$$

The ratio of total energy to warhead charge energy is

$$E_T/E_C = (22.8 \times 10^6 + 63.1 \times 10^6)/(63.1 \times 10^6) = 1.36$$

Note that the kinetic energy of the rocket baseline missile adds an additional 36% to the energy of the warhead charge.

As a reference, 1 kg of weight at Mach 3 has a kinetic energy of 391,000 J. This is the equivalent of the chemical energy of 0.4 lb of TNT.

Figure 6.47, based on Ref. 30, illustrates kinetic energy warhead penetration distance through a target. It is based on the equation

$$P/d = [(l/d) - 1](\rho_P/\rho_T)^{1/2} + 3.67(\rho_P/\rho_T)^{2/3}[(\rho_T V^2)/\sigma_T]^{1/3}$$

Assumptions for the equation are an impact velocity $V > 1000$ ft/s, penetrator length-to-diameter $l/d > 2$, and a non-deforming penetrator. The allowable maximum length of a non-deforming penetrator is $l \approx 10d$. The maximum allowable velocity of a non-deforming penetrator is given by

$$V_{\max} = [2(\sigma_P - 2.5\sigma_T)/\rho_T]^{1/2}$$

A non-deforming penetrator has the properties of high hardness, high strength, a relatively sharp nose, and $l/d < 10$. Candidate materials for a non-deforming penetrator include high strength steel and tungsten carbide.

Note from the above equation that kinetic energy penetration is a function of the penetrator length, diameter, density, and velocity, as well as the target density and ultimate stress. Target penetration increases with penetrator length, diameter, density, and velocity. Penetration is also greater against a low density target with a low value of ultimate stress, e.g., it is easier to penetrate the earth over a bunker target than a granite cover over the target.

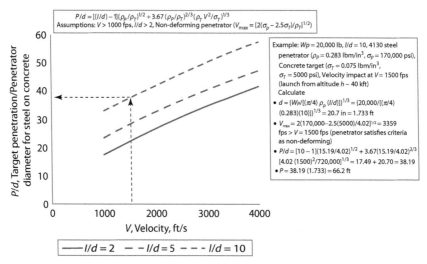

Fig. 6.47 Kinetic energy penetrator weight, density, length, and velocity increase target penetration. (Source: Christman, D. R., et al, "Analysis of High-Velocity Projectile Penetration," *Journal of Applied Physics*, Vol 37, 1966.)

As an example, assume a 20,000 lb 4130 steel penetrator ($\rho_P = 0.283$ lbm/in^3, $\sigma_P = 170{,}000$ psi) against a concrete target ($\rho_T = 0.075$ lbm/in^3, $\sigma_T = 5000$ psi). Assume that the penetrator has a vertical impact velocity $V = 1500$ fps (e.g., launch from an altitude $h \sim 40$k ft with a gravity drop). First, calculate the diameter of the penetrator

$$d \approx \{W_P/[(\pi/4)\rho_P(l/d)]\}^{1/3} = \{20000/[(\pi/4)(0.283)(10)]\}^{1/3}$$
$$= 20.7 \text{ in} = 1.733 \text{ ft}$$

Check the impact velocity against the maximum allowable velocity of a non-deforming projectile

$V_{\max} = \{2[170000 - 2.5(5000)]/4.02\}^{1/2} = 3359$ fps $> V = 1500$ fps (the penetrator satisfies the criteria as non-deforming)

Next, compute the non-dimensional penetration

$$P/d = [10 - 1](15.19/4.02)^{1/2} + 3.67(15.19/4.02)^{2/3}$$
$$\times \left[4.02(1500)^2/720000\right]^{1/3}$$
$$= 17.49 + 20.70 = 38.19$$

Finally, the penetration of the 20,000 lb steel penetration through concrete is

$$P = 38.19(1.733) = 66.2\,\text{ft}$$

This illustrates that even a very heavy, high fineness penetrator at 1500 fps has limited penetration capability through concrete. A deeply buried target under granite ($\sigma_T = 20{,}000$ psi) would be even more difficult to defeat. One approach to improve penetration against a deeply buried target is a successive use of accurately guided high density (e.g., tungsten carbide) boosted penetrators.

Examples of kinetic kill missiles are shown in Fig. 6.48. These missiles have no warhead charge; the kinetic energy of the hypersonic missile provides the kill mechanism. Most kinetic kill missile targets are either ballistic missile targets or armor targets. The high closing velocity of a missile defense interceptor against a ballistic missile target provides sufficient kinetic energy to kill the target in a hit-to-kill intercept. For an anti-armor application, an advantage of a kinetic energy warhead compared to a shaped charge warhead is that it is less susceptible to a reactive armor countermeasure.

In the upper left corner of the figure is a drawing of the US Navy Standard Missile 3 kinetic kill warhead. The SM 3 kinetic kill warhead replaces

Fig. 6.48 Most kinetic-kill missiles are used against ballistic missile and armor vehicle targets.

the warhead and seeker of the Standard Missile 2. It is part of the Navy Theater Wide (NTW) upper-tier, sea based capability for missile defense. The SM-3 kinetic kill warhead includes a third stage kick motor, a strap-down imaging 256×256 two color infrared seeker, guidance, autopilot, and solid propellant reaction jet control.

The upper left center section of the figure is a photograph of the US Army Theater High Altitude Area Defense (THAAD) missile. THAAD is an upper tier, land based missile defense system. Hit-to-kill accuracy is provided by a high resolution imaging infrared seeker and a Divert and Attitude Control System (DACS) that is similar to SM-3. The THAAD liquid propellant DACS has four divert thrusters (up, down, left, right) and eight attitude control thrusters (two for clock-wise roll, two for counter-clockwise roll, pitch up, pitch down, yaw right, and yaw left).

The upper right center photograph is the US Army Patriot Advanced Capability (PAC-3) missile. PAC-3 is a lower tier, endo-atmospheric missile defense system. Hit-to-kill accuracy is provided by a high resolution millimeter wave seeker and impulse reaction jet control.

The upper right photograph is the strategic defense Ground Based Interceptor (GBI). GBI is a silo-launched multi-stage exo-atmospheric long range interceptor that is used against ICBMs. The GBI Exo-atmospheric Kill Vehicle (EKV) is similar to the SM3 and THAAD kill vehicles, with a strap-down imaging infrared focal plane array seeker and reaction jet control.

The bottom left photograph is the US Army hypersonic Line-of-Sight Anti-Tank (LOSAT) missile. LOSAT provides kinetic energy on target that exceeds that of a tank round, without requiring the heavy weight of a tank gun. It is particularly suitable for rapidly deployed, light forces. The LOSAT system can be deployed using a C-130 aircraft, while an M-1 tank cannot be carried on a C-130 aircraft. Hit-to-kill accuracy is provided by following a narrow laser beam to the target. LOSAT guidance and control is laser beam rider guidance with impulse reaction jet flight control.

The bottom right section of the figure is a video of the LOSAT missile. Shown in the video are the light weight transportation vehicle and demonstrations of hit-to-kill firings against tank targets.

The United States is arguably the world leader in kinetic hit-to-kill missile technology.

In addition to designing a warhead for high lethality, we should also consider the problem of collateral damage. Figure 6.49 illustrates considerations to minimize collateral damage. These are a) precision targeting and accurate guidance, b) high reliability, and c) limiting the warhead energy to the target area.

One of the possible contributors to targeting error is human input error. The use of GPS coordinates for the target can enhance the accuracy of

- ◆ Precision targeting and guidance
  - • Accuracy
  - • Optimum impact angle
- ◆ High Reliability
- ◆ Limit warhead energy to target area
  - • Hit-to-kill warhead
    - • Kinetic energy
    - • EFP
    - • Shaped charge
  - • Blast/Frag warhead tailored to minimize collateral damage

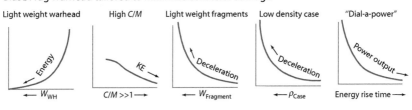

Fig. 6.49 Approaches to minimize collateral damage.

targeting. Missile GPS/INS provides guidance to the target area. The use of an imaging seeker also enhances guidance accuracy. In Chapter 5 we discussed the problem of attacking an urban target with minimum collateral damage. A vertical trajectory may be required to avoid impacting adjacent buildings. Also, an optimum impact angle will focus more of the warhead fragments toward the target, leaving fewer fragments for collateral damage.

The second consideration, high reliability of the warhead, is required to ensure proper detonation of the warhead. Electronic safe, arm, and fuzing is usually more reliable than mechanical.

Finally, approaches to limit the warhead energy to the target area include a hit-to-kill warhead and tailoring a blast/fragmentation warhead to minimize collateral damage.

Hit-to-kill warhead types include kinetic energy, explosively formed penetrator, and shaped charge warheads. These deposit their kinetic energy directly on the target, with little/no collateral damage.

The bottom portion of the figure illustrates approaches to reduce the collateral damage of a blast/fragmentation warhead. Compared to the cold war, today's blast/fragmentation warheads are typically smaller and lighter. One reason is greater emphasis on low collateral damage. An enabling technology that effectively allows a light weight, low collateral damage warhead that also has high lethality is more accurate guidance. Another approach to minimize collateral damage of a blast/fragmentation

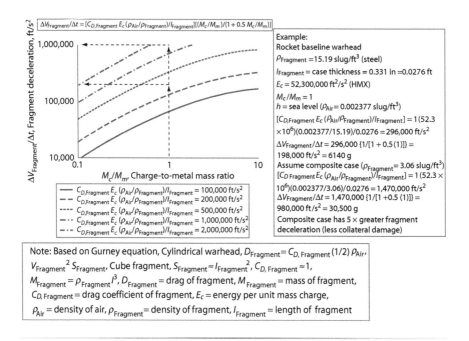

Fig. 6.50 A low density warhead case material has lower fragment collateral damage.

warhead is a high charge-to-metal ratio. There are fewer fragments extend outside the target area. Another approach is light weight fragments, which have a rapid decay in velocity. Powder metal fragments are embedded with the charge and breaking the warhead case into small, light weight fragments allows kinetic energy lethality with less collateral damage. A fourth approach is a low density case material, such as graphite composite. The low density fragments have a rapid velocity decay, confining most of the kinetic energy to the target area. A graphite composite case is also easier to qualify as an insensitive munition. A final approach that allows a multi-purpose blast/fragmentation warhead that can have low collateral damage is "dial-a-power." Based on the initiation, the warhead energy can be released in a small time interval to provide high power with high velocity fragments against a hard target. For a softer target, the energy can be released over a longer time interval, providing lower power with lower velocity fragments that are less hazardous outside the target area.

The benefit of a low density warhead case material to rapidly reduce the velocity of fragments is shown in Fig. 6.50. Assumptions are a cylindrical blast/fragmentation warhead with cube fragments that are accelerated to an initial velocity from the Gurney equation. The fragment deceleration equation is

$$\Delta V_{\text{Fragment}}/\Delta t = D_{\text{Fragment}}/M_{\text{Fragment}}$$

$$= C_{D,\text{Fragment}}(1/2)\rho_{\text{air}}V^2_{\text{Fragment}}S_{\text{Fragment}}/(\rho_{\text{Fragment}}l^3)$$

$$= [C_{D,\text{Fragment}}E_c(\rho_{\text{Air}}/\rho_{\text{Fragment}})/l_{\text{Fragment}}]$$

$$\times [(M_c/M_m)/(1 + 0.5\,M_c/M_m)]$$

Terms in the above equation are $D_{\text{Fragment}} = $ fragment drag $= C_{D,\,\text{Fragment}}(1/2)\rho_{\text{Air}}V^2_{\text{Fragment}}S_{\text{Fragment}}$, $S_{\text{Fragment}} = $ fragment surface area $\approx l^2_{\text{Fragment}}$, $C_{D,\,\text{fragment}} = $ fragment drag coefficient ≈ 1, $M_{\text{Fragment}} = $ fragment mass $= \rho_{\text{Fragment}}l^3$, $E_c = $ energy per unit mass charge, $\rho_{\text{Air}} = $ density of air, $\rho_{\text{Fragment}} = $ density of fragment, $l_{\text{Fragment}} = $ length of fragment, $M_c = $ warhead charge mass, $M_m = $ warhead case "metal" mass, and $V_{\text{Fragment}} = $ fragment initial velocity $= (2E_c)^{1/2}[(M_c/M_m)/(1 + 0.5M_c/M_m)]^{1/2}$.

Note from the figure the high deceleration $\Delta V_{\text{Fragment}}/\Delta t$ for large values of warhead charge to "metal" ratio and the parameter $C_{D,\text{Fragment}}E_c(\rho_{\text{Air}}/\rho_{\text{Fragment}})/l_{\text{Fragment}}$.

The rocket baseline missile warhead will be used to compare a low density warhead case with a high density case. Its warhead has a steel case ($\rho_{\text{Fragment}} = 0.283$ lbm/in^3 = 15.19 slug/ft^3), case thickness = 0.331 in. = 0.0276 ft, a charge-to-metal ratio $M_c/M_m = 1$, and a unit charge energy from its HMX charge $E_c = 52,300,000$ ft^2/s^2.

Compute the cube fragments average mass assuming $l_{\text{Fragment}} = 0.331$ in.

$$M_{\text{Fragment}} = \rho_{\text{Fragment}}l^3_{\text{Fragment}} = 0.283(0.331)^3 = 0.0103\,\text{lbm} = 4.7\text{g}$$

Next, assume fragment drag coefficient $C_{D,\text{Fragment}} = 1$ and warhead detonation at sea level ($\rho_{\text{Air}} = 0.002377$ slug/ft^3). Compute

$$[C_{D,\text{Fragment}}E_c(\rho_{\text{Air}}/\rho_{\text{Fragment}})/l_{\text{Fragment}}] = 1(52.3 \times 10^6)$$

$$\times (0.002377/15.19)/0.0276$$

$$= 296,000\,\text{ft/s}^2$$

The initial deceleration of the steel fragments is

$$\Delta V_{\text{Fragment}}/\Delta t = 296000\{1/[1 + 0.5(1)]\} = 198,000\,\text{ft/s}^2 = 6140\,\text{g}$$

Next, assume a 60% graphite/40% polyimide composite case ($\rho_{\text{fragment}} = 0.057$ lbm/in^3 = 3.06 slug/ft^3), with the other characteristics

US Navy Spike: Warhead weight = 1 lb

APKWS DAGR: Warhead weight = 10 lb

Video: Lockheed Martin DAGR

Fig. 6.51 A light weight warhead + guidance accuracy = lower collateral damage.

and conditions of the baseline warhead. Compute

$$[C_{D,\text{Fragment}}E_c(\rho_{\text{Air}}/\rho_{\text{Fragment}})/l_{\text{Fragment}}] = 1(52.3 \times 10^6)$$
$$\times (0.002377/3.06)/0.0276$$
$$= 1,470,000 \, \text{ft/s}^2$$

The initial deceleration of the composite case fragments is

$$\Delta V_{\text{Fragment}}/\Delta t = 1470000\{1/[1 + 0.5(1)]\} = 980,000 \, \text{ft/s}^2 = 30,500 \, \text{g}$$

Because the composite warhead has 5 × greater fragment deceleration, it should have less collateral damage.

Figure 6.51 shows the benefit of a light weight warhead with guidance accuracy for a limited region of lethality.

The top portion of the figure are flight sequence photographs of the US Navy Spike. Spike is an EO imaging guided 5 lb missile that has a range of about 3 km. The man portable Spike can be shoulder launched, launched from a remotely controlled box launcher, or air launched from a UCAV. The Spike 1 lb warhead was designed for small unarmored targets. Note that the blast is limited to the region near the truck target.

In the middle portion of the figure are flight sequence photographs of the Lockheed Martin Direct Attack Guided Rocket (DAGR), a version of

Advanced Precision Kill Weapon System (APKWS). APKWS is a semi-active laser guided 35 lb missile that has a range of about 6 km. It is based on a guidance kit for the Hydra 70 rocket. APKWS can be launched from combat vehicles, ships, helicopters, UCAVs, and fixed wing aircraft. The APKWs 10 lb warhead was designed to penetrate light armor. Note that the penetration and blast is limited to the region near the van target. The bottom portion of the figure is a video showing the effectiveness of the Lockheed Martin DAGR against a van target.

Missile warhead detonation can be initiated by either a contact fuze or by a proximity fuze. Many missiles have both.

Fuzes may be armed either mechanically or electronically. Both approaches require successfully completing a series of specified electrical and environmental events.

For a mechanical safe and arm (S&A), in a safe condition the detonator is not in-line with the warhead. If the detonator is accidentally initiated in a safe condition, it is designed to direct its energy away from the warhead, to avoid the detonation of the warhead. As an example of mechanical arming, an event, such as launch umbilical disconnect or a rocket motor firing, allows a specified voltage to be applied to the arming device. The arming device requires that the applied voltage be within a specified range to proceed to the next event. For a typical missile, the launch acceleration overcomes a spring force that prevents a mass from contacting and activating a solenoid. After satisfying a correct magnitude and duration of the launch acceleration, the solenoid is activated and the detonator is rotated or moved into the firing position, in-line with the warhead. The time duration of the movement is controlled by clock, to allow sufficient time for the missile to have a safe distance separation from the launch platform.

An electronic S&A has similar requirements as a mechanical S&A, except there is no mechanical movement and the explosives are always in-line. This reduces the parts count and enhances the reliability. Other advantages of electronic S&A include the capability to initiate multiple warheads/rocket motors with the same missile S&A. Similar to mechanical S&A, electronic S&A requires an application of a voltage of a specified level, followed by a series of prescribed environmental events, such as an accelerometer measurement of the correct magnitude and duration of the missile launch acceleration. If these satisfy measurement criteria, after a safe separation time interval the electronic S&A begins storing energy in a firing capacitor. Only after the firing capacitor has been fully charged is there is sufficient energy to detonate the warhead.

A contact fuze is actuated by a sufficiently high deceleration when the missile impacts the target. Contact fuzes are usually inexpensive and reliable.

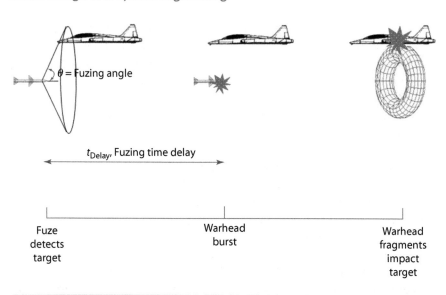

θ = Fuzing angle

t_{Delay}, Fuzing time delay

| Fuze
detects
target | Warhead
burst | Warhead
fragments
impact
target |

Fig. 6.52   Proximity fuze design for a blast/fragmentation warhead requires selecting fuze angle and time delay.

A proximity fuze is designed to initiate the warhead at a point in the flight trajectory that provides maximum effectiveness. Proximity fuzes may be optical, acoustic, pressure, electrostatic, radar, and laser. Most proximity fuzes are radar or laser. Initiating a proximity fuze at the optimum time is complicated. It depends upon the target (velocity, heading, size), the missile flight trajectory (velocity, heading), and the missile warhead (spray angle, fragment velocity). Figure 6.52 illustrates the sequence of events for proximity fuzing of a blast/fragmentation warhead against an air target. In the first event, the fuze detects the target. Usually the fuze beam is swept forward at an angle θ, shown in the left portion of the figure. This allows a time delay between target detection and detonation of the warhead, depending upon the closing velocity of the missile and the target. The fuze beam angle and the time delay may be variable or fixed, depending upon a tradeoff of cost, reliability, and performance. After the fuzing time delay, the warhead is detonated (middle portion of figure). Following warhead detonation, additional time is required for the warhead fragments to reach the target (right portion of figure).

The following is an example of a conceptual design approach to specify proximity fuzing requirements. The rocket baseline missile will be used to illustrate the process.

Our first consideration is the most forward fuzing angle requirement, θ_{min}. This establishes the zero-time delay condition for detonating the warhead. For other, lower closing velocity conditions, a time delay will delay the detonation. The most forward fuzing angle is usually driven by the maximum closing velocity between the missile/target and warhead fragments average velocity. The conceptual design process for specifying θ_{min} is as follows:

1. First, assume an initial value of the threshold (minimum) kill probability $(P_K)_{min}$. For this example we will assume $(P_K)_{min} = 0.5$. After completing the computation of the required θ_{min}, it is good design practice to go back and assume another value of $(P_K)_{min}$, to determine the robustness of θ_{min} to $(P_K)_{min}$.

2. Next, define the target vulnerability that corresponds to $(P_K)_{min}$. We will assume for this example that the missile blast/fragmentation warhead has a $P_K = 0.5$ against a typical fighter aircraft if it provides 130,000 ft-lb/ft^2 kinetic energy density on the target.

3. Next, compute the warhead lethal radius for the selected P_K. From the prior example

$$(r)_{P_K=0.5} = 17.7 \text{ ft}$$

4. Next, define the target velocity, altitude, and the contributors to miss distance. We will assume that target maneuverability and glint noise are the major contributors to miss distance. Assume

$$V_{Target} = 1000 \text{ fps}$$
$$h = 20 \text{ kft}$$
$$n_{Target} = 5 \text{ g}$$
$$W_{Target} = 27 \text{ ft}^2/\text{Hz} \text{ at } B = 2 \text{ Hz}$$

5. Based on the missile maximum velocity, compute the maximum closing velocity of the missile/target. For the rocket baseline missile, $(V_{Missile})_{max} = 2147 \text{ fps}$. Compute

$$(V_{closing})_{max} = 2147 + 1000 = 3147 \text{ fps}$$

6. Compute missile miss distance. Based on the methods later in this chapter

$$\sigma = 13.7 \text{ ft}$$

7. Select $\sigma = \text{Max}\left[(r)_{P_K=min}, \sigma\right]$

$$\sigma = \text{Max}[17.7, 13.7] = 17.7 \text{ ft}$$

8. Compute the average velocity of the warhead fragments. Neglecting drag, from a previous example for the rocket baseline missile warhead

$$V_{\text{Fragments}} = 8353 \text{ fps}$$

The time required for the warhead fragments to travel to the target is

$$t_{\text{Fragments}} = \sigma / V_{\text{Fragments}} = 17.7/8353 = 0.00212 \text{ s}$$

9. Finally, compute the most forward fuze angle $\theta_{\min}$

$$\theta_{\min} = \tan^{-1}\{\sigma/[(V_{\text{Closing}})_{\max} t_{\text{Fragments}}]\}$$
$$= \tan^{-1}[V_{\text{Fragments}}/(V_{\text{Closing}})_{\max}] = \tan^{-1}(8353/3147) = \tan^{-1}2.65$$
$$= 69.4 \text{ deg}$$

Figure 6.53 shows the most forward fuzing angle $\theta_{\min}$ as a function of the maximum closing velocity of the missile/target and the average velocity of the warhead fragments. Note that the most forward fuzing occurs for a high speed closing with low velocity warhead fragments. At the other extreme, a low speed closing with high velocity fragments requires much less forward fuzing ($\theta \approx 90$ deg). A tradeoff in proximity fuze design is a fixed versus a variable fuze angle. A fixed angle is less expensive and more reliable while a variable angle provides higher lethality. If there is a relatively small variation in closing velocity requirements for the missile,

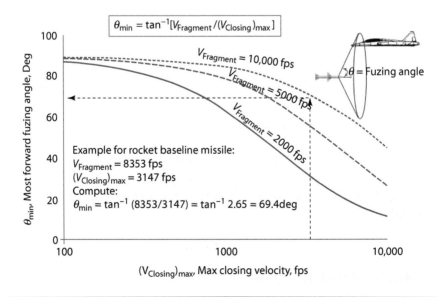

Fig. 6.53 Proximity fuzing minimum angle is driven by maximum closing velocity and the warhead fragments velocity.

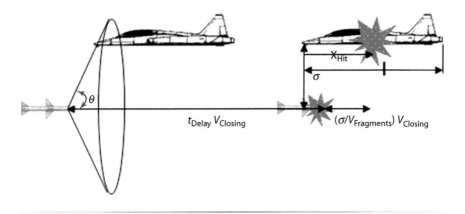

Fig. 6.54a Proximity fuzing time delay is driven by fuzing angle, miss distance, closing velocity, and the target length.

then a fixed fuzing angle is sufficient. However a high speed missile with a wide range in closing velocity (e.g., low supersonic to hypersonic) requires a variable fuzing angle for good lethality.

Conceptual design selection of the time delay for proximity fuzing may be simple or difficult, depending upon the missile mission requirements and the target performance. For a subsonic guided bomb with a wide spray warhead, it is usually possible to have a fixed time delay. However, for an air intercept target there are a number of proximity fuzing parameter tradeoffs, including the warhead spray angle, the fuzing angle, the missile miss distance, the closing velocity of the missile with the target, and the target length.

Figure 6.54 illustrates a conceptual design approach for predicting the fuzing time delay. Figure 6.54a illustrates the geometry of an air intercept of an aircraft target. Based on the intercept geometry, the warhead fragments hit location on the target and the fuzing time delay are respectively

$$x_{\text{Hit}} = V_{\text{Closing}}t_{\text{Delay}} - (\sigma/\tan\theta)[1 - \tan\theta(V_{\text{Closing}}/V_{\text{Fragments}})]$$
$$t_{\text{Delay}} = [\sigma/(V_{\text{Closing}}\tan\theta)][1 - \tan\theta(V_{\text{Closing}}/V_{\text{Fragments}})] + x_{\text{Hit}}/V_{\text{Closing}}$$

An example calculation will be made of conceptual design selection of the fuzing time delay, based on data from the prior example

$\theta = \theta_{\text{min}} = 69.4\,\text{deg}$

$V_{\text{Missile}} = 2147\,\text{fps}$

$V_{\text{Target}} = 1000\,\text{fps}$

$V_{\text{Closing}} = 3147\,\text{fps}$

$(P_K)_{\text{min}} = 0.5$

$(r)_{PK=0.5} = 17.7\,\text{ft}$

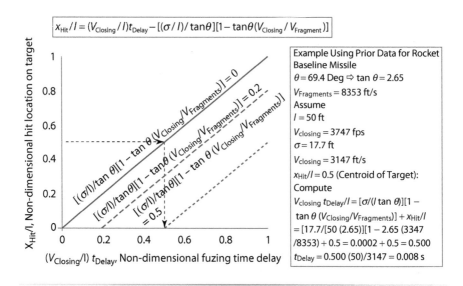

Fig. 6.54b Proximity fuzing time delay is driven by fuzing angle, miss distance, closing velocity, and the target length.

$$\sigma = 17.7 \text{ ft}$$

$$V_{\text{Fragments}} = 8353 \text{ fps}$$

We will assume the desired impact from the warhead fragments is the target centroid, located at 50% of the target length. We will also assume a target length $l = 50$ ft, a typical length of a fighter aircraft.

Compute

$$t_{\text{Delay}} = \left[\sigma/\left(V_{\text{Closing}} \tan \theta\right)\right]\left[1 - \tan \theta\left(V_{\text{Closing}}/V_{\text{Fragments}}\right)\right] + x_{\text{Hit}}/V_{\text{Closing}}$$
$$= [17.7/(3147 \tan 69.4 \text{ deg})][1 - \tan 69.4 \text{ deg}(3147/8353)]$$
$$+ 25/3147 = 0 + 0.0079 = 0.0079 \text{ s} = 8 \text{ ms}$$

Figure 6.54b shows the non-dimensional hit location on the target x_{Hit}/l versus the non-dimensional fuzing time delay $V_{\text{Closing}}t_{\text{Delay}}/l$. Note from the figure that increasing the time delay results in a more aft location of the warhead fragments impact on the target. A desired impact location, e.g., centroid or 50% of the length of the target, can be achieved by an appropriate value of the time delay. Also note that increasing the non-dimensional parameter $[\sigma/(l \tan \theta)][1 - \tan \theta(V_{\text{Closing}}/V_{\text{Fragments}})]$ provides a more forward location of the warhead fragments impact on the target. For the same fuzing time delay, increasing the closing velocity results in a more aft location of the warhead fragments on the target. It is especially difficult to accurately fuze the warhead against a small hypervelocity target, such as a ballistic missile reentry vehicle.

Next, we will calculate the fuzing time dealy for a tail chase of the same target. Assume $V_{Missile} = 2147$ fps and $V_{Target} = 1000$ fps. The closing velocity is

$$V_{Closing} = V_{Missile} - V_{Target} = 2147 - 1000 = 1147 \text{ fps}$$

Compute

$$t_{Delay} = [17.7/(1147 \tan 69.4 \text{ deg})][1 - \tan 69.4 \text{ deg} (1147/8353)]$$
$$+ 25/1147 = 0.0037 + 0.0218 = 0.0255 \text{ s} = 25 \text{ ms}$$

The fuzing time delay that is required for the rocket baseline missile cylindrical warhead fragments to impact the centroid of the target varies 8 ms to 25 ms, depending upon the closing velocity. Because of the large variation in the optimum time delay, a fixed time delay is not practical for the air target intercept missile. Active fuzing sensors (radar, LADAR) provide the capability to measure the air target range, length, and closing velocity as an input to computing the fuzing time delay.

6.4 Miss Distance

The third measure of merit of this chapter is miss distance. Miss distance is important in the missile design configuration development because it impacts the required flight performance and the required volume/weight for an appropriately matched warhead with high lethality.

The definition of how miss distance relates to circular error probable (CEP) is shown in Fig. 6.55 from Ref. 31. The CEP is the radius of a circle within which 50% of the flight trajectories with the closest distance

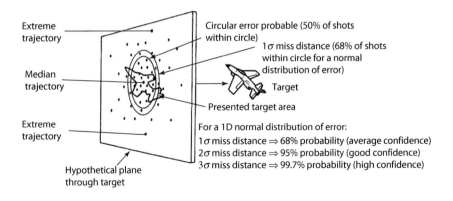

Fig. 6.55 CEP is approximately equal to the 1 σ miss distance. (Source: Heaston, R.J. and Smoots, C.W., "Introduction to Precision Guided Munitions," GACIAC HB-83-01, May 1983.)

to the target (e.g., miss distance) are expected to occur. If the miss distance is a one-dimensional normal distribution (a common assumption for conceptual design), then the probability that the miss distance is less than the $1\,\sigma$ value of the normal distribution is 68%. A common assumption for conceptual design, consistent with typical design accuracy, is to use the terminology of CEP and $1\,\sigma$ miss distance interchangeably. The probabilities that the miss distance is less than 2 and $3\,\sigma$ are 95 and 99.7% respectively. A typical approach to blast fragmentation warhead conceptual design is to set the warhead lethal radius greater than the estimate of the guidance miss distance, to provide a design margin for miss distance uncertainty.

Compared to unguided weapons, guided weapons are relatively new weapons that were first introduced in the 20th century. The first inertially guided weapon was the Kettering Bug, a 600 lb inertially guided cruise missile with a 300 lb warhead, that was introduced near the end of World War I. Technical challenges delayed seeker guided weapon development compared to that of inertially guided weapons. The first seeker guided weapons were not introduced until after World War II. After the successful application of SAL guided bombs in 1968 in Vietnam, the interest and funding in seeker guided weapons was accelerated. In recent years guided weapons have replaced unguided weapons for most beyond visual range, standoff missions. For within visual range surface target missions, cost is a driver and a tradeoff is the mix of guided versus unguided weapons. For most air target missions, guided weapons have replaced unguided weapons.

Type of guidance	Max range for 3 m accuracy against fixed target	Max range for 3 m accuracy against moving target	Unit cost	Countermeasure susceptibility	Reliability and maintainability
GPS/INS/Data link/Seeker guided	~ No limit ●	~ No limit ●	—	○	○
GPS/INS/Data link guided	~ No limit ●	Target speed ○	○	◔	◔
INS Guided	R ~ 5km ○	Target speed —	— ◔	●	◔
Unguided projectile Unguided bomb Unguided rocket	R ~ 600m R ~ 300 m — R ~150 m	Target speed —	●	●	●
● Superior	◔ Good	○ Average	— Poor		

Fig. 6.56 Guided weapons have advantages of accuracy and P_K—Unguided weapons have advantages of low unit cost, countermeasures resistance, and reliability and maintainability.

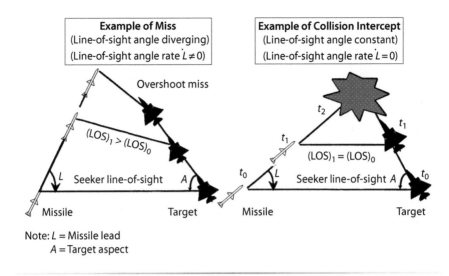

Fig. 6.57 An efficient intercept has a constant bearing for a constant velocity, non-maneuvering target.

The advantages and disadvantages of guided weapons versus unguided weapons are illustrated in Fig. 6.56. Primary advantages of guided weapons are accuracy and the smaller number that are required for a target kill. Unguided weapons have advantages of lower unit cost, they are less susceptible to countermeasures, and they are more reliable.

Guided weapons are especially useful in the early portion of a war. One mission is to remove the threat command, control, and communication (C^3) and other high value, highly defended targets. Later in the war, after the threat has been degraded, unguided weapons are more likely to be used. Because unguided weapons are lower unit cost, there is a higher inventory of unguided bombs, free flight rockets, and unguided projectiles.

In Fig. 6.57 a guided missile that has an overshooting miss trajectory is compared with a collision intercept trajectory. An assumption is a constant velocity, non-maneuvering target. An efficient flight trajectory can be followed in terminal guidance by directing the missile to an efficient lead of the target. A constant line-of-sight trajectory, or constant-looking course, can be provided by a guidance law known as proportional guidance. In the left section of the figure, the line-of-sight angle between the missile and the target is increasing, resulting in an overshoot miss. In the right section of the figure, the line-of-sight angle between the missile and the target is constant, resulting in a collision intercept. Proportional guidance homing adjusts the time rate-of-change in the missile velocity heading $\dot{\gamma}$, proportional to the time rate of change in the seeker line-of-sight angle $\dot{L}$. The objective is to make $\dot{L} \sim 0$, which results in $\dot{\gamma} \sim 0$. This usually

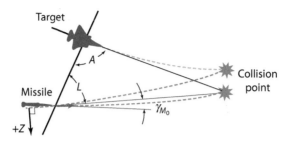

Proportional guidance: Step maneuver target

$$\tau \frac{d^2 Z}{dt^2} + \frac{dZ}{dt} + N' \frac{Z}{t_0 - t} = \frac{-N'}{t_0 - t} \frac{\cos A}{\cos L} \frac{1}{2} a_T t^2$$

Proportional guidance: Initial heading error

$$\tau \frac{d^2 Z}{dt^2} + \frac{dZ}{dt} + N' \frac{Z}{t_0 - t} = -V_M \gamma_{M_0}$$

Note: $t_0 - t = 0$ at intercept, causing discontinuity in above equations.
N' = Effective navigation ratio = $N [V_M \cos L/(V_M \cos L + V_T \cos A)]$
N = Navigation ratio = $(d\gamma/dt)/(dL/dt)$
τ = Missile time constant, V_M = Velocity of missile, γ_{M_0} = Initial flight path angle error of missile, t_0 = Total time of flight, a_T = Acceleration of target, V_T = Velocity of target

Fig. 6.58 A maneuvering target and an initial heading error cause miss distance. (Source: Jerger, J.J., *Systems Preliminary Design Principles of Guided Missile Design*, D. Van Nostrand Company, Inc., Princeton, New Jersey, 1960.)

provides a small miss distance. For most missiles, the proportional guidance gain is selected such that $\dot\gamma$ is about three-to-five times $\dot L$.

The proportional homing guidance trajectory equation for the missile flight path against a step maneuvering target and the trajectory equation for the missile flight path from an initial heading error are shown in Fig. 6.58 from Jerger [5]. A target step maneuver or an initial heading error will result in a missile flight path deviation from a collision course. Note that the equation of motion of the missile flight trajectory against the step maneuvering target and also the equation of motion for an initial heading error have a discontinuity of the term $(t_0 - t)$ in their denominators. For a flight trajectory attempting to follow proportional guidance, as the time t approaches the total time of flight t_0, the missile deviates from proportional guidance, resulting in a miss distance.

The navigation ratio N relates the flight path angle rate $d\gamma/dt$ to the line of sight rate dL/dt. The equation for the navigation ratio is

$$N = (d\gamma/dt)/(dL/dt)$$

The equation for the effective navigation ratio is

$$N' = N[V_M \cos L / (V_M + V_T \cos A)]$$

The effective navigation ratio N' also accounts for the influence of the missile velocity V_M, target velocity V_T, and target aspect A. The use of N' instead of N as feedback in the missile guidance system usually reduces the miss distance.

For conceptual design, the miss distance should be evaluated for a constant (step) maneuvering target and also for an initial heading error at seeker lock-on. It may be necessary to also evaluate the miss distance from other target dynamic maneuvers such as sinusoidal maneuvers and corkscrew maneuvers. The miss distance in conceptual design is usually based upon using proportional guidance. Augmented proportional guidance and modern guidance laws can theoretically provide smaller miss, particularly if the missile has an active, low noise seeker that can accurately provide additional information such as the target range, target range rate, and the target maneuver acceleration. These are usually investigated in the follow-on preliminary design activity.

Figure 6.59 from Jerger [5] shows the effect of target aspect A on the proportional guidance effective navigation ratio N'. Note that $N' = (N \, V_M \cos L)/V_C$ is less than N for a head-on ($A = 0$ deg) intercept. Also note that $N' > N$ for a tail intercept ($A = 180$ deg). Another driver of the value of N' is the closing velocity V_C. The variation in N' with V_C is especially large for a tail chase intercept. Note from the figure the divergent gain for $(V_M \cos L)/V_T = 1$, which reflects a non-solution for a closing velocity $V_C = 0$.

As an example calculation, assume a typical air intercept target with the flight conditions

$$V_M = 2000 \, \text{ft/s}$$
$$V_T = 1000 \, \text{ft/s}$$

Head-on intercept ($L = A = 0$ deg)
    Calculate

$$V_C = 2000(1) + 1000(1) = 3000 \, \text{ft/s}$$
$$N'/N = (V_M \cos L)/V_C = 2000(1)/3000 = 0.67$$

Next, assume a tail-chase intercept ($L = 0$ deg, $A = 180$ deg)
    Calculate

$$V_C = 2000(1) + 1000(-1) = 1000 \, \text{ft/s}$$
$$N'/N = 2000(1)/1000 = 2$$

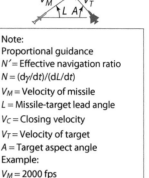

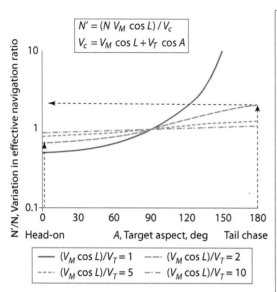

$N' = (N \, V_M \, \cos L)/V_c$

$V_c = V_M \, \cos L + V_T \, \cos A$

Note:
Proportional guidance
N' = Effective navigation ratio
$N = (dy/dt)/(dL/dt)$
V_M = Velocity of missile
L = Missile-target lead angle
V_c = Closing velocity
V_T = Velocity of target
A = Target aspect angle
Example:
$V_M = 2000$ fps
$V_T = 1000$ fps
Head-on: $L = A = 0$ deg
$(V_M \cos L)/V_T = 2000(1)/1000 = 2$
$V_c = 2000(1) + 1000(1) = 3000$ fps
$N'/N = 2000(1)/3000 = 0.67$
Tail-chase: $L = 0$ deg, $A = 180$ deg
$(V_M \cos L)/V_T = 2000(1)/1000 = 2$
$V_c = 2000(1) + 1000(-1) = 1000$ fps
$N'/N = 2000(1)/1000 = 2$

Fig. 6.59 A head-on engagement using proportional guidance has a lower effective navigation ratio. (Source: Jerger, J.J., *Systems Preliminary Design Principles of Guided Missile Design*, D. Van Nostrand Company, Inc., Princeton, New Jersey, 1960.)

In a proportional guidance trajectory, the target lead changes rapidly at the beginning of the trajectory before approaching a nearly constant bearing ($L \approx L_{CB}$ = constant) at the end of the trajectory. The sketches in the top right section of Fig. 6.60 illustrate this convergence. Based on Jerger [5], the equations for the target lead angle for an initial heading error are

$$\Delta L_{CB}/\gamma_{M_0} = -(N'-1)^{-1}\left\{-1 + N'\left[1 - (t/t_0)^{N'-1}\right]\right\}$$

$$L = \Delta L_{CB} + L_{CB},$$

$$L_{CB} = \sin^{-1}[(\sin A)/(V_M/V_T)]$$

Assumptions for the above equations are

V_M = constant

V_T = constant

$$n_T = 0$$

$$\tau = 0$$

$$\gamma_{M_0} \approx \sin \gamma_{M_0}$$

Definitions are ΔL_{CB} = deviation from constant bearing trajectory, γ_{M_0} = missile initial heading error, t = time, t_0 = total time of flight, N' = effective navigation ratio = $N [V_M \cos L/(V_M + V_T \cos A)]$, L_{CB} = missile-target lead angle for a constant bearing flight trajectory, V_M = missile velocity, V_T = target velocity, and A = target aspect angle.

Note from the figure that the error in the constant bearing lead angle ΔL_{CB} at time $t = 0$ (launch) is

$$\Delta L_{CB} = -\gamma_{M_0}$$

At intercept ($t = t_0$), ΔL_{CB} is

$$\Delta L_{CB} = \gamma_{M_0}/(N' - 1)$$

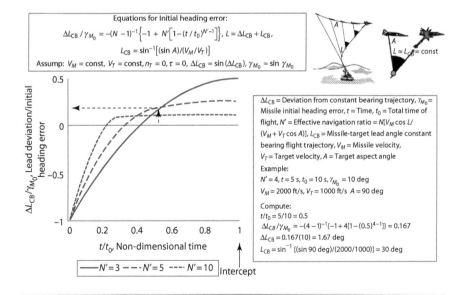

Fig. 6.60 A proportional guidance trajectory with a high value of navigation ratio quickly approaches a constant bearing trajectory. (Source: Jerger, J. J., *Systems Preliminary Design Principles of Guided Missile Design*, D. Van Nostrand Company, Inc., Princeton, New Jersey, 1960.)

Implementation	Robustness	Required sensors/ target data	Accuracy against off-boresight target	Accuracy against maneuvering target
$N = (d\gamma/dt)/(dL/dt)$	●	●	—	—
$N' = N\,[V_M \cos L / (V_M \cos L + V_T \cos A)]$	○	○	◗	○
"Optimal" Guidance (includes measurement of target acceleration)	—	—	◗	◗

● Superior   ◗ Good   ○ Average   — Poor

Fig. 6.61   Missile homing guidance law tradeoffs: robustness, required sensors and target data, and accuracy.

As an example calculation, assume

$N' = 4$

$t = 5\,\text{s}$

$t_0 = 10\,\text{s}$

$\gamma_{M_0} = 10\,\text{deg}$

$V_M = 2000\,\text{ft/s}$

$V_T = 1000\,\text{ft/s}$

$A = 90\,\text{deg}$

Compute:

$$t/t_0 = 5/10 = 0.5$$

$$\Delta L_{CB}/\gamma_{M_0} = -(4-1)^{-1}\{-1 + 4[1-(0.5)^{4-1}]\} = 0.167$$
$$\Delta L_{CB} = 0.167(10) = 1.67\,\text{deg}$$

$$L_{CB} = \sin^{-1}[(\sin 90\,\text{deg})/(2000/1000)] = 30\,\text{deg}$$

At 50% of the flight time the target lead $L = 31.67$ deg, which is 6% greater than a constant bearing trajectory ($L_{CB} = 30$ deg).

Figure 6.61 compares tradeoffs in selecting the type of homing guidance law. Tradeoffs include robustness, the required number of target sensors and the required amount of target data, the accuracy against an off-boresight target, and the accuracy against a maneuvering target. The simplest guidance law is a commanded flight path angle rate $d\gamma/dt$ that is proportional to the line-of-sight rate dL/dt. The gain N is

$$N = (d\gamma/dt)/(dL/dt)$$

One advantage of this simple guidance law is its robustness to noise and countermeasures. Also, the only required measurement is the seeker gimbal angle $\dot{L}$ tracking the target, which can be provided by a passive sensor such as an IR sensor.

A next level of complexity is to modify the simple guidance gain N to an effective gain N' that also includes the effects of missile velocity V_M, target velocity V_T, and target aspect A. The equation for the effective navigation ratio is

$$N' = N[V_M \cos L/(V_M \cos L + V_T \cos A)]$$

A disadvantage of N' is that it is more susceptible to noise and counter-measures than simple proportional guidance. It also requires either more on-board sensors or launch platform input data to the missile guidance law. V_M can be measured by a missile GPS/INS. V_T and A can be measured by an active radar or LADAR seeker or they may be an input from the launch platform fire control system. A big advantage is better accuracy against off-boresight and maneuvering targets.

"Optimal" guidance is theoretically the most accurate guidance law. It includes more sophisticated estimates of the target. An example is precognitive lead based on estimating the target maneuvering acceleration. Although it has been frequently investigated, its application to endo-atmospheric missiles has lagged its promise. Problems include high sensitivity to noise (e.g., it is difficult to accurately measure target acceleration), sensitivity to countermeasures (e.g., the target may not cooperate by continuing to maneuver in a predictable fashion), and latency (e.g., Kalman filtering increases the missile time constant).

Figure 6.62 shows the definition of the missile flight dynamics time constant that is used in this text. A single time constant τ represents the contributions from the flight control effectiveness τ_δ, flight control system actuator rate limit $\tau_{\dot{\delta}}$, and the filter for the seeker dome error slope $\tau_{\text{Dome filter}}$. Other contributors to the time constant from guidance and control filters $\tau_{\text{G\&C Filter}}$, other guidance and control contributors (gyro dynamics, accelerometer dynamics, digital processor latency, etc), and seeker errors (resolution, latency, blind range, tracking dynamics because of actuator bandwidth and rate limits, noise, glint, amplitude) are not usually evaluated in conceptual design, because they usually have less impact on the missile configuration design and there is usually insufficient information to adequately include them in the early evaluation. A

◆ Conceptual design typically uses a single time constant τ for entire missle (optimistic)
◆ τ is a measure of missile agility to respond to target condition changes
◆ τ equals elapsed time from input command maneuver until missile has completed 63% or $(1 - e^{-1})$ of the commanded maneuver ($t = \tau$)
◆ τ also called "rise time"
◆ Contributions to agility time constant τ
  - Flight control effectiveness (τ_δ)
  - Flight control actuator rate ($\tau_{\dot\delta}$)
  - Filter for seeker dome error slope ($\tau_{\text{Dome filter}}$)
  - Other guidance and control filters ($\tau_{\text{G\&C filter}}$)
  - Other G&C dynamics (gyro dynamics, accelerometer, processor latency, etc)
  - Seeker errors (resolution, latency, blind range, tracking, noise, glint, amplitude)
◆ Conceptual design approach to estimate τ

  • $\tau = \tau_\delta = \tau_{\dot\delta} + \tau_{\text{Dome filter}}$
  Note: Reaction jet divert thruster τ
  smaller than aero control τ

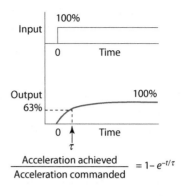

$$\frac{\text{Acceleration achieved}}{\text{Acceleration commanded}} = 1 - e^{-t/\tau}$$

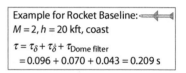

Example for Rocket Baseline:
$M = 2$, $h = 20$ kft, coast
$\tau = \tau_\delta + \tau_{\dot\delta} + \tau_{\text{Dome filter}}$
$= 0.096 + 0.070 + 0.043 = 0.209$ s

Fig. 6.62   Missile time constant is an indication of agility.

disadvantage of a single time constant to represent the complex dynamics of the multiple time constants of components/subsystems is that it leads to an optimistic estimate of miss distance.

Missile time constant is an aggregate measure of the agility of the missile to respond to target condition changes. It is usually represented in conceptual design as the elapsed time from receiving an input commanded maneuver for a required target correction until the missile has completed an exponential convergence to 63% or $(1 - e^{-1})$ of the required corrective maneuver. Missile time constant is also called "rise time." For this text it is assumed that the missile time constant is the sum of the following contributors to missile agility

$$\tau = \tau_\delta + \tau_{\dot\delta} + \tau_{\text{Dome filter}}$$

As an example, the rocket baseline missile coasting at Mach 2 and 20,000 ft altitude has an aggregate time constant

$$\tau = \tau_\delta + \tau_{\dot\delta} + \tau_{\text{Dome filter}} = 0.096 + 0.070 + 0.043 = 0.209 \text{ s}$$

To illustrate, for a rotational command for 10 degree angle of attack, the rocket baseline missile requires a time $t = \tau = 0.209$ s to achieve 63% (or 6.3 deg) of the command $[10(1 - e^{-1}) = 6.3]$. At a time $t = 4\tau = 0.836$ s, the missile achieves 98% (or 9.8 deg) of the command $[10(1 - e^{-4}) = 9.8]$. Similarly, for a 10-g command, the rocket baseline missile requires a time

$t = \tau = 0.209$ s to achieve 6.3 g of the command. At a time $t = 4\tau = 0.836$ s, the missile achieves 9.8 g of the 10 g command.

A missile with divert thrusters, which are located at the missile center-of-gravity, would have a smaller time constant for maneuvering than that of a missile using aerodynamic flight control. Divert thrusters provide normal and lateral acceleration directly, without requiring missile rotation. The time constant for the divert thrust rise time is very small, typically of the order of 10 ms. For example, for a divert acceleration command of 10 g with a divert time constant of 0.01 s, the missile would require a time $t = \tau = 0.01$ s to achieve 63% (or 6.3 g) of the command. At a time $t = 4\tau = 0.04$ s, the missile achieves 98% (or 9.8 g) of the command.

The primary drivers for missile time constant are usually the flight control effectiveness and the static margin. The effect of a limited pitching moment capability on aerodynamic flight control effectiveness is illustrated in Fig. 6.63. To determine this contribution to the missile time constant, we will assume that the flight control is deflection limited, operating in a race-break (bang-bang) deflection profile (see figure) to achieve a commanded angle of attack. This is representative of canard and tail control, which require missile body rotation to an angle of attack to provide the required maneuver acceleration. This approach provides a conservative result for wing control missiles, which use a divert maneuver with no/small body rotation. The assumption of a bang-bang control surface deflection is valid if the flight control actuator time that is required to reach maximum deflection is small compared to the time duration at the

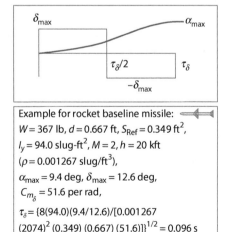

- ◆ Assumptions for τ_δ
  - Aero control
  - "Bang-bang" flight control
  - Fast actuator $(\delta_{max}/\dot{\delta} < \tau_\delta/2)$
  - Near neutral stability $(\alpha/\delta \gg 1)$
- ◆ Equation of motion is
  - $\ddot{\alpha} = [\rho\, V^2 S\, d\, C_{m_\delta}/(2\, l_y)]\, \delta_{max}$
- ◆ Intergrate to solve for α_{max}
  - $\alpha_{max} = [\rho\, V^2 S\, d\, C_{m_\delta}/(8\, l_y)]\, \delta_{max}\, \tau_\delta^2$
- ◆ τ_δ is given by
  - $\tau_\delta = [8\, l_y\, (\alpha_{max}/\delta_{max}/(\rho\, V^2 S_{Ref}\, d\, C_{m_\delta})]^{1/2}$
- ◆ Contributors to small τ_δ
  - Low fineness (small $l_y/(S_{Ref}\, d)$)
  - High dynamic pressure (low altitude/ high speed)
  - Large C_{m_δ}

Example for rocket baseline missile:
$W = 367$ lb, $d = 0.667$ ft, $S_{Ref} = 0.349$ ft^2,
$l_y = 94.0$ slug-ft^2, $M = 2$, $h = 20$ kft
$(\rho = 0.001267$ slug/ft$^3)$,
$\alpha_{max} = 9.4$ deg, $\delta_{max} = 12.6$ deg,
$C_{m_\delta} = 51.6$ per rad,

$\tau_\delta = \{8(94.0)(9.4/12.6)/[0.001267$
$(2074)^2\, (0.349)\, (0.667)\, (51.6)]\}^{1/2} = 0.096$ s

Fig. 6.63 Missile time constant contributor τ_δ is driven by flight control effectiveness.

maximum control surface deflection ($\delta_{\text{Max}}/\dot{\delta} < \tau_\delta/2$) and the missile has near-neutral static stability ($\alpha/\delta \gg 1$). The 1-DOF equation of motion is

$$\ddot{\alpha} = \left[\rho V^2 S d C_{m_\delta}/(2I_y)\right]\delta_{\text{max}}$$

Integrating the above equation to solve for α_{Max} gives

$$\alpha_{\text{max}} = \left[\rho V^2 S d C_{m_\delta}/(8I_y)\right]\delta_{\text{max}}\tau_\delta^2$$

τ_δ is given by

$$\tau_\delta = [8I_y(\alpha_{\text{max}}/\delta_{\text{max}})/(\rho V^2 S_{\text{Ref}} d C_{m_\delta})]^{1/2}$$

Inspecting the above equation, we can see that the contributors to a small value of τ_δ are low fineness [small value of $I_y/(S_{\text{Ref}}\,d)$], high dynamic pressure (low altitude/high speed flight), and a large pitching moment control effectiveness C_{m_δ}.

As an example of the τ_δ from limited pitching moment control effectiveness, the rocket baseline missile has a burnout weight $W = 367$ lb, diameter $d = 8$ in (0.667 ft), reference area $S_{\text{Ref}} = 0.349$ ft^2, and a burnout pitch moment-of-inertia $I_y = 94.0$ slug-ft^2. At an intercept Mach number and altitude of $M = 2$ and $h = 20{,}000$ ft respectively, the Chapter 7 maximum allowable angle of attack $\alpha_{\text{max}} = 9.4$ deg, maximum control deflection $\delta_{\text{max}} = 12.6$ deg, and the pitching moment control effectiveness derivative $C_{m_\delta} = 51.6$ per rad. Note that the assumption of near-neutral stability ($\alpha/\delta \gg 1$) is not valid. Because the rocket baseline missile has excess static stability, it is anticipated that the actual time constant would be larger. The time constant from limited pitching moment control effectiveness is computed to be

$$\tau_\delta = \left\{8(94.0)(9.4/12.6)/[0.001267(2074)^2(0.349)(0.667)(51.6)]\right\}^{1/2}$$
$$= 0.096\,\text{s}.$$

The next contributor to the missile time constant is $\tau_{\dot{\delta}}$, which represents the flight control system dynamics. $\tau_{\dot{\delta}}$ is usually driven by the actuator response, which is usually the slowest component of the flight control system. Actuator rate dynamics (e.g., $\tau_{\dot{\delta}}$ from the actuator rate limit) are illustrated in Fig. 6.64. Assume that the flight control is rate limited ($\dot{\delta} = \dot{\delta}_{\text{max}}$) and that the missile has near-neutral stability. The 1-DOF equation of motion for a race-break flight control deflection $\delta = \pm\delta_{\text{Max}}$ is

$$\ddot{\alpha} = \left[\rho V^2 S d C_{m_\delta}/(2I_y)\right]\dot{\delta}_{\text{max}}$$

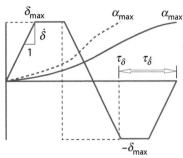

- Assumption for $\tau_{\dot{\delta}}$
  - Aero control
  - "Bang-bang" flight control
  - Fast actuator $(\delta_{max}/\dot{\delta} < \tau_{\delta}/2)$
    Near neutral stability $(\alpha/\delta \gg 1)$
- Equation of motion for $\dot{\delta} = +/- \dot{\delta}_{max}$
  - $\ddot{\alpha} = [\rho V^2 S d C_{m_\delta}/(2 I_y)]\dot{\delta}_{max}$
- Equation of motion for "perfect" response
  $\dot{\delta} = \infty, \delta = \delta_{max}$
  - $\ddot{\alpha} = [\rho V^2 S d C_{m_\delta}/(2 I_y)]\delta_{max}$
- $\tau_{\dot{\delta}}$ is difference between actual response to α_{max} and "perfect" (τ_δ) response
- Then
  - $\tau_{\dot{\delta}} = 2\delta_{max}/\dot{\delta}_{max}$

Example for rocket baseline missile

- $\dot{\delta}_{max} = 360 \deg/s, \delta_{max} = 12.6 \deg$
- $\tau_{\dot{\delta}} = 2(12.6/360) = 0.070 s$

—— Response for flight control rate limit
----- Response for no flight control rate limit

Fig. 6.64 Missile time constant contributor $\tau_{\dot{\delta}}$ for the flight control system is usually driven by the actuator.

As a comparison, the equation of motion from a "perfect" response $\dot{\delta} = \infty, \delta = +/- \delta_{max}$ is

$$\ddot{\alpha} = [\rho V^2 S d C_{m_\delta}/(2 I_y)]\delta_{max}$$

$\tau_{\dot{\delta}}$ is the difference between the actual response to α_{Max} and the "perfect" τ_δ response to α_{max}. Then

$$\tau_\delta = 2\delta_{max}/\dot{\delta}_{max}$$

As an example for the rocket baseline missile, the maximum wing control surface deflection rate $\dot{\delta}_{max} = 360$ deg/s and the maximum wing control surface deflection $\delta_{max} = 12.6$ deg for flight condition of Mach 2, $h = 20$ kft. Checking the criteria $\delta_{max}/\dot{\delta} < \tau_\delta/2$

$$\delta_{max}/\dot{\delta} = 12.6/360 = 0.035 s < \tau_\delta/2 = 0.096/2$$
$$= 0.048 s \text{ (satisfies criteria)}$$

The maximum wing control surface deflection occurs at wing stall, which has a maximum local angle of attack $\alpha' = \alpha + \delta = 22$ deg. For a nominal static margin of $\alpha/\delta = 0.75$, $\alpha = 9.4$ deg and $\delta = 12.6$ deg. The time constant from pitching moment control rate dynamics is computed to be

$$\tau_{\dot{\delta}} = 2(12.6/360) = 0.070 s$$

A third source of miss distance is from the radome error slope R. When the missile rotates there is a relative motion of the radome with respect to the seeker antenna look angle δ_{Seeker}, causing a look angle error ε. This appears to the seeker as an apparent change in the target line of sight. The radome error slope R is given by the equation $R = \Delta\varepsilon/\Delta\delta_{seeker}$. Radome error slope error may be destabilizing, depending upon its sign. A filter is usually required to avoid destabilization in the guidance system.

The conceptual design process for estimating the required filter time constant to avoid guidance destabilization from radome error slope is illustrated in Fig. 6.65. The magnitude of the seeker radome error slope for a typical high fineness curved dome (e.g., tangent ogive dome) is

$$|R| = |\Delta\varepsilon/\Delta\delta_{Seeker}| = 0.05(l_N/d - 0.5)[1 + 15(\Delta f/f)]/(d/\lambda)$$

The required stability in the guidance and control system feedback loop is given by Routh's Criteria. Assume conservatively that the required radome filter time constant $\tau_{Dome\ filter}$ for stability in the guidance and control system feedback loop is

$$\tau_{Dome\ filter} = N'(V_C/V_M)|R|(\alpha/\dot{\gamma})$$

The angle of attack sensitivity to turn rate is

$$\alpha/\dot{\gamma} = \alpha(W/g_c)V_M/\{qS_{Ref}[C_{N_\alpha} + C_{N_\delta}/(\alpha/\delta)]\}$$

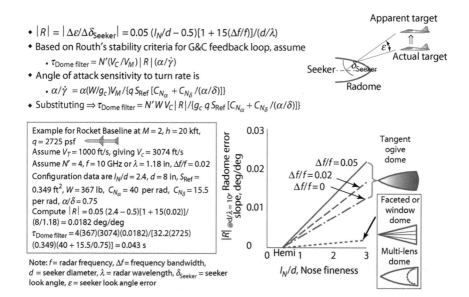

- $|R| = |\Delta\varepsilon/\Delta\delta_{Seeker}| = 0.05 (l_N/d - 0.5)[1 + 15(\Delta f/f)]/(d/\lambda)$
- Based on Routh's stability criteria for G&C feedback loop, assume
  - $\tau_{Dome\ filter} = N'(V_C/V_M)|R|(\alpha/\dot{\gamma})$
- Angle of attack sensitivity to turn rate is
  - $\alpha/\dot{\gamma} = \alpha(W/g_c)V_M/\{q S_{Ref}[C_{N_\alpha} + C_{N_\delta}/(\alpha/\delta)]\}$
- Substituting $\Rightarrow \tau_{Dome\ filter} = N'WV_C|R|/\{g_c q S_{Ref}[C_{N_\alpha} + C_{N_\delta}/(\alpha/\delta)]\}$

Example for Rocket Baseline at $M = 2$, $h = 20$ kft,
$q = 2725$ psf
Assume $V_T = 1000$ ft/s, giving $V_c = 3074$ ft/s
Assume $N' = 4$, $f = 10$ GHz or $\lambda = 1.18$ in, $\Delta f/f = 0.02$
Configuration data are $l_N/d = 2.4$, $d = 8$ in, $S_{Ref} = 0.349$ ft^2, $W = 367$ lb, $C_{N_\alpha} = 40$ per rad, $C_{N_\delta} = 15.5$ per rad, $\alpha/\delta = 0.75$
Compute $|R| = 0.05 (2.4 - 0.5)[1 + 15(0.02)]/(8/1.18) = 0.0182$ deg/deg
$\tau_{Dome\ filter} = 4(367)(3074)(0.0182)/[32.2(2725)(0.349)(40 + 15.5/0.75)] = 0.043$ s

Note: f = radar frequency, Δf = frequency bandwidth, d = seeker diameter, λ = radar wavelength, δ_{Seeker} = seeker look angle, ε = seeker look angle error

Fig. 6.65 Time constant contributor $\tau_{Dome\ Filter}$ is driven by radome error slope, N', closing velocity, and maneuverability.

Substituting for $\alpha/\dot{\gamma}$

$$\tau_{\text{Dome filter}} = N'WV_C|R|/\{g_c q S_{\text{Ref}}[C_{N_\alpha} + C_{N_\delta}/(\alpha/\delta)]\}$$

The contributors to a small value of $\tau_{\text{Dome filter}}$ are 1) a low value of missile weight per cross sectional area W/S_{Ref}, which implies a low value of body fineness ratio l/d; 2) low radome error slope $|R|$ such as the radome error slope of a hemispherical, faceted, window, or multi-lens dome; 3) low nose fineness l_N/d; 4) low change in angle of attack with flight control deflection α/δ, such as a statically stable missile with wing control; 5) low effective navigation ratio N'; 6) low closing velocity V_C, such as a tail chase intercept; 7) small frequency bandwidth Δf of the seeker transmitter; 8) high frequency f of the seeker transmitter, such as a mmW radar; 9) high normal force coefficient derivative from angle of attack C_{N_α}, such as a missile with a high aspect ratio, large wing; 10) high normal force coefficient derivative from flight control deflection C_{N_δ}, such as wing control; and 11) high dynamic pressure q, such as low altitude/high speed flight.

As an example for the rocket baseline missile, consider a head-on intercept of a target flying at an altitude of 20,000 ft with a velocity of $V_T = 1000$ ft/s. The assumed missile Mach number is $M = 2$, providing a dynamic pressure $q = 2725$ psf and a closing velocity $V_C = 3074$ ft/s. The assumed seeker and guidance parameters are a frequency $f = 10$ GHz, frequency bandwidth fraction $\Delta f/f = 0.02$, and an effective navigation ratio $N' = 4$. Configuration data from Chapter 7 are a tangent ogive nose fineness ratio $l_N/d = 2.4$, seeker diameter $d = 8$ in, reference area $S_{\text{Ref}} = 0.349$ ft^2, burnout weight $W = 367$ lb, normal force coefficient angle of attack derivative $C_{N_\alpha} = 40$ per rad, normal force control deflection coefficient derivative $C_{N_\delta} = 15.5$ per rad, and angle of attack sensitivity $\alpha/\delta = 0.75$.

Computing the dome error slope and the dome filter time constant

$$|R| = 0.05(2.4 - 0.5)[1 + 15(0.02)]/(8/1.18) = 0.0182\,\text{deg/deg}$$
$$\tau_{\text{Dome filter}} = 4(367)(3074)(0.0182)/\{32.2(2725)(0.349)(40 + 15.5/0.75)\}$$
$$= 0.043\,\text{s}$$

Note from the figure that an approach to greatly reduce the dome error slope would be to use either a hemispherical, faceted, window, or a multi-lens dome. The near-zero radome error slope would enhance the missile seeker tracking accuracy, reduce the missile time constant, and reduce the miss distance.

Figure 6.66 shows the missile maneuver acceleration that is required to eliminate an initial heading error for an ideal missile. It is based on proportional homing guidance for an ideal missile with zero time constant

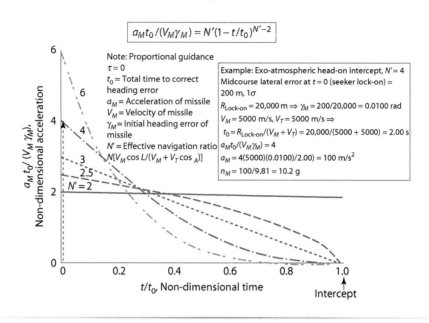

$$\boxed{a_{Mt_0}/(V_M\gamma_M) = N'(1 - t/t_0)^{N'-2}}$$

Note: Proportional guidance
$\tau = 0$
t_0 = Total time to correct heading error
a_M = Acceleration of missile
V_M = Velocity of missile
γ_M = Initial heading error of missile
N' = Effective navigation ratio
$N[V_M \cos L/(V_M + V_T \cos_A)]$

Example: Exo-atmospheric head-on intercept, $N' = 4$
Midcourse lateral error at $t = 0$ (seeker lock-on) = 200 m, 1σ
$R_{Lock\text{-}on} = 20{,}000$ m $\Rightarrow \gamma_M = 200/20{,}000 = 0.0100$ rad
$V_M = 5000$ m/s, $V_T = 5000$ m/s $\Rightarrow$
$t_0 = R_{Lock\text{-}on}/(V_M + V_T) = 20{,}000/(5000 + 5000) = 2.00$ s
$a_{Mt_0}/(V_M\gamma_M) = 4$
$a_M = 4(5000)(0.0100)/2.00 = 100$ m/s^2
$n_M = 100/9.81 = 10.2$ g

Fig. 6.66   High initial acceleration is required to eliminate heading error.

($\tau = 0$). The equation is

$$a_M = (V_M \gamma_M N'/t_0)(1 - t/t_0)^{N'-2}$$

The required maneuverability to correct a heading error is a function of 1) the effective navigation ratio N', 2) the time t that has elapsed since the initiation of guidance correction, 3) the total time t_0 that is available to correct the heading error, 4) the missile velocity V_M, and 5) the initial heading error γ_M. Note from the figure that for $N' > 2$, the missile maneuver acceleration to eliminate a heading error is largest at the initiation of the correction and decreases with time. A large value of the effective navigation ratio N' provides large initial missile maneuver acceleration and the acceleration decreases rapidly with time. A large value of N' also has an advantage of providing a larger off boresight intercept capability. For exo-atmospheric missile defense, at seeker lock-on, a large N' reduces the total impulse requirement for the divert thrusters, allowing more efficient use of the divert propellant. As a comparison, a value of $N' = 6$ provides 25% more divert capability than $N' = 3$. A disadvantage of $N' = 6$ is that it requires 2× the thrust of $N' = 3$, which may not be achievable. Also note from the figure that for a limiting small value of $N' = 2$ (not a practical case), the theoretical missile acceleration is constant.

For a theoretical missile with no lags in the system ($\tau = 0$) and no saturation in the commanded acceleration, there is theoretically zero miss distance with proportional homing guidance. However, as mentioned previously, a real missile with lags in the system will have a time constant and a resulting miss distance.

Consider an example of an exo-atmospheric missile interceptor correcting an initial heading error against a ballistic missile target at an assumed seeker lock-on range $R_{\text{lock-on}} = 20{,}000$ m. Assume that the target midcourse error at seeker lock-on is 200 m, 1σ. Also assume a head-on intercept with an interceptor velocity $V_M = 5000$ m/s and a target velocity $V_T = 5000$ m/s. Then the total time available to correct the initial heading error is $t_0 = R_{\text{lock-on}}/(V_M + V_T) = 2.00$ s. For the assumed seeker lock-on range of $R_{\text{Lock-on}} = 20{,}000$ m, the initial heading error $\gamma_M = 200/20000 = 0.0100$ rad. For an assumed missile effective navigation ratio $N' = 4$, the initial required maneuver acceleration

$$a_M = (V_M \gamma_M N'/t_0)(1 - t/t_0)^{N'-2} = 5000(0.0100)(4)(1 - 0)^{4-2}/2.00$$

$$= 100 \, \text{m/s}^2, \quad \text{or} \quad n_M = 10.2 \, \text{g}.$$

Consider another example of correcting an initial homing error against a fixed ground target. Based on a previous example, assume that the GPS/INS midcourse guidance has an error of 3 m, 1σ at $t = 0$ s (seeker lock-on). For an assumed seeker lock-on range $R_{\text{Lock-on}} = 125$ m, the initial heading error $\gamma_M = 3/125 = 0.024$ rad. Assume a missile velocity $V_M = 300$ m/s. Then the total time available to correct the initial heading error is $t_0 = 125/300 = 0.417$ s. For a missile effective navigation ratio $N' = 4$, the required maneuver acceleration is

$$a_M = 300(0.024)(4)/0.417 = 69.1 \, \text{m/s}^2, \quad \text{or} \quad n_M = 7.04 \, \text{g}$$

Miss distance from heading error is a function of 1) the total time t_0 that is available to correct heading error, 2) the missile time constant τ, 3) the heading error γ_M, 4) the missile velocity V_M, and 5) the effective navigation ratio N'. The adjoint method of References 32 and 33 gives the miss distance as

$$\sigma_{\text{HE}} = V_M \gamma_M \tau e^{-(t_0/\tau)} \sum_{j=1}^{N'-1} \{(N' - 2)![-(t_0/\tau)]^j /$$

$$[(j - 1)!(N' - j - 1)! \, j!]\}$$

If $N' = 3$, $\sigma_{\text{HE}} = V_M \gamma_M \tau e^{-(t_0/\tau)}[(t_0/\tau) - (t_0/\tau)^2/2]$
If $N' = 4$, $\sigma_{\text{HE}} = V_M \gamma_M \tau e^{-(t_0/\tau)}[(t_0/\tau) - (t_0/\tau)^2 + (t_0/\tau)^3/6]$
If $N' = 5$, $\sigma_{\text{HE}} = V_M \gamma_M \tau e^{-(t_0/\tau)}[(t_0/\tau) - (3/2)(t_0/\tau)^2 + (t_0/\tau)^3/2$
$\qquad - (t_0/\tau)^4/24]$
If $N' = 6$, $\sigma_{\text{HE}} = V_M \gamma_M \tau e^{-(t_0/\tau)}[(t_0/\tau) - 2(t_0/\tau)^2 + (t_0/\tau)^3 - (t_0/\tau)^4/6$
$\qquad + (t_0/\tau)^5/120]$

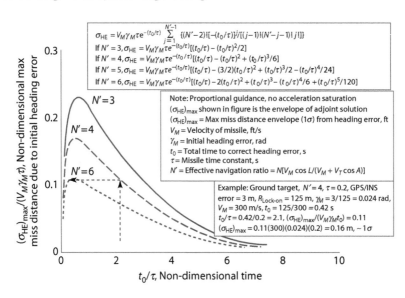

$$\sigma_{HE} = V_M \gamma_M \tau e^{-(t_0/\tau)} \sum_{j=1}^{N'-1} \{(N'-2)![-(t_0/\tau)]^j / [(j-1)!(N'-j-1)!j!]\}$$

If $N' = 3$, $\sigma_{HE} = V_M \gamma_M \tau e^{-(t_0/\tau)}[(t_0/\tau) - (t_0/\tau)^2/2]$

If $N' = 4$, $\sigma_{HE} = V_M \gamma_M \tau e^{-(t_0/\tau)}[(t_0/\tau) - (t_0/\tau)^2 + (t_0/\tau)^3/6]$

If $N' = 5$, $\sigma_{HE} = V_M \gamma_M \tau e^{-(t_0/\tau)}[(t_0/\tau) - (3/2)(t_0/\tau)^2 + (t_0/\tau)^3/2 - (t_0/\tau)^4/24]$

If $N' = 6$, $\sigma_{HE} = V_M \gamma_M \tau e^{-(t_0/\tau)}[(t_0/\tau) - 2(t_0/\tau)^2 + (t_0/\tau)^3 - (t_0/\tau)^4/6 + (t_0/\tau)^5/120]$

Note: Proportional guidance, no acceleration saturation
$(\sigma_{HE})_{max}$ shown in figure is the envelope of adjoint solution
$(\sigma_{HE})_{max}$ = Max miss distance envelope (1σ) from heading error, ft
V_M = Velocity of missile, ft/s
γ_M = Initial heading error, rad
t_0 = Total time to correct heading error, s
τ = Missile time constant, s
N' = Effective navigation ratio = $N[V_M \cos L/(V_M + V_T \cos A)]$

Example: Ground target, $N' = 4$, $\tau = 0.2$, GPS/INS
error = 3 m, $R_{Lock-on}$ = 125 m, γ_M = 3/125 = 0.024 rad,
V_M = 300 m/s, t_0 = 125/300 = 0.42 s
t_0/τ = 0.42/0.2 = 2.1, $(\sigma_{HE})_{max}/(V_M\gamma_M t_0)$ = 0.11
$(\sigma_{HE})_{max}$ = 0.11(300)(0.024)(0.2) = 0.16 m, $\sim 1\sigma$

Fig. 6.67 Minimum range miss distance is driven by the initial heading error, time available to correct the heading error, and the missile time constant. References: Bennett, R. R., et al, "Analytical Determination of Miss Distances for Linear Homing Navigation," Hughes Memo 260, March 1952; Zarchan, P., *Tactical and Strategic Missile Guidance*, Vol. 5, American Institute of Aeronautics and Astronautics, 2007.)

Figure 6.67 shows the envelope of the adjoint non-dimensional miss distance $(\sigma_{HE})_{max}/(V_M\gamma_M\tau)$ for effective navigation ratios of $N' = 3$, 4 and 6. Note that the heading error miss distance is smaller for large values of navigation ratio. The figure also shows that the peak miss distance occurs if the guidance to correct the heading error is initiated at about one time constant before intercept ($t_0 \approx \tau$). If guidance is initiated at about four-to-eight time constants prior to intercept, the miss distance due to an initial heading error is smaller and becomes negligible if t_0/τ is greater than 10.

As an example, assume the same conditions as those from a prior example on GPS/INS midcourse guidance. These are 1) an initial heading error against a ground target; 2) GPS/INS midcourse guidance with an error of 3 m at $t = 0$ s (seeker lock-on); 3) seeker lock-on range $R_{lock-on} = 125$ m; 4) missile velocity $V_M = 300$ m/s; 5) effective navigation ratio $N' = 4$; and 6) missile time constant $\tau = 0.2$ s. Assume that the initial tracking error is one pixel (0.07 m), which results in the GPS/INS error as the dominant driver for the initial heading error. The initial heading error is $\gamma = 3/125 = 0.024$ rad and the total time available to correct the heading error is $t_0 = 125/300 = 0.417$ s. Compute the number of available time constants to correct the heading error as

$$t_0/\tau = 0.417/0.2 = 2.1$$

From the figure, the envelope of the non-dimensional miss distance is

$$(\sigma_{HE})_{max}/(V_M \gamma_M \tau) = 0.11$$

Finally, compute the envelope (maximum value) of the missile miss distance from an initial heading error

$$(\sigma_{HE})_{max} = 0.11(300)(0.024)(0.2) = 0.16\,\text{m}, \sim 1\sigma$$

From the previous Fig. 6.66, the initial maneuverability requirement is $a_M t_0/(V_M \gamma_M) = N'(1 - t/t_0)^{N'-2}$. Solving for a_M

$$a_M = 300(0.024)(4)(1)/0.417 = 69.1\,\text{m/s}^2 = 7.04\,\text{g}$$

For this example, initiating seeker homing guidance at a range of 125 m provides better accuracy than the GPS uncorrected heading error (0.16 m versus 3 m), but it does require a relatively high maneuverability (7.04 g). Seeker lock-on at a longer range than 125 m would provide smaller miss distance and lower required maneuverability, because of the longer time available for seeker homing guidance. Although it would be possible in good weather and low clutter, it may be a higher risk because of factors that were not fully considered in treating the missile response as a simple first order time constant. For example, treating the missile as a more complex system of higher order time constants (e.g., five time constants) usually results in greater miss distance than a first order system [32].

The use an envelope of the adjoint miss distance rather than the actual computed value is a typical approach for conceptual design. This provides some conservatism in the result, to compensate for the typically optimistic result of a solution that is based on a single lag time constant. An illustration of this approach is shown in Fig. 6.68 for a value of $N' = 4$. The envelope in the figure first follows the adjoint miss distance computation to the first peak. The envelope then decays exponentially to follow the remaining peaks. As an example, assume the heading error computation of the previous figure. The parameters are $N' = 4$, $\tau = 0.2$, GPS/INS error = 3 m, $R_{\text{Lock-on}} = 75$ m, $\gamma_M = 3/75 = 0.04$ rad, $V_M = 300$ m/s, $t_0 = 75/300 = 0.25$ s. Compute

$$t_0/\tau = 0.25/0.2 = 1.25$$

$$\sigma_{HE} = 300(0.04)(0.2)e^{-1.25}\left[1.25 - (1.25)^2 + (1.25)^3/6\right]$$
$$= 2.4(0.287)\left[1.25 - 1.56 + 0.326\right] = 0.011\,\text{m}$$

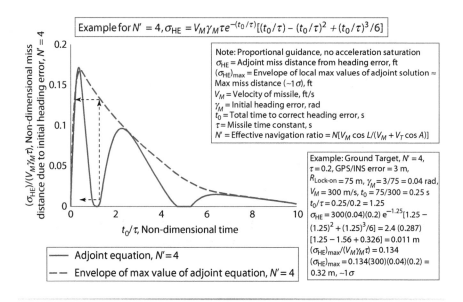

Left axis: $(\sigma_{HE})/(V_M\gamma_M\tau)$, Non-dimensional miss distance due to initial heading error, $N' = 4$

Top box: Example for $N' = 4$, $\sigma_{HE} = V_M\gamma_M\tau e^{-(t_0/\tau)}[(t_0/\tau) - (t_0/\tau)^2 + (t_0/\tau)^3/6]$

Note: Proportional guidance, no acceleration saturation
σ_{HE} = Adjoint miss distance from heading error, ft
$(\sigma_{HE})_{max}$ = Envelope of local max values of adjoint solution $\approx$ Max miss distance ($\sim 1\sigma$), ft
V_M = Velocity of missile, ft/s
γ_M = Initial heading error, rad
t_0 = Total time to correct heading error, s
τ = Missile time constant, s
N' = Effective navigation ratio = $N[V_M \cos L/(V_M + V_T \cos A)]$

Example: Ground Target, $N' = 4$,
$\tau = 0.2$, GPS/INS error = 3 m,
$R_{Lock-on} = 75$ m, $\gamma_M = 3/75 = 0.04$ rad,
$V_M = 300$ m/s, $t_0 = 75/300 = 0.25$ s
$t_0/\tau = 0.25/0.2 = 1.25$
$\sigma_{HE} = 300(0.04)(0.2) e^{-1.25}[1.25 - (1.25)^2 + (1.25)^3/6] = 2.4 (0.287)$
$[1.25 - 1.56 + 0.326] = 0.011$ m
$(\sigma_{HE})_{max}/(V_M\gamma_M\tau) = 0.134$
$(\sigma_{HE})_{max} = 0.134(300)(0.04)(0.2) = 0.32$ m, $\sim 1\sigma$

X-axis: t_0/τ, Non-dimensional time

— Adjoint equation, $N' = 4$
-- Envelope of max value of adjoint equation, $N' = 4$

Fig. 6.68   The adjoint equation maximum value envelope provides a first order estimate of the 1 σ miss distance. (Reference: Bennett, R. R., et al, "Analytical Determination of Miss Distances for Linear Homing Navigation," Hughes Memo 260, March 1952.)

Note from this figure that the envelope of miss distance is $(\sigma_{HE})_{max}/(V_M\gamma_M\tau) = 0.134$. This occurs at $t/\tau = 0.41$. Compute

$$(\sigma_{HE})_{max} = 0.134(300)(0.04)(0.2) = 0.32\,\text{m}, \sim 1\sigma$$

Also note from the figure that this is near the peak miss distance. The peak miss distance is $(\sigma_{HE})_{max}/(V_M\gamma_M\tau) = 0.17$. This occurs at $t_0/\tau = 0.41$.

Figure 6.69 shows the ideal missile maneuver acceleration that is required against a constant (step) maneuvering target. It is based on proportional homing guidance for a missile with the assumptions of a negligibly small time constant ($\tau = 0$) and the velocity of the missile greater than the velocity of the target. The equation is

$$n_M = n_T[N'/(N' - 2)]\left[1 - (1 - t/t_0)^{N'-2}\right]$$

The required maneuverability against a step maneuvering target is a function of the effective navigation ratio N', time t after the target initiates maneuvering, and the total time t_0 to the target intercept. Note from the figure that the missile maneuver acceleration increases with time and has the largest value at intercept. A benefit of a large value of the effective navigation ratio N' is less required maneuverability at intercept. Also note from the figure that the value of N' at intercept must be greater than 2.

As an example, assume a "perfect" system with a time constant $\tau = 0$ and a typical effective navigation ratio $N' = 3$. Then against a step maneuvering target, the ratio of the missile maneuverability to the target maneuverability at intercept $(t = t_0)$ is $n_M/n_T = 3/(3 - 2)[1 - (1 - 1)^{3-2}] = 3$. As a rule of thumb, the missile maneuverability must be about three times the maneuverability of the target. To intercept a highly maneuverable 9-g fighter aircraft requires about 30-g maneuverability for the missile.

Miss distance against a step maneuvering target is a function of the time-to-go t_0, the missile time constant τ, target maneuverability n_T, and the effective navigation ratio N'. Based on the adjoint method of Ref. 32 and 33, the equation for miss distance is

$$\sigma_{\text{Step man}} = gn_T \tau^2 e^{-(t_0/\tau)} \sum_{j=2}^{N'-1} \{(N' - 3)![-(t_0/\tau)]^j /$$

$$[(j - 2)!(N' - j - 1)! j!]\}$$

Substituting typical values for N' into the above equation gives for

$$N' = 3, \ \sigma_{\text{Step man}} = gn_T \tau^2 e^{-(t_0/\tau)}[(t_0/\tau)^2/2]$$

$$N' = 4, \ \sigma_{\text{Step man}} = gn_T \tau^2 e^{-(t_0/\tau)}[(t_0/\tau)^2/2 - (t_0/\tau)^3/6]$$

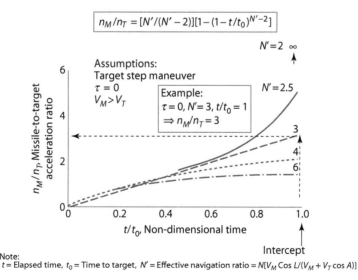

$$\boxed{n_M/n_T = [N'/(N' - 2)][1 - (1 - t/t_0)^{N'-2}]}$$

Assumptions:
Target step maneuver
$\tau = 0$
$V_M > V_T$

Example:
$\tau = 0, N' = 3, t/t_0 = 1$
$\Rightarrow n_M/n_T = 3$

$N' = 2 \ \infty$

$N' = 2.5$

3
4
6

n_M/n_T, Missile-to-target acceleration ratio

t/t_0, Non-dimensional time

Intercept

Note:
t = Elapsed time, t_0 = Time to target, N' = Effective navigation ratio = $N[V_M \cos L/(V_M + V_T \cos A)]$

Fig. 6.69 Required missile maneuverability is about 3x the target maneuverability.

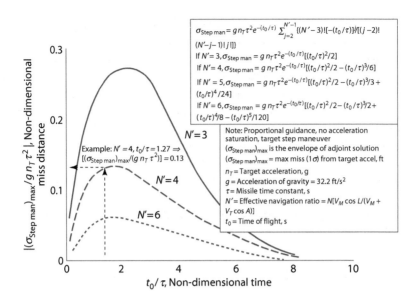

$$\sigma_{\text{Step man}} = g n_T \tau^2 e^{-(t_0/\tau)} \sum_{j=2}^{N'-1} \{(N'-3)![-(t_0/\tau)]^j / [(j-2)! \, (N'-j-1)! \, j!]\}$$

If $N'=3$, $\sigma_{\text{Step man}} = g \, n_T \tau^2 e^{-(t_0/\tau)}[(t_0/\tau)^2/2]$

If $N'=4$, $\sigma_{\text{Step man}} = g \, n_T \tau^2 e^{-(t_0/\tau)}[(t_0/\tau)^2/2 - (t_0/\tau)^3/6]$

If $N'=5$, $\sigma_{\text{Step man}} = g \, n_T \tau^2 e^{-(t_0/\tau)}[(t_0/\tau)^2/2 - (t_0/\tau)^3/3 + (t_0/\tau)^4/24]$

If $N'=6$, $\sigma_{\text{Step man}} = g \, n_T \tau^2 e^{-(t_0/\tau)}[(t_0/\tau)^2/2 - (t_0/\tau)^3/2 + (t_0/\tau)^4/8 - (t_0/\tau)^5/120]$

Note: Proportional guidance, no acceleration saturation, target step maneuver
$(\sigma_{\text{Step man}})_{\max}$ is the envelope of adjoint solution
$(\sigma_{\text{Step man}})_{\max}$ = max miss (1σ) from target accel, ft
n_T = Target acceleration, g
g = Acceleration of gravity = 32.2 ft/s²
τ = Missile time constant, s
N' = Effective navigation ratio = $N[V_M \cos L/(V_M + V_T \cos A)]$
t_0 = Time of flight, s

Example: $N' = 4$, $t_0/\tau = 1.27 \Rightarrow$
$[(\sigma_{\text{Step man}})_{\max}/(g \, n_T \tau^2)] = 0.13$

Fig. 6.70 A target step maneuver requires 6 to 10 time constants to settle out the miss distance. (Reference: Bennett, R.R., et al, "Analytical Determination of Miss Distances for Linear Homing Navigation," Hughes Memo 260, March 1952.)

$$N' = 5, \quad \sigma_{\text{Step man}} = gn_T\tau^2 e^{-(t_0/\tau)}[(t_0/\tau)^2/2 - (t_0/\tau)^3/3 + (t_0/\tau)^4/24]$$

$$N' = 6, \quad \sigma_{\text{Step man}} = gn_T\tau^2 e^{-(t_0/\tau)}[(t_0/\tau)^2/2$$
$$- (t_0/\tau)^3/2 + (t_0/\tau)^4/8 - (t_0/\tau)^5/120]$$

Shown in Fig. 6.70 is the envelope of the adjoint miss distance for effective navigation ratios of $N' = 3$, 4 and 6. Note that for $N' = 4$, the non-dimensional peak miss distance of $[(\sigma_{\text{Step man}})_{\max}/(gn_T\tau^2)] = 0.13$ occurs if the target initiates a step acceleration maneuver at 1.27 time constants prior to intercept. Also note that a high value of navigation ratio gives smaller miss distance. Finally, note that if the target initiates a step maneuver at greater than six to ten time constants prior to intercept and the missile has no acceleration saturation, there is negligible miss distance at intercept.

Figure 6.71 shows that the miss distance against a step maneuvering target increases with increased missile time constant and target maneuverability. The figure is based on the adjoint envelope of proportional guidance with an effective navigation ratio $N' = 4$. From the previous figure, the non-dimensional peak miss distance is

$$[(\sigma_{\text{Step man}})_{\max}/(gn_T\tau^2)] = 0.13$$

Note that the miss distance is a function of τ^2. For example, doubling the missile time constant increases the maneuvering target miss distance by $2^2 = 4$. Uncertainty in the value of time constant provides large uncertainty in the miss distance.

As an example, consider the rocket baseline missile in coasting flight at Mach 2 and 20,000 feet altitude. The time constant is $\tau = 0.209$ second. For a 5-g step maneuvering target, the rocket baseline missile maximum miss distance is computed to be

$$(\sigma_{\text{Step man}})_{\text{max}} = 0.13gn_T\tau^2 = 0.13(32.2)(5)(0.209)^2 = 0.9\,\text{ft}$$

This result is probably optimistic, because the adjoint method used in this text does not include other effects, such as seeker noise, that also contribute to miss distance.

Figure 6.72 shows the effect of intercept altitude and target maneuverability on the miss distance of the aerodynamic control rocket baseline missile. Assumptions are 1) proportional guidance; 2) no saturation of maneuver capability; 3) an effective navigation ratio $N' = 4$; 4) coasting flight at Mach 2; 5) head-on intercept of a target traveling at $V_T = 1000$ ft/s, 6) target step maneuver initiated at a time-to-go for maximum miss distance $(t_0/\tau = 1.27)$; and 7) negligible contributors to miss distance from other contributors (e.g., guidance filters, seeker noise, target glint). The

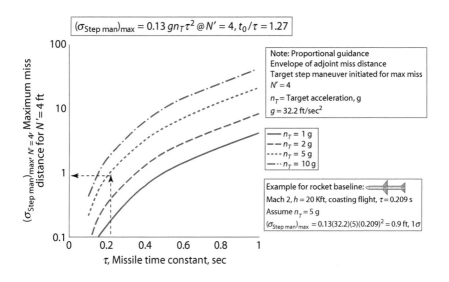

Fig. 6.71 A small time constant is required for a small miss distance against a maneuvering target.

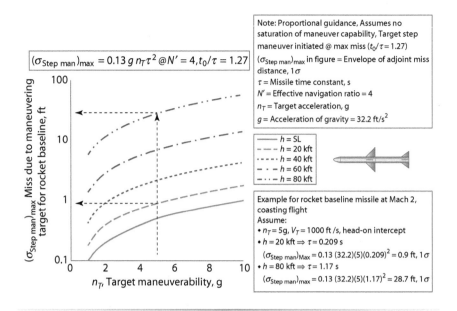

Fig. 6.72 An aerodynamic control missile has smaller miss distance at low altitude/high dynamic pressure.

equation for miss distance from a target step maneuver is

$$(\sigma_{\text{Step man}})_{\text{max}} = 0.13 g n_T \tau^2 \ @ \ N' = 4, \quad t_0/\tau = 1.27$$

Note from the figure that the miss distance increases with the intercept altitude. For the same velocity, a higher altitude results in lower dynamic pressure, which results in a larger value of the missile time constant. The missile miss distance also increases with target maneuverability. As an example, at an intercept altitude of $h = 20,000$ ft the rocket baseline missile has a time constant of $\tau = 0.209$ s. If the target conducts a step maneuver of $n_T = 5$ g, the maximum miss distance is

$$(\sigma_{\text{Step man}})_{\text{max}} = 0.13(32.2)(5)(0.209)^2 = 0.9 \text{ ft}, \quad 1\sigma$$

However, if the target could conduct a 5-g maneuver at an intercept altitude of 80,000 ft, the maximum miss distance is

$$(\sigma_{\text{Step man}})_{\text{max}} = 0.13(32.2)(5)(1.17)^2 = 28.7 \text{ ft}, \quad 1\sigma$$

The increased miss distance is because of an increased time constant, $\tau = 1.17$ s. The time constant contributions from limited control effectiveness and dome error slope are much larger at 80,000 ft altitude ($\tau_\delta = 0.38$ s, $\tau_{\text{Dome filter}} = 0.72$ s). For a high altitude intercept with hit-to-kill accuracy, unconventional flight control (e.g., reaction jet divert control) and a low error slope dome (e.g., window dome) would be required.

The miss distance against a weaving target is driven by the interceptor missile effective navigation ratio N'. The miss distance is also sensitive to the target acceleration n_T, the interceptor missile time constant τ, and the target weaving frequency ω. From Ref. 32, the miss distance is

$$\sigma_{\text{Weave}} = gn_T\tau^2(\omega\tau)^{N'-2}/[1 + (\omega\tau)^2]^{N'/2}$$

Assumptions in the above equation are proportional guidance, an adjoint solution with a single lag time constant, and the interceptor missile has infinite maneuver acceleration capability (no acceleration saturation). These assumptions result in an optimistic prediction of the miss distance.

Note from Fig. 6.73 that the non-dimensional peak miss distance $\sigma_{\text{Weave}}/(gn_T\tau^2)$ occurs if the product of the target weave frequency and the homing missile time constant is of the order of 1 ($\omega\tau \sim 1$ or $\tau \sim \omega^{-1}$). Also note that a high value of navigation ratio gives smaller miss distance against a weaving/cork screwing target.

The adjoint results for the miss distance due to initial heading error, step maneuvering target, and a weaving/cork screwing target have shown that a high value of N' gives the smallest miss distance. However, another consideration is that a high value of N' could require an increase in the filtering of the

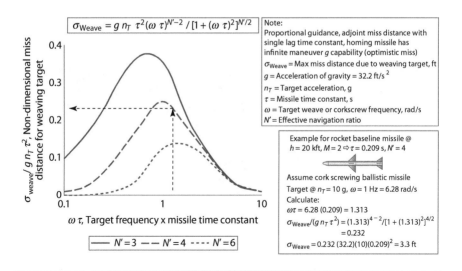

Fig. 6.73 A small miss distance against a weaving target requires a large value of N'. (Reference: Bennett, R. R., et al, "Analytical Determination of Miss Distances for Linear Homing Navigation," Hughes Memo 260, March 1952.)

radome error slope, which increases the missile time constant, which could increase the miss distance. Also, a high value of effective navigation ratio makes the missile more sensitive to seeker noise and seeker tracking error, such as glint. A missile that has a seeker with low noise and high resolution, such as a LADAR seeker or an imaging IR seeker, and also a low fineness radome may be most effective at a high value of effective navigation ratio (e.g., $N' = 6$). Because most current missile seekers have relatively high noise and relatively low resolution, especially radar missiles, the typical range of N' for most missiles is $3 < N' < 5$.

As an example calculation of the miss distance for a weaving target, assume the rocket baseline missile at a typical intercept condition of Mach 2, $h = 20$ kft altitude. From a prior example, the missile time constant $\tau = 0.209$. Also assume $N' = 4$. We will assume a ballistic missile target in a cork screwing flight trajectory with $n_T = 10$ g and $\omega = 1$ Hz $= 6.28$ rad/s. Calculate

$$\omega\tau = 6.28(0.209) = 1.313$$

$$\sigma_{\text{Weave}}/(gn_T\tau^2) = (1.313)^{4-2}/\left[1 + (1.313)^2\right]^{4/2} = 0.232$$

$$\sigma_{\text{Weave}} = 0.232(32.2)(10)(0.209)^2 = 3.3 \text{ ft}$$

Example of radar glint from F-16 frontal scatter centers

Video of Glint

Fig. 6.74 Radar glint error occurs from the angular flashes of target scatter centers.

Figure 6.74 illustrates radar glint from the scatter centers of a typical aircraft target. The target flight dynamic motions (e.g., short period mode), the target structural vibrations, and the local scattering centers as the missile seeker wanders across its field of view of the target can cause a fluctuating angular flash return from the target. Glint noise can be a driver for miss distance, particularly for missiles that do not have good seeker resolution, have a small value of time constant, and have a high navigation ratio. Glint is more of a problem for a relatively large target, which has a larger span of scattering centers. The reflections from the multiple scattering centers combine in a complex manner to give an error in the target location. In some cases the scattering centers can combine to give an apparent target location that lies outside the actual target. Glint is often one of the largest contributors to the miss distance of a radar missile. Because radar missiles are particularly sensitive to glint angle error, angular deception is often used as a countermeasure against a missile radar seeker. An advantage of an imaging infrared seeker, which has a high resolution, is that it typically has a small miss distance from glint. A millimeter wave radar seeker (e.g., 39 GHz) will also usually have lower glint than a conventional centimeter wave seeker (e.g., 10 GHz), because of its smaller field of view and its higher resolution.

Clicking on the figure illustrates flash returns from a typical fighter aircraft wing stores and the angular wander of the radar return.

The Ref. 32 adjoint equation for proportional guidance miss distance from glint is

$$\sigma_{\text{Glint}} = K_{N'}(W/\tau)^{1/2}$$

In the above equation

$$K_{N'} = 0.5(2K_{N'=4})^{N'/4}$$
$$K_{N'=4} = 1.206$$

The equation for the spectral density of glint noise is

$$W = (b_T)^2_{\text{Res}}/(3\pi^2 B)$$

Terms in the above equations are σ_{Glint} = miss distance (1σ) from glint noise, ft; W = glint noise spectral density from uniformly distributed target scatter across the seeker span resolution of the target, ft^2/Hz; τ = missile time constant, s; N' = effective navigation ratio; $(b_T)_{\text{Res}}$ = seeker resolution of the target span at the seeker blind range, ft; and B = noise bandwidth, Hz. The noise bandwidth is a function of the size and the flight dynamics motion of the target, which typically is over a range of

$$1 < B < 8 \, \text{Hz}.$$

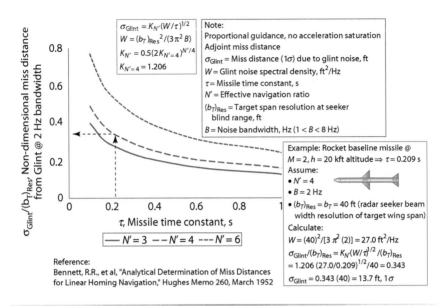

Fig. 6.75   Glint miss distance is driven by the missile seeker resolution, missile time constant, missile navigation ratio, and the target size. (Reference: Bennett, R. R., et al, "Analytical Determination of Miss Distances for Linear Homing Navigation," Hughes Memo 260, March 1952.)

Figure 6.75 shows the miss distance from glint noise for the rocket baseline missile. A typical noise bandwidth of $B = 2$ Hz of a fighter aircraft is assumed in the figure. For a relatively small target, such as a cruise missile, $B \sim 1$ Hz. For a large target, such as a bomber aircraft, $B \sim 8$ Hz. Note from the figure that the miss distance from glint is smaller for large values of τ and low values of N'.

For an example calculation we will use the rocket baseline missile, which has a radar seeker. Assume an intercept condition of Mach 2 and $h = 20$ kft altitude. It was previously shown that for this condition the missile time constant $\tau = 0.209$ s. Also assume 1) $N' = 4$, 2) $B = 2$ Hz, 3) $f = 10$ GHz ($\lambda = 0.03$ m), 4) $d = 8$ in $= 0.203$ ft, 5) $t_{blind} = \tau = 0.209$ s, 6) $b_T = 40$ ft (aircraft target with 40 ft wing span), and 7) $V_T = 1000$ ft/s. Calculate the closing velocity V_c and the blind range R_{Blind}

$$V_c = V_M + V_T = 2074 + 1000 = 3074 \text{ ft/s}$$
$$R_{Blind} = V_c t_{Blind} = 3074(0.209) = 642 \text{ ft}$$

From Ref. 25, the angular resolution $\theta_{angular}$ of a radar seeker is limited by the seeker beam width θ_{3dB}, signal-to-noise ratio S/N, and the number of pulses n that are integrated over the seeker beam width

$$\theta_{\text{Angular}} = \theta_{\text{3dB}}/\{2n(S/N)]^{1/2}\}$$

As an example, assume $S/N = 10$ and $n = 10$. Compute

$$\theta_{\text{Angular}} = \theta_{\text{3dB}}/\{2[(10)(10)]^{1/2}\} = \theta_{\text{3dB}}/20$$

Depending upon the target, the seeker angular resolution may be better or worse than the above. A typical fixed target would allow better angular resolution. However, an airborne high speed maneuver target would probably be worse than the above.

For a non-imaging radar seeker, angular resolution may do more harm then good against a large target with glint. A usually conservative approach to estimating the radar missile miss distance due to glint is to assume that the seeker resolution is the beam width. For an assumption of a typical missile seeker antenna that has a circular aperture and is uniformly illuminated

$$\theta_{\text{3dB}} = 1.02\lambda/d = 1.02(0.03)/0.203 = 0.1503\,\text{rad} = 8.6\,\text{deg}$$

Assuming that the seeker resolution is θ_{3dB}, the seeker resolution width at the blind range is

$$R_{\text{Blind}}\tan\theta_{\text{3dB}} = 642(0.1512) = 97\,\text{ft}$$

Comparing the seeker resolution width to the target span gives

$$(b_{\text{Res}})_{\text{min}} = \text{Min}(R_{\text{Blind}}\tan\theta_{\text{3dB}}, b_T) = \text{Min}(97, 40) = 40\,\text{ft}$$

Next, calculate the glint noise spectral density

$$W = (40)^2/[3\pi^2(2)] = 27.0\,\text{ft}^2/\text{Hz}$$

The non-dimensional miss distance from glint is

$$\sigma_{\text{Glint}}/b_T = 1.206(27.0/0.209)^{1/2}/40 = 0.343$$

Finally, substituting the target span into the above equation gives

$$\sigma_{\text{Glint}} = 0.343(40) = 13.7\,\text{ft}, \quad 1\sigma$$

Approaches to reduce glint miss distance for a non-imaging radar seeker include frequency agility, and polarization. Other potential approaches, that are specific target dependent, include an optimum guidance gain, filtering, and coherent pulse integration.

Minimizing miss distance requires a tradeoff of the missile time constant τ and the effective navigation ratio N'. Figure 6.76 shows the

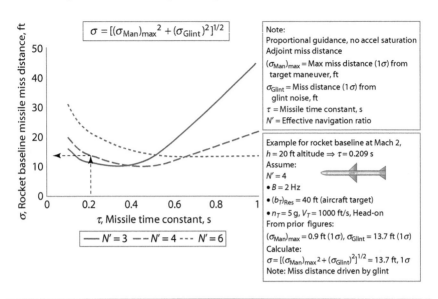

Fig. 6.76 Minimum miss distance requires optimum time constant and optimum navigation ratio. (Reference: Bennett, R. R., et al, "Analytical Determination of Miss Distances for Linear Homing Navigation," Hughes Memo 260, March 1952.)

root mean square (RMS) miss distance from target maneuverability $(\sigma_{Man})_{max}$ and seeker glint noise σ_{Glint}, given by the equation

$$\sigma = [(\sigma_{Man})^2_{max} + (\sigma_{Glint})^2]^{1/2}$$

Note from the figure that there is an optimum combination of τ and N' for minimum miss distance. The values of τ and N' for the minimum miss distance from target maneuver are at cross purposes with their values for the minimum miss distance from glint. For a large target, the miss distance is often driven by glint. A small target, such as a ballistic missile target, may have a relatively small miss distance from glint.

As an example, assume proportional guidance and an adjoint prediction of the miss distance for the rocket baseline missile. Also assume an intercept flight condition of Mach 2, $h = 20$ kft altitude, which has a missile time constant $\tau = 0.209$ s. Based on the previous examples, assume a maneuvering aircraft target with glint noise. The previous parameters are $N' = 4$, $B = 2$ Hz, $(b_T)_{Res} = 40$ ft, $n_T = 5g$, $V_T = 1000$ ft/s, and a head-on intercept. From the prior examples

$$(\sigma_{Man})_{max} = 0.9\,\text{ft}, \quad 1\sigma$$
$$\sigma_{Glint} = 13.7\,\text{ft}, \quad 1\sigma.$$

Calculate the RMS error

$$\sigma = \left(0.9^2 + 13.7^2\right)^{1/2} = 13.7 \,\text{ft}, \quad 1\sigma$$

Note from the above that the RMS miss distance for the aircraft target is driven by glint.

6.5 Carriage and Launch Observables

The fourth measure of merit to be discussed in this chapter is carriage and launch observables. Missile carriage and launch observables impact the survivability of the launch platform. Two areas of concern are the radar cross section (RCS) of the launch platform with weapon carriage and the missile plume visual signature at launch.

Illustrated in Fig. 6.77 are aircraft weapon carriage alternatives based on the consideration of RCS. The weapon carriage alternatives are 1) internal carriage, which has the lowest RCS in carriage; 2) conformal (semi-submerged) carriage, which provides a lower RCS than external carriage; and 3) conventional external pylon or rail carriage, which has the highest RCS in carriage. The examples are a Gripen aircraft for conventional external carriage, a Backfire bomber conformal carriage of the Kh-22 Kitchen, and an F-22 aircraft with internal carriage of the GBU-39B Small Diameter Bomb.

Conventional external pylon/
external rail carriage: High RCS

Conformal carriage: Reduced RCS

Internal carriage: Low RCS

Fig. 6.77 Internal weapon carriage is required for a low radar cross section launch platform.

Center weapon bay best for aircraft ejection launchers

F-22 semi-bay load-out: 2 SDB, 1 AIM-120C   F-117 bay load-out: 1 GBU-27, 1 GBU-10   B-1 single bay load-out: 8 GBU-31

Video

Side weapon bay best for aircraft rail launchers

F-22 carriage (AMRAAM/JDAM/AIM-9)   F-22 side bay: 1 AIM-9 in each side bay   RAH-66 side bay: 1 AGM-114, 2 FIM-92, 4 Hydra 70 in each side bay

Fig. 6.78   An aircraft center weapon bay is best for ejection launchers while a side weapon bay is best for rail launchers.

In addition to high RCS, other disadvantages of external weapon carriage include higher drag and potentially adverse aeroelastic stability and control interactions with the aircraft platform. An advantage of external carriage is higher firepower load-out, because of the large number of possible store attachment locations on the aircraft body and wings. Conformal carriage has an advantage of reduced RCS and lower drag compared to conventional carriage. A disadvantage is a need for specialized store and aircraft attachments for each type of aircraft. Internal carriage has the lowest carriage RCS and the lowest drag. A disadvantage of internal carriage is a weapon span and possibly a weapon length constraint, which results in a reduction in firepower, typically by factors of two-to-four compared to external carriage.

Figure 6.78 shows examples of internal carriage and load-outs for low observable fighters, bombers, and helicopters.

In the upper left of the figure is a photograph of the F-22 internal center bay. The F-22 center bay typically has a partition for air-to-air weapons (e.g., AMRAAM) and a partition for air-to-surface weapons (e.g., JDAM, Small Diameter Bomb). AMRAAM is ejection launched by the LAU-142/A pneudraulic (pneumatic plus hydraulic) launcher. The LAU-142 has a 9-in stroke, ejecting AMRAAM from the bay at a velocity of about 25 ft/s. The peak ejection acceleration is 40 g. Advantages of pneudraulic ejection compared to conventional pyrotechnic cartridge ejection include reduced logistics, faster turnaround time for weapon loading, and a more nearly constant ejection force that allows a shorter ejection stroke. For a heavier weapon, such as a GBU-32 JDAM (1000-lb class weapon), a conventional BRU-46/A bomb rack is provided. Examples of typical mixed (both air-to-air and air-to-surface) weapon load-outs in the F-22 center bay include 1) four Small Diameter Bombs plus two AIM-120C compressed carriage AMRAAM, 2) two AIM-120B AMRAAM (without compressed carriage) plus one 1000 lb JDAM, or 3) three AIM-120C AMRAAM plus one 1000 lb JDAM. The F-22 center bay can also be set up for air-to-air weapons only, such as four AIM-120B or six AIM-120C.

The F-117 aircraft (now retired) internal weapons bay is shown in the top center of the figure. The F-117 weapons bay is similar to that of the F-22, except that it has about twice the payload weight capability. A typical load-out for the F-117 is two Paveway guided bombs (2000-lb class). Shown in the foreground of the photograph is the GBU-27 laser guided bomb. Its warhead is based on the BLU-109 hardened structures penetrator bomb. In the background is the GBU-10 laser guided bomb. Its warhead is either the general-purpose Mk-84 bomb or the BLU-109 penetrator bomb.

The B-1 bomber weapons bay is shown in the upper right of the figure. The B-1 has three bays. Each bay has a rotary launcher for ejection of missiles and bombs. An ejector rack assembly is provided for each weapon that is attached to the rotary launcher. The ejector rack assembly has a 30-in spacing of the ejectors. Shown in the figure is a load-out of eight JDAM/BLU-109 2000 lb (GBU-31(V)3/B) guided bombs in the weapons bay.

The lower left section of the figure is a video of loading AMRAAM and AIM-9 into the center and side bays of the F-22 aircraft. Also shown in the video are launches of AMRAAM and JDAM from the center bay and AIM-9X from a side bay.

In the lower center of the figure is a photograph of an F-22 side bay. The F-22 has two side bays. Each bay is capable of carrying a single Sidewinder missile on a LAU-141/A trapeze rail launcher. A trapeze launcher is required for a lock-on-before-launch missile, such as AIM-9X. During the launch sequence the trapeze launcher extends the missile away from the aircraft, the missile seeker acquires the target, and the missile is launched. Following missile launch, the trapeze launcher retracts back into the side bay and the bay doors are closed. The LAU-141/A rail launcher has a deflector surface to keep the missile rocket motor plume from entering the weapon bay.

Finally, the lower right section of the figure is a photograph of a low observable combat helicopter, the cancelled RAH-66 Comanche. The Comanche had two side bays with rail launchers. Each bay had a typical mixed mission (combined ATA/ATS) load-out of one Hellfire missile

High smoke example: AIM-7	Reduced smoke example: AIM-120	Minimum smoke example: Javelin
Particles (e.g., metal fuel oxide) at all atmosphere temperature.	Contrail (HCl from AP oxidizer) at $T <$ $-10°F$ atmospheric temperature.	Contrail (H_2O) at $T < -35°F$ atmospheric temperature.

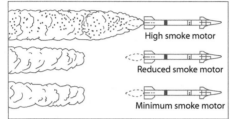

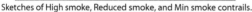

Sketches of High smoke, Reduced smoke, and Min smoke contrails.	Video of sparrow, Archer, AMRAAM, Javelin, and Hellfire smoke contrails

Fig. 6.79   Minimum smoke propellant reduces launch observables.

plus two Stinger missiles plus four Hydra 70 rockets. For an air-to-surface only mission, each bay could carry three Hellfire missiles, giving the Comanche a total bay load-out of six Hellfire missiles. As shown in the figure, the Comanche could also carry an additional eight Hellfire missiles externally, at the expense of increased RCS.

Illustrated in Fig. 6.79 are solid propellant rocket motor plume observables with high-smoke, reduced-smoke, and minimum-smoke propellants.

The relatively old Sparrow missile rocket motor is a representative high-smoke motor. The high-smoke contrail is shown in the photograph in the upper left corner of the figure. The Sparrow rocket motor has high-smoke Al_2O_3 particles from its aluminum fuel.

Shown in the upper center of the figure is a photograph of the contrail from a reduced-smoke propellant. AMRAAM has a more recent, reduced-smoke, rocket motor than Sparrow. It still has a contrail of HCl from the ammonium perchlorate oxidizer. The HCl contrail occurs if the atmospheric temperature is less than $-10°F$, typically corresponding to altitudes greater than about 20,000 ft.

Finally, the upper right photograph is a launch of the Javelin missile, which has a minimum-smoke rocket motor. Javelin has a boost-sustain motor. Boost occurs within the launch tube, eliminating exposure of the gunner to the boost exhaust plume and reducing the boost acoustic noise to less than 140 dB. Following boost ejection from the launch tube, a delayed signal ignites the sustain grain. This provides safe separation of the gunner from the missile sustain exhaust plume. Upon ignition, the sustain chamber pressure bursts a disk that separates the boost and sustain grains. Javelin has almost no smoke observable during either boost or sustain flight, enhancing the survivability of the gunner. Minimum-smoke propellants can have an H_2O (ice) contrail if the atmospheric temperature is less than $-35°F$, typically corresponding to altitudes greater than about 27,000 ft.

Most short range missiles use minimum smoke propellant, to minimize the probability of launch platform location by the threat. However, most beyond visual range (BVR) standoff missiles use high smoke propellant, for the higher performance and longer range. Because standoff missiles are usually launched at long range, there is less concern of the missile launch being observed by the threat.

In the bottom left section of the figure are sketches of the typical contrails from high-smoke, reduced-smoke, and minimum-smoke motors. The solid fuel oxide particles of the high smoke motor are visible immediately behind the nozzle under all atmospheric conditions. The contrail from a reduced-smoke motor occurs farther downstream of the nozzle. For an ammonium perchlorate oxidizer, a contrail is produced when the HCl gas from the reduced-smoke motor is absorbed by water and then freezes at low atmospheric temperature. Finally, water vapor from a minimum-smoke motor at low atmospheric temperature can freeze farther downstream of the nozzle, to produce a faint contrail.

The bottom right section of the figure contains a video of missile systems with high-smoke (Sparrow, Archer), reduced-smoke (AMRAAM, Hellfire-1), and minimum-smoke (Javelin, Hellfire-II) propellants.

6.6 Missile Survivability and Safety

The fifth measure of merit of this chapter is missile survivability and safety. Missile survivability examples will address cruise missile survivability from threat defenses. Safety will address the insensitive munition safety requirements.

Missile survivability is especially important for cruise missiles, which have a long exposure time to threat defenses because of their long range and their long flight duration. Also, cruise missiles are mostly used against high value targets, which are usually heavily defended. Figure 6.80 shows the approaches to survivability that are usually most appropriate for the typical flight phases of a cruise missile. Survivability enhancements include 1) low observables, 2) high altitude flight, 3) high speed flight, 4) mission planning to avoid the en-route threat, 5) terrain masking, and 6) maneuverability. The effectiveness of each approach to survivability

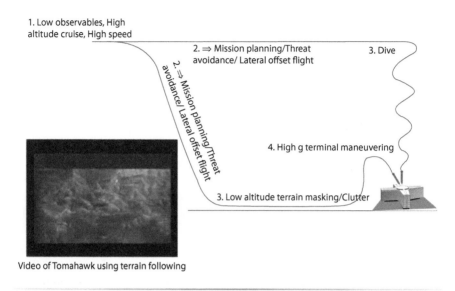

1. Low observables, High altitude cruise, High speed

2. ⇒ Mission planning/Threat avoidance/ Lateral offset flight

3. Dive

2. ⇒ Mission planning/Threat avoidance/ Lateral offset flight

4. High g terminal maneuvering

3. Low altitude terrain masking/Clutter

Video of Tomahawk using terrain following

Fig. 6.80　Approaches for survivability include stealth, high altitude, high speed, mission planning/threat avoidance, terrain masking, and maneuverability.

depends upon the capability of the missile, the flight environment of the missile, and the capability of the threat. During the en-route portion of the flight, before entering the target terminal area, the primary approach to survivability is usually low observables. Low observables allows the cruise missile to operate at an efficient altitude for maximum range. As shown previously in this chapter, the efficient cruise Mach number and altitude are about Mach $0.8/h = 30$ kft for a typical cruise missile with turbojet/turbofan propulsion and a wing (dynamic pressure $q \sim 300$ psf), about Mach $4/80$ kft for a typical ramjet missile ($q \sim 700$ psf), and about Mach $6.5/100$ kft ($q \sim 700$ psf) for a typical scramjet missile. The Mach number and speed for optimum cruise efficiency may also enhance the missile survivability, especially for a ramjet or a scramjet missile. Another survivability approach is mission planning, to route the cruise missile around the en-route threat defenses. A disadvantage of mission planning/threat avoidance is a loss in the maximum range capability, due to the routing around defenses. Another option, if the target is heavily defended in the terminal portion of the flight, is to descend and "fly-under-the-radar" at low altitude/high speed. The missile relies on the terrain masking/ground clutter of low altitude flight for survivability. This requires a tradeoff of the enhanced survivability versus the loss in range for a high dynamic pressure flight condition. Finally, high g maneuvering in terminal flight increases the miss distance from threat defenses, enhancing the cruise missile survivability. Weaving maneuvers to increase threat miss distance and improve survivability may also be conducted during en-route flight. A tradeoff is the loss in range versus improved survivability.

Figure 6.81 contrasts long range strike missile configurations that have survivability from high speed flight versus missiles that have survivability from low observables.

The SS-N-22 Sunburn and the 3M-54E Sizzler are anti-ship cruise missiles that rely on supersonic speed for their survivability. Sunburn, shown in the top left portion of the figure, has liquid fuel ramjet propulsion. Note the small wing and four inlets that are configured for supersonic flight. Sizzler, shown in the top right portion of the figure, has multi-mode propulsion. A subsonic turbojet provides efficient cruise for a long range fly-out. Note the large wing for subsonic aerodynamic efficiency. For terminal flight penetration, the turbojet engine and the wing in the aft portion of the airframe are separated from the missile. After staging, rocket propulsion provides supersonic terminal flight penetration of threat defenses.

The bottom portion of the figure shows examples of cruise missiles that rely primarily on low RCS for their survivability. Note for the Naval Strike Missile (NSM) its low RCS features, which include a faceted seeker dome, a seeker dome that is uncoupled from aft airframe, body chines, and graphite composite structure. The faceted dome is IR transmissive for the missile seeker but reflects threat radar off to the side. The forward airframe is roll stabilized to allow seeker tracking while the inlet can be rolled to

High speed

SS-N-22 Sunburn (Ramjet supersonic propulsion)   3M-54E Sizzler (Rocket supersonic penetrator/
Turbojet subsonic fly-out)

Low RCS

NSM (Faceted dome, Decoupled airframe, Body chines,   JASSM (Flush inlet, Window dome, Trapezoidal
Composite structure)   body, Single tail, Canted nozzle, Composite
structure)

Fig. 6.81 Most long range strike missiles use either high speed or low RCS for survivability.

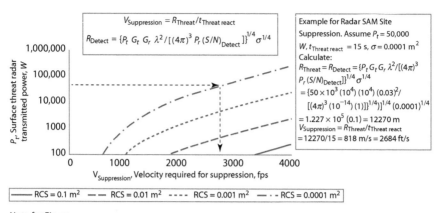

Note for Figure:

$R_{Threat} = R_{Detect}$ = Surface threat radar detection range, $(S/N)_{Detect}$ = Signal-to-noise required for detection = 1, Assumed unobstructed line-of-sight, G_t = Transmitter gain = 40 dB, G_r = Receiver gain = 40 dB, λ = Wavelength = 0.03 m, P_r = Receiver sensitivity = 10^{-14} W, σ = Target radar cross section, $V_{Suppression}$ = Velocity required for threat suppression, $t_{Threat\ react}$ = Threat reaction time detection to launch = Max allowable time for defense suppression = 15s

Fig. 6.82 High speed and low RCS enhance lethality and survivability by exploiting the threat response time.

either a bottom position (for efficient flight range), or a top position (for low RCS during terminal flight penetration). Body chines reduce RCS from creeping waves. Graphite composite structure absorbs radar energy, reducing RCS. The Joint Air-to-Surface Strike Missile (JASSM) is shown in the bottom right portion of the figure. Its low RCS features include a flush inlet, a flat window dome, a trapezoidal body, a single vertical tail, a canted nozzle, and graphite composite structure. The single vertical tail is shielded from a forward threat radar by the missile body. The canted nozzle prevents a rear ground threat radar from looking into the engine and also reduces the IR signature from the rear.

Shown in Fig. 6.82 is an example of the combined benefit of low RCS and high speed for threat radar defense suppression. Low RCS for the launch platform and high speed for the defense suppression missile provide higher survivability and higher lethality by exploiting the threat latency response time.

Assuming a worst case scenario of an autonomous SAM threat, the objective of the example is to destroy the threat radar site before it can launch a SAM. The required velocity $V_{Suppression}$ of the defense suppression missile is a function of the detection range by the threat R_{Threat} and the threat reaction time $t_{Threat\ react}$ to launch a SAM

$$V_{Suppression} = R_{Threat}/t_{Threat\ react}$$

A typical reaction time is about 15 s. The detection range of a radar is

$$R_{\text{Detect}} = \{P_t G_t G_r \lambda^2/[(4\pi)^3 P_r (S/N)_{\text{Detect}}]\}^{1/4} \sigma^{1/4}$$

In the above equation P_t = radar transmitted power, G_t = transmitter gain, G_r = receiver gain, λ = radar wavelength, P_r = receiver sensitivity, $(S/N)_{\text{Detect}}$ = signal-to-noise required for detection, and σ = target radar cross section. σ is the radar cross section of the aircraft that is launching the defense suppression missile.

Note from the figure the synergy of low RCS with high speed. A low RCS aircraft reduces the speed requirement of its defense suppression missile. However, since there is a lower limit of technology for cost-effective RCS, a high speed defense suppression missile is a complement to a low RCS aircraft.

As an example, assume a defense suppression aircraft with a radar cross section $\sigma = 0.001$ m^2. Assume a threat SAM site with the radar performance $(S/N)_{\text{Detect}} = 1$, unobstructed line-of-sight, $G_t = 40$ dB, $G_r = 40$ dB, $\lambda = 0.03$ m, $P_r = 10^{-14}$ W, and $t_{\text{Threat react}} = 15$ s. Compute

$$R_{\text{Detect}} = \{50 \times 10^3 (10^4)(10^4)(0.03)^2/[(4\pi)^3 (10^{-14})(1)]\}^{1/4}]^{1/4}(0.0001)^{1/4}$$
$$= 1.227 \times 10^5 (0.1) = 12{,}270 \, \text{m}$$

Next, compute the velocity that is required for the defense suppression missile to destroy a SAM site that has a 15 s reaction time to launch a SAM.

$$V_{\text{Suppression}} = 12270/15 = 818 \, \text{m/s} = 2684 \, \text{ft/s}$$

As a final comment, SAM site suppression is difficult. Even with a low RCS aircraft, the threat radar will usually detect a defense suppression missile at long range and shut down before missile impact. If the missile has an ARH-only seeker, it will cease homing if the threat radar shuts down. A multi-mode seeker has payoff in continued homing on the threat radar site after shut-down.

Shown in Fig. 6.83 is an example of survivability by avoiding detection from a ground-based radar SAM site threat. Two approaches are illustrated for survivability—reduced RCS and high altitude flight. Assumed are targets with three different values of RCS, from 0.001 to 0.1 m^2. Shown in the figure are the required flight altitude to avoid detection from the SAM site radar. Results are based on the radar range equation discussed previously, with an assumed signal-to-noise (S/N) for detection of $(S/N)_{\text{Detect}} = 1$. Another assumption is that there is an unobstructed line-of-sight to the target.

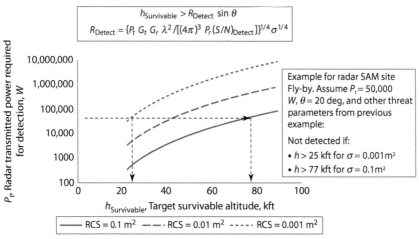

$$h_{\text{Survivable}} > R_{\text{Detect}} \sin \theta$$

$$R_{\text{Detect}} = \{P_t\, G_t\, G_r\, \lambda^2 / [(4\pi)^3\, P_r\, (S/N)_{\text{Detect}}]\}^{1/4}\, \sigma^{1/4}$$

Example for radar SAM site Fly-by. Assume $P_t =$ 50,000 W, $\theta =$ 20 deg, and other threat parameters from previous example:

Not detected if:
- $h >$ 25 kft for $\sigma =$ 0.001 m²
- $h >$ 77 kft for $\sigma =$ 0.1 m²

— RCS = 0.1 m²   — · — · RCS = 0.01 m²   ----- RCS = 0.001 m²

Note for Figure:
R_{Detect} = Surface threat radar detection range, $(S/N)_{\text{Detect}}$ = Signal-to-noise required for detection = 1, Unobstructed Line-of-sight, θ = Surface threat radar look angle = 20 deg, G_t = Transmitter gain = 40 dB, G_r = Receiver gain = 40 dB, λ = Wavelength = 0.03 m, P_r = Receiver sensitivity = 10^{-14} W, σ = Target radar cross section

Fig. 6.83   High altitude flight and low RCS enhance survivability by reducing the detection range.

The equations are

$$h_{\text{Survivable}} > R_{\text{Detect}} \sin \theta$$

$$R_{\text{Detect}} = \{P_t G_t G_r \lambda^2 / [(4\pi)^3 P_r (S/N)_{\text{Detect}}]\}^{1/4} \sigma^{1/4}$$

The assumed values of the ground threat radar parameters in the figure are the receiver threshold power sensitivity $P_r = 10^{-14}$ W, transmitter gain $G_t = 40$ dB, receiver gain $G_r = 40$ dB, and wavelength $\lambda = 0.03$ m ($f = 10 \times 10^9$ Hz). The threat transmitted power in the figure is varied by 5 orders of magnitude, from 100 to 10,000,000 W. Note the dramatic increase in the required power of the ground radar to detect the missile if the missile is at high altitude, which results in a large value of the slant range R. Reducing the radar cross section also requires a large increase in the power of the ground radar. A missile design tradeoff to avoid threat radar detection is the flight altitude versus reduced RCS. As an example, assume that a typical threat fire control radar has a transmitted power of 50,000 W and is looking up at a typical 20-deg elevation angle. A missile with a low RCS ($\sigma = 0.001$ m²) is not detected if it is above 25,000 ft altitude, a typical cruise altitude for a turbojet cruise missile. Similarly a missile with a much larger RCS ($\sigma = 0.1$ m²) is not detected if it is above 77,000 ft altitude, a typical cruise altitude for a ramjet cruise missile.

Drivers for radar cross section are the radar frequency, the target shape, the target orientation, and the target material. Figure 6.84 illustrates the principles of shaping and orientation to reduce RCS. Shown in the figure are a radar transmitter and the radar reflections from simple geometric shapes. Assumptions are a highly conductive (e.g., metal airframe) target, specular reflection, and a target dimension much larger than the radar wavelength ($l \gg \lambda$). The three example targets are 1) a sphere; 2) a flat plate oriented at a normal incidence to the radar transmitter; and 3) a flat plate oriented at a 30 deg incidence to the radar transmitter.

Note that for the first example, the spherical target in the far right portion of the figure, the radar reflections are isotropic, with reflection in all directions. An average portion of the radar transmitted energy is reflected back to the radar transmitter. For the assumption of specular reflection, the shadow region of the target has negligible backscatter return from traveling waves and creeping waves.

A mono-static radar has the transmitter and receiver at the same location. A bi-static radar has the receiver at a different location than the transmitter. The spherical target in the right portion of the figure illustrates radar reflections that are equally spaced on the target. The bi-static angles for target reflections at $y/r = 0, 25, 50, 75,$ and 100% radius locations are $\beta = 0, 29, 60, 97,$ and 180 deg, respectively. The radar cross section $\sigma_{\text{Bi-static}}$ for a bi-static radar is approximately the same as the mono-static radar,

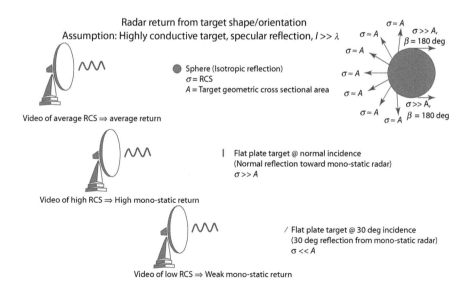

Fig. 6.84 Radar return/radar cross section drivers include target shape and target orientation.

except for $\beta = 180$ deg (bi-static radar directly behind the target and in-line with the transmitter. For $\beta = 180$ deg, the bi-static RCS is very large, $\sigma_{Bi\text{-static}} = 4\pi A/\lambda^2$. As an example, assume a spherical target with a presented area $A = 1$ m^2 and a radar wavelength $\lambda = 0.03$ m. Compute

$$\sigma_{Mono\text{-static}} = A = 1\,\text{m}^2$$

$$\sigma_{Bi\text{-static},\,\beta=180\,\text{deg}} = 4\pi A/\lambda^2 = 4\pi(1)/0.03^2 = 14{,}000\,\text{m}^2.$$

In the top left portion of the figure is an animation of the radar reflection from a spherical target. Note the isotropic reflection, with an average return for a mono-static radar. The next target animation, in the middle section of the figure, is a flat plate at normal incidence to the radar. For this case, most of the transmitted energy is reflected directly back toward the transmitter, resulting in a strong return, with a large radar cross section. Finally, the bottom section animation of the figure shows a flat plate oriented at a 30 deg incidence to the radar. As a first order effect, the radar is reflected at a mirror angle of 30 deg, with negligible reflected energy received by the radar. The flat plate at this orientation has a very small RCS.

A first order rule in shaping for low RCS is to avoid large flat surfaces that are facing the threat radar.

In Fig. 6.85 the ramjet baseline missile/ASALM PTV of Chapter 7 is used to illustrate geometry contributors to missile radar cross section. The ASALM PTV ramjet is similar to the ramjet baseline missile. One

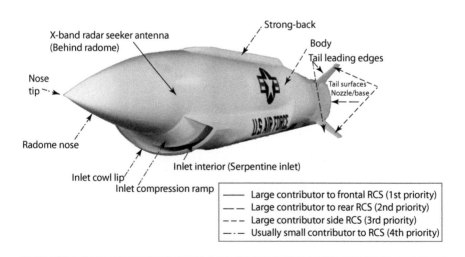

Fig. 6.85 Geometry contributors to radar cross section (ramjet baseline missile/ ASALM PTV example.)

difference is the ASALM PTV has a tangent ogive radome nose while the ramjet baseline missile has a conical radome nose.

The first priority to reducing the radar cross section of a missile is almost always to minimize the frontal RCS. Most engagements from the threat defenses are in the frontal aspect, especially in terminal flight. The second priority is to reduce the rear RCS. A rear engagement is less likely than a frontal engagement because it is more difficult for the threat to detect and intercept a retreating missile. A rear engagement is most likely to occur enroute to the target. The third and lowest priority is reduction of the side RCS. Side engagements are unlikely, especially for a high speed missile, because the exposure time to a side threat is usually small.

For a missile with a seeker, the seeker is usually the dominant contributor to the frontal RCS. An advantage of a seeker-less missile is reduced frontal RCS. For a missile with an inlet, the RCS contribution is design dependent. For the ramjet baseline missile, the inlet interior is a relatively small contributor to the frontal RCS. It has a serpentine inlet. A straight inlet would have a high frontal RCS and should be avoided if possible. The ramjet baseline missile has tail leading edges that are swept 37 deg, resulting in a small contribution to the frontal RCS. Although the ramjet baseline missile does not have a wing, if it did, the wing leading edge sweep should also be 37 deg, to avoid spreading the radar return over a larger angle than the tail return. Because of the time duration, a lobe spike flash from the leading edges is usually significant only if it is wider than about 3 deg aspect. The other contributors to the ramjet baseline missile frontal RCS are relatively small. These include the nose tip, radome nose, inlet cowl lip, and the inlet compression ramp.

The major contributor to the rear RCS of a missile is the nozzle/base. An advantage of a missile with a canted nozzle is reduced RCS and reduced IR signature. Also, a missile with wing, canard, and tail trailing edges that are swept 30 deg or more will have a smaller rear RCS.

The major contributor to side RCS is the body of the missile. Tail surfaces and other planar surfaces may also be large contributors to side RCS, depending upon the missile roll orientation, the number of tails, and the angle between the tails. For a cruciform missile flying in a typical x-roll orientation, the dihedral of two surfaces at a 90 deg angle provides a multiple bounce return, with a high return flash from the side of the missile. However, the RCS flash may be of short duration, and depending upon the missile roll activity and the threat radar processing capability, it may not be a problem.

An exact solution of the radar cross section of a missile is not a practical approach during the conceptual design and system engineering of a program. An exact solution requires solving Maxwell's electromagnetic field equations. Solving the partial differential equations with their boundary conditions would not be a good use of the limited time and resources that are typically available during the conceptual phase of a program. Instead, the recommended approach [34] for conceptual design and system engineering is to compute the missile RCS based on combining simple analytical shapes that already have exact solutions. An assumption is that the scattering contributions from each of the simple shapes can be added together without including their phase differences. Another typical assumption is no multiple bounce return from the simple shapes. For example, during conceptual design the RCS contribution of cruciform tails is usually predicted by adding the contribution from each tail without including the multiple bounce return from tail-to-body or tail-to-tail. A third assumption is that the simple shapes are metallic or highly conducting. A fourth assumption is high frequency specular optics, which requires that the missile geometry dimensions be much larger than the radar wave length ($l \gg \lambda$). This assumption typically limits reasonable accuracy to X-band (10 GHz) or higher radar frequency radar. This is usually not a problem, because for most threat fire control system radars are X-band. The RCS at the relatively low frequency (e.g., less than 1 GHz) of threat search radars is more of a function of the volume of the missile than that provided by airframe shaping and RAM. In the Rayleigh low frequency region the size of the missile is small compared to the wavelength. As a result, the phase of the radar and the current induced by the radar are nearly constant across the missile. As a first order effect, the radar cross section varies with λ^{-4}, and approaches the missile geometric cross section at low frequency. A fifth assumption is a free space return, with no ground effect. A sixth assumption that is typically used for conceptual design and system engineering is that the threat is a mono-static radar (threat transmitter/receiver in the same location) with circular polarization.

Shown in Fig. 6.86 are simple geometric shape approximations for the ramjet baseline missile/ASALM PTV. Simple shape approximations for the large contributors to the ramjet baseline missile RCS are a circular plate for the missile radar seeker antenna (for the frontal RCS), a plate for the nozzle base (rear RCS), plates for the tails (side RCS), and cylinders for the body and strong back (side RCS). The simple geometric shape representations of the other, less important, contributors are a prolate spheroid for the nose of a seeker-less missile, a cone for the nose tip, a wedge for the inlet compression ramp, a rectangular plate for the inlet interior, and wires for the inlet cowl lip and the leading/trailing edges of the tails.

A Pareto analysis is useful in identifying the relative importance of the missile RCS contributors. The example of Fig. 6.87 is the ramjet baseline missile, discussed in Chapter 7. Predictions are based on the frontal RCS of the simple shape methods of Ref 34.

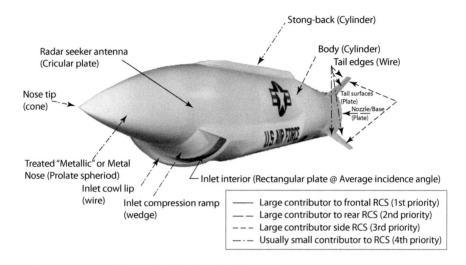

Fig. 6.86 Conceptual design radar cross section may be computed from modeling simple shapes scattering.

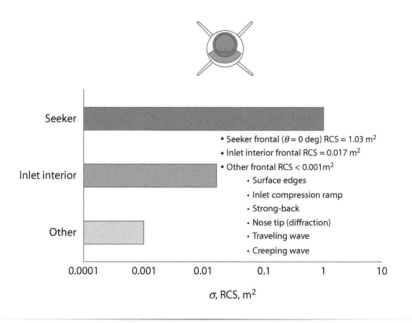

Fig. 6.87 A Pareto of the ramjet baseline missile/ASALM PTV frontal RCS shows that most of the frontal RCS is from the seeker antenna. (Source: Crispin, J. W., Jr., Goodrich, R. F., and Siegel, K. M., "A Theoretical Method for the Calculation of the Radar Cross Section of Aircraft and Missiles," Univeristy of Michigan Report 2591-1-H, July 1959.)

Note that the dominant parameter to the frontal RCS is the missile seeker ($\sigma_{Seeker} = 1.03$ m^2). The missile radome in front of the seeker was assumed to be transparent. The frontal RCS contribution from the inlet interior (0.017 m^2) and the other contributions from surface edges, inlet compression ramp, strong-back, nose tip diffraction, traveling wave, and creeping wave are much smaller (<0.001 m^2). An example of a relatively small type of contribution to RCS is diffraction. Diffraction occurs at an electromagnetic discontinuity such as a nose tip, a sharp leading edge, or a fastener that is slightly protruding. Diffraction occurs over a broad angle. Another type of contribution to RCS that is a relatively small contributor is a traveling wave. A traveling wave travels along the illuminated surface, scattering from protuberances or from a dielectric change (e.g., trailing edge). A creeping wave is somewhat similar to a traveling wave. A creeping wave creeps around the shadow region of body, scattering at gaps, a curvature change, or a dielectric change (e.g., trailing edge). It is more difficult to reduce the RCS from diffraction, traveling wave, and creeping wave. It is also expensive to logistically maintain an RCS < 0.001 m^2.

Based in this Pareto information, if the designer wishes to decrease the RCS of the ramjet baseline missile, the first priority should be given to reducing the specular RCS of the seeker. The following discussion will present a method of calculating the missile specular RCS. We will also present an example approach for reducing the ramjet baseline missile specular RCS.

Figure 6.88 shows the Ref. 34 prediction of the specular RCS of a circular disk and its application to a missile seeker antenna. The equations are

$$(\sigma/A)_{Disk} \approx [4\pi^2(d/\lambda)\sin\theta\,\tan^2\theta]^{-1}$$

$$(\sigma_{max}/A)_{Disk} = \pi^2(d/\lambda)^2$$

$$(\theta_{\sigma_{max}})_{Disk} = \tan^{-1}[(4\pi)^{4/3}(d/\lambda)]^{-1}$$

Definitions of the parameters in the above equations are

σ = radar cross section
A = area of circular plate
d = diameter of circular plate
λ = threat radar wavelength
θ = incidence angle, deg

The figure shows the non-dimensional radar cross section $(\sigma/A)_{Disk}$ as for $0 < \theta < 60$ deg and $d/\lambda = 5$, 10, and 20. Also shown as a reference is

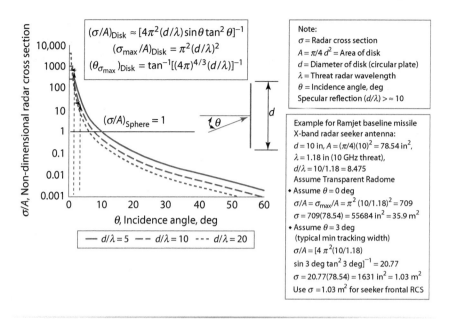

Fig. 6.88   The seeker radar antenna has a large RCS at near-normal incidence and low RCS at off boresight. (Source: Crispin, J. W., Jr., Goodrich, R. F., and Siegel, K. M., "A Theoretical Method for the Calculation of the Radar Cross Section of Aircraft and Missiles," Univerisity of Michigan Report 2591-1-H, July 1959.)

the non-dimensional RCS of a sphere, which is equal to its geometric area and is constant with θ, $(\sigma/A)_{\text{Sphere}} = 1$. Note from the figure that that value of the non-dimensional RCS of a circular disk for $\theta = 0$ deg is much larger than the non-dimensional sphere RCS/geometric area.

As an example, assume the ramjet baseline missile X-band radar seeker antenna is modeled as a circular disk, with an antenna diameter $d = 10$ in. Calculate

$$A = (\pi/4)(10)^2 = 78.54 \text{ in}^2$$

Assume the threat radar $\lambda = 1.18$ in (10 GHz threat). Calculate

$$d/\lambda = 10/1.18 = 8.475$$

Assume a transparent radome in front of the seeker. For $\theta = 0$ deg calculate

$$\sigma/A = \sigma_{\text{max}}/A = \pi^2 (10/1.18)^2 = 709$$

$$\sigma_{\theta=0 \text{ deg}} = 709(78.54) = 55684 \text{ in}^2 = 35.9 \text{ m}^2$$

The above result for RCS is probably higher than a realistic value, because the small width of the RCS flash spike at $\theta = 0$ deg. It is difficult for a fire control radar to track an RCS flash spike width less than about 3 deg, because of the short time. The flash spike width is

$$(\theta_{\sigma_{max}})_{Disk} = \tan^{-1}[(4\pi)^{4/3}(8.475)]^{-1} = \tan^{-1}(0.00404\,rad) = 0.23\,deg$$

At $\theta = 3$ deg, the RCS is

$$\sigma/A = [4\pi^2(10/1.18)\sin 3\,deg\,\tan^2 3\,deg]^{-1} = 20.77$$

$$\sigma_{\theta=3\,deg} = 20.77(78.54) = 1631\,in^2 = 1.03\,m^2$$

We will use $\sigma = 1.03\,m^2$ for the seeker frontal RCS, as a realistic value. However, this may be optimistic, depending upon the threat radar tracking capability.

For a rectangular flat surface, the RCS equations are [34]

$$(\sigma/A)_{Rectangular\ plate} = [4\pi(L/W)\sin^2\theta]^{-1}$$

$$(\sigma_{max}/A)_{Rectangular\ plate} = 4\pi A/\lambda^2$$

$$(\theta_{\sigma_{max}})_{Rectangular\ plate} = \sin^{-1}[4\pi(L/\lambda)]^{-1}$$

Definitions of the parameters in the above equations are

σ = radar cross section

$A = LW$ = area of plate

W = width of plate

L = length of plate

λ = threat radar wavelength

θ = incidence angle

Figure 6.89 shows the non-dimensional radar cross section $(\sigma/A)_{Rectangular\ plate}$ for $0 < \theta < 80$ deg, $L/W = 1$, 2 and $L/\lambda = 10$, 20. Note from the curves that L/λ has an effect on σ only if $\theta < \sin^{-1}[4\pi(L/\lambda)]^{-1}$. Also note that the sensitivity of σ to θ for a rectangular plate is similar to that of the last figure for a circular disk. The value of the RCS for $\theta = 0$ deg is much larger than the sphere RCS/geometric area. Also, the value of RCS for large θ is much less than the sphere RCS/geometric area.

As an example, assume the ramjet baseline missile/ASALM PTV inlet interior from Chapter 7. The chin inlet has a "smile" with an effective width $W = 18.2$ in, a cowl height $h = 3$ in, and a serpentine expansion to the combustor (which hides the rear face of the combustor). The effective length up to the shielded portion of the inlet is $L = 21.3$ in and the

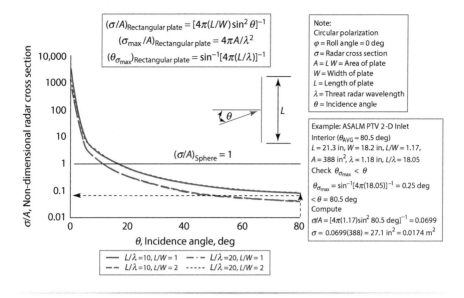

Fig. 6.89 A rectangular flat surface has large RCS at normal incidence and low RCS at an inclination angle. (Source: Crispin, J. W., Jr., Goodrich, R. F., and Siegel, K. M., "A Theoretical Method for the Calculation of the Radar Cross Section of Aircraft and Missiles," Univerisity of Michigan Report 2591-1-H, July 1959.)

average angle up to the shielded portion of the inlet is $\theta_{\mathrm{AVG}} \approx 80.5$ deg. Compute

$$L/W = 21.3/18.2 = 1.17$$

$$A = LW = 21.3(18.2) = 388\,\text{in}^2$$

Assume $\lambda = 1.18$ in. Compute

$$L/\lambda = 21.3/1.18 = 18.05$$

Check that $\theta_{\sigma_{\max}} < \theta$

$$\theta_{\sigma_{\max}} = \sin^{-1}[4\pi(L/\lambda)]^{-1} = \sin^{-1}[4\pi(18.05)]^{-1}$$
$$= 0.25\,\text{deg} < \theta = 80.5\,\text{deg}$$

Finally, compute

$$\sigma/A = [4\pi(1.17)\sin^2 80.5\,\text{deg}]^{-1} = 0.0699$$

$$\sigma = 0.0699(388) = 27.1\,\text{in}^2 = 0.0174\,\text{m}^2$$

It is noted that a straight inlet would have a much larger value of RCS. Assume that a straight inlet would act as a flat plate at normal incidence. For the same capture geometry as the ramjet baseline missile ($h = L = 3$ in, $W = 18.2$ in)

$$A = LW = 3(18.2) = 24.6 \text{ in}$$

At $\theta = 0$ deg the RCs is

$$(\sigma_{max}/A)_{\text{Rectangular plate}} = 4\pi A/\lambda^2 = 4\pi(24.6/1.18^2) = 222$$

$$\sigma = 222(24.6) = 12122 \text{ in}^2 = 7.82 \text{ m}^2$$

Comparing the angle for maximum RCS with a typical minimum flash width tracking angle of $\theta = 3$ deg

$$L/\lambda = 3/1.18 = 2.54$$

$$\theta_{\sigma_{max}} = \sin^{-1}[4\pi(L/\lambda)]^{-1} = \sin^{-1}[4\pi(2.54)]^{-1} = \sin^{-1}(0.0313)$$
$$= 1.79 \text{ deg} < 3 \text{ deg}$$

Using a typical value of $\theta = 3$ deg for a tracking radar

$$L/W = 3/18.2 = 0.1648$$

$$\sigma/A = [4\pi(0.1648)\sin^2 3 \text{ deg}]^{-1} = 176$$

$$\sigma_{\theta=3 \text{ deg}} = 176(24.6) = 9623 \text{ in}^2 = 6.21 \text{ m}^2$$

$\sigma = 6.21$ m^2 would probably be a more realistic value for a straight inlet.

Comparing the frontal RCS of the ramjet baseline serpentine inlet with a straight inlet, the serpentine inlet reduces the frontal RCS to only 0.3% of the RCS of a straight inlet (0.0174 versus 6.21 m^2).

The next simple shape to be considered is a prolate spheroid. A prolate spheroid has a length-to-diameter ratio (fineness ratio) $l/d \geq 0.5$. In the upper right section of Fig. 6.90 is a sketch of a prolate spheroid. From Ref. 34, the RCS of a prolate spheroid is

$$(\sigma/A)_{\text{Prolate spheroid}} = \{4(l/d)^2\{\sin^2\theta/[4(l/d)^2] + \cos^2\theta\}^2\}^{-1}$$

Parameter definitions in the above equation are

σ = radar cross section

$A = (\pi/4)d^2$ = cross sectional area of spheroid

l = length of spheroid

d = diameter of spheroid

λ = threat radar wavelength

θ = incidence angle, deg

Note from the figure that the RCS of a prolate spheroid is relatively low and becomes very low at high l/d. A hemisphere ($l/d = 0.5$) has the highest non-dimensional RCS, $(\sigma/A)_{\text{Sphere}} = 1$. Also note that RCS increases slowly with increasing θ.

As an example, assume that the ramjet baseline missile has either a metal nose (no seeker), a conformal seeker antenna, or a "metallic" radome that is reflective of the threat radar but has a band-pass at the seeker wavelength. An example is radome that is reflective of a threat X-band radar but has a band-pass for a mmW or an IR missile seeker. An approach for an IR band-pass is a thin film of gold over the IR dome. An approach for a mmW band-pass is a fine wire grid embedded in the

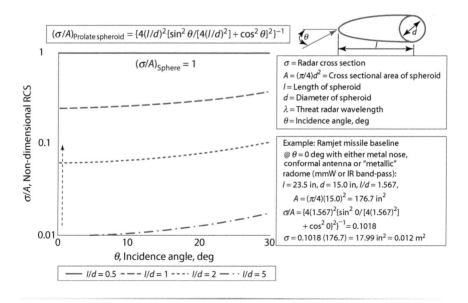

Fig. 6.90 A high fineness metallic nose has a low frontal RCS. (Source: Crispin, J. W., Jr., Goodrich, R. F., and Siegel, K. M., "A Theoretical Method for the Calculation of the Radar Cross Section of Aircraft and Missiles," Univerisity of Michigan Report 2591-1-H, July 1959.)

radome. For the example calculation, we will assume that the threat radar is at $\theta = 0$ deg. From the Chapter 7 data

$$l = 23.5 \text{ in}, \quad d = 15.0 \text{ in}$$

Calculate

$$l/d = 1.567$$

$$A = (\pi/4)(15.0)^2 = 176.7 \text{ in}^2$$

$$\sigma/A = \left\{ 4(1.567)^2 \left\{ \sin^2 0 / \left[4(1.567)^2 \right] + \cos^2 0 \right\}^2 \right\}^{-1} = 0.1018$$

$$\sigma = 0.1018(176.7) = 17.99 \text{ in}^2 = 0.0116 \text{ m}^2$$

Comparing the frontal RCS of the metal nose with the ramjet baseline missile seeker, the metal nose reduces the frontal RCS to only 1% of the RCS of the seeker (0.0116 versus 1.03 m²).

Depending upon the shaping, a missile RCS may be larger or smaller than its geometric area. Figure 6.91 compares the geometric frontal area of the ramjet baseline missile with the frontal RCS of the ramjet baseline missile and a reduced RCS missile.

In the top portion of the figure is a frontal view of the ramjet baseline missile. The frontal area is $A = 2.264 \text{ ft}^2 = 0.210 \text{ m}^2 = -7$ dB.

Ramjet baseline missile frontal geometric area
$A = 2.264 \text{ ft}^2 = 0.210 \text{ m}^2 = -7 \text{ dB}$

Ramjet baseline missile frontal RCS (untreated radome, X-band seeker)
$\sigma \approx \sigma_{\text{Seeker}} + \sigma_{\text{Inlet}} = 1.03 + 0.0174 = 1.05 \text{ m}^2 = 0.2 \text{ dB}$

Ramjet baseline missile with reduced RCS from either a metal nose (no seeker with GPS/INS/ data link guidance), Conformal antenna, or "Metallic" radome (block cmW threat radar with mmW or IR seeker band-pass)
$\sigma \approx \sigma_{\text{Nose}} + \sigma_{\text{Inlet}} = 0.0116 + 0.0174 = 0.029 \text{ m}^2 = -15 \text{ dB}$

Note: ● and ○ are relative RCS area comparisons with geometric area of ramjet baseline missile.

Fig. 6.91   An example of reduction of frontal RCS (ramjet baseline missile).

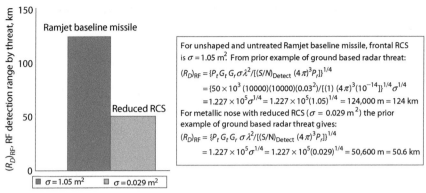

Fig. 6.92 Reduced RCS reduces radar detection range.

The middle section of the figure is a relative scale of the ramjet baseline missile frontal RCS compared to its geometric area. Note the relatively large RCS area compared to the geometric area (0.2 dB versus -7 dB). The frontal RCS is based on contributions from the missile seeker and inlet, neglecting the much smaller contributions from the inlet compression ramp, inlet cowl lip, tail leading edges, and strong back.

$$\sigma \approx \sigma_{\text{Seeker}} + \sigma_{\text{Inlet}} = 1.03 + 0.0174 = 1.05 \, \text{m}^2 = 0.2 \, \text{dB}$$

The bottom portion of the figure shows the relative scale of a reduced RCS for the ramjet baseline missile. Note the relatively small RCS area compared to the geometric area (-15 dB versus -7 dB). The reduced RCS is provided by either a metal nose (no seeker with GPS/INS/data link guidance), a conformal antenna, or a "metallic" radome that blocks a threat cmW radar, with a mmW or IR band-pass for the seeker. The frontal RCS is based on a prolate spheroid metal nose and inlet.

$$\sigma \approx \sigma_{\text{Nose}} + \sigma_{\text{Inlet}} = 0.0116 + 0.0174 = 0.029 \, \text{m}^2 = -15 \, \text{dB}$$

For most cruise missiles, reduced radar cross section is the primary approach to avoiding long range detection. A cruise missile without shaping and treatment for low RCS will be more easily detected at long range by the threat radar. The RCS calculations and RF threat characteristics from the prior examples will be used to illustrate the relative importance of RCS signature.

Figure 6.92 compares the RF detection range of the ramjet baseline missile with the detection range of a reduced RCS missile. From the prior example, the frontal RCS is $\sigma = 1.05 \ \mathrm{m}^2$. Detection range by the threat is

$$(R_D)_{RF} = \{P_t G_t G_r \sigma \lambda^2 / [(S/N)_{\mathrm{Detect}}(4\pi)^3 P_r]\}^{1/4} \sigma^{1/4}$$

$$= \left\{50 \times 10^3 (10000)(10000)(0.03^2) / [(1)(4\pi)^3(10^{-14})]\right\}^{1/4} \sigma^{1/4}$$

$$= 1.227 \times 10^5 \sigma^{1/4} = 1.227 \times 10^5 (1.05)^{1/4} = 124{,}000 \ \mathrm{m} = 124 \ \mathrm{km}$$

Note from the above equation that detection range is proportional to $\sigma^{1/4}$.

Based on prior RCS calculations and threat data, the detection range for a reduced RCS missile that is based on a metallic nose ($\sigma = 0.029 \ \mathrm{m}^2$) is

$$(R_D)_{RF} = 1.227 \times 10^5 \sigma^{1/4} = 1.227 \times 10^5 (0.029)^{1/4} = 50{,}600 \ \mathrm{m} = 50.6 \ \mathrm{km}$$

In Fig. 6.93 the ramjet baseline missile/ASALM PTV of Chapter 7 is used to illustrate contributors to missile infrared signature. The ramjet baseline missile is similar to the ASLAM PTV. The ASALM PTV has a tangent ogive radome nose, while the ramjet baseline missile has a conical radome nose.

The first priority to reducing the IR signature of a missile is almost always to minimize the frontal IR signature. Similar to RF threat engagements, most engagements from an IR threat are in the frontal aspect, especially in terminal flight. Also similar to the RF threat, the second

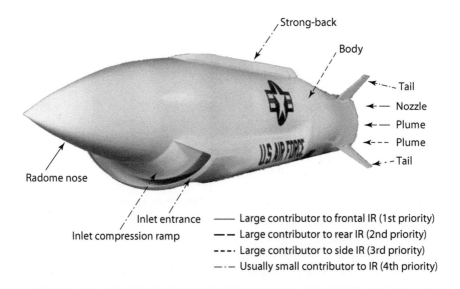

Fig. 6.93 Contributors to infrared signature (ramjet baseline missile/ASALM PTV example.)

priority is usually to reduce the rear IR signature. A rear engagement is usually less likely than a frontal engagement because most missiles are relatively high speed. It is usually more difficult for the threat to intercept a retreating missile. A rear engagement is most likely to occur enroute to the target. The third and lowest priority is a reduction of the side IR signature. Side engagements are unlikely, especially for a high speed missile, because the exposure time to a side threat is usually small.

Depending upon the missile thrust, the missile forebody is usually the largest contributor to the frontal RCS. For a high thrust rocket, the plume extends outside the missile body diameter, and also becomes a primary contributor to the frontal IR signature. For a relatively low thrust missile, such as an air-breathing cruise missile, the plume in a frontal engagement is often shrouded by the missile body and usually provides a relatively small contribution to the frontal IR signature. The plume signature is a function of the missile thrust, altitude, the combustion products with different radiation bands, and the combustion temperature.

The major contributors to rear IR signature are the plume and the nozzle/base of the missile. A canted nozzle is an approach to reduce the IR signature that is presented to a surface threat.

The major contributors to side IR signature are the plume and the body of the missile.

Conceptual design modeling of the missile airframe IR signature is based on computing the temperatures on the components of the airframe, their spectral emittance radiance, their spectral radiant power, and then combining the components to determine the total spectral radiant power. For a the frontal IR signature, this approach is usually accurate up to about ± 30 deg off boresight. The calculations of the frontal IR signature are based on the nose-on presented area.

An inherent characteristic of a high speed missile is a high infrared signature. As shown in Fig. 6.94, the infrared signature of a Mach 4 missile can be more than an order of magnitude greater than that of a Mach 2 missile. The figure is based on the body frontal signature of the ramjet baseline missile, which has a frontal presented area $A = S_{Ref} = 2.264 \text{ ft}^2 = 2103$ cm^2. The presented area of the tails is neglected. Also, a steady-state, aggregate temperature is used in this conceptual design analysis. A more detailed transient temperature distribution would be appropriate during the follow-on preliminary design and system engineering activity. The equations for radiant intensity and spectral radiance are

$$(I_T)_{\Delta\lambda} = \varepsilon L_\lambda (\lambda_2 - \lambda_1) A / \pi$$

$$L_\lambda = 3.74 \times 10^4 / \{\lambda^5 \{e^{[1.44 \times 10^4/(\lambda T)]} - 1\}\}$$

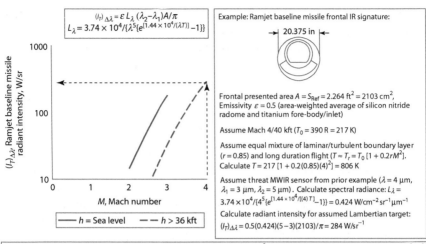

Fig. 6.94 A high speed missile has high infrared signature.

Parameters in the above equations are $(I_T)_{\Delta\lambda}$ = target radiant intensity between λ_1 and λ_2, W/sr; A = presented area, cm^2; ε = emissivity; L_λ = spectral radiance, Wcm^{-2} sr^{-2} μm^{-1}; λ_2, λ_1 = upper/lower cutoff wavelengths, μm; λ = average wavelength, μm; T = temperature, K; M = Mach number; h = flight altitude, ft; T_0 = free stream temperature, K; r = boundary layer recovery factor; and T_r = boundary layer recovery temperature, K.

The following is an example calculation of the radiant intensity of the ramjet baseline missile. The frontal area emissivity is $\varepsilon = 0.5$. This is an area-weighted emissivity of the silicon nitride radome and the titanium forebody/inlet.

We will assume $M = 4$, $h = 40$ kft ($T_0 = 390$ R), $r = 0.85$ (mixture of laminar/turbulent boundary layer), and a long duration flight with a thermally soaked airframe ($T = T_r$). Then

$$T = T_r = T_0\left[1 + 0.2rM^2\right] = 217\left[1 + 0.2(0.85)(4)^2\right] = 1451\,\text{R} = 806\,\text{K}$$

Assume the threat MWIR sensor from the prior example (wavelength $\lambda = 4$ μm). Calculating the spectral radiance at 4 μm wavelength

$$L_\lambda = 3.74 \times 10^4/\{\lambda^5\{e^{[1.44\times10^4/(\lambda T)]} - 1\}\}$$

$$= 3.74 \times 10^4/\{4^5\{e^{[1.44\times10^4/4(806)]} - 1\}\}$$

$$= 0.424\,\text{Wcm}^{-2}\text{sr}^{-2}\,μm^{-1}$$

Assume that the threat sensor upper and lower wavelength cutoffs are $\lambda_2 = 5\ \mu$m and $\lambda_1 = 3\ \mu$m. Finally, calculate the radiant intensity for an assumed Lambertian (hemispherical emission) target

$$(I_T)_{\Delta\lambda} = \varepsilon L_\lambda(\lambda_2 - \lambda_1)A/\pi = 0.5(0.424)(4.4 - 3.6)(2103)/\pi = 113.5\ \text{Wsr}^{-1}$$

Previously in this chapter we discussed the atmospheric attenuation of an IR signal. In clear weather, the MWIR wavelength (3 to 5 μm) is primarily attenuated by molecular interaction with the "greenhouse" gases H_2O and CO_2. For an LWIR (8 to 12 μm) wavelength, the clear weather attenuation is primarily from H_2O, CO_2, and O_3 gases. The IR detection range including the atmospheric transmission and the one-way atmospheric transmission are given by

$$(R_D)_{\text{IR}} = \{(I_T)_{\Delta\lambda}\eta_a A_0\{D^*/[(\Delta f_p)^{1/2}(A_d)^{1/2}]\}(S/N)^{-1}_{\text{Detect}}\}^{1/2}$$

$$\eta_a = (1 - \alpha)^R$$

Parameters in the above equations are

$(R_D)_{\text{IR}}$ = detection range for passive IR seeker, m

$(I_T)_{\Delta\lambda}$ = Lambertian target radiant intensity between λ_1 and λ_2, W/sr

η_a = atmospheric transmission

α = atmospheric extinction coefficient, km

Figure 6.95 shows $(R_D)_{\text{IR}}$ based on the characteristics of the previous IR threat example. Results are shown for low-to-high values of $(I_T)_{\Delta\lambda}$ (10 to 1000 W/sr) and low-to-high values of α (0 to 0.1/km).

The figure is based on the following values of the IR threat characteristics:

$$A_o = \text{optics aperture area} = 0.01267\ \text{m}^2$$

$$D^* = \text{specific detectivity} = 1 \times 10^{11}\ \text{cm Hz}^{1/2}/\text{W}$$

$$\Delta f_p = \text{pixel bandwidth} = 50\ \text{Hz}$$

$$A_d = \text{individual pixel detector area} = 0.000016\ \text{cm}^2$$

$$(S/N)_{\text{Detect}} = \text{signal-to-noise ratio for detection} = 5$$

$$\lambda_2 = \text{upper cutoff wavelength} = 4.4\ \mu\text{m}$$

$$\lambda_1 = \text{lower cutoff wavelength} = 3.6\ \mu\text{m}$$

$$\lambda = \text{average wavelength} = 4\ \mu\text{m}$$

The value of $(S/N)_{\text{Detect}} = 5$ is a typical value. $(S/N)_{\text{Detect}}$ could be as low as 1 for an exo-atmospheric target with a space background and as

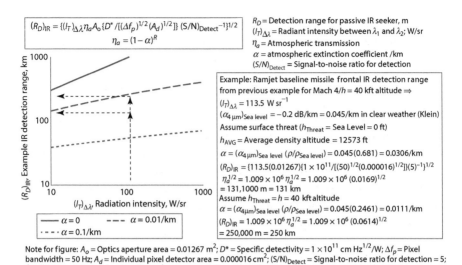

$$(R_D)_{IR} = \{[(I_T)_{\Delta\lambda}\eta_a A_o \{D^* /[(\Delta f_p)^{1/2}(A_d)^{1/2}]\} (S/N)_{Detect}^{-1}\}^{1/2}$$
$$\eta_a = (1-\alpha)^R$$

R_D = Detection range for passive IR seeker, m
$(I_T)_{\Delta\lambda}$ = Radiant intensity between λ_1 and λ_2; W/sr
η_a = Atmospheric transmission
α = atmospheric extinction coefficient /km
$(S/N)_{Detect}$ = Signal-to-noise ratio for detection

Example: Ramjet baseline missile frontal IR detection range from previous example for Mach 4/h = 40 kft altitude ⇒
$(I_T)_{\Delta\lambda}$ = 113.5 W sr^{-1}
$(\alpha_{4\,\mu m})_{Sea\,level}$ = −0.2 dB/km = 0.045/km in clear weather (Klein)
Assume surface threat (h_{Threat} = Sea Level = 0 ft)
h_{AVG} = Average density altitude = 12573 ft
$\alpha = (\alpha_{4\,\mu m})_{Sea\,level}\,(\rho/\rho_{Sea\,level})$ = 0.045(0.681) = 0.0306/km
$(R_D)_{IR}$ = {113.5(0.01267){1 × 10^{11}/[(50)$^{1/2}$(0.000016)$^{1/2}$]}(5)$^{-1}$}$^{1/2}$
$\eta_a^{1/2}$ = 1.009 × 10^6 $\eta_a^{1/2}$ = 1.009 × 10^6 (0.0169)$^{1/2}$
= 131,1000 m = 131 km
Assume h_{Threat} = h = 40 kft altitude
$\alpha = (\alpha_{4\,\mu m})_{Sea\,level}\,(\rho/\rho_{Sea\,level})$ = 0.045(0.2461) = 0.0111/km
$(R_D)_{IR}$ = 1.009 × 10^6 $\eta_a^{1/2}$ = 1.009 × 10^6 (0.0614)$^{1/2}$
= 250,000 m = 250 km

Note for figure: A_o = Optics aperture area = 0.01267 m^2; D^* = Specific detectivity = 1 ×10^{11} cm Hz$^{1/2}$/W; Δf_p= Pixel bandwidth = 50 Hz; A_d = Individual pixel detector area = 0.000016 cm^2; (S/N)$_{Detect}$ = Signal-to-noise ratio for detection = 5; λ_2 = Upper cutoff wavelength = 5 μm; λ_1 = Lower cutoff wavelength = 3 μm; λ = Average wavelength = 4 μm

Fig. 6.95 IR detection range is reduced by atmospheric attenuation, especially at low altitude.

high as 10 for a target in ground clutter and solar noise. Another possible detection mechanism is contrast.

As an example, we will calculate IR detection range of the ramjet baseline missile in a frontal engagement. The assumed Mach number and altitude are Mach 4/h = 40 kft. From the prior example

$$(I_T)_{\Delta\lambda} = 113.5 \text{ W sr}^{-1}$$

Next, calculate η_a.

The atmospheric attenuation at sea level for a 4 μm (MWIR) signal is − 0.2 dB/km in clear weather (Ref. 25). This provides 0.955/km transmission. The atmospheric extinction coefficient is

$$(\alpha_{4\mu m})_{Sea\,level} = 1 - 0.955 = 0.045/\text{km}$$

As a comparison, the atmospheric attenuation at sea level for a 10 μm (LWIR) signal is −0.05 dB/km in clear weather (Ref. 25). This provides 0.989/km transmission. The atmospheric extinction coefficient is

$$(\alpha_{10\mu m})_{Sea\,level} = 1 - 0.989 = 0.011/\text{km}$$

A tradeoff is an LWIR versus MWIR sensor. Although LWIR has less atmospheric attenuation in clear weather than MWIR, other considerations such as detector detectivity, contrast, and aperture optics are other tradeoffs in MWIR versus LWIR selection. For detecting a hot target, such as the ramjet baseline missile, an MWIR sensor is usually the better choice.

First assume that the threat sensor is at sea level (h_{Threat} = Sea level = 0 ft), looking up at its target, which is at h = 40 kft altitude. The density ratio is

$$(\rho_{h=40\,\text{kft}}/\rho_{\text{Sea level}}) = 0.000585\;\text{slug/ft}^3/0.002377\;\text{slug/ft}^3 = 0.2461$$

Because the density variation with altitude is non-linear, we will use a weighted average for the density between sea level and 40 kft latitude. An approximate equation for the density ratio of the 1976 Standard Atmosphere is

$$\rho/\rho_{\text{Sea level}} = \left(1 - 6.875 \times 10^{-6}\,h\right)^{4.2561}$$

Between sea level and h = 40 kft, the average density altitude is

$$h_{\text{AVG}} = (1 - \rho_{h=40\,\text{kft}}/\rho_{\text{Sea level}})/6.875 \times 10^{-6}$$
$$- \left\{\left[(1 - \rho_{h=40\,\text{kft}}/\rho_{\text{Sea level}})^{1.2350}\right]/8.491 \times 10^{-6}\right\}$$
$$= (1 - 0.2461)/6.875 \times 10^{-6} - \left(1 - 0.2461^{1.2350}\right)/8.491 \times 10^{-6}$$
$$= 12{,}573\;\text{ft}$$

Between sea level and h = 40 kft, the weighted average density is

$$\rho_{\text{AVG}}/\rho_{\text{Sea level}} = \left[1 - 6.875 \times 10^{-6}(12573)\right]^{4.2561} = 0.681$$

It is assumed that the extinction coefficient is proportional to the density of the atmosphere. Computing the average extinction coefficient

$$\alpha_{\text{AVG}} = (\alpha_{4\mu\text{m}})_{\text{Sea level}}(\rho/\rho_{\text{Sea level}}) = 0.045(0.681) = 0.0306/\text{km}$$

Iterating with $\eta_a = (1 - \alpha)^R$, the maximum detection range for a 4 µm sensor looking up from sea level to h = 40 kft altitude is

$$(R_D)_{\text{IR}} = 16730(I_T)_{\Delta\lambda}^{1/2}\eta_a^{1/2} = 16730(113.5)^{1/2}\left(0.0169^{1/2}\right) = 131{,}000\;\text{m}$$
$$= 131\;\text{km}$$

As a comparison of a surface based sensor versus a high altitude sensor, assume that the threat 4 µm sensor is at the same altitude as its target, h = 40 kft. The atmospheric extinction coefficient is

$$\alpha = (\alpha_{4\mu\text{m}})_{\text{Sea level}}(\rho/\rho_{\text{Sea level}}) = 0.045(0.2461) = 0.0111/\text{km}$$

Again, iterating with $\eta_a = (1 - \alpha)^R$, compute

$$(R_D)_{\text{IR}} = 94700(113.5)^{1/2}(0.0614)^{1/2} = 250{,}000\;\text{m} = 250\;\text{km}$$

The high altitude IR sensor has 91% longer range than a sea level IR sensor (250 km versus 131 km). An IR sensor would probably be more effective with a high altitude UAV than with a ground platform.

Figure 6.96 compares the RF and IR frontal detection range for the ramjet baseline missile at Mach $4/h = 40$ kft altitude. From prior examples, the frontal RCS is $\sigma = 1.05$ m^2 and the frontal radiant intensity is $(I_T)_{\Delta\lambda} = 113.5$ W/sr. Based on assumed threats of a 50 KW radar at sea level and a 4 µm threat sensor at sea level ($h = 0$ kft), the detection ranges are

$$(R_D)_{RF} = 124 \text{ km}$$
$$(R_D)_{IR} = 131 \text{ km}$$

For the ramjet baseline missile, with the assumed threats, it could be a higher payoff to reduce the IR signature than the RCS. However other considerations include the difficulty/cost in achieving signature reduction, the probability of facing the different threats, and the relative importance of signature reduction compared to other approaches (e.g., speed, altitude) for survivability.

A consideration that favors signature reduction is its synergy with improved lethality effectiveness. A lower signature reduces the time

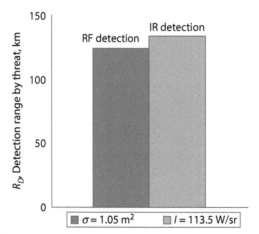

Note:
For ramjet baseline missile, frontal RCS is $\sigma = 1.05$ m^2. From prior example, with threat RF sensor at sea level, $(R_D)_{RF} = 124$ km

From prior example, frontal radiant intensity of ramjet baseline missile at Mach $4/h = 40$ kft $\Rightarrow (I_T)_{\Delta\lambda} = 113.5$ W/sr and threat IR sensor at h = sea level (0 ft) altitude with clear weather $\Rightarrow (R_D)_{IR} = 131$ km

Fig. 6.96 The Mach 4 ramjet baseline missile IR detection range is larger than its RCS detection range.

available for the threat to employ countermeasures, enhancing the effectiveness. Defense suppression is an example where reduced observables enhances lethality and mission effectiveness.

It is difficult to accurately predict the signature of a missile during conceptual design. Conceptual design methods are typically limited to missiles with an RCS $> \sim 0.02$ m^2 and an IR signature $(I_T)_{\Delta\lambda} > \sim 10$ W/sr. Although preliminary design methods have better accuracy for low observable missiles, they are difficult to apply. RCS prediction methods such as the geometric theory of diffraction (GTD), physical theory of diffraction (PTD), method of moments (MoM), and finite difference time domain (FDTD) are applicable to complex shapes and provide better accuracy for low observable missiles. However, these have a steep learning curve and are difficult modeling. Preliminary design IR signature methods require a more detailed temperature distribution over the airframe and details of the plume combustion products excitation frequencies.

Missiles that usually require signature tests include 1) cruise missiles (RCS, IR, and possibly contrail), 2) indirect fire missiles with a time of flight greater than about 60 s (RCS), 3) anti-radiation homing (ARH) missiles (RCS), 4) hypersonic missiles (IR, RCS), 5) any reduced signature missile (RCS/IR) and possibly laser cross section (LCS), and 6) active seeker out-of-band emissions (RF).

RCS ground tests usually begin with subscale metal models in a small compact indoor range. High frequency radar is required for model scaling. This test evaluates first order shaping and the accuracy of the design prediction methods. The next step, if required, is a full scale dielectric missile in a large anechoic chamber. This test evaluates the effectiveness of radar absorbing material (RAM). The next level of sophistication, if required, is the actual full scale dielectric missile mounted on a low dielectric strut support on an outdoor range. Finally, RCS measurements may be conducted during the flight test of the missile. Test parameters include frequency, polarization, azimuth, and elevation.

IR ground tests usually begin with subscale models in a low Reynolds number wind tunnel, with less than full scale temperature. Techniques such as temperature sensitive paint with thermographic imagery provide an estimate of the airframe IR signature and local hot spots. The next test, if required, is a high temperature wind tunnel test. A spectrometer/radiometer provides a more accurate airframe IR signature. For the plume signature, a radiometer/spectrometer provides IR signature during full scale propulsion static firing tests. Results are scaled to other altitude flight conditions. Finally, IR signature measurements may be conducted during the flight tests of the missile. Predictions such as emissivity variation with temperature, full scale Reynolds number, and the plume geometry variation with Mach number and altitude are confirmed in flight test.

Another consideration in missile survivability and effectiveness is the threat latency time. The latency response time of the threat may be sufficiently long to allow missile survivability. The typical human response time is about 10 to 20 s.

In Fig. 6.97 a frontal exposure to a surface-to-air threat is used to illustrate the relationship of detection range, velocity, and exposure time. For a forward surface threat, the exposure time to the threat is

$$t_{\text{Exposure}} \approx R_D/V$$

The above equation is based on an assumption of frontal exposure and constant heading toward the surface threat. Parameters are

$$t_{\text{Exposure}} = \text{exposure time}$$
$$R_D = \text{detection range by threat}$$
$$V = \text{velocity}$$

The ramjet baseline missile will be used as an example calculation. Assume a flight condition of Mach 4, $h = 40$ kft altitude. The missile velocity is $V = 3872$ ft/s $= 1180$ m/s. From a prior example, the frontal RCS $\sigma = 1.05$ m^2 and $R_D = 124$ km $= 124{,}000$ m. Calculate

$$t_{\text{Exposure}} = 124000/1180 = 105\,\text{s}$$

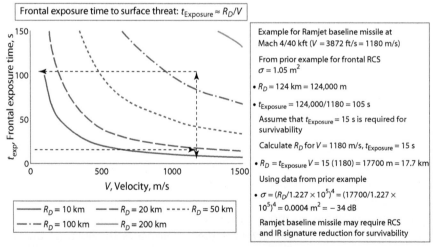

Frontal exposure time to surface threat: $t_{\text{Exposure}} \approx R_D/V$

Example for Ramjet baseline missile at Mach 4/40 kft ($V = 3872$ ft/s $= 1180$ m/s)

From prior example for frontal RCS
$\sigma = 1.05$ m^2

• $R_D = 124$ km $= 124{,}000$ m

• $t_{\text{Exposure}} = 124{,}000/1180 = 105$ s

Assume that $t_{\text{Exposure}} = 15$ s is required for survivability

Calculate R_D for $V = 1180$ m/s, $t_{\text{Exposure}} = 15$ s

• $R_D = t_{\text{Exposure}} V = 15\,(1180) = 17700$ m $= 17.7$ km

Using data from prior example

• $\sigma = (R_D/1.227 \times 10^5)^4 = (17700/1.227 \times 10^5)^4 = 0.0004$ m$^2 = -34$ dB

Ramjet baseline missile may require RCS and IR signature reduction for survivability

Note: Based on assumption of frontal exposure, constant heading toward SAM threat.
$t_{\text{exposure}} = $ exposure time, $R_D = $ detection range by threat, $V = $ velocity

Fig. 6.97   A short detection range and high speed reduce threat exposure time, enhancing survivability and effectiveness.

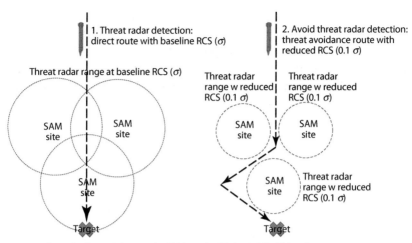

Fig. 6.98 Mission planning/threat avoidance and reduced observables enhance survivability.

Assume that $t_{\text{exposure}} = 15$ s is required for survivability. Calculating R_D for $V = 1180$ m/s and $t_{\text{Exposure}} = 15$ s

$$R_D = t_{\text{Exposure}} V = 15(1180) = 17{,}700 \text{ m} = 17.7 \text{ km}$$

Using data from a prior example, the required frontal RCS for survivability is

$$\sigma = \left(R_D/1.227 \times 10^5\right)^4 = \left(17700/1.227 \times 10^5\right)^4 = 0.0004 \text{ m}^2 = -34 \text{ dB}$$

In the above example, an extensive signature reduction activity would be required to avoid an engagement from the threat. A tradeoff would be reduced signature (RCS, IR) to avoid an engagement versus surviving the engagement through other approaches (e.g., speed, altitude, maneuvering).

Another consideration for survivability is mission planning/threat avoidance. One approach to mission planning is a reduced observables missile, which provides more flexibility in mission planning/routing to avoid threat defenses. A reduced observables missile may be able to survive by flying between the seams of the coverage of threat defenses.

Figure 6.98 compares the survivability of a baseline cruise missile with that of a reduced observables cruise missile. Both missiles are attacking a notional target that is defended by three SAM sites.

For the baseline missile routing, shown as Case 1 in the left portion of the figure, the SAM sites have overlapping coverage. A direct attack, without mission planning, has exposure to all three SAM sites. Each SAM site has an assumed lethality of $P_K = 0.7$ if a target is within their radar range. The survivability of the baseline cruise missile exposed to three SAM engagements is

$$P_{\text{Survival}} = (1 - P_K)^3 = (1 - 0.7)^3 = 0.03$$

Case 2 in the right section of the figure shows the more effective routing of a reduced observables missile. The assumed RCS is 10% that of the baseline missile. The SAM site detection range against the reduced observable missile is

$$(R_D)_{\text{Reduced RCS}} = (\sigma_{\text{Reduced RCS}} / \sigma_{\text{Baseline RCS}})^{1/4} (R_D)_{\text{Baseline RCS}}$$
$$= (0.1)^{1/4} (R_D)_{\text{Baseline RCS}} = 0.56 (R_D)_{\text{Baseline RCS}}$$

The right section of the figure shows the reduction in the effective envelope of the SAM sites, which eliminates overlapping coverage. The reduction in the SAM site envelope allows the reduced observables missile to survive by routing around the SAM sites, avoiding SAM engagements, with

$$P_{\text{Survival}} = (1 - P_K)^3 = (1 - 0)^3 = 1$$

Mission planning to minimize the exposure time to known threats has payoff in survivability and effectiveness. A threat exposure time less than about 15 s usually provides survivability because the human reaction time is about 15 s.

Shown in the left portion of Fig. 6.99 is the non-dimensional exposure time to a SAM threat. It is based on the equation

$$t_{\text{Exposure}} = 2(R_{\text{max}}/V)\cos\left[\sin^{-1}(y_{\text{Offset}}/R_{\text{max}})\right] - t_{\text{React}}$$

The parameters are exposure (front, side, rear) time t_{Exposure}, maximum detection range by the SAM threat R_{max}, flyby velocity V, flyby offset y_{Offset}, and the reaction time of the SAM site t_{React}. The SAM site reaction time is the time from initial detection to launch. An assumption is that the flyby is with a constant altitude and a constant heading. It is also assumed that the SAM site has an unobstructed line-of-sight.

Shown in the upper right portion of the figure is a sketch illustrating the flyby of a threat SAM site. The circle is the envelope of possible engagement by the SAM site. The maximum engagement range may be set by the SAM detection range (which is a function of the target observables and terrain masking), kinematic range, and other parameters. The maximum time available for a SAM to engage during the flyby would be a direct over-flight of a SAM site. A lateral offset flyby enhances survivability by reducing the

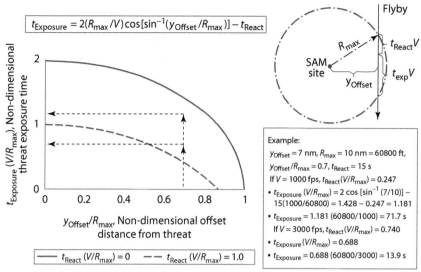

$$t_{Exposure} = 2(R_{max}/V)\cos[\sin^{-1}(y_{Offset}/R_{max})] - t_{React}$$

Example:

$y_{Offset} = 7$ nm, $R_{max} = 10$ nm $= 60800$ ft,

$y_{Offset}/R_{max} = 0.7$, $t_{React} = 15$ s

If $V = 1000$ fps, $t_{React}(V/R_{max}) = 0.247$

- $t_{Exposure}(V/R_{max}) = 2\cos[\sin^{-1}(7/10)] - 15(1000/60800) = 1.428 - 0.247 = 1.181$
- $t_{Exposure} = 1.181(60800/1000) = 71.7$ s

If $V = 3000$ fps, $t_{React}(V/R_{max}) = 0.740$

- $t_{Exposure}(V/R_{max}) = 0.688$
- $t_{Exposure} = 0.688(60800/3000) = 13.9$ s

Note: Based on assumption of constant altitude, constant heading flyby of threat SAM site with an unobstructed line-of-sight. $t_{Exposure}$ = exposure time to SAM threat, R_{max} = max detection range by SAM threat, V = flyby velocity, y_{Offset} = flyby offset, t_{React} = SAM site reaction time from detection to launch

Fig. 6.99 Mission planning/threat avoidance and high speed provide enhanced survivability.

exposure time. This is illustrated in the flyby trajectory on the upper right portion of the figure.

For an over-flight of a "perfect" SAM site that that has no time delay in reacting from detection to launch, the exposure time is given by the equation $t_{Exposure} = 2(R_{max}/V)$. As an example, if the SAM site detection range $R_{max} = 10$ nm against a typical turbojet missile with $V = 1000$ ft/s, then $t_{Exposure} = 2(60800/1000) = 121$ s. The SAM site would have about 60 s for a frontal shot at the incoming trajectory. It would also have about 60 s for a rear shot at the outgoing trajectory. More than one shot would probably be possible in both the closing and retreating trajectories. Because the exposure time is so large and multiple shots (e.g., shoot-look-shoot) are possible, survivability is a concern for an over-flight trajectory. A previous example illustrated the enhanced survivability by reducing the frontal observables to the frontal detection range, which results in a lower exposure time. For this example, an exposure time of 15 s would require a reduction in the detection range by the SAM threat to $15/121 = 0.124$ of the nominal range. For a radar threat and a nominal radar cross section $\sigma = 1$ m^2, the 88% reduction in detection range to minimize the exposure time to 15 s would require an RCS that is -36 dB.

Rather than overflying the SAM site, a better approach to cruise missile survivability is to use mission planning to reduce the threat exposure time.

In the bottom right portion of the figure is an example calculation based on an assumed lateral offset $y_{Offset} = 7$ nm, maximum detection range by the SAM site $R_{max} = 10$ nm, and a SAM site reaction time from detection to launch $t_{React} = 15$ s. For a low speed flyby representative of a subsonic cruise missile with $V = 1000$ ft/s, the exposure time is still large, $t_{Exposure} = 71.7$ s. However, for a very high speed flyby, such as a ramjet missile with $V = 3000$ ft/s, the exposure time is 13.9 s, a reduction of 81%.

The above examples illustrate that the combination of mission planning to avoid SAM sites, reduced observables, and high speed provides enhanced survivability for a cruise missile.

Another approach to survivability through mission planning is to fly at low altitude and exploit terrain masking, clutter, and transmission line-of-sight (LOS) limitations. Figure 6.100 shows the benefit of low altitude flight in reducing the LOS range of a surface-to-air threat. The disadvantages of low altitude flight may include increased fuel consumption, a higher probability of terrain clobber, and an exposure to an increased number of infrared SAM threats.

The equation for the required altitude to provide masking from a surface-to-air threat is

$$h_{Mask} = h_{Obstacle}(R_{los}/R_{Obstacle}) + (R_{los}/7113)^2$$

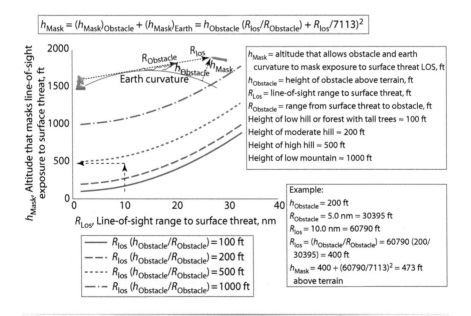

Fig. 6.100   Low altitude flight and terrain obstacles provide masking from the threat.

The above equation is based on the assumptions that the obstacle height is much larger than the threat height above the terrain and that the earth has a spherical curvature. Parameters are h_{Mask} = altitude that allows the obstacle and the earth's curvature to mask exposure to the surface threat LOS, ft; $h_{Obstacle}$ = height of the obstacle above the terrain, ft; R_{los} = line-of-sight range to the surface threat, ft; and $R_{Obstacle}$ = range from the surface threat to the obstacle, ft. Terrain obstacles shown in the figure have the following typical heights above the terrain 1) height of a low hill or a forest that is dominated by tall trees ≈ 100 ft, 2) height of a moderate hill ≈ 200 ft, 3) height of a high hill ≈ 500 ft, and 4) height of a mountain ≈ 1000 ft. Most fire control radar tracking is limited to about a 1 deg grazing angle above the LOS. Although a low frequency surveillance radar may be able to detect a target over the horizon, usually more information would be required to launch a SAM.

As an example, assume an obstacle height $h_{Obstacle}$ = 200 ft, range from the threat to the obstacle $R_{Obstacle}$ = 5.0 nm = 30395 ft, and a line-of-sight range to the threat R_{los} = 10.0 nm = 60790 ft. The parameter

$$R_{los}(h_{Obstacle}/R_{Obstacle}) = 60790(200/30395) = 400\,\text{ft}$$

Substituting into the equation for h_{Mask} gives

$$h_{Mask} = 200(60790/30395) + (60790/7113)^2 = 400 + 73 = 473\,\text{ft}$$

Note from the example that flying at a height that is 273 ft higher than the obstacle avoids detection. Two approaches for a cruise missile to take advantage of terrain masking are terrain following and terrain avoidance. Terrain following is the easiest to implement. The missile follows the terrain in 1-DOF with clearance of peak-to-peak obstacles. Disadvantage of this approach is a higher probability of clobber and the mission planning predictability may reduce survivability. Terrain avoidance is a 2-DOF approach that allows the missile to fly around obstacles. An advantage is a lower probability of clubber. A potential disadvantage is that it may not provide as much masking as peak-to-peak terrain following.

Insensitive munitions have payoff in improving the launch platform safety and survivability. As noted in Figure 6.101, the missile critical energetic subsystems are the rocket motor, engine fuel and the warhead. Other energetic subsystems include fuzes, batteries, initiators, and gas bottles. An example of a missile that has received high emphasis in the area of insensitive munitions is JASSM.

In terms of hazard severity, detonation (Type 1) is considered the most severe, because of the high power output. A detonation has a rise time of about 2 μs. The power output during a detonation is about six orders of

- Critical subsystems
  - Propellant/fuel.. Propellant
  - Warhage ....W/H
- Severity concerns ranking of power output-type
  1. Detonation ($\sim 2 \times 10^{-6}$ s rise time)
  2. Partial detonation ($\sim 10^{-4}$ s rise time)
  3. Explosion ($\sim 10^{-3}$ s rise time)
  4. Deflagration or propulsion rise time ($\sim 10^{-1}$ s rise time)
  5. Burning (>1s)
- Design and Test conditions (MIL STD 2105C)
  - Fragment/bullet/shaped charge impact or blast
  - Sympathetic detonation
  - Fast/slow cook-off fire
  - Drop
  - Temperature
  - Vibration
  - Carrier landing (18 ft/s sink, 12 g impact)

Video of Forrestal aircraft carrier fire

Fig. 6.101   Insensitive munitions improve launch platform safety and survivability.

magnitude greater than the power output during normal rocket motor combustion. The decreased severity ranking order for other hazard concerns are a partial detonation (Type 2, rise time about 0.1 ms), an explosion (Type 3, rise time about 1 ms), a deflagration or the propulsion rise time (Type 4, rise time about 0.1 s), and burning (Type 5, rise time greater than 1 s).

In the US, the design and test considerations for insensitive munitions are based on MIL-STD-2105C, Hazard Assessment Tests for Non-Nuclear Munitions. MIL-STD-2105C includes considerations of hardening against threat weapons, fast and slow cook-off fires, dropping the weapon, extremes in environmental temperature, missile vibration, and operation off an aircraft carrier. Hardening against threat weapons includes considerations of fragment impact, bullet impact, shaped charge impact, and blast. Hardening also considers sympathetic detonation of adjacent weapons. Cook-off from a fire requires consideration of the type of fire (slow cook-off without direct exposure to the fire and a slow rise in temperature, fast cook-off with direct exposure to the thermal radiation of an intense fire temperature $\sim 1800°F$ and a rapid rise in temperature) and the warhead or rocket motor reaction to the fire (e.g., burning, detonation). Approaches to alleviate the sudden release of energy include a vent plug and a composite case. Drop shock sensitivity is a concern for ground maintenance personnel dropping the missile during handling. The environmental temperature extremes range from a very low temperature that could damage the rocket motor (e.g., crack the propellant grain) to a very high temperature that could cause detonation of the warhead. Missile vibration consideration includes the dynamic acceleration imparted during store carriage on the launch platform. Aircraft carrier operation includes the landing shock of aircraft landing sink rate as high as 18 ft/s and impact deceleration as high as 12 g.

The bottom right section of the figure is a video of the Forrestal aircraft carrier horrific fire of July 29, 1967. An F-4 aircraft on the deck of the Forrestal was subjected to an electrical power surge while switching from external (auxiliary) power for engine start to internal (self) power. The power surge accidently fired a Zuni rocket that was mounted on the F-4 aircraft. Normal safety precautions during refueling using a safety pin and a disconnected electrical pigtail had been overridden. The Zuni shot across the deck, impacting a wing-mounted external fuel tank of an A-4 aircraft. As a result of the Zuni impact, the A-4 external fuel tank caught on fire, spilling burning fuel onto the deck. Two 1000 lb bombs mounted on the wing of the A-4 aircraft subsequently dropped into the burning fuel on the deck. The bombs exploded, the first of eight subsequent explosions over the next 30 minutes. The video shows three of the explosions. Note from the video that after each explosion, sailor firefighters returned to fight the fire. A total of 134 sailors died in the fire. There were 27 aircraft destroyed. It was the largest US naval loss since World War II. There is a saying of the Army that each soldier is a rifleman; a saying of the Navy is that each sailor is a firefighter. This video illustrates why insensitive munitions is such a high priority for the Navy.

6.7 Reliability

The sixth measure of merit to be discussed is reliability. Because most missiles are designed with no redundancy, missiles require highly reliable subsystems to avoid failure. An approach to predicting missile reliability is to assume that the system reliability is a serial product of the individual event/subsystem reliabilities. Figure 6.102 shows representative system hardware and event/subsystem reliabilities for a modern operational missile. For an operational missile, the system reliability is usually between 90 and 99%, depending upon the parts count and the type of subsystems/parts. Moving parts tend to be less reliable than non-moving parts. For a typical missile an individual subsystem failure rate should be about one-tenth the system design failure rate, to provide a balance of emphasis in the individual subsystem reliabilities. As an example, a typical missile with 90% system reliability and having ten subsystems would require about 99% reliability ($0.9 = 0.99^{10}$) for each subsystem. The requirement

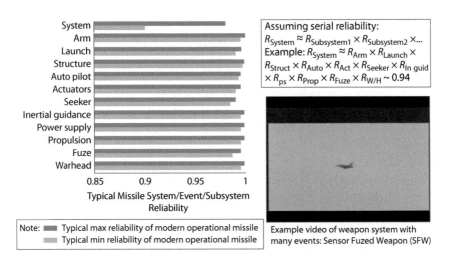

Note: ▬ Typical max reliability of modern operational missile
▨ Typical min reliability of modern operational missile

Example video of weapon system with many events: Sensor Fuzed Weapon (SFW)

Fig. 6.102 Reliability is provided by few events, reliable parts, few parts, short time of flight, and a benign environment.

for component reliability is even higher. A typical missile may have about ten components in each subsystem, giving a total of 100 components. A system reliability of 90% would require very high component reliability, about 99.9% reliability ($0.9 = 0.999^{100}$) for each component. Design considerations for high reliability are to minimize the number of events/subsystems, minimize components/parts count, minimize moving parts, minimize the complexity of the subsystems, minimize the time of flight, and minimize a harsh environment.

In recent years the electronic subsystems and components have become much more reliable, as the manufacturing processes have reduced the effective parts count. A computer chip may be the equivalent of millions of transistors, but a quality manufacturing process provides a high reliability.

The example of the notional missile of the figure has an overall reliability of 0.94. If the allocation of subsystem reliabilities were equally allocated, then each of the 11 events/subsystems would have a reliability of 0.994 (i.e., $0.994^{11} = 0.94$). However, the cost of achieving a reliability of 0.994 for some events/subsystems (e.g., gimbaled seeker) would be too high for most missiles. A less expensive subsystem (e.g., structure) could be allocated a reliability requirement greater than 0.994 to compensate for the inherent lower reliability of the seeker.

Figure 6.103 characterizes the contributors to the failure of missile hardware and software into three categories—infant mortality, environmental overload, and reliability.

Infant mortality failure occurs at the initial operation of the hardware or the software. Sources of hardware infant mortality are usually either a design error or a manufacturing error. Approaches to identify hardware design errors for correction include comparing alternative design prediction methods and comparing the design prediction with ground test data. Approaches to identify manufacturing errors for correction include quality control inspection and conducting acceptance tests in a representative environment. Sources of software infant mortality are usually either a modeling error or a coding error. A modeling error may be an inaccurate description of the physics of the missile. Another modeling error may be a misinterpretation of the specification. A software coding error is a mistake that is made in translating the missile analytical model into the software code. The process of software debugging exercises the software over the design environment, comparing the software output with the results from an independent computation of the missile physics.

The second contributor to failure, environmental overload, occurs from exceeding the missile design environment. Hardware failure may occur from exceeding the design environment in the missile storage, transportation, launch platform integration, or during its flight. Software failure may occur from exceeding the design environment for launch platform integration or during missile flight.

The third contributor, reliability failure, is the normal wear-out of hardware that is operating within the design environment. For a constant failure rate, reliability follows an exponential distribution $R = e^{-\lambda t}$, with the probability of failure increasing with time.

Infant Mortality	Hardware	Software
Poor design/modeling	x	x
Poor manufacturing/coding	x	x
Environmental Overload		
Storage	x	
Transportation	x	
Launch platform integration	x	x
Flight	x	x
Reliability		
Random wear-out vs time	x	

Note:

For constant failure rate, reliability follows an exponential distribution $R = e^{-\lambda t}$

A short time of flight missile (e.g., Hellfire) typically has higher reliability than a long time of flight missile (e.g., Harpoon).

Fig. 6.103 Missile failures can be characterized by infant mortality, environmental overload, and reliability.

In recent years software failure has replaced mechanical reliability as the major contributor to failure of missile systems. Software failures are reduced during missile development as coding errors are found and corrected and operating conditions are identified that are outside of the original design specification. Software failures also often occur after deployment, when the missile may be subjected to conditions that were not part of the development testing. Another problem is the introduction of software updates, usually to correct errors. Software updates may have new hidden faults that may not be discovered until later.

An example of a failure of "mature" software is the Patriot missile radar accumulative clock error. The Patriot radar clock rate of 0.1 s was calculated using a 24 bit fixed point register, which resulted in a clock rate error of 0.0000095%. For a typical reboot time of 10 hours, the clock rate error would result in a relatively small clock error of 0.034 s. However, during the 1991 Gulf War an operational Patriot had been on-line about 100 hours, which is 10× longer than the design reboot time. This resulted in a much larger clock error of about 0.34 s. Because of the clock error, an incoming Scud missile was outside the range gate of the radar, which resulted in a failed intercept.

6.8 Cost

The seventh measure of merit of this chapter is cost. The typical subsystems that have high unit production cost are shown in Fig. 6.104. The seeker is usually the highest cost subsystem for most missiles, usually exceeding 25% of the missile production cost. The guidance and control system is also usually high cost. It typically accounts for more than 10% of the missile unit production cost. A difference in the cost of missiles with air-breathing propulsion compared to rockets is the cost of the propulsion system and the missile structure. The propulsion system cost of an air-breathing missile is higher, usually exceeding 25% of the missile production cost, while the propulsion system of a rocket powered missile is usually between 10 and 25%. The relatively complex structure cost of an air-breathing missile is usually between 5 and 10% of the missile production cost, while the structure cost of a rocket powered missile is usually less than 5%. The cost of the missile seeker dome varies widely, depending upon the guidance accuracy and speed requirement of the missile. For a low speed missile, the cost of the seeker dome is about 5 to 10% of the missile cost. However, for a hypersonic hit-to-kill missile, the cost of the seeker dome usually exceeds 10% of the missile cost. The cost of the warhead and fuzing also vary widely. A blast fragmentation or a shaped charge warhead with contact fuzing is usually inexpensive. At the other

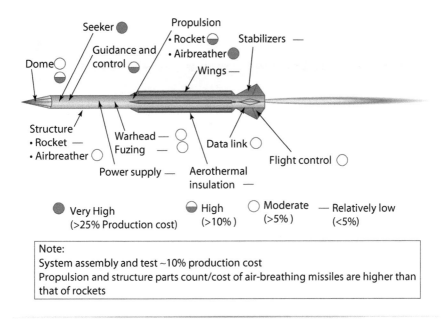

Fig. 6.104 Sensors, electronics, and propulsion typically drive missile unit production cost.

extreme, a multi-purpose warhead with smart fuzing can be expensive. Also, a nuclear warhead would be very expensive. System assembly and system test is usually about 10% of the missile production cost for a moderately complex missile. For a complex missile, which has more parts and is more labor intensive, system assembly and system test may be more than 15% of the missile production cost. For a simple missile, system assembly and test may be as low as 5% of the missile production cost.

The top portion of Fig. 6.105 illustrates the emphasis on sensors and electronics for most high performance, high cost missiles. Note that about 40% of the volume of the relatively large Derby/R-Darter missile is devoted to a variety of sensors and electronics. In addition to its radome, radar seeker, inertial navigation system, proximity fuze, autopilot, and four flight control actuators for pitch/yaw control, the Derby/R-Darter also has two additional flight control actuators for roll control and a data link. As a contrast, the bottom portion of the figure illustrates the lesser emphasis on sensors and electronics for a relatively inexpensive missile. The example is the Bolide missile. Bolide is a relatively small, command guided missile with a simple laser detector.

The total life cycle cost of a missile system includes the cost of the engineering manufacturing and development (EMD), the cost of production, and the cost of logistics. EMD cost may be predicted fairly accurately, based on data from previous missile programs. There is always some risk after

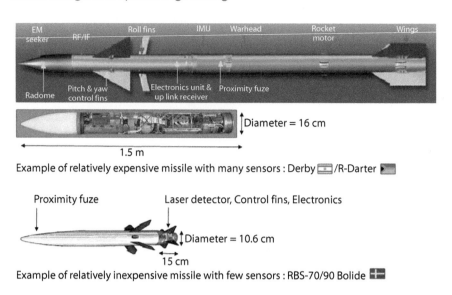

Example of relatively expensive missile with many sensors : Derby /R-Darter

Example of relatively inexpensive missile with few sensors : RBS-70/90 Bolide

Fig. 6.105 Missiles with a large fraction of sensors and electronics are more expensive.

completing the EMD program, which can impact the production cost and require follow-on development to fix problems. Production cost is often difficult to predict accurately, particularly for complex missiles with new types of subsystems and technology. Also, there may be pressure to provide optimistic predictions of production cost, to sell the missile program. Finally, although logistics cost is a major component of the missile life cycle cost, historically there has been little incentive for the contractor to design and develop a missile with reduced logistics cost, especially if a projected reduction in logistics cost would require increased development or production cost. In recent years logistic cost has received more emphasis because of environmental considerations, including disposal. The following figures will provide more information on design considerations for EMD, production, and logistics cost.

The culture and processes that emphasize quality will result in lower cost, through a more efficient design and reduced scrap. The culture of the tactical missile community, the strategic missile community, the unmanned air vehicle (UAV) community, and the aircraft community are different. For example, the tactical missile community usually puts more emphasis on reducing cost with less emphasis on performance, reliability, and the organization structure. In the strategic missile community and the other aerospace vehicle communities the emphasis on performance, reliability, and a relatively large organization structure is usually greater than the emphasis on reducing cost. A tactical missile may have 90% of the performance and reliability of a comparable strategic missile at 1/2 the cost and 2/3 of the development time. A missile development and production decision that impacts cost is the make-or-buy decision for the subsystems. Most missile system primes develop and make internally about 50% of the subsystems and farm out about 50% of the cost to suppliers. The make-or-buy decision depends upon the core competency of the missile system prime. Most missile system primes develop and make their own sensors and electronics. The propulsion, warhead, power supply, actuators, and structure are usually manufactured by suppliers, with the system integration conducted by the missile system prime. Another example of culture is the customer's expectations on the application of military standards. If the customer allows the relaxed and tailored use of military standards, there is usually a more cost-effective design. As an example, relaxed military standards may allow the use of lower cost commercial components. Also, customer participation in the design development through a team process, such as integrated product and process development (IPPD), usually results in a more cost-effective design. Another attribute by the customer that usually allows a more cost-effective design is the view toward profit. A profit incentive contract provides motivation for the contractor to reduce cost, which increases his profit while reducing cost for the customer. Unfortunately, many customers have a negative view of using profit as an incentive to reduce cost.

Competition is another approach to reduce cost. Competition also enhances creativity, especially during the missile development. Production buys with two competing contractors improve efficiency and may reduce the unit production cost by 50% compared to that of a sole source contractor. Competition also reduces the possibility of a cost overrun and a contractor "buy-in" for development. Unfortunately in the current environment there is less available funding for defense programs and the downsizing of the number of contractors has reduced competition. As a result of fewer competing contractors and less funding, the unit cost of missiles is likely to continue to increase in the future.

As a first order estimate, the cost of an EMD program is driven by the duration of EMD. A low risk EMD usually requires less than four years duration. A moderate risk EMD usually requires about four-to-six years in duration. A high risk EMD is usually longer than six years duration. Shown in Fig. 6.106 is the cost of twenty-one US EMD programs. The source of the data is Ref. 2. The cost of EMD in FY 99 US dollars is correlated as

$$C_{EMD} = \$24,500,000 \, t_{EMD}^{2.02}$$

In the above equation t_{EMD} is duration of the EMD in years.

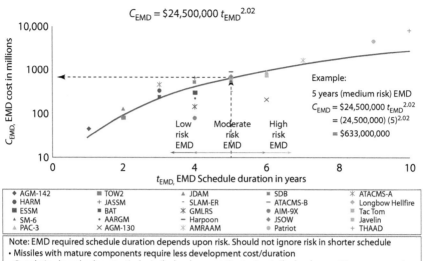

$$C_{EMD} = \$24,500,000 \, t_{EMD}^{2.02}$$

Example:

5 years (medium risk) EMD
$C_{EMD} = \$24,500,000 \, t_{EMD}^{2.02}$
$= (24,500,000) (5)^{2.02}$
$= \$633,000,000$

◆ AGM-142	■ TOW2	▲ JDAM	■ SDB	✳ ATACMS-A
● HARM	+ JASSM	– SLAM-ER	– ATACMS-B	◆ Longbow Hellfire
■ ESSM	■ BAT	✳ GMLRS	● AIM-9X	▥ Tac Tom
▲ SM-6	• AARGM	– Harpoon	◆ JSOW	▥ Javelin
▲ PAC-3	✕ AGM-130	✳ AMRAAM	● Patriot	+ THAAD

Note: EMD required schedule duration depends upon risk. Should not ignore risk in shorter schedule
• Missiles with mature components require less development cost/duration
• Correlation based only on tactical missile development. Strategic missile development is more expensive
• Correlation based only on US missile development. Multi-national missile development is more expensive
• EMD cost adjusted to year 2011 US$

Fig. 6.106 Missile EMD cost is driven by schedule duration and risk. (Source: Nicholas, T. and Rossi, R., *U.S. Missile Data Book*, Data Search Associates, 2011.)

Note from the figure that an EMD program that costs significantly less than prediction is AGM-130. Part of the reason for the relatively low EMD cost of AGM-130 is that it was a firm, fixed price contract. The cost of a three-year delay due to unforeseen technical difficulties was absorbed by the contractor.

Sometimes management will force the engineers to accept an unrealistically short duration schedule. However, the risk will eventually catch up, and as a result overrun funding and schedule slippage will be probably be required to complete the program. If there is insufficient funding for an overrun, it is possible that the missile requirements will have to be waived or that the program will have to be cancelled.

As an example of using the equation to predict EMD cost, the cost of a five year/medium risk EMD program is predicted to be

$$C_{EMD} = \$24,500,000(5)^{2.02} = \$633,000,000.$$

The average duration of EMD of the twenty-five missiles shown in the figure is 4.6 years. The average cost of EMD of the twenty-five missiles is $948,000,000 in US 2011 dollars.

An example of a short duration and low cost EMD program is the US acquisition of the AGM-142 Raptor missile. The US EMD program was low risk, short duration, and low cost, because the missile had been previously developed by Israel. The US EMD was primarily limited to the integration of the missile on the B-52 and F-111 aircraft. At the other extreme is the long EMD development and high EMD cost of the PAC-2 Patriot missile. The long duration of EMD for Patriot was a combination of high risk and a shortage of funding, which resulted in extending the EMD program and adding additional total program cost.

Missile development by a single country is usually more efficient, is shorter duration, and is less expense than a multi-national development program. Problems with multi-national development programs often include an inefficient work share allocation, politicized funding, problems with technology transfer, and poor system engineering.

As a first order design consideration, missile production cost is a function of weight. The equation is

$$C_{1000} \approx \$13,300 W_L^{0.596}$$

The above equation is based on correlating the data from Ref. 2. The derived cost of the 1000th missile C_{1000} is in US 2011 dollars. Missile launch weight W_L is in lb. The correlation shown in Fig. 6.107 covers two orders of magnitude in missile weight, ranging from 27 lb for the light weight, man-portable Javelin to 3200 lb for the Tomahawk.

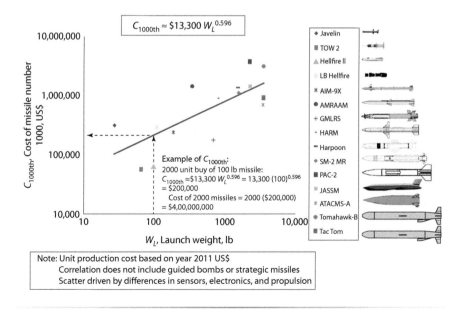

Note: Unit production cost based on year 2011 US$
Correlation does not include guided bombs or strategic missiles
Scatter driven by differences in sensors, electronics, and propulsion

Fig. 6.107 A light weight missile has a lower unit production cost. (Source: Nicholas, T. and Rossi, R., *U.S. Missile Data Book, 2011*, Data Search Associates, 2011.)

As an example, the predicted unit production cost of the 1000th unit for a missile with a launch weight of 100 lb is

$$C_{1000th} \approx \$13,300(100)^{0.596} = \$200,000$$

The cost of a total missile buy of 2000 units would be equal to the total number of missiles (2000) times the cost of the average (1000th) missile ($200,000), or $2000 \times 200000 = \$400,000,000$.

Note from the figure that the actual cost of Javelin is higher than predicted. Javelin is more complex than a typical light weight missile. For example, it has both aerodynamic control and thrust vector control, two motors (launch, flight), two warheads (pre-cursor, main), and also has an expensive imaging infrared seeker. As a contrast, note from the figure that the actual cost of the guided MLRS and JSOW are less than predicted. MLRS is a less complex than most heavy missiles and has no seeker, relying on inertial guidance. JSOW is also less complex than most heavy missiles. JSOW has no propulsion; it is a guided glide bomb. For both MLRS and JSOW, a relatively large fraction of the missile weight is the warhead, which is a relatively low cost subsystem.

A factor in manufacturing cost is controlled cleanliness. Clean rooms are necessary for optical manufacturing, inertial instrument manufacturing, electromechanical manufacturing, thermal insulation blankets, and electronics manufacturing (e.g., printed circuit boards). Optical, inertial, and electromechanical manufacturing require a facility cleanliness standard of 100 (fewer than 100 particles per ft^3). Thermal insulation blanket and electronics manufacturing require a standard of 10,000. Other manufacturing processes such as machining, mechanical assembly, plating, chemical treatment, composite forming, adhesive bonding, heat treatment, assembly tests, and system level tests do not need a clean room and are usually less expensive.

The unit production cost of a missile is dependent upon the learning curve from the past production of the missile, given by the equation

$$C_x = C_{1st}L^{\log_2 x}$$

In the above equation C_x is the unit cost of the current missile, C_{1st} is the unit cost of the first production missile, x is the number of missiles produced to date, and L is the coefficient of the learning curve. Another expression for the learning curve is the relationship of the unit cost C_x to the unit cost of doubling the number of units in production

$$C_{2x} = LC_x$$

The learning curve is used to predict production cost, not only in the aerospace industry, but also in other industries such as the automotive industry. The contributors to the learning curve include motivated workers and labor efficiency, reduced scrap, improved production process (e.g., setup time), and the maturity of the components that are used in the production process.

For a labor intensive process, such as building a developmental missile or a complex missile, the value of the coefficient of the learning curve is usually less than 0.8. For a machine intensive process, such as high rate production or a simple missile, the value of the coefficient of the learning curve is usually greater than 0.8.

Figure 6.108 illustrates the impact of the learning curve and the number of units produced on the missile production cost. As an example, for a value of the learning curve coefficient of $L = 0.80$, the cost of the 1000th missile is 11% of the cost of the first missile. It is noted that changing a production process will change the learning curve. The production process (and its value of L) that is used for the first missile is different from the production process (and its value of L) that is used for the 1000th missile. The first missile is probably a developmental missile that is labor intensive and produced in the laboratory using soft tooling. The 1000th missile is probably a rate production missile produced in the factory using hard tooling.

Shown in the figure is production cost as a function of the number of units produced for the BAE APKWs. The source of the data is

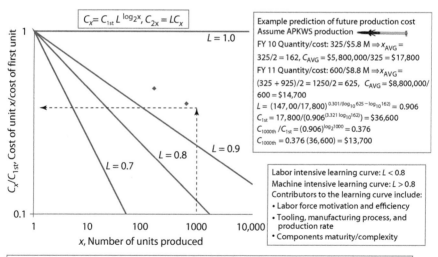

Note: APKWS $C_{1000th} = \$13,700$ Is lower than correlation $C_{1000th} = \$13,300\,W_L^{0.596} = \$105,000$. Reasons include simple/mature/light seeker, simple/mature rocket motor, warhead and fuzing (GFP), and high rate production.

Fig. 6.108 The learning curve and a large production reduce the missile unit production cost. (Source: Nicholas, T. and Rossi, R., *U.S. Missile Data Book,* Data Search Associates, 2011.)

Ref. 2. The data cover the FY10 quantity and cost (325 units/$5.8M) and the FY11 quantity and cost (600 units/$8.8M). The average cost and average number of units of the FY10 missile buy are

$$C_{\text{AVG}} = \$5,800,000/325 = \$17,800$$
$$X_{\text{AVG}} = 325/2 = 162$$

Similarly, the average cost and average unit number of the Fy11 missile buy are

$$C_{\text{AVG}} = \$8,800,000/600 = \$14,700$$
$$X_{\text{AVG}} = 325 + 600/2 = 625$$

Compute the learning curve L, first unit cost $C_{1\text{st}}$, and the projected cost of unit number 1000

$$L = (C_{162}/C_{625})^{(\log_{10} 2)/(\log_{10} 625 - \log_{10} 162)}$$

$$= (14700/17800)^{0.30/(2.796-2.210)}$$

$$= 0.906$$

$$C_{1\text{st}} = 17800/(0.906)^{3.321\log_{10}162} = \$36,000$$

$$C_{1000}/C_{1\text{st}} = 0.906^{\log_{10}1000} = 0.376$$
$$C_{1000} = 0.376(36600) = \$13,700$$

The revolutionary advancement in the performance of low cost commercial chips over the last 40 years has led to the movement to incorporate commercial parts into missiles. Figure 6.109 shows the decreasing presence of military parts in the integrated circuit (IC) market and the relative decline of military procurement. The military IC presence has declined to where it is now less than 1% of the IC market. At this level, the military exerts essentially no influence on most IC manufacturers to supply the technology needed for military parts. The relatively low level of military chip procurement caused many of the traditional high-reliability IC manufacturers to leave the military market. The result is less available selection of military-type parts. As a result, most military electronics is now based on commercial parts.

Ruggedized commercial electronics is usually based on plastic encapsulated microcircuits (PEMS). However, the environmental protection from PEMS is often not sufficient for missile applications. The commercial parts must often be cocooned for protection against the harsher military environment (temperature, vibration, shock, acoustics, moisture, dust, salt, EMI, EMP, radiation, etc.). New technology is required to develop cocoons for the commercial off the shelf (COTS) parts. Another

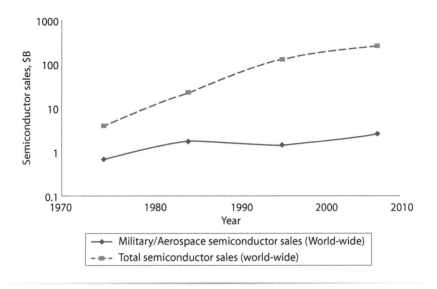

Fig. 6.109 Missile electronics are usually based on COTS, because of a much larger commercial market. (Source: "A Complete Analysis and Forecast of the Integrated Circuit Industry," The McClean Report 2007.)

consideration is the rapid introduction of new commercial products compared to the long development time of a military product. As a result, the military products are often one-to-three generations behind the commercial state-of-the-art (SOTA) by the time the military product is introduced. In addition, the military product may not have a logistical support base due to obsolete commercial parts. This requires robust program flexibility to handle the frequent upgrades of the commercial parts. The frequent upgrades require a streamlined process for military qualification test, to make the more frequent qualification tests affordable. As an example, if a military INS uses a commercial chip, then based on Moore's Law, the chip is obsolete in about two years. A effective system engineering activity is required to incorporate a new chip into an existing INS at a relatively cost and a low risk.

New technology can enhance the producibility and reduce the cost of weapons. Examples of precision strike weapons that include low cost technologies include JDAM, JSOW, and JASSM. Technologies to reduce cost are also being introduced into existing weapons, with large savings. An example shown in Fig. 6.110 is Tactical Tomahawk, with a unit production cost of about $570,000 for 1300 missiles. It has a simple low cost cast aluminum airframe (see figure) with extruded wings that results in a reduced parts count for the structure. Low cost commercial parts are used for guidance and control and propulsion. The earlier Tomahawk has 11,500 parts, 2500 fasteners, 45 circuit cards, 160 connectors, and requires 610

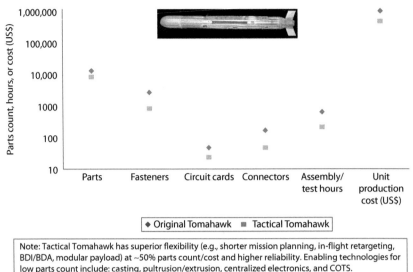

Note: Tactical Tomahawk has superior flexibility (e.g., shorter mission planning, in-flight retargeting, BDI/BDA, modular payload) at ~50% parts count/cost and higher reliability. Enabling technologies for low parts count include: casting, pultrusion/extrusion, centralized electronics, and COTS.

Fig. 6.110   A low parts count missile has a lower unit production cost.

assembly/test hours. The Tactical Tomahawk missile has approximately 35% fewer parts, 68% fewer fasteners, 51% fewer circuit cards, 72% fewer connectors, and 68% fewer assembly/test hours, resulting in approximately a 50% reduction in cost. Tactical Tomahawk also has superior flexibility (e.g., shorter mission planning time, data link capability for in-flight targeting, data link capability for battle damage indication/battle damage assessment, a modular payload capability) and higher reliability at the same launch weight and flight range (~1000 nm) as the earlier Tomahawk.

Another factor in missile production cost is the production rate. There is normally an economy of high rate production. High rate production allows hard tooling, which is usually more efficient. The labor work force is also usually more efficient in rate production.

A difference of the tactical missile culture compared to the related cultures of the strategic missile, UAV, and combat aircraft communities is the emphasis on low cost manufacturing and high rate production. A tactical missile production rate may be more than 5000 missiles per year. This may be 10 times the production rate of a strategic missile and 100 times the production rate of a UAV or combat aircraft.

Examples of relatively high rate production processes are shown in Fig. 6.111. Shown in the left side of the figure is an example of a work station production integration of Copperhead seeker and electronics. The top right section of the figure is an example of a work station production integration of the Patriot flight control. In the bottom right section of the figure is a circa 1990 video of the Hellfire seeker and electronics production processes. The production processes of the Copperhead, Patriot, and Hell-fire weapons are labor intensive, with some automation of electronics, such as circuit boards. System assembly and system test are a significant portion of the production cost. A simpler missile that is produced at a relatively high rate, such as TOW, is less labor intensive. The production for TOW is highly automated. There is relatively little assembly and testing. Missile system assembly and system tests are a relatively small portion of the TOW production cost. At the other extreme is the AMRAAM missile. AMRAAM is a more complex missile that is produced at a lower rate and is more labor intensive. The production process for AMRAAM has less automation. Missile subsystem, subsystem assembly, and system tests are a large portion of the AMRAAM production cost.

A skilled labor work force is desirable for missile production. The higher wage cost of skilled production workers is usually more than compensated by fewer missile failures and a lower unit production cost, from the reduced scrap and less rework of a skilled labor work force.

The logistics cost of the missile system over the years following production can be comparable to or even greater than the EMD and production costs. Note in Fig. 6.112 that logistics considerations can be grouped into two major categories: peacetime logistics and wartime logistics. Design tradeoffs for logistics include of the cost allocation to each category and the allocation of cost within each category.

Copperhead seeker/Electronics work station   Patriot control section work station

Video of Hellfire seeker and electronics production

Fig. 6.111 Missile culture is driven by rate production of sensors and electronics.

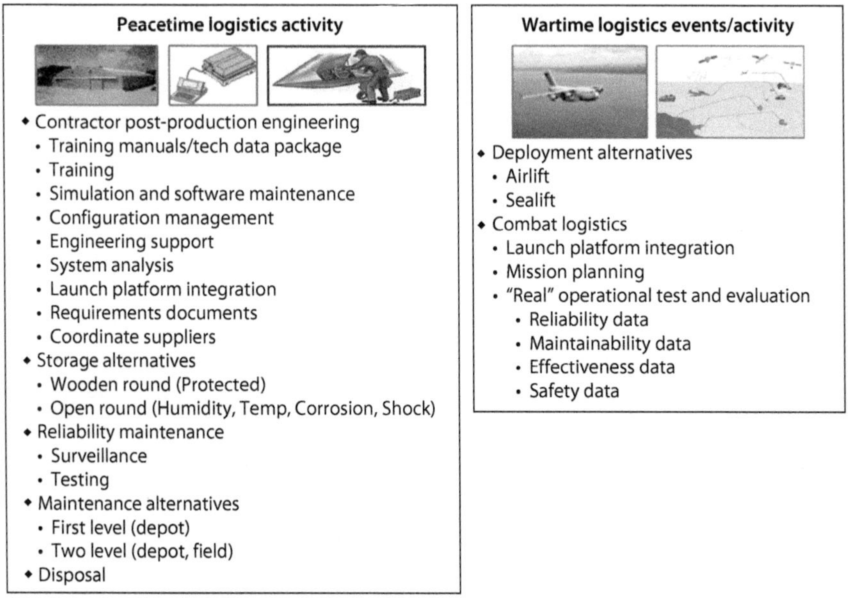

Peacetime logistics activity	Wartime logistics events/activity

◆ Contractor post-production engineering
  • Training manuals/tech data package
  • Training
  • Simulation and software maintenance
  • Configuration management
  • Engineering support
  • System analysis
  • Launch platform integration
  • Requirements documents
  • Coordinate suppliers
◆ Storage alternatives
  • Wooden round (Protected)
  • Open round (Humidity, Temp, Corrosion, Shock)
◆ Reliability maintenance
  • Surveillance
  • Testing
◆ Maintenance alternatives
  • First level (depot)
  • Two level (depot, field)
◆ Disposal
	◆ Deployment alternatives
	  • Airlift
	  • Sealift
	◆ Combat logistics
	  • Launch platform integration
	  • Mission planning
	  • "Real" operational test and evaluation
	    • Reliability data
	    • Maintainability data
	    • Effectiveness data
	    • Safety data

Fig. 6.112 Missile logistics in war and peace.

Peacetime logistic considerations from a system prime contractor perspective may be categorized as the contractor's post-production storage, maintenance, and disposal activities.

Following the production of the missile, the system prime contractor maintains and updates the training manuals for the military user. The contractor may also provide training for military personnel. Another activity may include maintaining the technical data package that documents the weapon system characteristics. A configuration management system is used to provide order and accuracy for the missile data. Other activities following production include maintenance of the 6 degree-of-freedom (6-DOF) digital simulation, hardware-in-loop (HWL) simulation, and software. The system prime contractor also provides engineering support if it is necessary to analyze and correct problems that develop after delivery of the missile. System engineering support provided by the prime contractor after production includes maintaining a capability for system analysis, maintaining a capability for launch platform integration, and maintaining the requirements documents. Much of the system analysis capability emphasizes the guidance and control system, with validation conducted through the 6-DOF and HWL simulations. The system prime contractor work on launch platform integration often addresses the impact of changes in the launch platform avionics on the missile. Work on requirements documents often addresses the flow down and allocation of new system and launch platform requirements. Finally, the prime contractor continues to coordinate with suppliers following production.

A typical missile production provides more than a single load-out of missiles for the launch platforms. Most missiles are stored following production, awaiting deployment. For a long term storage, for example, ten years of storage, a wooden round is cost effective. The missiles are stored in a sealed, insulated, and cushioned container, protected from diurnal temperature fluctuation, humidity, shock, and corrosion. For short term storage, for example one year of storage, a simple hinged container may provide sufficient protection from the environment.

The missile stockpile is periodically assessed for reliability through surveillance and testing. Strategic missiles have more emphasis on reliability surveillance and testing than tactical missiles. Two philosophies that apply to maintenance are first-level versus two-level maintenance. In first level maintenance, all of the maintenance is conducted by a contractor at the depot. First level maintenance is particularly applicable to naval weapons, because ships and submarines have limited available space. Two-level maintenance is particularly applicable to air force and army weapons. A field maintenance facility can be used for routine maintenance, for example, sealing gaps to ensure low observables, adding new desiccant to a wooden round storage container, replacing a discharged battery. If sophisticated maintenance is required, the missile is shipped back to the central depot.

A final consideration during peacetime logistics is disposal of obsolete missiles without harming the environment. The total number of missiles in the US inventory is relatively large, more than 500,000 missiles. However, only a fraction of the inventory will require disposal. Some may be used in wartime, others will be used for training, and some may be approved for foreign military sale. Typical cost of disposal of a tactical missile varies from about $100 to about $2000, depending upon the number of hazardous components, the type of hazard, environmental impact, the complexity of the missile, security classification, and the size of the missile. Disposal of most missiles is at their depot storage. The disposal process of the warhead charge and rocket motor propellant usually consists of removal and destruction. After the removal of the guidance and control system, it is usually disposed, but sometimes parts are salvaged. The airframe and rocket motor case are usually salvaged.

Environmental impact and the avoidance of law suits have become increased concerns in recent years. Hazardous materials such as asbestos, mercury, and beryllium that were used in older missiles are no longer allowed. The application of new technologies for future missiles will be limited by environmental restrictions. For example, gel rocket motors will not be able to use toxic propellants such as hydrazine, nitrogen tetroxide, or nitric acid. Because environmental requirements are becoming stricter, current practices that are now deemed to be potentially hazardous, such as the use of lead solder in electronics, thermal batteries for power supply, and chromium/cadmium corrosion resistant coatings are likely to be replaced in the future by other approaches.

Wartime logistics may be categorized as deployment and combat considerations.

A tradeoff of deploying the missiles from the storage facility to the theater of operation is the cost and time required for deployment. Airlift is rapid, but has limited capacity and is expensive. Sealift has a large capacity and is inexpensive, but may take a month or longer to deliver a weapon from the storage facility to the theater.

After delivery to the theater of combat, the missiles are integrated with the launch platform for physical and electrical compatibility. Prior to launching the missile, mission planning and check-out tests are conducted. During combat ("real" operational test and evaluation), statistical data are acquired on the reliability, maintainability, effectiveness, and the safety of the missile. These data are used to develop any necessary fixes and provide guidelines for future design.

The three top left photographs of Fig. 6.113 compare a simple surface-to-air missile (SAM) system (Stinger), that has low cost, wooden round logistics, to more sophisticated missile systems that include a launch vehicle and radar (Hawk and Surface Launched AMRAAM/NASAMS (National

Simple: Stinger   More sophisticated: Hawk and SLAMRAAM/NASAMS   Complex: PAC-3

 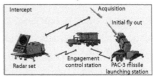

Very complex: THAAD

Video of SAM logistics alternatives

Fig. 6.113 Logistics cost is lower for a simple missile system.

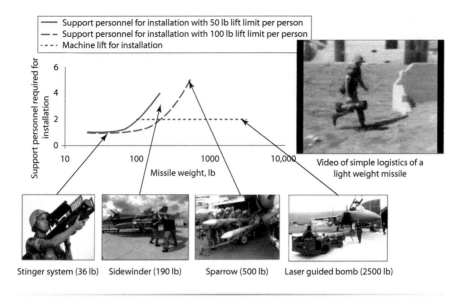

Stinger system (36 lb)   Sidewinder (190 lb)   Sparrow (500 lb)   Laser guided bomb (2500 lb)

Fig. 6.114 Logistics is usually simpler for a light weight missile.

Surface-to-Air Missile System)). Continuing with the comparison, shown in the top right section of the figure is a more complex missile system (PAC-3) that has higher cost logistics from three vehicles—a radar van, an engagement control station, and a missile launching station. Finally, the bottom left section of the figure illustrates a very complex missile system, THAAD, which has an entourage of vehicles and support personnel for transportation, maintenance, launch, fire control, and command and control.

Shown in the bottom right section of the figure is a video that compares the operational logistics of a progression of surface-to-air missiles from simple to complex logistics. The progressions are from Stinger, to Hawk, to Surface Launched AMRAAM (SLAMRAAM), to PAC 3, and finally to THAAD. Also shown in the video are missile firings, fly-outs, and intercepts against air targets.

Shown in Fig. 6.114 are examples of the impact of missile weight on the support manpower requirements. A typical maximum lift requirement per person is between 50 to 100 lb. For a light weight man-portable missile system such as Stinger, a single gunner can prepare and launch the missile. As an example of a moderately heavy missile, the 190-lb Sidewinder requires two-to-four personnel to install the missile on the launch aircraft. A heavier missile, such as a 500-lb Sparrow, requires additional support personnel plus ground support equipment. Finally, a very heavy weapon, such as a 2000 lb laser guided bomb, requires specialized, heavy ground support equipment.

The video in the upper right corner of the figure illustrates the logistics simplicity of a light weight missile. The 21-lb Predator system (missile/launcher) is easily carried, set up, and fired by a single gunner in a broad range (e.g., open terrain, urban building) of battlefield engagements. Also shown in the video is the effectiveness of the Predator's explosively formed projectile (EFP) warhead and the top attack flyover trajectory against tank targets.

Predator's use of an EFP warhead in a top flyover trajectory allows a light weight warhead to penetrate the relatively soft top armor of a tank. Also, Predator's simple flyover trajectory minimizes the maneuvering requirement of the missile, allowing lighter weight/lower cost flight control actuators and gyros.

The application of Micro-machined Electro-Mechanical Systems (MEMS) devices to logistics health monitoring after missile production provides a more accurate assessment of the health and lifetime of each individual missile. This reduces logistics cost and improves missile reliability. MEMS devices also have payoff during missile development. Because high performance missiles, such as ramjets, are especially weight and volume limited, there is leverage in reducing weight. Reduced weight is consistent with reduced cost, improved performance, and improved launch platform compatibility. One approach to reduce missile weight is to reduce the required factor of safety (which is really a factor of ignorance). The higher confidence from MEMS data allows weight reduction by eliminating the excess weight in the over designed areas of the structure.

MEMS devices are fabricated from a single piece of silicon by semiconductor manufacturing processes, resulting in a small size, low-cost package.

- ◆ Micro-machined Electro-Mechanical Systems (MEMS)
  - Small size/low cost semiconductor manufacturing process
  - 2000 to 5000 devices on a 5 in silicon wafer
- ◆ Wireless (RF) data collection and health monitoring
- ◆ Distributed sensors over missile
  - Acceleration
  - Stress/strain
  - Vibration
  - Acoustics
  - Temperature
  - Pressure
  - Propellant aging
- ◆ Reduced logistics cost and improved reliability
  - Health monitoring
- ◆ Reduced weight and production cost
  - More efficient design

Fig. 6.115   Small MEMS sensors provide health monitoring, reduce cost, and reduce weight.

Between 2000 and 5000 MEMS sensor devices can be produced from a single 5 in silicon wafer. An example of the small size of a MEMS device is shown in Fig. 6.115. Future missiles could have low cost/small size MEMS sensors for data collection during missile development and also for health monitoring after production. Localized stress/strain, vibration, acoustics, temperature, pressure, and other measurements can be monitored through many low cost/small size sensors distributed around the airframe.

6.9 Launch Platform Integration

The final measure of merit of this chapter is launch platform integration. Launch platform integration sets constraints on the missile that must be considered early in the development process. Moreover, the design process requires iteration to harmonize the outputs from the diverse areas of mission/scenario definitions, missile requirements, launch platform integration, missile concepts, and technologies. In a few cases it may be possible to modify a launch platform to accommodate a new missile, but in most cases this is not an option. Generally the launch platform is a constraint that drives the missile design. For example, AMRAAM was originally developed as a light weight radar missile for carriage on the wing tips of the F-16, which has a 300-lb (135 kg) weight limit. Later, AMRAAM was modified to a compressed carriage configuration (clipped wings and tails) to better accommodate internal carriage in the F-22 center weapons bay. Missiles are driven as much by launch platform compatibility as other measures of merit. Cross-platform compatibility is desirable for a missile system. A larger total buy of missiles for cross-platform application has a benefit of a lower unit production cost. Weapon compatibility with multiple launch platforms also has a payoff in the neck-down benefit cost savings of fewer missile logistics systems.

Carriage constraints for missiles on US surface ships, submarines, fighter/bomber aircraft, helicopters, UCAVs, and ground vehicles are shown in Fig. 6.116.

In the United States, the Vertical Launch System (VLS) is a standard sea carriage and launch system for many missiles (Tomahawk, Standard Missile, Sea Sparrow, ASROC) on surface ships such as cruisers and destroyers. The Arleigh Burke class destroyer has 90 VLS cells. The larger Ticonderoga class cruiser has 122 VLS cells. VLS length constraint is approximately 263 in. The cross sectional geometry constraint of the current standard canister is approximately 22×22 in $(56 \times 56$ cm), depending upon the missile folded surface geometry. Maximum missile weight constraint for the current standard canister is approximately 3400 lb. A ship typically has two magazines of missiles, located fore and

US launch platform	Launcher	Carriage span/shape	Length	Weight
Surface ships	VLS	~22″ × ~22″ (diamond)	263″	3400 lb
Surbmarines	CLS	22″ (circle)	263″	3400 lb
Fighters/ bombers/ large UCAVs	Rail/ ejection	~24″ x ~24″	~168″	~500 lb to ~3000 lb
Ground vehicles	Launch pods	~28″ × ~28″ (diamond)	158″	3700 lb
Helos/small UCAVs	Helo rail, UCAV rail/ ejection	~13″ x ~13″	~70″	~120 lb
Tanks	Gun barrel	120 mm (circle)	~40″	~60 lb

Fig. 6.116 Missile carriage size, shape, and weight limits may be driven by launch platform compatibility.

aft. Each magazine could have six modules, with eight launchers in each module, providing a total of 96 VLS launchers for two magazines per ship. Each VLS launcher can carry from one missile (e.g., Standard Missile, Tomahawk) to four missiles (e.g., Sea Sparrow) per launcher.

United States submarines have a missile launcher that is similar to the VLS, but it has a circular cross section. The tactical submarine Canister Launch System (CLS) has a diameter constraint of 22 in and a length constraint of 263 in. Maximum missile weight for the CLS is the same as that of the VLS, 3400 lb (1540 kg). The VLS also has a maximum limit of the mass flow rate that is delivered, to avoid choking the flow in the launcher plenum and to avoid burning through the launch platform structure in the event of a restrained launch. Refurbishment is required after about three firings. Some Trident missile launch tubes on strategic submarines (SSGM) have been adapted to launch conventional missiles such as Tomahawk and ATACMS, providing high firepower. As an example, a modified Trident launch tube can store and launch up to seven Tomahawk missiles, allowing an SSGM to carry up to 154 Tomahawk missiles.

Fixed wing aircraft launch platforms for missiles include tactical fighters, bombers, and UCAVs. Shown in the figure is an example of a fighter aircraft, the F-18C. The F-18C carries weapons externally for pylon ejection launch and rail launch. The launcher photograph shows three missiles on their launchers: a rail-launched AMRAAM carried on the wing tip, an ejection launched AMRAAM carried under the wing, and an ejection launched

HARM carried under the wing. Other aircraft, such as the F-22, F-35, B-1, and B-2 have an additional capability of internal carriage. Internal launchers are capable of vertical ejection launch, rail trapeze launch, and rotary ejection launch. Missile span constraint for a typical fixed wing aircraft carriage is about 24×24 in. Length constraint for a typical fixed wing aircraft is about 168 in and the maximum allowable missile weight varies from about 500 to 3000 lb, depending upon the aircraft. A heavy bomber (e.g., B-52) is capable of external carriage of even heavier stores (e.g., 30,000 lb penetrator). There is a desire for light weight missiles to maximize the firepower of small aircraft such as the F-18 fighter and UCAVs. The US Navy fleet current combat aircraft is dominated by the F-18. UCAVs will be assuming a greater role in weapon delivery in future years.

Helicopters and small UCAVs require small and light weight weapons. Most helicopters and small UCAVs have rail launchers. Helicopters and small UCAVs have severe integration constraints, with the Hellfire missile representing a typical constraint. A typical missile length constraint is about 70 in and a typical maximum allowable missile weight is about 120 lb. An exception is the relatively small number of helicopters that carry anti-ship missiles, such as Penguin and Naval Strike Missile, which can weigh up to 900 lb.

An example of a ground launch platform is the US Army M270 Armored Vehicle, which is based on a modified M2 Bradley armored personnel carrier. It is the standard US Army platform for surface-to-surface artillery rockets and missiles. The M270 has two launch pods. Either twelve MLRS rockets or two ATACMS missiles can be launched from the M270. The MLRS rocket and ATACMS payloads can be either submunition or unitary warheads.

The bottom portion of the figure illustrates guided weapon compatibility constraints for tanks. Tanks require very small and light weight weapons. The maximum diameter of a gun-launched guided projectile is 120 mm. Maximum length and weight are about 40 in and 60 lb respectively. Examples of tank-launched guided projectiles are XM-1111 and Lahat.

Technologies for improved weapon/launch platform aeromechanics compatibility and high firepower include low volume propulsion, ordnance and airframe; store carriage and store separation wind tunnel tests; computational fluid dynamics (CFD) predictions; and finite element modeling (FEM) predictions.

In an ideal world, new combat aircraft development would be conducted in concert with new missile development, for a more cost-effective weapon system. Examples of system-level trades for fighter aircraft survivability and effectiveness include aircraft maneuverability versus missile maneuverability and aircraft observables versus missile standoff range. The reality is that new aircraft are usually developed based on the

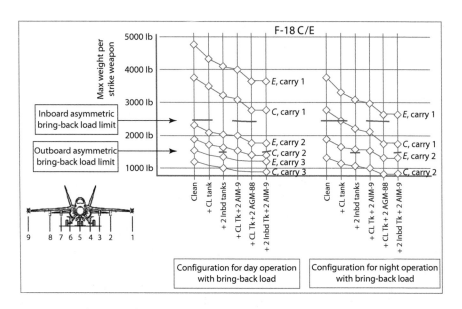

Fig. 6.117 Light weight missiles enhance firepower.

current weapons with little consideration of the new weapons or the new missile technology that is currently in development. The lack of consideration of new weapons may be an aircraft developer's concern that the consideration of new weapons may endanger the new aircraft program funding.

Figure 6.117 illustrates how an aircraft carrier bring-back load limits, day/night operation, firepower objectives, and weapons load-out impact the maximum allowable weight of a precision strike missile. Shown are examples for the F-18C and F-18E aircraft. Note that the F-18C aircraft has less capability than the F-18E in all load-out configurations. The figure also shows a large difference in the maximum allowable missile weight for day operation versus night operation. The difference is because of the additional fuel that must be reserved for night operation off an aircraft carrier. The maximum weapon weight shown in the curves may be driven by the asymmetric carriage bring-back load limits (2500 lb maximum weight for inboard asymmetric carriage and 1500 lb maximum weight for outboard asymmetric carriage). Finally, note the reduction in maximum allowable missile weight as the load-out configuration is changed from that of a clean aircraft, carrying only precision strike missile(s), to other configuration load-outs. Five other load-out configurations are the precision strike missile(s) plus either 1) a centerline fuel tank, 2) two inboard fuel tanks, 3) a centerline fuel tank plus two AIM-9 Sidewinder air-to-air missiles, 4) a centerline fuel tank plus two AGM-88 anti-radiation missiles (ARM), or

5) two inboard fuel tanks plus two AIM-9 Sidewinders. Note that the maximum allowable weight of carrying only a single precision strike missile on the F-18E is about 4800 lb under ideal conditions. At the other extreme is an F-18C operating under more typical, limited conditions. For an F-18C operating at night with two inboard fuel tanks and two AIM-9 Sidewinders, the maximum allowable weight of a single precision strike missile is much lower, about 1800 lb. In the case of carriage of two precision strike missiles, each missile for F-18E carriage under ideal conditions can weigh up to 2400 lb. At the other extreme for an F-18C load-out of two precision strike missiles, operating at night with the addition of two inboard fuel tanks and two AIM-9 Sidewinders requires that each precision strike missile weigh less than 900 lb. A precision strike missile design weight of about 1400 lb is probably a good design tradeoff compromise for the example of F-18C/E aircraft integration. It allows two weapons on the F-18C for unrestricted day operation, two weapons on the F-18E for near unrestricted night flight operation, and three weapons on the F-18E for day operation with two inboard fuel tanks.

An advantage of a light weight missile is high firepower for the launch platform. An example of the firepower benefit of a light weight missile is the light weight, precision strike Brimstone missile. Brimstone is based on a Hellfire missile airframe with a mmW seeker, instead of a SAL seeker. Its frequency modulation continuous waveform (FMCW) mmW seeker provides an adverse weather capability with lighter weight than that from a conventional pulsed waveform cmW seeker. FMCW mmW also provides a relatively high average power and relatively good clutter suppression/smoothing (sub-clutter visibility) compared to a conventional pulsed waveform cmW seeker. The mmW seeker also provides a high contrast of the typical metal target compared to natural terrain. Another advantage of a mmW seeker is polarization in the target return provides the capability to extract information on the target's physical shape characteristics, facilitating automatic target recognition (ATR). The return from the features that are unique to the target be related to a unique combination of elemental scatterers such as dihedrals, trihedrals, diploes, and cylinders. A disadvantage of FMCW mmW is a limited capability against a moving target, because of its relatively short range lock-on. Other disadvantages compared to a SAL seeker include a clutter-limited look-down angle of about 20 deg and a relatively high cost.

Shown in the top portion of Fig. 6.118 is the Brimstone triple rail launcher. The bottom left photograph of the figure shows the high firepower of twelve Brimstone missiles on a Tornado aircraft. In the bottom right portion is a video illustrating Brimstone's high firepower carriage, lock-on-before launch (LOBL), lock-on-after-launch (LOAL), salvo-firing, terrain following/terrain avoidance, and ATR capabilities.

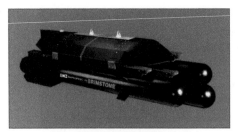

Brimstone launcher

Brimstone/F-18 carriage

Brimstone/Tornado carriage

Video: Brimstone firepower

Fig. 6.118 Example of a light weight/high firepower missile: the precision strike Brimstone.

In addition to firepower, weight, and fitment constraints, other considerations in missile/launch platform integrations include the missile off-boresight limitations, minimum range limitations, and safety concerns, illustrated in Fig. 6.119a for a fixed wing aircraft launch platform. In addition to aircraft launch platforms, the limitations may also be applicable to helicopter, ship, and ground vehicle launch platforms. Off-boresight limitations include the missile seeker field of regard (FOR) obscured by the launch platform and a limited field-of-regard of the fire control system. Examples of contributors to the missile minimum range limitations include the launch tip off from the missile lugs/hangers clearance on the launch rail, launcher aeroelasticity, and a crosswind/downwash induced velocity from either the crosswind of a vertical launcher or the downwash from the rotor blades for a helicopter launch. A Monte Carlo probabilistic simulation is usually used to determine the effect of launch tip off on the missile miss distance/minimum range. Safety concerns include the launcher rail retention and release system (locks the missile on the rail during carriage prior to launch and then releases the missile at launch), launch platform maneuvering local flow field (α, β) and its effect on the safe separation trajectory, missile store carriage excitation of the launch platform aeroelasticity modes, and the launch platform bay or canister acoustics and vibration environment.

A possible concern in launch platform/missile integration during carriage is that the missile seeker field of regard (FOR) may be obscured by the launch platform. For a lock-on-before-launch (LOBL) missile, launch platform obscuration limits the off-boresight capability against threats on the opposite side of the launch platform. As an example, the left portion of Fig. 6.119b shows the F-22 side bay with a AIM-9x Sidewinder. To alleviate obscuration, F-22 has a trapeze launcher that extends laterally from the side bay. This enables the Sidewinder seeker to have a target lock-on before launch without being obscured by the F-22 aircraft.

Another concern is the off-boresight capability of the fire control system compared to the inherent off-boresight capability of a LOBL missile. The photograph in the right portion of the figure is an example of a fire control system with a wide field-of-regard, the Tactical Acquisition and Designation System (TADS) of the Apache helicopter, which does not limit the off-boresight capability of the Hellfire missile seeker.

In the bottom section of the figure is a video showing a missile carriage that allows a wide FOR of the missile seeker. The video shows the F-16 aircraft outboard wing carriage of the IRIS-T missile and the Apache helicopter forward carriage of the Hellfire missile. The IRIS-T seeker has a 3-axis gimbal (pitch, yaw, roll) that provides a wide FOR. Also shown in the video is the Apache helicopter wide FOR fire control system, which does not limit the FOR of the Hellfire seeker.

Another possible concern in launch platform/missile integration is the missile lug/hanger clearance for a rail launch may result in a tip-off rotation

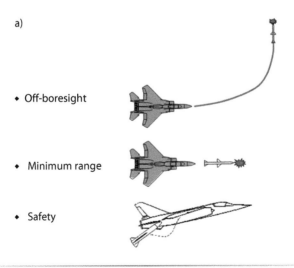

a)

• Off-boresight

• Minimum range

• Safety

Fig. 6.119a Examples of missile — launch platform integration problems/limitations.

b) Launch platform obscures seeker field-of-regard ⇒ limited off-boresight
fire control system field-of-regard ⇒ may limit off-boresight

F-22 side bay with AIM-9X

Apache fire control system

Video of F-16 wing tip carriage of IRIS-T and Apache fire control system

Fig. 6.119b Examples of missile — launch platform integration
problems/limitations.

at launch. A rail-launched missile has pitch, yaw, and roll rates when it
leaves the rail. The time that is required for the missile seeker and flight
control system to correct tip-off rate and angle errors results in miss distance and a minimum effective range.

The typical design clearances are set by a minimum value to avoid
binding on the launcher and by a maximum value to minimize the
tip-off. These are illustrated in Fig. 6.119c. Typical minimum/maximum

c) Lug/hanger clearance on rail ⇒ tip-off rotation @ launch ⇒ miss at
min range

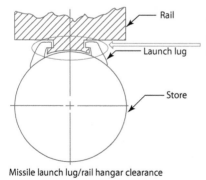

Missile launch lug/rail hangar clearance

Rail

Launch lug

Store

Typical allowable lug/hanger rail clearance
• Pitch: ±/−0.04 (binding) to 0.08 deg (high tip-off)
• Yaw: ±/−0.02 (binding) to 0.05 deg (high tip-off)

Fig. 6.119c Examples of missile — launch platform integration
problems/limitations.

d) Launcher aeroelasticity ⇒ tip-off @ launch ⇒ miss at min range

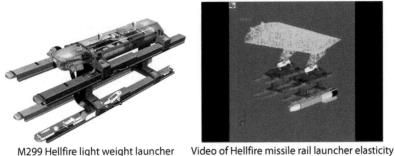

M299 Hellfire light weight launcher   Video of Hellfire missile rail launcher elasticity

Fig. 6.119d   Examples of missile — launch platform integration problems/limitations.

values of the missile lug/hanger rail clearances are ± 0.04 in to ± 0.08 in for pitch, and ± 0.02 to ± 0.05 in for yaw.

A design tradeoff is two versus three lugs/hangers. Two lugs/hangers have less drag, but three lugs/hangers may be required to reduce the tip-off error when the missile leaves the rail.

A third consideration in missile/launch platform integration is launcher aeroelasticity. The aeroelasticity of a lightweight launcher causes a tip-off at launch, which causes a missile miss distance that may set the minimum effective range. Launcher aeroelasticity is of particular concern for rail launchers on UCAVs and helicopters because they are more weight driven to light weight launchers. The flight loads and missile thrust results in launcher elasticity tip-off error when missile leaves the rail.

Shown in the left portion of Fig. 6.119d is an example of a light weight rail launcher, the M299 launcher. The M299 launcher weighs 145 lb without missiles. The total weight of the launcher with four Hellfire missiles is much larger, 541 lb. The M299 is a "smart" digital launcher that recognizes the Hellfire missile variants as well as the Joint Air-to-Ground Missile (JAGM) and guided 2.75-inch rockets. It is compatible with multiple helicopter and aircraft launch platforms. In the right portion of the figure is a video illustrating the launch of the Hellfire missile and the rail launcher elasticity.

A fourth consideration in missile/launch platform integration is the impact of a crosswind or a downwash on the missile tip-off at launch. A high angle of attack at launch causes a miss distance at the minimum effective range and may also cause a loss of flight control, especially for an aerodynamically controlled missile.

In the top left portion of Fig. 6.119e is a photograph showing the vertical launch of a Sea Sparrow in a crosswind. Sea Sparrow uses TVC for flight control during launch. Correcting for the cross wind impacts the missile miss distance and the minimum effective range. The photograph in the top right portion of the figure is a helicopter hovering near the ground. Note the large downwash beneath the rotor blades. During launch the missile must fly through the high local angle of attack from the downwash, followed by a transient change in the angle of attack after the missile clears the downwash. The corrections impact the missile miss distance at its minimum effective range. At the bottom of the figure is a video showing a Sea Sparrow launch in a cross wind and the rotor blade downwash of the Apache helicopter.

Figure 6.119f is a first-order method of calculating the angle of attack for a missile launch from a low speed launch platform in a crosswind or in a downwash. The angle of attack α_{cw} is a function of the cross wind velocity V_{cw}, and the missile launch velocity $V_{\text{Missile launch}}$. The equation is

$$\alpha_{cw} = \tan^{-1}\left(V_{cw}/V_{\text{Missile launch}}\right)$$

The equation for the missile launch velocity is

$$V_{\text{Missile launch}} = \left[2g(T/W)s\right]^{1/2}$$

e) Cross wind/downwash $\Rightarrow$ tip-off and possible instability of missile
    leaving launcher $\Rightarrow$ miss at min range and possible loss of control

ESSM Sea Sparrow launch in cross wind

Helo downwash

Video

Fig. 6.119e   Examples of missile — launch platform integration problems/limitations.

f) High cross wind/downwash ⇒ high angle of attack @ launch

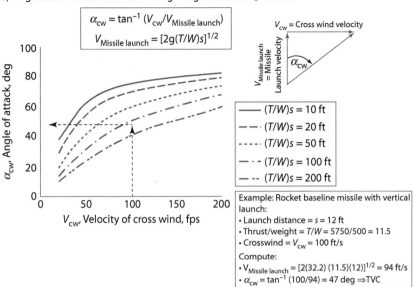

Fig. 6.119f Examples of missile — launch platform integration problems/limitations.

In the above equation $g =$ acceleration of gravity $= 32.2 \text{ ft/s}^2$, $T/W =$ missile thrust-to-weight ratio during launch, and $s =$ length of the launcher. The figure shows α_{cw} from a cross wind velocity ranging from $V_{cw} = 20$ to 200 ft/s. The parameter $(T/W)s$ varies from 10 to 200 ft. Note from the figure that a high angle of attack occurs for a high cross wind, a low thrust-to-weight ratio, and a short length launcher. Angles of attack greater than about 30 deg require TVC, to provide sufficient stability and control.

As an example, from Chapter 7, assume the rocket baseline missile with a vertical launch in a crosswind. Assume that the launch distance is the length of the missile, $s = 12$ ft. The missile thrust-to-weight during launch is

$$T/W = 5750/500 = 11.5$$

Assume that the crosswind is $V_{cw} = 100 \text{ ft/s}$. Calculate

$$V_{\text{Missile launch}} = [2(32.2)(11.5)(12)]^{1/2} = 94 \text{ ft/s}$$

$$\alpha_{cw} = \tan^{-1}(100/94) = 47 \text{ deg}$$

The high value of $\alpha_{cw} = 47$ deg requires that TVC be used in the crosswind, because aerodynamic control would not be effective.

A fifth concern for missile/launch platform integration is either an accidental release or a hang-fire for a rail launched missile. A rail launched missile requires a retention and release system. During the carriage prior to launch, the retention system prevents the missile from an accidental release. During launch, the retention system is removed and the missile is released to be powered down the rail by the thrust of its rocket motor.

In the top left portion of Fig. 6.119g is a schematic of the rail launch retention and release system for the Hellfire missile. Under a normal condition the missile is locked to the rail except for launch, as shown with the position of the latch. In a locked position, an aft travel of the missile is blocked by the missile shoe pressing against an aft stop on the launcher. Forward travel is restrained by a latch on the launcher, which is pressed in front of the missile shoe. The latch is held in place by the compression force of a spring. When the launch command is given by the pilot, a solenoid is activated, which pulls the latch away from the rail and unlocks the missile. The unlocked position of the latch is shown as the dashed line in the figure. The retention force on the unlocked missile is usually about 50% of the thrust of the rocket motor, which allows the missile thrust to overcome the retention force. If the missile does not leave the rail within a normal time period, the retention system is designed to

g) Launcher retention/release $\Rightarrow$ potential inadvertent release/hang-fire

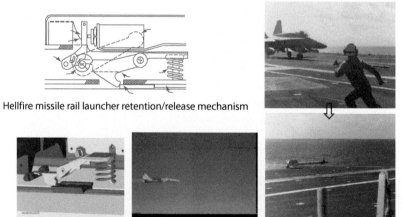

Hellfire missile rail launcher retention/release mechanism

Video of release   Video of hang-fire   Inadvertent release-Sidewinder from F-18

Fig. 6.119g   Examples of missile — launch platform integration
problems/limitations.

automatically relock the missile to the rail. In the bottom left section of the figure is an animation video of the rail launch of a Hellfire missile.

The top right and bottom right sections of the figure show an inadvertent release of a Sidewinder missile from an F-18 aircraft landing on the aircraft carrier Midway (June 3, 1987). Accidental release of a rail launch missile is more likely to occur for aircraft carrier operation than for a fixed base operation, because the landing shock loads are usually higher.

A hang-fire occurs if the retention system does not unlock the missile from the rail following the launch command. A concern of hang-fire is the hot rocket exhaust from the missile, which can damage the adjacent launch platform structure. Another concern is the thrust load on the launch platform. Shown in the bottom center of the figure is a video of a hang-fire of a rocket motor. Finally, in addition to the concern of a hang-fire if the launcher retention/release system fails to unlock the missile from the rail, a hang-fire may also occur if the igniter fails to sufficiently pressurize the rocket motor to full thrust.

The missile rocket plume may provide an unsafe heating environment on the launch platform, especially for a hang-fire of a rail launched missile. An assessment of the lateral spread and length of the missile rocket plume, based on Ref. 36 is

$$y_{max} = 0.4(T/q_\infty)^{1/2}$$

$$x_{Mach\,disk} = 3.3(T/q_\infty)^{1/2}$$

In the above equations, y_{max} = maximum lateral spread in ft of the rocket plume; $x_{Mach\,disk}$ = longitudinal distance in ft from the nozzle exit to the first diamond Mach disk, where the plume begins subsonic mixing with the free stream; T = missile thrust in lb; and q_∞ = free stream dynamic pressure in $lb/ft^2 = (1/2)\rho M_\infty^2 a^2$. Assumptions are an under-expanded plume, inviscid flow, the nozzle expansion ratio $\varepsilon < 10$, and a free stream Mach number $M_\infty \geq 0.5$. If $M_\infty < 0.5$, $M_\infty = 0.5$ is used to compute q_∞.

Note from the above equation and Fig. 6.119h that y_{max} increases with increased thrust and decreased dynamic pressure. At large values of thrust and low dynamic pressure the maximum diameter is larger than the diameter of the missile, and can provide a safety hazard for the adjacent structure of the launch platform.

As an example calculation, assume the rocket baseline missile from Chapter 7, which has a diameter $d = 8$ in $= 0.67$ ft and a nominal boost thrust $T = 5750$ lb. We will also assume a flight altitude $h = 20$ kft ($\rho = 0.001267$ slug/ft^3, $a = 1037$ ft/s) and a free stream Mach number

h)   Rocket plume ⇒ potential unsafe heating of launch platform

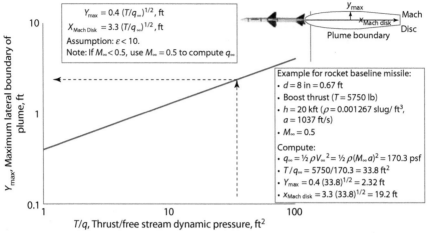

Fig. 6.119h Examples of missile — launch platform integration problems/
limitations. (Source: Jarvinen, P. O., and Hill, J. A. F., Universal Model for
Underexpanded Rocket Plumes in Hypersonic Flow, *Proceedings of the 12th
JANAF Liquid Propulsion Meeting, Nov. 1970.*)

$M_\infty = 0.5$. Compute

$$q_\infty = (1/2)\rho V_\infty^2 = (1/2)\rho(M_\infty a)^2 = (1/2)(0.001267)[0.5(1037)]^2$$
$$= 170.3\,\text{psf}$$

$$T/q_\infty = 5750/170.3 = 33.8\,\text{ft}^2$$

$$y_{\text{max}} = 0.4(33.8)^{1/2} = 2.32\,\text{ft}$$

$$x_{@y_{\text{max}}} = 3.3(33.8)^{1/2} = 19.2\,\text{ft}$$

Note from the above calculation and the figure that the maximum
lateral spread of the rocket plume is larger than the missile radius (2.32 ft
versus 0.33 ft).

A concern for qualifying an air launched missile is safe separation from
the launch platform. Safe separation is of particular concern for high angle
of attack maneuvering fighter aircraft and aircraft flying at a high dynamic
pressure. Program guidelines for considering store separation are included
in MIL-HDBK-244A (Guide to Aircraft/Stores Compatibility) and MIL-
STD-1763 (Aircraft/Stores Compatibility: Systems Engineering Data
Requirements and Test Procedures).

In the left portion of Fig. 6.119i is a photograph of an F-18 aircraft at
high angle of attack, indicated by the vortex shedding. The middle sketch
of the figure illustrates an unsafe separation of a missile from an aircraft,

with the missile returning to impact the aircraft. In the far right portion of the figure is a video of examples of unsafe store separation of fuel tanks, bombs, and missiles. Finally, store separation problems tend to occur for large stores, buoyant stores (e.g., empty fuel tanks), and close proximity/ multiple adjacent stores.

Because of the limited funding of today's environment, most combat aircraft are multi-purpose aircraft. An example of a multi-purpose aircraft is the F-18 E/F, shown in Fig. 6.119j, with its large number of stores. Included are anti-aircraft missiles, precision strike missiles, defense suppression missiles, guided bombs, unguided bombs, decoys, targeting pods, and fuel tanks. The store qualification program is a major activity in the development of a new combat aircraft and ideally it should be addressed early in the aircraft development process. Store qualification is especially time consuming and expensive for a multi-purpose aircraft.

Figure 6.119k illustrates shows examples of safe store separation. In the top section of the figure are photographs of the launch separation of a rail-launched AMRAAM from the F-16, a rapid bomb drop from the B-2, and an ejection-launched CALCM from the B-1.

In the bottom left corner of the figure is a video of the launch separation of AMRAAM from the F-16, Phoenix from the F-14, bomb drops from the B-2, bomb drops from the B-1, GBU-24 separation from the F-4, and Taurus separation from the C-130. The first portion of the video shows examples of launch separation of AMRAAM using rail and ejection launchers. AMRAAM is capable of either rail launch or ejection launch. The second portion of the video shows ejection launch, roll stabilization, and motor ignition for Phoenix. Note that Phoenix has a stable roll condition in the x-roll orientation. The third portion of the video illustrates B-2

i) Aircraft launch platform maneuvering/local flow filed (α, β) and high dynamic pressure $\Rightarrow$ potential unsafe separation

 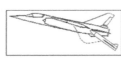 

| F-18 at High angle of attack | Unsafe store separation | Video of unsafe store separation |

Fig. 6.119i Examples of missile — launch platform integration problems/limitations.

j) A multi-purpose fighter aircraft must qualify a large number of stores

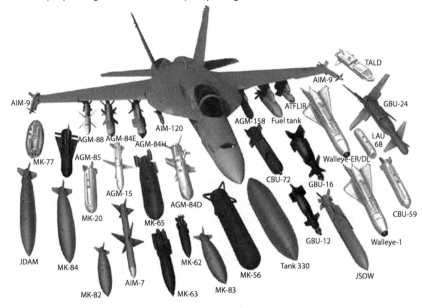

Fig. 6.119j Examples of missile — launch platform integration problems/limitations.

K)

Examples of safe store separation

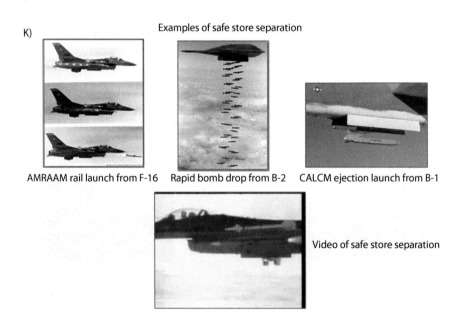

AMRAAM rail launch from F-16   Rapid bomb drop from B-2   CALCM ejection launch from B-1

Video of safe store separation

Fig. 6.119k Examples of missile — launch platform integration problems/limitations.

bomb drop separations. The B-2 rapid bomb drop is about one per second. A rapid bomb drop is desirable to minimize the exposure time with the high observables from the open weapon bay. An exposure time less than about 15 s is desirable to prevent threat radars from establishing a track file. The next portion of the video is the separation of the GBU-24 low level laser guided bomb from the F-4 aircraft. Note the GBU-24 rapid roll rate during separation. The rapid roll rate is induced by a fixed roll deflection of the flight control surfaces, to aid in safe separation. Finally, the last portion of the video is a parachute extraction of Taurus from the C-130.

A tradeoff in launch separation analysis is fixed flight control versus active flight control. Fixed flight control, with the flight control surfaces in a locked position, is usually preferable during launch. There is the possibility of a hard-over failure in using active flight control. The use of fixed flight control during launch separation usually requires that the missile be statically stable. For a statically unstable missile, active flight control is almost always required during launch, to avoid impacting the aircraft. The use of active flight control and a statically unstable store requires a additional reliability analysis to ensure there is a negligible probability of a flight control hard-over failure, requires more extensive store separation wind tunnel and flight testing, and requires the application of a Monte Carlo probability analysis to ensure there is a low probability of the missile impacting the launch platform.

Analytical predictions of an aircraft missile store separation flight trajectory are often inaccurate, especially during the early conceptual design of the missile. The store separation trajectory is influenced by many parameters, with complex interactions among the parameters, and uncertainty in the values of the parameters. These are illustrated in Figure 6.119l.

In the right portion of the figure is a sketch of the rocket baseline missile mounted on a pylon under an aircraft wing. Shown are the aircraft's velocity V_∞, its angle of attack α, its flight path angle γ, and its pitch attitude θ. Note from the sketch that the local velocity magnitude and orientation changes as it flows over the aircraft wing and pylon. The missile is immersed in a non-uniform field. As a result of the non-uniform flow field, the missile aerodynamic coefficients (e.g., C_N, C_m, C_A) and the local dynamic pressure are a function of the location of the missile relative to the launch aircraft.

Store parameters and their uncertainties have a large effect on the store separation trajectory. These include the shape, size, weight, cg, moments of inertia, and the time interval for the deployment of compressed carriage surfaces. Based on MIL-HDBK-1763 (Aircraft/Stores Compatibility: System Engineering Data Requirements and Test Procedures), the missile

l)   Conceptual criteria for safe separation $\Rightarrow C_{N_\alpha}\alpha q S_{Ref}/(W \cos \gamma) < 1$

- ◆ Store parameters/uncertainties
  - Shape
  - Size
  - Weight
  - cg
  - Moments of inertia
  - Time for surface deployment
- ◆ Launcher parameters/uncertainties
  - Location
  - Total impulse
  - Pitch rate
- ◆ Aircraft parameters/uncertainties
  - Mach number
  - Angle of attack, angle of sideslip, roll angle
  - Flight path angle
  - Altitude/Reynolds number
  - Load factor
  - Rotation rates
  - Stores loading

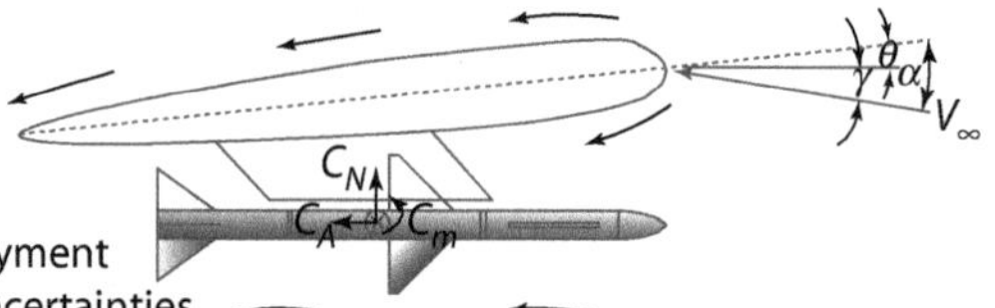

Fig. 6.119l   Examples of missile — launch platform integration problems/limitations.

cg location, the suspension lugs locations, and the time for missile surfaces deployment are often the most critical concerns.

Ejection launcher parameters and their uncertainties also have a large effect on the store separation trajectory. These include the location, the total impulse, and the pitch rate of an ejection launcher.

There are many aircraft parameters and their uncertainties that affect the store separation trajectory. These include the aircraft Mach number, angle of attack, angle of sideslip, roll angle, flight path angle, altitude/ Reynolds number, load factor, rotation rates, and its stores loading configuration. According to MIL-HDBK-1763, the aircraft Mach number, angle of attack, and angle of sideslip may be critical concerns.

There may not be sufficient time or funding during missile development to confidently evaluate the impact of store/launcher/aircraft parameters and their uncertainties on the missile store separation trajectory. The store separation qualification process is usually initially based on prediction methods, such as CFD, to identify the most critical conditions. Next, wind tunnel testing is conducted to address the critical store separation flight conditions and to also develop a general data base on the aircraft store separation across the flight envelope of the aircraft. Finally, flight testing is conducted, focusing on the critical store separation flight conditions.

A conceptual design and system engineering criteria for store safe separation is that the store weight W and the aircraft light path angle γ should drive the store separation trajectory more than the store normal force $N = C_{N\alpha}\alpha q S_{\text{Ref}}$. The criteria is

$$C_{N\alpha}\alpha q S_{\text{Ref}}/(W\cos\gamma) < 1$$

Aircraft store compatibility wind tunnel tests are conducted to determine store carriage loads and store separation forces, moments, and trajectories. Figure 6.119m shows examples of wind tunnel installations of aircraft and store models. Note that a typical aircraft store load-out has closely spaced stores. The local airflow around a store is difficult to predict. There is a complex flow field interaction of a store with the aircraft and also with the adjacent stores.

The types of wind tunnel testing for store compatibility include:

1. Flow field mapping underneath the aircraft with a pitot static pressure probe. This measures the local values of the static pressure, total pressure, and the angle of attack/sideslip. Based on the collected data, a later computer simulation calculates the store separation trajectories. The advantage of this type of test is that the effect of the launch aircraft flow field on the store separation trajectory is available at the start of the missile development program. This approach works well with a small store immersed in the flow field of large aircraft. It does not work as well

m)   Examples of store separation wind tunnel tests

F-18 store compatibility test in AEDC 16T   AV-8 store compatibility test in AEDC 4T

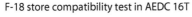

Types of wind tunnel testing for store compatibility

- Flow field mapping with probe
- Flow field mapping with store
- Captive trajectory simulation
- Drop testing
- Carriage loads

Example stores with flow field interaction: Kh-41 + AA-10

Fig. 6.119m Examples of missile — launch platform integration problems/limitations.

for a large store in the flow field of a small aircraft. It is also deficient in accounting for the influence of adjacent stores.

2. Flow field mapping with an instrumented store model on a sting. This measures the forces and moments on the store that is immersed in the aircraft flow field. The instrumented store has a internal balance to measure the loads and moments on the store. Based on the collected data, a later computer simulation (usually 6-DOF) calculates the store separation trajectories. An advantage of this approach is that it provides aircraft/store mutual flow field interaction data.

3. Captive trajectory simulation (CTS), using an instrumented store model on a sting. Based on the measured loads and moments of the store in the wind tunnel, the CTS computer program provides the store trajectory. An advantage of this approach is that it provides immediate information on safe separation for specified flight conditions. A disadvantage is the information has limited applicability to other flight conditions.

4. *Drop testing of store models.* An advantage of drop testing is there is no sting support interference with the flow field. Disadvantages of drop testing are fewer tests with the limited wind tunnel time that is available and there may be inaccuracy in scaling the wind tunnel results to a full scale store and full scale flight conditions. Because the wind tunnel models are sub-scale, it is not possible to simultaneously simulate Mach number, static aerodynamic forces and moments, and dynamic aerodynamic forces and moments. Three scaling approaches may be used

   1. *Heavy Scaling.* This is the most popular approach. Heavy scaling duplicates the free stream Mach number and the flow field. It provides the correct ratio of static aerodynamic forces to missile weight. However, dynamic derivatives (e.g., C_{m_q} pitch rate damping) are improperly scaled and angular motion does not have sufficient damping. The store models are usually constructed of lead, tungsten, or even gold to provide weight scaling to simulate full-scale buoyancy in the wind tunnel test.

   2. *Froude Scaling.* Froude scaling is often the second most popular approach for drop testing. Froude scaling preserves static and dynamic forces and moments but does not match Mach number. Froude scaling is most applicable at low subsonic Mach number.

   3. *Light scaling.* Light scaling duplicates the free stream Mach number and properly scales the aerodynamic forces and moments. However, the correct ratio of static aerodynamic forces to gravity is not maintained. The store weight is deficient by the ratio of the model-to-aircraft characteristic length. The store angular motion is proper, but linear accelerations are incorrect. This technique is most applicable to simulating the initial angular motion of the store.

5. *Carriage Loads.* A store carriage loads wind tunnel test measures the forces and moments on the store attached to the aircraft. Two measurement techniques may be used:
    1. *Strain gauge balance inside store.* This approach is often used for small models because does not require a sting support for the store.
    2. *Dual-sting.* This approach uses separate stings/struts to support the store and aircraft. An advantage of this approach is that the balance inside the store can not only measure loads in captive flight, but can also measure loads in the store trajectory. A disadvantage is the store sting support changes the local flow field.

Because each type of wind tunnel store separation testing has advantages and disadvantages, it is usually a good idea to conduct both flow field mapping/captive trajectory tests and drop tests. Also, if affordable, it is often a good idea to conduct more than one type of drop testing and compare the results. The problem is the complex flow field and low Reynolds number (sub-scale store laminar boundary layer instead of full-scale store turbulent boundary layer) may result in relatively inaccurate forces and moments compared to flight test.

Another concern in missile/launch platform integration is the aeroelastic instability of the launch aircraft due to stores. At low dynamic pressure with light weight stores mounted on a stiff portion of the aircraft structure, aeroelasticity is not a problem. Under normal design conditions the amplitude of structural vibration is small and is damped out. However, for relatively heavy stores mounted on relatively flexible portions of the aircraft, such as the wing tips, flight at high dynamic pressure can induce divergent vibration. This is illustrated in the left portion of Fig. 6.119n. The divergence can damage the aircraft, degrade the flying qualities, and may even lead to the loss of the aircraft.

Aeroelastic flight test qualification of stores requires that the instrumented flight test store match the weight, size, and geometry of the operational store. Instrumentation includes accelerometer and acoustic sensors. Shown in the bottom right portion of the figure is a video with examples of aircraft aeroelastic instability from stores.

A tradeoff in missile/launch platform integration is the aircraft wing bending frequency with attached stores. A heavy store reduces the bending frequency, which may reduce the structure life of the wing. Also, if the first mode bending frequency ω_1 is reduced to the same frequency as the aircraft short period frequency ω_{SP}, there is a problem of flutter divergence. For light weight inboard stores at low dynamic pressure, the aircraft wing bending frequency is higher than the frequencies of the aircraft flight dynamics and there is relatively small aeroelastic coupling. However the bending fundamental first mode frequency deceases for a heavy store,

n)   Aircraft launch platform aeroelasticity with store ⇒ potential flutter/
unsafe handling qualities/wing fatique

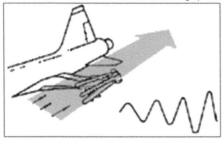

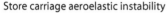

Store carriage aeroelastic instability   Video of store wind tunnel flutter, wind
tunnel limit cycle oscillation, and flight test
limit cycle oscillation

Fig. 6.119n Examples of missile — launch platform integration
problems/limitations.

especially for a store on the wing tip. Also, the aircraft flight dynamics frequencies increase for an aircraft flying at high dynamic pressure. As a result, the aircraft wing first mode bending frequency ω_1 may approach an aircraft flight dynamics frequency, such as the short period frequency ω_{SP}. Limit cycle oscillations and flutter will result from resonance when the aircraft wing first mode frequency coincides with the aircraft flight dynamics short period frequency. A limit cycle oscillation has large amplitude and only a small amount of damping. Flutter is worse. It is an increasing amplitude, divergent oscillation (negative damping).

A conceptual design and system engineering criteria to avoid flutter is

$$\omega_1 > \omega_{SP}$$

An equation for ω_1 is

$$\omega_1 = 15.32\{c_{mac}(t/c)^3 E/[A^3 W_{Wing}[(W_{Launcher} + W_{Store})/$$

$$W_{Wing} + 0.118]]\}^{1/2}, \text{ Hz}$$

The source of the above equation is Ref 3. Assumptions are that each wing panel can be modeled as 1-DOF cantilever beam and that the store plus launcher mass is located at the wing tip (worst case for a low value of ω_1). Definitions are

ω_1 = aircraft wing first mode bending frequency, Hz

c_{mac} = aircraft wing mean aerodynamic chord, ft

$(t/c) = $ aircraft wing thickness-to-chord ratio

$E = $ aircraft wing modulus of elasticity, psi

$A = $ aircraft wing aspect ratio

$W_{\text{Wing}} = $ weight of aircraft wing, lb

$W_{\text{Launcher}} = $ weight of wing tip launcher, lb

$W_{\text{Store}} = $ weight of wing tip store, lb

Figure 6.119o shows the effect of the store weight on the structural frequency of an aircraft wing. Note from the figure and the above equation that the parameters that lead to a low structural frequency are a heavy store, a heavy launcher, a short chord wing, a thin wing, a low structural elasticity of the wing, and a high aspect ratio wing.

As an example calculation, assume an F-16 Aircraft with carriage of a LAU-129 launcher plus an AIM-9 missile on each wing tip. For this case $c_{\text{mac}} = 8.51$ ft, $(t/c) = 0.04$, $E = 10.6 \times 10^6$ psi, $A = 3.05$, $W_{\text{Wing}} = 2700$ lb, $W_{\text{Launcher}} = 87$ lb, and $W_{\text{Store}} = W_{\text{AIM-9}} = 200$ lb. Compute

$$\omega_1 = 15.32 \{ 8.51(0.04)^3 (10.6 \times 10^6) /$$

$$[3.05^3(2700) \times [(87 + 200)/2700 + 0.118]] \}^{1/2} = 8.88 \text{ Hz}$$

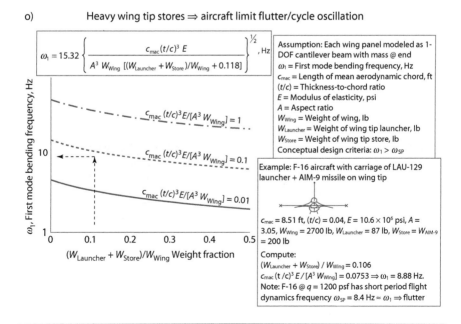

o)   Heavy wing tip stores ⇒ aircraft limit flutter/cycle oscillation

Fig. 6.119o Examples of missile — launch platform integration problems/limitations. (Source: *AIAA Aerospace Design Engineers Guide*, 1993.)

The highest value of the short period frequency ω_{SP} of the F-16 aircraft occurs at its maximum dynamic pressure flight condition ($\omega_{SP} \approx 8.4$ Hz @ $q = 1200$ psf). Note that for $q = 1200$ psf, $\omega_1 = 8.88$ Hz $\approx \omega_{SP} \approx 8.4$ Hz. This indicates that there is likely a flutter limit for an F-16 with AIM-9 stores if it is flying at its maximum dynamic pressure flight condition $q = 1200$ psf.

Internal carriage of a weapon inside an aircraft bay is normally a more benign environment than external carriage. However, when the aircraft bay doors are open, the weapons may be subjected to a severe vibration and acoustics environment, especially if the aircraft is at a high dynamic pressure flight condition.

The upper portion of Fig. 6.119p compares the flow over a shallow bay with that over a deep bay. A shallow bay has a length-to-depth ratio with $l/d > \approx 10$. A deep bay has $l/d < \approx 10$. For a shallow bay, there may be a problem from the airflow intruding into the bay and attaching to the inner wall, causing flow separation. Weapons that are within the region of flow separation have especially high loads from vibration and acoustics. Also, for supersonic flight, the shock wave/boundary layer attachment is a source of high localized heating. For a deep bay, there is less flow intrusion into the bay with less flow separation, and the vibration and acoustic loads are smaller.

p)   Aircraft launch platform bay acoustics and vibration ⇒ missile factor of safety

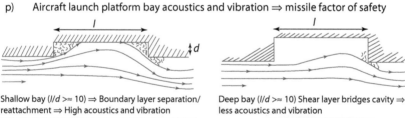

Shallow bay ($l/d > \approx 10$) ⇒ Boundary layer separation/ reattachment ⇒ High acoustics and vibration

Deep bay ($l/d > \approx 10$) Shear layer bridges cavity ⇒ less acoustics and vibration

F-35 shallow bay

B-1 deep bay (180 in x 44 in)

Fig. 6.119p Examples of missile — launch platform integration problems/ limitations.

Example rail launcher: Hellfire/Brimstone   Example ejection launcher: AGM-86 ALCM

Video of Hellfire/Brimstone carriage/launch   Video of AGM-86 carriage/launch

Fig. 6.120 Examples of aircraft rail launched and ejection launched missiles.

The bottom portion of the figure shows photographs of a shallow bay and a deep bay. The bottom left photograph is the F-35 weapons bay with a mixed payload of an AMRAAM (on the bay door) and a JDAM. The bottom right photograph is a B-1 weapons bay, with a load-out of eight JDAMs.

The mechanical and electrical interface between a missile and the launch aircraft is provided by the launcher. The mechanical interface by the launcher includes the attachment of the missile to the launcher, structural support by the launcher for the missile, and the launch mechanism for the missile. The electrical interface by the launcher supports the cockpit controls and displays, enabling the pilot to launch the missile.

Figure 6.120 has examples of US standard rail and ejection launchers for aircraft. In the upper left of the figure is an example of a rail launcher. Shown in the figure are AGM-114 Hellfire II missiles on the rail launchers of a helicopter. Rail launchers are particularly suited to light weight, high thrust missiles such as Hellfire. Hellfire II weighs about 100 lb, with a launch thrust-to-weight ratio of about 10 : 1. Hellfire II has a semi-laser seeker (SAL) with a field of regard of ± 30 deg.

Most heavy weight missiles use ejection launch. In the upper right corner of the figure is an example of an ejection launcher. Shown are AGM-86 ALCM precision strike missiles that are installed on a rotary launcher of a bomb bay. ALCM is ejected from the bay at an ejection velocity of about 20 ft/s. The ejection stroke is about 12 in, providing an average acceleration of about 6 g. The ejection launcher contains cartridges that provide the downward velocity and a downward pitch rate to the missile at launch, aiding safe and accurate separation. Suspension of the missile is such that the missile center-of-gravity is midway between the ejectors. A concern during launch is the local angle of attack and the local angle of sideslip and the effect on the missile flight trajectory, especially at high dynamic pressure. Up to eight ALCM missiles can be carried on a rotary launcher in each of the bays of the B-1, B-2, and B-52 bombers. The ALCM has compressed carriage (switchblade wing, folded tails), providing a high missile load-out efficiency in the bomb bay. The wing and tails are unfolded immediately after separation from the bay. Concerns for internal bay carriage include bay acoustics, bay vibration, flow field angularities near the aircraft, and safe separation at high dynamic pressure.

The left bottom section of the figure is a video of the rail launcher loading of the mmW Brimstone missile. The missile is loaded on the launcher by sliding onto the rail and into a "shotgun" connector that interfaces with the aircraft avionics. The video also shows the rail loading and the launch of the SAL Hellfire missile from a helicopter launch platform.

The bottom right section of the figure has a video of the loading, carriage, ejection launch, separation, and flight of the ALCM missile. Note the deployment of the compressed carriage switch blade wing and the folded tails.

Store suspension requirements for ejection launchers, based on US military standard MIL-A-8591, are summarized in Fig. 6.121. Shown are the store weight and the store/launcher dimension parameters for light weight stores (up to 100 lb), medium weight stores (101 to 1450 lb), and heavy weight stores (1451 to 3500 lb) that are suspended from lugs. Lug suspension alternatives are 30-in and 14-in suspension systems. For an ejected store weight up to 100 lb, only the 14-in suspension can be used. A light weight (up to 100 lb) missile requires a lug height and an ejector pad area of 0.75 in and 4.0 × 26.0 in respectively. For a medium weight missile, with a weight between 101 and 1450 lb, either the 14 or a 30-in suspension may be used. Medium weight ejected stores have larger required lug height. They also require lug wells. The required lug wells could have a strong impact on the missile internal structure design. For example, in some cases the rocket motor may overlap the missile center of gravity. Accommodating the lug wells in the rocket motor case is difficult and expensive. A strong back may be required, similar to that of the AGM-69 SRAM missile. For a heavy missile with a weight that is over 1451 lb, only the 30-in suspension must be used. MIL-STD-8591 requires that the lugs have a deeper well if the missile weighs more than 1451 lb.

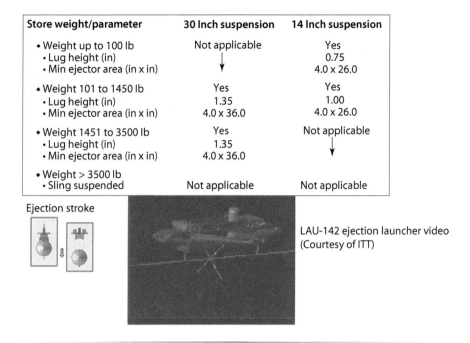

Store weight/parameter	30 Inch suspension	14 Inch suspension
◆ Weight up to 100 lb • Lug height (in) • Min ejector area (in x in)	Not applicable ↓	Yes 0.75 4.0 x 26.0
◆ Weight 101 to 1450 lb • Lug height (in) • Min ejector area (in x in)	Yes 1.35 4.0 x 36.0	Yes 1.00 4.0 x 26.0
◆ Weight 1451 to 3500 lb • Lug height (in) • Min ejector area (in x in)	Yes 1.35 4.0 x 36.0	Not applicable ↓
◆ Weight > 3500 lb • Sling suspended	Not applicable	Not applicable

Ejection stroke

LAU-142 ejection launcher video
(Courtesy of ITT)

Fig. 6.121 MIL-STD-8591 imposes aircraft store suspension and ejection launcher requirements.

A store with a weight over 3501 lb is not suspending by lugs but is sling-suspended, either externally or in a bomb bay. It is not ejected, but is gravity dropped. Stores with a weight up to 30,000 lb have been carried and dropped from bombers.

The bottom left portion of the figure illustrates the ejection launch sequence of a store separating from the launcher. In the bottom center portion of the figure is a video animation of the ejection launch sequence. The animation shows the LAU-142 pneudraulic launcher ejection launching an AMRAAM. The end-of-stroke ejection velocity is about 27 ft/s.

The traditional store ejection launchers use one-shot pyrotechnic cartridges, to provide a downward velocity and a downward pitch rate for safe separation from the aircraft launch platform. The newer "smart" ejection launchers do not have pyrotechnic cartridges, but instead use pneumatic, electromechanical, or hydraulic forces to provide the store ejection velocity and pitch rate.

Figure 6.122 compares the older pyrotechnic store ejection launchers with the newer non-pyrotechnic launchers. One disadvantage of conventional pyrotechnic launchers is that the store ejection pitch rate is fixed. For a non-pyrotechnic launcher the ejection pitch rate can be automatically set, to provide the best separation at the launch condition. Another

Ejection launcher type	Pitch rate matched to launch (M, h, α)	Logistics	Ejection velocity	Example
Pyrotechnic cartridges	No ☹	☹	☺	 LAU-106/A with AMRAAM  BRU-33/A with Mk-82
Pneumatic, electromech, or hydraulic	Yes ☺	☺	☺☺	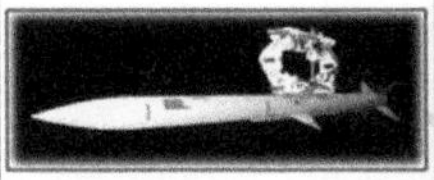 LAU-142/A with AMRAAM  BRU-69/A with Mk-82

Fig. 6.122   Pyrotechnic ejection launchers for aircraft stores are being replaced by smart launchers.

disadvantage of a pyrotechnic launcher is it is logistically intensive. The pyrotechnic cartridges must be replaced after each launch. Also, maintenance is required to clean up the residue buildup in the racks. The non-pyrotechnic launchers are lower maintenance. Also, they do not require the inventory storage and the hazardous waste cleanup/disposal of a pyrotechnic launcher. Both types of launchers provide high ejection velocity for a medium weight store, such as an AMRAAM. For a heavy store, some pyrotechnic launchers can provide a somewhat higher ejection velocity. Shown in the right portion of the figure are photographs comparing pyrotechnic launchers with non-pyrotechnic launchers. AMRAAM is shown with the older LAU-106/A pyrotechnic launcher and the newer LAU-142/A pneudraulic launcher. Mk-82 is shown with the older BRU-33/A pyrotechnic launcher and the newer BRU-69/A pneumatic launcher.

The rail length for launching a modern missile is typically shorter than the length of the missile. A short length rail launcher requires a higher missile thrust-to-weight at launch and more consideration of the missile stability & control at launch. Examples of missile rail launchers that are compatible with MIL-STD-8591 are shown in Fig. 6.123. Most rail launchers suspend the missile at two locations, a forward hanger and an aft hanger. Some rail launchers suspend the missile at three locations, for added stiffness and for reduced tip off at launch. A disadvantage of three hangers is additional missile drag.

The rail launcher shown in the top of the figure is the LAU-7. It has a store weight limit of 300 lb and a store diameter limit of 7 in. The LAU-7 is a standard launcher for the Sidewinder missile. Sidewinder has three hangers (forward, center, and aft), with a shoe width of 2.26 in.

The LAU-117 rail launcher, shown in the bottom of the figure, has a store weight limit of 600 lb and a store diameter limit of 10 in. The LAU-117 is a standard launcher for the Maverick missile. Maverick has a forward T-shaped hanger with a shoe width of 1.14 in and an aft U-shaped hanger with a shoe width of 7.23 in. Only two hangers are required for Maverick because the relatively long length of the aft hanger.

An advantage of a missile that has reduced span surfaces during carriage is that it allows a closer spacing of the adjacent missiles on the launch platform. Approaches for compressed carriage include reduced span surfaces, folded surfaces, wraparound surfaces, and planar surfaces that extend (such as switch blade wings, Diamond Back wings, and the Longshot wings).

Figure 6.124 illustrates the benefit of compressed carriage for AMRAAM in the F-22 bay. The F-22 internal center weapons bay typically has two partitions, with one partition for air-to-air (e.g., AMRAAM) missiles. A baseline AMRAAM AIM-120B load-out in an F-22 center bay partition allows two missiles per partition. However, compressed carriage AMRAAM AIM-120C can be packaged three missiles per partition, a 50% increase in the firepower load-out. For an air-to-air mission only,

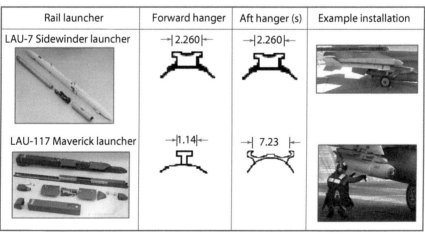

Rail launcher	Forward hanger	Aft hanger (s)	Example installation
LAU-7 Sidewinder launcher	→|2.260|←	→|2.260|←	
LAU-117 Maverick launcher	→|1.14|←	→| 7.23 |←	

Note: Dimension in inches.
- LAU 7 rail launched store weight and diameter limits are ≤300 lb, ≤7 in
- LAU 117 rail launched store weight and diameter limits are ≤600 lb, ≤10 in

Fig. 6.123 MIL-STD-8591 aircraft store rail launcher examples.

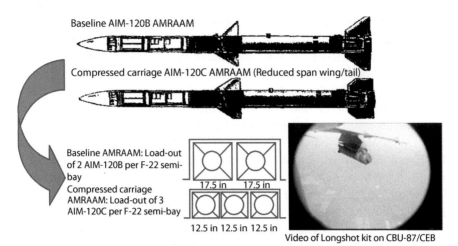

Baseline AIM-120B AMRAAM

Compressed carriage AIM-120C AMRAAM (Reduced span wing/tail)

Baseline AMRAAM: Load-out of 2 AIM-120B per F-22 semi-bay

Compressed carriage AMRAAM: Load-out of 3 AIM-120C per F-22 semi-bay

17.5 in   17.5 in

12.5 in 12.5 in 12.5 in

Video of Longshot kit on CBU-87/CEB

Note: Alternative approaches to compressed carriage include surfaces with small span, folded surfaces, wrap around surfaces, and planar surfaces than extend (e.g., switch blade, Diamond Back, longshot).

Fig. 6.124   Compressed carriage missiles provide higher firepower.

both partitions of the F-22 center bay are allocated to air-to-air missiles, allowing a bay lead-out of six compressed carriage AIM-120C.

It was noted previously in Chapter 2 that missiles that have low aspect ratio surfaces, such as AMRAAM AIM-120C, usually have a larger supersonic hinge moment. This is from the larger variation in the aerodynamic center. However, an advantage of a low aspect ratio surface is a lower

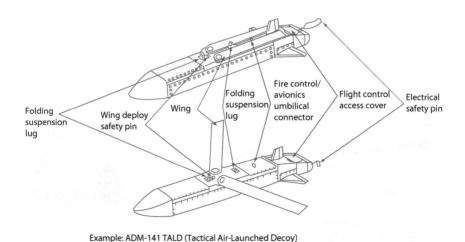

Folding suspension lug

Wing deploy safety pin

Wing

Folding suspension lug

Fire control/ avionics umbilical connector

Flight control access cover

Electrical safety pin

Folding suspension lug

Example: ADM-141 TALD (Tactical Air-Launched Decoy)
Note: Military standard guidelines: MIL-STD-1760, MIL-STD-1553, NATO STANAG 3837

Fig. 6.125   Example of aircraft carriage and fire control interfaces.

bending moment, because of the reduced span. The lower bending moment on the control surface shaft reduces the frictional bearing torque. Frictional bearing torque versus hinge moment is a tradeoff in the performance and weight of the flight control actuator.

Another example of compressed carriage is in the video of the bottom right section of the figure. The Longshot wing and GPS guidance adaptor kit provide extended range and accuracy for the CBU-87/CEB dispenser. The compressed carriage wings and folded tails are deployed at launch.

Figure 6.125 shows an example of aircraft carriage and fire control interface. It is based on the ADM-141 TALD (Tactical Air-Launched Decoy). Shown are the electrical safety pin lanyard for wing and control surfaces deployment, which is removed just prior to aircraft takeoff; the flight control access cover for maintenance check-out and tests; the fire control/avionics umbilical connector to the aircraft store management computer and displays in the cockpit; folding suspension lugs; deployable wings after launch; and a safety pin to prevent wing deployment prior to launch from the aircraft. Applicable guidelines for the interface of a missile with the aircraft avionics include MIL-STD-1760, MIL-STD-1553, NATO STANAG 3837.

The commitment to launch a missile from a launch platform is usually based on the fire control system display of the combat situational awareness. An advantage of network centric warfare is improved situational awareness by providing a capability to sort out the threat forces, friendly forces, and neutrals in the battlefield area. There is less likelihood of a firing on friendly forces and neutrals.

The left portion of Fig. 6.126 illustrates a display in an aircraft of information from the Link 16/Joint Tactical Information Display System

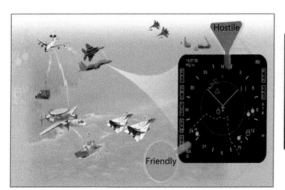

Link 16/JTIDS/MIDS

Video of F-18 cockpit display and control stick functions

Fig. 6.126 The launch platform fire control system display provides combat situational awareness.

(JTIDS)/Multifunctional Information Distribution System (MIDS). Displayed are the locations of the friendly and the threat combat forces. The aircraft shows its own position as a blue+ in the center of the display. The friendly forces are shown as the nearby wingman to the left (blue open circle), two friendly aircraft to the right (green closed circle), a friendly ship that is aft and to the right (green object), a friendly command and control aircraft that is aft and to the right (green closed circle), and a friendly command and control aircraft that is aft and to the left (green closed circle). The hostile systems are the red objects shown in the display, which indicates each threat range, aspect, and heading. The Link 16/JTIDS/MIDS provides enhanced situational awareness is provided through automatic transmission of near real time digital data over a jam-resistant and secure network.

The video in the right portion of the figure presents the F-18 cockpit display and control stick functions. Shown are the pilot's actions to launch air-to-air and air-to-surface weapons.

The control stick of a combat aircraft can provide a capability for the pilot to launch a missile while also maintaining situational awareness through eye contact with the target. Figure 6.127 shows the weapon parameter functions that are available on the F-18 control stick. These are identified in the solid red arrows. The F-18 control stick can be used to select the type of weapon, release the weapon for firing, and fire the weapon.

The helmet mounted sight enhances the capability of the fixed wing aircraft and helicopter pilot to more effectively launch a missile, by providing a

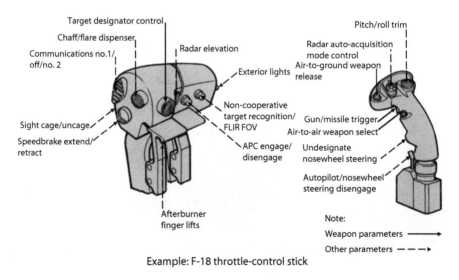

Example: F-18 throttle-control stick

Fig. 6.127 An aircraft control stick can provide a head up weapon selection, release, and firing.

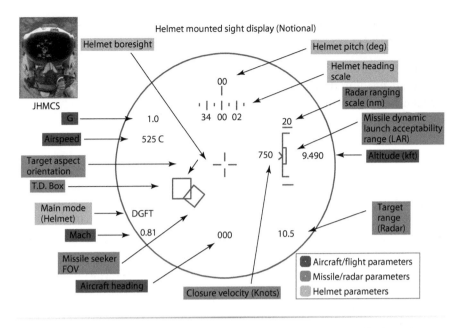

Fig. 6.128 A helmet mounted sight provides a head up display of missile parameters.

head up display of missile parameters and other combat parameters. The typical helmet mounted sight parameters are shown in Fig. 6.128.

Missile/radar parameters displayed on the helmet mounted sight are shown in red. Parameters are:

• Missile dynamic launch acceptability range (LAR). The upper limit of the scale is 20 nm. The minimum/maximum launch ranges are shown in the rectangle. The carrot shows that the missile can be launched in a "sweet spot", midway between max/min range.
• Target radar range (10.5 nm)
• Closure velocity (750 knots) of the launch aircraft on the target. This is displayed next to the carrot in the LAR.
• Missile seeker look angle box. This is shown next to the target direction box.
• Target aspect angle (approximately 210 deg). This is shown as an arrow next to the target direction box.

Helmet parameters that are displayed on the helmet mounted sight are shown in blue. Parameters are:

• Helmet pitch angle (0 deg). An indicated value of 01 would be 10 deg.
• Helmet heading scale (0 deg). An indicated value of 02 would be a look angle of 20 deg right.

Aircraft/flight parameters displayed on the helmet mounted sight are shown in black. Parameters are:

* Altitude (9490 ft)
* Aircraft heading (0 deg or north)
* Mach number (0.81)
* Operating mode (DGFT or dogfight)
* Airspeed (525 knots)
* Normal acceleration g (1.0)

In the upper left corner of the figure is a photograph of the Joint Helmet Mounted Cueing System (JHMCS). JHMCS is used on the F-15, F-16, and F-18 aircraft. JHMCS is an effective complement to the AIM-9X missile, providing a large off-boresight capability in air-to-air combat. A new helmet mounted sight is in development for the F-35. It provides a virtual head up display capability, presenting flight symbology as well as displaying day and night imagery from the F-35's 360° distributed-aperture infrared sensor and electro-optical targeting sensor.

Examples of launch platform integration options and the impact on missile terminal guidance are shown in Fig. 6.129. The typical guidance phases for a missile are launch, midcourse, and terminal.

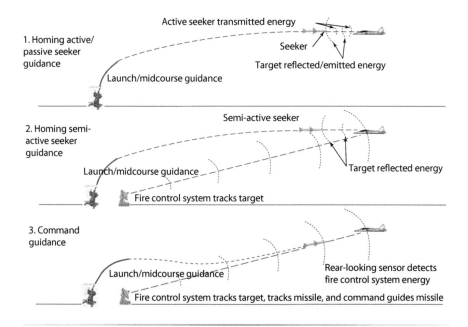

Fig. 6.129   Missile guidance/launch platform integration varies from autonomous missile guidance to command guidance from the fire control system.

The launch phase is usually a programmed phase to safely separate from the launch platform.

The midcourse phase begins when commands are initiated to direct the missile to the target, prior to the missile seeker lock-on. Some short-range missiles do not have a midcourse phase, but proceed immediately into a terminal phase. Approaches to direct the missile during midcourse guidance include an in-flight data link and/or an inertial navigation system. A reference system may be used to update the missile inertial navigation system. Reference update systems include Global Positioning System (GPS) satellites, map matching, and loran. One of the design tradeoffs is the accuracy versus cost and weight of the midcourse guidance system. An advantage of an accurate mid-course guidance system is that it reduces the performance requirements and the cost of a terminal seeker. For a non-moving target, the inertial navigation system may provide sufficient accuracy to eliminate the need for a seeker, which is often the most expensive subsystem of a missile.

The figure illustrates three approaches for terminal guidance. The first approach is autonomous homing guidance, using either an active or a passive seeker. For active seeker guidance, the missile seeker (radar, LADAR) transmits energy to illuminate the target and detects the reflected energy from the target. A processor continuously commands the seeker angle rate to track the target. For passive seeker guidance, the seeker detects infrared (IR) or radar radio frequency (RF) energy that is naturally emitting from the target. A missile with active or passive seeker guidance may operate independently after launch. The second approach is semi-active guidance. The missile seeker receives and tracks the reflected energy (laser, RF) from a target that is illuminated by the fire control system. The third approach is command guidance. Elements of command guidance are 1) the tracking and guiding fire control system, 2) the launcher, 3) the missile, and 4) the target. For command guidance, the fire control system tracks both the missile and the target. Guidance commands are sent from the fire control system to the missile. A command guided missile has a sensor receiver in the back of the missile, looking rearward toward the fire control system. Command guidance can also be used to provide midcourse guidance of longer range missiles, prior to the transition to terminal homing guidance.

Figure 6.130 compares five approaches to missile terminal guidance. Comparisons are shown for 1) active homing (RF, laser), 2) passive homing (IR, RF, ARH), 3) semi-active homing (RF, laser), 4) command (RF, laser, wire), and 5) multi-mode guidance (command updates, inertial, active or passive homing).

Advantages of active guidance include better accuracy at long range and launch platform survivability from "fire-and-forget" autonomous homing

Type of guidance	Launch platform survivability	Missile sensor cost/weight	Long range accuracy	CCM	Fire control corrections/fuzing
Active homing (RF, laser)	◐	— ○	○ ●	◐	—
Passive homing (IR, RF, ARH)	●	○ ◐	◐ ●	— ●	—
Semi-active homing (RF, laser)	— ○	○ ◐	○ ◐	○	●
Command (RF, laser, wire)	—	●	— ◐	●	●
Multi-mode (command updates, inertial, active or passive homing)	○	○	○ ●	○ ●	●
Note:	● Superior ◐ Good ○ Average — Poor				

Fig. 6.130 Comparison of terminal guidance laws.

missile guidance. An example of an active homing RF guided missile is AIM-120 AMRAAM. The tracking accuracy of an active radar seeker is a function of the sub-beam width processing. Because a laser has fine resolution, an active laser homing missile usually has better accuracy than an active RF homing missile.

Passive guidance has an advantage of better launch platform survivability. An example of a passive IR guided missile is AIM-9 Sidewinder. Because an imaging infrared seeker has fine resolution, accuracy for imaging IR homing is usually better than passive non-imaging IR and RF homing.

Semi-active guidance usually has a smaller size, lighter weight, and a lower cost seeker than active guidance, because it does not require that the missile have a transmitter. However, semi-active guidance may result in reduced survivability of the launch platform. Again, accuracy for semi-active laser homing is usually better than semi-active RF. A special type of semi-active RF homing is track-via-missile. The missile seeker tracking information is data linked back to the ground radar for processing, with the processing commands sent back to the missile. This may provide more accurate tracking in terminal flight. Examples of missile that have semi-active laser (SAL), semi-active RF, and track-via-missile semi-active RF guidance are the Hellfire, SM-2 Standard, and the PAC-2 Patriot missiles respectively.

An advantage of a command guided missile is the relatively small size and low cost of the command guidance sensor compared to that of a seeker. Another advantage is less susceptibility to threat countermeasures

(CM). Command guidance also allows the capability for a possible "regrets avoidance" guidance correction, early warhead fuzing, or fuze lock-out by the fire control system if it is determined before impact that the missile has been launched at a friendly or a neutral target. Disadvantages of command guidance are reduced survivability of the launch platform and reduced accuracy at long range. TOW, Star Streak, Rapier, Roland, and RBS-70 are examples of command guided missiles.

Finally, multi-mode guidance has become more popular in recent years. It allows the benefit of short duration command inertial updates to provide "regrets avoidance" combined with much of the launch platform survivability and accuracy benefits of active or passive homing guidance.

Figure 6.131 shows examples of missile systems that use command guidance, where the launch platform fire control system tracks the target, tracks the missile, and issues command guidance to the missile.

In the upper left portion of the figure is an example of a laser command guided missile that is multi-mission, Starstreak. In the upper middle portion of the figure is a laser command guided SAM, the RBS-70/Bolide. An example of a more sophisticated command guided SAM is Roland, shown in the upper right portion of the figure. Roland has an RF/FLIR tracker with RF command guidance. In the bottom left portion of the figure is an example of a relatively simple command guided battlefield missile, TOW. TOW is a wire guided missile, with commands provided by a FLIR tracker.

Example of laser command guidance: Starstreak | Example of laser command guidance: RBS-70/Bolide | Example of RF/FLIR track–RF command guidance: Roland

Example of FLIR track-wire command guidance: TOW | Video of Starstreak, RBS-70, Roland, and TOW command guidance

Fig. 6.131 Command guidance: the fire control system tracks the missile, tracks the target, and commands the missile.

Example of semi-active radar guidance: Sea Dart   Example of semi-active TVM radar guidance: Patriot PAC-2

Example of semi-active laser guidance: SAL Maverick   Video of semi-active Sea Dart, Patriot PAC-2, Maverick

Fig. 6.132 Semi-active guidance: the fire control system tracks the target and illuminates the target for missile guidance.

In the bottom right portion of the figure is a video of Starstreak, RBS-70, Roland, and TOW. Starstreak provides laser command guidance to three darts, each of which has a rearward looking laser detector. The high velocity darts have high kinetic energy that is effective against air targets as well as light armor ground targets. The RBS-70 portion of the video shows its set-up on a tripod, the gunner tracking the target, its identification-friend-foe (IFF) hardware, and its low altitude intercept capability. The Roland portion of the video shows its automatic launcher and its corkscrew flight trajectory. Finally, the TOW portion of the video shows the crew assisted set-up, its flight trajectory with a top-attack warhead, and the FLIR tracker.

Figure 6.132 shows examples of missile systems that use semi-active guidance. The launch platform fire control system illuminates the target with its radar or laser transmitter and tracks the target from the reflected energy that it receives from the target. The missile homes on the reflected energy off the target.

In the top left portion of the figure is an RF semi-active guided SAM, Sea Dart. In the upper right portion is an RF semi-active track-via-missile (TVM) SAM, Patriot PAC-2. In the bottom left portion of the figure is the laser semi-active guided Maverick.

A video of Sea Dart, Patriot PAC-2, and SAL Maverick is shown in the bottom right portion of the figure. The Maverick portion of the video first shows an A-10 autonomous designation and launch of a Maverick. Also shown is a ground designation of the target. In addition to Sea Dart, Patriot PAC-2, and SAL Maverick, other weapons that use semi-active laser guidance include SAL Hellfire and SAL guided bombs, such as GBU-24.

Figure 6.133 shows an example of a ship weapon carriage and launcher, the Mk41 Vertical Launch System (VLS). VLS is a standard missile launcher for US Navy ships. Advantages of VLS include a high firing rate against all-aspect targets, reduced radar cross section, lighter weight, environmental protection, and multi-role modularity for a variety of missiles. Disadvantages include below deck safety concerns and an inability to reload at sea, because of ship motion.

VLS has multiple configurations, ranging from a single module with eight cells to sixteen modules with 122 cells. The Mk41 VLS has three size lengths—Strike, Tactical, and Self-Defense. The Strike Mk41 can accommodate missiles up to about 22 ft in length. The Tactical MK41 can accommodate missiles up to 18.5 ft in length. Finally, the Self-Defense Launcher (SDL) is used for vertically launched self-defense missiles such as ESSM Sea Sparrow. SDL is shorter and lighter. It is more suitable for smaller ships (e.g., corvettes, frigates) and aircraft carriers (constrained deck area/hull depth).

The VLS specifications for missile launch include a temperature range of -18 to $144°F$, roll angle up to 29 deg, cross wind up to 75 knot, maximum gas flow rate up to 200 lb/s, and a maximum gas flow rate increase of 2000 lb/s.

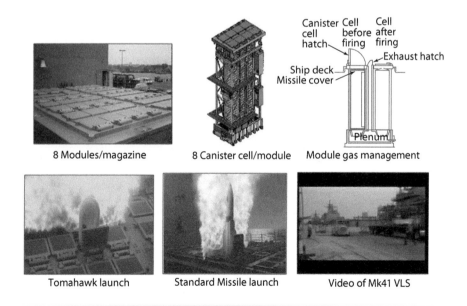

Fig. 6.133 Example of ship weapon carriage and launcher — Mk41 VLS.

In the upper left section of the figure is a photograph of a VLS magazine consisting of eight modules. The upper center of the figure is a schematic of the VLS module. There are eight canister cells in the module. The top right section of the figure shows an internal view of a VLS canister before and after a missile firing. Note the canister hatch and frangible cover, which provide maritime environmental protection for the missile prior to launch. Also note the plenum gas management, which directs the missile exhaust flow through a vertical exhaust. The required area of the exhaust vent is driven by the mass flow and the backpressure. As a rule of thumb, the exhaust vent area should be much larger than missile nozzle throat area, to avoid choking the flow through the vent and creating a large back pressure.

Shown in the bottom portion of the figure are photographs of the Tomahawk missile and the Standard missile launches. Note the missile exhaust exiting through the exhaust hatch that is shared by eight cells. Finally, the bottom right section of the figure is a video, which shows the Mk41 VLS installation on a cruiser, the Aegis phased array radar, and a near-simultaneous launch of three Standard missiles.

Missiles should have sufficient robustness in their design to avoid failure in a broad climatic environment during storage, shipping, and launch platform carriage. Contributors to failure include an excessively high temperature, a very low temperature, corrosion, shock, and fatigue. Figure 6.134 has examples of surface environmental requirements for temperature, humidity, rain, wind, salt fog, dust/sand/dirt, vibration, shock, acoustics, and

Environment parameter	Typical requirement
♦ Surface temperature	– 60°F to 160°F*
♦ Surface humidity	5% to 100%
♦ Rain rate	120 mm/h**
♦ Surface wind	150 km/h***
♦ Salt fog	3 g/mm² per year
♦ Dust/sand/dirt	2 g/m³, wind @ 18 m/s
♦ Vibration	10 g rms at 1000 Hz: MIL STD 810G, 648, 1670A
♦ Shock	Drop height 0.5 m, half sine wave 100 g/10 ms
♦ Acoustic	160 dB
♦ External power fluct	±10%, MIL-HDBK-781

ATACMS launch   Video: Ground/sea environment

Note: MIL-HDBK-310 and earlier MIL-STD-210B suggest 1% world-wide climatic extreme typical requirement.
*Highest recorded temperature 136°F. Lowest recorded temperature = –129°F ≈ 20% probability temperature lower than –60°F during worst month/location.
**Highest recorded rain rate = 436 mm/h ≈ 0.5% probability greater than 120 mm/h during worst month/location.
***Highest recorded wind = 407 km/h ≈ 1% probability greater than 100 km/h during worst month/location.
Typical external air carriage maximum hours for aircraft ~100 h. Typical external carriage max hours for helicopter ~1000 h.

Fig. 6.134 Missile climatic environment requirements are typically based on the 1% probability extreme.

the external interface (e.g., launch platform) power fluctuation. Shown in the figure is a photograph of an example of a severe environment, the launch of an ATACMS.

An example of concern at the temperature extremes is the propulsion and the warhead safety, reliability, and performance. Another concern is the adverse effects of high rain rate, such as seeker dome erosion during carriage at high aircraft velocity. A third example of a surface environmental concern is corrosion from salt fog, particularly for naval operation. Although it is not a surface environmental concern, another concern is the vibration and acoustics of missile carriage on an aircraft. An advantage of internal bay carriage over external carriage is that many of the carriage environment concerns are alleviated. However, some carriage environment concerns could be greater for internal carriage than that of external carriage. Examples of concerns for aircraft internal carriage are high vibration and acoustic loads when the bay doors are open at a flight condition with high dynamic pressure. A shallow bay is particularly susceptible to vibration/acoustics failures. Another concern for a shallow bay is that it often has a high thermal environment when the bay doors are closed.

MIL-HDBK-310 (Global Climatic Data for Developing Military Products) and the earlier MIL-STD-210 (Military Standard of Climatic Extremes for Military Equipment) were developed to provide design data on the surface environmental extremes of climate for global conflict in the areas north of 60 deg south latitude and less than 15,000 ft (4.6 km) elevation. The extremes have near zero probability of being exceeded in the natural environment. It provides sets of climatic extremes for designing missiles for land, sea, and air operation.

It would not be cost effective to design a missile for the world-wide surface climate extremes, such as the highest recorded temperature ($136°F = 58°C$ at Azizia, Libya on September 13, 1922), the lowest recorded temperature ($-129°F = -89°C$ at Vostok Station, Antarctica on 21 July 1963), the highest recorded rain rate (436 mm/h at Chilaos, La Reunion Station, Indian Ocean on 15 March 1952), and the highest recorded wind speed (253 mph $= 407$ km/h on Barrow Island, Western Australia, on April 10, 1996). A typical approach is to design a missile for operation in the 1% world-wide climatic extreme. An exception is the surface low temperature requirement, where the approximately 20% extreme of $-60°F = -51°C$ is typically used for missiles because combat is less likely to occur in extremely cold areas of the world. The cold temperature requirement often varies, depending upon the missile program emphasis of cost versus performance. As an example, the emphasis on developing a low cost motor and seeker for Hellfire led to the selection of $-40°F$ for the minimum surface temperature requirement. At the other extreme, the SRAM strategic missile had a minimum surface temperature requirement of $-80°F$, because of less emphasis on cost and higher emphasis on reliability, performance, and northern basing that is typical of a strategic missile. Another exception to the 1% guideline is the rain rate requirement, where the approximately 0.5% extreme is typically used. The 0.5% extreme of 120 mm/h is typically used because periods of high rain rate usually extend over more than one month each year and areas with high rain rate are also often areas of combat. Surface wind velocity is based on the approximately 1% climatic extreme value of 150 km/h. For a sea-launched missile, a wind speed of 100 km/h (54 knots) is representative of the upper boundary of a storm (wind speed 48–55 knots, sea state 10, and a wave height 29 ft). A violent storm would be sea state 11, with a wind speed of 56–63 knots and a wave height of 37 ft.

Air launched missiles that are externally carried at high altitude may be subjected to even lower carriage temperature. For example, Mach 0.6 external carriage at 50,000 ft (15 km) altitude with a MIL-HDB-310 1% cold day results in a recovery temperature of $-95°F$ ($-71°C$). Also, air launched missiles that are externally carried at high speed may be subjected to high temperature. As an example, Mach 1.2 external carriage at sea level with a MIL-HDBK-310 hot day results in a recovery temperature of $310°F$ ($154°C$). A safety concern for high speed external carriage is the warhead charge and rocket motor propellant become very sensitive at temperatures above $160°F$ ($71°C$). External carriage of air-launched missiles shortens the service life of the missile. For an aircraft launch platform, a typical total maximum allowable time for external carriage is about 100 h. For a helicopter launch platform, a typical total maximum allowable time for external carriage is greater, about 1000 h.

Designing a missile for world-wide expeditionary warfare or for foreign sales requires more consideration of climatic extremes. Missiles that are designed for use only in a local/smaller geographic area usually have more relaxed environmental requirements.

The video in the right section of the figure illustrates the carriage and launch environments of the ground vehicle launched Multiple Launch Rocket System (MLRS), the surface ship launched Standard Missile, and the surface ship/submarine launched Tomahawk missile. For the MLRS, in addition to natural environment considerations such as temperature and rain, the tracked propulsion M270A1 and the wheeled propulsion High Mobility Artillery Rocket Systems (HIMARS) launchers may also subject the MLRS to a severe vibration and shock environment. For the Standard Missile, the sea salt corrosive environment is a particular concern. For submarine launch of the Tomahawk missile, the initial underwater environment is a concern.

A low temperature environment is of particular concern for the propellant grain of a rocket motor. Concerns include cracking due to strain, the propellant insulation detaching from the motor case due to a difference in thermal expansion, and accelerated failure from shock/vibration. A low temperature concern for a turbojet/ramjet is the fuel freezing.

For a first order conceptual design and system engineering prediction of temperature, the missile components may be approximated as plates, cylinders, or spheres. As an example, the temperature at the center of the rocket motor case of an end burning propellant grain may be approximated as the temperature at the center of a long cylinder. Also, the temperature at the center of a radial burning propellant grain may be approximated as the temperature at the inner surface of a long hollow cylinder. From Cengel [35], a first order method to predict the transient conduction temperature at the center of a plate, cylinder, or sphere is

$$(T_{\text{Inner}} - T_{\text{Outer}})/(T_i - T_{\text{Outer}}) \approx A_1 e^{-\lambda_1^2 [\alpha t/(r_{\text{Outer}} - r_{\text{Inner}})^2]}$$

Assumptions in the above equation include negligible radiation and negligible convection. For actual cooling, the effects of convection and radiation result in faster cooling than the prediction. The values of the geometric parameters in the above equation are:

For a plate: $A_1 = 1.2732$, $\lambda_1 = 1.5708$

For a cylinder: $A_1 = 1.6021$, $\lambda_1 = 2.4048$

For a sphere: $A_1 = 2$, $\lambda_1 = \pi$

Based on the above equation, the drivers for the cooling time are the object's radius, geometry (plate, cylinder, sphere), and thermal diffusivity. The non-dimensional temperature $(T_{\text{Inner}} - T_{\text{Outer}})/(T_i - T_{\text{Outer}})$ has less than 2% difference from an exact solution if the parameter $\alpha t/(r_{\text{Outer}} - r_{\text{Inner}})^2 > 0.2$.

Figure 6.135 shows the non-dimensional center temperature $(T_{\text{Inner}} - T_{\text{Outer}})/(T_i - T_{\text{Outer}})$ of a plate, cylinder, or a sphere for the non-dimensional time $\alpha t/(r_{\text{Outer}} - r_{\text{Inner}})^2 > 0.2$. Note from the figure that 1) as time $t \to \infty$, $T_{\text{Inner}} \to T_{\text{Outer}}$, 2) a sphere cools faster than a cylinder, which cools faster than a plate, and 3) a large radius object cools slower (parameter $\alpha t/(r_{\text{Outer}} - r_{\text{Inner}})^2$ is smaller) than a small radius object.

As an example, assume that the baseline rocket motor is taken from an initial conditioned storage temperature $T_i = +70°F$ and suddenly subjected for $t = 4\,\text{h} = 14,400\,\text{s}$ of exposure to a cold environment ambient temperature $T_{\text{Ambient}} = -60°F$. We will model the baseline motor case as a hollow cylinder, with an insulated plug at the throat of the nozzle. The frangible plug provides environmental protection of the propellant prior to ignition. It is ejected by the chamber pressure during the ignition process. The thermal diffusivity of the rocket motor case structure, insulation, and propellant are $\alpha_{\text{Structure}} = 0.0001196\,\text{ft}^2/\text{s}$, $\alpha_{\text{Insulation}} = 0.00000222\,\text{ft}^2/\text{s}$, and $\alpha_{\text{Propellant}} = 0.00000200\,\text{ft}^2/\text{s}$ respectively. The outer radius of the motor case is $r_{\text{Outer}} = 8/2 = 4$ in. The average inner

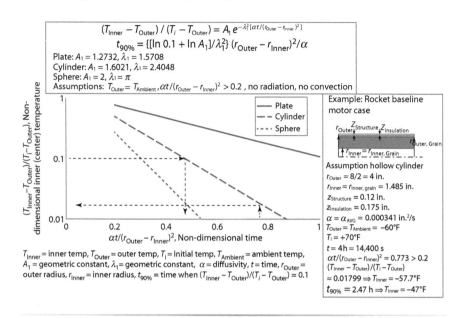

$$(T_{Inner} - T_{Outer}) / (T_i - T_{Outer}) = A_1 e^{-\lambda_1^2 [\alpha t/(r_{Outer} - r_{Inner})^2]}$$

$$t_{90\%} = \{[\ln 0.1 + \ln A_1]/\lambda_1^2\} (r_{Outer} - r_{Inner})^2/\alpha$$

Plate: $A_1 = 1.2732$, $\lambda_1 = 1.5708$
Cylinder: $A_1 = 1.6021$, $\lambda_1 = 2.4048$
Sphere: $A_1 = 2$, $\lambda_1 = \pi$
Assumptions: $T_{Outer} = T_{Ambient}$, $\alpha t/(r_{Outer} - r_{Inner})^2 > 0.2$, no radiation, no convection

Example: Rocket baseline motor case

Assumption hollow cylinder
$r_{Outer} = 8/2 = 4$ in.
$r_{Inner} = r_{Inner, grain} = 1.485$ in.
$z_{Structure} = 0.12$ in.
$z_{Insulation} = 0.175$ in.
$\alpha = \alpha_{AVG} = 0.000341$ in.^{2}/s
$T_{Outer} = T_{Ambient} = -60°F$
$T_i = +70°F$
$t = 4h = 14,400$ s
$\alpha t/(r_{Outer} - r_{Inner})^2 = 0.773 > 0.2$
$(T_{Inner} - T_{Outer})/(T_i - T_{Outer})$
$= 0.01799 \Rightarrow T_{Inner} = -57.7°F$
$t_{90\%} = 2.47$ h $\Rightarrow T_{Inner} = -47°F$

T_{Inner} = inner temp, T_{Outer} = outer temp, T_i = Initial temp, $T_{Ambient}$ = ambient temp, A_1 = geometric constant, λ_1 = geometric constant, α = diffusivity, t = time, r_{Outer} = outer radius, r_{Inner} = inner radius, $t_{90\%}$ = time when $(T_{Inner} - T_{Outer})/(T_i - T_{Outer}) = 0.1$

Fig. 6.135 Cooling time drivers include dimension, geometry, and diffusivity. (Source: Cengel, Y. A., *Heat and Mass Transfer: A Practical Approach*, McGraw-Hill, 2006.)

radius of the propellant grain is $r_{Inner} = 1.485$ in. The assumed case structure thickness and the insulation thickness are $z_{Structure} = 0.12$ in and $z_{Insulation} = 0.175$ in respectively. A lumped capacitance approach will be used to calculate the average thermal diffusivity.

$$\alpha = \alpha_{AVG} = [\alpha_{Structure} z_{Structure}^2 + \alpha_{Insulation} z_{Insulation}^2$$

$$+ \alpha_{Propellant} (r_{Outer} - r_{Inner})^2]/[z_{Case}^2 + z_{Insulation}^2$$

$$+ (r_{Outer} - r_{Inner})^2]$$

$$= 0.00000237 \text{ ft}^2/\text{s} = 0.000341 \text{ in}^2/\text{s}$$

Calculate

$$\alpha t/(r_{Outer} - r_{Inner})^2 = 0.000341(14400)/(4 - 1.485)^2 = 0.773$$

$$> 0.2 \text{ (less than 2\% difference from exact solution)}$$

$$(T_{Inner} - T_{Outer})/(T_i - T_{Outer}) = 1.6021 e^{-(2.4048)^2(0.773)} = 0.01799$$

$$T_{Inner} = 0.01799[70 - (-60)] - 60 = -57.7°F$$

After four hours of cold temperature exposure, the predicted temperature of the center of the baseline motor case is near the ambient temperature.

Theoretically, according to the above equation it takes infinite time to reach an ambient temperature. A typical design criteria is the time that is required to achieve 90% of the decrease to the ambient temperature. The equation for $(T_{Inner} - T_{Outer})/(T_i - T_{Outer}) = 0.10$ is

$$t_{90\%} = -[\ln(1 - 0.9) + \ln A_1]/\lambda_1^2 (r_{Outer} - r_{Inner})^2/\alpha$$

Substituting $A_1 = 1.6021$ and $\lambda_1 = 2.4048$ for a hollow cylinder, the predicted cooling time of the center of a rocket motor case to reach 90% of the decrease to the ambient temperature is

$$t_{90\%} = -[\ln(1 - 0.9) + \ln 1.6021]/2.4048^2 (r_{Outer} - r_{Inner})^2/\alpha$$
$$= 0.4797(r_{Outer} - r_{Inner})^2/\alpha$$

For the baseline motor case

$$t_{90\%} = -0.4797(4 - 1.485)^2/0.000341 = 8898 \text{ s} = 148 \text{ m} = 2.47 \text{ h}$$

Another first order method to determine the cooling time of a missile that is exposed to a cold environment is to assume that the cooling follows the radiative cooling equation [37]

$$t_{Cooling} = [mN_A k/(2M\varepsilon\sigma A)][T^{-3} - T_i^{-3}]$$

In the above equation $t_{Cooling}$ = cooling time, s; m = mass, kg; N = Avogadro's number = 6.02×10^{23}; k = Boltzmann constant = 1.38×10^{-23} m²kg/s²/T; M = molecular weight, kg; ε = emissivity; σ = Stefan-Boltzmann constant = 5.67×10^{-8} Wm^{-2}T^{-4}; A = surface radiation area = m²; T = temperature, K; and T_i = initial temperature, K.

The above equation assumes that the body is thermally thin, with a uniform temperature. The inner temperature is assumed to be equal to the surface (outer) temperature.

Figure 6.136 shows the cooling time of the baseline rocket motor case from a typical range of the storage temperature (0 to 80°F) to a typical range of the minimum ambient temperature (−40 to −80°F). At a given time, the actual temperature of the outer surface will be somewhat lower and the inner temperature will be somewhat higher than that predicted from the above equation. This is because of the thermally thin assumption of a uniform temperature throughout the body.

Additional assumptions for the figure are negligible radiation input from the sky, clouds, and nearby objects; and negligible convection cooling. Radiative cooling is greatest at night with a clear sky, a low temperature, and a low humidity. The low humidity of deserts and at high elevation results in more radiative cooling. Convection cooling is greatest if there is an exposure to wind.

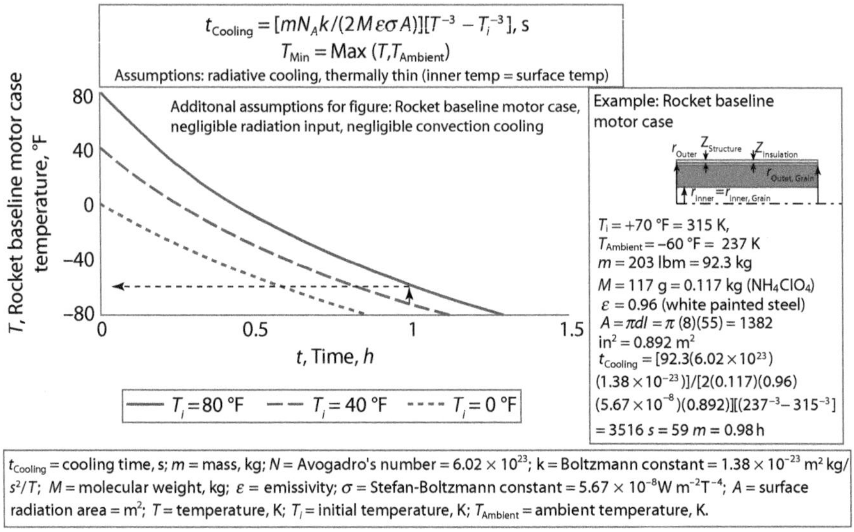

t_Cooling = [mN_A k/(2MεσA)][T^-3 – T_i^-3], s
T_Min = Max (T,T_Ambient)
Assumptions: radiative cooling, thermally thin (inner temp = surface temp)
Additonal assumptions for figure: Rocket baseline motor case, negligible radiation input, negligible convection cooling
T, Rocket baseline motor case temperature, °F
80
40
0
-40
-80
0
0.5
1
1.5
t, Time, h
T_i = 80 °F
T_i = 40 °F
T_i = 0 °F
Example: Rocket baseline motor case
T_i = +70 °F = 315 K,
T_Ambient = –60 °F = 237 K
m = 203 lbm = 92.3 kg
M = 117 g = 0.117 kg (NH4ClO4)
ε = 0.96 (white painted steel)
A = πdl = π (8)(55) = 1382 in² = 0.892 m²
t_Cooling = [92.3(6.02 × 10^23)(1.38 × 10^-23)]/[2(0.117)(0.96)(5.67 × 10^-8)(0.892)][(237^-3 – 315^-3]
= 3516 s = 59 m = 0.98 h
t_Cooling = cooling time, s; m = mass, kg; N = Avogadro's number = 6.02 × 10^23; k = Boltzmann constant = 1.38 × 10^-23 m² kg/s²/T; M = molecular weight, kg; ε = emissivity; σ = Stefan-Boltzmann constant = 5.67 × 10^-8 W m^-2 T^-4; A = surface radiation area = m²; T = temperature, K; T_i = initial temperature, K; T_Ambient = ambient temperature, K.

Fig. 6.136 Cooling time drivers include temperature, mass, molecular weight, emissivity, and surface area. (Source: Hyperphysics, Georgia State University.)

The minimum temperature predicted from the above equation is subject to the limitation of the ambient temperature, which results in thermal equilibrium.

$$T_{\min} = \mathrm{Min}(T,\, T_{\mathrm{Ambient}})$$

As an example, assume that the rocket baseline missile is taken from an initial conditioned storage temperature $T_i = +70^\circ\mathrm{F}$ and suddenly subjected to a cold environment ambient temperature $T_{\mathrm{Ambient}} = -60^\circ\mathrm{F}$. We will calculate the cooling time of the rocket baseline motor case. The baseline motor case characteristics are

$$m = 203\,\mathrm{lbm} = 92.3\,\mathrm{kg}$$

$$\varepsilon = 0.96\,(\text{white painted steel})$$

$$A = \pi \mathrm{dl} = \pi(8)(55) = 1382\,\mathrm{in.}^2 = 0.892\,\mathrm{m}^2$$

For a first order estimate of molecular weight M, we will use $M = 117$ g $= 0.117$ kg, the molecular weight of ammonium perchlorate (NH_4ClO_4). Ammonium perchlorate is the dominant weight constituent of the rocket baseline propellant. A more precise approach would be to calculate the average molecular weight of the rocket motor case, based on the molecular weights of the motor case structure, insulation, oxidizer, fuel, binder, burning rate modifier, plasticizer, curing agent, bonding agent, stabilizer, catalyst, and other constituents.

Substituting into the radiative cooling equation, the time for the baseline motor case to cool from $T_i = +70°F = 294$ K to $T_{Ambient} = -60°$ F $= 222$ K is

$$t_{Cooling} = [92.3(6.02 \times 10^{23})(1.38 \times 10^{-23})]/$$
$$[2(0.117)(0.96)(5.67 \times 10^{-8})(0.892)](222^{-3} - 294^{-3})$$
$$= 3516\,\text{s} = 59\,\text{m} = 0.98\,\text{h}$$

Note that the prediction of cooling time based on radiative cooling is lower than the prediction of $t_{90\%}$ based on conduction (0.98 h versus 2.47 h). These results illustrate the value of comparing different methods during conceptual design and system engineering, to help establish the accuracy requirements for follow-on analysis and tests. A more sophisticated prediction technique (e.g., finite element modeling) with the combined contributors to cooling time (conduction, convection, radiation) is usually required in the follow-on preliminary design and system engineering.

A missile with an un-insulated metal airframe, un-insulated metal rocket motor case, or an un-insulated metal fuel tank will heat up quickly if it is exposed to solar heating. Problems from an excessively high temperature environment include the possibility of rocket motor propellant explosion, possibility of warhead explosion, increased moisture penetration, possibility of electronics failure, propellant and fuel degradation, and increased salt fog corrosion. The following discussion and Fig. 6.137 illustrate first order conceptual design and system engineering approaches to predict the temperature of a missile that is exposed to solar heating.

For a first order analysis of solar heating, one approach is to compute the equilibrium temperature. From Cengel [35], for assumptions of a steady equilibrium temperature (solar input flux = surface output radiation), gray body radiation, and negligible convection, the equilibrium temperature is

$$T_{Equilibrium} = [5.84 \times 10^8 (\Lambda/\varepsilon)\dot{q} + T_{amb}^4]^{1/4}$$

Definitions are $T_{Amb} =$ ambient temp, R; $\dot{q} =$ input flux, $BTU/ft^2/h$; $T_{Equilibrium} =$ equilibrium temp, R; $\Lambda =$ absorptivity; and $\varepsilon =$ emissivity.

$T_{Equilibrium}$ predicted by the above equation is usually higher than the actual temperature, because it neglects convection. Natural convection from air circulating over the surface will cool the surface to a lower temperature.

The average solar input flux is dependent upon the latitude, the date, the time of day, the atmospheric transmission, and the inclination of the object toward the sun. Because of the rotation of the earth, the solar radiation input varies with time, with a maximum at "high noon". There is a transmission loss in solar radiation through the atmosphere. For a cloudy day, there is relatively low transmission of solar flux. For a clear day in a desert, the transmission is high, about 80%. The solar constant, or the solar flux at the edge of the atmosphere is

$$\dot{q}_{Solar} = 1368 \, \text{W/m}^2 = 433.6 \, \text{BTU/ft}^2/\text{h}$$

Assuming an 80% transmission through the atmosphere, the average solar flux reaching the surface of the earth is

$$\dot{q}_{Solar\,transmitted} = 0.8(433.6) = 347 \, \text{BTU/ft}^2/\text{h}$$

For an assumed "high noon" environment, the solar radiation is perpendicular to the side of the rocket motor case. Neglecting surface reflection, the average incidence angle of the rocket motor case is

$$\theta_{AVG} = \int_0^{\pi} \sin\theta \, d\theta = 2/\pi = 0.637 \, \text{rad} = 36.5 \, \text{deg}$$

Figure 6.137a shows the thermal equilibrium temperature rise of the rocket baseline motor case from solar heating. Note the lower temperature

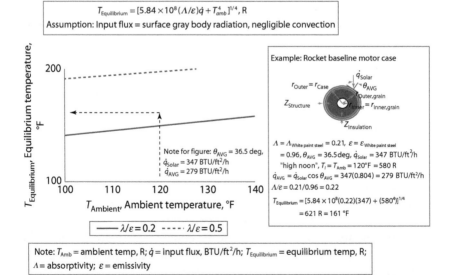

a) Thermal equilibrium temperature from solar heating is lower for a low value of Λ/ε

Note: T_{Amb} = ambient temp, R; $\dot{q}$ = input flux, BTU/ft²/h; $T_{Equilibrium}$ = equilibrium temp, R; Λ = absorptivity; ε = emissivity

Fig. 6.137a Exposure to solar heating requires design for higher than ambient temperature. (Source: Cengel, Y. A., *Heat and Mass Transfer: A Practical Approach*, McGraw-Hill, 2006.)

advantage of a low value of the parameter Λ/ε. Many missiles are painted white for this reason. A white pained steel motor case has an absorptivity $\Lambda = \Lambda_{\text{White paint steel}} = 0.21$ and an emissivity $\varepsilon = \varepsilon_{\text{White paint steel}} = 0.96$. The parameter $\Lambda/\varepsilon = 0.22$. An advantage of a white painted motor case is a lower temperature in exposure to the sun. A potential disadvantage of a white motor case is an increased probability of detection by the threat, because of its higher visual observables. As a contrast, an unpainted stainless steel rocket motor case would have a lower visual signature. However, it would have a higher equilibrium temperature from solar radiation, from the high value of its Λ/ε ($\Lambda = 0.50$, $\varepsilon = 0.21 \rightarrow \Lambda/\varepsilon = 2.4$).

As an example calculation, assume the motor case of the rocket baseline missile shown in the top right portion of the figure. Also assume a "high noon" environment, with the solar radiation perpendicular to the side of the rocket motor case, a white painted steel motor case, and $T_{\text{amb}} = 120°F = 580$ R. Calculate

$$\dot{q}_{\text{AVG}} = \dot{q}_{\text{Solar transmitted}} \cos \theta_{\text{AVG}} = 347(0.804) = 279 \text{ BTU/ft}^2/\text{h}$$

$$T_{\text{Equilibrium}} = \left[5.84 \times 10^8 (0.21/0.96)(279) + (580)^4\right]^{1/4} = 621 \text{ R} = 161°F$$

After a long duration exposure (e.g., greater than 1 h) to the sun, the predicted equilibrium temperature, neglecting convection, is 41°F higher than the ambient temperature.

A first order prediction of the transient temperature rise of a missile that is exposed to solar heating can be based on modeling the missile as a lumped (average) capacitance body that is thermally thin, with a zero-dimensional temperature distribution. This method works best for a high conductivity metal structure, such as aluminum or steel. From Cengel [35], the equation is

$$T = T_i + \Delta T = T_i + [\dot{q} A_{\text{Presented}}/(mc)]\Delta t$$

Assumptions are a constant input heat flux, a thermally thin body (inner temperature ≈ outer temperature), negligible convection, and negligible surface radiation. The maximum temperature predicted from the above equation is subject to the limitation of the equilibrium temperature from output radiation, shown in the previous example.

$$T_{\text{max}} = \text{Min}(T, T_{\text{Equilibrium}})$$

In the above equation T_i = initial temperature, R; ΔT = incremental temperature, R; Δt = incremental time, h; $A_{\text{Presented}}$ = presented area, ft^2; m = mass, lbm; c = specific heat, BTU/lbm/R; and t = time, h.

b) Temperature from solar input driven by Area, Mass, Capacitance, and Time

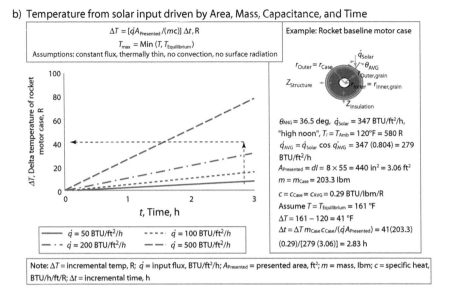

$$\Delta T = [\dot{q} A_{Presented} /(mc)] \,\Delta t, R$$

$$T_{max} = Min \,(T, T_{Equilibrium})$$

Assumptions: constant flux, thermally thin, no convection, no surface radiation

Example: Rocket baseline motor case

$\theta_{ANG} = 36.5$ deg, $\dot{q}_{Solar} = 347$ BTU/ft²/h,

"high noon", $T_i = T_{Amb} = 120°F = 580$ R

$\dot{q}_{AVG} = \dot{q}_{Solar}$ cos $q_{AVG} = 347 \,(0.804) = 279$

BTU/ft²/h

$A_{Presented} = dl = 8 \times 55 = 440$ in² = 3.06 ft²

$m = m_{Case} = 203.3$ lbm

$c = C_{Case} = C_{AVG} = 0.29$ BTU/lbm/R

Assume $T = T_{Equilibrium} = 161$ °F

$\Delta T = 161 - 120 = 41$ °F

$\Delta t = \Delta T \, m_{Case} \, C_{Case}/(\dot{q} A_{Presented}) = 41\,(203.3)$

$(0.29)/[279 \,(3.06)] = 2.83$ h

— $\dot{q} = 50$ BTU/ft²/h ···· $\dot{q} = 100$ BTU/ft²/h
— · — $\dot{q} = 200$ BTU/ft²/h — — $\dot{q} = 500$ BTU/ft²/h

Note: ΔT = incremental temp, R; $\dot{q}$ = input flux, BTU/ft²/h; $A_{Presented}$ = presented area, ft²; m = mass, lbm; c = specific heat, BTU/h/ft/R; Δt = incremental time, h

Fig. 6.137b Exposure to solar heating requires design for higher than ambient temperature. (Source: Cengel, Y. A., *Heat and Mass Transfer: A Practical Approach*, McGraw-Hill, 2006.)

Figure 6.137b shows the temperature rise of the rocket baseline motor case from solar heating. Note the increase in temperature from increasing solar radiation input flux.

As an example calculation, assume the rocket baseline motor case ($d = 8$ in, $l = 55$ in), shown in the top right portion of the figure. Assume $T_i = T_{Ambient} = 120°F$. From the prior example, for an assumed "high noon" environment, $\dot{q}_{AVG} = 279$ BTU/ft²/h. Also, from Chapter 7

$$A_{Presented} = dl = 8 \times 55 = 440 \,in^2 = 3.06 \,ft^2$$

$$m = m_{Case} = m_{Structure} + m_{Insulation} + m_{Propellant}$$

$$= 47.3 + 23.0 + 133.0 = 203.3 \,lbm$$

$$c = c_{Case} = c_{AVG} = [c_{Structure} t^2_{Structuree} + c_{Insulation} t^2_{Insulation} + c_{Propellant} t^2_{Propellant}]$$

$$/[t^2_{Structure} + t^2_{Insulation} + t^2_{Propellant}]$$

$$= [0.12(0.12)^2 + 0.30(0.175)^2 + 0.29(2.22)^2]/$$

$$[0.12^2 + 0.175^2 + 2.22^2]$$

$$= 0.29 \,BTU/lbm/R$$

Calculate the time required to reach thermal equilibrium $T_{\text{Equilibrium}} = 161°F$

$$\Delta t = \Delta T m_{\text{Case}} c_{\text{Case}} / (\dot{q} A_{\text{presented}})$$
$$= (161 - 120)(203.3)(0.29) / [279(3.06)]$$
$$= 2.83 \, h$$

Another first order method for predicting the transient temperature rise of a missile that is exposed to solar heating is based on modeling the missile as a lumped capacitance body that is assumed to be thermally thick, with a one-dimensional temperature distribution. This method usually has best accuracy for a low conductivity structure, such as graphite epoxy. From Cengel [35], the equation is

$$T(z, t)/T_i = 1 + [\dot{q} z/(k T_i)][e^{-x^2}/(\pi^{1/2} x) - erfc(x)], \quad \text{where } x = z/[2(\alpha t)^{1/2}]$$

Assumptions are a constant input heat flux, a thermally thick body, negligible convection, and negligible surface radiation. A criteria for a thermally thick body is $r/[2(\alpha t)^{1/2}] > 1$.

The maximum temperature from the above equation is limited to the steady equilibrium temperature (solar input flux = surface output radiation), discussed in the previous example.

$$T_{\max} = \text{Min}(T, T_{\text{Equilibrium}})$$

In the above equations $T_i =$ initial temp, R; $\dot{q} =$ input flux, BTU/ft²/h; $k =$ conductivity, BTU/h/ft/R; $\alpha =$ diffusivity, ft²/h; $t =$ time, h; z is distance, ft; erfc = complementary error function; and $r =$ radius, ft.

Figure 6.137c shows the non-dimensional temperature rise from a constant heat flux input as a function of non-dimensional time $(\alpha t)^{1/2}/z$ and the non-dimensional heat flux $\dot{q} z/(k T_i)$. Note from the figure that the predicted temperature increases with time without a theoretical upper limit. Not shown in the figure is an imposed practical limit

$$T_{\max} = \text{Min}(T, T_{\text{Equilibrium}})$$

An example calculation of the temperature rise from solar heating of the rocket baseline motor case is shown in the right portion of the figure. From the prior example, its diffusivity is

$$\alpha = \alpha_{\text{AVG}} = 0.00000237 \, \text{ft}^2/\text{s} = 0.00853 \, \text{ft}^2/\text{h}$$

c) A Thermally thick body has a large variation in its internal temperature

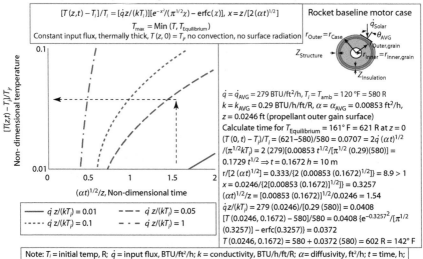

Fig. 6.137c   Exposure to solar heating requires design for higher than ambient temperature. (Source: Cengel, Y. A., *Heat and Mass Transfer: A Practical Approach*, McGraw-Hill, 2006.)

The average conductivity is

$$k = k_{\mathrm{AVG}} = [k_{\mathrm{Structure}} t^2_{\mathrm{Structure}} + k_{\mathrm{Insulation}} t^2_{\mathrm{Insulation}} + k_{\mathrm{Propellant}} t^2_{\mathrm{Propellant}}] /$$

$$[t^2_{\mathrm{Structure}} + t^2_{\mathrm{Insulation}} + t^2_{\mathrm{Propellant}}]$$

$$= [25.0(0.12)^2 + 0.06(0.175)^2 + 0.22(2.22)^2] /$$

$$[0.12^2 + 0.175^2 + 2.22^2]$$

$$= 0.29 \, \mathrm{BTU/h/ft/R}$$

From the prior example, assume a "high noon" environment $\dot{q}_{\mathrm{AVG}} = 279 \, \mathrm{BTU/ft^2/h}$. Also assume an initial temperature $T_i = 120°\mathrm{F}$. We will first calculate the time at which the temperature of the surface of the rocket motor case reaches the thermal equilibrium temperature $T_{\mathrm{Equilibrium}} = 161°\mathrm{F} = 621 \, \mathrm{R}$. We will then calculate the corresponding temperature of the rocket motor propellant.

For thermal equilibrium at the surface of the rocket motor case

$$[T(0, t) - T_i]/T_i = (621 - 580)/580 = 0.0707 = 2\dot{q}(\alpha t)^{1/2}/(\pi^{1/2} k T_i)$$

$$= 2(279) \, 0.00853 \, t^{1/2}/[\pi^{1/2}(0.29)(580)] = 0.1729 \, t^{1/2}$$

From above, the time required to reach thermal equilibrium is

$$t = 0.1672\,\text{h} = 10\,\text{m}$$

Comparing with the previous result, note that the surface of the thermally thick body reaches thermal equilibrium much faster than the uniform temperature of the thermally thin body (0.1672 versus 2.83 h). The solar input flux energy deposited on the thermally thick body penetrates slowly, because of its low conductivity and low diffusivity. For a thermally thin body, the solar input flux energy is more readily conduced into the body, because of its high conductivity and high diffusivity. As a result, a thermally thin body has a lower surface temperature at a given time than a thermally thick body. Metals are often used as heat sinks, because of their high conductivity and high diffusivity.

Next, checking the assumption of a thermally thick surface

$$r/[2(\alpha t)^{1/2}] = 0.333/\{2[0.00853(0.0413)^{1/2}]\} = 8.9 > 1,$$

which satisfies the criteria of thermally thick.

The value of the parameter x is

$$x = 0.0246/\{2[0.00853(0.1672)]^{1/2}\} = 0.3257$$

The value of the non-dimensional time is

$$(\alpha t)^{1/2}/z = [0.00853(0.1672)]^{1/2}/0.0246 = 1.54$$

The value of the non-dimensional input flux is

$$\dot{q}z/(kT_i) = 279(0.0246)/[0.29(580)] = 0.0408$$

Solving for temperature

$$[T(0.0246, 0.1672) - 580]/580$$

$$= 0.0408\{e^{-0.3257^2}/[\pi^{1/2}(0.3257) - erfc(0.3257)\}$$

$$= 0.0372$$

$$T = (0.0246, 0.1672) = 580 + 0.0372(580) = 602\,\text{R} = 142^\circ\text{F}$$

The predicted temperature of the propellant is less than the motor case structure temperature (142 versus 161°F). The lower temperature of the propellant is from the insulation between the motor case structure and the propellant.

A third approach to predict the temperature from solar heating, which is usually more accurate for a metal structure, is based on separating the missile into thermally thin and thermally thick sections. This approach is most appropriate for a highly conductive (e.g., metal) structure over the less conductive components (e.g., insulation, warhead explosive, rocket motor propellant). From Ref. 20, an equation for the internal temperature from a constant input heat flux is

$$[T(z, t) - T_i]/[T(0, t) - T_i] = e^{-x^2} - \pi^{1/2} x \, erfc(x),$$

$$\text{where } x = z/[2(\alpha t)^{1/2}]$$

The assumptions are one-dimensional conduction heat transfer, constant heat flux, negligible surface radiation, negligible convection, and a thermally thick body ($x > 1$).

Figure 6.137d shows the non-dimensional temperature $[T(z, t) - T_i]/[T(0, t) - T_i]$ versus the non-dimensional time $(\alpha t)^{1/2}/z$. Note that the interior temperature of the thermally thick body increases with time, eventually approaching the temperature of the thermally thin surface covering.

From Cengel [35], the equation for the temperature throughout the thermally thin surface covering is

$$T(0, t) = T_i + \Delta T = T_i + [\dot{q} A_{Presented}/(mc)]\Delta t$$

As before, the maximum temperature predicted from the above equation is subject to the limitation of the steady equilibrium temperature

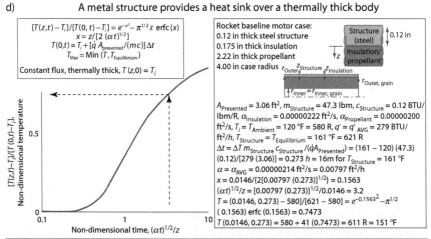

Fig. 6.137d Exposure to solar heating requires design for higher than ambient temperature. (Reference: Carslaw, H. S. and Jaeger, J. C., *Conduction of Heat in Solids*, Clarendon Press, 1989).

(solar input flux = surface output radiation).

$$T_{max} = Min\left(T, T_{Equilibrium}\right)$$

As an example, the rocket baseline motor case has a steel alloy structure (assumed thickness = 0.12 in, $A_{Presented} = dl = 8 \times 55 = 440 \text{ in}^2 = 3.06 \text{ ft}^2$, $m_{Structure} = 47.3 \text{ lbm}$, $c_{Structure} = 0.12 \text{ BTU/lbm/R}$). Beneath the structure is MA-255 insulation (thickness = 0.175 in = 0.0146 ft, $\alpha_{Insulation} = 0.00000222 \text{ ft}^2/\text{s}$) and propellant (thickness = 2.22 in = 0.185 ft, $\alpha_{Propellant} = 0.00000200 \text{ ft}^2/\text{s}$). Assume $T_i = T_{Ambient} = 120$ $^\circ$F = 580 R. From the prior example, assume a "high noon" environment, $\dot{q}_{AVG} = 279 \text{ BTU/ft}^2/\text{h}$. We will calculate the temperature of the rocket motor propellant at its outer surface, behind the insulation ($z = 0.175 \text{ in} = 0.0146 \text{ ft}$), when the motor case structure has reached equilibrium temperature $T_{Equilibrium} = 161°\text{F} = 621 \text{ R}$.

The time that is required for the structure to reach $T_{Equilibrium} = 161°\text{F}$ is

$$\Delta t = \Delta T \, m_{Structure} c_{Structure} / (\dot{q} A_{Presented})$$
$$= (161 - 120)(47.3)(0.12)/[279(3.06)] = 0.273 \, \text{h} = 16 \, \text{m}$$

The average diffusivity of the rocket motor insulation and propellant is

$$\alpha = \alpha_{AVG} = [\alpha_{Insulation} z_{Insulation}^2 + \alpha_{Propellant} z^2]/[z_{Insulation}^2 + z_{Propellant}^2]$$
$$= [0.00000222(0.0146)^2 + 0.00000200(0.200)^2]/[0.0146^2 + 0.185^2]$$
$$= 0.00000214 \, \text{ft}^2/\text{s} = 0.00797 \, \text{ft}^2/\text{h}$$

The thermally thick criteria is

$$r/[2(\alpha t)^{1/2}] = 0.200/\{2[0.00797(0.273)]^{1/2}\} = 2.14$$
$$> 1, \text{ which satisfies the criteria of thermally thick}$$

The value of the parameter x is

$$x = 0.0146/\{2[0.00797(0.273)]^{1/2}\} = 0.1563$$

Solving for $T(0.0146, 0.273)$

$$[T(0.0146, 0.273) - 580]/[621 - 580] = e^{-0.15632} - \pi^{1/2}(0.1563)\,\text{erfc}(0.1563)$$
$$= 0.9759 - \pi^{1/2}(0.1563)(0.8251)$$
$$= 0.7473$$
$$T(0.0146, 0.273) = 580 + 41(0.7473) = 611 \, \text{R} = 151°\text{F}$$

Comparing the methods for predicting solar heating, the predicted temperature of the rocket baseline propellant at the time the motor case first reaches thermal equilibrium temperature $T_{Equilibrium} = 161°F$ is 1) 161°F @ 2.83 h for a thermally thin lumped parameter assumption, 2) 142°F @ 0.17 h for a thermally thick lumped parameter assumption, and 3) 151°F @ 0.27 h for a thermally thin structure with a thermally thick lumped insulation and propellant parameters assumption. For the rocket baseline missile with a metal structure, the third method is probably more accurate. Again, these results illustrate the value of comparing different prediction methods during conceptual design and system engineering, to help establish the accuracy requirements for follow-on analysis and tests. A more sophisticated prediction technique (e.g., finite element modeling) with the combined contributors (conduction, convection, input radiation, output radiation) is usually required for follow-on preliminary design and system engineering.

6.10 Summary

This chapter addressed the broad considerations of missile measures of merit and launch platform integration/system engineering. Considerations for robustness included the effectiveness of alternative sensors operating in adverse weather and clutter, the capability of the missile in off-design flight conditions, changes in missile performance with uncertainty, and the performance in countermeasures. Considerations for warhead lethality included warhead effectiveness against a broad range of targets, synergy with guidance accuracy, and the type of warhead (e.g., blast fragmentation, kinetic energy). Also addressed were approaches to reduce warhead collateral damage. Fuzing alternatives and requirements addressed the optimum fuzing angle and time delay. Considerations for miss distance included the miss distance because of an initial heading error at seeker lock-on, miss distance because of a maneuvering target, miss distance from glint noise, and the contributions to the missile time constant by limited control effectiveness, flight control dynamics, and seeker dome error slope. Included in the considerations for carriage and launch observables were launch platform carriage RCS and missile plume visual signature for reduced observables. Missile survivability and safety considerations included missile radar cross section, missile infrared signature, missile flight altitude, mission planning, speed, terrain masking, terminal maneuvering, and insensitive munitions. Considerations for reliability included the number of subsystems, parts count, the types of parts (e.g., moving, non-moving), and subsystem complexity. Other considerations that contribute to failure included design errors, manufacturing errors, software errors, and exceeding the design environment. Cost considerations included the types of subsystems, weight, system development duration and risk, production quantity/learning curve, parts count, logistics, production rate, culture/processes, and competition. Considerations for launch platform integration and system engineering included firepower, weight, and fitment; launch envelope limitations; store separation; launch platform handling qualities; aircraft aeroelasticity; hang-fire; vibration; compatibility with standard launchers; compressed carriage; avionics interface; alternative guidance laws; and the carriage/storage environment.

6.11 Problem Review

1. IR signal attenuation is greater than 100 dB per km through a c____.

2. GPS/INS enhances seeker lock-on in adverse weather and ground c_____.

3. A data link update can enhance missile seeker lock-on against a mo____ target.

4. One missile counter-counter measure to flares is an i_____ i_____ seeker.

5. Compared to a mid wave IR seeker, a long wave IR seeker receives more energy from a c___ target.

6. High fineness kinetic energy penetrators are required to defeat bu____ targets.

7. For the same lethality with a blast fragmentation warhead, a small decrease in miss distance allows a large decrease in the required weight of the w_____.

8. A conceptual design tool for a blast/fragmentation warhead is the G_____ equation.

9. For a blast/fragmentation warhead, a charge-to-metal ratio of about one is required to achieve a high total fragment k_____ e_____.

10. A blast fragmentation warhead tradeoff is the number of fragments versus the individual fragment w_____.

11. Kinetic energy penetration is a function of the penetrator diameter, length, density, strength, and v_____.

12. Autonomous guidance improves launch platform su_____.

13. Proportional homing guidance drives the line-of-sight angle rate equal to z___.

14. Aeromechanics contributors to missile time constant include flight control effectiveness, flight control system dynamics, and the dome e____ s____ .

15. Miss distance due to heading error is a function of the missile navigation ratio, velocity, time to correct the heading error, and the missile t___ c_____ .

16. Missile maneuverability is typically at least t____ times that of the target.

17. Miss distance against a weaving target is large if the missile time constant is comparable to the inverse of the target weave f_____ .

18. Minimizing miss distance due to radar glint requires a high resolution seeker, an optimum time constant and an optimum na_____ ra___ .

19. Weapons on low observable launch platforms use i_____ carriage.

20. Weapons on low observable launch platforms use m_____ smoke propellant.

21. Alternative approaches to improve precision strike missile survivability include 1) high altitude cruise, 2) high speed, 3) mission planning/ threat avoidance, 4) terrain masking, 6) maneuvering, and 7) low o_____ .

22. Two drivers for RCS are the target geometric sh___ and the target or_____ .

23. The largest contributor to the ramjet baseline missile frontal RCS is its ra___ se____ .

24. The hypersonic ramjet baseline missile has a high i_____ signature.

25. For an insensitive munition, burning is preferable to detonation because it releases less p____ .

26. System reliability is enhanced by a high subsystem reliability and a low p____ count.

27. High cost subsystems of missiles are sensors, electronics, and p_____ .

28. Missile EMD cost is driven by the program duration and ri__ .

29. Missile unit production cost is driven by the number of units produced, the learning curve, and the missile w_____ .

30. First level maintenance is conducted at a d____ .

31. Store compatibility problems include aeroelasticity, hang-fire, and s_____ .

32. A standard launch system for U.S. Navy ships is the V_____ L_____ S_____ .

33. Most air-launched missiles that are light weight use rail launchers, while most heavy weight air-launched missiles use e_____ launchers.

34. Higher firepower is provided by com_____ carriage.

35. A typical environmental requirement in MIL-HDBK-310 is _% world-wide extreme.

36. A missile exposed to the sun probably has greater than ambient t_____.

Chapter 7

Sizing Examples and Sizing Tools

- Missile Sizing Examples
- Conceptual Design and System Engineering Sizing Tools
- Rocket, Ramjet, and Turbojet Baseline Missile Characteristics
- Soda Straw Rocket Design, Build, and Fly Activity
- House of Quality
- Design of Experiment

7.1 Introduction

This chapter presents examples of sizing missile configurations and examples of computer-aided sizing tools for missile conceptual design and system engineering. The topics presented are 1) sizing examples for the rocket baseline missile, 2) sizing examples for the ramjet baseline missile, 3) sizing examples for the turbojet baseline missile, 4) computer-aided sizing tools, and 5) an example of a "hands on" design, build and fly activity based on a soda straw rocket. The rocket baseline missile sizing examples address the air-to-air standoff range requirement, wing sizing requirement and turn performance, multi-parameter design harmonization, and the maximum range flight trajectory. The ramjet baseline missile sizing examples are range robustness, ramjet propulsion and fuel alternatives, and velocity control. The turbojet baseline missile sizing examples are turbojet thrust prediction, specific impulse prediction, low altitude range prediction, maximum range prediction, and engine rotational speed. The computer-aided sizing tools for conceptual design and system engineering that are addressed are a DOS-based code and a spreadsheet code. The soda straw rocket examples are a design, build, and fly sizing activity, a flight range Pareto and uncertainty analysis, a house of quality analysis, and a design of experiment (DOE) analysis.

7.2 Rocket Baseline Missile Standoff Range Requirement

The rocket baseline missile will be used to illustrate the establishment and substantiation of an air-to-air missile standoff range requirement, the missile wing sizing for maneuverability, a multi-parameter harmonization of missile weight/miss distance, and a lofted trajectory range comparison with conventional line-of-sight flight trajectories.

The first example is sizing the rocket baseline missile to meet an air-to-air standoff range requirement. The air-to-air missile flight range in this example is derived from the speed and range required for standoff survivability of the launch aircraft. The assumed requirement is to provide an F-pole range, which allows the kill of a head-on threat outside the threat weapon launch range. For air-to-air combat, the visual detection range by the threat is $R_D \approx 3.3$ nm for a typical aircraft contrast against a typical background of $C = 0.18$. We will assume for this example that the threat fire control system does not have a beyond visual range engagement capability. The maximum launch range of the threat missile is assumed to be the visual detection range. This sets the required F-pole range of 3.3 nm. The assumed altitude and speed of the launch aircraft (blue), target aircraft (red, threat), and the launch aircraft missile (blue) for this analysis are $h = 20,000$ ft, $V_L = 820$ ft/s (Mach 0.8), $V_T = 820$ ft/s, and $V_M = 2\ V_T = 1640$ ft/s respectively.

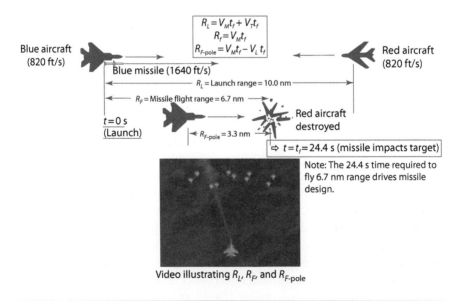

$$R_L = V_M t_f + V_T t_f$$
$$R_f = V_M t_f$$
$$R_{F\text{-pole}} = V_M t_f - V_L t_f$$

Blue aircraft (820 ft/s)

Blue missile (1640 ft/s)

Red aircraft (820 ft/s)

$R_L =$ Launch range $= 10.0$ nm

$R_f =$ Missile flight range $= 6.7$ nm

$t = 0$ s (Launch)

$R_{F\text{-pole}} = 3.3$ nm

Red aircraft destroyed

$\Rightarrow t = t_f = 24.4$ s (missile impacts target)

Note: The 24.4 s time required to fly 6.7 nm range drives missile design.

Video illustrating R_L, R_F, and $R_{F\text{-pole}}$

Fig. 7.1 Assumed air-to-air engagement scenario for head-on intercept.

The assumed air-to-air scenario is shown in Fig. 7.1. The required launch range R_L and F-pole range $R_{\text{F-pole}}$ are functions of the missile average velocity V_M, missile time of flight t_f, and the target average velocity V_T. The equations are

$$R_L = V_M t_f + V_T t_f$$
$$R_{\text{F-pole}} = V_M t_f - V_L t_f$$

Also, the missile flight range R_f is

$$R_f = V_M t_f$$

Referring to Fig. 7.1, note that to provide an $R_{\text{F-pole}} = 3.3$ nm, the rocket baseline missile must be launched at 10.0 nm from the target and have a flight range of 6.7 nm within 24.4 s. Because the launch range is greater than the visual detection range, a non-cooperative target identification (NCTID) capability is required for the launch aircraft fire control system to avoid fratricide to friendly or neutral aircraft.

The video at the bottom of the figure illustrates the launch aircraft fire control system tracking range (yellow event), the missile launch range (red event), missile fly-out, and the F-pole range (orange event) for a simultaneous threat engagement. At the beginning of the video the launch aircraft radar is tracking twelve threat aircraft. Four missiles are targeted against four of the threat aircraft. The missiles are launched, fly out, and impact the threat aircraft. The F-pole range is the final range between the launch aircraft and the threat aircraft when the missiles impact the threat aircraft.

A simplified model of the typical ranges at which a pilot can detect and recognize a typical aircraft target is shown in Fig. 7.2. The detection range and the recognition range are assumed to be primarily driven by the target contrast C, target presented area A_p, and the threshold contrast C_T. The equation for visual detection range R_D is

$$R_D = 1.15[A_p(C - C_T)]^{1/2}$$

The equation for visual recognition range R_R is

$$R_R = 0.29\, R_D$$

Referring to Fig. 7.2, note that the detection range is reduced as the contrast is reduced. A design consideration for aircraft integration of missiles is to use a paint scheme for the missile that matches the paint scheme of the launch aircraft.

As an example, assume a target contrast $C = 0.18$, a target presented area $A_p = 50$ ft^2, and a threshold contrast $C_T = 0.02$. The visual detection range is

$$R_D = 1.15[50(0.18 - 0.02)]^{1/2} = 3.3 \text{ nm}$$

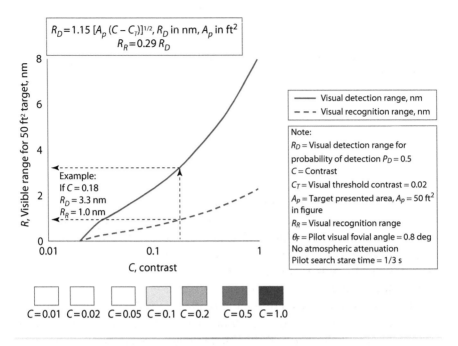

Fig. 7.2 Target contrast and size drive visual detection and recognition range.

The visual recognition range is typically about 29% of the detection range, giving

$$R_R = 0.29(3.3) = 1.0 \text{ nm}$$

Assumptions for the analysis are:

1. The threat does not have NCTID or a beyond visual range missile.
2. The threat will launch a within-visual-range missile (e.g., Sidewinder-type) when it is within visual detection range.
3. Probability of detection by the threat is $P_D = 0.5$.
4. Threat pilot visual acuity angle θ_F (foveal angle of the eye) = 0.8 deg.
5. Negligible atmospheric attenuation. This is most applicable at high altitude.
6. Threat pilot uses an optimum stare time for an air-to-air search-stop-stare ($\approx 1/3$ s).

Assumption 5, negligible atmospheric attenuation, can result in a large error for long range detection. As an example, assume that the engagement altitude is $h = 40$ kft. From Chapter 6, the atmospheric attenuation coefficient for clear weather at sea level is $\sigma_{SL} = 0.26/\text{km}$. Scaling to $h = 40$ kft, the apparent contrast at $R_D = 2.7$ nm $= 5.00$ km is

$$\sigma_{h=40\,\text{kft}} = \sigma_{\text{SL}}(\rho_{h=40\,\text{kft}}/\rho_{h=\text{SL}}) = 0.26(0.2461) = 0.064/\text{km}$$

$$C = C_i e^{-\sigma R} = 0.18e^{-0.064(5.00)} = 0.131$$

The apparent contrast has been reduced from an initial contrast $C_i = 0.18$ to $C = 0.131$, due to atmospheric attenuation. The detection range including atmospheric attenuation is

$$R_D = 1.15[50(0.131 - 0.02)]^{1/2} = 2.7 \text{ nm}$$

The detection range R_D has been reduced from 3.3 to 2.7 nm, due to atmospheric attenuation.

At the bottom of the figure is a grayscale of contrast ranging from $C = 0.01$ to 1.0. Note that it is difficult to distinguish the difference between the contrast and the white background for $C = 0.02$.

In addition to the target size and contrast, a more complete analysis of visual detection could also include the considerations of target texture, color, relative motion, and scintillation.

An example of contrast, texture and color is shown at the top of Fig. 7.3, with a "camouflage" aircraft against an earth background. The aircraft camouflage is a good match of contrast, texture, and color against the background. However, the aircraft stores are painted white, which provides high contrast, low texture, and a color difference that stands out against the aircraft/background. As discussed in Chapter 6, stores are often painted

Example of F-16 "Camouflage" (Note store contrast, texture, color)

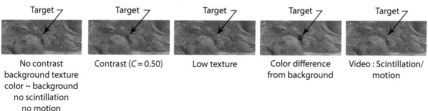

Target	Target	Target	Target	Target
No contrast background texture color ~ background no scintillation no motion	Contrast ($C = 0.50$)	Low texture	Color difference from background	Video : Scintillation/ motion

Fig. 7.3 Target contrast, low texture, color difference, and scintillation/motion increase visual detection in clutter.

white to reduce the temperature from solar radiation, at the expense of visual observables.

Shown at the bottom of the figure are five examples of target visual signature in a clutter background. In the far left example, the target blends into the background. It has no contrast, has the same texture as the background, is the same color as the background, and has no scintillation/motion. In the next example, the target has 50% greater contrast than the background, enhancing detection. In the third example, the target has low texture, also enhancing detection. Most man-made objects without camouflage are low texture. The fourth example shows a color difference with the background. A two color seeker is required to discriminate color. Finally, the fifth example is an animation of the effect of scintillation/motion on discrimination.

Figure 7.4 shows the relative standoff range $R_{\text{F-pole}}$ between the launch platform and the target for a missile head-on intercept. $R_{\text{F-pole}}$ is a function of the launch range R_L, missile velocity V_M, target aircraft velocity V_T, and the launch platform velocity V_L. The equation is

$$R_{\text{F-pole}}/R_L = 1 - (V_T + V_L)/(V_M + V_T)$$

Again, an assumption is a head-on intercept engagement. Note that the longest F-pole range is for a missile velocity that is much greater than the target velocity ($V_T/V_M \ll 1$) and the missile velocity is much greater than

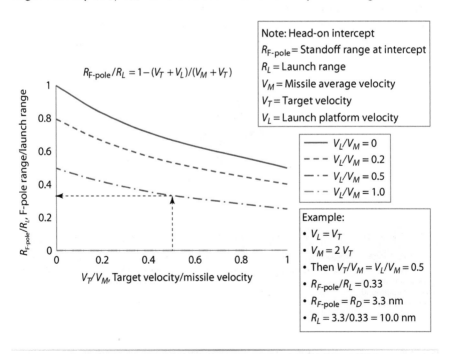

Fig. 7.4 High missile velocity improves standoff range.

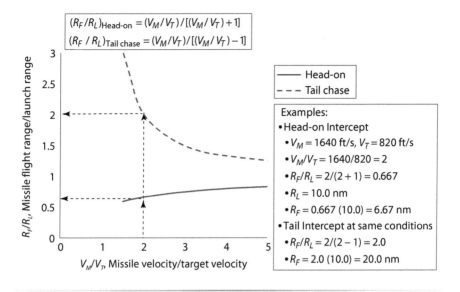

Fig. 7.5 Missile flight range/no escape zone requirement is greatest for a tail chase intercept.

the launch platform velocity ($V_L/V_M < 1$). The longest standoff range is a surface launch ($V_L/V_M = 0$) against a surface target ($V_T/V_M = 0$).

As an example, assume that the average missile velocity is twice that of the target ($V_M/V_T = 2$). Also assume that the launch platform is an aircraft with the same velocity as the target aircraft ($V_L/V_T = 1$). Then $V_T/V_M = 0.5$ and $V_L/V_M = 0.5$. If the F-pole range is required to be the same as the visual detection range, then from the previous discussion, $R_{\text{F-pole}} = R_D = 3.3$ nm. Substituting into the above equations, the missile launch range is calculated to be

$$R_L = R_{\text{F-pole}}/[1 - (V_T/V_M + V_L/V_M)/(1 + V_T/V_M)]$$
$$= 3.3/[1 - (0.5 + 0.5)/(1 + 0.5)] = 10 \, \text{nm}$$

As shown in Fig. 7.5, the missile flight range R_F that is required to intercept a target is a function of the launch range R_L, missile velocity V_M, target velocity V_T, and the target aspect (i.e., head-on, tail chase). The equations are

$$(R_F/R_L)_{\text{Head-on}} = (V_M/V_T)/[(V_M/V_T) + 1]$$
$$(R_F/R_L)_{\text{Tail chase}} = (V_M/V_T)/[(V_M/V_T) - 1]$$

Note from the figure that a higher speed missile reduces the required flight range for a tail chase intercept and increases the required flight range for a head-on intercept. However, the flight range requirement for a head-on intercept is always less than the flight range required for a tail chase.

As an example using the rocket baseline missile, assume the head-on intercept engagement discussed previously. For an average missile velocity $V_M = 1640$ ft/s, an average target velocity of $V_T = 820$ ft/s, and a launch range $R_L = 10$ nm, the non-dimensional flight range $(R_F/R_L)_{\text{Head-on}}$ is

$$(R_F/R_L)_{\text{Head-on}} = (1640/820)/[(1640/820) + 1] = 0.667$$

For a launch range $R_L = 10.0$ nm, the required missile flight range is

$$R_F = 0.667(10) = 6.67 \text{ nm.}$$

If the target in the engagement discussed previously were retreating from the launch aircraft, for the same assumptions of launch range $(R_L = 10.0 \text{ nm})$, missile average velocity $(V_M = 1640 \text{ ft/s})$, and target average velocity $(V_T = 820 \text{ ft/s})$, the required flight range of the missile is

$$(R_F/R_L)_{\text{Tail chase}} = (1640/820)/[(1640/820) - 1] = 2$$
$$R_F = 2(10) = 20 \text{ nm}$$

The required flight range is increased by 200% (20.0 versus 6.67 nm) for a tail chase. In general, the no escape zone launch acceptability region is greater for a head-on intercept than for a tail-chase intercept.

A configuration drawing of the rocket baseline missile, which is similar to the Sparrow missile, circa 1982, is shown in Fig. 7.6 from Ref. 19. The rocket baseline missile is a beyond visual range and adverse weather (radar guided) missile. It has a design flight range of about 7 nm when launched at a typical altitude of 20,000 ft. The missile uses cruciform wings as control surfaces. Fixed cruciform tail surfaces provide static stability. Missile launch weight is 500 lb, including 133 lb of propellant. Its

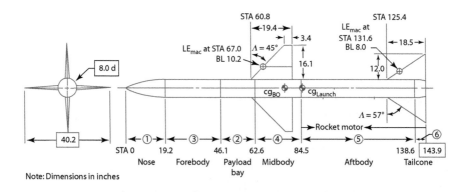

Fig. 7.6 Drawing of rocket baseline missile configuration. (Source: Bithell, R. A. and Stoner, R. C., "Rapid Approach for Missile Synthesis, Vol. 1, Rocket Synthesis Handbook," AFWAL-TR-81-3022, Vol. 1, March 1982.)

Table 7.1 Mass Properties of Rocket Baseline Missile.

Component	Weight, lb.	C.G. STA, in.
① Nose (Radome)	4.1	12.0
② Forebody structure	12.4	30.5
Guidance	46.6	32.6
③ Payload Bay Structure	7.6	54.3
Warhead	77.7	54.3
④ Midbody Structure	10.2	73.5
Control Actuation System	61.0	75.5
⑤ Aftbody Structure	0.0	–
Rocket Motor Case	47.3	107.5
Insulation (EPDM - Silica)	23.0	117.2
⑥ Tailcone Structure	6.5	141.2
Nozzle	5.8	141.2
Fixed Surfaces	26.2	137.8
Movable Surfaces	38.6	75.5
Burnout Total	367.0	76.2
Propellant	133.0	107.8
Launch Total	**500.0**	**84.6**

rocket motor has a boost-sustain thrust profile with 32,272 lb-s total impulse at a nominal temperature. The motor grain configuration is an internal burner type with three radial slots, aft end longitudinal slots, and a center web grain. The nozzle has a 1.81 in.^{2} throat area and provides an expansion ratio of 6.2.

Note from the figure that the missile diameter $d = 8$ in. total wing span $b_w = 40.2$ in. and length $l = 143.9$ in. Shown are the length of the rocket motor and the section lengths/bulkhead locations. The missile is divided into nose, forebody, payload bay, midbody, aftbody, and the tailcone sections. The wing geometry data in the figure includes the wing span, sweep angle, location of the mean aerodynamic chord, the length of the root chord and its location, and the length of the tip chord. The tail geometry data shown in the figure includes the tail span, sweep angle, location of the mean aerodynamic chord, length of the root chord, and the location of the root chord.

The rocket baseline missile weight and balance statement is given in Table 7.1, derived from Ref. 19. Note that the burnout weight $W_{BO} = 367$ lb, the launch weight $W_L = 500$ lb, and the propellant weight $W_P = 133$ lb. The center-of-gravity location is 84.6 in. from the nose tip at launch and 76.2 in. from the nose tip at burnout. There is a large forward movement (1.05 diameter) in the center-of-gravity from the motor burn, which results in an excess static margin after motor burn-out. The total weight of the aluminum airframe body structure, aluminum wing structure, aluminum tail surfaces structure, and the steel motor case structure is 30% of the missile launch weight.

Reference 19 also provides the rocket baseline missile detailed geometric data, material data, configuration reference data, and propulsion data. Table 7.2, based on Ref. 19, shows a more detailed definition of the

Table 7.2 Rocket Baseline Missile Definition.

Body	
Dome material	Pyroceram
Airframe structure material	Aluminum (2219-T81)
Length, in.	143.9
Diameter, in.	8.0
Airframe structure thickness, in.	0.16
Fineness ratio	17.99
Volume, ft^3	3.82
Wetted area, ft^2	24.06
Nozzle exit area, ft^2	0.078
Boattail fineness ratio	0.38
Nose fineness ratio	2.40
Nose bluntness	0.0
Boattail angle, deg	7.5
Movable surfaces (forward)	
Material	Aluminum 2219-T81
Planform area, ft^2 (2 panels exposed)	2.55
Wetted area, ft^2 (4 panels)	10.20
Aspect ratio (2 panels exposed)	2.82
Taper ratio	0.175
Root chord, in.	19.4
Tip chord, in.	3.4
Span, in. (2 panels exposed)	32.2
Leading edge sweep, deg	45.0
Mean aerodynamic chord, in.	13.3
Thickness ratio	0.044
Section type	Modified double wedge
Section leading edge total angle, deg	10.01

(Continued)

Table 7.2 Rocket Baseline Missile Definition (Continued).

x_{mac}, in.	67.0
y_{mac}, in. (from root chord)	6.2
Actuator rate limit, deg/s	360.0
Fixed surfaces (aft)	
Material	Aluminum 2219-T81
Modulus of elasticity, 10^6 psi	10.5
Planform area, ft^2 (2 panels exposed)	1.54
Wetted area, ft^2 (4 panels)	6.17
Aspect ratio (2 panels exposed)	2.59
Taper ratio	0.0
Root chord, in.	18.5
Tip chord, in.	0.0
Span, in (2 panels exposed)	24.0
Leading edge sweep, deg	57.0
Mean aerodynamic chord, in.	12.3
Thickness ratio	0.027
Section type	Modified double wedge
Section leading edge total angle, deg	6.17
x_{mac}, in.	131.6
y_{mac}, in. (from root chord)	4.0
References values	
Reference area, ft^2	0.349
Reference length, ft	0.667
Pitch/Yaw Moment of inertia at launch, slug-ft^2	117.0
Pitch/Yaw Moment of inertia at burnout, slug-ft^2	94.0
Rocket Motor Performance (altitude = 20 kft, temp = 70°F)	
Burning time, sec (boost/sustain)	3.69/10.86
Maximum pressure, psi	2042
Average pressure, psi (boost/sustain)	1769/301
Average thrust, lbf (boost/sustain)	5750/1018
Total impulse, lbf-s (boost/sustain)	21217/11055
Specific impulse, lbf-s/lbm (boost/sustain)	250/230.4
Propellant	
Weight, lbm (boost/sustain)	84.8/48.2
Flame temperature @ 1,000 psi, °F	5282/5228
Propellant density, lbm/in.^{3}	0.065

(Continued)

Table 7.2 Rocket Baseline Missile Definition (Continued).

Characteristic velocity, ft/s	5200
Burn rate @ 1000 psi, in./s	0.5
Burn rate pressure exponent	0.3
Burn rate sensitivity with temperature, %/°F	0.10
Pressure sensitivity with temperature, %/°F	0.14
Rocket Motor Case	
Yield/ultimate tensile strength, psi	170,000/190,000
Material	4130 Steel
Modulus of elasticity, psi	29.5×10^6 psi
Length, in.	59.4
Outside diameter, in.	8.00
Thickness, in. (minimum)	0.074
Burst pressure, psi	3140
Volumetric efficiency	0.76
Grain configuration	Three slots + web
Dome ellipse ratio	2.0
Nozzle	
Housing material	4130 Steel
Exit geometry	Contoured (equiv. 15°)
Throat area, in.^{2}	1.81
Expansion ratio	6.2
Length, in.	4.9
Exit diameter, in.	3.78

rocket baseline missile. The material for the body, wing, and tail structure is aluminum 2219–T81. The material for the rocket motor case structure is 4130 steel. The aluminum body airframe and steel motor case thicknesses are 0.16 and 0.074 in. respectively. The radome material is pyroceram.

Continuing with Table 7.2, additional information is provided on the movable wings, fixed aft stabilizers, and the configuration reference values. The configuration reference area for the rocket baseline missile is $S_{Ref} = 0.349$ ft^2. It is the body cross sectional area. The configuration reference length of the rocket baseline missile is $l_{Ref} = d = 8$ in. (0.667 ft). It is the body diameter.

Also shown in the table are the pitch/yaw moments of inertia reference values, rocket motor performance data, and the propellant characteristics. The pitch/yaw moment-of-inertia is 117.0 slug-ft^2 at launch and 94.0 slug-ft^2 at burnout. The rocket motor boost thrust and boost burn time are 5750 lb and 3.69 s respectively at a nominal temperature. The sustain thrust and sustain burn time are 1018 lb and 10.86 s respectively at a nominal temperature. The assumed altitude and the propellant temperature are 20,000 ft and 70°F respectively. Boost and sustain propellant weight are 84.8 lb and 48.2 lb respectively.

The conclusion of Table 7.2 provides data on the rocket motor case and nozzle. The structural material for the rocket motor case and the nozzle housing is 4130 heat treated steel. It has a yield and an ultimate tensile strength of 170,000 psi and 190,000 psi respectively. The rocket motor case length is 59.4 in. and the cylindrical case thickness is 0.074 in. The nozzle has an expansion ratio of 6.2. Nozzle length is 4.9 in.

A graph of the rocket baseline simplified thrust-time history is shown in Fig. 7.7. The boost thrust is 5.6 times the sustain thrust (5750 versus 1018 lb). The sustain burn time is 2.9 times longer than the boost burn time (10.86 versus 3.69 s). The boost and sustain thrust profiles shown in the figure are simplified approximations of the actual thrust profiles. The simplified thrust-time profiles were selected to match the total impulse $\int T\,dt$ of the actual rocket motor. Because thrust is much larger than drag during boost, the incremental velocity during boost is driven by the boost total impulse $\int T\,dt = 21{,}217$ lb-s. The total impulse during sustain is $\int T\,dt = 11{,}055$ lb-s.

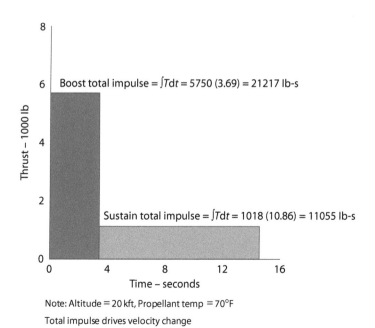

Fig. 7.7 The rocket baseline missile has a boost-sustain thrust-time history.

Figure 7.8 from Ref. 19 provides the aerodynamic performance, stability, and control characteristics of the rocket baseline missile.

Shown in Fig. 7.8a are the pitching moment C_m and normal force coefficient C_N as a function of angle of attack and Mach number. The figure is based on undeflected control surfaces ($\delta = 0$ deg). Note that the pitching moment coefficient and normal force coefficient decrease with increasing supersonic Mach number. The reference center-of-gravity location for the aerodynamic data is $x_{CG} = 75.7$ in from the nose tip, slightly forward of the burnout center-of-gravity.

Figure 7.8b shows other aerodynamic data consisting of the rocket baseline missile normal force coefficient derivative from control surface deflection C_{N_δ}, zero-lift drag coefficient ($C_{D_0} = C_A$ at $\alpha = 0$ deg), corrections to the axial force coefficient because of control surface deflection and angle of attack (K_1, K_2), and the pitching moment coefficient derivative from control surface deflection C_{m_δ}. The power-off (coast) drag coefficient is higher, because of the additional drag from the base pressure. Note the decrease in the aerodynamic coefficients and derivatives with increasing supersonic Mach number.

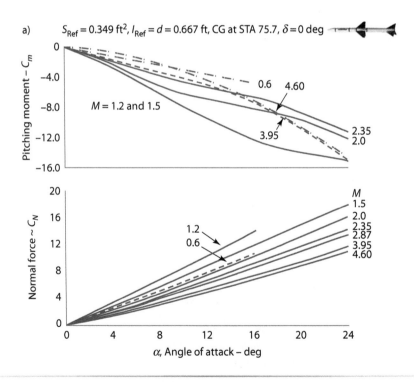

Fig. 7.8a   Rocket baseline missile aerodynamic characteristics—pitching moment and normal force coefficients.

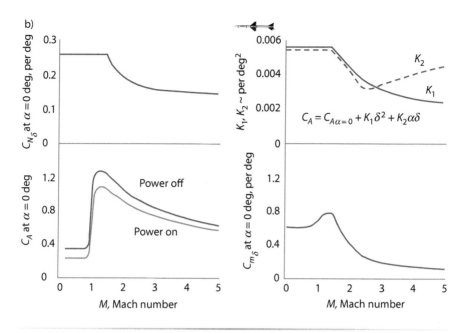

Fig. 7.8b Rocket baseline missile aerodynamic characteristics—normal force derivative, drag, and pitching moment coefficients.

The maximum forward flight range performance for an assumed Mach 0.7 launch and Mach 1.5 flight termination is shown in Fig. 7.9, based on Ref. 19. The flight range increases with high altitude launch, because of the lower drag and higher L/D at high altitude. Note that for sea level flight the sustain thrust Mach number is Mach 1.5, the same as the end-of-boost Mach number.

Off boresight maneuverability performance of the rocket baseline missile is shown in Fig. 7.10 from Ref. 19. Missile cross range and down range are shown, with time tics every 2 s. The termination criteria is Mach 1.0. Note that the best turn performance is at low altitude with high angle of attack, curves ① and ②. However, the "sustain" thrust for a low altitude turn cannot maintain $M > 1$ for the duration of the rocket motor burn time ($t_{Burn} = 14.55$ s).

It is noted that the missile turn envelope shown in the figure is an ideal, unconstrained envelope. A typical seeker gimbal angle limit (e.g., $+/-30$ deg) and a requirement for lock-on before launch would limit the missile off boresight envelope to about $+/-30$ deg. A seeker with high gimbal angle (e.g., $+/-90$ deg) and a lock-on after launch capability facilitate a large off boresight envelope.

A flight performance Pareto sensitivity study was conducted of the flight range of the rocket baseline missile, to determine the most significant

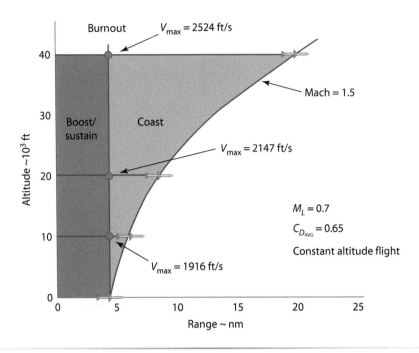

Fig. 7.9 High altitude launch enhances the rocket baseline missile flight range.

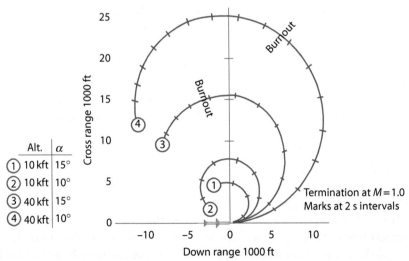

Note: Off boresight envelop that is shown does not include the rocket baseline missile seeker field-of-regard limit (30 deg).

Fig. 7.10 A low altitude launch and a high angle of attack maneuver enhance the rocket baseline missile turn capability.

parameters and the sensitivity of accuracy for prediction methods. Note from Fig. 7.11 that the flight range is most sensitive to changes in the specific impulse, propellant weight, zero-lift drag coefficient, drag-due-to-lift, and the static margin. In the Pareto, these provide more than 90% of the sensitivity. The sensitivity study was conducted at a nominal flight condition of an altitude $h_L = 20$ kft, launch Mach number $M_L = 0.7$, and an end-of-coast Mach number $M_{EC} = 1.5$. The nominal flight range is $R_{@M_L=0.7, \, h_{L=20 \text{ kft}}} = 9.5$ nm.

As an example, note from the figure that a 10% increase in propellant weight provides an 8.8% increase in flight range.

The prediction methods for specific impulse, zero-lift drag coefficient, and drag-due-to-lift usually have sufficient accuracy (e.g., $+/-5\%$, $1 \, \sigma$) for conceptual design. However, there is usually larger uncertainty in predicting the subsystem packaging volume available for the propellant weight and predicting the static margin. Inboard profile drawings and wind tunnel tests are required to reduce the design uncertainty.

Assumptions for the following conceptual analysis of the boost-sustain-coast flight trajectory include 1 degree-of-freedom and a constant altitude flight. The simplified equation for axial acceleration based on thrust, drag, and weight is

$$n_x = (T - D)/W$$

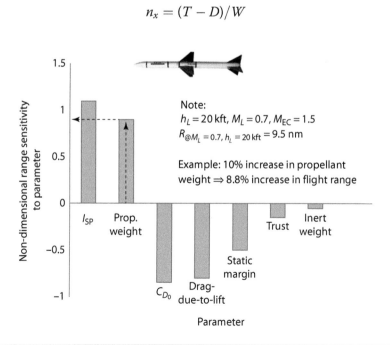

Fig. 7.11 A Pareto sensitivity shows that the flight range of the rocket baseline missile is driven by specific impulse, propellant weight, drag, and static margin.

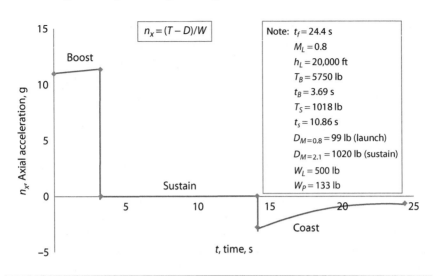

Fig. 7.12   Rocket baseline missile boost, sustain, and coast axial acceleration.

Missile weight varies with burn rate and time

$$W = W_L - W_P t/t_B$$

Missile drag is approximated by

$$D = C_{D_0} q S$$

Figure 7.12 shows the rocket baseline missile axial acceleration during the boost, sustain, and coast phases of flight. As mentioned previously, the equation for axial acceleration is $n_x = (T - D)/W$. During boost the acceleration is positive (increasing flight velocity), during sustain the acceleration is nearly zero (nearly constant flight velocity), and during coast the acceleration is negative (decreasing flight velocity). The assumed flight conditions are:

1. Total time of flight $t_f = 24.4$ s (required to provide F-pole range)
2. Launch Mach number $M_L = 0.8$
3. Launch altitude $h_L = 20{,}000$ ft
4. Boost thrust $T_B = 5750$ lb
5. Boost time $t_B = 3.69$ s
6. Sustain thrust $T_S = 1018$ lb
7. Sustain time $t_S = 10.86$ s
8. Drag $D_{M=0.8} = 99$ lb at launch
9. Drag $D_{M=2.1} = 1020$ lb during sustain
10. Launch weight $W_L = 500$ lb
11. Propellant weight $W_P = 133$ lb

The aerodynamic efficiency of the rocket baseline missile is relatively low for most of the flight conditions shown in the figure. For the 1-g constant altitude flyout, the lift is equal to the missile weight. At the Mach 0.8, 20 kft altitude launch condition, the L/D is relatively high ($L/D \approx 500/99 = 5.1$). At the end of the Mach 2.1 sustain, the L/D is much lower ($L/D \approx 367/1020 = 0.36$). For most of the flight trajectory the L/D is much lower than $(L/D)_{Max}$. The rocket baseline missile would have to fly at a higher altitude and a nearly constant (cruise) velocity for an $(L/D)_{Max}$ flight trajectory.

From Chapter 5, the non-dimensional incremental velocity equation during boost-sustain is

$$\Delta V/(gI_{SP}) = -(1 - D_{AVG}/T) \ln(1 - W_P/W_i)$$

ΔV is a function of the initial weight W_i, propellant weight W_P, thrust T, average drag D_{AVG}, and the specific impulse I_{SP}. Also from Chapter 5, the non-dimensional velocity at the end of coast is

$$V/V_{BO} = 1/\{1 + t/\{2W_{BO}/[g_c\rho_{AVG}S_{Ref}(C_{D_0})_{AVG}V_{BO}]\}\}$$

V is a function of the begin-of-coast (burnout) velocity V_{BO}, burnout weight W_{BO}, average atmospheric density ρ_{AVG}, reference area S_{Ref}, average zero-lift drag coefficient $(C_{D_0})_{AVG}$, and the coast time t_C. Figure 7.13 shows the rocket baseline missile velocity versus time history for the flight phases of boost, sustain, and coast. The launch condition is Mach 0.8, 20 kft altitude. The peak (sustain) velocity is 2151 ft/s (Mach 2.07). The velocity at the end of 24.4 s time of flight is 1588 ft/s (Mach 1.53). Note that the missile has a rapid velocity increase during boost,

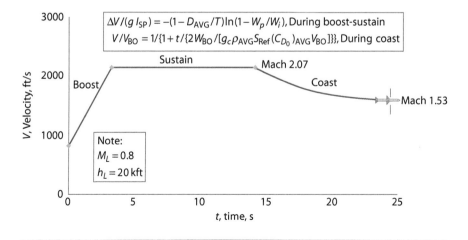

Fig. 7.13 The rocket baseline missile has a boost–sustain–coast velocity profile.

nearly constant velocity during sustain, and a velocity decay during coast. These results are based on the Ref. 19 data for a circa 1982 Sparrow missile. It is noted that the current Sparrow has higher performance.

The rocket baseline missile computed flight range is shown in Fig. 7.14 as a function of time. The launch conditions are Mach 0.8, 20 kft altitude. Note that the flight range at a time of flight $t_f = 24.4$ s exceeds the assumed requirement by 16% (7.8 versus 6.7 nm). The rocket baseline missile achieves the required flight range of 6.7 nm at a time that is 14% shorter than the required time-of-flight (21 versus 24.4 s).

The total flight range R is the sum of the incremental flight ranges during boost ΔR_{boost}, sustain $\Delta R_{sustain}$, and coast ΔR_{coast}. The incremental range during boost is a function of the propellant weight W_P, launch weight W_L, specific impulse I_{SP}, thrust T, average drag D_{AVG}, launch velocity V_L, and the boost time t_B. Substituting into the Chapter 5 equation for the incremental range during boost

$$\Delta R_{Boost} = (V_L + \Delta V/2)t_B$$
$$= \{V_L + [-g_c I_{SP}(1 - D_{AVG}/T)\ln(1 - W_p/W_L)]/2\}t_B$$
$$= \{820 + [-32.2(250)(1 - 635/5750)\ln(1 - 84.8/500)]/2\}(3.69)$$
$$= 5481 \text{ ft}$$
$$= 0.90 \text{ nm}$$

Similarly, the incremental range during sustain $\Delta R_{sustain}$ is a function of the propellant weight W_P, missile weight at the beginning of sustain W_{BS},

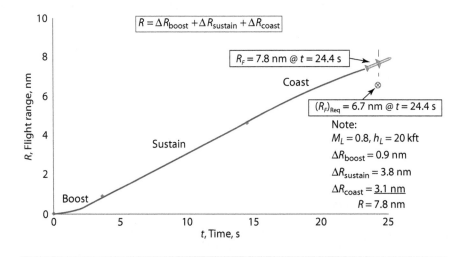

Fig. 7.14 The flight range and time-to-target of the rocket baseline missile satisfy the assumed requirements.

specific impulse I_{SP}, thrust T, average drag D_{AVG}, velocity at the beginning of sustain V_{BS}, and the sustain burn time t_S. Substituting into the equation for the incremental range during sustain

$$
\begin{aligned}
\Delta R_{\text{sustain}} &= (V_{BS} + \Delta V/2)t_S \\
&= \{V_{BS} + [-g_c I_{SP}(1 - D_{AVG}/T)\ln(1 - W_p/W_{BS})]/2\}(t_S) \\
&= \{2151 + [-32.2(230.4)(1 - 1020/1018) \\
&\quad \times \ln(1 - 48.2/415.2)]/2\}(10.86) \\
&= 23,350\,\text{ft} \\
&= 3.84\,\text{nm}
\end{aligned}
$$

The incremental range during coast ΔR_{coast} is a function of the begin-of-coast velocity V_{BC}, burnout weight W_{BO}, atmospheric density ρ, reference area S_{Ref}, zero-lift drag coefficient C_{D_0}, and the coast time t_C. Substituting into the Chapter 5 equation for the incremental range during coast

$$
\begin{aligned}
\Delta R_{\text{coast}} &= [2W/(g_c \rho S_{\text{Ref}} C_{D_0})]\ln\{1 + t_C/[2W/(g_c \rho S_{\text{Ref}} C_{D_0} V_{BC})]\} \\
&= \{2(367)/[(32.2)(0.00127)(0.349)(0.9)]\} \\
&\quad \times \ln\{1 + 10.28/\{(2)(367)/[(32.2)(0.00127)(0.349)(0.9)(2150)]\}\} \\
&= 18,685\,\text{ft} = 3.07\,\text{nm}
\end{aligned}
$$

Finally, the total flight range for 24.4 s of flight is

$$
R_F = R = \Delta R_{\text{Boost}} + \Delta R_{\text{Sustain}} + \Delta R_{\text{Coast}} = 0.90 + 3.84 + 3.07 = 7.8\,\text{nm}
$$

Although the rocket baseline missile flight range and time-to-target satisfy the F-pole requirement, the design margin is relatively small ($R_F = 7.8$ nm in 24.4 s versus $(R_F)_{\text{Req}} = 6.7$ nm in 24.4 s). Consideration should be given to designing a higher speed/longer range missile (e.g., AMRAAM) for more design robustness.

7.3 Wing Sizing Requirement and Turn Performance

The next sizing example for the rocket baseline missile is the wing sizing to meet a maneuverability requirement and the missile turn performance. In this example, the wing size is evaluated against an assumed maneuverability requirement of 30 g, required for a small miss distance against a 9-g maneuvering target. Also assumed are flight conditions of Mach 2, 20 kft altitude, and 367 lb weight (burnout). It is assumed that the total missile maneuver g is provided by the individual contributions from the missile body, tail, and wing. The Ref. 8 interference effects of the body-wing, body-tail, wing-body, tail-body, and wing-tail are neglected.

The maximum local angle of attack of the rocket baseline missile movable wing is $\alpha'_{max} = 22$ deg, established by wing stall. The relationship of the local wing angle of attack to the missile body angle of attack is

$$\alpha_{Wing} = \alpha'_{max} = (\alpha + \delta)_{max} = 22 \text{ deg}$$

The missile body maximum angle of attack is

$$\alpha_{max} = \alpha'_{max}/[1 + 1/(\alpha/\delta)]$$

The rocket baseline missile maximum trim angle of attack for a nominal static margin $\alpha = 0.75\delta$ is

$$\alpha_{max} = \alpha_{Body} = \alpha_{Tail} = 22/(1 + 1/0.75) = 9.4 \text{ deg}$$

Using the results from a prior example in Chapter 2, the incremental maneuverability contribution from the isolated body is

$$\Delta(n_Z)_{Body} = qS_{Ref}(C_N)_{Body}/W = 2725(0.349)(1.28)/367$$
$$= 3.3 \text{ g (from body)}$$

Also, based on the prior result in Chapter 2, the aerodynamic contribution from the tail at Mach 2, with an angle of attack $\alpha_{Tail} = 9.4$ deg is $(C_N)_{Tail}(S_{Ref}/S_{Tail}) = 0.425$. The incremental maneuverability contribution from the isolated tail is

$$\Delta(n_Z)_{Tail} = qS_{Tail}[(C_N)_{Tail}(S_{Ref}/S_{Tail})]/W = 2725(1.54)(0.425)/367$$
$$= 4.9 \text{ g (from tail)}$$

The wing must be designed to meet the shortfall in maneuverability. Compute

$$\Delta(n_Z)_{Wing} = (n_Z)_{Required} - \Delta(n_Z)_{Body} - \Delta(n_Z)_{Tail} = 30 - 3.3 - 4.9 = 21.8 \text{ g}$$

Based on the Chapter 2 example, the aerodynamic contribution from the wing at Mach 2, with an effective angle of attack of $\alpha_{Wing} = 22$ deg is $(C_N)_{Wing}(S_{Ref}/S_{Wing}) = 1.08$. The required wing area is therefore

$$S_W = \Delta(n_Z)_{Wing} W/\{q[(C_N)_{Wing}(S_{Ref}/S_{Wing})]\}$$
$$= 21.8(367)/\{(2725)(1.08)\} = 2.72 \text{ ft}^2$$

The wing area of the rocket baseline missile $(S_W)_{Rocket\ baseline} = 2.55$ ft², which is slightly less than the predicted required wing area $S_W = 2.72$ ft². Based on this conceptual design prediction, the rocket baseline missile requires about 7% additional wing area to satisfy the maneuverability requirement of 30 g at Mach 2, 20 kft altitude. A 7% larger wing would increase the missile wing weight by 7% (38.6 to 41.2 lb) and the missile weight by about 1%

(367 to 369.6 lb). The increased wing weight of 2.6 lb would have a small effect on missile maneuverability, speed, and flight range.

The video in the top right corner of Fig. 7.15 illustrates the maneuverability of a typical air intercept missile (Roland) against a maneuvering target. Note that the missile must lead the target, have high velocity, have a high turn rate, and have a small turn radius to intercept the target.

Turn rate performance is the capability to make a rapid rate of change in the flight path angle γ. From Chapter 5, the equation for turn rate using aerodynamic control is

$$\dot{\gamma} = gn/V = [qSC_{N_\alpha}\alpha + qSC_{N_\delta}\delta - W\cos\gamma]/[(W/g_c)V]$$

An example of a requirement for turn rate performance is the capability of an anti-aircraft missile to match the turn rate of the target, which is necessary for a successful intercept. As discussed in Chapter 5, for manned fighter aircraft, typical aircraft maneuvering capability is a normal acceleration of about $n = 9$ g (pilot limit), with a velocity of about $V = 1000$ ft/s. Substitution into the turn rate equation gives a typical maximum turn rate of a manned aircraft of

$$\dot{\gamma} = 32.2(9)/1000 = 0.290 \text{ rad/s or } 16.6 \text{ deg/s}$$

Because the missile must have a speed advantage to intercept the aircraft, it requires higher maneuverability to match the turn rate of the

- Size wing for assumptions
  - $(n_z)_{Required} = 30$ g to counter 9 g maneuvering target
  - $(n_z) = \Delta(n_z)_{Wing} + \Delta(n_z)_{Body} + \Delta(n_z)_{Tail}$
- Rocket baseline missile @ 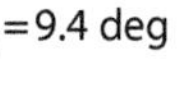
  - Mach 2
  - 20,000 ft altitude
  - 367 lb weight (burnout)
- From prior example, compute
  - $\alpha_{Wing} = \alpha'_{max} = (\alpha+\delta)_{max} = 22$ deg for rocket baseline
  - $\alpha = 0.75\delta$, $\alpha_{Body} = \alpha_{Tail} = 9.4$ deg

$\Delta(n_z)_{Body} = qS_{Ref}(C_N)_{Body}/W = 2725(0.349)(1.28)/367 = 3.3$ g (from body)

$\Delta(n_z)_{Tail} = qS_{Tail}[(C_N)_{Tail}(S_{Ref}/S_{Tail})]/W = 2725(1.54)(0.425)/367 = 4.9$ g (from tail)

$\Delta(n_z)_{Wing} = (n_z)_{Required} - \Delta(n_z)_{Body} - \Delta(n_z)_{Tail} = 30-3.3-4.9 = 21.8$ g

$(S_W)_{Required} = \Delta(n_z)_{Wing}W/\{q[(C_N)_{Wing}(S_{Ref}/S_{Wing})]\} = 21.8(367)/\{(2725)(1.08)\} = 2.72$ ft²

Note: $(S_W)_{Rocket\ baseline} = 2.55$ ft² $\Rightarrow \approx 30$ g maneuverability

Video of Roland lead-intercept of maneuvering aircraft

Fig. 7.15 Example of wing sizing to satisfy a required maneuver acceleration.

aircraft. For example, a missile with a velocity $V = 3000$ ft/s requires about 27-g maneuverability to achieve a turn rate $\dot{\gamma} = 16.6$ deg/s.

The aerodynamically controlled rocket baseline missile from a prior example in Chapter 5 will be used to illustrate the drivers for turn rate. Assume that a vertical maneuver is commanded for a typical post-burnout intercept condition of Mach 2, $h = 20$ kft altitude ($V = 2074$ ft/s) in horizontal flight. The maximum wing local angle of attack $|\alpha'| = |\alpha + \delta| < 22$ deg. The rocket baseline missile is statically stable, with $\alpha/\delta = 0.75$. The missile maximum angle of attack is $\alpha_{max} = 9.4$ deg. Substituting into the turn rate equation

$$\dot{\gamma} = [2725(0.349)(0.60)(9.4) + 2725(0.349)(0.19)(12.6)$$
$$- 367(1)]/[(367/32.2)(2074)]$$
$$= 0.314 \text{ rad/s or } 18 \text{ deg/s}$$

Thus, the rocket baseline missile wing area ($S_W = 2.55$ ft^2) is predicted to provide a sufficient turn rate capability to counter a typical highly maneuverable aircraft.

A metric for missile response time is the angle of attack sensitivity to turn rate, or $\alpha/\dot{\gamma}$. For the rocket baseline missile at Mach 0.8 launch and $h = 20\,000$ ft altitude ($V = 830$ ft/s)

$$\alpha/\delta = 1.5$$

Compute maximum angle of attack α_{max} and the control surface deflection δ

$$\alpha_{max} = 22/(1 + 1/1.5) = 13.2 \text{ deg}$$
$$\delta = 13.2/1.5 = 8.8 \text{ deg}$$

The turn rate $\dot{\gamma}$ is

$$\dot{\gamma} = [436(0.349)(0.80)(13.2) + 436(0.349)(0.27)(8.8)$$
$$- 3500(1)]/[(500/32.2)(830)]$$
$$= 0.114 \text{ rad/s or } 6.5 \text{ deg/s}$$

Compute the missile response time metric $\alpha/\dot{\gamma}$ at launch

$$\alpha/\dot{\gamma} = 13.2/6.5 = 2.0 \text{ s}$$

As a comparison, the response time metric for Mach 2 coast at 20, 000 ft altitude is better

$$\alpha/\dot{\gamma} = 9.4/18 = 0.52 \text{ s}$$

Although an aerodynamic control missile may have a relatively high control effectiveness at launch ($\alpha/\delta > 1$), it may not have sufficient maneuverability if there is a relatively low dynamic pressure. An advantage of a thrust vector control missile is the capability of high turn rate at a low velocity, such as launch velocity. A TVC missile at launch usually has a higher turn rate than an aerodynamically controlled missile.

Another concern in sizing the wing for maneuverability is the required turn radius capability. To achieve an intercept, the missile turn radius must be less than the turn radius of a maneuvering target. As an example, assume a maneuvering aircraft target with $\dot\gamma = 18$ deg/s $= 0.314$ rad/s, $V = 1000$ ft/s. Compute the instantaneous turn radius using the Chapter 5 equation

$$(R_T)_\text{Target} = V/\dot\gamma = 1000/0.314 = 3183 \text{ ft}$$

Also, assume that the intercept missile is the rocket baseline missile at Mach 2, 20 kft altitude, and 367 lb weight (burnout). From the prior example, $\dot\gamma = 18$ deg/s. Compute

$$(R_T)_\text{Rocket baseline t} = V/\dot\gamma = 2074/0.314 = 6602 \text{ ft}$$

Note that the rocket baseline missile turn radius is larger than the turn radius of the target, $(R_T)_\text{Rocket baselinet} > (R_T)_\text{Target}$. Because the rocket baseline missile has a larger turn radius, it can be counter-measured by a maneuverable target in a tight turn. Candidate counter-countermeasure approaches for the rocket baseline missile include a larger wing, a higher angle of attack capability from reduced static margin, the use of thrust vector control (TVC) with either a longer burn motor or thrust magnitude control at intercept, and the use of reaction jet control.

7.4 Multi-Parameter Harmonization

The next example of sizing for the rocket baseline missile is multi-parameter harmonization. The example is harmonization of the measures of merit of light weight and a small miss distance.

A sensitivity study was conducted to determine which parameters have the greatest impact on weight and miss distance for the rocket baseline missile. Baseline sensitivities to parametric changes are shown in Table 7.3 from Ref. 38. If an increase in the value of a subsystem parameter results in an increase in the value of a measure of merit parameter (weight, miss distance), the value of the measure of merit sensitivity parameter will be positive. The measure of merit sensitivity parameters are:

$$W^* = (\Delta W/W)/(\Delta P/P) = \text{non-dimensional weight sensitivity}$$
$$\sigma^* = (\Delta\sigma/\sigma)/(\Delta P/P) = \text{non-dimensional miss distance sensitivity}$$

In the above equations $\Delta P/P$ represents a relative change in a parameter.

Table 7.3 The Rocket Baseline Missile Weight and Miss Distance Synergistic Drivers are Nozzle Expansion and Motor Propellant Volumetric Efficiency.

Parameter	Baseline	Sensitivity Variation	W^*	σ^*
Number of fixed surface panels (tail)	4	3	+0.054	+0.100[d]
Number of movable surface (wing)	4	2	+0.071	+0.106[d]
Design static margin at launch	0.40	0.30	+0.095	+0.167[d]
Wing (movable surface) sweep (deg)	45.0	49.5	−0.205[b]	+0.015
Tail (fixed surface) sweep (deg)	57.0	60.0	+0.027	+0.039
Wing (movable surface) thickness ratio	0.044	0.034	+0.041	+0.005
Nose fineness ratio	2.4	2.6	−0.016	−0.745[b]
Rocket chamber sustain pressure (psi)	301	330	−0.076	−0.045
Boattail fineness ratio (length/diameter)	0.38	0.342	+0.096	+0.140[d]
Nozzle expansion ratio	6.2	6.82	−0.114[c]	−0.181[c]
Motor propellant volumetric efficiency	0.76	0.84	−0.136[c]	−0.453[a]
Propellant density (lbm/in^3)	0.065	0.084	−0.062	+0.012
Boost thrust (lb)	5750	6325	+0.014	−0.018
Sustain thrust (lb)	1018	1119	+0.088	+0.246[b]
Propellant characteristic velocity (ft/s)	5200	5720	−0.063	−0.077
Wing location (percent total length)	47.5	42.75	+0.181[d]	−0.036

Baseline:
Weight = 500 lb, Miss distance = 62.3 ft
W^* = weight sensitivity for parameter variation = $\Delta W/W$
σ^* = miss distance sensitivity for parameter variation = $\Delta\sigma/\sigma$

Note:
[a]Strong impact with synergy
[b]Strong impact
[c]Moderate impact with synergy
[d]Moderate impact

The table shows that there is moderate-to-strong synergistic benefit in reducing both the weight and the miss distance by increasing the rocket nozzle expansion ratio and by increasing the rocket motor propellant volumetric efficiency. For example, a 10% increase in motor propellant volumetric efficiency (0.76 to 0.84) reduces the missile weight by 14% (500 to 432 lb) and also reduces the miss distance by 45% (62 to 34 ft). Other sensitivities that have a moderate-to-strong impact on either weight or miss distance, but not a significant impact on both are reducing the number of tails, reducing the number of wings (which requires bank-to-turn maneuvering), reducing the static margin, increasing the wing sweep, increasing the nose fineness ratio, decreasing the boattail fineness ratio, increasing the sustain thrust, and moving the wing forward. Examples of sensitivities that have a slight anti-synergy are wing sweep (reduced weight, slightly increased miss distance), propellant density (reduced weight, slightly increased miss distance), boost thrust (slightly increased weight, slightly decreased miss distance), and wing location (increased weight, slightly decreased miss distance).

Missile parameters were selected that resulted in the lightest weight and smallest miss distance missiles without exceeding the state-of-the-art. These parameters and their values for the four missiles (baseline, lightest weight, smallest miss distance, and harmonized missile) are shown in Table 7.4 from Ref. 38. The harmonized missile compared to the baseline missile has the following characteristics:

1. higher fineness nose (2.6 versus 2.4)
2. higher expansion nozzle (15 versus 6.2)
3. higher sustain pressure (1000 versus 301 psi)
4. smaller boattail fineness (0.21 versus 0.38)
5. fewer wing panels (two versus four)
6. fewer tail panels (three versus four)
7. higher wing leading edge sweep (55 versus 45 deg)
8. smaller static margin at launch (0 versus 0.4 diameter)
9. higher propellant density (0.084 versus 0.065 lbm/in^3), and
10. higher propellant loading for higher motor propellant volumetric efficiency (84 versus 76%)

The measures of merit comparison of the harmonized missile with the baseline missile shows that the harmonized missile has lighter weight (390 versus 500 lb), smaller miss distance (17 versus 62 ft), and shorter length (115 versus 144 in). A comparison of the harmonized missile with the minimum weight missile shows that the harmonized missile is only slightly heavier (390 versus 386 lb). It is also slightly longer (115 versus 113 in). Comparing the harmonized missile with the minimum miss distance missile shows that the harmonized missile has only slightly larger miss distance (17 versus 16 ft). The harmonized missile was selected based on synergistic parameters for weight and miss distance that are within the state-of-the-art.

The configuration of the harmonized missile, which has lighter weight and smaller miss distance, is compared with the rocket baseline missile in Fig. 7.16 from Ref. 38. Both missiles were assumed to have the same diameter, to package the same subsystems. Note the 20% shorter length/ smaller size of the harmonized missile compared to the baseline. The harmonized missile is also 22% lighter in launch weight and has a 73% reduction in miss distance. A disadvantage for the harmonized missile is 10% longer time of flight for a flight range of 6.7 nm. However, the time

Table 7.4 A Harmonized Missile Can Have Smaller Miss Distance and Lighter Weight.

Parameter	Baseline Value	Min Weight	Min Miss	Harmonized
Judicious changes				
Boost thrust (lb)	5750	3382	3382	3382
Wing location (percent missile length to 1/4 mac)	47.5	47	44	46
Wing taper ratio	0.18	0.2	0.2	0.2
Nose fineness ratio	2.4	3.2	**2.55**	2.6
Nose bluntness ratio	0.0	0.05	0.05	0.05
Nozzle expansion ratio	6.2	**15**	15	15
Sustain chamber pressure (psi)	301	**1000**	1000	1000
Boattail fineness ratio	0.38	0.21	**0.21**	0.21
Tail leading edge sweep (deg)	57	50	50	50
Technology limited changes				
No. wing panels	4	2	**2**	2
No. tail panels	4	3	**3**	3
Wing thickness ratio	0.044	0.030	0.030	0.030
Wing leading edge sweep (deg)	45	**55**	55	55
Static margin at launch (diam)	0.4	0.0	**0.0**	0.0
Propellant density (lbm/in^3)	0.065	**0.084**	0.084	0.084
Motor propellant volumetric efficiency	0.76	**0.84**	0.84	0.84
Measures of Merit				
Total weight (lb)	500	**385.9**	395.0	390.1
Miss distance (ft)	62.3	63.1	**16.2**	16.6
Time to target (s)	21.6	23.8	23.6	23.8
Length (in)	144	**112.7**	114.7	114.9
Mach No. at burnout	2.20	2.08	2.09	2.07
Weight of propellant (lb)	133	**78.3**	85.4	85.9
Wing area (in^2)	368.6	**175.5**	150.7	173.8
Tail area (in^2)	221.8	**109.1**	134.5	112.0

Note: Bold numbers represent value of driving parameter

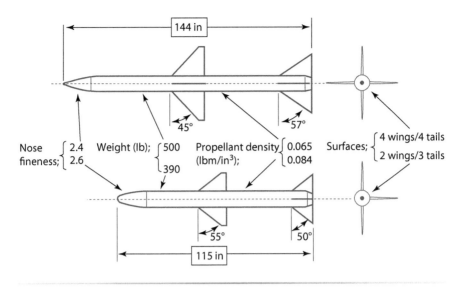

Fig. 7.16 Rocket baseline missile versus smaller size harmonized missile with same diameter.

of flight of the harmonized missile still meets the F-Pole requirement of 24.4 s to 6.7 nm. A design consideration for follow-on analysis is its robustness to provide sufficient F-Pole standoff range against future threats.

7.5 Maximum Range Trajectory

The final example of the rocket baseline missile sizing discusses maximizing the missile flight range by selecting a trajectory that provides more time at $(L/D)_{max}$. The flight range advantage of a loft-glide trajectory will be compared to alternatives of a loft-ballistic trajectory and a constant altitude trajectory.

Surface launch ($h = 0$ ft) is assumed with an initial inclination angle of 45 deg and the same flight path angle ($\gamma = 45$ deg) during boost and sustain. From the Chapter 5 equation, the velocity at the end of the initial boost is

$$\Delta V = -gI_{SP}[1 - (D_{AVG}/T) - (W_{AVG}\sin\gamma)/T]\ln(1 - W_P/W_i)$$
$$= -32.2(250)[1 - (419/5750) - 458(0.707)/5750]\ln(1 - 84.8/500)$$
$$= 1303 \text{ ft/s}$$

The distance traveled at the end of the initial boost is

$$\Delta R = (V_i + \Delta V/2)t_B = (0 + 1303/2)3.69 = 2404 \text{ ft}$$

The horizontal range at the end of the initial boost is

$$\Delta R_x = \Delta R \cos \gamma_i = 2404(0.707) = 1700 \, \text{ft}$$

Similarly, the altitude at the end of the initial boost is

$$h = h_i + \Delta R_y = 0 + \Delta R \sin \gamma_i = 1700 \, \text{ft}$$

The velocity, incremental horizontal range, and the altitude at the end of rocket motor sustain (burnout) are

$$\Delta V = -gI_{\text{SP}}[1 - (D_{\text{AVG}}/T) - (W \sin \gamma)/T]\ln(1 - W_P/W_i)$$
$$= -32.2(230.4)[1 - (650/1018) - 391(0.707)/1018]$$
$$\times \ln(1 - 48.2/415.2) = 81 \, \text{ft/s}$$
$$V_{\text{BO}} = 1303 + 81 = 1384 \, \text{ft/s}$$
$$\Delta R = (V_i + \Delta V/2)t_S = (1303 + 81/2)10.86 = 14{,}590 \, \text{ft}$$
$$\Delta R_x = \Delta R \cos \gamma_i = 14590(0.707) = 10{,}315 \, \text{ft}$$
$$\Delta R_y = \Delta R \sin \gamma_i = 14590(0.707) = 10{,}315 \, \text{ft}$$
$$h = h_i + \Delta R_y = 1700 + 10315 = 12{,}015 \, \text{ft}$$

Following motor burnout, the missile is assumed to coast at a flight path angle of $\gamma = 45$ deg. Coast continues until the missile reaches an altitude that provides maximum aerodynamic efficiency $h_{(L/D)\text{max}}$. This occurs after 21 s of coast. The velocity, coast range, coast horizontal range, and the incremental altitude, using the equations of Chapter 5 are

$$V_{\text{coast}} = V_i\{1 - [(g \sin \gamma)/V_i]t\}/\{1 + \{[g_c\rho_{\text{AVG}}S_{\text{Ref}}(C_{D_0})_{\text{AVG}}V_i]/(2W)\}t\}$$
$$= 1384\{1 - [32.2(0.707)/1384]21\}/$$
$$\{1 + \{[32.2(0.001338)(0.349)(0.7)(1384)]/(2(367))\}21\}$$
$$= 674 \, \text{ft/s} \, @ \, t_{\text{coast}} = 21 \, \text{s}$$
$$R_{\text{coast}} = \{2W/[g_c\rho_{\text{AVG}}S_{\text{Ref}}(C_{D_0})_{\text{AVG}}]\}$$
$$\times \ln\{1 - [g_c^2\rho_{\text{AVG}}S_{\text{Ref}}(C_{D_0})_{\text{AVG}}/(2W)][\sin\gamma]t^2$$
$$+ \{[g_c\rho_{\text{AVG}}S_{\text{Ref}}(C_{D_0})_{\text{AVG}}V_i]/(2W)\}t\}$$
$$= \{2(367)/[32.2(0.001338)(0.349)(0.7)]\}$$
$$\times \ln\{1 - [(32.2)^2(0.001338)(0.349)(0.7)/((2(367))][0.707](21)^2$$
$$+ \{[32.2(0.001338)(0.349)(0.7)(1384)]/(2(367))\}21\}$$
$$= 17{,}148 \, \text{ft} \, @ \, t_{\text{coast}} = 21 \, \text{s}$$
$$(R_x)_{\text{coast}} = (R_y)_{\text{coast}} = R_{\text{coast}} \sin \gamma = 17148(0.707) = 12{,}124 \, \text{ft}$$

The flight conditions at the end of coast are

$t = 35.6\,\text{s}$

$V = 674\,\text{ft/s}$

$h = 24{,}189\,\text{ft}$

$q = 251\,\text{psf}$

$M = 0.66$

$(L/D)_{\text{max}} = 5.22$

$\alpha_{(L/D)\text{max}} = 5.5\,\text{deg}$

At the end of coast the angle of attack is set to

$$\alpha = \alpha_{(L/D)\text{max}} = 5.5\,\text{deg}$$

Incremental horizontal range at the end of the $(L/D)_{\text{max}}$ glide, using the equation in Chapter 5, is

$$\Delta R_x = (L/D)\Delta h = 5.22(24189) = 126{,}267\,\text{ft}$$

Finally, the total horizontal range for the loft-glide trajectory is

$$R_x = \Sigma\Delta R_x = \Delta R_{x,\text{Boost}} + \Delta R_{x,\text{Sustain}} + \Delta R_{x,\text{Coast}} + \Delta R_{x,\text{Glide}}$$
$$= 1700 + 10315 + 12124 + 126267 = 150{,}406\,\text{ft} = 24.8\,\text{nm}$$

Figure 7.17 compares a loft-glide trajectory versus loft-ballistic and co-altitude flight trajectories. For lofted flight, the initial launch angle is assumed to be 45 deg and during rocket motor burn the flight path angle is held constant at 45 deg. For a loft-glide trajectory, the missile continues at 45 deg flight path angle following motor burnout, coasting until it reaches an apogee altitude of $h = 24{,}189\,\text{ft}$, which occurs 35.6 s after launch. After reaching the apogee, where lift approximately equals weight, the rocket baseline missile begins a glide at maximum aerodynamic efficiency. The angle of attack is maintained at $\alpha = \alpha_{(L/D)\text{max}} = 5.5\,\text{deg}$ during the glide. The dynamic pressure during the $(L/D)_{\text{max}}$ glide is relatively constant at $q \approx 285\,\text{psf}$. Impact occurs after 298 s of flight. The impact velocity is relatively low, 459 ft/s. The impact angle is $-10.8\,\text{deg}$. Impact range is 24.8 nm.

The loft-ballistic trajectory alternative has an apogee of 21,590 ft, which occurs at 35 s after launch. Impact occurs at 68 s, with an impact velocity of 1368 ft/s and an impact angle of $-71\,\text{deg}$. The ballistic trajectory has a flight range of 9.6 nm. A gliding flight trajectory after apogee provides greater range, while a ballistic flight trajectory provides a higher velocity impact.

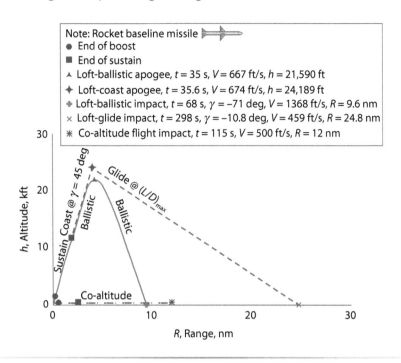

Note: Rocket baseline missile
- End of boost
- End of sustain
- Loft-ballistic apogee, t = 35 s, V = 667 ft/s, h = 21,590 ft
- Loft-coast apogee, t = 35.6 s, V = 674 ft/s, h = 24,189 ft
- Loft-ballistic impact, t = 68 s, γ = –71 deg, V = 1368 ft/s, R = 9.6 nm
- Loft-glide impact, t = 298 s, γ = –10.8 deg, V = 459 ft/s, R = 24.8 nm
- Co-altitude flight impact, t = 115 s, V = 500 ft/s, R = 12 nm

Fig. 7.17 A loft-glide trajectory provides extended range for a high performance rocket.

Note from the figure that a co-altitude flight has a range of 12 nm, which is longer than a loft-ballistic trajectory, but shorter than a loft-glide trajectory. Its impact velocity (500 ft/s) is less than a loft-ballistic trajectory (1368 ft/s) and is comparable to that of a loft-glide trajectory (459 ft/s).

In addition to range, other design considerations in selecting an optimum trajectory include the time-to-target, survivability, and buried target penetration. The low altitude trajectory may benefit from terrain masking survivability. The loft-ballistic trajectory has a supersonic impact velocity, which improves penetration of buried targets and may enhance survivability.

7.6 Ramjet Missile Range Robustness

A generic baseline of a ramjet missile, derived from the Advanced Strategic Air Launched Missile (ASALM), will be used to illustrate the typical characteristics of a ramjet powered missile. Sizing examples are presented for ramjet flight range robustness, alternative propulsion systems, alternative fuels, and surface impact velocity.

The baseline ramjet engine is sized for cruise at Mach numbers up to Mach 4.0 at 80,000 ft altitude and up to Mach 3.0 at sea level. An integral solid propellant rocket motor boosts the missile to a ramjet thrust takeover Mach number of about 2.5. After rocket motor burnout, the rocket motor case becomes the ramjet combustor. Unlike the rocket baseline missile, the ramjet baseline missile is able to cruise at constant velocity and high altitude, maintaining an aerodynamic efficiency near $(L/D)_{max}$.

The ramjet baseline missile configuration is shown in Fig. 7.18. It is a chin inlet integral rocket ramjet based on Ref. 19. The aerodynamic configuration has a conical forebody with a half angle of 17.7 deg, followed by a nearly circular cross-sectional body. From body station 23.5 to 43.5 in, the nose diameter gradually increases. The fineness ratio of the nose is $f_N = 43.5/20.375 = 2.13$. Downstream of body station 43.5 in, the average diameter $d = 20.375$ in. The ASALM diameter and length were set by the diameter and length constraints to efficiently package eight ASALM missiles within a B-1 rotary launcher/weapon bay. Flight control is provided by four tail surfaces. The tails are folded for compressed carriage in the weapons bay. The missile uses bank-to-turn maneuvering to minimize the sideslip air flowing into the inlet. The fuel is liquid hydrocarbon RJ-5 fuel, packaged in a fuel tank around the inlet duct. Shown in the figure are the section bulkhead locations and lengths of the nose, forebody, payload bay, midbody, aftbody, and tail cone sections. Also shown are frontal and aft views of the nose and tail sections. A planform view is provided of the tail geometry, showing the tail leading edge sweep, root chord location and length; tip chord length; and the exposed tail semi-span.

Shown in Table 7.5 from Ref. 19 is a weight and balance statement of the ramjet baseline missile. The launch weight $W_L = 2230$ lb and the end of cruise weight $W_{EC} = 1263$ lb. The fuel weight $W_f = 476$ lb and the booster propellant weight $W_P = 449$ lb. There is a small forward movement

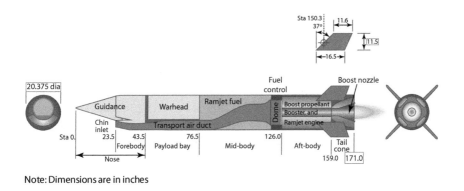

Note: Dimensions are in inches

Fig. 7.18 The ramjet baseline missile is a chin inlet integral rocket ramjet (IRR). (Source: Bithell, R. A. and Stoner, R. C. "Rapid Approach for Missile Synthesis," Vol. II, Air-breathing Synthesis Handbook, AFWAL TR 81-3022, Vol. II, March 1982.)

Table 7.5   Mass Properties of Ramjet Baseline Missile.

Component	Weight, lb	CG Sta, in
Nose	15.9	15.7
Forebody Structure	42.4	33.5
Guidance	129.0	33.5
Payload Bay Structure	64.5	60.0
Warhead	510.0	60.0
Midbody Structure	95.2	101.2
Inlet	103.0	80.0
Electrical	30.0	112.0
Hydraulic System for Control Actuation	20.0	121.0
Fuel Distribution	5.0 .	121.0
Aftbody Struct (Eng Combustor/Booster Case)	44.5	142.5
Engine Trans (Injectors, Igniter, Flameholder)	33.5	142.5
Tailcone Structure	31.6	165.0
Ramjet Nozzle	31.0	165.0
Flight Control Actuators	37.0	164.0
Fins (4)	70.0	157.2
End of Cruise	1262.6	81.8
Ramjet Fuel (11900 in^3)	476.0	87.0
Start of Cruise	1738.6	83.2
Boost Nozzle (Ejected)	31.0	164.0
Frangible Port	11.5	126.0
End of Boost	1781.1	84.9
Boost Propellant	449.0	142.5
Booster Ignition	2230.1	96.5

(0.07 diameter) in the center-of-gravity during the ramjet cruise portion of flight. The center-of-gravity at the start of cruise is 83.2 in from the nose tip. The center-of-gravity at the end of cruise is 81.8 in from the nose tip. Most of the missile structure is titanium alloy. The total weight of the titanium airframe, inlet, and fins is 17% of the launch weight.

The ramjet baseline missile detailed geometric and material definition of the inlet, body, and tails are shown in Table 7.6 from Ref. 19. The inlet is a mixed compression type with a total of four compressions prior to the normal shock, consisting of 1) the shock wave on the conical nose, followed by 2) the shock wave on the ramp leading to the cowl, followed by 3)

Table 7.6 Ramjet Baseline Missile Definition.

Inlet	
Type	Mixed compression
Material	Ti-6Al-2Sn-4Zr-2Mo-Si
Yield internal pressure load @ 1300 °F, psi	200
Backside Insulation	3/16 in Min-K
Conical forebody half angle, deg	17.7
Ramp wedge angle, deg	8.36
Cowl angle, deg	8.24
Internal contraction ratio	12.2 Percent
Capture area, ft^2	0.79
Throat area, ft^2	0.29
Exit area, ft^2	0.54
Length, in	102.5
Body	
Seeker Dome Material	Silicon nitride
Forebody Airframe Material	Titanium Ti-6424S
Airframe Insulation	Min-K
Combustor Material	Inconel 718
Combustor Insulation	DC 93-104
Nozzle Material	Silica Phenolic
Length, in	171.0
Diameter, in	20.375
Fineness ratio	8.39
Volume, ft^3	28.33
Wetted area, ft^2	68.81
Base area, ft^2 (cruise)	0.58
Boattail fineness ratio	N/A
Nose half angle, deg	17.7
Nose length, in	23.5
Tail (Exposed)	
Material	Titanium Ti-6424S
Planform area (2 panels), ft^2	2.24
Wetted area (4 panels), ft^2	8.96
Aspect ratio (2 panels exposed)	1.64
Taper ratio	0.70
Root chord, in	16.5
Span (2 panels exposed), in	23.0

(Continued)

Table 7.6 Ramjet Baseline Missile Definition (Continued).

Leading edge sweep, deg	37.0
Mean aerodynamic chord, in	14.2
Thickness ratio	0.04
Section type	Modified double wedge
Section leading edge total angle, deg	9.1
x_{mac}, in	150.3
y_{mac} (from root chord), in	5.4
Reference values	
Reference area, ft^2	2.264
Reference length, ft	1.698

the shock wave on the cowl, and finally 4) a series of nearly isentropic internal contraction shock waves leading to a normal shock. The missile has a hot structure, with no external insulation. The forebody airframe structure and the elliptical duct inlet are a titanium alloy, with internal insulation to protect the subsystems. The tails are made of a titanium alloy built-up structure. A ballistic actuator located inside each tail unfolds the tail after the missile has separated from the launch aircraft. The combustor is constructed from Inconel super alloy, with internal insulation. The seeker dome material is silicon nitride.

Also shown in the table are data on the missile reference geometry parameters. The ramjet baseline missile reference area $S_{Ref} = 2.264$ ft^2 is based on the body cross-sectional area. The reference length $l_{Ref} = d_{Ref} = 1.698$ ft is based on an equivalent circular diameter of the body cross-sectional area.

Definitions of the propulsion parameters and the flow path are shown in Fig. 7.19 based on Ref. 19. The ramjet baseline inlet captures the air that flows over the bottom one-third of the nose (120 deg). In the thrust – drag accounting system the nose corrected drag accounts for the air that is captured by the inlet. It is given by the equation

$$(C_{D_0})_{\text{Nose corrected}} = (C_{D0})_{\text{Nose uncorrected}} \times (1 - A_c/S_{Ref})$$

The flow path in the figure is described by the stations number 1 (free stream conditions) through number 6 (nozzle exit). The largest flow path areas are located at the subsonic combustion stations 3 (flame holder plane) and 4 (combustor exit), each having an area of 287.1 in^2. The other areas of the flow path are the inlet throat (41.9 in^2), diffuser exit (77.3 in^2), ramjet nozzle throat (103.1 in^2), and the ramjet nozzle exit (233.6 in^2). The smallest area in the flow path is the inlet throat, which is 15% of the combustor area.

At station number 0 the free stream flow conditions apply. The capture area A_c is the theoretical flow area into the inlet if the missile is in a cruise condition and if there are no shock waves in front of the inlet. A_0 is the actual flow area into the inlet in the presence of the forebody. As an example, referring to Chapter 3, at Mach 4 with angles of attack of 0 deg and 10 deg respectively, the free stream area to capture area ratios of the ramjet baseline are $A_0/A_c = 0.91$ and 0.61 respectively.

The axial force, normal force, and pitching moment aerodynamics of the ramjet baseline missile are presented in Fig. 7.20 from Ref. 19. Aerodynamics for the ramjet baseline missile were developed using an early version (year 1974) of the computer program described in Ref. 43.

Axial force C_A and normal force C_N coefficients are presented as a function of Mach number and angle of attack in Fig. 7.20a. Note the decrease in the aerodynamic coefficients with increasing supersonic Mach number. It is noted that the axial force is usually nearly equal to the zero-lift drag coefficient. The reference center-of-gravity for the aerodynamic data is 82.5 in from the nose tip, representative of the cruise center-of-gravity.

Pitching moment coefficient C_m with undeflected controls is presented in Fig. 7.20b as a function of Mach number and angle of attack. Again, the reference center-of-gravity location for the aerodynamic data is 82.5 in from the nose tip. Note that compared to the rocket baseline missile, the

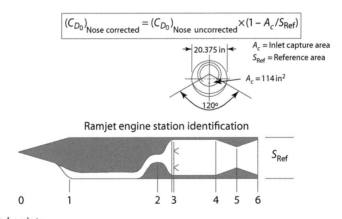

$$(C_{D_0})_{\text{Nose corrected}} = (C_{D_0})_{\text{Nose uncorrected}} \times (1 - A_c/S_{\text{Ref}})$$

20.375 in

A_c = Inlet capture area
S_{Ref} = Reference area

$A_c = 114\,\text{in}^2$

120°

Ramjet engine station identification

S_{Ref}

0   1   2 3   4 5 6

Subscripts
0   Free stream flow into inlet
    (Example, Ramjet baseline at March 4, $\alpha = 0$ deg $\Rightarrow A_0 = 104\,\text{in}^2$. Note: $A_c = 114\,\text{in}^2$)
1   Inlet throat (Ramjet baseline $A_1 = A_{IT} = 4.19\,\text{in}^2$)
2   Diffuser exit (Ramjet baseline $A_2 = 77.3\,\text{in}^2$)
3   Flame holder plane (Ramjet baseline $A_3 = 287.1\,\text{in}^2$)
4   Combustor exit (Ramjet baseline $A_4 = 287.1\,\text{in}^2$)
5   Nozzle throat (Ramjet baseline $A_5 = 103.1\,\text{in}^2$)
6   Nozzle exit (Ramjet baseline $A_6 = 233.6\,\text{in}^2$)
Ref Reference area (Ramjet baseline body cross-sectional area, $S_{\text{Ref}} = 326\,\text{in}^2$)

Fig. 7.19 Engine nomenclature and flow path geometry for ramjet baseline.

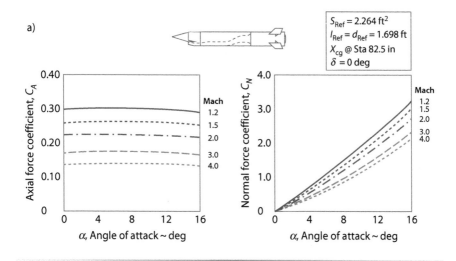

Fig. 7.20a Aerodynamic characteristics of ramjet baseline missile—axial force C_A and normal force C_N coefficients. (Source: Bithell, R. A. and Stoner, R. C. "Rapid Approach for Missile Synthesis", Vol. II, Air-breathing Synthesis Handbook, AFWAL TR 81-3022, Vol. II, March 1982.)

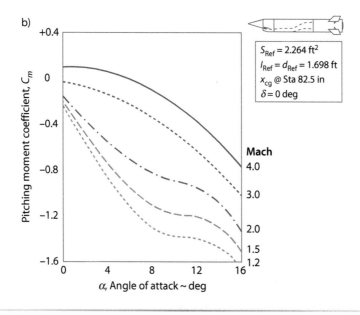

Fig. 7.20b Aerodynamic characteristics of ramjet baseline missile—pitching moment coefficient C_m. (Source: Bithell, R. A. and Stoner, R. C. "Rapid Approach for Missile Synthesis", Vol. II, Air-breathing Synthesis Handbook, AFWAL TR 81-3022, Vol. II, March 1982.)

ramjet baseline missile has a smaller value of pitching moment and a smaller variation with angle of attack and Mach number. This enhances the control effectiveness and reduces the trim drag of the missile.

Zero-lift drag coefficient C_{D_0} and the stability and control derivatives C_{m_δ} and C_{N_δ} are presented in Fig 7.20c as a function of Mach number. Note the decrease of the zero-lift drag coefficient and the stability and control derivatives with increasing supersonic Mach number. The zero-lift drag coefficient in the figure is based on power-on flight. Also, it includes a correction to account for inlet capture. C_{D_0} is based on a flowing inlet, which reduces the drag.

Supersonic inlets are usually designed for shock-on-lip operation at the highest Mach number cruise condition.

For a shock-on-lip design Mach number, a higher flight Mach number should be avoided. A higher Mach number would result in the shock wave entering the inlet, causing shock-wave boundary layer interaction, possibly flow separation, a loss in total pressure, and a loss in thrust. For a shock-on-lip design, operating at a lower Mach number results in a larger shock wave angle, streamlines spilling outside the inlet, a reduction in the captured air, a reduction in thrust, and spillage drag.

The ramjet baseline missile inlet capture efficiency is shown in Fig. 7.21 as a function of Mach number ($2 < M < 4$). Also shown is the relatively small effect of altitude on inlet capture efficiency. Data are based on

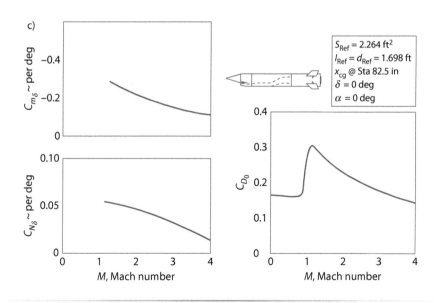

Fig. 7.20c Aerodynamic characteristics of ramjet baseline missile-zero-lift drag coefficient C_{D_0} and the stability and control derivatives C_{m_δ} and C_{N_δ}. (Source: Bithell, R. A. and Stoner, R. C. "Rapid Approach for Missile Synthesis", Vol. II, Air-breathing Synthesis Handbook, AFWAL TR 81-3022, Vol. II, March 1982.)

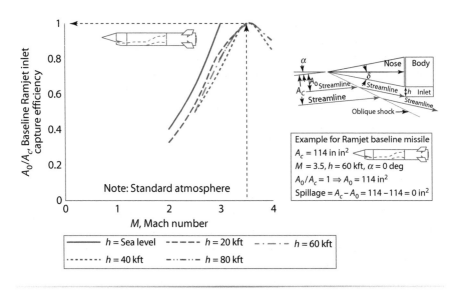

Fig. 7.21 Inlet capture efficiency of the ramjet baseline missile increases with free stream Mach number. (Source: Bithell, R. A. and Stoner, R. C. "Rapid Approach for Missile Synthesis", Vol. II, Air-breathing Synthesis Handbook, AFWAL TR 81-3022, Vol. II, March 1982.)

Ref. 19. It is noted that the inlet capture efficiency in the figure is about 20 to 30% higher than the prediction of Chapter 3.

Note from the figure that the ramjet baseline inlet has approximately 100% capture efficiency (shock-on-lip operation) at the cruise design maximum Mach number $M = 3.5$. Lower capture efficiency and spillage occur at lower Mach number, because of the larger value of the shock wave angle θ.

As an example, the capture efficiency at Mach 3.5 is approximately 100%. For the ramjet baseline missile capture area $A_c = 114$ in^2, the free stream flow area is computed $A_0 = 1.00(114) = 114$ in^2 and the air spillage is given by $A_c - A_0 = 114 - 114 = 0$ in^2. For the ramjet baseline missile, a slightly smaller value of inlet height would be required for shock-on-lip operation at Mach 4.0.

Maximum thrust of the ramjet baseline is shown in Fig. 7.22 as a function of Mach number and altitude, for standard atmospheric conditions. The figure is not based on data, but was generated based on the computer program of Ref. 19. The Mach number range is 2 to 4 and the altitude range is sea level to 80,000 ft. Note that the peak thrust is produced at about Mach 3.5.

As an example, at Mach 3.5 and 60,000 ft altitude the maximum thrust from the figure is

$$T_{\max} = 1750\,\text{lb}$$

Maximum thrust may be limited either by stoichiometric combustion ($\phi = 1$) or the combustor insulation temperature limit. From Chapter 3, the combustion temperature for Mach $3.5/60$ kft/$\varphi = 1$, RJ-5 fuel ($H_f = 17,900$ BTU/lbm/R) is

$$T_4 \approx T_0\{1 + [(\gamma_0 - 1)/2]M_0^2\} + (H_f/c_p)(f/a)$$

$$= 390\{1 + [(1.4 - 1)/2]\}(3.5)^2\} + (17900/0.302)(0.0667)$$

$$= 1345 + 3953 = 5298 \text{ R}.$$

A combustion temperature of $T_4 = 5298$ R from operation at $\phi = 1$ exceeds the ramjet baseline combustor insulation material temperature limit of $T_4 = 4000$ R. For this reason, the ramjet baseline cannot achieve maximum thrust and must operate at $\phi < 1$.

Thrust is also limited by inlet efficiency. A shock-on-inlet lip design condition provides highest inlet capture efficiency, with $A_0 = A_c$. From Ref. 19 data, the thrust at an off-design condition can be estimated from

$$T \approx [\phi/(A_0/A_c)]T_{\max} \quad \text{if } \phi \leq A_0/A_c$$
$$T \approx T_{\max} \quad \text{if } \phi \geq A_0/A_c$$

Specific impulse of the ramjet baseline at maximum thrust is shown in Fig. 7.23 as a function of Mach number for standard atmospheric conditions. The figure is based on the computer predictions of Ref. 19. Note that the peak value of specific impulse occurs at a Mach number of

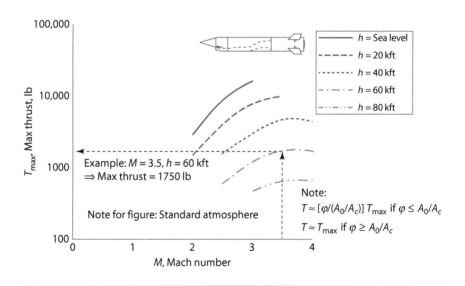

Fig. 7.22 Thrust modeling of the ramjet baseline. (Source: Figure based on Bithell and Stoner.)

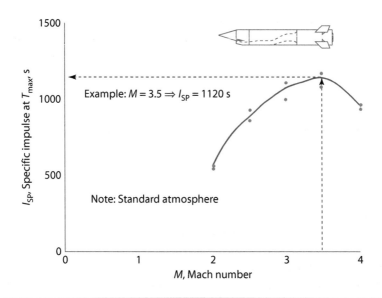

Fig. 7.23   Specific impulse modeling of the ramjet baseline. (Source: Figure based on Bithell and Stoner.)

about Mach 3.5. Also, the specific impulse of the ramjet baseline is nearly independent of altitude.

As an example, the figure shows that the specific impulse at Mach 3.5 is

$$I_{SP} = 1120\,s$$

The standard atmosphere performance of the rocket boost motor is shown in Fig. 7.24 from Ref. 19. The booster thrust and burn time are 22,000 lb and 5.05 s respectively. The booster thrust-to-launch-weight ratio is 9.9:1. A high thrust-to-weight ratio is required to provide safe separation from the launch aircraft and to minimize the propellant that is required for boost to the ramjet thrust takeover Mach number (about Mach 2.5). The incremental flight range during boost is about 1.3 nm for a launch Mach number of 0.8. The end-of-boost burnout Mach number for Mach 0.8 launch varies from Mach 2.3 to 2.7, depending upon the launch altitude.

Flight range performance for constant altitude flight is shown in Fig. 7.25 from Ref. 19. Note that the ramjet baseline missile is much more efficient in high altitude flight than in low altitude flight.

As an example, for a Mach 3/60 kft fly-out, the range is 445 nm. As a comparison, the Chapter 5 Breguet range prediction is

$$R = VI_{SP}(L/D)\ln\left[W_{BC}/(W_{BC} - W_f)\right]$$
$$= 2901(1040)(3.15)\ln(1739/(1739 - 476)) = 3{,}039{,}469\,\text{ft or }500\,\text{nm}$$

Note that the predicted range is 10% greater than baseline missile data.

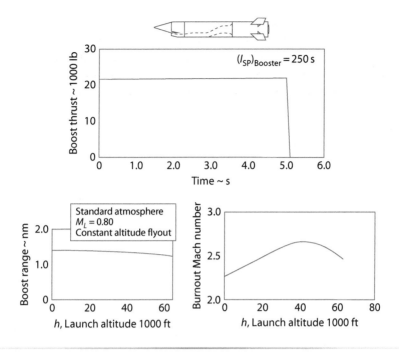

Fig. 7.24   Rocket booster acceleration/performance of ramjet baseline missile.

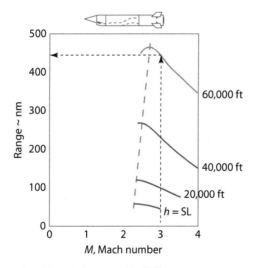

Note: $M_L = 0.8$, Constant altitude Fly-out
Example, March 3/60k ft flyout $\Rightarrow$ 445 nm. Brequet Range Prediction is $R = V I_{SP}$
$(L/D) \ln [W_{BC}/(W_{BC} - W_f)] = 2901(1040)(3.15) \ln(1739/(1739 - 476)) = 3,039,469$ ft
or 500 nm. Predicted range is 10% greater than baseline missile data.

Fig. 7.25   The ramjet baseline missile has best performance at high
altitude cruise.

A Pareto sensitivity study was conducted to define the ramjet baseline missile most significant parameters for flight range and the required accuracy for prediction methods. Note from Fig. 7.26 that flight range is most sensitive to the ramjet specific impulse, fuel weight, ramjet thrust, and the zero-lift drag coefficient. The flight range is relatively insensitive to inert weight and lift curve slope, especially for low altitude flight (high dynamic pressure).

As an example, note from the figure that a 10% increase in fuel weight for a Mach 3/60 kft altitude cruise provides a 9.6% increase in flight range.

The figure shows that the ramjet baseline missile does not require a wing for efficient flight at low altitude. The lift-curve-slope coefficient C_{L_α} for sea level flight at Mach 2.3 has a negligible effect on range. However, at 60k ft altitude with Mach 3.0 flight, a 10% increase in C_{L_α} would provide a 4% increase in range. Adding a small wing would provide enhanced range for high altitude flight but would reduce the range for low altitude flight.

The prediction methods for ramjet specific impulse, zero-lift drag coefficient, and ramjet thrust usually have sufficient accuracy (e.g., $+/-5\%$, 1σ) for conceptual design. However, similarly to the rocket baseline missile, there is often larger uncertainty in predicting the conceptual design subsystem packaging volume available to package the fuel, providing uncertainty in the fuel weight. Inboard profile drawings of subsystem packaging are

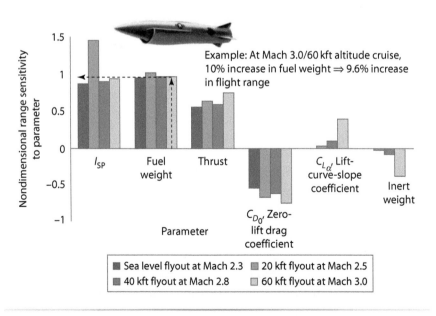

Fig. 7.26   From a Pareto sensitivity, the ramjet baseline missile range is driven by I_{SP}, fuel weight, thrust, and C_{D_0}.

Table 7.7   Ramjet Baseline Missile Flight Range Uncertainty Is $+/-7\%$, 1σ.

Parameter	Baseline Value at Mach 3.0/60k ft	Uncertainty in Parameter	$\Delta R/R$ from Uncertainty
1. Specific Impulse	1040 s	$+/-5\%$, 1σ	$+/-5\%$, 1σ
2. Ramjet Fuel Weight	476 lb	$+/-1\%$, 1σ	$+/-0.9\%$, 1σ
3. Cruise Thrust ($\phi = 0.39$)	458 lb	$+/-5\%$, 1σ	$+/-2\%$, 1σ
4. Zero-Lift Drag Coefficient	0.17	$+/-5\%$, 1σ	$+/-4\%$, 1σ
5. Lift Curve Slope Coefficient	0.13/deg	$+/-3\%$, 1σ	$+/-1\%$, 1σ
6. Inert Weight	1205 lb	$+/-2\%$, 1σ	$+/-0.8\%$, 1σ

required in the design process, to reduce the uncertainty in the available fuel volume/weight.

The uncertainties of the values of the ramjet baseline missile parameters that define the cruise flight range can be used to determine the uncertainty in flight range, as shown in Table 7.7. The assumed cruise flight condition is Mach 3.0 at 60,000 ft altitude. It was previously shown that the parameters affecting flight range, in order of their Pareto sensitivity are

1. Specific impulse
2. Ramjet fuel weight
3. Cruise thrust ($\phi = 0.39$)
4. Zero-lift drag coefficient
5. Lift curve slope coefficient
6. Inert weight

The level of maturity of the ramjet baseline missile used in this text is based on an advanced technology demonstration (ATD) of a flight prototype of the ASALM missile. Subsystem technology tests included wind tunnel tests; direct connect, inlet, and freejet propulsion tests; booster firings; and structure tests. Integration/system engineering included a mock-up, launch aircraft (B-1) fitment test, and hardware-in-loop simulation.

Based on the above tests, for the assumed cruise flight condition of Mach 3, 60 kft altitude, the ramjet baseline missile parameters are assumed to have the following values and uncertainties: specific impulse: 1040 s $+/-5\%$, 1σ; ramjet fuel weight: 476 lb $+/-1\%$, 1σ; cruise thrust: 458 lb ($\phi = 0.39$) $+/-5\%$, 1σ; zero-lift drag coefficient: 0.17 $+/-5\%$, 1σ; lift curve slope coefficient: 0.13/deg $+/-3\%$, 1σ; and inert weight: 1205 lb $+/-2\%$, 1σ. The effect of uncertainty of each parameter on flight range was obtained by multiplying the uncertainty in the value of the parameter times the Pareto sensitivity of the parameter. The ranking of parameter uncertainty on flight range, in order of importance is

1. Specific impulse: $+/-5\%$, 1σ
2. Zero-lift drag coefficient: $+/-4\%$, 1σ
3. Cruise thrust ($\phi = 0.39$): $+/-2\%$, 1σ
4. Lift curve slope coefficient: $+/-1\%$, 1σ
5. Ramjet fuel weight: $+/-0.9\%$, 1σ
6. Inert weight: $+/-0.8\%$, 1σ

Uncertainty analysis is an aid in planning the development program. As an example, to meet the flight range requirement, based on the above ranking, the development program should give more emphasis to reducing the uncertainty in specific impulse than in reducing the uncertainty in inert weight. The uncertainty in specific impulse has over 6x the impact on flight range than that of inert weight ($+/-5\%$ versus $+/-0.8\%$).

The ramjet baseline missile total flight range uncertainty for the Mach 3.0/60 kft cruise condition is assumed to be the root mean square (RMS) of the contributors

$$\Delta R/R = +/- [(\Delta R/R)_1^2 + (\Delta R/R)_2^2 + (\Delta R/R)_3^2 + (\Delta R/R)_4^2$$
$$+ (\Delta R/R)_5^2 + (\Delta R/R)_6^2]^{1/2}$$
$$= +/- 6.9\%, 1\sigma$$

The ramjet baseline missile cruise flight range with uncertainty in the Fig. 7.25 cruise range is therefore

$$R = 445 \text{ nm} +/-31 \text{ nm}, 1\sigma$$

From above, the prediction gives a 99% confidence (3σ) that the ramjet baseline missile range would exceed 352 nm. However, if the customer requires that the ramjet baseline missile achieve a range of 400 nm with 99% confidence, the missile would not satisfy the requirement. The program manager would have to either develop a missile with a nominal range greater than 445 nm or reduce the uncertainty with more development testing.

Note that because the engine burnout is at 60,000 ft altitude, the missile has additional range available in gliding from the high altitude.

7.7 Ramjet Propulsion/Fuel Alternatives

The second example of ramjet missile sizing is the effect of ramjet propulsion system alternatives and fuel alternatives on the missile flight range. Shown in Fig. 7.27 is a comparison of the baseline liquid fuel ramjet with the propulsion/fuel alternatives of low smoke ducted rocket, high performance ducted rocket, solid fuel ramjet, and slurry fuel ramjet propulsion. The

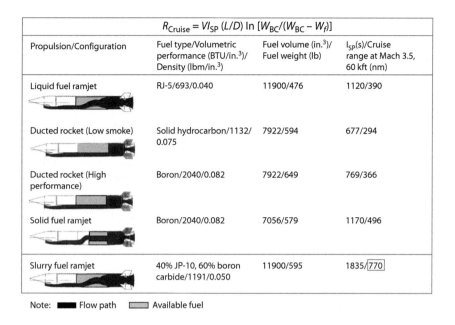

$R_{Cruise} = VI_{SP} (L/D) \ln [W_{BC}/(W_{BC} - W_f)]$			
Propulsion/Configuration	Fuel type/Volumetric performance (BTU/in.³)/ Density (lbm/in.³)	Fuel volume (in.³)/ Fuel weight (lb)	I_{SP}(s)/Cruise range at Mach 3.5, 60 kft (nm)
Liquid fuel ramjet	RJ-5/693/0.040	11900/476	1120/390
Ducted rocket (Low smoke)	Solid hydrocarbon/1132/ 0.075	7922/594	677/294
Ducted rocket (High performance)	Boron/2040/0.082	7922/649	769/366
Solid fuel ramjet	Boron/2040/0.082	7056/579	1170/496
Slurry fuel ramjet	40% JP-10, 60% boron carbide/1191/0.050	11900/595	1835/770

Note: ▮▮ Flow path   ▭ Available fuel

Fig. 7.27 Slurry fuel and efficient packaging provide an extended range ramjet.

assumed cruise condition is Mach 3.5 at an altitude of 60,000 ft. The comparison is conducted for a volume limited missile.

Note that the solid hydrocarbon ducted rocket has 75% of the range of the liquid fuel ramjet (294 versus 390 nm), because of lower specific impulse (667 versus 1120 s) and less available fuel volume (7922 versus 11,900 in.³). Although a solid hydrocarbon ducted rocket has less range than a liquid fuel ramjet, other attributes such as simpler logistics and higher acceleration capability may make it attractive for some missions.

The high performance boron ducted rocket has 94% of the range of the liquid fuel ramjet (366 versus 390 nm). A tradeoff could be made of the simpler logistics and higher acceleration of the ducted rocket versus the lower observables of the liquid fuel ramjet plume.

The solid boron fuel ramjet has 27% longer range than the liquid fuel ramjet (496 versus 390 nm). Although boron fuel has higher volumetric performance and density than liquid hydrocarbon fuel, some of the potential performance benefit is lost in the reduced fuel volume from design integration. As shown in the figure, a grain cavity must be provided for the burn area, reducing the volumetric efficiency of the solid fuel ramjet. The solid fuel boron ramjet has disadvantages of increased plume observables and the lack of a throttle capability compared to the liquid hydrocarbon fuel baseline. A solid fuel boron ramjet is also higher risk.

Finally, the slurry fuel ramjet (40% JP-10, 60% boron carbide) has almost two times the range of the liquid fuel ramjet (770 versus 390 nm). The adverse characteristic of the high observables of the plume of the slurry fuel ramjet must be traded off with the outstanding range performance. Another design consideration is the need for a higher performance fuel pump, because of the highly viscous slurry fuel.

In addition to the benefit of a high density and a high specific impulse fuel, this example illustrates the benefit of packaging efficiency to provide fuel volume. It is important to develop good drawings and packaging in the design process to have confidence in the resulting performance.

7.8 Velocity Control

The last example of ramjet missile sizing is the thrust and fuel flow rate requirements to achieve a high velocity vertical impact on a surface target or a deeply buried target. It illustrates the process of matching thrust and fuel flow rate to the required values for flight performance.

Figure 7.28 illustrates the benefit of ramjet fuel control as a means of velocity control. The previous cruise performance data for the ramjet baseline missile showed that the liquid fuel ramjet has relatively low thrust and fuel flow rate requirements in the efficient cruise at high altitude. For example, the thrust for efficient cruise at Mach 3, 60 kft altitude is $T = 458$ lb. At Mach 3, 60 kft altitude the dynamic pressure q, fuel flow rate $\dot{w}$, and the equivalence ratio φ are 945 psf, 0.46 lb/s, and 0.39 respectively. The liquid fuel ramjet can also provide the higher thrust that is

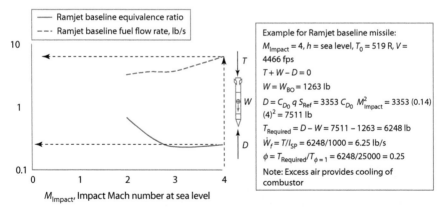

Note: Ramjet baseline missile, vertical impact at sea level, steady state velocity at impact, T = thrust, W = Weight, D = drag, W_{BO} = burnout weight, C_{Do} = zero-lift drag coefficient, M_{Impact} = impact Mach number, $T_{Required}$ = required thrust for steady state flight, $\dot{w}_f$ = fuel flow rate, I_{sp} = specific impulse, ϕ = equivalence ratio (ϕ = 1 stoichiometric)

Fig. 7.28 Example of ramjet velocity control through fuel control.

required for a high impact speed on a hardened surface target or a deeply buried target. As an example, assume an impact Mach number $M_{\text{Impact}} = 4$ at an impact altitude $h = $ sea level ($T_0 = 519$ R). For a vertical impact at constant velocity, the summation of forces is

$$T + W - D = 0$$

The weight of the ramjet baseline missile at burnout is

$$W = W_{\text{BO}} = 1263 \text{ lb}$$

Drag is

$$D = C_{D_0} q S_{\text{Ref}} = C_{D_0}[(1/2)\rho M^2 c^2] S_{\text{Ref}}$$

$$= C_{D_0}[(1/2)(0.002377)M^2(1116)^2](2.264)$$

$$= 3353 C_{D_0} M_{\text{Impact}}^2 = 3353(0.14)(4)^2 = 7511 \text{ lb}$$

Substituting for the required thrust

$$T_{\text{Required}} = D - W = 7511 - 1263 = 6248 \text{ lb}$$

The fuel flow rate is

$$\dot{w}_f = T/I_{\text{SP}} = 6248/1000 = 6.25 \text{ lb/s}$$

Calculating equivalence ratio

$$\phi = T_{\text{Required}}/T_{\phi=1} = 6248/25000 = 0.25$$

The thrust required for a Mach 4 vertical impact on a sea level target is much larger than the thrust required for high altitude cruise. At Mach 4, sea level impact, the dynamic pressure is $q = 23{,}700$ psf, fuel flow rate $\dot{w} = 6.25$ lb/s and $\phi = 0.25$. The fuel-to-air ratio at Mach 4 impact is $f/a = 0.25(0.0667) = 0.0167$. Note that the equivalence ratio is much less than stoichiometric for both the low thrust/high altitude cruise and the high thrust/sea level impact flight conditions. The ramjet baseline missile takes on more air than is nominally required for high efficiency in aerodynamics and propulsion. For the Mach 4 impact condition, the combustor exit temperature using the equation from Chapter 3 is calculated to be

$$T_4 \approx T_0\{1 + [(\gamma - 1)/2]M_0^2\} + (H_f/c_p)(f/a)$$

$$= 519\{1 + [(1.29 - 1)/2]\}(4)^2\} + (17900/0.30)(0.0167)$$

$$= 1723 + 996 = 2719 \text{ R}$$

The excess air has a benefit of cooling the combustor insulation.

Operating the ramjet engine over the broad range of throttle ratio of this example ($\dot{w}_{\text{Mach 4, }h=\text{Sea level}}/\dot{w}_{\text{Mach 3, }h=60\text{ kft}} = 6.25/0.46 = 13.6$) is pushing the state-of-the-art in combustion stability technology and fuel pump technology.

Another concern is the ramjet baseline missile was also designed for a maximum dynamic pressure cruise of Mach 3.0, sea level flight. A heavier structure would likely be required for Mach 4, sea level flight. For example, the titanium alloy inlet was designed for an internal pressure of 200 psi at 1300°F. At Mach 4.0 sea level the dynamic pressure and the turbulent boundary layer recovery temperature are

$$q = 1/2(\rho M^2 a^2) = 1/2(0.002377)(4)^2(1116)^2 = 23700\,\text{psf} = 165\,\text{psi}$$

$$T_r = T_0(1 + 0.2rM^2) = (519)\left[1 + 0.2(0.9)(4)^2\right] = 2014\,\text{R} = 1554°\text{F}$$

7.9 Turbojet Baseline Thrust Prediction

Five sizing examples were selected to illustrate the prediction of the turbojet missile conceptual design sizing. The sizing examples are:

1. Turbojet baseline thrust prediction
2. Turbojet baseline specific impulse prediction
3. Turbojet baseline missile low altitude range prediction
4. Turbojet baseline missile maximum range prediction
5. Turbojet baseline engine rotational speed

The first sizing example is prediction of the turbojet baseline missile thrust and comparison with data.

The turbojet baseline missile used for this analysis is based on the Ref. 19 circa 1982 data for the Harpoon missile. Harpoon is a short-to-medium range anti-ship cruise missile that has multiple launch platforms. For ship, submarine, and ground launch platforms, Harpoon is enclosed in canisters with its folded surfaces. A drop-off booster stage boosts the missile to a take-over Mach number, for efficient flight control and turbojet thrust. The booster provides about 12,000 lb thrust for approximately 2.9 s. The submarine launched Harpoon is enclosed in a buoyant canister. The encapsulated Harpoon is first ejected from its torpedo tube and glides to the surface. After reaching the surface, the missile is separated from the canister and its booster is ignited. The air launched Harpoon does not require a booster, canister, or folded surfaces.

Figure 7.29 has example photographs of Harpoon applications for ship, submarine, aircraft, and ground vehicle launch platforms. In the bottom right portion of the figure is a video of Harpoon. The video shows missile

Ship launch   Submarine launch   Aircraft launch

Ground vehicle launch   Video of Harpoon anti-ship missile

Fig. 7.29 The turbojet baseline missile has ship, submarine, aircraft, and ground vehicle launch platforms.

assembly, seeker test, and launches from ship, submarine, aircraft, and ground vehicle platforms.

The turbojet baseline missile aerodynamic configuration is shown in Fig. 7.30 from Ref. 19. It has a cylindrical body, with a diameter of 13.5 in and a length of 151.5 in, for compatibility with a torpedo tube launch. The nose is a tangent ogive shape with a fineness ratio of 0.86. Four wing panels and four in-line fin control surfaces are in a cruciform arrangement. They are folded for ship, submarine, and ground vehicle launch platform carriage and are deployed after launch. The inlet is flush with the bottom surface of the body. The turbojet baseline missile uses bank-to-turn maneuvering, to maintain low sideslip. Low sideslip is necessary to maintain the inlet capture efficiency and total pressure efficiency.

Table 7.8 from Ref. 19 is a weight and balance statement of the turbojet baseline missile. It does not include the booster weight (required for surface launch missions but not required for air launch missions). Note that the weight of fuel (108.5 lb) is about 10% of the total missile weight. The weight and center-of-gravity (cg) at the beginning of cruise are 1165.0 lb and 77.4 in (distance from nose tip) respectively. The weight and cg at the end of cruise are 1056.5 lb and 75.4 in respectively. Because the turbojet baseline missile has only a small cg travel and operates at subsonic Mach number with a relatively low angle of attack, the stability and control variations are relatively mild.

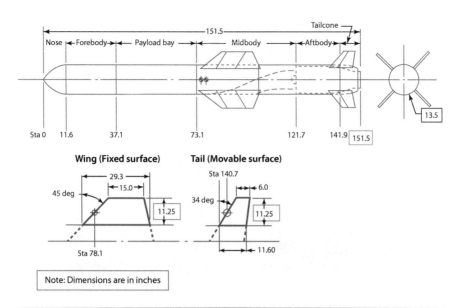

Note: Dimensions are in inches

Fig. 7.30   Drawing of the turbojet baseline missile configuration. (Source: Bithell, R. A. and Stoner, R. C. "Rapid Approach for Missile Synthesis", Vol. II, Air-breathing Synthesis Handbook, AFWAL TR 81-3022, Vol. II, March 1982.)

Table 7.9 from Ref. 19 provides the geometric characteristics of the turbojet baseline missile. The low aspect ratio ($A = 1.02$) cruciform wings are relatively small in area, with an exposed planform area of 3.46 ft^2. The missile body has a much larger wetted area than the wings (43.45 versus 13.84 ft^2). Most of the contribution to the missile skin friction and the zero-lift drag coefficient comes from the body. Exposed tail span and aspect ratio are 22.50 in and 2.56 respectively. The reference area is the body cross section area (0.994 ft^2). The reference length is the body diameter (1.125 ft).

Figure 7.31 from Ref. 19 provides axial force, normal force, pitching moment, and control effectiveness coefficients as functions of Mach number and angle of attack. The reference area, length, and center-of-gravity location are 0.994 ft^2 (body cross-sectional area), 1.125 ft (body diameter), and 73.9 in respectively.

Figure 7.31a shows the axial and normal force coefficients for an undeflected control surface ($\delta = 0$ deg). The axial force coefficient at low angle of attack is approximately equal to the zero-lift drag coefficient. Note that maximum axial force coefficient occurs near Mach 1. Also note from the figure that the normal force coefficient has a small variation with Mach number and a nearly linear variation with angle of attack.

Figure 7.31b shows the pitching moment C_m versus angle of attack and Mach number for undeflected ($\delta = 0$ deg) control surfaces. The figure is based on an assumed center-of-gravity location $x_{cg} = 73.9$ in from the nose. Note that the turbojet baseline missile has its least static stability at $\alpha = 0$ deg.

Figure 7.31c shows the turbojet baseline missile aerodynamic control effectiveness. The change in the pitching moment coefficient with control surface deflection (C_{m_δ}) and the change in the normal force coefficient with control surface deflection (C_{N_δ}) are shown as a function of Mach number. The figure is applicable to low angle of attack. Note that C_{m_δ} is largest at a Mach number near $M \sim 1$ and C_{N_δ} is smallest at $M \sim 1$.

Finally, Figure 7.31d provides the aerodynamic efficiency lift-to-drag ratio (L/D) of the turbojet baseline missile as a function of Mach number and angle of attack. It is based on the data of Ref. 19. As before, the reference area is the body cross sectional area $S_{Ref} = 0.994 \text{ ft}^2$. The reference

Table 7.8 Mass Properties of the Turbojet Baseline Missile.

Component	Weight, lb	CG Sta, in
Nose	4.6	7.7
Forebody Structure	21.5	24.0
Guidance	89.0	22.0
Instrumentation	5.5	34.0
Payload Bay Structure	0.0	-
Warhead	510.0	55.1
Midbody Structure	124.0	97.4
Electrical	49.9	94.2
Fuel Distribution	10.0	104.0
Inlet	15.0	107.0
Aftbody Structure	19.0	131.8
Engine	101.5	136.0
Tailcone Structure	15.0	146.7
Flight Control Actuators	33.8	144.2
Wings (4 Fixed Surfaces)	41.4	89.6
Tails (4 Movable Surfaces)	16.3	145.3
End of Cruise	1056.5	75.4
Fuel	108.5	97.4
Start of Cruise	1165.0	77.4

Source: Bithell, R. A. and Stoner, R. C. "Rapid Approach for Missile Synthesis", Vol. II, Air-breathing Synthesis Handbook, AFWAL TR81-3022, Vol. II, March 1982.

Table 7.9 Turbojet Baseline Missile Geometry Definition.

Body	
Length, in	151.5
Diameter, in	13.5
Fineness ratio	11.2
Volume, ft^3	12.02
Wetted area, ft^2	43.45
Base area, ft^2	0.567
Boattail fineness ratio	0.44
Nose fineness ratio	0.86
Nose bluntness	0.0
Wing (Fixed Surface)	
Planform area (2 panels exposed), ft^2	3.46
Wetted area (4 panels), ft^2	13.84
Aspect ratio (2 panels exposed)	1.02
Taper ratio	0.512
Root chord, in	29.30
Tip chord, in	15.00
Span (2 panels exposed), in	22.50
Leading edge sweep, deg	45.0
Mean aerodynamic chord, in	22.92
Thickness ratio	0.06
x_{mac}, in	78.1
y_{mac}, in	5.02
Tail (Movable Surfaces)	
Planform area (2 panels exposed), ft^2	1.375
Wetted area (4 panels), ft^2	5.50
Aspect ratio (2 panels exposed)	2.56
Taper ratio	0.52
Root chord, in	11.60
Tip chord, in	6.00
Span (2 panels exposed), in	22.50
Leading edge sweep, deg	34.0
Mean aerodynamic chord, in	9.11
Thickness ratio	0.09
x_{mac}, in	140.7
y_{mac} (from root chord), in	5.03
Reference Values	
Reference area, ft^2	0.994
Reference length, ft	1.125

Source: Bithell, R. A. and Stoner, R. C. "Rapid Approach tor Missile Synthesis",
Vol. II, Air-breathing Synthesis Handbook, AFWAL TR 81-3022, Vol. II, March 1982.

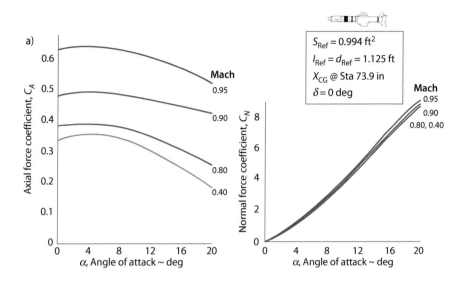

Fig. 7.31a Aerodynamic characteristics of the turbojet baseline missile—axial force and normal force coefficients. (Source: Bithell, R. A. and Stoner, R. C. "Rapid Approach for Missile Synthesis", Vol. II, Air-breathing Synthesis Handbook, AFWAL TR 81-3022, Vol. II, March 1982.)

length is the body diameter $l_{Ref} = d_{Ref} = 1.125$ ft. Note from the figure that maximum L/D occurs at relatively high angle of attack. This is typical for a missile with a relatively small wing.

As an example, assume a flight Mach number $M = 0.8$ and an angle of attack $\alpha = 9.7$ deg. The lift-to-drag ratio $L/D = (L/D)_{max} = 3.65$.

A summary of the turbojet baseline engine (Teledyne J402-CA-400) is given in Fig. 7.32. It is based on the data of Ref. 39. As shown in the drawing, the engine width and length are 12.52 in and 29.44 in respectively. The missile applications of this engine include the AGM-84A and RGM-84 Harpoon and the AGM-84E SLAM and AGM-84H SLAM-ER.

Engine components are:

1. Two-stage, axial–centrifugal compressor ($d_{Entrance} = 8.4$ in, $p_3/p_2 = 5.4$)
2. Annular combustor ($T_4 = 1800$ R maximum combustion temperature)
3. Single stage axial flow turbine
4. Convergent nozzle ($T_{exit} = 1090$ R, $d_{exit} = 8.4$ in)

Other characteristics of the engine are:

1. Weight: 101.5 lb
2. Low parts count because of extensive use of castings
3. Shelf life: 20 years

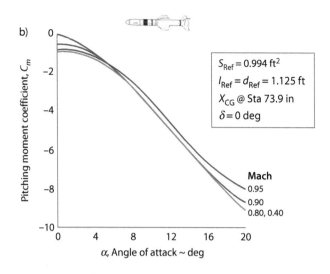

Fig. 7.31b   Aerodynamic characteristics of the turbojet baseline missile—pitching moment coefficient. (Source: Bithell, R. A. and Stoner, R. C. "Rapid Approach for Missile Synthesis", Vol. II, Air-breathing Synthesis Handbook, AFWAL TR 81-3022, Vol. II, March 1982.)

4. Reliability: 99%
5. Maximum rotational speed: 41,200 rpm
6. Fuel: JP-4, JP-5, JP-8, JP-10

Figure 7.33 from Ref. 39 provides performance data of thrust versus engine rotational speed and flight Mach number for the J402-CA-400

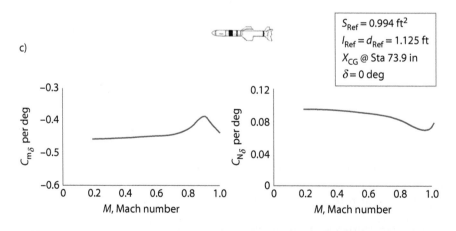

Fig. 7.31c   Aerodynamic characteristics of the turbojet baseline missile—pitching moment and normal force control effectiveness. (Source: Bithell, R. A. and Stoner, R. C. "Rapid Approach for Missile Synthesis", Vol. II, Air-breathing Synthesis Handbook, AFWAL TR 81-3022, Vol. II, March 1982.)

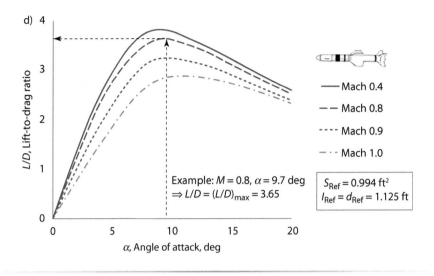

d)

Fig. 7.31d Aerodynamic characteristics of the turbojet baseline missile—lift-to-drag ratio. (Source: Bithell, R. A. and Stoner, R. C. "Rapid Approach for Missile Synthesis", Vol. II, Air-breathing Synthesis Handbook, AFWAL TR 81-3022, Vol. II, March 1982.)

turbojet baseline engine. Also shown are the specific fuel consumption (sfc) and the weight flow rate of air (w_a). Note that the maximum flight Mach number is $M = 1.0$. Maximum altitude is $h = 40$ kft. The maximum thrust for Mach 1.0 at sea level with 100% rpm engine speed is $T = 710$ lb. Note that the maximum thrust decreases with altitude. For example, maximum thrust at Mach 1.0, $h = 40$ kft altitude with 100% rpm engine speed is $T = 215$ lb.

The turbojet baseline missile flight range performance is shown in Fig. 7.34 from Ref. 19. Item ① denotes the sea level cruise maximum range performance (83 nm at Mach 0.7). Item ② denotes the $h = 5000$ ft altitude cruise maximum range performance (92 nm at Mach 0.75). Item ③ denotes the $h = 10$ kft altitude cruise maximum range performance (99 nm at Mach 0.8). Note that the best range is at higher altitude. At higher altitude the turbojet baseline missile has a higher value of aerodynamic efficiency L/D.

The turbojet baseline missile range sensitivity to weight, aerodynamics, and propulsion are shown in Fig. 7.35, based on data from Ref. 19. Note that the flight range is most sensitive to fuel weight, specific impulse, and zero-lift drag coefficient. These parameters should be given emphasis in the turbojet missile design study tradeoffs and optimization.

As an example, assume sea level cruise at an optimum Mach number $M = 0.7$. For this case, a 10% increase in fuel weight provides a 6.7% increase in flight range. Because the turbojet baseline missile is volume

- Applications
  - AGM-84A and RGM-84 Harpoon
  - AGM-84E SLAM and AGM-84H SLAM-ER
- Components
  - 2-Stage, axial – centrifugal compressor ($d_{Entrance}$ = 8.4 in, p_3/p_2 = 5.4)
  - Annular combustor (T_4 = 1800 R)
  - Single stage axial flow turbine
  - Convergent nozzle (T_{Exit} = 1090 R, d_{Exit} = 8.4 in)
- Other
  - Weight: 101.5 lb
  - Low parts count (castings)
  - Shelf life: 20 years
  - Reliability: 99%
  - Maximum rotational speed: 41,200 rpm
  - Fuel: JP-4, JP-5, JP-8, JP-10

Width: 12.52 in   Length: 29.44 in

Fig. 7.32 Turbojet baseline engine data—Teledyne J402-CA-400. (Source: Teledyne Turbine Engines Brochure, "Model 370, J402-CA-400 Performance", 2006.)

limited, with diameter and length constraints, emphasis of developing low volume/light weight subsystems has payoff in allowing more volume/weight available for fuel, allowing longer range.

Note from the figure that a 10% increase in the lift curve slope coefficient C_{L_α} for flight at sea level, Mach 0.7 would increase the range by about 3%. However, the opposite is true for flight at 5 kft, Mach 0.75 and 10 kft, Mach 0.8. This indicates that the baseline wing is a near-optimum size.

The ideal thrust (isentropic inlet, compressor, turbine, and nozzle; low subsonic flow through the inlet exit; low subsonic, constant pressure combustion; exit pressure = free stream pressure) is predicted using Ashley [14]. Ideal thrust is then corrected to account for the non-ideal effects such as total pressure loss, inlet capture efficiency, and imperfect gas ($\gamma < 1.4$). This example predicts the turbojet baseline maximum thrust at Mach 0.8, sea level. The three-step process is as follows:

1. Assume the turbojet baseline Teledyne J402-CA-400 engine and inlet, using data from Ref. 19, 14, 39, and 40:

$$T_4 = (T_4)_{max} = 1800\,\text{R}$$
$$p_3/p_2 = 5.4$$
$$M = 0.8$$

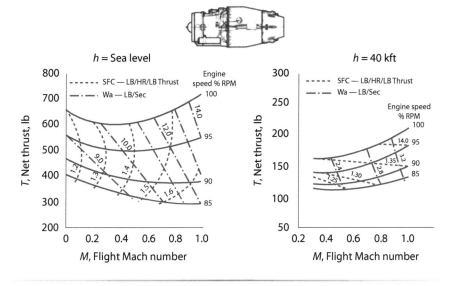

Fig. 7.33 Turbojet baseline engine performance—Teledyne J402-CA-400. (Source: Teledyne Turbine Engines Brochure, "*Model 370, J402-CA-400 Performance,*" 2006.)

h = sea level ($T_0 = 519\,\text{R}$, $p_0 = 2116\,\text{psf}$, $a_0 = 1116\,\text{ft/s}$)
Flush inlet
Cruise with $A_c = A_0 = 0.287\,\text{ft}^2$

2. Calculate the ideal thrust.

   Figure 7.36 and the equation below, based on Ashley [14], show that the turbojet baseline thrust is driven by the turbine temperature, compressor pressure ratio, inlet area, Mach number, and altitude. Note from the figure the increase in thrust with increasing turbine entrance temperature and free stream subsonic Mach number. The ideal thrust equation [14] is

   $$T_{\text{Ideal}}/(p_0 A_0) = \gamma_0 M_0^2 \{\{1 + \{2/[(\gamma_0 - 1)M_0^2]\}\}[(p_3/p_2)^{(\gamma_0 - 1)/\gamma_0} - 1]$$
   $$\times \{(T_4/T_0)/\{[(p_3/p_2)^{(\gamma_0 - 1)/\gamma_0}]$$
   $$\times \{[1 + (\gamma_0 - 1)/2]M_0^2\}\} - 1\}$$
   $$+ \{(T_4/T_0)/\{[(p_3/p_2)^{(\gamma_0 - 1)/\gamma_0}]$$
   $$\times \{[1 + (\gamma_0 - 1)/2]M_0^2\}\}^{1/2} - 1\}$$

   Again, assumptions are an ideal turbojet with perfect gas ($\gamma = \gamma_0 = 1.4$).

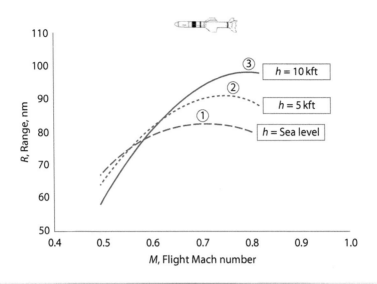

Fig. 7.34 Turbojet baseline missile cruise performance. (Source: Bithell, R. A. and Stoner, R. C. "Rapid Approach for Missile Synthesis", Vol. II, Air-breathing Synthesis Handbook, AFWAL TR 81-3022, Vol. II, March 1982.)

Symbols are:

T_4 = Turbine entrance temperature
T_0 = Free stream temperature
p_0 = Free stream pressure
A_0 = Inlet free stream flow area
γ_0 = Free stream ratio of specific heat = 1.4
M_0 = Free stream Mach number
p_3 = Compressor exit pressure
p_2 = Compressor entrance pressure

As an example for the turbojet baseline engine (Teledyne J402-CA-400) and inlet of Ref. 19, 39, and 40 ($p_3/p_2 = 5.4$, $A_0 \approx A_c = 0.287$ ft^2), assume: $T_4 = (T_4)_{\max} = 1800$ R, $h =$ sea level ($p_0 = 2116$ psf, $T_0 = 519$ R) $\Rightarrow T_4/T_0 = 3.47$, $M_0 = 0.8$.
Then

$$T_{\text{Ideal}}/p_0 = 0.287(1.4)(0.8)^2\{\{1+\{2/[(1.4-1)(0.8)^2]\}\}[(5.4)^{(1.4-1)/1.4}-1]$$

$$\times \{3.47/\{[(5.4)^{(1.4-1)/1.4}]\{[1+(1.4-1)/2](0.8)^2\}\}-1\}$$

$$+\{3.47/\{[(5.4)^{(1.4-1)/1.4}]\{[1+(1.4-1)/2](0.8)^2\}\}\}^{1/2}-1\}$$

$$=0.414\,\text{ft}^2$$

Finally, the turbojet baseline ideal thrust is

$$T_{\text{Ideal}} = 0.414(2116) = 875\,\text{lb}$$

3. Calculate predicted non-ideal thrust. Based on the propulsion system assumed typical total pressure and inlet capture efficiency of Chapter 3, predicted thrust is

- $T_{\text{Predicted}} = \eta(A_0/A_c)T_{\text{Ideal}}$
- $\eta = \eta_{\text{Inlet}}\,\eta_{\text{Compressor}}\,\eta_{\text{Combustor}}\,\eta_{\text{Turbine}}\,\eta_{\text{Nozzle}}$

  $= 0.91(0.90)(0.95)(0.90)(0.99) = 0.69$
- $(A_0/A_c) = 1$
- $T_{\text{Predicted}} = 0.69(1)(875) = 607\,\text{lb}$

Based on the Fig. 7.33 data from Ref. 39, the actual thrust is 650 lb. The actual thrust (650 lb) is 7% greater than the predicted thrust (607 lb).

7.10 Turbojet Baseline Specific Impulse Prediction

The second turbojet sizing example is prediction of the turbojet baseline specific impulse, with comparison to data. The process for this example is similar to that of the previous example. The ideal specific impulse of Ashley [14] will be corrected to account for non-ideal effects such as the total pressure loss and a calorically imperfect gas ($\gamma < 1.4$). This example

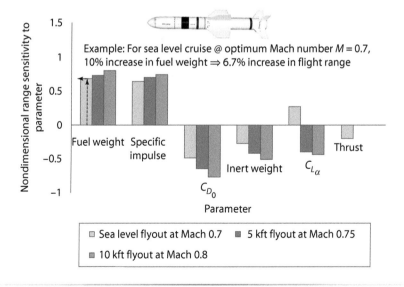

Fig. 7.35 From a Pareto sensitivity, the turbojet baseline missile range is driven by specific impulse, fuel weight, and zero-lift drag coefficient.

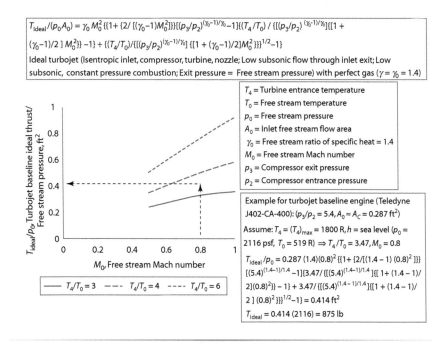

$T_{ideal}/(p_0A_0) = \gamma_0 M_0^2 \{1+ \{2/ [(\gamma_0-1)M_0^2]\}[(p_3/p_2)^{(\gamma_0-1)/\gamma_0}-1]\{(T_4/T_0) / \{[(p_3/p_2)^{(\gamma_0-1)/\gamma_0}]\{[1 +$

$(\gamma_0-1)/2] M_0^2\} -1\} + \{(T_4/T_0)/\{[(p_3/p_2)^{(\gamma_0-1)/\gamma_0}] \{1 + (\gamma_0-1)/2]M_0^2\}\}^{1/2}-1\}$

Ideal turbojet (Isentropic inlet, compressor, turbine, nozzle; Low subsonic flow through inlet exit; Low subsonic, constant pressure combustion; Exit pressure = Free stream pressure) with perfect gas ($\gamma = \gamma_0 = 1.4$)

T_4 = Turbine entrance temperature
T_0 = Free stream temperature
p_0 = Free stream pressure
A_0 = Inlet free stream flow area
γ_0 = Free stream ratio of specific heat = 1.4
M_0 = Free stream Mach number
p_3 = Compressor exit pressure
p_2 = Compressor entrance pressure

Example for turbojet baseline engine (Teledyne J402-CA-400): ($p_3/p_2 = 5.4, A_0 \approx A_c = 0.287 \text{ ft}^2$)

Assume: $T_4 = (T_4)_{max} = 1800$ R, h = sea level ($p_0 = 2116$ psf, $T_0 = 519$ R) $\Rightarrow T_4/T_0 = 3.47, M_0 = 0.8$

$T_{ideal}/p_0 = 0.287 (1.4)(0.8)^2 \{1+ \{2/[(1.4 - 1) (0.8)^2]\}$

$[(5.4)^{(1.4-1)/1.4} -1]\{3.47/\{[(5.4)^{(1.4-1)/1.4}]\{[1+ (1.4 - 1)/$

$2](0.8)^2\} - 1\} + 3.47/ \{[(5.4)^{(1.4-1)/1.4}]\{[1 + (1.4 - 1)/$

$2] (0.8)^2\}\}^{1/2}-1\} = 0.414 \text{ ft}^2$

$T_{ideal} = 0.414 (2116) = 875$ lb

Fig. 7.36 Turbojet thrust is driven by turbine temperature, compressor pressure ratio, inlet area, Mach number, and altitude. (Reference: Ashley, H., *Engineering Analysis of Flight Vehicles*, 1974).

predicts the specific impulse at Mach 0.8, sea level. The three-step process is as follows:

1. Assume the turbojet baseline Teledyne J402-CA-400 engine and inlet with

    $T_4 = (T_4)_{max} = 1800 \text{ R}$

    JP-10 Fuel$(H_f = 18{,}700 \text{ BTU/lbm})$

    $p_3/p_2 = 5.4$

    $M = 0.8$

    h = sea level $(T_0 = 519 \text{ R}, p_0 = 2116 \text{ psf}, a_0 = 1116 \text{ ft/s})$

    Flush inlet

    Cruise at $A_c = A_0 = 0.287 \text{ ft}^2$

2. Calculate the ideal I_{SP}.

    The Ref. 14 equation for ideal I_{SP} is

    $$[gc_pT_0/(a_0H_f)](I_{SP})_{Ideal}O = T/(p_0A_0)/\{\gamma_0M_0[(T_4/T_0)$$

    $$- (p_3/p_2)^{(\gamma_0-1)/\gamma_0}]\}$$

Assumptions are an ideal turbojet with perfect gas ($\gamma = \gamma_0 = 1.4$).

Symbols are g = acceleration of gravity = 32.2 ft/s², c_p = specific heat at constant pressure, a_0 = free stream speed of sound, H_f = heating value of fuel, $(I_{SP})_{ideal}$ = ideal specific impulse, T = thrust, T_4 = turbine entrance temperature, T_0 = free stream temperature, p_0 = free stream pressure, A_0 = inlet free stream flow area, γ_0 = free stream ratio of specific heat = 1.4, M_0 = free stream Mach number, p_3 = compressor exit pressure, p_2 = compressor entrance pressure.

Figure 7.37 shows the turbojet baseline non-dimensional specific impulse $[gc_pT_0/(a_0H_f)]$ $(I_{SP})_{ideal}$ as a function of free stream Mach number and turbine entrance temperature. Note that the highest specific impulse is at low Mach number and low values of turbine entrance temperature. However, a low turbine entrance temperature is not a practical design consideration because high temperature combustion is necessary to satisfy the missile thrust requirement.

As an example for the turbojet baseline engine (Teledyne J402-CA-400) and inlet of Ref. 19, 39, and 40: ($p_3/p_2 = 5.4, A_c = A_0 = 0.287$ ft²), H_f = 18700 BTU/lb(JP-10), c_p = 0.276 BTU/lb/R, $T_4 = (T_4)_{max}$ = 1800 R, h = sea level(p_0 = 2116 psf, a_0 = 1116 ft/s, T_0 = 519 R) $\Rightarrow T_4/T_0 = 3.47$ and $M_0 = 0.8$.

From the prior example, $T_{Ideal}/p_0 = 0.414$ ft².

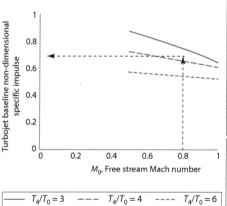

Fig. 7.37 The turbojet baseline specific impulse decreases with Mach number. (Reference: Ashley, H., *Engineering Analysis of Flight Vehicles*, 1974).

Calculate:

$$[gc_pT_0/(a_0H_f)](I_{SP})_{Ideal} = 0.414/\{0.287(1.4)(0.8)$$

$$\times [3.47 - (5.4)^{(1.4-1)/1.4}]\} = 0.696$$

Ideal specific impulse of the turbojet baseline is

$$(I_{SP})_{Ideal} = 0.696/\{32.2(0.276)(519)/[1116(18700)]\}$$
$$= 0.696/0.000221 = 3149 \text{ s}$$

3. Compute non-ideal specific impulse.

Based on the typical propulsion system total pressure efficiency of Chapter 3, predicted specific impulse is

- $(I_{SP})_{Predicted} = \eta(I_{SP})_{Ideal}$
- $\eta = \eta_{Inlet}\eta_{Compressor}\eta_{Combustor}\eta_{Turbine}\eta_{Nozzle}$

$$= 0.91(0.90)(0.95)(0.90)(0.99) = 0.69$$

- $(I_{SP})_{Predicted} = 0.69(3149) = 2173 \text{ s}$

From the Fig. 7.33 specific fuel consumption sfc data of Ref. 39, the actual specific impulse is

$$(I_{SP})_{Actual} = \text{sfc}^{-1} = (1.51 \text{ lbm fuel/h/lbf thrust})^{-1}(3600 \text{ s/h}) = 2384 \text{ s}.$$

The actual specific impulse (2384 s) is 9.7% higher than the predicted specific impulse (2173 s).

7.11 Turbojet Baseline Missile Low Altitude Range Prediction

The third turbojet sizing example is a prediction of the turbojet baseline missile low altitude range, with comparison to data. The process is as follows:

1. Assume a cruise altitude and Mach number, such as sea level ($T_0 = 519$ R, $p_0 = 2116$ psf, $a_0 = 1116$ ft/s, $\rho_0 = 0.002377$ slug/ft^3) and $M = 0.8 \Rightarrow V_0 = Ma_0 = 0.8(1116) = 893$ ft/s

2. Assume an average missile weight based on the Table 7.8 (Ref. 19) beginning of cruise weight W_{BC} and the end of cruise weight W_{EC}

$$W = (W_{BC} + W_{EC})/2 = (1165.0 + 1056.5)/2 = 1110.8 \text{ lb}$$

3. Calculate the required lift coefficient C_L for cruise

During cruise, lift ≈ weight, thrust ≈ drag
Then for $L = C_L q S_{Ref} = W = 1110.8$ lb

Calculate $q = (1/2)\rho_0 V_0^2 = (1/2)(0.002377)(893)^2 = 947$ psf
Since $S_{Ref} = 0.994$ ft$^2 \Rightarrow C_L = 1110.8/[947(0.994)] = 1.18$

4. Next, calculate α, C_D, and L/D for $C_L = 1.18$, $M = 0.8$

Figure 7.38 shows the turbojet baseline missile lift and drag coefficients at Mach 0.8 with the control surface deflection $\delta = 0$ deg. The
figure is based on the data of Ref. 19. The assumption $\delta \approx 0$ deg is
usually appropriate accuracy for conceptual design analysis of a
missile at a relatively low angle of attack with a relatively low static
margin. Reference area is $S_{Ref} = 0.994$ ft^2 and reference length is
$l_{Ref} = d_{Ref} = 1.125$ ft.

From the figure, for the low altitude cruise condition of $C_L = 1.18$,
then $\alpha = 4.3$ deg and $C_D = 0.49$. Note that the turbojet baseline
missile at Mach 0.8, sea level cruise is at a relatively low angle of attack.

Figure 7.39, based on Ref. 19, shows the turbojet baseline missile
lift-to-drag ratio (L/D) as a function of Mach number and angle of
attack. Note that L/D is higher for low Mach number. For the low altitude cruise condition of Mach 0.8, $\delta \approx 0$ deg, $\alpha = 4.3$ deg $\Rightarrow L/
D = 2.42$. The L/D in low altitude Mach 0.8 cruise is 66% of $(L/D)_{max}$
(2.42 versus 3.65).

5. Next, calculate the drag and the required thrust for cruise

$$D = C_D q S_{Ref} = 0.49(947)(0.994) = 461 \text{ lb}$$

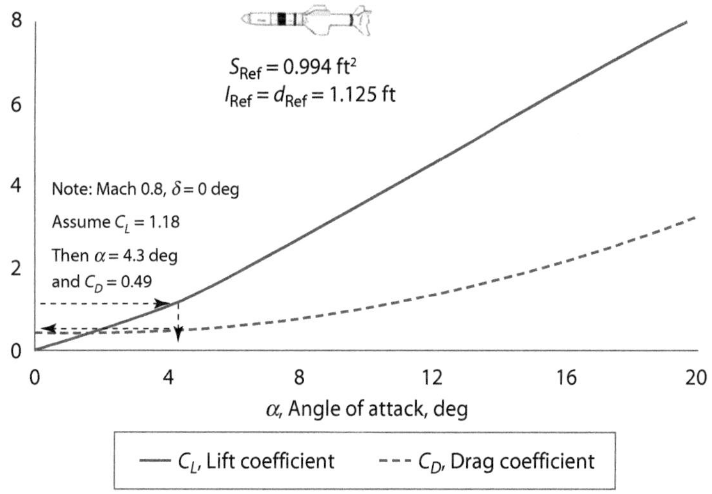

Fig. 7.38 The turbojet baseline missile at Mach 0.8, sea level cruise is at low
angle of attack ($\alpha = 4.3$ deg). (Source: Bithell, R. A. and Stoner, R. C., "Rapid
Approach for Missile Synthesis", Vol. II, Air-breathing Synthesis Handbook, AFWAL
TR 81-3022, Vol. II, March 1982.)

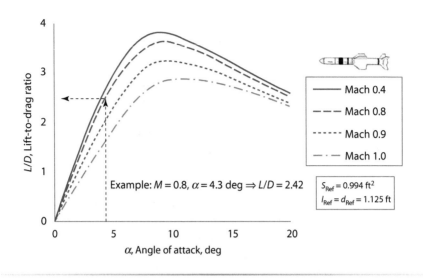

Fig. 7.39 The turbojet baseline missile cruise at Mach 0.8, sea level has a relatively low lift-to-drag ratio. (Source: Bithell, R. A. and Stoner, R. C. "Rapid Approach for Missile Synthesis", Vol. II, Air-breathing Synthesis Handbook, AFWAL TR 81-3022, Vol. II, March 1982.)

From the turbojet baseline engine data of Fig. 7.33 (Ref. 39), $T_{\text{Available}} = 650$ lb at sea level with the engine speed at 100% rpm ($T_4 = (T_4)_{\text{max}} = 1800$ R)

Therefore, there is sufficient thrust available for this example. Also $T_4 < 1800$ R. Next, search for the value of T_4 that satisfies $T_{\text{Available}} = D = 461$ lb

6. Calculate the ideal thrust for an assumed value of T_4 (e.g., $T_4 = 1470$ R)

Figure 7.40 shows the turbojet baseline ideal thrust for the assumed $T_4 = 1470$ R. Again, it is based on the equation from Ashley [14]

$$T_{\text{ideal}}/(p_0 A_0) = \gamma_0 M_0^2 \{\{1 + \{2/[(\gamma_0 - 1)M_0^2]\}\}$$
$$\times [(p_3/p_2)^{(\gamma_0 - 1)/\gamma_0} - 1]\{(T_4/T_0)/\{[(p_3/p_2)^{(\gamma_0 - 1)/\gamma_0}]$$
$$\times \{[1 + (\gamma_0 - 1)/2]M_0^2\}\} - 1\}$$
$$+ \{(T_4/T_0)/\{[(p_3/p_2)^{(\gamma_0 - 1)/\gamma_0}]$$
$$\times \{[1 + (\gamma_0 - 1)/2]M_0^2\}\}^{1/2} - 1\}$$

For this example of the turbojet baseline engine (Teledyne J402-CA-400) and inlet ($p_3/p_2 = 5.4$, $A_0 \approx A_c = 0.287$ ft^2) in the low altitude cruise condition:

Assume $T_4 = 1470$ R, $h = $ sea level ($p_0 = 2116$ psf, $T_0 = 519$ R) $\Rightarrow$ $T_4/T_0 = 2.83$, $M_0 = 0.8$. Then

$$T_{\text{Ideal}}/p_0 = 0.287(1.4)(0.8)^2\{\{1 + \{2/[(1.4-1)(0.8)^2]\}\}$$

$$\times [(5.4)^{(1.4-1)/1.4} - 1]\{2.83/\{[(5.4)^{(1.4-1)/1.4}]$$

$$\times \{[1 + (1.4-1)/2](0.8)^2\}\} - 1\}$$

$$+ \{2.83/\{[(5.4)^{(1.4-1)/1.4}]\{[1 + (1.4-1)/2](0.8)^2\}\}\}^{1/2} - 1\}$$

$$= 0.292 \text{ ft}^2$$

Ideal thrust is $T_{\text{Ideal}} = 0.292(2116) = 618$ lb

Note from the figure that for this example the turbojet baseline has relatively low thrust, because of its relatively low combustion temperature (1470 R).

7. Next, substitute the propulsion system assumed typical total pressure efficiency and inlet capture efficiency into the predicted thrust equation $T_{\text{Predicted}} = \eta(A_0/A_c)T_{\text{Ideal}}$

$$\eta = 0.69 \quad A_0/A_c = 1 \quad T_{\text{Predicted}} = 0.69(1)(618) = 426 \text{ lb}$$

$T_{\text{Ideal}}/(p_0 A_0) = \gamma_0 M_0{}^2 \{\{1 + \{2/[(\gamma_0 - 1)M_0{}^2]\}\}[(p_3/p_2)^{(\gamma_0-1)/\gamma_0} - 1]\}(T_4/T_0)/\{[(p_3/p_2)^{(\gamma_0-1)/\gamma_0}]\{[1 + (\gamma_0 - 1)/2]M_0{}^2\}\} - 1\} + \{(T_4/T_0)/\{[(p_3/p_2)^{(\gamma_0-1)/\gamma_0}][1 + (\gamma_0 - 1)/2]M_0{}^2\}\}^{1/2} - 1\}$

Assumptions: Ideal turbojet (isentropic inlet, compressor, turbine, nozzle; low subsonic, constant pressure combustion; exit pressure = free stream pressure) with perfect gas ($\gamma = \gamma_0 = 1.4$)

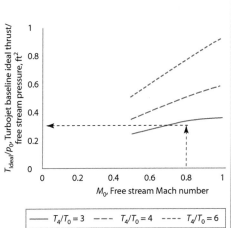

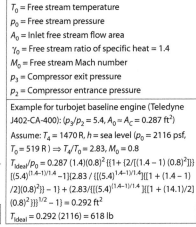

T_4 = Turbine entrance temperature
T_0 = Free stream temperature
p_0 = Free stream pressure
A_0 = Inlet free stream flow area
γ_0 = Free stream ratio of specific heat = 1.4
M_0 = Free stream Mach number
p_3 = Compressor exit pressure
p_2 = Compressor entrance pressure

Example for turbojet baseline engine (Teledyne J402-CA-400): ($p_3/p_2 = 5.4$, $A_0 \approx A_c = 0.287$ ft^2)

Assume: $T_4 = 1470$ R, $h = $ sea level ($p_0 = 2116$ psf, $T_0 = 519$ R) $\Rightarrow T_4/T_0 = 2.83$, $M_0 = 0.8$

$T_{\text{Ideal}}/p_0 = 0.287 (1.4)(0.8)^2 \{\{1 + \{2/[(1.4-1)(0.8)^2]\}\}[(5.4)^{(1.4-1)/1.4} - 1]\{2.83/\{[(5.4)^{1.4-1)/1.4}]\{[1 + (1.4-1)/2](0.8)^2\}\} - 1\} + (2.83/\{[(5.4)^{(1.4-1)/1.4}][1 + (1.4.1)/2](0.8)^2\}\})^{1/2} - 1\} = 0.292$ ft^2

$T_{\text{Ideal}} = 0.292 (2116) = 618$ lb

Fig. 7.40 The turbojet baseline engine at Mach 0.8, sea level cruise has relatively low thrust. (Reference: Ashley, H., Engineering Analysis of Flight Vehicles, 1974).

8. Based on the previous example, assume the thrust correction factor = 1.07. Corrected thrust is

$$T_{\text{Corrected}} = (T_{\text{Actual}}/T_{\text{Predicted}})\,T_{\text{Predicted}} = 1.07(426)$$
$$= 456\,\text{lb} \approx \text{Drag}\,D = 461\,\text{lb}$$

9. Next, calculate the ideal specific impulse.
   Again, from Ashley [14], the non-dimensional ideal specific impulse equation is

$$[gc_p T_0/(a_0 H_f)]\,(I_{\text{SP}})_{\text{Ideal}} = T/(p_0 A_0)/\{\gamma_0 M_0[(T_4/T_0)$$
$$- (p_3/p_2)^{(\gamma_0-1)/\gamma_0}]\}$$

   Repeating, the ideal specific impulse is based on the assumption of an ideal turbojet with perfect gas ($\gamma = \gamma_0 = 1.4$).
   Symbols are: g = acceleration of gravity = 32.2 ft/s², c_p = specific heat at constant pressure, a_0 = free stream speed of sound, H_f = heating value of fuel, $(I_{\text{SP}})_{\text{Ideal}}$ = ideal specific impulse, T = thrust, T_4 = turbine entrance temperature, T_0 = free stream temperature, p_0 = free stream pressure, A_0 = inlet free stream flow area, γ_0 = free stream ratio of specific heat = 1.4, M_0 = free stream Mach number, p_3 = compressor exit pressure, p_2 = compressor entrance pressure
   Figure 7.41 shows the turbojet baseline specific impulse for the assumed T_4 = 1470 R. Again, it is based on the data of Ref. 19, 39, and 40: (p_3/p_2 = 5.4, $A_0 \approx A_c$ = 0.287 ft²).
   For this example calculation at the low altitude cruise condition, assume H_f = 18700 BTU/lb (JP-10), c_p = 0.276 BTU/lb/R, T_4 = 1470 R, h = sea level (p_0 = 2116 psf, a_0 = 1116 ft/s, T_0 = 519 R) $\Rightarrow T_4/T_0$ = 2.83, and M_0 = 0.8. From the prior example, T_{Ideal}/p_0 = 0.292 ft²
   Calculate the non-dimensional ideal specific impulse:

$$[gc_p T_0/(a_0 H_f)]\,[(I_{\text{SP}})_{\text{Ideal}} = 0.292/\{0.287(1.4)(0.8)$$
$$\times [2.83 - (5.4)^{(1.4-1)/1.4}]\} = 0.748$$

   The ideal specific impulse is

$$(I_{\text{SP}})_{\text{Ideal}} = 0.748/\{32.2(0.276)(519)/[1116(18700)]\}$$
$$= 0.748/0.000221 = 3383\,\text{s}$$

10. Next, based on the propulsion system assumed typical total pressure efficiency, the predicted specific impulse is

$$(I_{\text{SP}})_{\text{Predicted}} = \eta(I_{\text{SP}})_{\text{Ideal}}$$

   Where η = 0.69.
   Calculate $(I_{\text{SP}})_{\text{Predicted}}$ = 0.69(3383) = 2334 s.

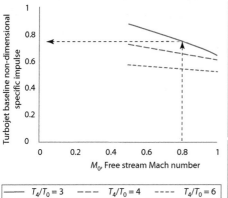

$[g C_p T_0/(a_0 H_f)] (I_{SP})_{Ideal} = [T/(p_0 A_0)]/\{ \gamma_0 M_0[(T_4/T_0) - (p_3/p_2)^{\gamma_0 - 1)/\gamma_0}]\}$

Assumptions: Ideal Turbojet (isentropic inlet, compressor, turbine, nozzle; low subsonic flow through inlet exit; low subsonic, constant pressure combustion; exit pressure = free stream pressure) with perfect gas ($\gamma = \gamma_0 = 1.4$)

Example for turbojet baseline engine (Teledyne J402-CA-400) and inlet: $(p_3/p_2 = 5.4, A_0 \approx A_c = 0.287 \text{ ft}^2)$

Assume: $H_f = 18,700$ BTU/lb (JP-10), $C_p = 0.276$ BTU/lb/R, $T_4 = 1470$ R, h = sea level ($p_0 = 2116$ psf, $a_0 = 1116$ ft/s, $T_0 = 519$ R) $\Rightarrow T_4/T_0 = 2.83, M_0 = 0.8$

From prior example: $T_{Ideal}/p_0 = 0.292 \text{ ft}^2$

Calculate: $[g c_p T_0/(a_0 H_f)](I_{SP})_{Ideal} = 0.292/\{0.287$

$(1.4) (0.8) [2.83 - (5.4)^{(1.4-1)/1.4}]\} = 0.748$

$(I_{SP})_{Ideal} = 0.748/\{32.2 (0.276) (519)/[1116 (18700)]\} = 0.748/0.000221 = 3383$ s

Note: g = acceleration of gravity = 32.2 ft/s², c_p = specific heat at constant pressure, a_0 = free stream speed of sound, H_f = heating value of fuel, $(I_{SP})_{Ideal}$ = ideal specific impulse, T = thrust, T_4 = turbine entrance temperature, T_0 = free stream temperature, p_0 = free stream pressure, A_0 = inlet capture area, γ_0 = free stream ratio of specific heat = 1.4, M_0 = free stream Mach number, p_3 = compressor exit pressure, p_2 = compressor entrance pressure

Fig. 7.41   The turbojet baseline engine at Mach 0.8, sea level cruise has relatively high specific impulse. (Reference: Ashley, H., *Engineering Analysis of Flight Vehicles*, 1974).

11. Solve for (I_{SP}) corrected.

    Based on the previous example, assume a specific impulse correction factor = 1.097. The corrected specific impulse is

$$(I_{SP})_{Corrected} = 1.097 (I_{SP})_{Predicted} = 1.097(2334) = 2561 \text{ s}$$

12. Finally, the Breguet range equation is

$$R = V I_{SP}(L/D)\ln[W_{BC}/(W_{BC} - W_F)]$$

Definitions are

R = cruise range
L/D = lift/drag
W_{BC} = weight at the beginning of cruise
W_F = weight of fuel

Substituting, the turbojet baseline missile predicted range at Mach 0.8, sea level is

$$R = 893(2561)(2.42)\ln[1165/(1165 - 108.5)] = 541,000 \text{ ft} = 89 \text{ nm}$$

Note that the predicted range from the Breguet range equation is 11% higher than the turbojet baseline missile data from Ref. 19 (89 nm versus 80 nm).

7.12 Turbojet Baseline Missile Maximum Range Prediction

The fourth turbojet sizing example is a prediction of the turbojet baseline missile maximum cruise range, which occurs at maximum aerodynamic efficiency $(L/D)_{max}$. A comparison will be made of the prediction against data. This example will use a somewhat different approach from the prior examples of cruise at a specified altitude. The process is as follows:

1. Assume an efficient cruise Mach number (e.g., $M = 0.8$) @ $(L/D)_{max}$
2. Calculate α, C_L, C_D, and $(L/D)_{max}$

   Figure 7.42, based on Ref. 19, shows that for this example of the turbojet baseline at $M = 0.8$: $(L/D)_{max} = 3.65$ and $\alpha_{(L/D)max} = 9.7$ deg. From Fig. 7.43, based on Ref. 19, for Mach 0.8, $\delta = 0$, $\alpha = 9.7$ deg:

$$C_D = 0.96, \; C_L = 3.50$$

3. Next, calculate the lift, dynamic pressure, altitude, velocity, and drag for cruise @ $(L/D)_{max}$.

   During cruise, lift $\approx$ weight, thrust $\approx$ drag. Calculate

$$L = C_L q S_{Ref} = W = 1110.8 \; \Rightarrow \; q = 1110.8/[3.50(0.994)] = 319\,\text{psf}$$

$$q = (1/2)\rho_0 V_0^2 = (1/2)\rho_0 M^2 a_0^2 = (1/2)[\rho_0(0.8)^2 a_0^2] = 0.32\rho_0 a_0^2$$

$$= 319\,\text{psf} \; \Rightarrow \; \rho_0 a_0^2 = 997\,\text{psf}$$

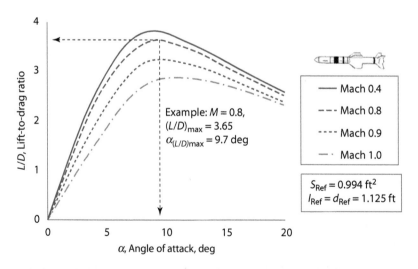

Fig. 7.42 For the turbojet baseline missile at Mach 0.8, $(L/D)_{max}$ occurs at a relatively high angle of attack ($\alpha = 9.7$ deg). (Source: Bithell, R. A. and Stoner, R. C. "Rapid Approach for Missile Synthesis", Vol. II, Air-breathing Synthesis Handbook, AFWAL TR 81-3022, Vol. II, March 1982.)

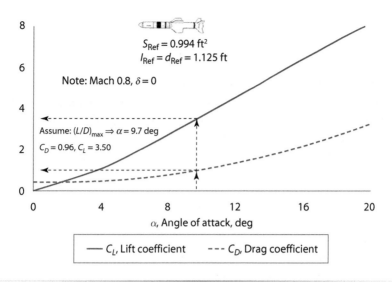

Fig. 7.43   For the turbojet baseline missile at Mach 0.8, $(L/D)_{max}$ is at a relatively high C_L and C_D. (Source: Bithell, R. A. and Stoner, R. C. "Rapid Approach for Missile Synthesis", Vol. II, Air-breathing Synthesis Handbook, AFWAL TR 81-3022, Vol. II, March 1982.)

$$\rho_0 a_0^2 = 997 \text{ psf is satisfied for}$$

$$h = 27 \text{ kft } (\rho_0 = 0.000992 \text{ slug/ft}^3, \ a_0 = 1008 \text{ ft/s}).$$

Next calculate

$$V_0 = Ma_0 = 0.8(1008) = 806 \text{ ft/s}$$
$$D = C_D q S_{Ref} = 0.96(319)(0.994) = 304 \text{ lb}$$

4. Determine if a value of engine speed provides $T = D = 304$ lb at Mach 0.8, $h = 27$ kft altitude.

  Assume 100% engine rpm. From Fig. 7.33 (Ref. 39) of the turbojet baseline engine data

  $T_{Available} = 650$ lb at Mach 0.8, $h =$ sea level, 100% engine rpm ($T_4 = (T_4)_{max} = 1800$ R)

  $T_{Available} = 185$ lb at Mach 0.8, $h = 40$ kft, 100% engine rpm ($T_4 = (T_4)_{max} = 1800$ R)

  Assume that the turbojet engine thrust scales with the pressure altitude p_0.

$$T_{h=27 \text{ kft}} = T_{h=\text{sea level}} + \left\{ (T_{h=40k \text{ ft}} - T_{h=\text{sea level}}) / \right.$$
$$\left. [(p_0)_{h=\text{sea level}} - (p_0)_{h=40 \text{ kft}}] \right\} [(p_0)_{h=\text{sea level}} - (p_0)_{h=27\text{kft}}]$$

Solving for thrust at $h = 27$ kft

$$T_{h=27\text{kft}} = 650 + [(185 - 650)/(2116 - 392)](2116 - 719) = 273\,\text{lb}$$

Because $T_{h=27\text{ kft}} = 273$ lb and $D_{h=27\text{ kft}} = 304$ lb, there is not quite sufficient thrust available at 100% engine rpm to maintain Mach 0.8 cruise at $h = 27$ kft. Another iteration, assuming either a slightly lower cruise Mach number (e.g., $M = 0.75$) or a slightly higher cruise altitude (e.g., $h = 30$ kft) could be conducted to investigate a convergence of thrust = drag. However, the present result is consistent with typical conceptual design accuracy ($\sim 10\%$).

5. Next, determine the specific impulse at maximum available thrust (100% engine rpm, $T_4 = (T_4)_{\max} = 1800$ R) from the Fig. 7.33 (Ref. 39) turbojet baseline data.

Specific fuel consumption sfc = 1.51 lbm fuel/h/lbf thrust at Mach 0.8, $h =$ sea level, 100% engine rpm

Specific fuel consumption sfc = 1.40 lbm fuel/h/lbf thrust at Mach 0.8, $h = 40$ kft, 100% engine rpm

Note that the baseline turbojet sfc is nearly independent of altitude. Assume that sfc scales with pressure altitude p_0.

$$\text{sfc}_{h=27\text{k ft}} = \text{sfc}_{h=\text{sea level}} + \{(\text{sfc}_{h=40\text{k ft}} - \text{sfc}_{h=\text{sea level}})/$$
$$[(p_0)_{h=\text{sea level}} - (p_0)_{h=40\text{k ft}}]\}[(p_0)_{h=\text{sea level}} - (p_0)_{h=27\text{k ft}}]$$

Solving for sfc at $h = 27$ kft

$$\text{sfc}_{h=27\text{kft}} = 1.51 + [(1.40 - 1.51)/(2116 - 392)](2116 - 719)$$
$$= 1.42\,\text{lbm fuel/h/lbf thrust}$$

Compute specific impulse

$$I_{\text{SP}} = (1.42\,\text{lbm fuel/h/lbf thrust})^{-1}(3600\,\text{s/h}) = 2535\,\text{s at Mach 0.8,}$$
$$h = 27\,\text{kft}$$

6. Finally, the Breguet range equation gives

$$R = VI_{\text{SP}}(L/D)\ln[W_{\text{BC}}/(W_{\text{BC}} - W_F)]$$
$$= 806(2535)(3.65)\ln[1165/(1165 - 108.5)] = 729{,}063\,\text{ft} = 120\,\text{nm}$$

So, to achieve maximum range for the turbojet baseline missile at Mach 0.8 cruise requires cruising at an optimum altitude of $h \approx 27$ kft. Cruising at $h \approx 27$ kft provides 35% longer range than cruising at Mach 0.8 at sea level (120 versus 89 nm).

7.13 Turbojet Baseline Engine Rotational Speed

The fifth and last turbojet sizing example for the turbojet baseline missile is a prediction of its engine rotational speed and a comparison with data.

From Ref. 13, the rotational speed of a centrifugal compressor ($N_{\text{Centrifugal}}$) is a function of its impeller tip velocity $u_{\text{Impeller tip}}$ and its diameter d.

$$N_{\text{Centrifugal}} = 60 u_{\text{Impeller tip}}/(\pi d), \text{rpm}$$

The impeller tip velocity is obtained from the local Mach number $M_{\text{impeller tip}}$ and speed of sound $a_{\text{Impeller tip}}$

$$u_{\text{Impeller tip}} = M_{\text{Impeller tip}} a_{\text{Impeller tip}}$$

Because local supersonic flow over the impeller tip will often cause flow separation, a typical design has $M_{\text{Impeller tip}} \approx 1$

The local speed of sound at the impeller tip is obtained from the local temperature

$$a_{\text{Impeller tip}} = (\gamma R T_{\text{Impeller tip}})^{1/2}$$

In the above equation γ = ratio of specific heat $\approx 1.29 + 0.16\, e^{-0.0007 T_{\text{Impeller tip}}}$ and R = gas constant = 1716 ft^2/s^2/R. The impeller tip temperature is given by

$$T_{\text{Impeller tip}} = T_{\text{Diffuser}}/\{1 + [(\gamma - 1)/2] M_{\text{Impeller tip}}^2\}$$

The diffuser temperature $T_{\text{Diffuser}} \approx T_{\text{Exit}} = T_3$ is obtained using an assumption of an isentropic compressor pressure ratio $p_{\text{Exit}}/p_{\text{Entrance}}$.

Figure 7.44 shows the turbojet baseline engine centrifugal compressor rotational speed as a function of free stream Mach number M_0 and altitude h. Assumptions are

$$M_{\text{Impeller tip}} = 0.94$$
$$(p_{\text{Exit}}/p_{\text{Entrance}}) = 3.2$$
$$d = 8.4 \text{ in} = 0.7 \text{ ft}$$

Note from the figure that the engine rotational speed is relatively constant.

As an example, assume $M_0 = 0.8$, h = sea level ($T_0 = 519$ R). Calculate

$$T_{\text{Exit}} \approx 519\{1 + [(1.4 - 1)/2]0.8^2\}(3.2)^{(1.38-1)/1.38} = T_{\text{Diffuser}}$$
$$= 806 \text{ R if } \gamma_{\text{Exit}} = 1.38$$

Check: $\gamma_{\text{Exit}} \approx 1.29 + 0.16\, e^{-0.0007(806)} = 1.38$

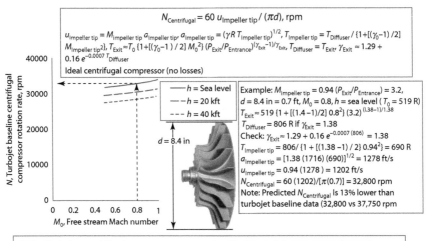

Fig. 7.44 The turbojet baseline centrifugal compressor has nearly constant rotational speed. (Source: Durham, F. P., *Aircraft Jet Powerplants*, Prentice-Hall, 1961.)

Calculate

$$T_{\text{Impeller tip}} = 806/\{1 + [(1.38 - 1)/2]0.94^2\} = 690\,\text{R}$$

$$a_{\text{Impeller tip}} = [1.38(1716)(690)]^{1/2} = 1278\,\text{ft/s}$$

$$u_{\text{Impeller tip}} = 0.94(1278) = 1202\,\text{ft/s}$$

$$N_{\text{Centrifugal}} = 60(1202)/[\pi(0.7)] = 32,800\,\text{rpm}$$

Note that the predicted $N_{\text{Centrifugal}}$ is 13% lower than the turbojet baseline data (32,800 versus 37,750 rpm).

7.14 Examples of Computer-Aided Conceptual Design Sizing Tools

The next sizing examples are computer-aided sizing tools that are suitable for conceptual design and system engineering.

Two fundamental requirements for computer programs used in conceptual design and system engineering are fast turnaround time and ease of use. Fast turnaround is necessary to search a broad solution space with a sufficient number of iterations for design convergence to a harmonized design. A good design code connects the prediction of the missile aeromechanics and physical parameters directly to a trajectory code that calculates flight performance. The conceptual design methods should be simple physics-based methods, incorporating only the most important, driving parameters. A simple physics based-code with only a few, driving parameters allows easier insight into the relationships of the parameters. Pareto analysis shows that the top four most sensitive parameters usually provide greater than 80% of the design drivers. Another advantage of a simple, analytical code is its computation is usually more stable than a detailed design and analysis code. Finally, baseline missile data should be imbedded in the code to facilitate startup.

More detailed computational methods are used later in preliminary design, when the number of alternative geometric, subsystem, and flight parameters has been reduced to a smaller set of possibilities. As an example, it is usually inappropriate to use computational fluid dynamics (CFD) in conceptual design. The mathematical considerations of CFD (e.g., mesh size, time interval, numerical stability, turbulence modeling, smoothing) are impediments to the fast turnaround time that is required for conceptual design. Similarly, a 6-DOF trajectory simulation is inappropriate during conceptual design for the convenient evaluation of guided flight. The development of the required autopilot for 6-DOF guided flight is time consuming, diverting emphasis from other more appropriate considerations for conceptual design and system engineering. Similarly, missile optimization codes are generally not appropriate for conceptual design. First order optimization in conceptual design is usually best left to the creativity and the intuition of the designer. Optimization codes work best when there is a continuous smooth variation in parameters, which is usually not the case in conceptual design. For example, optimization codes do not work well in comparing ramjet propulsion versus rocket propulsion. The CFD, 6-DOF guided flight trajectory simulations, and optimization codes have seductive "precision." However, their accuracy in conceptual design may be worse than simpler methods. Simple aerodynamic, propulsion, weight, and flight trajectory methods, combined with a well defined baseline missile and the designer's creativity and intuition are usually a preferable approach for the initial alternatives selection, sizing, and harmonization. They are usually sufficiently accurate, they are more robust, and they provide better insight into the relationships of the driving parameters for conceptual design and system engineering. References 38, 41, and this text illustrate examples of conceptual design computer-aided sizing methods that are fast and usually have sufficient accuracy for the relative screening of missile concept alternatives. These methods require that the designer, not the computer, make the creative decisions. A computer program, even adaptive programs such as genetic algorithms and swarming algorithms, lacks the creativity to consider a novel concept (e.g., lattice fins, faceted dome). Finally, a non-proprietary code is preferable to a proprietary code for conceptual design. A proprietary code typically has insular and institutional bias that often limits its application to new missile concepts.

The following discussion of the Advanced Design of Aerodynamic Missiles (ADAM) [41] is provided as an example of a non-proprietary computer program that generally meets the conceptual design criteria of fast turnaround, ease of use, and applicable to a broad range of configurations and flight conditions. ADAM is a old DOS code that runs on a personal computer. A disadvantage of ADAM is that it may have compatibility problems with high speed computers. It may require a compatible timing hardware emulation setting, to reduce the rate at which the computer's timer sends timing calls. Another disadvantage is that most young engineers are not familiar with DOS.

The aerodynamics predictions of ADAM are based on References 8 and 9. The aerodynamic methods cover subsonic to hypersonic Mach numbers and angles of attack up to 180 deg. The ADAM aerodynamics module calculates force and moment coefficients, static and dynamic stability derivatives, trim conditions, control effectiveness, and center-of-pressure location.

ADAM modeling of the equations of motion can be in three, four, five, or even six-degrees-of-freedom (it is limited to unguided flight for 6-DOF). The 3-DOF flight trajectory model runs faster than real time. The 6-DOF flight trajectory simulation can be used to analyze the nutation/precession modes of missiles during their unguided portion of flight, as well as unguided bombs and unguided projectiles. It requires longer run time. For homing missiles, proportional guidance can be used as well as other guidance laws. The input to the flight trajectory module is provided automatically by the aerodynamics module, simplifying the user input.

The benchmark missiles used in the aerodynamics module have corrected coefficients and derivatives based on wind tunnel data. Greater than fifty input parameters are available. The input default is the baseline missile parameters, simplifying the input data preparation. The baseline missiles in ADAM include air-to-air (e.g., Archer), surface-to-air (e.g., Patriot), air-to-surface (e.g., Hellfire), and surface-to-surface (e.g., ATACMS) missiles.

The aerodynamic modeling of the body includes the diameter, nose configuration (geometry, fineness, bluntness), body bulge, boattail, and length. The body cross section may be circular or elliptical. Up to three surfaces (stabilizers, wings, and controls) can be specified. The geometric modeling of each surface includes the leading edge root and tip station, span, trailing edge root and tip station, thickness, control surface deflection limit, and the number of surfaces. Modeling includes the Ref. 8 body-surface and surface-surface interactions. The program models the missile center-of-gravity variation from launch to burnout.

For propulsion, the thrust is modeled as a two-value thrust profile, of a given time duration. The propellant weight of each thrust-time phase can also be specified.

The target can be modeled as fixed or moving. Down range and cross range of the target are specified, as well as the target altitude and velocity. Launch conditions for the missile are specified, including altitude, velocity, launch angle, and the guidance law.

The output of the ADAM 3-DOF pitch simulation modeling includes a drawing of the missile geometry with dimensions, aerodynamic coefficients and derivatives, center-of-pressure location, flight performance parameters (velocity, trim angle of attack, acceleration, range, trim control surface deflection) versus time, and missile miss distance.

A second computer technique suitable for conceptual design is spreadsheet analysis. A simple physics-based tool for rapid sizing of missiles is the Tactical Missile Design (TMD) Spreadsheet. It is based on the design methods from the author's previous AIAA textbook *Tactical Missile Design* [42]. Appendix I provides a summary. The TMD Spreadsheet is included on the website in support of this textbook.

Figure 7.45 shows the design parameters of the TMD Spreadsheet. More recent methods and data developed for this textbook have not been incorporated in the spreadsheet. The spreadsheet software is Windows Excel, which has wide availability for personal computers. Recommendations for a future revision of the spreadsheet are given in Appendix I.

Aerodynamics of the missile body is from slender body theory [8] and cross flow theory [9]. The fixed and movable surface aerodynamic predictions are based on linear wing/slender wing theory [8,10] and Newtonian impact theory [9]. The methods are applicable to low aspect ratio wing and wingless configurations at an angle of attack up to 90 deg and Mach number from subsonic to hypersonic.

For a ramjet-powered missile, the propulsion module output includes the inlet total pressure recovery, specific impulse, and thrust [14, 16, 17]. The ramjet thrust and specific impulse predictions include the oblique and normal shock losses in total pressure.

The rocket motor thrust and specific impulse are based on the isentropic flow equations, adjusted for the change in specific heat ratio with temperature. Thrust is modeled as a two-value thrust profile, each with a given time duration. The propellant weight of each thrust time duration can also be specified as an option.

The system and subsystem weight scaling (i.e., density scaling) and material data (e.g., stress-strain versus temperature) in the TMD Spreadsheet weight module are from Ref. 42. Predictions of aerodynamic

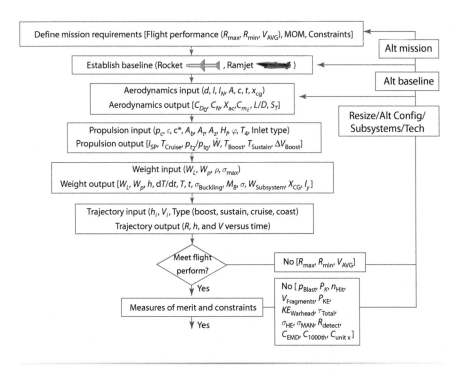

Fig. 7.45 Example of a spreadsheet based conceptual sizing computer code—TMD Spreadsheet.

heating and temperatures from References 4, 16, and 17 are used to evaluate structure and insulation thickness/weight. The body localized buckling stress from bending moment and axial loads, motor case stress, and the required motor case and airframe thickness are based on the methods used in Ref. 42. Reference 42 is also used to predict the weight of the missile dome, power supply, and actuators.

Flight trajectory methods are based on closed-form analytical methods. Cruise range prediction is the Breguet range equation. The thrust required for steady cruise is based on Jerger [5]. Boost velocity, coast velocity, boost range, and coast range are based on Ref. 42.

Warhead blast pressure is based on Ref. 27. Fragment velocity, kill probability, number of warhead fragments impacting the target, kinetic energy warhead penetration, and the penetrator kinetic energy are based on Ref. 29 and Ref. 42. Kinetic energy penetration depth is based on Ref. 30. In the area of guidance, miss distance prediction and parameters (e.g., missile time constant, heading error, maneuvering target acceleration) are based on Ref. 32, Ref. 42, and Ref. 43. Survivability detection range and other design considerations for survivability are based on Ref. 42. Finally, production cost due to weight and the learning curve and EMD cost are based on Ref. 42.

Reference 44 presents a more detailed discussion of the TMD spreadsheet.

Following definition of mission requirements such as range and velocity and selection of a baseline configuration (either rocket or ramjet), the TMD aerodynamics module is exercised. Aerodynamic data input to the aerodynamics module includes the missile diameter d, missile length l, nose length l_N, surfaces aspect ratio A, surfaces chord c, surfaces thickness t, and the missile center-of-gravity x_{cg}. The aerodynamics module then calculates the zero-lift drag coefficient (C_{D_0}), normal force coefficient C_N, aerodynamic center location x_{ac}, pitching moment control effectiveness C_{m_δ}, lift-to-drag ratio L/D, and the required tail stabilizer surface area S_T. Although the TMD spreadsheet can size the tails for neutral stability at a specified Mach number flight condition, it is important to check a number of flight conditions to make sure that the tails provide sufficient stability at the worse case flight condition. The worse case flight condition for stability is often the highest Mach number. However, because the highest Mach number may occur at burnout, with a forward location of the center-of-gravity, it is important to also check the stability at the launch condition, which usually has a more aft location of the cg. It is also necessary to check that the missile has sufficient control effectiveness. The output of the aerodynamics module, along with the default data of the baseline missile, is an input into the propulsion module.

Propulsion data input to the propulsion module for the rocket includes the motor chamber pressure p_c, nozzle expansion ratio ε, characteristic velocity c^*, burn area A_b, and the throat area A_t. For a ramjet engine, the input data also includes the inlet capture area A_0, heating value of the fuel H_f, equivalence ratio ϕ, combustor exit temperature T_4, and the type of inlet. The propulsion module output for a rocket motor includes incremental velocity ΔV, thrust T, and specific impulse I_{SP}.

A weight module is next used to revise the missile weight. Input data includes the initial estimate of missile launch weight W_L, propellant weight W_p, density ρ, and the maximum allowable stress σ_{max} of the structure materials. The weight module provides an estimate of aerodynamic heating, surface and inner wall temperatures, required airframe and motor case thickness, localized buckling stress, bending moment, motor case stress, total weight, center-of-gravity, moment-of-inertia, and the density/weight of subsystems.

The flight trajectory spreadsheet has closed form, analytical equations for one- and two-degrees-of-freedom trajectories. The closed form, analytical equations provide design insight into the driving parameters and usually eliminate computational instabilities, which can be a problem for a more sophisticated time marching numerical integration of the equations of motion. The input includes the initial altitude, initial velocity, and the type of flight profile (e.g., boost, sustain cruise, coast). The output of the flight trajectory spreadsheet includes flight range, altitude, and velocity versus time.

Finally, the designer compares the output of the flight trajectory spreadsheet against the mission flight performance requirements. If the missile design does not meet the performance requirements, the process is repeated until the requirements are satisfied. The modularity of the spreadsheet and the default baseline missile data reduce the time required for data input in the next iteration.

Once flight performance requirements are met, the other measures of merit (e.g., lethality, miss distance, survivability, cost) and launch platform constraints are evaluated. For example, the warhead lethality parameters include the blast pressure and kinetic energy penetration. Miss distance parameters include the missile time constant and the miss distances from heading error and a maneuvering target. EMD cost, production cost of the 1000th missile, and the unit production cost of other missile quantities (based on the year 1999) are provided. Again, the design is manually iterated until the measures of merit and constraints are satisfied.

The verification process of a computer sizing code includes debugging the source code, comparing the source code with the original algorithms, comparing results with another computer code, and when possible comparing the results with at least one set of test data. Verification of the TMD Spreadsheet was based on comparing the source code with the equations from Ref. 42, comparing results with the ADAM code, and also comparing the results with the Ref. 42 examples based on the data of Ref. 19. The rocket and ramjet missile baselines, which are based on test data, were used in the verification of the TMD Spreadsheet.

The validation process of a computer sizing code confirms that the code accurately models reality. Validation is a comparison of code results with the actual system and subsystem data, ideally including flight test data. A limited validation of the TMD Spreadsheet has been accomplished, based on comparisons with Sparrow and ASALM test data. A complete validation of the TMD Spreadsheet has not been accomplished, because the broad range of applicability of the TMD Spreadsheet would require an extensive comparison with a large set of test data.

Figure 7.46 is an example of verification based on the air-to-air range requirement discussed previously in this chapter. The launch condition is Mach 0.8 launch at 20,000 ft altitude. In the example the rocket baseline missile has straight ahead flight at a constant altitude. Based on the F-Pole requirement, the missile must fly 6.7 nm in less than 24.4 s. In this example the time of flight to 6.7 nm based on a 3-DOF trajectory using wind tunnel data is 21 s. It is assumed that the wind tunnel data/3-DOF trajectory result is the most accurate. However, it would be good to also

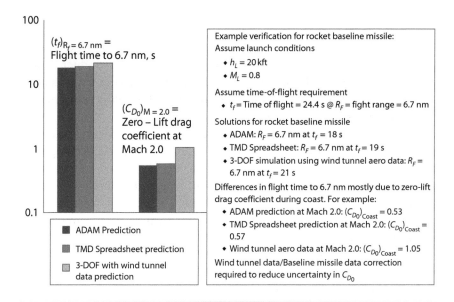

Fig. 7.46 Example of TMD Spreadsheet verification: rocket baseline missile air-to-air range requirement.

compare with another set of wind tunnel data and another flight trajectory code. As a comparison, the ADAM computer program gives a time of flight of 18 s. The TMD Spreadsheet gives a time of flight of 19 s. Discussed previously, the flight range of the rocket baseline missile is most sensitive to the parameters of specific impulse, propellant weight, zero-lift drag coefficient, drag-due-to-lift, and static margin. Results may also be sensitive to the modeling assumptions for the equations of motion. In this example, specific impulse, weight, and static margin were specified. An examination of the solutions shows that the major contributor to the difference in time of flight is attributable to the difference in the zero-lift drag coefficient (C_{D_0}). For example, at Mach 2, the ADAM prediction of zero-lift drag coefficient during coast is $(C_{D_0})_{coast} = 0.53$. The TMD Spreadsheet prediction is slightly higher, $(C_{D_0})_{coast} = 0.57$. However, wind tunnel data for the rocket baseline missile is a much larger value, $(C_{D_0})_{coast} = 1.05$. Because of the large difference between the predictions and wind tunnel data, comparison with another set of wind tunnel data is recommended. Also, because the uncertainty in the predicted value of zero-lift drag coefficient has an impact on flight range and time to target, it is desirable to correct the TMD Spreadsheet with wind tunnel data to reduce the uncertainty. The wind tunnel data on a baseline missile can be used to reduce the uncertainty. It is also desirable to provide a sufficient F-Pole design margin to handle the uncertainty.

7.15 Soda Straw Rocket Design, Build, and Fly

The final sizing examples are based on a soda straw rocket sizing. Included are a "hands on" process for the student to conduct a soda straw rocket design, build, and fly activity; a Pareto analysis and uncertainty assessment; a house of quality example; and a DOE process to harmonize the parameters for maximum range.

Soda Straw Rocket Science is an aerospace engineering outreach program to demonstrate the physics of flight and missile development, using a small air rocket. Up to eighteen projects introduce students and their teachers to the aerospace environment - including the design, build, and fly process; teamwork; and competition. Additional information is available in Appendix J and at the website http://genefleeman.home.mindspring.com/.

Examples of postulated customer requirements for this design, build, and fly activity include the objective, availability of furnished property, use of furnished material, launch conditions, and the requirement to compare predictions with test. The general objective is to design, build, and fly a soda straw rocket that meets customer requirements of flight range (e.g., greater than 90 ft) and weight (e.g., less than 2 grams). There are no customer explicit environmental requirements (e.g., elevation, atmospheric temperature, wind).

The furnished property includes a launch system and a distance measuring wheel, to measure the flight range. It may also include weight scales, engineer's scales, and scissors.

Furnished material includes a large diameter soda straw for the rocket body, strip tabbing for the tails, an ear plug for the nose, tape, and a smaller diameter straw for the launch tube. The rocket body is a conventional "giant" soda straw of 0.28 in diameter, 7.75 in length, and 0.6 g weight. Adhesive strip tabbing, provided for construction of the tails, is available at office supply stores. A flexible ear plug for the nose is 0.33 to 0.45 in diameter by 0.90 in length, with a weight of 0.6 g. Tape is wrapped around the nose and body, to ensure a tight fit. Finally, a conventional "super jumbo" soda straw for the launch tube is slightly smaller diameter (0.25 in) and at the same length (7.75 in) compared to the "giant" soda straw.

The specified launch tube length after inserting the launch straw inside the launcher pipe fitting exit is 6 in. A typical (adjustable) launch pressure is 30 psi and a typical (adjustable) launch angle is 40 deg (for maximum range). Finally, a comparison should be conducted of predicted range with the flight test result.

The furnished property soda straw rocket launcher is compact size, allowing storage/carriage in a travel case, for use in the author's Missile

Design and System Engineering short course and also as an aerospace engineering outreach program for K-12+ students. Shown in Fig. 7.47 is a photograph of the launcher and its components. An air compressor (1) pressurizes an air supply tank (2). An air hose (3) leads from the air supply tank through a pressure gauge (4) to a fast responding (0.025 s average response time) solenoid valve (5), which allows the air to flow into the launch tube (6) and rocket (7). An inclinometer (8) sets the angle of the launch tube and rocket. Shown in the left side of the figure is a collection of some of the rockets (9) that have been previously built by students, a measuring wheel (10) to measure flight range, and a launch button (11) that activates the solenoid valve.

The soda straw rocket initial baseline configuration is shown in Fig. 7.48. It is a body-tail design consisting of a nose plug, a soda straw body, and four strip tabs for tails. The initial baseline has a diameter of 0.28 in and a length of 7.0 in. The inside chamber length is 6.0 in, to maximize the total impulse from the 6.0 in length launcher. The cruciform tails are 0.25 in exposed semi-span × 0.5 in chord.

Note that the initial baseline soda straw rocket was selected as a representative, but not an optimum configuration. It is anticipated that the student can design a lighter weight, longer range configuration.

Table 7.10 is a cost, weight, and balance statement for the initial baseline soda straw rocket. The 0.33 – 0.45 in × 0.9-in nose plug weighs 0.6 g. Its

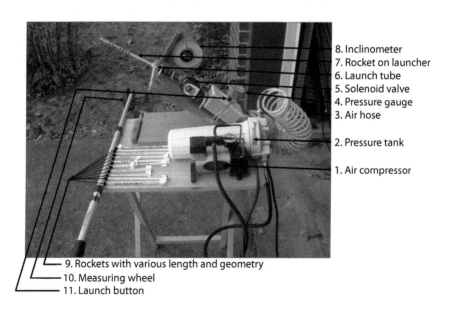

8. Inclinometer
7. Rocket on launcher
6. Launch tube
5. Solenoid valve
4. Pressure gauge
3. Air hose

2. Pressure tank

1. Air compressor

9. Rockets with various length and geometry
10. Measuring wheel
11. Launch button

Fig. 7.47 Soda straw rocket launcher.

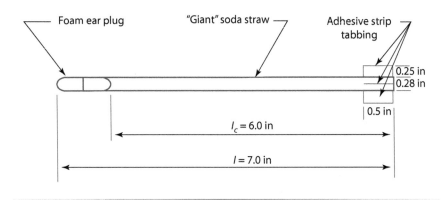

Fig. 7.48   Soda straw rocket initial baseline configuration.

unit cost is $0.10. The nose plug center-of-gravity is located approximately in its middle, 0.5 in from the beginning of the nose. The "Giant" soda straw body weighs 0.5 g, with its cg located in the middle of the body, 3.5 in from the nose. Its unit cost is $0.01. Total weight of the four plastic tail panels is 0.5 g. The unit cost of the plastic strip tabbing for the tails is $0.23. Center-of-gravity of the tails is 6.75 in from the nose. Total cost of the initial soda straw rocket baseline is $0.34, which satisfies the customer requirement that the unit cost be less than $0.50. Total weight of the soda straw rocket is 1.6 g, which satisfies the requirement that the weight be less than 2 g. The soda straw rocket cg is located approximately in the middle, 3.39 in from the nose.

Table 7.11 is a description of the soda straw rocket initial baseline geometry, its structure materials, and the propulsion. The body is made of a thin wall (0.004 in) high density polyethylene (HDPE) plastic soda straw. Nominal ultimate stress is $\sigma_{\text{ultimate}} = 4600$ psi. According to the hoop stress equation, the soda straw should theoretically withstand a gauge pressure of

$$p = \sigma_{\text{ult}} t / r = 4600(0.004)/0.14 = 131 \text{ psi}$$

Table 7.10   Soda Straw Rocket Initial Baseline Cost, Weight and Balance.

Component	Cost, $	Weight, g	cg Station, in
Nose (Plug)	0.10	0.6	0.5
Body (Soda Straw)	0.01	0.5	3.5
Fins (Four)	0.23	0.5	6.75
Total*	0.34	1.6	3.39

*Neglects assembly labor cost.

Table 7.11 Soda Straw Rocket Initial Baseline Definition.

Body	
Material type	HDPE Plastic
Material density, lbm/in.^{3}	0.043
Material strength, psi	4600
Thickness, in.	0.004
Length, in.	7.0
Diameter, in.	0.28
Fineness ratio	25.0
Nose fineness ratio	0.5
Fins	
Material	Plastic
Planform area (2 panels exposed), in.^{2}	0.25
Wetted area (4 panels), in.^{2}	1.00
Aspect ratio (2 panels exposed)	1.00
Taper ratio	1.0
Chord, in.	0.5
Span (exposed), in.	0.5
Span (total including body), in.	0.78
Leading edge sweep, deg	0
x_{mac}, in.	6.625
Nose	
Material type	Foam
Material density, lbm/in.^{3}	0.012
Average diameter (before insertion)	0.39 in.
Length	0.90 in.
Reference Values	
Reference area, in.^{2}	0.0616
Reference length, in.	0.28
Thrust Performance	
Inside cavity length, in.	6.0
Typical pressure, psi	30
Maximum thrust @ 30 psi pressure, lb	1.47
Launcher solenoid time constant (standard temperature), s	0.025

Although tests have been conducted for gauge pressures up to a maximum of 120 psi without failure, soda straw rockets have experienced side wall failure about 10% of the time at a gauge pressure as low as 60 psi. This is probably because of a variation in the wall thickness and voids from the low cost extruded plastic manufacturing process. A safe gauge pressure that allows multiple launches without failure/exceeding the yield limit is 40 psi.

The initial baseline fins are cut from office file tabbing. They are made of thin wall plastic, with self-adhesive tabs for attachment to the body. The initial baseline fin geometry was selected as an initial tradeoff of weight, stability, and drag. The nose plug is a 0.9-in length soft foam ear plug with a density of $\rho = 0.012$ lbm/in^3. The nose plug is inserted inside the soda straw and reinforced by wrapping tape around it, to prevent a blow-out during launch.

Reference diameter and area are based on the body diameter and the cross-sectional area respectively. Nominal thrust for a 30 psi gauge pressure is $T = 1.47$ lb. The thrust rise time constant, from the response time required to fully open the launcher solenoid valve, is $\tau = 0.025$ s.

Figure 7.49 illustrates the process to calculate the static margin of the soda straw rocket initial baseline. For the body-tail geometry, static margin is given by the equation from Chapter 2

$$(x_{AC} - x_{CG})/d = -\{(C_{N_\alpha})_B\{[x_{CG} - (x_{AC})_B]/d\}$$
$$+ (C_{N_\alpha})_T\{[x_{CG} - (x_{AC})_T]/d\}(S_T/S_{Ref})\}/[(C_{N_\alpha})_B$$
$$+ (C_{N_\alpha})_T S_T/S_{Ref}]$$

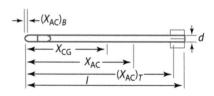

- For body-tail geometry, static margin given by
  - $(x_{AC} - x_{CG})/d = -\{(C_{N_\alpha})_B \{[x_{CG} - (x_{AC})_B]/d\} + (C_{N_\alpha})_T \{[x_{CG} - (x_{AC})_T]/d\}(S_T/S_{Ref})\}/[(C_{N_\alpha})_B + (C_{N_\alpha})_T S_T/S_{Ref}]$
- For initial baseline soda straw configuration ($x_{CG} = 3.39$ in, $d = 0.28$ in, $l = 7.0$ in, $S_T = 0.25$ in^2, $S_{Ref} = 0.0616$ in^2) @ $\alpha = 0$ deg
  - $(C_{N_\alpha})_B = 2$ per rad
  - $(x_{AC})_B = [(x_{AC})_B / l_N] l_N = 0.63\,(0.14) = 0.09$ in
  - $(C_{N_\alpha})_T = \pi A_T/2 = \pi\,(1)/2 = 1.57$
  - $(x_{AC})_T = 6.5 + 0.25\,(c_{mac})_T = 6.63$
- Substituting
  - $(x_{AC} - x_{CG})/d = -\{2\,(3.39 - 0.09)/0.28 + [1.57\,(3.39 - 6.63)/0.28]\,[(0.25)/0.0616]\}/[2 + 1.57\,(0.25)/0.0616] = 6.00$ (excess static stability)
  - $x_{AC} = 6.00\,(0.28) + 3.39 = 5.07$ in from nose

Fig. 7.49   The soda straw rocket initial baseline has excess static margin.

The input data for the initial baseline soda straw configuration is $x_{CG} = 3.39$ in, $d = 0.28$ in, $S_T = 0.25$ in^2, and $S_{Ref} = 0.0616$ in^2. From the slender body equation of Chapter 2, compute the aerodynamic center of the body

$$(x_{AC})_B = [(x_{AC})_B/l_N]l_N = 0.63(0.14) = 0.09 \text{ in}$$

The normal force coefficient of the tail, from the slender wing equation in Chapter 2, is

$$(C_{N_\alpha})_T = \pi A_T/2 = \pi(1)/2 = 1.57$$

Compute the aerodynamic center location of the tail

$$(x_{AC})_T = 6.5 + 0.25(c_{mac})_T = 6.5 + 0.25(0.5) = 6.63 \text{ in}$$

Substituting the static margin equation of Chapter 2, the static margin of the initial baseline soda straw rocket is

$$(x_{AC} - x_{CG})/d = -\{2(3.39 - 0.09)/0.28 + [1.57(3.39 - 6.63)/0.28]$$
$$[(0.25)/0.0616]\}/[2 + 1.57(0.25)/0.0616] = 6.0 \text{ (statically stable)}$$

Note from the above result that the initial baseline soda straw rocket has a static margin of 6.0 diameters. A soda straw rocket with less static margin would probably have better performance. It would be lighter weight and have lower drag, resulting in a higher launch velocity and longer range. It would also be less likely to weather-cock, resulting in less dispersal and longer range in a cross-wind.

The location of the aerodynamic center of the initial baseline is $x_{AC} = 6.00(0.28) + 3.39 = 5.07$ in from nose.

Figure 7.50 and the following discussion describe the method for predicting flight performance and an example of the performance of the initial baseline soda straw rocket.

Thrust is assumed to be equal to the differential pressure in the launch tube multiplied by the cross sectional area of the launch tube. The equation is

$$T = (p - p_0)A$$

The pressure in the launch tube is assumed to have the same rise time as that of the solenoid valve, and exponentially rises to the gauge pressure, giving

$$T = p_{Gauge}(1 - e^{-t/\tau})A$$

The actual thrust force is less than the theoretical thrust, because of the pressure loss in the line, boundary layer restriction of the effective flow area, launch tube leakage around the soda straw rocket, and launch tube friction.

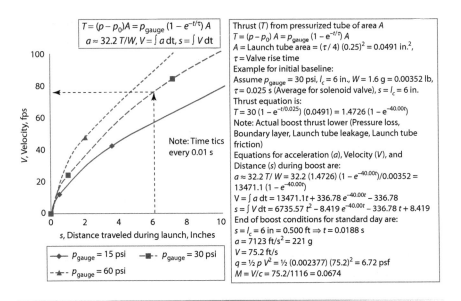

The box contents:

$$T = (p - p_0)A = p_{gauge}(1 - e^{-t/\tau})A$$
$$a \approx 32.2\,T/W,\ V = \int a\,dt,\ s = \int V\,dt$$

Thrust (T) from pressurized tube of area A
$T = (p - p_0)A = p_{gauge}(1 - e^{-t/\tau})A$
A = Launch tube area $= (\pi/4)(0.25)^2 = 0.0491$ in.^{2},
τ = Valve rise time
Example for initial baseline:
Assume p_{gauge} = 30 psi, l_c = 6 in., W = 1.6 g = 0.00352 lb,
τ = 0.025 s (Average for solenoid valve), $s = l_c$ = 6 in.
Thrust equation is:
$T = 30(1 - e^{-t/0.025})(0.0491) = 1.4726(1 - e^{-40.00t})$
Note: Actual boost thrust lower (Pressure loss,
Boundary layer, Launch tube leakage, Launch tube
friction)
Equations for acceleration (a), Velocity (V), and
Distance (s) during boost are:
$a \approx 32.2\,T/W = 32.2\,(1.4726)(1 - e^{-40.00t})/0.00352 = $
$13471.1\,(1 - e^{-40.00t})$
$V = \int a\,dt = 13471.1t + 336.78\,e^{-40.00t} - 336.78$
$s = \int V\,dt = 6735.57\,t^2 - 8.419\,e^{-40.00t} - 336.78\,t + 8.419$
End of boost conditions for standard day are:
$s = l_c = 6$ in. = 0.500 ft $\Rightarrow t = 0.0188$ s
$a = 7123$ ft/s^2 = 221 g
$V = 75.2$ ft/s
$q = \tfrac{1}{2}\,p\,V^2 = \tfrac{1}{2}(0.002377)(75.2)^2 = 6.72$ psf
$M = V/c = 75.2/1116 = 0.0674$

Graph axis: V, Velocity, fps (y-axis, 0 to 100); s, Distance traveled during launch, Inches (x-axis, 0 to 10)

Note: Time tics every 0.01 s

Legend:
$P_{gauge} = 15$ psi
$P_{gauge} = 30$ psi
$P_{gauge} = 60$ psi

Fig. 7.50   The soda straw rocket has high acceleration boost performance.

Drag can be neglected during boost, because the thrust force is relatively large, more than two orders of magnitude larger than the drag. Therefore from Newton's 2nd Law, the equation for acceleration of weight W is

$$a \approx 32.2\,T/W$$

Integrating the acceleration gives the velocity during boost ($V = \int a\,dt$) and the distance traveled ($s = \int Vt$). The graph shows the velocity as a function of time during boost. It is based on the launch tube diameter of 0.25 in [area $A = (\pi/4)(0.25)^2 = 0.0491$ in^2], the soda straw rocket initial baseline weight $W = 1.6$ g $= 0.00352$ lb, and a solenoid valve average rise time $\tau = 0.025$ s. It is noted that the solenoid valve response time is a function of the ambient temperature and the losses in the electrical power connector cord to the solenoid valve. A cold day and a long length power connector cord will increase the solenoid time constant.

As an example, for a gauge pressure of 30 psi and a launch length of 6 in,

$$T = 30(1 - e^{-t/0.025})(0.0491) = 1.4726(1 - e^{-40.00t})$$

The equations for acceleration (a), velocity (V), and distance (s) during boost are

$$a \approx 32.2T/W = 32.2(1.4726)(1 - e^{-40.00t})/0.00352$$
$$= 13471.1(1 - e^{-40.00t})$$

$$V = \int a\,dt = 13471.1t + 336.78e^{-40.00t} - 336.78$$

$$s = \int V\,dt = 6735.57t^2 - 8.419e^{-40.00t} - 336.78t + 8.419$$

Finally, the end-of-boost conditions are

$$s = l_c = 6 \text{ in} = 0.500 \text{ ft} \Rightarrow t = 0.0188 \text{ s}$$

$$a = 7123 \text{ ft/s}^2 = 221 \text{ g}$$

$$V = 75.2 \text{ ft/s}$$

Assume a sea level launch on a standard day ($\rho = 0.002377 \text{ slug/ft}^3$). Compute

$$q = 1/2\rho V^2 = 1/2(0.002377)(75.2)^2 = 6.72 \text{ psf}$$

$$M = V/c = 75.2/1116 = 0.0674$$

Figure 7.51 shows the soda straw rocket drag coefficient, based on summing the contributions from the body skin friction drag, base drag, and the tail skin friction drag. The equation is

$$C_{D_0} = (C_{D_0})_{Body,Friction} + (C_{D_0})_{Base,Coast} + (C_{D_0})_{Tail,Friction}$$

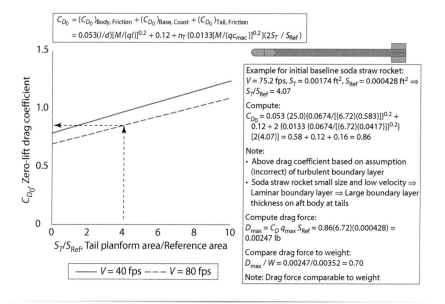

Fig. 7.51   Most of the soda straw rocket drag coefficient is from skin friction.

The Chapter 2 equation for the body skin friction drag coefficient, from Jerger [5], is

$$(C_{D_0})_{Body,Friction} = 0.053(l/d)[M/(ql)]^{0.2}$$

Note from the equation that body skin friction drag coefficient is primarily driven by body fineness ratio. The assumption of a turbulent boundary layer is in error for the very low Mach number of the soda straw rocket, which has a laminar boundary layer.

The Chapter 2 base drag coefficient equation for coasting flight at subsonic Mach number is

$$(C_{D_0})_{Base,Coast} = 0.12$$

The Chapter 2 tail skin friction drag coefficient prediction, based on Jerger [5], is the equation

$$(C_{D_0})_{Tail,Friction} = n_T[0.0133[M/(qc_{mac})]^{0.2}](2S_T/S_{Ref})$$

In the equation the units of dynamic pressure q and mean aerodynamic chord c_{mac} are lb/ft^2 and ft respectively. Major contributors to the tail skin friction drag are the number of tails n_T and the tail planform area S_T. The total wetted area for tail skin friction drag is equal to $2n_TS_T$. Tail skin friction drag is a weak function of Mach number, dynamic pressure, and the length of the mean aerodynamic chord. Again, an error in using this equation is the assumption of a turbulent boundary layer. A laminar boundary layer, with larger thickness, would probably have higher drag. Note from the figure that for a typical tail size, the major contributor to the zero-lift drag coefficient is from the body, with a lesser contribution from the tails.

As an example, assume that the initial baseline soda straw rocket is launched at 30 psi launch pressure, which results in an end-of-boost velocity of 75.2 ft/s. The initial baseline tail area is $S_T = 0.00174$ ft^2 and the reference area is $S_{Ref} = 0.000428$ ft^2, providing a ratio of tail area-to-reference area of $S_T/S_{Ref} = 4.07$. The zero-lift drag coefficient is computed to be

$$C_{D_0} = 0.053(25.0)\{0.0674/[(6.72)(0.583)]\}^{0.2} + 0.12$$

$$+ 2\{0.0133\{0.0674/[(6.72)(0.0417)]\}^{0.2}\}[2(4.07)]$$

$$= 0.58 + 0.12 + 0.16 = 0.86$$

The maximum total drag force will occur at launch, which is maximum velocity. Computing for a standard day sea level launch

$$D_{max} = C_D q_{max} S_{Ref} = 0.86(6.72)(0.000428) = 0.00247 \text{ lb}$$

Comparing the drag force to weight

$$D_{max}/W = 0.00247/0.00352 = 0.70$$

Note that the drag is comparable to the weight, but somewhat smaller. Although the rocket follows a nearly ballistic trajectory, it has somewhat shorter range than that of an ideal (no drag) trajectory.

The ballistic deterministic trajectory of the soda straw rocket initial baseline shown in Fig. 7.52 is a function of the time of flight t, weight W, atmospheric density ρ, reference area S_{Ref}, zero-lift drag coefficient C_{D_0}, initial velocity V_i, and the initial flight path angle γ_i. It is based on the one-degree-of-freedom (1-DOF) equation of motion with the assumptions of no thrust ($T = 0$) after launch, zero angle of attack ($\alpha = 0$ deg), standard atmosphere sea level launch ($\rho = 0.002377$ slug/ft^3), still air (no wind), and drag force greater than the component of weight along the drag axis ($D > W\sin\gamma$).

Horizontal flight range during ballistic flight is given by the Chapter 5 equation

$$R_x = \{2W\cos\gamma_i/[g_c\rho S_{Ref}C_{D_0}]\}\ln\{1 + t/\{2W/[g_c\rho S_{Ref}C_{D_0}V_i]\}\}$$

In the above equation the term g_c is the gravitational constant, with $g_c = 32.2$ lbm/slug. The altitude during ballistic flight is given by the

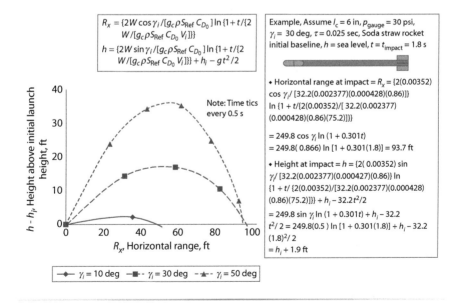

Fig. 7.52   The soda straw rocket initial baseline deterministic ballistic flight range is greater than 90 feet.

Chapter 5 equation

$$h = h_i + \{2W\sin\gamma_i/[g_c\rho S_{\text{Ref}}C_{D_0}]\}\ln\{1 + t/\{2W/[g_c\rho S_{\text{Ref}}C_{D_0}V_i]\}\} - gt^2/2$$

Examination of the equations above shows that the contributors to long-range ballistic flight include high initial velocity, low zero-lift drag coefficient, an optimum launch angle, and high altitude (low atmospheric density) flight.

Note from the figure that launches at $\gamma_i = 30$ deg and 50 deg provide almost the same range. A delay in the $\gamma_i = 30$ deg launch time of about 0.7 s would result in a nearly simultaneous impact time of a $\gamma_i = 50$ deg launch. It can be shown that the maximum range (including drag) is at launch angle of about 40 deg. For an ideal ballistic flight with zero drag, the launch angle for maximum range would be 45 deg.

As an example, assume $l_c = 6$ in, $p_{\text{gauge}} = 30$ psi, $\gamma_i = 30$ deg, $\tau = 0.025$ s, soda straw rocket initial baseline, and $t = t_{\text{impact}} = 1.8$ s. Then the predicted horizontal range at impact is

$$R_x = \{2(0.00352)\cos\gamma_i/[32.2(0.002377)(0.000428)(0.86)]\}$$
$$\times \ln\{1+t/\{2(0.00352)/[32.2(0.002377)(0.000428)(0.86)(75.2)]\}\}$$
$$= 249.8\cos\gamma_i\ln(1+0.301t) = 249.8(0.866)\ln[1+0.301(1.8)] = 93.7 \text{ ft}$$

Similarly, the height at impact ($t = 1.8$ s) is

$$h = \{2(0.00352)\sin\gamma_i/[32.2(0.002377)(0.000428)(0.86)\}$$
$$\times \ln\{1 + t/\{2(0.00352)/[32.2(0.002377)(0.000428)(0.86)(75.2)]\}\}$$
$$+ h_i - 32.2t^2/2 = 249.8\sin\gamma_i\ln(1 + 0.301t) + h_i - 32.2t^2/2$$
$$= 249.8(0.5)\ln[1+0.301(1.8)] + h_i - 32.2(1.8)^2/2 = h_i + 1.9 \text{ ft} \approx h_i$$

7.16 Soda Straw Rocket Range Pareto and Uncertainty Analysis

The next sizing example is a Pareto sensitivity analysis to rank the most important, driving parameters for the flight range of the soda straw rocket. Also, an uncertainty analysis will be conducted to determine the sensitivity of the predicted flight range to the uncertainty in the input data.

As stated previously, the customer requirements for the soda straw rocket are a flight range greater than 90 ft and a weight less than 2 g. A Pareto sensitivity study (Fig. 7.53) was conducted of the flight range of the initial baseline soda straw rocket, to determine the most important drivers and the required accuracy for prediction methods. Note from the figure that more than 80% of the sensitivity in flight range is from the

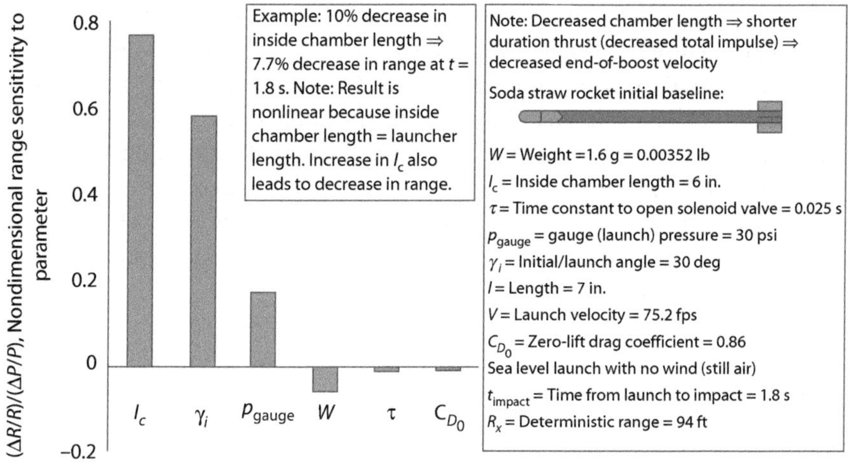
(ΔR/R)/(ΔP/P), Nondimensional range sensitivity to parameter
0.8
0.6
0.4
0.2
0
−0.2
l_c
γ_i
p_{gauge}
W
τ
C_{D_0}
Example: 10% decrease in inside chamber length ⇒ 7.7% decrease in range at t = 1.8 s. Note: Result is nonlinear because inside chamber length = launcher length. Increase in l_c also leads to decrease in range.
Note: Decreased chamber length ⇒ shorter duration thrust (decreased total impulse) ⇒ decreased end-of-boost velocity
Soda straw rocket initial baseline:
W = Weight = 1.6 g = 0.00352 lb
l_c = Inside chamber length = 6 in.
τ = Time constant to open solenoid valve = 0.025 s
p_{gauge} = gauge (launch) pressure = 30 psi
γ_i = Initial/launch angle = 30 deg
l = Length = 7 in.
V = Launch velocity = 75.2 fps
C_{D_0} = Zero-lift drag coefficient = 0.86
Sea level launch with no wind (still air)
t_{impact} = Time from launch to impact = 1.8 s
R_x = Deterministic range = 94 ft

Fig. 7.53 From a range Pareto analysis: soda straw rocket range is driven by chamber length and launch angle.

inside chamber length and the launch angle. The most sensitive parameter is the inside chamber length l_c. A 10% decrease in the inside chamber length results in a 7.7% decrease in range. If the chamber length decreases, the boost time and total impulse also decrease, resulting in a decrease in the launch velocity. Note that there is no increase in range for a chamber length greater than 6 in, because the launcher length is also 6 in. Another significant parameter is the initial flight path angle γ_i, which is the launch angle. The baseline launch angle was assumed to be 30 deg. Increasing the launch angle provides increased range for launch angles up to 40 deg. A launch angle of $\gamma_i = 40$ deg provides 21% greater range than a launch angle of 30 deg (114 versus 94 ft). For launch angles greater than 40 deg, the range decreases. A third, less sensitive parameter is the launch (gauge) air pressure p_{gauge}. An increase in gauge pressure increases the thrust, resulting in an increase in the launch velocity, which increases range. Also shown in the figure is the sensitivity to changes or uncertainties in other parameters that have less impact on range. Shown are the sensitivities from weight W, solenoid valve opening time τ, and zero-lift drag coefficient C_{D_0}. For weight, an increase in the soda straw rocket weight results in lower acceleration during boost and therefore a lower launch velocity. For the solenoid valve, an increase in the valve opening time results in a slower rise in thrust, which results in a decrease in the launch velocity, which decreases the flight range. The nominal opening time of the baseline solenoid valve is 0.025 s. As a comparison, the nominal valve opening time of a manual valve is longer, about 0.1 s. A manual, hand operated valve is limited by the typical human muscular response time. The use of the faster responding baseline solenoid valve (0.025 versus 0.1 s) results in a 44% greater launch velocity (75 versus 52 ft/s), providing longer range. Finally, note that zero-lift drag coefficient C_{D_0} has a relatively small influence on range. The relatively low drag of the soda straw rocket is because of the low velocity/low dynamic pressure. As a result, the flight trajectory of the relatively low speed soda straw rocket is dominated more by inertial forces rather than aerodynamic forces. The soda straw rocket follows a nearly ballistic flight trajectory of somewhat shorter range than the ideal (no drag) ballistic trajectory.

The engineering parameters that are under the control of the designer are the inside chamber length, weight, the zero-lift drag, and the tail sizing. In this case, it is assumed that the launch angle, gauge pressure, and the solenoid valve time constant are fixed by the customer and are not under the control of the designer. Another assumption is that the launch is in a standard atmosphere at sea level with still air (no wind). As previously discussed, the most important design characteristic is the inside chamber length.

The uncertainties of the values of the soda straw rocket initial baseline parameters are used to determine the uncertainty in flight range, as shown in Table 7.12. The assumed launch conditions are a gauge pressure of 30 psi, a launch angle of 30 deg, and a launch at sea level in still air. The parameters and their uncertainties are

1. l_c = inside chamber length = 6 in +/−2%, 1σ
2. γ_i = initial (launch) angle = 30 deg +/−3%, 1σ

Table 7.12 Because of Range Uncertainty, the Initial Baseline Soda Straw Rocket does not Meet a 3σ Range Requirement.

P, Parameter	Baseline Value	$(\Delta P/P)$	$(\Delta R/R)/(\Delta P/P)$	$\Delta R/R$
1. l_c	6 in	+/−2%, 1σ	0.77	+/−1.5%, 1σ
2. γ_i	30 deg	+/−3%, 1σ	0.58	+/−1.7%, 1σ
3. p_{gauge}	30 psi	+/−3%, 1σ	0.17	+/−0.5%, 1σ
4. W	1.6 g	+/−6%, 1σ	−0.06	+/−0.4%, 1σ
5. τ	0.025 s	+/−20%, 1σ	−0.01	+/−0.2%, 1σ
6. C_{D_0}	0.86	+/−20%, 1σ	−0.01	+/−0.2%, 1σ

- Estimate of Level of Maturity/Uncertainty of Soda Straw Rocket Baseline Parameters Based on
  - Wind tunnel test
  - Thrust static test
  - Weight measurement
  - Structure static test
  - Prediction methods
- Total Flight Range Uncertainty for 30 psi Launch at 30 deg at Sea Level Standard Atmosphere in Still Air
  - $\Delta R/R = [(\Delta R/R)_1^2 + (\Delta R/R)_2^2 + (\Delta R/R)_3^2 + (\Delta R/R)_4^2 + (\Delta R/R)_5^2 + (\Delta R/R)_6^2]^{1/2} = +/−2.4\%, 1\sigma$
  - $R = 94$ ft +/−2.3 ft, $1\sigma \Rightarrow 87$ ft $< R < 101$ ft, 3σ

3. p_{gauge} = gauge pressure = 30 psi $+/-3\%$, 1σ
4. W = weight = 1.6 g $+/-6\%$, 1σ
5. τ = solenoid valve time constant = 0.025 s $+/-20\%$, 1σ
6. C_{D_0} = zero-lift drag coefficient = 0.86 $+/-20\%$, 1σ

The estimated levels of maturity/uncertainty in the parameters of the soda straw rocket initial baseline are based on conducting tests and prediction. Ground tests included a wind tunnel test, thrust static test, weight measurement, and a structure static test. These are summarized in Appendix J and presented on the website that is in support of this text.

From Fig. 7.53 and Table 7.12, the flight range sensitivity to uncertainty in each of the parameters is

1. $\Delta R_1/R = +/-0.02(0.77) = +/-0.015$, 1σ
2. $\Delta R_2/R = +/-0.03(0.58) = +/-0.017$, 1σ
3. $\Delta R_3/R = +/-0.03(0.17) = +/-0.005$, 1σ
4. $\Delta R_4/R = +/-0.06(-0.06) = +/-0.004$, 1σ
5. $\Delta R_5/R = +/-0.20(-0.01) = +/-0.002$, 1σ
6. $\Delta R_6/R = +/-0.20(-0.01) = +/-0.002$, 1σ

Total flight range uncertainty for a 30 psi/30 deg/still air launch is assumed to be the root mean square (RMS) of the contributors

$$\Delta R/R = +/-\left[(\Delta R/R)_1^2 + (\Delta R/R)_2^2 + (\Delta R/R)_3^2 + (\Delta R/R)_4^2\right.$$

$$\left. +(\Delta R/R)_5^2 + (\Delta R/R)_6^2\right]^{1/2}$$

$$= +/-[0.015^2 + 0.017^2 + 0.005^2 + 0.004^2 + 0.002^2 + 0.002^2]^{1/2}$$

$$= +/-0.024, 1\sigma$$

The soda straw rocket initial baseline probabilistic flight range is the sum of the deterministic flight range plus the uncertainty

$$R = 94 \text{ ft} +/-2.3 \text{ ft}, \ 1\sigma$$

From above, there is a predicted 99% confidence (3σ) in achieving a range exceeding 87 ft in still air. If a 99% confidence is required for the customer requirement of a 90 ft range, options to satisfy the customer requirement include 1) conduct more accurate testing, measurement, and/or prediction to reduce the uncertainty, 2) request customer approval of a deviation in the specified launch conditions, such as a higher launch angle (the optimum launch angle for maximum range is about 40 deg), or 3) develop a new design concept with longer range performance. As an example, we will elect to conduct option 3), develop a new design concept to provide a flight range of 90 ft, 3σ.

Concept	Tail planform area	Length	Weight	Unit cost	Drag coefficient @ 75 ft/s	Static margin	3σ range
Initial baseline 	0.250 in.²	7.0 in.	1.6 g	$0.34	0.86	6.00 diam	87 to 101 ft (Fails req)
Revised baseline 	0.0784 in.²	7.0 in.	1.2 g	$0.13	0.75	0.00 diam	93 to 107 ft (Meets req)

Fig. 7.54   The revised soda straw rocket baseline meets the range requirement with lighter weight and lower cost.

A revised baseline with neutral static stability was selected to provide a longer flight range to satisfy a customer requirement of 90 ft range, with an implied 3σ confidence. It has smaller tails that are made from paper adhesive strip tabbing. The revised tails are lower drag, lighter weight, and lower cost. Figure 7.54 gives a summary comparison of the revised baseline with the initial baseline. Compared to the initial baseline, the revised baseline characteristics are

$R = 100$ versus 94 ft
$W = 1.2$ g versus 1.6 g
$C = \$0.13$ versus $\$0.34$
$(x_{AC} - x_{CG})/d = 0$ versus 6.0
$C_{D_0} = 0.75$ versus 0.86
$S_T = 0.0784$ versus 0.250 in²
$b_e = 0.28$ versus 0.50 in.
$c = 0.28$ versus 0.50 in.
$A_e = 1.00$ (same)
Nose cost $= \$0.10$ (same)
Body cost $= \$0.01$ (same)
Tails cost (4 panels) $= 0.02$ versus $\$0.23$
$l = 7.0$ in (same)
$d = 0.28$ in (same)

It takes about 15 to 30 m to make a soda straw rocket. The steps for construction are shown in Fig. 7.55. The rocket body consists of a large diameter "giant" soda straw, which is cut (1) to a desired length. Next (2), a flexible ear plug is cut and trimmed to a desired length and shape. A shorter length/smaller diameter ear plug is lighter weight. However, a smaller ear plug is more likely to blow out. Twist and squeeze the ear plug to reduce its diameter and then (3) insert the ear plug into the front of the soda straw. Trim (4) the nose to a desired shape (e.g., hemisphere). A symmetrical shape is desirable to minimize the flight trajectory dispersal/loss in range. Surfaces (tails, wings, canards) with two, three, or four panels are made from paper adhesive filing tabs. Select the number and type of surfaces (5). The surfaces are wrapped (6) around the soda straw and cut (7) to the desired size and planform shape. Next (8) over wrap the joint of the ear plug and soda straw with tape, to prevent the ear plug from blowing out of the straw. Finally, the soda straw rocket slides over the smaller diameter launch tube (9).

7.17 House of Quality

The house of quality is a template that is uses customer priorities to drive the engineering emphasis for design solutions. The objective is to develop a balanced design(s) that is most responsive to the customer requirements and priorities.

Figure 7.56a is a notional illustration of the envelope of possible design solutions that address the customer requirements for the soda straw rocket flight range, weight, and cost. An example of a design consideration is the maximum flight range. Note from the figure that a high value of flight range may be satisfied only for a limited envelope of weight and cost. For very low and very high values of weight and cost, the range may be much less than the maximum range. Another consideration is the constraints of the minimum acceptable range, the maximum acceptable weight, and the

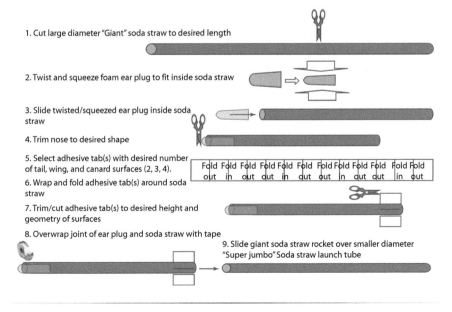

1. Cut large diameter "Giant" soda straw to desired length

2. Twist and squeeze foam ear plug to fit inside soda straw

3. Slide twisted/squeezed ear plug inside soda straw

4. Trim nose to desired shape

5. Select adhesive tab(s) with desired number of tail, wing, and canard surfaces (2, 3, 4).

6. Wrap and fold adhesive tab(s) around soda straw

Fold out	Fold in	Fold out	Fold out	Fold in	Fold out	Fold out	Fold in	Fold out	Fold out	Fold in	Fold out

7. Trim/cut adhesive tab(s) to desired height and geometry of surfaces

8. Overwrap joint of ear plug and soda straw with tape

9. Slide giant soda straw rocket over smaller diameter "Super jumbo" Soda straw launch tube

Fig. 7.55 Work instructions for soda straw rocket.

- Broad envelope of possible design soultion, e.g. extremes:

  1. Longest flight range that also meets weight and cost requirements
  2. Lightest weight that also meets range and cost requirements
  3. Lowest cost that also meets range and weight requirements

- House of quality translates customer requirements/ emphasis into engineering emphasis for design solution(s)

- Soda straw rocket customer requirements/emphasis:

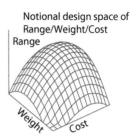

Notional design space of Range/Weight/Cost

Customer requirement	Customer emphasis
Flight Range	50%
Weight	20%
Cost	30%
Total	100%

Fig. 7.56a   The house of quality translates customer requirements into engineering emphasis.

maximum acceptable cost. These requirements provide boundary limits on the solutions. Particular design solutions of interest are

1. Longest fight range that also meets weight and cost requirements
2. Lightest weight that also meets range and cost requirements
3. Lowest cost that also meets range and weight requirements

If the customer provides a weighting of the importance of the requirements it greatly facilitates the design solution. As an example for the soda straw rocket requirements, we shall assume that the customer has also provided the following emphasis for the requirements

Flight Range	50%
Weight	20%
Cost	30%
Total	100%

Figure 7.56b shows the house of quality process applied to the soda straw rocket baseline. It is made up of seven rooms, with each room contributing to the task of mapping customer requirements to engineering design characteristics. Because the process of populating these rooms requires brainstorming, discussion with the customer, and analysis by the design team, a benefit of the house of quality is a better understanding of the problem. The house of quality should not be a static document. It should continue to be updated and evolve as the design progresses.

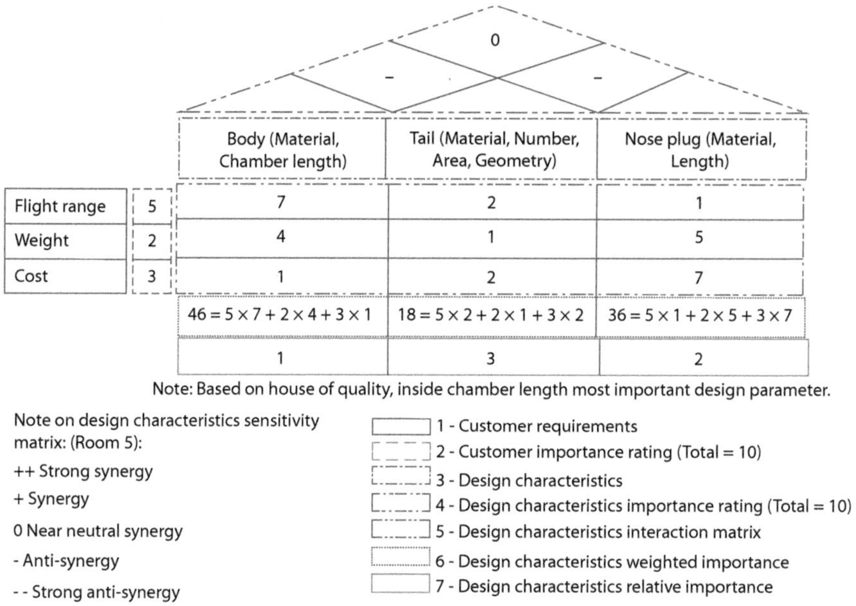

		Body (Material, Chamber length)	Tail (Material, Number, Area, Geometry)	Nose plug (Material, Length)
Flight range	5	7	2	1
Weight	2	4	1	5
Cost	3	1	2	7
		$46 = 5 \times 7 + 2 \times 4 + 3 \times 1$	$18 = 5 \times 2 + 2 \times 1 + 3 \times 2$	$36 = 5 \times 1 + 2 \times 5 + 3 \times 7$
		1	3	2

Note: Based on house of quality, inside chamber length most important design parameter.

Note on design characteristics sensitivity matrix: (Room 5):

++ Strong synergy

+ Synergy

0 Near neutral synergy

- Anti-synergy

- - Strong anti-synergy

1 - Customer requirements
2 - Customer importance rating (Total = 10)
3 - Design characteristics
4 - Design characteristics importance rating (Total = 10)
5 - Design characteristics interaction matrix
6 - Design characteristics weighted importance
7 - Design characteristics relative importance

Fig. 7.56b The house of quality translates customer requirements into engineering emphasis (cont).

The first room of the house of quality is the *Customer Requirements*. It is frequently referred to as the *whats* of the house of quality. Customer requirements can fall into three categories

1. Formal requirements directly indicated by the customer organization. These are flight range (>90 ft), weight (<2 g), and cost (<$0.50).
2. Unspoken requirements or "hidden" requirements of the customer's implicit needs. An example of an unspoken requirement is an acceptable uncertainty in the flight range requirement of greater than 90 ft. We have assumed that 90 ft with 99% confidence (3σ) is acceptable.
3. Exciters or "softer" customer requirements that can be traded off against other needs. Examples of softer requirements are weight and cost, which have less emphasis than flight range (20 versus 50%) and (30 versus 50%) respectively.

The customer requirements may be derived from formal sources such as the request for proposal (RFP) and technical requirements document (TRD), as well as informal discussions with customer. The informal discussions with the customer may provide further insight into the formal requirements, as well as implied requirements, such as safety, preferred technologies, and launch platform compatibility. Informal discussions with the customer organization may also indicate contradictory desires from different members of the customer organization.

The second room, just to the right of customer requirements, is the *Customer Importance Rating.* It shows the relative importance of each customer requirement. It is at this stage, above all others, where clear customer input is required to accurately map the customer needs. Ideally, the customer is present in the discussion of the customer importance rating and concurs with the rating. Often the summation of the values of the rating for each requirement is set equal to 10. This forces a relative priority ranking of each of the customer requirements. As an example, the soda straw rocket flight range is considered by the customer to be more important than weight (rating of 5 versus 2) and cost (rating of 5 versus 3).

The third room of the house of quality is *Design Characteristics.* These are frequently referred to as the *hows* of the house of quality. Design characteristics are a translation of customer needs into engineering product or process attributes. They identify how the customer requirements can be satisfied. The design characteristics are based on the important engineering design parameters that can be controlled and measured. Engineering insight and sensitivity analysis of a baseline design are ideally used in selecting the design characteristics. For example, we know from analyzing the soda straw rocket baseline that the end-of-boost velocity drives the flight range, and that the end-of-boost velocity increases with increasing inside chamber length until the chamber length is equal to the launcher length. Also, the weight and drag of the soda straw rocket is a function of the length of the body. It is therefore expected that inside chamber length would be an important design parameter, with a maximum reasonable length less than the launcher length. Another design parameter is the tail planform area. Benefits of a small tail planform area are less weight and drag, providing longer range. However, some tail area is required for neutral stability. At the other extreme, too much tail area (such as the initial baseline) results in increased weight, increased drag, and excess stability. Excess stability causes the soda straw rocket to weathercock (and lose range) in a cross wind. A third design parameter is the nose plug length. A short nose plug length is lighter weight, providing longer range. However, the nose plug must be of sufficient length to provide structural integrity, preventing a blow-out of the nose plug. The values of the engineering design characteristics are derived from a baseline design sensitivity study that is used to initiate the design process. For a soda straw rocket baseline with specified values of launch angle, launch length, launch gauge pressure, and solenoid valve response time, the primary sensitivity of flight range to the engineering design characteristics is from the inside chamber length, tail planform area, and the nose plug length. Similarly, the primary sensitivity of the weight and cost is from the inside chamber length, tail planform area, and nose plug length.

Room four is the engineering *Design Characteristics Importance Rating*. It is here that the quantifiable metrics, controllable by the designer, are defined. The design characteristics importance rating identifies the correlation between the customer requirements and the engineering design characteristics. Engineering design characteristics are assigned quantitative values that are selected based upon their impact on the customer requirements. The total for each customer requirement is often set to 10, to force a ranking of importance. An empty column indicates that an engineering characteristic that was previously thought to be significant does not have a significant impact on any of the customer requirements, and therefore should probably be eliminated as a design parameter. An empty row shows that a customer requirement is not being properly addressed with the current set of engineering characteristics and therefore additional engineering design characteristics should be added to accommodate it. The goal of this matrix is to match the important engineering associations with customer requirements. Based on a sensitivity study of the baseline soda straw rocket, the flight range is driven about 70% by inside chamber length, 20% by tail planform area, and about 10% by nose plug length. The weight is driven about 40% by inside chamber length, 10% by tail planform area, and about 50% by nose plug length. The cost is driven about 10% by the body, 20% by the tail, and 70% by the nose plug. These values were used as the basis for the design characteristics importance rating.

The fifth room of the House of Quality is the *Design Characteristics Interaction Matrix*. It identifies the interactions that exist among the engineering design characteristics. Five different interactions are often used: strong synergy, synergy, near neutral, anti-synergy, and strong anti-synergy. A synergistic interaction means that a beneficial change in the value of an engineering design characteristic also benefits another engineering characteristic. An anti-synergy interaction means that a beneficial change in the value of an engineering design characteristic unfortunately degrades another engineering characteristic, requiring a design tradeoff. Areas requiring the most attention are those with strong sensitivities that can lead to either strong synergy or require major design tradeoffs. For the soda straw rocket, there is a slight anti-synergy between the inside chamber length and tail planform area (i.e., an increase in chamber length, resulting in a longer rocket, requires a slightly larger tail area for flight stability). The reason is an increase in chamber length moves the body normal force farther forward, resulting in a decrease in static stability. As a result, the tail planform area must be increased to maintain static margin. An example of a near-neutral interaction is between the inside chamber length and nose plug length. Another example of slight anti-synergy is between the tail planform area and nose plug length (a smaller tail area requires a larger/heavier nose plug length to provide the required static margin).

The two lowest rooms (six and seven), represent the outcome of the house of quality process. They focus on the most important engineering design characteristics. Room six is the *Design Characteristics Weighted Importance.* It indicates which engineering design characteristics are most important in meeting the customer requirements. The design characteristics weighted importance matrix is obtained by multiplying the design characteristic importance rating by the corresponding customer requirements rating, and summing the results. For the soda straw rocket, the weighted importance of the soda straw body ($46 = 5 \times 7 + 2 \times 4 + 3 \times 1$) is considered to be more important than the weighted importance of either the tail ($18 = 5 \times 2 + 2 \times 1 + 3 \times 2$) or the nose plug ($36 = 5 \times 1 + 2 \times 5 + 3 \times 7$). Finally, room seven, *Design Characteristics Relative Importance*, facilitates the quick identification of the most important engineering characteristics, by providing a ranking of the design characteristics. The most important design characteristics should receive the greatest attention during the design study. In the case of the soda straw rocket, the inside chamber length of the soda straw body receives the highest ranking and should receive the greatest attention in the design.

7.18 Design of Experiment

The Design of Experiment (DOE) process provides a structured approach for designing a missile. The objective is to improve the quality of information that can be obtained within the schedule and resource constraints, in order to allow more efficient convergence to an "optimum" design.

Table 7.13, based on Ref. 45, shows three approaches to applying the DOE process to conceptual missile design and system engineering.

A parametric study using one-factor-at-a-time (OFAT) was used previously in the Pareto sensitivity analyses of the flight range of the rocket, ramjet, and turbojet baseline missiles and also the soda straw rocket baseline. This approach works best when the baseline design is a near-optimum design. The sensitivity of the flight range to the parameters indicates which parameters are the most important and the desired changes in the parameters for the next design iteration. Although a parametric OFAT is great for identifying the most important parameters, a disadvantage is that it does not disclosure the interactions between the design parameters. For example, room 5 of the soda straw rocket house of quality has a slight anti-synergy between the inside chamber length and tail planform area (i.e., an increase in chamber length, resulting in a longer rocket, requires a slightly larger tail area for flight stability).

The number of designs required for a parametric OFAT is a function of the number of parameters and the number of levels of the parameters. If k = number of design parameters and l = number of levels of the parameters, then the number of designs required is

$$n_{\text{Parametric OFAT}} = 1 + k(l - 1)$$

As an example, for a simple design with $k = 2$ and $l = 2$

$$n_{\text{Parametric OFAT}} = 1 + 2(2 - 1) = 3$$

For a more complex design, with $k = 5$ and $l = 2$

$$n_{\text{Parametric OFAT}} = 1 + 5(2 - 1) = 6$$

As a notional illustration, assume that each design iteration for $k = 5$ and $l = 2$ requires 1 month. An actual missile design study, even a conceptual design study, would probably have a larger value of k. For this notional illustration, a typical six-month conceptual design study duration would allow 6 designs to be evaluated within the time available. A parametric OFAT with five parameters and two levels could be completed within the time available. However, it would not include the interactions among the parameters, with some uncertainty in the quality of the design.

A second approach to DOE is an adaptive OFAT. An adaptive OFAT checks to see if there is an improvement from changing a factor. If there is an improvement, the change is retained. If there is no improvement, then the original factor is maintained. This continues until each factor has been changed. The number of designs that are required for an adaptive OFAT is the same as the parametric OFAT

$$n_{\text{Adaptive OFAT}} = 1 + k(l - 1)$$

The advantage of an adaptive OFAT over a parametric OFAT is that it provides more information for the same number of designs. An adaptive OFAT includes some of the synergy and anti-synergy interactions among parameters.

A third approach to DOE is a full factorial evaluation. A full factorial DOE includes all of the combinations of parameters and levels. The number of designs that are required for a full factorial DOE is

$$n_{\text{Full factorial}} = l^k$$

As an example for five parameters with two levels

$$n_{\text{Full factorial}} = 2^5 = 32$$

Table 7.13 DOE Approaches are a Tradeoff of the Time Required for the DOE Study Versus the Confidence in Result.

DOE Approach	Number Required Designs	Designs Required for Simple Design (2 Parameters), 2 Levels	Designs Required for More Complex Design (5 Parameters), 2 Levels	Time Required for Each Design	Interactions/Confidence in Predicted Optimum
Parametric Study Using One-Factor-at-a-Time (OFAT)	$1 + k(l - 1)$	☺(3)	☺(6)	☺	☹ No interactions
Adaptive OFAT	$1 + k(l - 1)$	☺(3)	☺(6)	☺	☹ to ☺ (Some)
Full Factorial	l^k	⊕(4)	☹(32)	☹	☺ (Excellent)

☺ Superior ⊕ Average ☹ Below Average

Note: k = number of parameters, l = number of levels

Reference: Montgomery, D.G., *Design and Analysis of Experiments*, John Wiley & Sons, 2001.

Although a full factorial DOE has an advantage in that it includes all of the interactions among the parameters, it has a disadvantage of the larger number of designs that are required. For a typical time and resource limited conceptual design study, a full factorial DOE is usually not a practical approach.

Table 7.14 presents an example of a parametric OFAT with four parameters and two levels. The number of designs is

$$n_{\text{Parametric OFAT}} = 1 + k(l-1) = 1 + 4(2-1) = 5$$

The process of evaluation is

1. Specify the levels for each parameter. One approach is to pick a baseline level that is a best guess as to a near-optimum value and a second level that is the best guess as to a direction that may improve the design. Another approach is to pick lower and upper levels that bracket the best guess as to the near-optimum value.
2. Change one parameter at a time, with all others at the row 1 level
3. Compare each row with the y_1 row to find the best result (y_{Best}) for each x
   1. Compare $y_1, y_2 \Rightarrow (x_1)_{\text{Best}}$

Table 7.14 A DOE Parametric Study Changes One Factor at a Time, with All Others Held at a Base Level.

Example of Parametric Study: 4 parameters, 2 Levels $\Rightarrow 1 + k(l-1) \Rightarrow$ $1 + 4(2-1) = 5$ DOE Designs					
Design Number	Parameter (x_1)	Parameter (x_2)	Parameter (x_3)	Parameter (x_4)	Result (y)
1	Low	Low	Low	Low	y_1
2	High	Low	Low	Low	y_2
3	Low	High	Low	Low	y_3
4	Low	Low	High	Low	y_4
5	Low	Low	Low	High	y_5

Process:

1. Specify levels for each parameter
2. Change one parameter at a time, with all others at row 1 level
3. Compare row 1 with other rows to find best result (y_{Best}) for each x
   1. Compare $y_1, y_2 \Rightarrow (x_1)_{\text{Best}}$
   2. Compare $y_1, y_3 \Rightarrow (x_2)_{\text{Best}}$
   3. Compare $y_1, y_4 \Rightarrow (x_3)_{\text{Best}}$
   4. Compare $y_1, y_5 \Rightarrow (x_4)_{\text{Best}}$
4. DOE "best" design is the x for each best row result. y_{Best} consists of $((x_1)_{\text{Best}}, (x_2)_{\text{Best}}, (x_3)_{\text{Best}}, (x_4)_{\text{Best}})$
5. Compare DOE "best" design with baseline and refine baseline for next iteration

Table 7.15   A DOE Adaptive One-Factor-at-a-Time Study Sequentially Selects the Values of Parameters, Based on a Comparison of Results.

Example of Adaptive OFAT Study with 4 parameters, 2 Levels $\Rightarrow 1 + k(l - 1) \Rightarrow$ $1 + 4(2 - 1) = 5$ DOE Designs					
Design Number	Parameter (x_1)	Parameter (x_2)	Parameter (x_3)	Parameter (x_4)	Result (y)
1	Low	Low	Low	Low	y_1
2	High	Low	Low	Low	y_2
3	Best	High	Low	Low	y_3
4	Best	Best	High	Low	y_4
5	Best	Best	Best	High	y_5

Process:

1. Specify row 1 and row 2 levels for first parameter x_1
2. Compare results for first parameter x_1
3. Set new level for x_1 in row 3 based on row 1 vs row 2 that gives best result
4. Move on to next parameter (x_2) and repeat until all rows evaluated
5. Assume row that provides best y is y_{Best}
6. Compare y_{Best} with baseline and refine baseline for next iteration

   2. Compare $y_1, y_3 \Rightarrow (x_2)_{Best}$
   3. Compare $y_1, y_4 \Rightarrow (x_3)_{Best}$
   4. Compare $y_1, y_5 \Rightarrow (x_4)_{Best}$
4. The DOE "best" design is the x for each best row result. y_{best} consists of $((x_1)_{Best}, (x_2)_{Best}, (x_3)_{Best}, (x_4)_{Best}, (x_5)_{best})$
5. After comparing y_{Best} with the baseline, refine the baseline for the next iteration.

Table 7.15 presents an example of an adaptive OFAT DOE with four parameters and two levels. The number of designs is

$$n_{\text{Adaptive OFAT}} = 1 + k(l - 1) = 1 + 4(2 - 1) = 5$$

The process for evaluation is

1. Specify the two levels for first parameter x_1 of rows 1 and 2
2. Compare results for first parameter x_1
3. Set new level for x_1 in row 3, based on the row 1 versus row 2 comparison that gives best result
4. Move on to next parameter (x_2) and repeat until all of the rows have been evaluated
5. Assume that the row that provides the best y is y_{Best}
6. Compare y_{Best} with the baseline and refine the baseline for the next iteration

Table 7.16 presents an example of a full factorial DOE, with four parameters and two levels. The number of designs is

$$n_{\text{Full factorial}} = l^k = 2^4 = 16$$

The process is straightforward, but more time consuming. After evaluating all combinations, the row that provides the best result is selected. An advantage of a full factorial DOE is that it includes the interactions among all of the parameters.

Since the soda rocket revised baseline design meets the customer standard of weight and cost requirements, the primary design tradeoff is the flight range. One approach to conducting a DOE is to use an aggregate measure of merit based on the customer priority ranking (50% range, 20% weight, 30% cost). Another approach, since the weight and cost requirements are already satisfied, is to focus on range only. A third approach is to request customer input for goals that exceed the standard requirements and conduct a DOE based on the customer priority ranking of the goals. For this exercise we will address the second approach, focusing on a DOE for maximizing the flight range.

It is instructive to select a set of concepts that illustrate the practical limits of the driving engineering characteristics and the driving customer requirements for range. Engineering should guide the selection of an envelope of design concepts that make sense. As an example for the soda straw rocket concepts in Fig. 7.57

- A no tail concept is not a valid concept because it is statically unstable and has a high dispersal, resulting in short range.
- A two panel tail concept is not a valid concept because it is also statically unstable and has a high dispersal, resulting in short range.
- A three panel tail concept is a valid concept (it can be statically stable).
- A four panel tail concept is a valid concept (it can also be statically stable).
- A mono-wing concept is not a valid concept because it adds unnecessary drag, weight, and dispersal for the ballistic ($\alpha = 0$ deg) trajectory, reducing the range.
- A cruciform wing concept is not a valid concept because it also adds unnecessary drag, weight, and dispersal for the ballistic trajectory, reducing the range.
- Canards are not a valid concept because they add unnecessary drag, weight, and dispersal for the ballistic trajectory, reducing the range.
- A short length ($l < 7$ in) concept is not a valid concept because the lighter weight and lower drag does not compensate for lower launch velocity from the shorter inside chamber length l_c, reducing the range.

Table 7.16   A DOE Full Factorial Study Evaluates All Combinations of Parameters, but it Requires More Time.

Example of Full Factorial Study with 4 parameters, 2 Levels $\Rightarrow l^k = 2^4 = 16$ DOE Designs						
Design Number	Parameter (x_1)	Parameter (x_2)	Parameter (x_3)	Parameter (x_4)	Result (y)	Process: Select Row that Provides y_{Best}
1	Low	Low	Low	Low	y_1	
2	High	Low	Low	Low	y_2	
3	Low	High	Low	Low	y_3	
4	High	High	Low	Low	y_4	
5	Low	Low	High	Low	y_5	
6	High	Low	High	Low	y_6	
7	Low	High	High	Low	y_7	
8	High	High	High	Low	y_8	
9	Low	Low	Low	High	y_9	
10	High	Low	Low	High	y_{10}	
11	Low	High	Low	High	y_{11}	
12	High	High	Low	High	y_{12}	
13	Low	Low	High	High	y_{13}	
14	High	Low	High	High	y_{14}	
15	Low	High	High	High	y_{15}	
16	High	High	High	High	y_{16}	

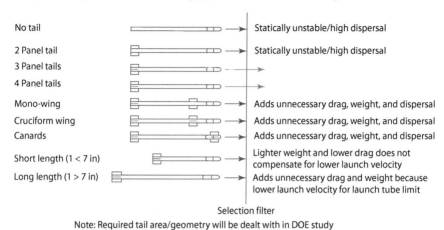

Example: DOE Geometric design space for soda straw rocket range

No tail	Statically unstable/high dispersal
2 Panel tail	Statically unstable/high dispersal
3 Panel tails	
4 Panel tails	
Mono-wing	Adds unnecessary drag, weight, and dispersal
Cruciform wing	Adds unnecessary drag, weight, and dispersal
Canards	Adds unnecessary drag, weight, and dispersal
Short length (1 < 7 in)	Lighter weight and lower drag does not compensate for lower launch velocity
Long length (1 > 7 in)	Adds unnecessary drag and weight because lower launch velocity for launch tube limit

Selection filter

Note: Required tail area/geometry will be dealt with in DOE study

Fig. 7.57 A DOE study should use engineering intuition in searching the broad possible design space.

- A long length ($l > 7$ in) concept is not a valid concept because it overmatches the launch tube length of 6 in and adds unnecessary drag and weight, reducing the range.

Based on the above analysis, the primary driving engineering geometry parameters for the range of the soda straw rocket are the choices of three versus four tail panels and the tail planform area. The primary driver for the effect of tail sizing on the flight range of the soda straw rocket is its stability. Shown in Table 7.17 are the driving parameters for stability. The table addresses the effect of static stability on the ballistic flight range and provides a basis for the geometric design solution and geometry-related tests, such as wind tunnel tests. Assuming that the revised baseline is a reasonable starting point for a design solution, the design tradeoffs are the number of tail panels $n_{\text{Tail panels}}$ (3 versus 4) and the tail planform area S_T. The lower value selected ($S_T = 0.0392$ in^2) is based on 1/2 of the revised baseline tails area. It is considered a lower reasonable lower value limit because it is probably results in a statically unstable rocket, with short range and large dispersal. The upper value selected ($S_T = 0.1568$ in^2) is based on two times the revised baseline tails area. It is considered an upper reasonable value because it probably results in an excess static stability rocket, with reduced range and increased dispersal. The best design is probably an intermediate value, subject to the uncertainty in the data. It is noted that there is interaction among the

Table 7.17   A DOE Study Should Search the Broad Possible Design Space.

Example: Geometric Design Space for Soda Straw Rocket		
Engineering Characteristics Envelope	$n_{\text{Tail Panels}}$, Number of Tail Panels	S_T, Tail Planform Area, in^2
Lower Value	3	0.0392
Upper Value	4	0.1568

Note:
Lower value of S_T, based on 1/2 revised baseline tails area. It is considered a lower reasonable value because it is probably statically unstable.
Upper value of S_T, based on 2× revised baseline tails area. It is considered an upper reasonable value because it probably has excess static stability.

number of tail panels and the tail area. For the same static margin, a tri-tail ($n_{\text{Tail panels}} = 3$) requires more planform area than a cruciform tail ($n_{\text{Tail panels}} = 4$).

The characteristics of an operational free flight unguided rocket, such as the Hydra-70, can be used as a guide in developing the DOE set of alternatives and a baseline design. Figure 7.58 compares the total length-to-body diameter ratio (fineness ratio), tail span-to-body diameter ratio, and tail chord-to-diameter ratio of the Hydra-70 to the revised baseline soda straw rocket. Because free flight rockets such as Hyda-70 are designed to be near neutrally stable, the tail geometry of the soda straw rocket should be somewhat similar.

For a neutrally stable rocket, the destabilizing moment from the body is equal to the stabilizing moment from the tail. Because the moment arm from the body is located at the nose and is approximately equal to the moment arm from the tail, the normal force derivative of the body should be approximately equal to the normal force derivative of the tail.

As an example, Soda Straw Rocket geometry should be comparable to an operational unguided rocket with near-neutral static stability (e.g., Hydra-70)

Concept	Sketch	l/d, Total length/ Diameter	b/d, Total tail span/ Diameter	c/d, Tail chord/ Diameter
Revised baseline		25	2.00	1
Hydra-70		15.1	2.66	1

Note: For a subsonic rocket with the centre-of-gravity in the center of the rocket, slender body theory and slender surface theory give total tail span (tail exposed span + body diameter) and chord for neutral stability of $b_{\text{Neutral stability}} \approx 2\,d$ and $c_{\text{Neutral stability}} \approx d$ respectively

Fig. 7.58   Engineering experience should guide DOE study and design.

Table 7.18   A DOE Parametric OFAT Study Provides a Quick Evaluation but Has Lowest Confidence.

DOE Parametric OFAT Study Example with $1 + k(l - 1) = 1 + 2(2 - 1) = 3$ Designs			
Design Number	Number of Tail Panels (x_1)	Tail Planform Area (x_2)	Range (y)
1	3	0.0392 in.^{2}	TBD
2	4	0.0392 in.^{2}	TBD
3	3	0.1568 in.^{2}	TBD

Process:

1. Compare y_1, y_2 $\Rightarrow$ $(x_1)_{Best}$
2. Compare y_1, y_3 $\Rightarrow$ $(x_2)_{Best}$
3. Compare DOE best design range with revised baseline design range for next iteration

Based on slender body theory [8], subsonic slender wing theory [10] (low aspect ratio), and an assumed center-of-gravity near the center of the rocket, the total span and chord of the tail should be about $b_{Neutral\ stability} \approx 2d$ and $c_{Neutral\ stability} > \approx d$ respectively. Note from the figure that the soda straw rocket revised baseline satisfies the criteria for neutral stability. Also note that the Hydra-70 total tail span is 2.66 times the body diameter and the tail chord is equal to the body diameter, providing a sanity check.

An example of a parametric OFAT DOE of the soda straw rocket is shown in Table 7.18. The range is to be determined (TBD); it is left as a possible exercise by the student. The process is

1. Compare row 1 and row 2 to determine the number of tail panels ($n_{Tail\ panels}$ = 3 versus 4) that provides the best range
2. Compare row 1 and row 3 to determine the tail planform area (S_T = 0.0392 in^2 versus 0.1569 in^2) that provides the best range
3. Compare the DOE best design range with the revised baseline design range for the next iteration

Only three designs are required for the evaluation, $n_{Parametric\ OFAT} = 1 + k (l - 1) = 1 + 2(2 - 1) = 3$. However, it does not include the effect of the interaction among the number of tail panels and the planform area.

An adaptive OFAT DOE of the soda straw rocket is shown in Table 7.19. The process is

1. Compare row 1 and row 2 to determine the number of tail panels ($x_1 = n_{Tail\ panels}$ = 3 versus 4) that provides the best range
2. Set level for $(x_1)_3 = (x_1)_{Best}$

3. Compare row 2 and row 3 to determine the tail planform area ($x_2 = S_T = 0.0392$ versus 0.1568 in^2) that provides best range
4. Compare DOE best design range with revised baseline design range for next iteration

Only three designs are required for the evaluation, $n_{\text{Adaptive OFAT}} = 1 + k\ (l - 1) = 1 + 2(2 - 1) = 3$. An advantage of the adaptive OFAT DOE compared to the parametric OFAT is that the adaptive OFAT somewhat includes the interaction of the number of tails with the tail area.

Finally, a full factorial DOE of the soda straw rocket is shown in Table 7.20. The process is to select the row that provides the best range. The number of designs is

$$n_{\text{Full factorial}} = l^k = 2^2 = 4$$

The full factorial DOE adds only one more design case compared to the parametric OFAT and the adaptive OFAT DOEs. A full factorial DOE may not be practical if there are a large number of parameters (2^k very large). The advantage of a full factorial DOE is that the results include the interaction of the design parameters (number of tail panels and the tail planform area). It provides more information to determine the optimum values of the design parameters.

A process to determine the x_1 (number of tail panels) and x_2 (tail planform area) that provides maximum range is

1. Assume $y = \beta_0 + \beta_1 x_1 + \beta_2 x_2 + \beta_{12} x_1 x_2$
2. Find values of β_0, β_1, β_2, β_{12}, by solving equations from results of 4 designs

Table 7.19 A DOE Adaptive One Factor at A Time Provides a Quick Evaluation with More Confidence.

DOE Adaptive OFAT Study Example with $1 + k(l - 1) = 1 + 2(2 - 1) = 3$ Designs			
Design Number	Number of Tails (x_1)	Tail Planform Area (x_2)	Range (y)
1	3	0.0392 in.^{2}	TBD
2	4	0.0392 in.^{2}	TBD
3	$(x_1)_3 = (x_1)_{Best}$	0.1568 in.^{2}	TBD

Process:

1. Compare y_1, $y_2 \Rightarrow (x_1)_{Best}$
2. Set level for $(x_1)_3 = (x_1)_{Best}$
3. Compare y_2, $y_3 \Rightarrow (x_2)_{Best}$
4. Compare DOE best design range with revised baseline design range for next iteration

Table 7.20 A Full Factorial DOE Study Provides the Highest Confidence but it Requires More Time.

DOE Full factorial Study Example with $l^k = 2^2 = 4$ Designs			
Design Number	Number of Tail panels (x_1)	Tail Planform Area (x_2)	Range (y)
1	3	0.0392 in.^{2}	TBD
2	4	0.0392 in.^{2}	TBD
3	3	0.1568 in.^{2}	TBD
4	4	0.1568 in.^{2}	TBD

Process: Select Row that Provides y_{Best}
Process to Determine x_1, x_2 for Optimum (max/min):

1. Assume $y = \beta_0 + \beta_1 x_1 + \beta_2 x_2 + \beta_{12} x_1 x_2$
2. Find values of β_0, β_1, β_2, β_{12} by solving equations from results of 4 designs
3. Optimum (max/min) occurs if

$$\Delta y / \Delta x_1 = 0$$
$$\Delta y / \Delta x_2 = 0$$

3. An optimum (max/min) occurs if

$$\Delta y / \Delta x_1 = 0$$
$$\Delta y / \Delta x_2 = 0$$

Usually two values ($l = 2$) are used for the DOE parameters (low, high). The levels are selected to cover the design envelope of interest. Selecting two levels implies the solution is driven by monotonicity. Using $l = 3$ (low, medium, high) provides an improved capability to include the non-linear curvature in the solution. However, $l = 3$ requires more design cases. For the soda straw rocket, with $l = 3$ and $k = 2$

$$n_{\text{Full Factorial}} = l^k = 2^3 = 8$$

A final comment is that the amount of work in design refinement/harmonization should be consistent with the accuracy of the data. The typical accuracy for conceptual design is about $+/-10\%$, 1σ.

7.19 Summary

Chapter 7 provided examples of the missile sizing process. Examples were shown for a rocket powered missile, a ramjet powered missile, a turbojet powered missile, computer programs for conceptual design, and a soda straw rocket. The Sparrow missile was used as a baseline missile to illustrate 1) the flight performance sizing to meet an air-to-air standoff range requirement, 2) wing sizing to meet maneuverability, turn rate, and turn radius requirements, 3) multi-parameter harmonization of weight and miss distance, and 4) lofted glide flight range. A ramjet missile based on the Advanced Strategic Air launched Missile was used to illustrate 1) the robustness in the uncertainty of the cruise flight range, 2) ramjet propulsion and fuel alternatives, and 3) surface target impact velocity. A turbojet missile based on Harpoon was used to illustrate 1) correction of turbojet thrust and specific impulse, 2) low altitude versus high altitude cruise range, and 3) engine rotational speed. Examples were shown of computer-aided sizing codes for conceptual design. ADAM is a DOS-based aerodynamic sizing code that includes a time-marching numerical solution of the equations of motion. TMD Spreadsheet is a Windows-based sizing code consisting of a spreadsheet that is based on the analytical methods of Ref. 42. Finally, a soda straw rocket design, build, and fly project was presented. Predictions of static margin, drag, and flight performance were shown. A Pareto sensitivity study identified the most important driving parameters. A house of quality was developed to illustrate the interface of customer requirements to the engineering design characteristics. Finally, a DOE was conducted to illustrate candidate design concepts and an efficient process to evaluate the design space.

7.20 Problem Review

1. Required flight range is shorter for a head-on intercept and it is longer for a ta__ ch___ intercept.
2. The rocket baseline missile center-of-gravity moves f_____ with motor burn.
3. The rocket baseline missile has an al_____ airframe.
4. The rocket baseline motor case and nozzle are made of st___.
5. The rocket baseline missile flight range is driven by specific impulse, propellant weight fraction, drag, and st___ ma____.
6. Configuration contributors to the maneuverability of the rocket baseline missile are its body, tail, and w___.
7. Although the rocket baseline missile has sufficient g's and turn rate to intercept a maneuvering aircraft, it needs a smaller turn r_____.
8. Compared to a co-altitude trajectory, the rocket baseline missile has extended range with a lo____ glide trajectory.
9. The ramjet baseline missile has a ch__ inlet.
10. The Mach 4 ramjet baseline missile has a ti_____ airframe.
11. The ramjet baseline combustor is a nickel-based super alloy, i_____.

12. The flight range of the ramjet baseline missile is driven by specific impulse, thrust, zero-lift drag coefficient, and the weight fraction of fu__.

13. Extended range for the ramjet baseline missile would be provided by more efficient packaging of subsystems and the use of sl____ fuel.

14. The flight range of the turbojet baseline missile is driven by fuel weight, specific impulse, and d___.

15. Efficiency corrections to the turbojet prediction account for total pressure losses in the compressor, combustor, turbine, nozzle, and i____.

16. A turbojet cruises most efficiently at high a_____.

17. A small diameter centrifugal compressor has higher ro_____ sp___.

18. A conceptual design sizing code should be based on the simplicity, speed, and robustness of ph_____ based methods.

19. The house of quality room for design characteristics has engineering characteristics that are most important in meeting cu_____ re_____.

20. A Pareto sensitivity identifies design parameters that are most im_____.

21. DOE provides a systematic evaluation of the broad possible de____ sp___.

Chapter 8

Development Process

- Missile Development Activities/Funding/Time frame
- Missile History/Follow-on Programs
- Cost, Risk, Performance Tradeoffs
- Tests/Integration
- State-of-the-Art Advancements
- New Technologies for Missiles

8.1 Introduction

The relationship of missile design and system engineering to the missile development process is presented in this chapter. It addresses the phases of missile development, missile development activities, Technology Readiness Level (TRL), cost-risk-performance trade-offs, examples of development tests and facilities, technology assessment/technology roadmap, typical attributes of a successful development program, the frequency of and the rationale for new missile system follow-on programs, examples of missile state-of-the-art advancement, and new technologies for missiles.

8.2 Missile Technology and System Development Process

Summarized in Fig. 8.1 is a summary of the research, technology, and acquisition (RT&A) funding process for missile systems of the United States. The middle portion of the process, technology development, is focused on the key enabling technologies that are driven by the requirements, but are in need of additional development and demonstration for a required level of maturity. Conceptual design and system engineering studies provide guidance for the development of the technologies. The

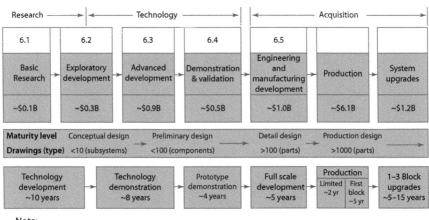

Fig. 8.1   Relationship of design maturity to the US Research, Technology, and Acquisition (RT&A) process.

technology development program addresses alternative approaches and risk mitigation. It has exit criteria for each phase, and an exit plan in the event of failure. The technology development and demonstration activities lead to a level of readiness for entry into Engineering and Manufacturing Development (EMD).

Early technology work addresses laboratory tests and demonstrations of a critical component of a subsystem in a representative environment, but not necessarily a full-scale environment. The next step of technology development is a laboratory or a flight demonstration of a subsystem in a representative, but not a full-scale environment. This is followed by either a laboratory demonstration or a flight Advanced Technology Demonstration (ATD) of a subsystem in a full-scale environment. Finally, there is a flight demonstration, based on either an Advanced Concept Technology Demonstration (ACTD) or a Program Definition and Risk Reduction (PDRR) of a full-scale prototype missile in a full-scale environment. This progression of technology development and demonstration is typically required for a missile to enter into EMD.

The figure also shows the relationship of missile design to the RT&A process. Conceptual design is most often conducted during the exploratory development phase of missile development. A primary objective of exploratory development is to investigate and evaluate technology alternatives. Research and technology funds are allocated to promising alternatives to demonstrate performance/cost as a hedge against uncertainties and risk. The next phase, advanced technology development, is intended to mature the enabling technologies of key subsystems. Although conceptual design may also be conducted later during advanced development, preliminary design methods are usually more appropriate during advanced development. The concept risk is reduced during preliminary design through the use of the more sophisticated prediction methods, parameter optimization, and testing. Preliminary design continues during advanced development demonstration of the prototype missile. Following successful demonstration of a prototype, the program moves into EMD. At this point more detail design methods are appropriate for the operational missile. However, the assessment of possible future block upgrades may require the reintroduction of preliminary design and conceptual design activities.

Conceptual design and system engineering studies should be conducted early in the exploratory development process, and continued into advanced development. Many of the cost and performance drivers may be locked in during the conceptual design phase. During conceptual design and system engineering it is important to quickly evaluate a large number of alternatives that cover the feasible design solution space as part of the downselect process.

Figure 8.2 relates the maturity of a subsystem or a technology for its application to a missile system. The technology levels that characterize the type of funding are derived from the Technology Readiness Level

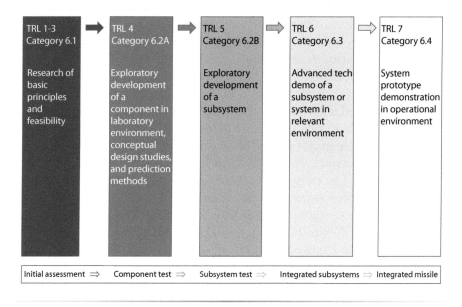

Fig. 8.2 Technology Readiness Level (TRL) indicates the maturity of technology.

(TRL) model, developed by NASA. TRLs for missile technology may be characterized as:

1. TRL 1-3 is research. The category of funding is 6.1. The technology goals of this category generally have limited consideration of the constraints of other component interactions or a specific application for the technology. An example of a basic research program is determining the basic strength characteristics of a new high temperature composite material, which may have numerous applications (e.g., missiles, ground vehicles, ships, submarines, aircraft, spacecraft). The differences of the TRL 1-3 levels are the degree of consideration of the interaction with the other components of the subsystem and the depth of consideration of operational applications. TRL 1 is basic research while an example of TRL 3 is research to evaluate its feasibility.
2. TRL 4 is laboratory development and laboratory test demonstration of a component. The category of funding is 6.2A exploratory development. In this category a component is usually tested in a representative laboratory environment, but not a full-scale environment. The component usually has general application (e.g., follow-on to AMRAAM, follow-on to JASSM). Conceptual design and analysis studies are also conducted in this category. These set the technology into a military context. Analytical prediction methods are usually developed under this category of funding. The accuracy of the analytical prediction methods is established by the laboratory experiments under this category.
3. TRL 5 is a laboratory development or demonstration of a subsystem. The subsystem usually has full-scale components and is tested in a representative, but not full-scale environment. The category of funding is 6.2B exploratory development category.
4. TRL 6 is a laboratory or a flight ATD of a full-scale subsystem in a relevant full-scale environment, with integration of some of the other subsystems and some of the other technologies of a follow-on missile system. Missile system digital and hardware-in-loop simulations are usually available in this phase. The software that is used in the phase is usually documented. This is the Concept Definition Phase of program development. The category of funding is 6.3 advanced development.
5. TRL 7 flight demonstration is either an ACTD or a PDRR full-scale prototype in a operational full-scale environment. The category of funding is 6.4 demonstration and validation. All of the new critical technologies and subsystems will be demonstrated in this phase. A driving consideration is to assure the system engineering and the confidence in the technologies. An ACTD or PDRR is normally performed when the technology and/or subsystem application is critical

and high risk. The technology availability date (TAD) for entry into EMD is based on successfully completing TRL 7.

Indications of design maturity include the number and type of drawings that describe the design and the number of alternative concepts that are currently under consideration. These are shown in Fig. 8.3 and the earlier Fig. 8.1. Conceptual design may be characterized by approximately five drawings for each concept, describing perhaps five subsystems. The stage of drawing maturity for conceptual design is typically TRL 4-5. A large number of alternative missile system concepts, perhaps up to ten, are in evaluation during conceptual design. Conceptual design drawings include the overall dimensions of the missile, major subsystems layout, and the major subsystems mass properties. The next step is preliminary design. The stage of drawing maturity for preliminary design is typically TRL 6. Preliminary design drawings of a prototype missile are usually characterized by up to 100 drawings, with greater detail and showing up to 100 components. Preliminary design drawings have fully dimensioned subsystems, inboard layouts showing the subsystems, individual subsystem and component drawings, and dimension tolerances. A fewer number of alternative missile system concepts, perhaps two-to-four, are under evaluation during preliminary design. Following preliminary design, the next step is detail design. The stage of drawing maturity is TRL 7. Detail design for EMD usually requires more than 100 drawings and often has more than 1000 drawings.

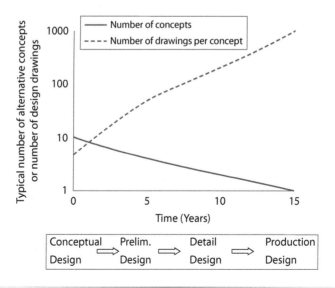

Fig. 8.3 Conceptual design has broad alternatives while detail design has high definition.

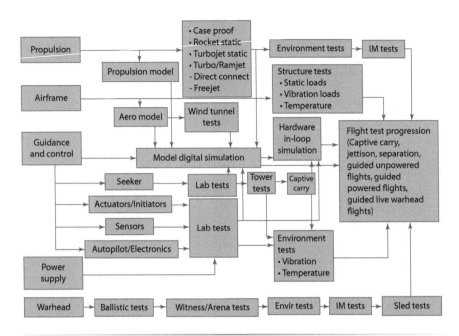

Fig. 8.4 Missile technology development and design validation activities.

Production drawings have even more detail, including drawings of each part, detailed work assembly instructions, and descriptions of the manufacturing processes. During EMD and production there is usually only one design concept (e.g., sole source contractor) or perhaps at most two similar design concepts (two competitive contractors).

Figure 8.4 shows the typical technology development and design validation activities for missiles. A primary integration/system engineering tool for missile design development/validation is system simulation. The initial simulations used in conceptual and preliminary design activities are digital simulations. As missile hardware becomes available, a hardware-in-loop (HWL) simulation is also developed. HWL simulation incorporates the missile guidance and control hardware (e.g., seeker, gyros, accelerometers, actuators, autopilot) mounted on a flight table that provides full-scale rotation rates and accelerations. It also includes a simulated target signal for the seeker to track. Either an all-digital or a hybrid computer may be used in HWL simulation. In the case of hybrid HWL simulation, fast analog computers simulate the rapidly changing parameters, such as the flight trajectory equations of motion. Digital computers for a hybrid HWL simulation are used for the more slowly changing parameters, such as computing the forces and moments from aerodynamics and propulsion. More modern HWL simulation is based on multiple all-digital computers with parallel processing that is sufficiently fast to model the rapidly changing dynamics. As an example, the required update rate for solving the equations of motion may be less than a ms, to provide sufficient accuracy to the simulation. HWL and digital simulations are the primary system analysis tools that are used in missile development. The simulation results and its input data from wind tunnel, seeker, and propulsion tests are validated with flight test results. HWL and digital simulations are also used to determine the cause of flight test anomalies. In recent years the number of developmental flight tests has been reduced, primarily because of the increased confidence in the HWL and digital simulations. HWL and digital simulations provide a large amount of information at a relatively low cost and are cost-effective complements to flight test. The approximately $4 million per year cost to maintain an HWL and digital simulation capability is relatively small compared to the cost of a typical flight test program. Each missile launch in development flight test typically costs from about 100,000 to $2 million, depending upon the unit cost of the development missile, the cost of the range, the complexity of the flight test, and the frequency of testing. Also, the time required to initiate and complete an HWL evaluation is relatively short (e.g., $\sim$1 month) compared to the time that is required to initiate and complete a flight test program (e.g., $\sim$2 years).

Launch platform integration should be considered from the start of the subsystems development, continuing as the subsystems evolve into a missile system. In the area of propulsion, propulsion environmental tests, motor case proof loads tests, static firings, and insensitive munition tests are conducted before a missile with a live rocket motor is fired from a launch platform. For the airframe, wind tunnel configuration development tests are conducted. Store separation wind tunnel tests are also conducted for an air launched missile. Structure tests confirm the missile structural integrity from static and vibration loads at low and high temperature. In the guidance and control area, laboratory tests are conducted in a simulated ground and flight environment for the missile seeker, inertial navigation system, data link, flight control gyros and accelerometers, flight control actuators, and electronics. The laboratory tests include environmental tests that simulate the environmental conditions such as the operational temperature, humidity, rain rate, shock, and vibration. The missile modeling and simulation activities of an air launched missile include a safe separation analysis. Modeling of a missile with active flight control during separation includes the flight control system sensors, actuators, and electronics. Similar to the propulsion area, the warhead has insensitive munition tests prior to firing a missile with a live warhead from the launch platform. For the missile system, flight test validation is a progressive activity of increasing complexity. The objective of progressively complex testing is to minimize the risk and enhance the safety in the flight test activity. For example, a typical progression of flight demonstration for an air launched missile begins with captive carriage of the missile and ends with launches of the guided missile with a live warhead. Intermediate flight testing may include store jettison tests, safe separation tests, guided unpowered flights with an inert warhead, and guided powered flights with an inert warhead. Telemetry (TM) data from flight test include the flight control deflections, missile accelerations, missile rotation rates, guidance and control gains, and the seeker tracking rate. A good flight test program will compare the flight test data (e.g., control surface deflections) with simulation and analytical predictions. Following completion of development flight test, which is conducted by the contractor, the next phase is operational test and evaluation that is conducted by the military.

Examples of missile development tests and test facilities are shown in Figure 8.5. Figure 8.5a gives examples of aerodynamics and propulsion tests and facilities. The top right photograph is an example of a wind tunnel test, a ramjet missile model in the ONERA wind tunnel facility. The types of data that are acquired in a wind tunnel test include six component aerodynamic force and moment data, dynamic stability derivatives data, surface pressure data, flow field data, aerodynamic heat transfer data, infrared signature data, and aeroelastic data. The next example is a propulsion test of a static rocket motor firing with TVC. Measurements are made

a) • Airframe wind tunnel test ....

• Propulsion static firing with TVC ....

• Propulsion direct connect test ....

• Propulsion freejet test ....

Fig. 8.5a Examples of missile development tests and facilities—aerodynamics and propulsion.

b) • Warhead arena test ....

• Warhead sled test ....

• Insensitive munition test ....

• Structure load test ....

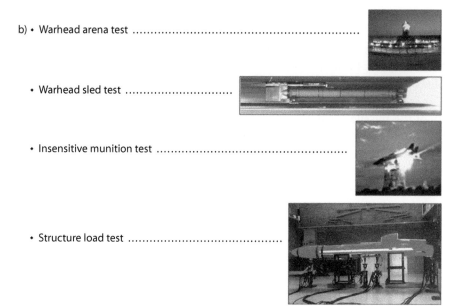

Fig. 8.5b Examples of missile development tests and facilities—warhead and structure.

of thrust versus time. Measurements also include the side forces and moments to evaluate thrust misalignment. Also for a missile with TVC, measurements are made of the six forces and moments provided by the TVC. The bottom right photograph shows an example of an air breathing propulsion direct connect test, in this case the Armiger ducted rocket missile. In the left side of the photograph are four direct connect pipes that supply preheated air to simulate the inlet flow into the combustor. Actual hardware can be tested for the gas generator, combustor, and nozzle. Finally, the bottom left photograph is a freejet test of the HyFly Dual Combustor Ramjet-Scramjet (DCR). The freejet test operates the entire propulsion system, including the inlet, over the angle of attack, Mach number, and altitude envelope. Propulsion tests may also acquire infrared signature data.

Figure 8.5b shows examples of warhead and structure tests and the facilities. The top photograph is a warhead arena test conducted at the Naval Air Warfare Center—China Lake, California. The warhead fragments that penetrate the witness plates provide information on the size and the spatial distribution of the fragments. The next photograph shows a sled test of a warhead. Warhead sled tests are conducted to evaluate the warhead effectiveness in a dynamic environment. Sled tests provide data on the warhead performance as a function of the missile velocity and the orientation of the target at impact. The third photograph is an insensitive munitions live fire test. Insensitive munition tests are conducted with fragment impact, blast, fire cook-off, and other hostile environments. The photograph shows an insensitive munition test of a threat missile impact. The insensitive munition tests provide measurements of the hazards severity of the missile warhead and the propulsion subsystems. Hazard severity measurements may require instrumentation capable of very short time measurements. For example, the rise time of a warhead detonation is about 2 μs. The bottom photograph in the figure shows a structure load test. Structure load tests of the missile airframe are conducted using hydraulic actuators to provide simulated loads. Testing may be conducted at elevated temperature. The missile structure is instrumented with strain gauges to measure the stain, structural displacement, and structural failure mode conditions. Structure load tests are usually conducted only on high cost, long range missiles, such as cruise missiles.

Figure 8.5c shows examples of missile seeker, HWL, environmental, and submunition dispenser tests and facilities.

The upper right photograph is a Standard Missile seeker test in an anechoic chamber. The seeker performance against a simulated target is evaluated, along with its interfaces with the guidance section.

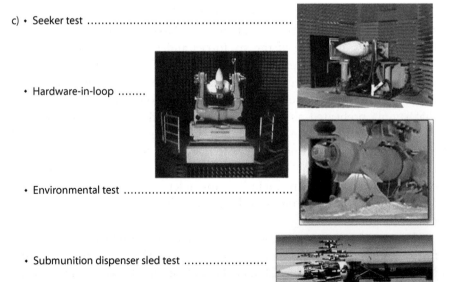

c) • Seeker test ....

• Hardware-in-loop ....

• Environmental test ....

• Submunition dispenser sled test ....

Fig. 8.5c Examples of missile development tests and facilities—seeker, HWL, environmental, and submunition dispenser.

d) • RCS test ....

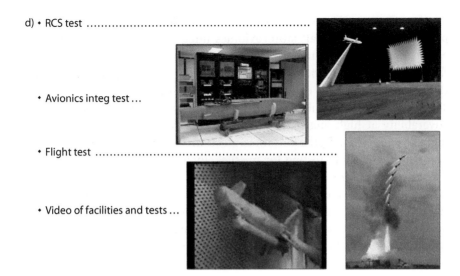

• Avionics integ test ...

• Flight test ....

• Video of facilities and tests ...

Fig. 8.5d Examples of missile development tests and facilities—RCS, store/ avionic integration, and flight test.

The left photograph is a rate table for AMRAAM guidance and control HWL simulation. The rate table provides simulated flight trajectory pitch, yaw, and roll rates for rate-sensitive guidance and control hardware such as missile gyros and actuators. The rate table requires high performance actuators, usually hydraulic, to move at the required rates ($\sim$1000 deg/s) and bandwidth ($\sim$40 Hz). The AMRAAM seeker in the figure is surrounded by an anechoic chamber that includes the simulated target.

Shown in the middle right photograph is an AGM-130 environmental test to demonstrate the reliability and performance of guidance and control hardware at low temperature. The environment used in reliability demonstration tests is usually based on a simulation of the missile mission profiles. During development the missile is subjected to a sequence of environmental conditions with a level, duration, and order that match the mission. About 50% of failures of an operational missile are due to the environmental conditions. A non-environmental event that may contribute to failure is handling.

The bottom right photograph shows a submunition dispenser test to evaluate the flight trajectory pattern of submunitions. Accurate dispensing of submunitions is a challenge, particularly at high dynamic pressure, because of the complex aerodynamic interactions of the submunitions. High speed sleds may be used in the development of a submuntion dispenser.

Figure 8.5d shows concluding examples of missile system development and integration testing and the test facilities. In the top right of the figure is a JSOW RCS test in the Bi-static Anechoic Chamber at the Naval Air

Warfare Center—Weapons Division. In the top left section of the figure is a photograph of an aircraft store/avionics integration laboratory test at the Naval Air Warfare Center—China Lake. Tests are conducted to determine the launch platform avionics compatibility with the weapon. The bottom right photograph is an example of a flight test of a surface-to-air missile. The Aster FSAF 15 missile is demonstrating its stability and control and maneuverability at high angles of attack over the Mach number and altitude flight envelope. Finally, the bottom left section of the figure is a video of development facilities and testing for missiles. Included are examples of a wind tunnel force and moment test, wind tunnel store separation test, rocket motor static test including radiography measurement, thrust vector control static test, reaction jet control hover flight test demonstration, propellant development, scramjet freejet test, warhead arena test, warhead sled test, penetrator warhead (BLU-109) test, insensitive munitions tests, hardware-in-loop simulation, explosive device initiator test, environmental tests, submunition dispense test, aircraft avionics/store integration laboratory test, TVC flight demonstration test, and launch demonstration flight tests.

New facilities may be required for the development of future missiles. As an example, the current hypersonic facilities for aerodynamic and propulsion testing have limited capability to simulate the Mach number and altitude of large hypersonic missiles. A benefit of conceptual design and system engineering studies is the timely identification of new facility requirements for future missiles.

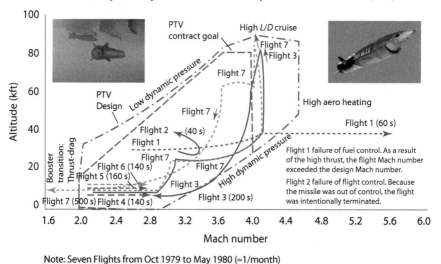

Example: Ramjet baseline missile Propulsion Test Validation (PTV)

Note: Seven Flights from Oct 1979 to May 1980 (≈1/month)

Fig. 8.6 Missile development flight test should cover the extremes/corners of the design flight envelope.

Figure 8.6 is an example of a typical missile technology flight test validation program. Flight test validation was discussed previously in Fig. 8.1. The example is based on the ASALM Propulsion Test Validation (PTV) flight test program for the ramjet baseline missile. It was an efficient flight test, with seven flights conducted from October 1979 to May 1980 (approximately one flight per month).

A normal plan for a flight test demonstration is that it should progress from an initial low risk demonstration of nominal performance to an evaluation of the limits of the design flight envelope. Note from the figure that the areas of concern for the ASALM PTV flight test were booster transition to ramjet thrust take-over, aerodynamic maneuver performance, cruise performance at high dynamic pressure, engine operation and cruise at low dynamic pressure, structural integrity at high aerodynamic heating, and high L/D cruise performance.

The objectives of Flight 1 were to simply conduct a nominal launch, transition from rocket boost to ramjet propulsion, and then operate in the middle of the flight envelope. However the missile did not operate in accordance with the plan. In this case, the fuel control stuck wide open, driving the missile outside of the design flight envelope. Flight 1 accidentally went Mach 5.7, exceeding the design requirement for Mach number, dynamic pressure, and temperature. Finally, after fuel exhaustion and 60 s of flight, the missile structure failed. In addition to controlling the missile outside the design Mach number, during Flight 1 the flight control system had to contend with an anomaly of large oscillatory moments. The ASALM inlet was designed with splitter plates, for a lighter weight inlet structure. Unfortunately, the flow in the channels of the splitter plates was oscillatory, with the normal shocks occurring at different locations in the channels. This resulted in large oscillatory moments that nearly overwhelmed the flight control system. Another anomaly that was observed in Flight 1 was a reduction in the flight control effectiveness, due to plume-induced flow separation over the tail control. Fortunately, there was sufficient design margin in the flight control system to handle the anomalies. The next flight (Flight 2) also had a failure, of the flight control system. The range safety officer terminated the flight of the out-of-control missile after 40 s of flight. However, the flight did demonstrate high angle of attack maneuverability. ASALM was designed for both an air-to-surface mission and an air-to-air mission. The air-to-air bomber defense mission required the capability for a rapid heading change up to 180 deg for an aft intercept of an aircraft target. The next flight, Flight 3, was successful. It demonstrated operation in the high dynamic pressure environment of low altitude supersonic cruise. It also demonstrated operation at a high Mach number cruise and a split level trajectory consisting of a powered dive from high altitude with a pullout at low altitude. Total time of flight was 200 s, including 40 s of high L/D cruise at Mach 4.1/80 kft.

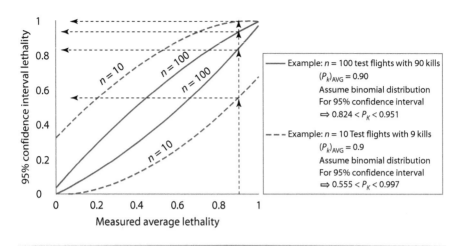

Fig. 8.7 A large number of test flights are required for a high confidence missile system. (Reference: Dixon W.J. and Massey, F.J., *Introduction to Statistical Analysis*, McGraw-Hill, 1969.)

Inspection of the missile after the flight showed that the combustor insulation had performed well in the long duration flight, without a burn through. Flights 4, 5, and 6 demonstrated inlet start and acceleration at low supersonic Mach number (Mach 2), low altitude (5000 ft) cruise duration (up to 160 s) and range, and pitch/yaw maneuver capability. The last flight, Flight 7 demonstrated the high Mach number cruise duration and range. Total time of flight was 500 s, including 300 s cruise at Mach 4.1/80 kft altitude.

A lesson learned in missile development is to be prepared to address anomalies from the "unknown unknowns"—problems that occur during the development flight test that were not envisioned in the design and were not uncovered during the preceding ground tests and simulations. Another lesson learned is to plan for a sufficient number of test missiles to compensate for flight test failures.

Again referring back to Fig. 8.1, note that flight test validation occurs near the end of EMD. Figure 8.7 shows a typical confidence interval in the flight test validation of missile lethality as a function of the number of flight tests n. It is based on an assumed binomial distribution, with a pass/fail result from each test. Note from the figure that a high confidence requires a large number of tests. As an example, assume that a large number of test flights ($n = 100$) provides 90 kills. Then

$$(P_K)_{\text{AVG}} = 90/100 = 0.90$$

From Ref. 46, for a binomial distribution with a 95% confidence interval

$$0.824 < P_K < 0.951$$

Now assume that there is a lower number of test flights ($n = 10$) that provides 9 kills. The average kill probability is the same

$$(P_K)_{AVG} = 9/10 = 0.9$$

However, there is much lower confidence in the second result. From a binomial distribution with a 95% confidence interval

$$0.555 < P_K < 0.997$$

The number of tests in development testing and evaluation (DT&E) and operational tests and evaluation (OT&E) have been reduced in recent years because there is higher confidence in simulation. However, as discussed previously, a simulation is no better than the quality of its input data and the quality of its modeling. A flight test program that evaluates the extremes/corners of the flight envelope with enough tests to provide high confidence is recommended. A problem with an austere flight test program is that it is likely that it will not identify all of the major problems. It is more expensive to correct problems and retrofit missiles after the missile has gone into production. It may be difficult for management to accept a realistic probability of failures in development testing and to provide sufficient funding for the required number of test missiles. For example, if a missile is expected to have an operational probability of kill of $P_K = 0.9$, an austere development test program may allocate only 10% additional missiles to account for failures. However, additional missiles are probably necessary to allow re-tests because of events such as propulsion failure, guidance failure, flight control failure, TM lost, target failure, anomalies in performance, and a lower developmental reliability than that that of the operational missile. A missile with an operational effectiveness of $P_K = 0.9$ typically has an effectiveness $P_K \sim 0.6$ during development testing. Approximately 70% additional assets should be planned for its development testing, to allow re-tests of unsuccessful flights.

Most missile block upgrades that were discussed in Fig. 8.1 address the areas of improved guidance, flight control, and propulsion. An example of a block upgrade plan is the Fig. 8.8 evolution plan for SM-3 for the years 2006 to 2014. The SM-3 basic block IA year 2006 missile is shown in the left portion of the figure. It has a one color seeker and a pulsed divert and attitude control system (DACS). Block upgrade IB introduces a two color seeker (with improved target acquisition and discrimination), an improved DACS (with throttle capability), and an improved electronics processor. The Block II upgrade introduces larger diameter (21 in.) second and third stage rocket motors, consistent with the maximum diameter constraint of the Mk 41 VLS launcher. The larger rocket motors provide a longer range intercept capability. Block IIA introduces a larger diameter (21 in.) kill vehicle. The seeker and DACs of the new kill vehicle provide longer range discrimination and a larger divert capability.

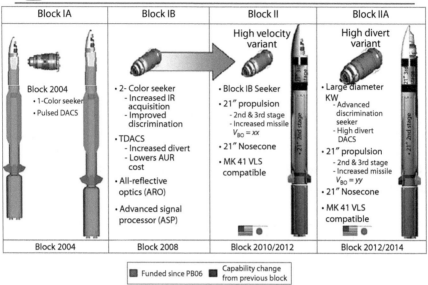

Aegis BMD SM-3 Evolution plan

Block IA	Block IB	Block II	Block IIA
		High velocity variant	High divert variant

Block 2004
• 1-Color seeker
• Pulsed DACS
	• 2- Color seeker
	  - Increased IR acquisition
	  - Improved discrimination
	• TDACS
	  - Increased divert
	  - Lowers AUR cost
	• All-reflective optics (ARO)
	• Advanced signal processor (ASP)
		• Block IB Seeker
		• 21" propulsion
		  - 2nd & 3rd stage
		  - Increased missile
		    $V_{BO} = xx$
		• 21" Nosecone
		• MK 41 VLS compatible
			• Large diameter KW
			  - Advanced discrimination seeker
			  - High divert DACS
			• 21" propulsion
			  - 2nd & 3rd stage
			  - Increased missile
			    $V_{BO} = yy$
			• 21" Nosecone
			• MK 41 VLS compatible

Block 2004	Block 2008	Block 2010/2012	Block 2012/2014

■ Funded since PB06   ■ Capability change from previous block

Fig. 8.8   Most missile block upgrades provide improved guidance, control, and propulsion. (Source: 06-MDA-1922, September 13, 2006.)

Block upgrade evolution plans need to flexible, to accommodate future funding uncertainty. Most block upgrade plans do not meet their original schedule dates because of lack of funding.

8.3   New Missile Program Planning and Development

An activity for planning a new missile program is the development of a technology roadmap. Products of technology assessment and technology road-mapping include the identification of the key, enabling, high payoff technologies; the technology drivers; key decision points; critical paths; facility requirements; and the resource needs for technology development. The technology roadmap establishes the time phase relationships that are required for the missile technology development activity. This includes 1) development of plans for technology development and validation, 2) identification of the technology options, 3) setting time-phased technology goals, and 4) development of a plan for technology transition. The technology plan provides an approach in maturing the missile technology through the development phases. As a result of technology development, the level of maturity will move from that of exploratory development, to advanced technology development, to a prototype demonstration. For most new missiles, a technology development, risk reduction, and maturity demonstration activity is required prior to entering EMD.

An optimum allocation of funding for technology investment is a difficult task. Some technologies may have the potential to satisfy the requirements but may be highly immature. There may be insufficient time or insufficient funding available to mature the technology to the required level of performance, cost, and confidence in the time frame of interest. As a result, the highly immature technologies would not be included in the technology roadmap for a specific missile. Other technologies may be mature, with high confidence in their performance and cost. However, the technologies may fall short of meeting the requirements and a funding investment may do little to improve their performance/cost. As a result, the mature technologies would not be included in the technology roadmap. Technologies that would be included in the technology roadmap are those that have high potential payoff and can be matured within the available time and funding.

Some attributes of a good technology development and demonstration program are

1. Balanced Emphasis of Analytical/Experimental. A program with little emphasis on analytical activity is likely to have a non-optimum design. At the other extreme, a program with little emphasis on experimental activity is likely have either a high risk, under-designed missile or a highly over-designed missile. Also, it is good practice to compare analytical results with experimental results and resolve their differences.
2. Contractor Competition. Competition is a motivator to provide high quality work at lower cost.
3. Team Camaraderie and Performance Under Pressure. The technology development and demonstration team is relatively small group compared to the larger groups that conduct missile system development and production. A technology team has little redundancy in the personnel, with typically one or two persons for each area. The technology program success/failure reflect directly on the individuals of the team. Because technology development programs do not usually fit a universal template, it is good practice to have dedicated members for all areas, including
Management
Design
Technology
Test
Manufacturing
Contracts
Security

Example design concept	Example constraints
Lowest Cost concept	Risk and Performance Threshold/ Standard requirements
Lowest Risk concept (e.g., Derivative concept)	Cost and Performance Threshold/ Standard requirements
Highest Performance concept	Cost and Risk Threshold/Standard requirements
Best Value concept (e.g., Best combination of Cost, Risk, Performance)  — Performance, Cost, Risk	Cost, Risk, and Performance Standard/Goal requirements

Questions to be answered before picking a preferred concept/approach
1. The preferred concept/approach strengths will lead to a successful program
2. The preferred concept/approach weaknesses are minor
3. Alternative concepts/approaches have more serious weaknesses

Conceptual design and system engineering studies are required to evaluate cost, risk, and performance of candidate, alternative concepts

Fig. 8.9   Conceptual design and system engineering is required to explore alternative approaches.

4. Broad/Honest Assessment of Alternatives. Ideally, the alternatives that are considered in conceptual design and system engineering should not be overly constrained by the biases of the culture of the organization.
5. Program Manager Authority. The program manager should have the support of the team members and upper management.
6. Stability. Program funding and requirements should be stable during the program development. "Peanut butter funding", or stretching out a program to accommodate a funding shortfall after the program initiation can kill a program. Also, changing the requirements (requirements creep) during the program can kill a program.

A conceptual design and system engineering activity is required to explore the typically large design space of alternative approaches. Often the primary drivers of the design are its cost, performance, and risk. These are illustrated in Fig. 8.9. It is usually instructive to develop individual designs that emphasize these attributes, such as

1. Lowest cost concept that also satisfies the risk and performance threshold/standard requirements
2. Lowest risk concept (e.g., derivative concept from an existing missile) that also satisfies the cost and performance threshold/ standard requirements

3. Highest performance concept that also satisfies the cost and risk threshold/standard requirements
4. Best value concept that is the "best" combination of cost, risk, and performance that satisfies the standard/goal requirements

Questions to be answered before picking a preferred concept/approach include

1. The preferred concept/approach has strengths that should lead to a successful program.
2. The preferred concept/approach weaknesses are minor and can be corrected during development.
3. Alternative concepts/approaches have more serious weaknesses than the preferred concept.

Conceptual design studies and system engineering are required to evaluate the cost, risk, and performance of candidate, alternative concepts. The best value concept is often the preferred approach.

Over the last 50 + years missiles have provided a transformational operational capability for the military and have largely replaced unguided weapons such as guns and bombs. Because of their enhanced range and accuracy—air-to-air missiles have largely replaced aircraft guns, air-to-surface missiles have largely replaced dumb bombs, surface-to-air missiles have largely replaced anti-aircraft artillery, and surface-to-surface missiles have largely replaced artillery.

Figure 8.10 illustrates the initial operational application of the following missile transformational technologies and the operational benefits:

IOC Year 1956: the proportional guidance accuracy of AIM-9 Sidewinder led to better lethality and higher exchange ratio in air-to-air combat. As an example, on the first combat application of Sidewinder in September 1958, Republic of China F-86 aircraft destroyed People's Republic of China MIG-17 gun-only aircraft, with no losses.

IOC Year 1957: The R-7 missile provided a capability for long range intercontinental strategic missile strike.

IOC Year 1957: The SA-2 Guideline (V-77) two-stage high performance rocket motor provided a capability for high altitude intercept. On 1 May 1960 the SA-2 shot down a high altitude U-2 reconnaissance aircraft.

IOC Year 1969: the semi-active laser precision guidance accuracy of the GBU-10 guided bomb reduced the number of required aircraft sorties, providing higher aircraft survivability. A historical example of the value of precision guided weapons is the 13 May 1972 attack on the Thanh Hoa Bridge in Vietnam. For more than six years, a total of 871 aircraft sorties dropped unguided bombs but failed to close the bridge. However, the first operational application of laser-guided bombs resulted in direct

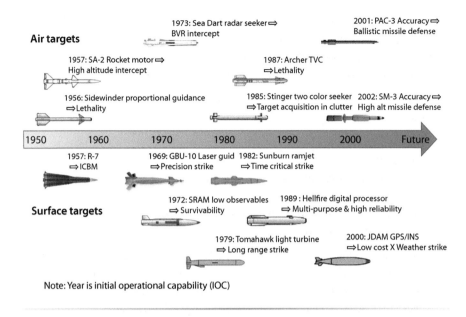

Fig. 8.10 Missile technologies have transformed warfare.

hits on the supporting piers, successfully closing the bridge. Eleven aircraft had been lost in the 871 previous sorties. No aircraft were lost in the four sorties using precision guided munitions. More recent examples are the growing use of precision strike weapons are their applications in Desert Storm, Kosovo, and Enduring Freedom. In the year 1991 Desert Storm operation, 9% of the strike weapons were guided weapons. In Kosovo, 35% of the strike weapons were guided weapons. In the year 2002 Enduring Freedom operation, 69% of the strike weapons were guided weapons.

IOC Year 1972: The low observables of SRAM provided a higher projected capability for missile survivability, a greater number of targets killed per bomber, and enhanced bomber survivability. SRAM provided the B-52 and B-1 bombers with enhanced survivability for standoff attack against defended targets.

IOC Year 1973: The radar seeker of Sea Dart led to the first combat demonstration of a beyond visual range (BVR) surface-to-air missile. Sea Dart had seven kills in the 1982 Falkland Islands War, including BVR kills against long range, high altitude aircraft.

IOC Year 1979: The light weight turbine of Tomahawk led to the long range standoff, relatively small size cruise missile. Tomahawk became a weapon of choice for long range strike. During Desert Storm (year 1991), 297 Tomahawks were fired at long range standoff, with more than 90% destroying their targets.

IOC Year 1982: The ramjet propulsion of SS-N-22 Sunburn led to the capability of time critical attack of ship targets, with enhanced missile survivability from high speed, high altitude, and long range standoff.

IOC Year 1985: The two color (infrared/ultraviolet) seeker of Stinger led to better target acquisition in clutter (atmosphere ozone layer filters out solar UV) and better countermeasure resistance. Introduced in Afghanistan in 1986, Stingers shot down more than 200 fixed wing aircraft and helicopters.

IOC Year 1987: The thrust vector control (TVC) of AA-11 Archer led to large off-boresight, reduced time for firing, and enhanced capability against maneuvering aircraft. This provided high lethality and exchange ratio in short range air-to-air combat. Its introduction made the AIM-9L missile obsolete.

IOC Year 1989: The digital processor of 1989 Hellfire led to flight trajectory flexibility and a multi-mission missile with higher reliability. In the opening salvo of Desert Storm, Apache helicopters used Hellfire missiles to destroy Iraq low frequency early warning radar sites, clearing the way for F-117 aircraft.

IOC Year 2000: The Global Positioning System/inertial navigation system (GPS/INS) guidance of JDAM led to a low cost adverse weather fire-and-forget weapon. As of the year 2009, more than 200,000 JDAMs have been produced, with more than 20,000 dropped in combat.

IOC Year 2001: The kinetic hit-to-kill kill accuracy of PAC-3 led to a high lethality for terminal ballistic missile defense. During Iraqi Freedom (year 2003), PAC-3 successfully destroyed threat ballistic missiles.

IOC Year 2002: The exo-atmospheric accuracy of SM-3 led to a capability for long range/high altitude missile defense. During the year 2008 an SM-3 demonstrated the capability to destroy a satellite, with limited debris.

Figure 8.11 shows that the frequency of a follow-on program is about every 24 years for most US tactical missiles. For a strategic missile, the time interval to the follow-on program is likely to be longer. For example, ALCM (EMD year 1974), Minuteman III (EMD year 1966), and Trident (EMD year 1968) have not yet had follow-on programs. Follow-on programs for strategic missiles are often limited by political considerations. Once a missile is in production, it usually has a long lifetime, including block upgrades. Block upgrades often incorporate the emerging new technologies in electronics, sensors, and propulsion. Block upgrades are also often necessary for new launch platform integration. However, eventually a capability is needed that is not easily achievable through a block upgrade, requiring a new follow-on missile development. Examples are shown in the figure of the driving requirements in the follow-on missile programs. These are the improved maneuverability of AIM-9X; autonomous seeker, lighter weight, improved speed and longer range of AIM-120; improved speed and range of AGM-88; improved accuracy (hit-to-kill) of PAC-3; higher gunner survivability (lower observables, launch-and-leave), lethality, and lighter weight of Javelin; reduced RCS of AGM-129 (partial follow-on to ALCM); and the

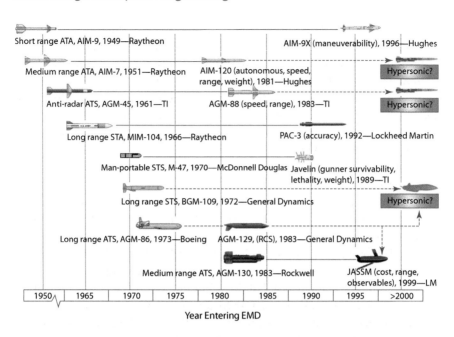

Fig. 8.11   US tactical missile follow-on programs occur about every 24 years.

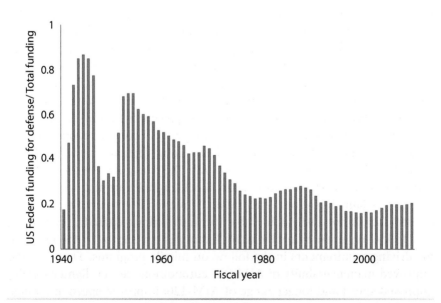

Fig. 8.12   There is currently relatively low US emphasis on funding defense programs. (Source: US Office of Management and Budget, FY 2009 Budget, Table 6-1.)

Year 1985   **Year 1997**

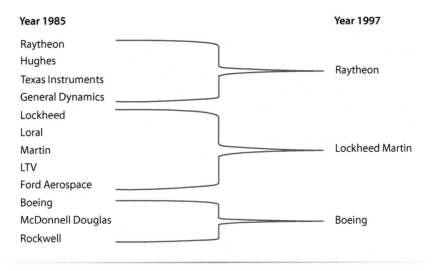

Fig. 8.13 US missile system development is conducted by three contractors (1985–1997 consolidations). (Source: US Defense Science Board, May 1997.)

combined robustness of lower cost, longer range and reduced observables of JASSM. It is interesting to note that in almost no case does a missile follow-on program go to the incumbent contractor of the current missile.

Because of a lack of funding, there were no US new missile EMD programs during the 2000 decade. There may be opportunities for a new start for a US hypersonic air-breathing missile in the post-2010 year time frame. A hypersonic air-breathing missile provides faster time-to-target and may also provide longer range (compared to an endo-atmospheric rocket). Opportunities include follow-on programs for the air-to-air AIM-120 AMRAAM, the air-to-surface defense suppression AGM-88 HARM, and cruise missiles (BGM-109 Tomahawk, AGM-86 CALCM).

There is currently relatively little funding available for new missile programs. Figure 8.12 shows the fraction of US defense funding compared to the total US federal funding for the fiscal years 1940-2009. Note that the current defense funding emphasis is the lowest since just before World War II.

Another concern is the relatively low number of missile system contractors. Figure 8.13 shows the US missile contractor consolidations, going from twelve contractors in the year 1985 to three contractors in the year 1997. Implications of the consolidations include less competition, less creativity, and more vertical integration (fewer suppliers).

8.4 Example of Missile Technology Development

An example of a missile technology development activity will be presented for the area of aerodynamics. It illustrates the maturity development and risk reduction activities of missile aerodynamics. Conceptual design is usually based on predicted aerodynamics using simple methods, such as the methods described in this text, without the benefit of test data for the new configuration. Preliminary design may also be initially based on prediction, using more sophisticated codes. The accuracy is improved when wind tunnel data become available. Relatively low fidelity simulation (e.g., 3-DOF digital) is conducted during conceptual design, to provide an initial estimate of flight performance and stability and control. The 6-DOF digital simulation and the hardware-in-loop simulation are usually initiated during preliminary design, continuing with refinement through flight test. The 6-DOF simulation provides integration of aerodynamics with flight control and other subsystems.

Examples of preliminary design aerodynamic prediction codes are Missile DATCOM, MISL3, SUPL, and AP09.

The Missile DATCOM (DATa COMpendium) is a Fortran 90 computer code [47] that was developed under the sponsorship of the Air Force Research Laboratory, Wright-Patterson Air Force Base, Ohio. It is available at low cost. The generalized methods are applicable to wing-body-tail configurations with circular and noncircular body cross section at any angle of attack. It can model inlets and protuberances. Surfaces may be at arbitrary roll orientation and deflection. Missile DATCOM is more applicable to preliminary design because of the large number of input parameters and the time required to prepare input data and to analyze output. Missile DATCOM is a complex computer program, with 405 subroutines.

The Nielsen Engineering and Research (NEAR) MISL3 computer code [11] is based on the equivalent angle of attack method developed by NEAR. It includes the effects of vortex shedding, configuration geometry, and Mach number. MISL3 is applicable to wing-body-tail configurations at high angle of attack, arbitrary roll angle, and arbitrary control surface deflection. Bodies may have conical changes in diameter, which allows the modeling of body flares and boattails. Surfaces may be in-line or interdigitated. The output includes forces and moments, loads, hinge moments, bending moments, and dynamic stability derivatives. MISL3 is more applicable to preliminary design because it does not automatically transfer output data to a flight trajectory code, requiring a longer input time.

The NEAR MISDL computer code [11] is a subsonic and supersonic panel method that models up to two different planar surfaces at different locations, including the effect of planar surface-body interference. The body cross section can be noncircular, including bodies with chines. Surfaces may have two, three, or four panels. The body and planar surface separation vortices are tracked aft of their separation points. Either two-dimensional shock expansion theory or Newtonian impact theory can be selected to provide lifting surface pressure calculations. Surface pressures are integrated to provide loads, forces, and moments. MISDL is limited to relatively low angles of attack and control surface deflection. The code handles arbitrary surface geometry and roll angle. It is more applicable to preliminary design because of the time required to model the surface panels.

The Aeroprediction Incorporated Code AP09 [48] includes bodies of elliptical cross section, high angle of attack, arbitrary control surface deflection, arbitrary roll angle, and base bleed. It has been periodically updated over the years. The output includes forces and moments, dynamic stability derivatives, pressure distribution, load distribution, the airframe temperature response, and a three-degree-of-freedom flight trajectory simulation. It is user-friendly for preliminary design, with a plotting program for aerodynamic coefficients, a geometric sketch of the input configuration, and compatibility with personal computers. The integrated three-degree-of-simulation expedites design convergence.

Computational fluid dynamics (CFD) provides a solution of the Navier-Stokes equations that can be suitable for complex flow fields and configuration geometry. Disadvantages of CFD include a long setup time and usually a requirement for parallel processing. However, CFD is useful as a check of selected cases of results from the more traditional approaches to aerodynamic prediction. As an example of CFD, ESI has a relatively user friendly/relatively fast CFD program (CFD-FASTRAN) that can run on a PC. It is applicable to complex problems such as complex aerodynamic shape, jet interaction, and store separation. CFDRC has conducted a number of missile application studies using CFD-FASTRAN.

Examples of preliminary design optimization techniques are the response surface methods based on meta-models, probabilistic analysis, and flight trajectory optimization. Response surface methods provide a meta-model polynomial approximation of the results from running a more sophisticated aerodynamic prediction code. Only the most important, Pareto-type, driving parameters are included in the polynomial approximation. This allows a rapid assessment of the available design space and the use of probabilistic analysis to evaluate design robustness. Probabilistic analysis provides an assessment of the robustness of the design to design uncertainty in areas such as cost and performance. Flight trajectory optimization tools, such as OTIS and POST, allow an evaluation of the sensitivity of the optimum flight trajectory to performance parameters. OTIS has an advantage of a broad range of applicability while POST has an advantage of a shorter set-up time.

Wind tunnel testing develops the aerodynamic configuration and verifies the conceptual and preliminary design prediction. Wind tunnel testing is a progressive series of tests of increasing complexity. The initial tests are usually simple body build-up evaluations of the aerodynamic configuration alternatives. The initial data are six component forces and moments with undeflected control surfaces. An objective is to define a baseline configuration that has low drag, high lift, and a small variation in aerodynamic center. Following body build-up tests, a missile baseline configuration is selected, and a wind tunnel test is conducted to determine flight control effectiveness and the control surface hinge moment. In the control effectiveness test the control surfaces are systematically deflected in "pure" pitch, yaw, or roll and asymmetric combined pitch, yaw, and roll configurations over their limits for the Mach number, angle of attack, and roll attitude envelope. The combined control deflections measure cross coupling forces and moments. The control surface hinge moment measurements focus on the flight conditions of high dynamic pressure, high angle of attack, and high control surface deflection, where the maximum hinge moment is likely to occur.

Additional wind tunnel tests may be required, depending upon the missile type. Examples are store compatibility, flow field, pressure distribution, plume, heat transfer, aeroelasticity, dynamic stability, and inlet wind tunnel tests. Aircraft store carriage and separation wind tunnel tests were discussed previously. A flow field test investigates the quality of the flow over the missile. Areas of concern include flow separation and shock wave-boundary layer interaction. Flow field measurements may be made using a laser velocimeter, wind tunnel model paint, oil flow over the model, smoke, water bubbles (for a water tunnel test), or Schlierens. The pressure distribution test provides surface pressure data that are used for the air loads prediction. Pressure distribution may be obtained using either pressure taps or pressure sensitive paint. The other wind tunnel tests such as thrust plume, reaction jet plume, heat transfer, aeroelasticity, and dynamic stability testing are usually not required, depending upon the missile and flight characteristics. Plume measurements may be required for missiles that fly at high angle of attack (e.g., $\alpha > 30$ deg) or high altitude (e.g., $h > 40$ kft) and have high thrust. Cold gas air is usually used to simulate the rocket plume, with momentum flux scaling to full scale conditions. Heat transfer measurements are usually required for Mach numbers greater than 4. Heat transfer may be measured using either gauges or temperature sensitive paint. Aeroelasticity tests on an aeroelastic scaled model may be required if the missile has a large aspect ratio wing. Dynamic stability testing of roll damping (C_{l_p}) is usually required for a rolling airframe missile. Similarly, inlet tests are required for an air-breathing missile. Inlet tests usually require a scaled flowing inlet model with matched internal geometry and bleed exhaust ports.

The aerodynamic data from the wind tunnel tests are used to provide increasing confidence in the digital and hardware-in-loop simulations. During conceptual design only a few (typically fewer than 50) aerodynamic parameters are required. However, for detail design more than 200 aerodynamic parameters may be required in the simulation. A potential problem in a more detailed computer simulation is the interaction of the large number of parameters may lead to computer instability. Another potential problem is the increased likelihood of a data input error.

Autopilot design is conducted after the acquisition of wind tunnel 6-component control effectiveness data, in concert with the development of six-degree-of freedom simulation.

The flight test missile typically has about 50 channels available for telemetry (TM) data. Aerodynamic data from the TM typically include the missile acceleration, angle of attack, Mach number, altitude, roll attitude, control surface deflection, hinge moment, propulsion system temperature, and the surface temperature. Ideally, the flight test program would include a correlation of the flight test aerodynamic data with the wind tunnel data and aerodynamic prediction. Unfortunately, this rarely happens.

8.5 Examples of State-of-the-Art Advancement

Two examples of missile state-of-the art advancement will be shown. These are the areas of air-to-air missile maneuverability and supersonic airbreathing missile cruise Mach number.

An assessment of the state-of-the-art advancement in air-to-air missile maneuverability is shown in Fig. 8.14. The figure is based on the maximum

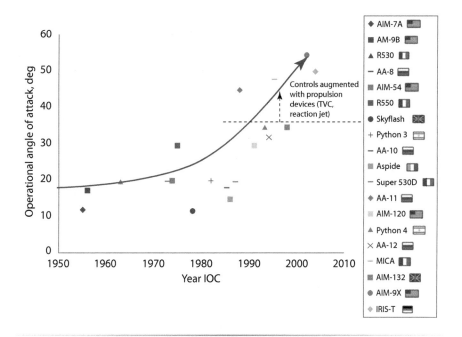

Fig. 8.14 Example of missile technology state-of-the-art advancement: air-to-air missile maneuverability.

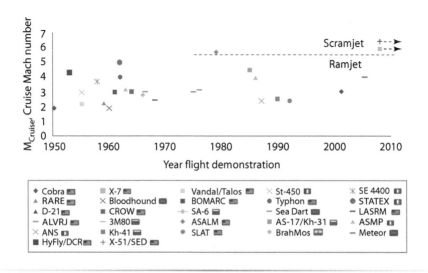

Fig. 8.15 Example of missile technology state-of-the-art advancement: ramjet propulsion.

angle of attack of air-to-air missiles at the date of their initial operational capability (IOC). Note that there is a trend of increased angle of attack capability, especially for short range air-to-air missiles. Aerodynamic flight control missiles have a limited angle of attack capability because they are susceptible to flow separation and asymmetric vortex shedding at high angle of attack. They are limited by technology to about 35-deg angle of attack. For very high angles of attack, unconventional flight control (i.e., TVC, reaction jet/jet interaction control) is required. Examples of modern highly maneuverable air-to-air missiles with unconventional flight control are the Archer AA-11, Mica, AIM-9X, and IRIS-T.

Ramjet propulsion was investigated as early as the 1940s and has been used on several production missile systems in the United States, United Kingdom, France, Russia, China, Taiwan, and India. Figure 8.15 shows a history of most of the ramjet Mach number demonstrations over the last 50 years. As shown in the figure, the Mach 4.31 ramjet cruise Mach number demonstration in the year 1953 by the X-7 has had little advancement over the last fifty years. The ASALM accidental demonstration of Mach 5.7 in the year 1979 probably represents the practical limit of subsonic combustion ramjet technology. A future flight demonstration of a HyFly Dual Combustion Ramjet-scramjet (DCR) engine may demonstrate Mach 6.5 cruise in the post 2011 year time frame. Another program, the X-51 Scramjet Engine Demonstrator (SED) may demonstrate a "pure" scramjet in the post 2011 year time frame. In recent years France, Russia, and the United Kingdom have maintained a steady commitment to ramjet propulsion technology and have ramjet missile systems that are currently deployed.

8.6 New Technologies for Missiles

Figure 8.16 is a summary of the high payoff, enabling technologies for missiles that were presented in this text. High payoff technologies are as follows.

1. *Dome*: Faceted/window and multi-lens domes have reduced dome error slope, resulting in improved guidance accuracy, low observables, and low drag at supersonic speed. Multi-mode and multi-spectral domes will also be developed.

2. *Seeker*: Multi-spectral/multi-mode imaging seekers enhance performance for ATR in countermeasures and clutter. SAR seekers have good effectiveness against surface targets in adverse weather and ground clutter. Strap down and uncooled IR seekers provide reduced parts count/lower cost. High gimbal seekers enhance off-boresight capability. Phased array enhances resolution.

3. *G&C*: Integrated GPS/INS permits precision guidance of a low cost seeker-less missile against fixed targets. Multi-mode (command/inertial/autonomous terminal homing) guidance provides a balance of missile effectiveness and launch platform survivability. Using in-flight

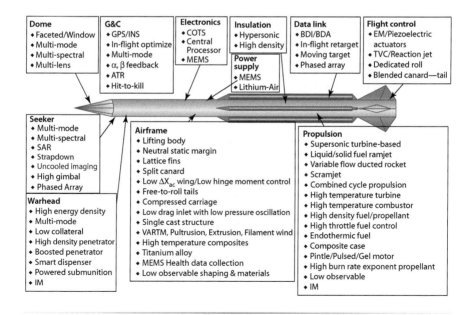

Fig. 8.16 Enabling technologies for missiles.

digital prediction of the trajectory flight and derived flight conditions from the GPS/INS, missiles will continuously optimize the flight trajectory to maximize performance parameters. Advancements in ATR technology will provide new capabilities of near real-time ATR and lower false alarm rate. Hit-to-kill guidance accuracy will be improved.

4. *Electronics*: Processing capability is ceasing to be a limitation for the application of processors to sensor data fusion and near real-time trajectory optimization to missiles. Commercial off-the-shelf (COTS) electronics, a single central processor, and micro-electromechanical systems (MEMS) provide lower cost.

5. *Airframe*: Lifting body airframes provide enhanced maneuverability and efficiency. Enhancements are also provided by configurations that maintain near-neutral static margin over the flight envelope. Split canard control and free-to-roll tails also enhance maneuverability. Aerodynamic surface planform shaping can reduce the shift of static margin with Mach number and minimize hinge moment. Lattice fins have advantages of smaller hinge moment and higher control effectiveness. Compressed carriage aerodynamic surfaces will be developed for internal carriage. Inlets with low drag and low pressure oscillation are in development for hypersonic missiles. Increased usage will be made of castings, vacuum assisted resin transfer molding, pultrusion, extrusion, and filament winding to reduce parts count/cost. High temperature composite and titanium materials will be used in hypersonic missiles. Low cost/small size MEMS sensors will be used in development data collection and logistics health monitoring. Airframe shaping and composite materials technology will provide reduced observables.

6. *Power Supply*: Development of a MEMS micro turbine generator and lithium-air battery will provide a large reduction in the weight of power supply compared to a conventional battery of the same power output.

7. *Warhead*: Higher energy density explosive charge such as the US Navy China Lake CL-20 will be developed. Modular multi-mode warheads will be developed that tailor the type of kill mechanism (e.g., blast, kinetic energy) to fit the target. Low collateral damage warheads will developed that confine lethality to the target area. Kinetic energy warheads will be developed that have higher density and boosted penetrators for defeating hard and deeply buried targets. Smart submunition dispensers and autonomous submunitions will counter mobile, time-critical targets. Improved insensitive munition warheads will be developed.

8. *Insulation*: Higher density insulation will be developed to improve the volumetric efficiency of hypersonic missiles.

9. *Propulsion*: Turbojet, air turbo-rocket, ramjet, ducted rocket, scramjet, and combined cycle propulsion will be developed for high speed air-breathing missiles. High temperature turbines and combustors will be developed. High density fuels and propellants will provide higher volumetric performance. Endothermic fuels will provide higher specific impulse, shorter combustor length, and cooling for scramjets. Composite motor cases will provide reduced weight. Thrust management technologies will be developed for pintle, pulse, and gel motors. In the case of a pintle motor, high burn rate exponent propellants will be developed to maintain high specific impulse over a broad range of thrust. Reduced observable propellants will be developed that have higher specific impulse and greater safety. Higher thrust motors to quickly accelerate missiles to hypersonic speed will be developed for kinetic kill missiles. Finally, improved insensitive munition propulsion will be developed.

10. *Data Link*: BDI/BDA will be enhanced by continued development of data links with target imagery. In-flight retargeting by a high bandwidth data link will be developed for mobile and moving targets. A high bandwidth data link will provide a seeker-less missile with a hit-to-kill capability against moving targets. Phased array antennas will be developed for high data rate and mission flexibility.

11. *Flight Control*: High power density electromagnetic and piezoelectric actuators will provide high bandwidth and high rate with reduced weight. TVC and reaction jet control performance will be enhanced for highly maneuverable and hit-to-kill missiles. Dedicated roll control surfaces will provide higher control effectiveness at high angle of attack and simplify the autopilot design. Finally, blended canard-tail control will provide divert maneuvering at low angle of attack to minimize radome error slope miss distance, facilitating hit-to-kill accuracy.

8.7 Summary

Chapter 8 addressed the development process for missiles. The areas of discussion included the application of a technology roadmap to the development process; the development activities and the time frame for the phases of basic research, exploratory development, advanced technology development, advanced development, and EMD; and the levels of design and drawing maturity as related to the stage of missile system development. Also discussed were the frequency of missile follow-on programs and examples of follow-on programs. Examples were given of cost, risk, and performance tradeoffs. The process for the integration/system engineering of missile subsystems (propulsion, airframe, guidance and control, power supply, warhead) development to the missile system development/integration activities (e.g., HWL, environmental tests, launch platform compatibility) and the process leading to a flight demonstration of the missile system were presented. Examples were given of missile development tests and facilities. Examples were also given of the state-of-the-art advancement for the areas of air-to-air missile maneuverability and ramjet cruise Mach number. Finally, new technologies for missiles were summarized.

8.8 Problem Review

1. A technology roadmap establishes the high payoff technologies go____.

2. The levels of design maturity from the most mature to least mature are production, detail, preliminary, and c_____ design.

3. Technology transitions occur from basic research to exploratory development, to advanced development, to d_____ and v_____.

4. Approximately 11% of U.S. RT&A budget is allocated to t_____ m_____.

5. In the U.S., a new missile follow-on program occurs about every ___ years.

6. Compared to the AIM-9L, the AIM-9X has enhanced m_____.

7. Compared to the AIM-7, the AIM-120 has autonomous guidance, lighter weight, higher speed, and longer r____.

8. Compared to the PAC-2, the PAC-3 has h__ t_ k___ accuracy.

9. A best value proposal strives for the best balance of low cost, low risk, and high p_____.

10. Guidance and control is verified in the h_____ in l___ simulation.

11. Air-breathing propulsion ground tests include direct connect and f_____.

12. Aerodynamic force and moment data are acquired in w___ t_____ tests.

13. Many flight tests are required to develop a high c_____ missile system.

Chapter 9 Summary and Lessons Learned

9.1 Introduction

This final chapter is a summary of the material presented in this text, a reiteration of conceptual design and system engineering criteria, and a discussion of lessons learned from the author's experience in the development of missiles and their technologies. We will begin with a discussion of twenty two guidelines from lessons learned in missile conceptual design and system engineering.

9.2 Conduct Unbiased and Creative System-of-Systems Design, with Rapid Evaluation and Iteration

Again, Fig. 9.1 illustrates that the missile conceptual design and system engineering process requires a broad unbiased assessment of alternatives and fast iteration at all levels. This figure was discussed in detail in Chapter 1. A common mistake is to select a design too quickly without sufficient consideration of the broad range of possible system-of-systems alternatives.

9.3 Exploit Diverse Skills

Figure 9.2 illustrates that the missile design activity is an opportunity to harmonize diverse inputs early in the development process. The military customer has the lead in providing the "requirements pull" initial input for the mission/scenario definition task and in providing the relative weighting for the most important requirements (MIRs). A useful tool in reaching a consensus on the MIRs and their weighting is constructing a "house of quality." In many cases it is not possible to put a single value on a requirements parameter. Instead, a requirements parameter may be specified with threshold, standard, and goal values that are based on considerations such as cost, performance, risk, and the projected state-of-the-art. The mission/scenario definition, the relative weighting of the MIRs, and the values of the requirements parameters may be modified later, based on the emerging results from the study. For example, the customer may change the requirements as a result of a previously unidentified "technology push" of a new projected available capability in the time frame of interest. The customer may also change the requirements to satisfy other types of opportunities that were not foreseen at the beginning of the study. For example, if a precision strike missile design warhead weight and flight range are only slightly greater than the constraints of the Military Technology Control Regime (MCTR), the customer may ask that the warhead weight and the flight range be limited to 500 kg and 300 km, to allow the possibility of future foreign sales. The system-of-systems weapon requirements analysis (including C^3 targeting), trade studies, and sensitivity analysis is usually conducted by operations analysis personnel. System integration engineers usually lead the task to integrate the missile with the launch platform. Missile design engineers lead the task to synthesize the alternative missile concepts. Finally, technical specialists provide the lead input for the "technology push" of potentially available technical capability and the technology development roadmap.

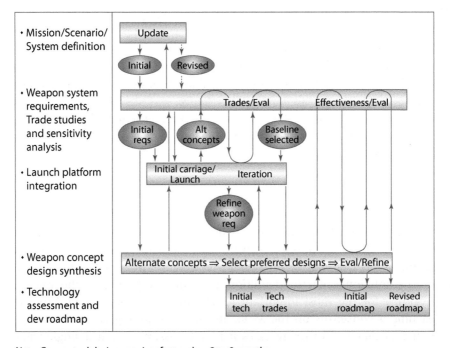

Note: Conceptual design requires fast cycle, ~3 to 9 months.

Fig. 9.1 Conduct unbiased and creative system-of-systems design, with rapid evaluation and iteration.

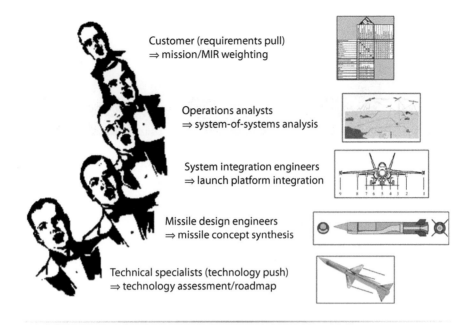

Customer (requirements pull)
⇒ mission/MIR weighting

Operations analysts
⇒ system-of-systems analysis

System integration engineers
⇒ launch platform integration

Missile design engineers
⇒ missile concept synthesis

Technical specialists (technology push)
⇒ technology assessment/roadmap

Fig. 9.2 Exploit diverse skills for a balanced design.

9.4 Quickly Switch Focus from the Big Picture to a Detail Picture to . . .

Conceptual design and system engineering has multiple solutions, with some better than others. The "best" solution is a harmonized solution that provides a good balance of its strengths and weaknesses. This requires that the engineer be able to quickly switch focus between two thought processes—a creative overview oriented (right brain) process and a deductive detail task oriented (left brain) process. It is a mistake to overly focus only on the creative process or only on the deductive process. Because most engineers are left brain oriented, there is often a tendency to develop tunnel vision, focusing too much on a detailed task. It is good to periodically step back for a strategic overview of the problem, to ensure that a task is well integrated with other tasks and the approach is leading in a good direction.

Figure 9.3 has two photographs that were taken by my grandson on a trip to New York City. The upper photograph was taken from the top of the Chrysler Building. It has a perspective overview of Central Park and the boundaries of the city. The bottom photograph has a more detailed, close-up perspective of the marsh trees near the lake in Central Park. Standing in the marsh you can see the detail of the trees but you can't see the surrounding forest and the boundary of the forest. It is important for an engineer to "see the forest, not just the trees."

Fig. 9.3   Quickly switch focus from the big picture to a detail picture to ....

9.5 Utilize Creative Skills

Missile conceptual design and system engineering is a creative process that requires unique skills (Fig. 9.4). Creative skills are required for 1) consideration of a broad range of alternatives, 2) questioning the basis of requirements and constraints, to ensure that they are not artificially limiting the range of alternative approaches, 3) projecting into the future (e.g., 5–15 years) the state-of-the-art (SOTA), threat, scenarios, tactics, military

◆ Use creative skills to consider broad range of alternatives
◆ Ask why? of requirements/constraints
◆ Project into future (e.g., 5–15 years)
   • State-of-the-art (SOTA)
   • Threat
   • Scenario/Tactics/Doctrine
   • Concepts
   • Technology impact forecast
◆ Recognize and distill the most important, key drivers
◆ Develop missile concept that is synergistic within a system-of-systems
◆ Develop synergistic/Balanced combination of high leverage subsystems/Technologies

Fig. 9.4   Utilize creative skills.

doctrine, alternative concepts, and technology impact forecast, 4) recognizing and distilling the most important, key drivers from a large number of possibilities, 5) developing a missile concept that is synergistic within a system-of-systems and 6) developing a synergistic/balanced combination of high leverage subsystems, and technologies.

9.6 Utilize the Skills of the Entire Organization

Missile conceptual design and system engineering is usually conducted by a small group of engineers in an advanced programs department. The advanced programs organization is usually part of a larger organization. Overall management of each conceptual design and system engineering activity is usually conducted by a program manager and a systems engineer. The program manager usually focuses on the cost performance, schedule performance, and the outside customer interface. The systems engineer usually provides the inside technical interface with the engineering team and addresses the system engineering concerns. The conceptual design and system engineering team usually consists of about 10 engineers, representing the key technical areas. It is important that the team function as a synergistic group rather than a set of individuals with each primarily promoting their individual technical areas. However, it is also important that the group is not overly consensus oriented. The group should be sensitive to dissent from the individual members.

Figure 9.5, based on Ref. 49, shows that the size of the conceptual design and system engineering team is typically about 2% of the engineering

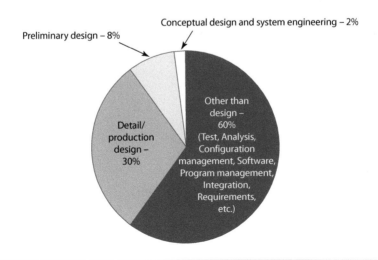

Fig. 9.5 Utilize the skills of the entire organization. (Source: Nicolai, L.M., *Designing a Better Engineer*, AIAA Aerospace America, April 1992.)

organization. The size of the typical advanced programs organization is about 10–30 engineers, with about two engineers in each broad technical area (e.g., system design, aerodynamics, propulsion, structures, performance, flight control, guidance and navigation, sensors, warhead, flight trajectory, launch platform integration, system effectiveness, cost). Usually there is a senior engineer as a mentor for each junior engineer. The experience and skills of the senior engineer are often complemented by the new ideas and computer skills of the junior engineer. Most of the junior engineers move out of the conceptual design organization after a few years. The junior system engineers often become program managers, while the junior technical specialists may move on to either providing technical support to specific programs or to conducting more detailed work in their technical specialty. It is important for the conceptual design and system engineering team to maintain a good relationship with the larger outside organization, drawing upon their expertise when necessary for areas such as manufacturing, flight test, and suppliers.

9.7 Balance the Tradeoff of Importance Versus Priority

The advanced programs/conceptual design and system engineering team works on future business opportunities that are important, but usually have relatively low priority in comparison to the more near-term concerns of the larger organization. As illustrated in Fig. 9.6, it is important to be agile to survive in a dynamic environment of the shifting priority for the EMD and production programs. When the large programs get into trouble, there is a tendency to "mortgage the future" or "eat

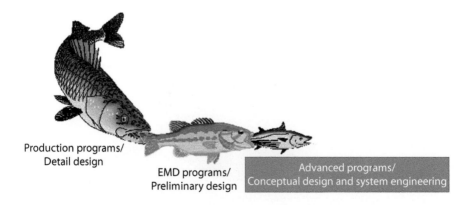

Production programs/
Detail design

EMD programs/
Preliminary design

Advanced programs/
Conceptual design and system engineering

Fig. 9.6 Balance the tradeoff of importance versus priority.

the seed corn" by taking away the funding and personnel in advanced programs. The large current programs may also view advanced programs as a threat to their future long-term survival and a competitor for discretionary funding. In many organizations the senior engineering managers and program managers began their careers in advanced programs. There may be unspoken management support for advanced programs in spite of the relatively low priority and the lack of a short-term return on investment.

9.8 Identify, Quantify, and Balance the Measures of Merit, within Cost Constraints

One objective of conceptual missile design and system engineering is to identify, quantify, and balance the high payoff performance measures of merit while also meeting cost constraints. Because missiles are cost constrained, it is not possible to use the latest state-of-the art for all areas. Measures of merit such as range, time to target, robustness, lethality, reliability, miss distance, survivability, observables, and weight impact the missile production cost. Also, the development cost is limited, requiring a tradeoff of performance, risk, and cost. As illustrated in Fig. 9.7, judicious selection must be made for a balanced cost-effective design.

Analysis techniques such as the house of quality and DOE, discussed in Chapter 7, should be used in the design and system engineering process. The house of quality provides a process for meeting customer requirements. A properly tailored DOE provides a process for more efficiently covering the design solution space in the time that is available. A full factorial DOE of the 10 measures of merit illustrated in the figure requires $2^{10} = 1024$ design concepts to cover the solution space of cost based on minimum/maximum reasonable values for each measure of merit. Engineering judgment is required to efficiently guide the DOE mathematical process to fit the time available.

Participation by the military customer is required to obtain a consensus on the relative weighting of the most important requirements (MIRs)/ system measures of merit. As an example for a typical volume- and weight-limited missile, one contractor may overly emphasize the warhead lethality, and as a result develop a larger/heavier warhead at the expense of insufficient range. Another contractor may overly emphasize the launch platform survivability and, as a result, develop a longer range stand-off missile at the expense of insufficient warhead weight/lethality. The customer preference of lethality versus launch platform survivability should be a consideration in the relative weighting of the MIRs/system measures of merit.

Fig. 9.7 Identify, quantify, and balance the measures of merit, within cost constraints.

9.9 Start with a Good Baseline Design

As discussed in Chapter 1, starting with a good baseline enhances the accuracy and speed of the missile design and system engineering process. Figure 9.8 illustrates that the selection of a baseline missile should not be overly biased by the previous experience with another missile. As an example, the Sparrow missile was a good baseline missile in the development of designs for a lighter weight, longer range, higher speed, and autonomous guidance (active radar seeker) missile (which later became AMRAAM).

9.10 Evaluate Alternative Prediction Methods and Compare with Data, for Accuracy and Precision

It is good practice to evaluate alternative prediction methods and compare the results with data, to investigate their accuracy and precision. Conceptual design prediction methods typically have large uncertainty (e.g. $+/-10\%$, 1σ) in their accuracy. As discussed previously, the use of a

Fig. 9.8 Start with a good baseline design.

baseline missile that has data is an approach to improve the accuracy and precision of conceptual design prediction methods. Preliminary design prediction methods usually have better precision, because of the larger number of parameters, but they may also lack precision as well as accuracy because of a built-in bias. Again, comparison with other prediction methods and data is a good practice.

Precise
but not accurate

Good average accuracy
but not precise

Fig. 9.9 Evaluate alternative prediction methods and compare with data, for accuracy and precision.

Accuracy indicates how close the prediction is to the true value, such as the spacing of the arrows compared to the bull's eye in the right portion of Fig. 9.9. Note that the average spacing of the arrows is near the bull's eye. It has good average accuracy but poor precision. Precision indicates the repeatability of the prediction, shown in the left portion of the figure. This example has good precision, but because of a large bias, there is poor accuracy.

9.11 Confirm Accuracy of Computer Input Data and Modeling

Errors in the computer input data and errors in the computer modeling can lead to a bad output and a poor design (Fig. 9.10). Input error is of more

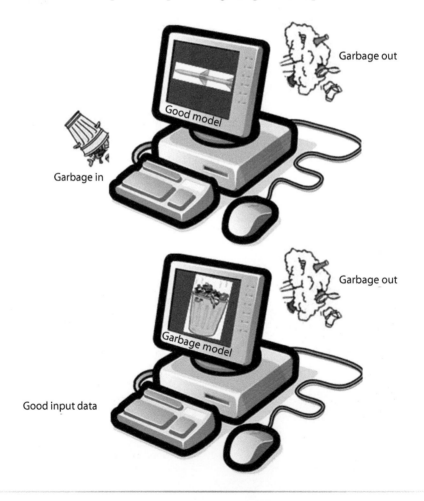

Fig. 9.10   Confirm the accuracy of computer input data and the modeling (bad input or bad modeling leads to bad output).

concern for the larger, more complex preliminary design codes than for the simpler, conceptual design codes, because preliminary design codes require more input data. Also, it is of more concern for empirical codes than physics based codes, because of a greater possibility of extrapolating outside the data base. It may be difficult to detect a bias in the input data for a larger code, allowing someone to "cook the books" in disguising the output to fit a pre-conceived notion of what the result should be.

An independent check should be conducted of the computer input data and the computer modeling. Verification/validation of the computer output should be conducted, including comparisons with data. There may be a tendency to blindly accept a computer result, especially if the computer program is well known and appears to have high precision.

9.12 Conduct Balanced, Unbiased Tradeoffs

As shown in Fig. 9.11, what is important is in the eye of the beholder. Based on experience, if a subsystem is taken to an extreme limit of its capability, it is usually at cross purposes to the other subsystems and results in a non-optimum missile. If there is sufficient time in conceptual

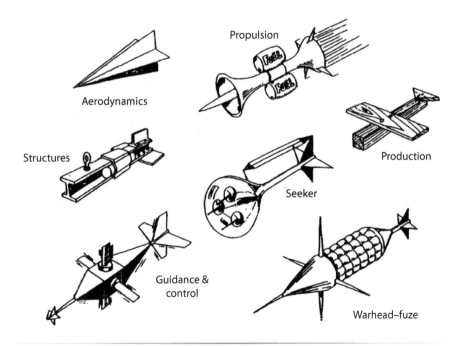

Fig. 9.11 Conduct balanced, unbiased tradeoffs.

design and system engineering, it may be instructive to design alternative missiles that emphasize different attributes/subsystems. The missile designer must harmonize the different attributes/subsystems to create a cost-effective design.

9.13 Include System Integration in Missile Conceptual Design and System Engineering

Missile design and system engineering is often driven by system integration. Examples of missile span and length geometric constraints include box, canister, and tube launchers and aircraft weapon bays. Also, the program schedule of a new launch platform development may be delayed if weapon integration is not considered in the early portion of the program. The problem of timely consideration of weapon integration is often more of a political problem than a technical problem. Weapon programs and launch platform programs are usually funded separately by different organizations.

Figure 9.12 illustrates how the V-2 tail span was driven by system integration. A requirement was that the fully assembled V-2 had to comply with rail transport from the Mittelwerk V-2 factory through the Mittelbau-Dora tunnels in Kohnstein Mountain. The smallest tunnel width was 4 m. The 4 m tunnel clearance set the V-2 fin span dimension of 3.6 m. Aerodynamics was not the primary driver for the V-2 tail span.

Example of system integration: V-2 tail span was limited by a railroad tunnel

V-2 on Railroad car   Mittelbau-Dora tunnel in Kohnstein Mountain, Leading to Mittelwerk V-2 factory

Fig. 9.12 Include system integration in missile conceptual design and system engineering.

9.14 Evaluate Many Alternatives

There are usually many configuration candidates for a missile design. A balanced, harmonized conceptual design requires the consideration of the broad range of alternatives. For example, Fig. 9.13 shows air-to-air missile alternatives that are very different in their aerodynamic configurations. As expected, aircraft launch platform constraints and supersonic flight considerations result in air-to-air missiles with high fineness ratio. Also, the relatively soft/small air target results in a relatively small warhead. Although all of the missiles in the figure have high maneuverability (e.g., 30+ g), the approach to surface area and geometry varies widely. Some missiles have wings (e.g., IRIS-T), whereas others are wingless (e.g., ASRAAM). Flight control alternatives include thrust vector control, tail control, canard control, and wing control. There are a variety of propulsion alternatives (e.g., rocket, ducted rocket, ramjet). Relatively small differences in the system requirements flow-down of the measures of merit (e.g., targeting, aircraft compatibility, launch maneuverability, turn radius, rate of turn, velocity, accuracy) will often drive the selection of a specific aerodynamic configuration.

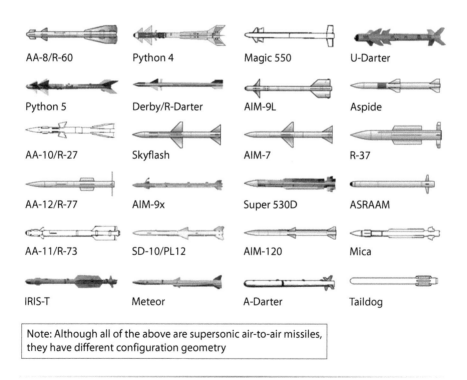

AA-8/R-60	Python 4	Magic 550	U-Darter
Python 5	Derby/R-Darter	AIM-9L	Aspide
AA-10/R-27	Skyflash	AIM-7	R-37
AA-12/R-77	AIM-9x	Super 530D	ASRAAM
AA-11/R-73	SD-10/PL12	AIM-120	Mica
IRIS-T	Meteor	A-Darter	Taildog

Note: Although all of the above are supersonic air-to-air missiles, they have different configuration geometry

Fig. 9.13 Evaluate many alternatives.

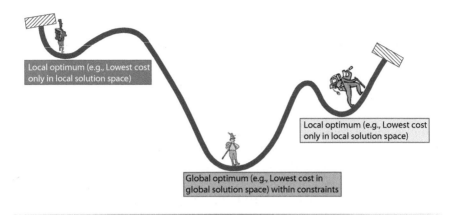

Fig. 9.14 Quickly search a broad design solution space (global optimization versus local optimization).

9.15 Quickly Search a Broad Design Solution Space (Global Optimization Versus Local Optimization)

Figure 9.14 illustrates the problem of quickly finding a harmonized design within a broad design space that is nonlinear, with local curvatures. Missile conceptual design and system engineering is a complex problem consisting of many parameters. The measures of merit are often interacting and are often conflicting. The best design optimum is often not obvious. Prior experience may not necessarily be applicable and intuition may not necessarily lead in the correct direction. The best approach is usually to quickly search the broadest possible solution space to the greatest depth in the available time.

9.16 Evaluate and Refine as Often as Possible

Figure 9.15 illustrates a natural bias of the original missile developer, that changes to his missile are not necessary. The pride of authorship reflects the time and money that went into developing the original missile. However, time does not stand still. The developer of a missile should not ignore new technologies, new capabilities, or new requirements because of a "not invented here" attitude. A good design will eventually be replaced by a better design.

9.17 Apply OODA Loop Process for Faster and Higher Confidence Design Convergence

A conceptual design and system engineering activity that is based on the process to observe, orient, decide, act (OODA) [50] usually has a faster and

Fig. 9.15 Evaluate and refine as often as possible.

a more accurate approach to search the broad design space. The OODA loop, shown in Fig. 9.16, is analogous to the feedback loops of the missile guidance and control system. A fast feedback using the OODA loop expedites the design convergence. The objective of the first activity in the

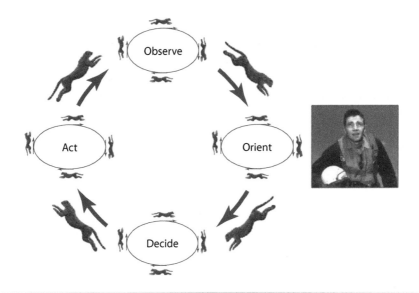

Fig. 9.16 Apply OODA loop process for faster and higher confidence design convergence. (Source: Boyd, John R., *The Essence of Winning and Losing*, Jan. 1996.)

OODA loop, shown in the top portion of the figure, is to quickly and accurately observe the situation. This may be difficult because we often have preconceived ("Don Quixote type") biases. A preconceived but incorrect perspective may change slowly before accurately recognizing the real situation. The OODA inner loop feedback of fast successive observations hastens the convergence to an accurate assessment of the situation. Moving quickly to the next inner loop (orient), the objective is to quickly orient our thinking to accurately address the situation. This may also be difficult, because of culture and previous experience. If a new situation does not match our background it may be difficult to quickly reorient our thinking. Again, the faster we can change our orientation to respond to the actual situation, the faster we can move on to the next inner loop. As difficult as it may be for an individual to quickly reorient thinking to respond to a new situation, it is usually even more difficult for an organization to quickly change its orientation. Some large organizations are inherently stagnant and may require years to achieve a reorientation. The next inner loop is to quickly decide a course of action. Individuals and organizations sometimes become paralyzed when confronted with making a major decision, especially if there are multiple options with possibly bad consequences. Management will sometimes "kick the can down the road" with "paralysis by analysis" to avoid making a decision on a course of action. The last inner loop is to quickly act on the decision. Quickly developing a design (e.g., the results of a conceptual design and system engineering study) is often better than taking a longer time to develop a more defined design (e.g., the results of a preliminary design study). Finally, we begin the OODA loop again by observing the situation again for new changes. It is usually faster to complete the OODA loop the second time, because we have a now have a better observation of the situation, we have oriented our thinking to better match the situation, we are more comfortable in quickly deciding on a course of action, and we can more quickly act on a new design activity because of a better baseline design and a more refined solution space than that generated in the first OODA loop.

The OODA loop process works best in conceptual design and system engineering studies, which sometimes have changing requirements during the course of the study. An objective is to complete the study before the requirements change. The advantage of the OODA loop process is that it usually provides more rapid and a more accurate convergence to a solution.

9.18 Provide Balanced Emphasis of Analytical Versus Experimental

Aerospace engineering is by its nature a synthesis profession, requiring a balance of emphasis of analytical activity and experimental activity. Each

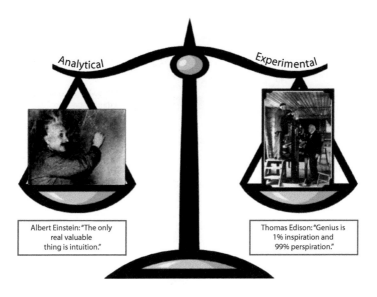

Fig. 9.17 Provide balanced emphasis of analytical versus experimental.

has value, each has its advocates and role model examples (Fig. 9.17), and each can be a career path unto itself. Although most of the individual functional disciplines of aerospace engineering (e.g., propulsion, aerodynamics, structure, materials, flight control) could be accommodated within a mechanical engineering program, one of the things that makes aerospace engineering unique is the requirement for synergistic synthesis of its disciplines into aerospace systems. This requires a system development process with a balanced emphasis of analytical versus experimental and feedback at each stage of the development process.

9.19 Use a Design, Build, and Fly Process, for Feedback Leading to Broader Knowledge and Understanding

Figure 9.18 illustrates the benefit of the feedback and synergy of the design, build, and fly process. The initial stage, design synthesis, requires synergistic selection of subsystems, with prediction of subsystem and system performance and cost. Iteration is required for convergence of the design predicted characteristics to a balanced emphasis that is consistent with customer requirements. The next step is building the flight vehicle in accordance with the design drawings/work instructions. A lesson learned here is that the engineering drawings/work instructions need to be clear and producible. The third step is test. In the case of flight test,

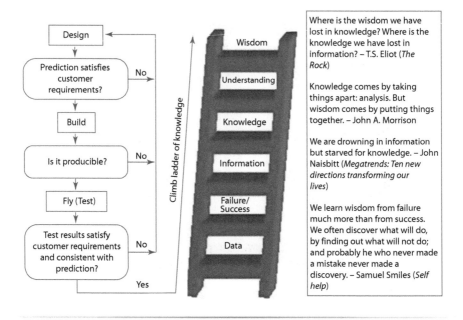

Fig. 9.18 Use the design, build, and fly process, for feedback leading to broader knowledge and understanding.

comparisons can be made of predicted performance versus actual performance. Often the prediction does not match the data, and you have to explain possible reasons for the differences. Also, for repeat tests there are differences in the results, introducing the problem of probabilistic uncertainties.

Illustrated in the right side of the figure is the classical ladder of knowledge. Advancing up each step of the ladder of knowledge involves multiple and diverse experiences. Steps lead from collecting data, to the outcomes of failure/success, to acquiring information, to obtaining knowledge. Knowledge may (or it may not) lead to a more general understanding, which may finally lead to wisdom.

9.20 Consider Potential Consequences (Good and Bad) of Decisions

The consequences (good and bad) of design decisions should be considered. For example, immature technologies often have unknown and adverse interactions with other subsystems. Unfortunately the technical specialist will often present only the favorable features of a technology and may not present the possible unintended consequences. A technology should not be inserted into a future EMD or production program unless the technology is mature and the risk, performance, schedule, cost, and customer acceptance have been fully characterized. Figure 9.19 illustrates that there may be hidden, perhaps even disguised, undesirable consequences of actions/decisions. In addition to a static analysis prediction of the effect of a design decision, a dynamic analysis prediction should also be conducted to see if there may be unintended adverse consequences.

9.21 Keep Track of Assumptions and Develop Real-Time Documentation

As illustrated in Fig. 9.20, it is good practice to maintain real-time documentation of the assumptions and results during the design process, rather than waiting until the end. A common mistake is to delay the documentation until the end of the study. However, key assumptions and results may be lost during the study unless there is timely and accurate documentation. Also, there may be insufficient time to complete the documentation before moving on to the next activity.

Fig. 9.19 Consider potential consequences (good and bad) of decisions.

Fig. 9.20   Keep track of assumptions and develop real-time documentation.

9.22 Develop Good Documentation

Figure 9.21 is an example of typical documentation requirements for missile conceptual design and system engineering. Good documentation should provide a traceable flow-down of information from the system-level requirements to subsystem requirements to component performance to the technology rationale. An example output of a missile conceptual design and system engineering process is the following:

1. Most important requirements (MIRs)/system measures of merit weighting. Meetings are held with the customer to develop a consensus on the most important requirements and their weighting. A "house of quality" is usually constructed to facilitate the process.
2. Sketches of alternative concepts.
3. Justification of the recommended concept(s), including reasons for the concept(s) being selected, measures of merit, design tradeoffs, criteria for selection, and advantages/disadvantages compared to alternative concepts. Measures of merit include maximum range, minimum range, maximum speed, and accuracy. A DOE should be conducted with alternative concepts.
4. Aerodynamics and propulsion characteristics, including aerodynamic stability, aerodynamic control effectiveness, normal force, axial force, specific impulse, thrust, weight of propellant/fuel, and the methods used for prediction.
5. Mission flight profiles of the preferred concept(s).
6. Sensitivity of the system/subsystem parameters to measures of merit.

7. Traceability of flowing down the system driving MIRs to concept performance, subsystem performance, component performance, and technology selection.
8. Three-view drawing of preferred concept(s), including an outboard profile showing external features with dimensions and inboard profiles showing subsystems and their dimensions.
9. Weight and balance statement, including subsystems weight, subsystems location, launch and burnout center-of-gravity, launch and burnout moments-of-inertia, and the methods used for weight and balance prediction.
10. Unit production cost, including the number of units that are produced, the learning curve, and the basis for the learning curve.
11. Technology roadmap of technologies that require development to demonstrate their maturity and their readiness for an operational application. The technology roadmap includes the required schedule and milestones for the timely insertion of technology into an operational system.

Fig. 9.21 Develop good documentation.

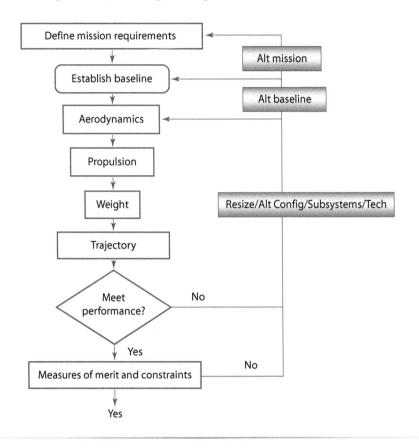

Fig. 9.22 Conceptual design and system engineering require creative, rapid, and iterative evaluations.

9.23 Rapidly Evaluate Alternatives and Iterate the Design

Figure 9.22 was repeated in each of the first six chapters of this text. It is shown here for one last time. The point is that the conceptual design and system engineering process is a rapid evaluation of a broad range of alternatives that requires iteration, iteration, and iteration. A conceptual design and system engineering study is typically only as good as the number of iterations and the number of alternatives that are considered.

9.24 Missile Conceptual Design and System Engineering Configuration Sizing Guidelines

Table 9.1 shows missile conceptual design and system engineering configuration sizing guidelines that were presented in this text. Table 9.1a has eleven design guidelines related to the area of aeromechanics and Table 9.1b has eleven guidelines related to the area of guidance and control.

The Table 9.1a configuration design guidelines that are related to missile aeromechanics include missile body fineness ratio, nose fineness ratio, boattail or flare angle, efficient cruise dynamic pressure, missile homing velocity, ramjet combustion temperature, oblique shocks prior to the inlet normal shock, inlet flow capture, ramjet minimum cruise Mach number, subsystem packaging, and aging lifetime.

A design guideline for an endo-atmospheric missile body fineness ratio (length-to-diameter ratio) is that it should be between 5 and 25, to harmonize the tradeoffs of drag, subsystem packaging available volume, launch platform integration, seeker and warhead effectiveness, and body bending. The second guideline is that the nose fineness ratio for a supersonic homing missile should be $l_N/d \approx 2$, for a tradeoff of a relatively low drag and a relatively good seeker tracking accuracy. Another guideline is the boattail or flare angle should be less than 10 deg, to avoid flow separation. This is particularly important for supersonic missiles, to avoid increased drag at high speed. A design guideline for efficient cruise flight is that the dynamic pressure be less than 1000 psf. For a missile with a relatively large wing, the optimum dynamic pressure is somewhat lower. A fifth guideline is the missile velocity should be at least 50% greater than the target velocity to capture the target. A sixth guideline is the ramjet combustion temperature should be greater than

Table 9.1a   Conceptual Design and System Engineering Configuration Sizing Guidelines: Aeromechanics.

Configuration Sizing Parameter	Aeromechanics Design Guideline
Body fineness ratio	$5 < l/d < 25$
Nose fineness ratio	$l_N/d \approx 2$ if $M > 1$
Boattail or flare angle	<10 deg
Efficient cruise dynamic pressure	$q < 1000$ psf
Missile homing velocity	$V_M/V_T > 1.5$
Ramjet combustion temperature	$>4,000°F$ (need high temp insulation)
Oblique shocks prior to inlet normal shock to satisfy MIL-E-5008b MIL-E-5008B	>2 oblique shocks/compressions if $M > 3.0$, >3 shocks/compressions if $M > 3.5$
Inlet flow capture	Shock on cowl lip at M_{max} cruise
Ramjet minimum cruise Mach number	$M > 1.2 \times M_{inlet\ start}$, $M > 1.2\ M_{max\ Thrust=Drag}$
Subsystems packaging	Maximize available volume for fuel/propellant
Aging lifetime	Lifetime average temperature less than specification.

Table 9.1b Conceptual Design and System Engineering Configuration Sizing Guidelines: Guidance and Control.

Configuration sizing parameter	G&C design guideline
Body bending frequency	$\omega_{BB} > \omega_{Act}$
Trim control power	$\alpha/\delta > 1$
Neutral stability tail-body	If low aspect ratio $\Rightarrow$ $b/d \approx 2$, $c/d > \approx 1$
Stability & control cross coupling	$<30\%$
Missile time constant	$\tau < 0.2$ s, $\tau < \omega^{-1}$
Missile maneuverability	$n_M/n_T > 3$
Proportional guidance ratio	$3 < N < 5$
Target span resolution by seeker	$< b_{Target}$
Missile heading rate	$\dot{\gamma}_M > \dot{\gamma}_T$
Missile turn radius	$R_{T_M} < R_{T_T}$
Fire control system range	$R_{FCS} > 2R_F$

4000°F for high specific impulse and thrust at Mach numbers greater than 3.5. This requires high temperature insulation for the combustor. Efficient inlet integration for supersonic missiles to satisfy MIL-E-5008B requires more than two oblique shocks/compressions prior to the inlet normal shock, for good inlet total pressure recovery at Mach numbers greater than 3.0. For Mach numbers greater than 3.5, more than three oblique shocks/compressions prior to the inlet normal shock are desirable for inlet total pressure recovery. Also, the forebody shock wave should impact the inlet cowl lip at the highest Mach number cruise condition, to maximize the air flow capture and thrust. It also minimizes the spillage drag at lower Mach number. A concern for a ramjet is a sufficiently high cruise Mach number for the inlet to swallow the shock, avoiding inlet buzz, and having sufficient thrust to overcome drag. Design criteria are $M > 1.2 \times M_{\text{Inlet start}}$ and $M > 1.2\, M_{\text{max Thrust=Drag}}$. The tenth criteria is subsystems, which should be synergistically and efficiently packaged to maximize the available volume for fuel or propellant. Finally, the lifetime average temperature should be less than the specification. A 10°F increase in average temperature reduces the rocket motor lifetime by 50%.

Table 9.1b provides conceptual design and system engineering configuration sizing guidelines related to missile guidance and control. These include the missile body bending frequency, trim control power, tail span/chord for neutral stability, stability and control derivatives cross coupling, missile time constant, missile maneuverability, proportional guidance ratio, target span resolution by the seeker, missile heading rate capability, missile turn radius capability, and the fire control system range requirement.

A guideline is the body bending frequency in the first mode should be greater than the flight control actuator frequency if possible, to avoid the complication and risk of notch filters. A second guideline is trim control power (trim angle of attack-to-control surface deflection ratio) should be $\alpha/\delta > 1$ for tail and canard flight control maneuverability. For a neutrally stable body-tail missile (no canard), the total tail span (including body diameter) of a low aspect ratio tail should be approximately twice the body diameter and the tail chord length should be larger than the body diameter. A fourth guideline is stability and control derivatives cross coupling should be less than 30% for efficient dynamics. A fifth guideline is the missile system time constant should be less than 0.2 s for precision accuracy (3 m) and less than the inverse of the weaving target frequency ω^{-1} for low miss distance against an air target. Contributors to a low value of the airframe time constant include a high maneuverability capability, neutral static margin, high rate control surface actuators, low dome error slope for the seeker, and a low noise seeker. A sixth guideline is missile maneuverability should be at least three times the target maneuverability, for small miss distance. The proportional guidance ratio should be between 3 and 5 to minimize miss distance. Values less than 3 will result in excessive time to correct heading error and target maneuver error, while values greater than 5 make the missile overly sensitive to glint noise input from the seeker and the dome error slope. An eighth guideline is the seeker should be capable of resolving the target geometry to a fraction of the target span, to minimize the miss distance from glint. A ninth guideline is the missile heading rate capability should be greater than that of the target in order to achieve an intercept. Also, the missile turn radius capability should be less than that of the target in order to achieve an intercept. Finally, the range of the fire control system should be at least twice the missile flight range, to allow sufficient time for launch decisions.

9.25 Wrap-Up

Missile conceptual design and system engineering is a creative, fast, and iterative process that includes system-of-systems engineering requirements flow-down and integration considerations, missile sizing, technology assessment, flight trajectory evaluation, and measures of merit evaluation. Because many of the cost, performance, and risk drivers may be "locked in" early during the design process, the emphasis of this text has been on conceptual design and system engineering.

Missile conceptual design and system engineering is an opportunity to harmonize the diverse inputs early in the missile development process.

The military customer, operations analysts, system integration engineers, conceptual design engineers, technical specialists, and others work together in harmonizing the mission/scenario definition, system-of-systems requirements, launch platform integration, missile concept synthesis, and technology assessment/roadmaps.

Missile conceptual design and system engineering is a highly integrated process requiring synergistic compromise and tradeoffs of many parameters. The synthesis of an effective compromise requires balanced emphasis in subsystems, unbiased tradeoffs, efficient packaging of subsystems, and the evaluation of many alternatives. It is important to keep track of assumptions to maintain traceable results. It is necessary to be aware not only of the current state-of-the-art, but also to conduct a technology impact forecast of the projected state-of-the-art in the time frame of interest. Starting with a well-defined baseline that has similar propulsion and performance expedites design convergence and provides a more accurate design.

Conceptual design and system engineering is an open-ended problem and has no single right answer. The available starting point information is never sufficient to provide only one solution. The design engineer makes assumptions in coming up with candidate concepts, subsystems, and technologies to satisfy mission requirements and cover the design solution space. Weighting of the most important measures of merit is required in coming up with a cost-effective solution. The military customer buy-in is important in achieving a consensus weighting of the most important measures of merit. Trade studies are conducted to investigate the impact of design parameters. Sensitivity analyses are also conducted to evaluate the effects of uncertainty in the design and the benefit of new technology. The missile should be designed for robustness to handle risk and uncertainty of both a deterministic and a stochastic nature.

Finally, a good conceptual design code is a physics-based code that connects the missile geometric, physical, and subsystem performance parameters directly into a flight trajectory evaluation. Good conceptual design codes do not automatically change the design or resize automatically. It is best that the missile designer make the creative decisions.

Appendix A

Homework Problems/ Classroom Exercises

These homework problems/classroom exercises are designed to comp-lement the problems at the end of the chapters. The problems at the end of the chapters can be posed as verbal questions to the students, providing an indication that the students were listening to the lecture. The following homework problems/classroom exercises are designed to provide a more in-depth learning reinforcement. Points associated with each homework problem/classroom exercise indicate the degree of difficulty, as a consideration in assigning the student's grade for the problem.

1. *(20 points). Chapter I (Introduction/Key Drivers in the Missile Design and System Engineering Process).* Compare measures of merit for the following alternative concepts to destroy threat ballistic missiles during their boost phase:
   - Space-based interceptors
   - Space-based lasers
   - Airborne laser
   - Air-launched interceptors
   - Ship-launched interceptors
   - Ground-launched interceptors

2. *(10 points). Chapter I (Introduction/Key Drivers in the Missile Design and System Engineering Process).* Develop a state-of-the-art comparison of tactical missile characteristics with the current state-of-the-art (SOTA) of UCAVs. Show examples where missiles are driving technology. Also show examples where the missile is not driving technology.

3. *(10 points). Chapter I (Introduction/Key Drivers in the Missile Design and System Engineering Process).* For the examples shown of air-launched and surface-launched missiles, which have been applied to more than one mission?

4. *(20 points). Chapter II (Aerodynamic Considerations in the Missile Design and System Engineering Process).* Based on the example, calculate radar seeker detection range and 3-dB beam width for a target cross section $\sigma = 1 \text{ m}^2$, mmW transmitter frequency $f = 35 \times 10^9$ Hz, transmitted power $P_t = 100$ W, and antenna diameter $d = 4$ in.

5. *(20 points). Chapter II (Aerodynamic Considerations in the Missile Design and System Engineering Process). Based on the example, calculate imaging IR seeker detection range and instantaneous field of view for rainfall at 4 mm/hr and optics diameter $d_0 = 2$ in.*

6. *(10 points). Chapter II (Aerodynamic Considerations in the Missile Design and System Engineering Process). Based on the example, calculate the first mode body bending frequency for a missile weight of 367 lb.*

7. *(10 points). Chapter II (Aerodynamic Considerations in the Missile Design and System Engineering Process). In the body-flare example, what is the required diameter of the flare to provide neutral stability at launch?*

8. *(20 points). Chapter II (Aerodynamic Considerations in the Missile Design and System Engineering Process). What are the strengths and weaknesses of the China SD-10/PL-12 tail planform?*

9. *(10 points). Chapter II (Aerodynamic Considerations in the Missile Design and System Engineering Process). Calculate the rocket baseline wing normal force coefficient $(C_N)_{\text{Wing}}$ at Mach 1.1, $\delta = 13$ deg, $\alpha = 9$ deg.*

10. *(40 points). Chapter II (Aerodynamic Considerations in the Missile Design and System Engineering Process). Calculate C_{D_0}, C_N, and C_m for the ramjet baseline at Mach 2.5 end-of-cruise and Mach 4.0 end-of-cruise. Compare with the aerodynamic data of Chapter VII. Why is it difficult to accurately predict (or even obtain accurate data) for C_m?*

11. *(20 points). Chapter II (Aerodynamic Considerations in the Missile Design and System Engineering Process). What are the dynamic pressures at cruise $(L/D)_{\text{max}}$ for a circular cross section missile and an $a/b = 2$ lifting body cross section missile if the weight $W = 500$ lb, cross sectional reference area $S_{\text{Ref}} = 0.5$ ft², length-to-diameter ratio $l/d = 10$, and zero-lift drag coefficient $C_{D_0} = 0.2$?*

12. *(20 points). Chapter II (Aerodynamic Considerations in the Missile Design and System Engineering Process). Calculate hinge moment for the ramjet baseline at the initiation of a pitch-over dive. Flight conditions are Mach 4.0, $h = 80$ kft altitude, end-of-cruise, $\delta_e = -30$ deg control deflection, and $\alpha = \alpha_{\text{max}}$ angle of attack.*

13. *(20 points). Chapter II (Aerodynamic Considerations in the Missile Design and System Engineering Process). Using the approach of the text example, calculate the required tail area of the rocket baseline to provide neutral static stability at launch.*

14. *(20 points). Chapter III (Propulsion Considerations in the Missile Design and System Engineering Process). Using the approach of the text example, compare compressor exit temperature at Mach number*

$M = 3$, altitude $h =$ sea level with the Mach 2, $h = 60$ kft compressor temperature result of the text example.

15. *(20 points). Chapter III (Propulsion Considerations in the Missile Design and System Engineering Process).* For the turbojet text example ($T_4 = 3000$ R, $A_0 = 114$ in^2, RJ-5 fuel, $M = 2$, $h = 60$ kft) show the impact on maximum ideal thrust and specific impulse of $+/-$ 10% uncertainty in specific heat ratio.

16. *(30 points). Chapter III (Propulsion Considerations in the Missile Design and System Engineering Process).* For an ideal turbojet, calculate thrust, specific impulse, equivalence ratio, and nozzle exit area for the following conditions/assumptions: liquid hydrocarbon fuel, free stream Mach number $= 2$, angle of attack $= 0$ deg, altitude $= 60$ kft, compressor pressure ratio for maximum thrust, turbine maximum temperature $= 2000$ R, and inlet capture area $= 114$ in^2. Compare with the text example.

17. *(20 points). Chapter III (Propulsion Considerations in the Missile Design and System Engineering Process).* Using the approach of the text example of a centrifugal compressor, what is the rotation rate if the impeller tip Mach number $M_{\text{Impeller tip}} = 1.2$?

18. *(20 points). Chapter III (Propulsion Considerations in the Missile Design and System Engineering Process).* For an axial compressor stage with a pressure coefficient $c_p = 0.6$ and rotor entrance local Mach number $M_{\text{Entrance}} = 1.4$, what is stage pressure ratio $p_{\text{Exit}}/p_{\text{Entrance}}$?

19. *(10 points). Chapter III (Propulsion Considerations in the Missile Design and System Engineering Process).* For an assumed axial compressor single stage pressure ratio $p_{\text{Exit}}/p_{\text{Entrance}} = 2$, what is the overall compressor pressure ratio p_3/p_2 of a four-stage compressor?

20. *(20 points). Chapter III (Propulsion Considerations in the Missile Design and System Engineering Process).* For an assumed turbine entrance temperature $T_4 = 4000$ R, compare the thrust T and specific impulse I_{SP} with the example in the text ($T_4 = 3000$ R).

21. *(20 points). Chapter III (Propulsion Considerations in the Missile Design and System Engineering Process).* At what combustion temperature does dissociation of water become a significant contributor to real gas effects?

22. *(30 points). Chapter III (Propulsion Considerations in the Missile Design and System Engineering Process).* Calculate the thrust, specific impulse, equivalence ratio, and nozzle exit area of an ideal ramjet for the following conditions/assumptions: liquid hydrocarbon fuel, free stream Mach number $= 2.5$, angle of attack $= 0$ deg, altitude $= 60$ kft, ramjet combustor maximum temperature 4000 R, and inlet capture area $= 114$ in^2. Compare with the ramjet baseline data of Chapter VII.

23. *(40 points). Chapter III (Propulsion Considerations in the Missile Design and System Engineering Process).* The corrected specific impulse of a ramjet is a function of the individual efficiencies of the combustor, nozzle, and inlet. Assuming that the driving parameter for the efficiencies is the total pressure recovery, derive an expression for correcting theoretical specific impulse.

24. *(100+ points). Chapter III (Propulsion Considerations in the Missile Design and System Engineering Process).* Derive the one-dimensional equations for thrust and specific impulse for an ideal scramjet. Calculate thrust, specific impulse, combustor area, and nozzle exit area for the following conditions/assumptions: hydrocarbon fuel, free stream Mach number $= 6.5$, angle of attack $= 0$ deg, altitude $= 100$ kft, Mach 3 initial combustion, thermal choking limit, combustor maximum temperature $= 4000$ R, and inlet capture area $= 114$ in^2. How is a scramjet similar to a ramjet? How is it different?

25. *(10 points). Chapter III (Propulsion Considerations in the Missile Design and System Engineering Process).* In the example, what is the inlet start Mach number if the inlet throat area $A_{IT} = 0.4$ ft^2? Is there a problem in having a large area for the inlet throat?

26. *(30 points). Chapter III (Propulsion Considerations in the Missile Design and System Engineering Process).* Calculate the total pressure ratios entering the combustor for the ramjet baseline cruising at Mach 2.5, sea level and at Mach 4.0, 80 kft. The inlet is a mixed compression type with a total of four compressions prior to the normal shock, consisting of 1) the shock wave on the conical nose, followed by 2) the shock wave on the ramp leading to the cowl, followed by 3) the shock wave on the cowl, and finally 4) a series of nearly isentropic internal contraction shock waves leading to a normal shock. Compare with the maximum available total pressure ratio from four optimum compressions.

27. *(100+ points). Chapter III (Propulsion Considerations in the Missile Design and System Engineering Process).* Derive the one-dimensional equations for thrust and specific impulse for an ideal ducted rocket. Calculate thrust, specific impulse, equivalence ratio, inlet throat area, and diffuser exit area for the following conditions/assumptions: 40% boron fuel, 8% aluminum fuel, 27% binder fuel, 25% ammonium perchlorate oxidizer, free stream Mach number $= 4$, angle of attack $= 0$ deg, altitude $= 80$ kft, gas generator pressure $= 1000$ psi, combustor maximum temperature $= 4000$ R, combustor area $= 287$ in^2, and inlet capture area $= 114$ in^2.

28. *(10 points). Chapter III (Propulsion Considerations in the Missile Design and System Engineering Process).* Compute the turbojet specific impulse I_{SP} of a 40% JP-10/60% boron carbide slurry fuel that has a heating

value $H_f = 23,820$ BTU/lbm. Compare with the text example (JP-10 fuel with $H_f = 18,700$ BTU/lbm).

29. *(20 points). Chapter III (Propulsion Considerations in the Missile Design and System Engineering Process).* Calculate the rocket baseline thrust at altitudes of sea level, 20 kft, and 50 kft. Compare results with Chapter VII.

30. *(20 points). Chapter III (Propulsion Considerations in the Missile Design and System Engineering Process).* If the rocket baseline throat area were reduced by 50%, with the propellant, burn area, and nozzle expansion ratio the same, what would be the resulting boost/sustain chamber pressure, thrust, specific impulse, and propellant weight flow rate?

31. *(30 points). Chapter III (Propulsion Considerations in the Missile Design and System Engineering Process).* Assume a propellant burn rate exponent $n = 0.9$. Also assume the same nominal propellant burn rate $r_{p_c} = 1000$ psi, propellant characteristic velocity c^*, propellant density ρ, nozzle geometry, and thrust profile as the rocket baseline. Calculate the chamber pressures and burn areas for boost/sustain. Compare with the rocket baseline chamber pressures and burn areas.

32. *(20 points). Chapter IV (Weight Considerations in the Missile Design and System Engineering Process).* The rocket baseline propellant grain is a slotted tube with a propellant volumetric efficiency of 90%. For the same volume of the motor case, what is the boost propellant weight and end-of-boost velocity for a grain with a propellant volumetric efficiency of 80%?

33. *(20 points). Chapter IV (Weight Considerations in the Missile Design and System Engineering Process).* A typical strategic ballistic missile motor has a much larger propellant fraction than a typical tactical ballistic missile, resulting in longer range. Assume a strategic ballistic missile has a typical inert subsystems weight fraction of 0.1 of the propellant weight. Also assume a payload weight of 1000 lb. Neglecting drag and the curvature of the earth, calculate the maximum range of a three-stage 100,000 lb missile with specific impulse of $I_{SP} = 250$ s (Minuteman-type solid propellant). As a comparison, calculate the maximum range of a two-stage 100,000 lb missile with specific impulse of $I_{SP} = 300$ s (Titan-type liquid propellant). Discuss the trade-off of the number of stages vs type of propellant/specific impulse.

34. *(20 points). Chapter IV (Weight Considerations in the Missile Design and System Engineering Process).* Calculate the center-of-gravity and pitch/yaw moment-of-inertia of the rocket baseline if the propellant density were increased by 50%, assuming the same weights for subsystems (e.g., motor case) in Chapter VII. Compare with the data in Chapter VII.

35. *(30 points). Chapter IV (Weight Considerations in the Missile Design and System Engineering Process).* Based on an average heat transfer coefficient, estimate the rocket baseline airframe temperature at the end of the flight trajectory example of Chapter 7.1 (Mach 0.8 launch at 20 kft altitude, 3.26 s boost, 10.86 s sustain, 9.85 s coast).

36. *(30 points). Chapter IV (Weight Considerations in the Missile Design and System Engineering Process).* Calculate the ramjet baseline radome internal wall temperature and surface wall temperature after 10 s flight at Mach 3, sea level.

37. *(30 points). Chapter IV (Weight Considerations in the Missile Design and System Engineering Process).* Estimate the ramjet baseline internal insulation required thickness to maintain warhead temperature less than 160°F for 10 m time of flight at Mach 4/80 kft. Assume an initial temperature of 70°F.

38. *(40 points). Chapter IV (Weight Considerations in the Missile Design and System Engineering Process).* For the ramjet baseline, compare the weight of an aluminum airframe with external micro-quartz insulation to that of the baseline uninsulated titanium airframe.

39. *(30 points). Chapter IV (Weight Considerations in the Missile Design and System Engineering Process).* Using the ramjet baseline inlet geometry and material data of Chapter VII, estimate the required inlet thickness and the required inlet weight based on an inlet start at Mach 2.5, sea level altitude. Compare with the inlet weight of Chapter VII.

40. *(20 points). Chapter IV (Weight Considerations in the Missile Design and System Engineering Process).* Calculate motor case weight for the rocket baseline if the case were titanium, with a forward dome ellipse ratio of 3 and a cylindrical cross section aftbody. Compare with the example calculation for a steel motor case and the data in Chapter VII.

41. *(20 points). Chapter IV (Weight Considerations in the Missile Design and System Engineering Process).* Calculate required tail thickness and the resulting weight of the rocket baseline tail surfaces. Assume a flight condition of Mach 2, altitude = 20 kft, motor burnout, angle of attack = 9.4 deg, and an ultimate stress factor of safety = 1.5. Compare result with the data of Chapter VII.

42. *(20 points). Chapter IV (Weight Considerations in the Missile Design and System Engineering Process).* Calculate radome weight for the rocket baseline if the radome were silicon nitride with an optimum transmission thickness. Compare with the example calculation for a pyroceram radome and the data in Chapter VII.

43. *(20 points). Chapter IV (Weight Considerations in the Missile Design and System Engineering Process).* Calculate the required thickness and the resulting weight of the rocket baseline radome to withstand the load from Mach 2, 20 kft altitude, and angle of attack = 9.4 deg for an

ultimate stress factor of safety = 1.5. Compare with the Chapter IV
example of optimum transmission thickness and the data of
Chapter VII.

44. *(10 points). Chapter IV (Weight Considerations in the Missile Design
and System Engineering Process).* Calculate actuation system weight for
the rocket baseline if the actuators were electromechanical. Compare
with the text example calculation and the data in Chapter VII.

45. *(10 points). Chapter V (Flight Performance Considerations in Missile
Design and System Engineering).* Using the Breguet range equation,
calculate the Mach 2.5, sea level cruise range of the ramjet baseline,
using data from Chapter VII. Compare with the range in Chapter VII.

46. *(10 points). Chapter V (Flight Performance Considerations in Missile
Design and System Engineering).* Calculate the steady state rate of climb
and the climb flight path angle for the ramjet baseline at Mach 2.5, sea
level, maximum thrust. Use data from Chapter VII.

47. *(20 points). Chapter V (Flight Performance Considerations in Missile
Design and System Engineering).* Calculate turn radius and turn rate of
the ramjet baseline for horizontal and pitch-over turns at Mach 4,
$h = 80$ kft altitude, end of cruise, angle of attack $\alpha = 15$ deg. Use data
from Chapter VII.

48. *(20 points). Chapter V (Flight Performance Considerations in Missile
Design and System Engineering).* Calculate the velocity and range of the
rocket baseline after 10 s of coast at a flight path angle of $+30$ deg for an
initial velocity of 2151 ft/s and an initial altitude of 20 kft.

49. *(20 points). Chapter V (Flight Performance Considerations in Missile
Design and System Engineering).* Calculate booster burnout Mach
number and ramjet acceleration capability following booster burnout at
sea level for the ramjet baseline. Compare with the performance data of
Chapter VII.

50. *(10 points). Chapter V (Flight Performance Considerations in Missile
Design and System Engineering).* Assuming a non-accelerating target at
Mach 0.8, $h = 20$ kft altitude, and 30 deg aspect, what is the required
missile lead angle for a constant bearing Mach 3 fly-out at $h = 20$ kft?

51. *(10 points). Chapter VI (Measures of Merit and Launch Platform
Integration/System Engineering).* For fog cover of 20 m height over the
target, what is the required look-down angle to achieve less than 5 dB
attenuation of a passive IR seeker?

52. *(20 points). Chapter VI (Measures of Merit and Launch Platform
Integration/System Engineering).* Compare the performance of an
MWIR seeker vs an LWIR seeker using the data of the text example, but
with a target temperature of 500 K.

53. *(10 points). Chapter VI (Measures of Merit and Launch Platform
Integration/System Engineering).* Assume a missile with a velocity

$V = 300$ m/s, strapdown seeker with a field of view $\theta = 20$ deg, and seeker detection range $R_D = 1$ km. Assume that an off-board sensor (e.g., UAV) provides the missile with a target location error TLE $= 10$ m. Assume the target has a velocity $V_T = 10$ m/s, laterally to the flight path of the missile. If the update time from the off-board sensor is equal to the target latency time (i.e., $t_{Update} = t_{Latency}$), what is the required update time from the off-board sensor?

54. (10 points). Chapter VI (Measures of Merit and Launch Platform Integration/System Engineering). For the text example rocket baseline warhead, what is the blast overpressure Δp at a distance from the center of explosion of $r = 5$ ft and an altitude $h =$ sea level?

55. (20 points). Chapter VI (Measures of Merit and Launch Platform Integration/System Engineering). Calculate the maximum miss distance requirement of a 5 lb warhead with $C/M = 1$ to achieve a lethality of 0.5 for a typical air target vulnerability (overpressure $\Delta p = 330$ psi, fragments impact energy $= 130$ kft-lb/ft^2).

56. (10 points). Chapter VI (Measures of Merit and Launch Platform Integration/System Engineering). Assume a revised rocket baseline warhead that has reduced collateral damage, with a warhead metal case mass $M_m = 0.4$ slug. For a warhead charge mass $M_c = 1.207$ slug, what is the total kinetic energy KE of the warhead?

57. (10 points). Chapter VI (Measures of Merit and Launch Platform Integration/System Engineering). Compare the text example of penetration through concrete with the penetration of the same penetrator through granite of density $\rho = 0.0897$ lb/in^3 and ultimate strength $\sigma = 20,000$ psi.

58. (30 points). Chapter VI (Measures of Merit and Launch Platform Integration/System Engineering). Assume a missile defense interceptor has a time constant of $\tau = 0.05$ s, an effective navigation ratio of $N' = 4$, and the target glint noise bandwidth is $B = 2$ Hz. What is the miss distance from glint for the imaging IR seeker example in Chapter II?

59. (10 points). Chapter VI (Measures of Merit and Launch Platform Integration/System Engineering). In the text example for survivability through high altitude flight and low radar cross section (RCS), if the flight altitude $h = 80$ kft, what is the required RCS to avoid detection by a threat radar that has a transmitted power $P_t = 10^6$ W and a wavelength $\lambda = 0.01$ m?

60. (20 points). Chapter VI (Measures of Merit and Launch Platform Integration/System Engineering). Calculate the frontal RCS of the rocket baseline.

61. (20 points). Chapter VI (Measures of Merit and Launch Platform Integration/System Engineering). Using data from the example in the

text, calculate the frontal radiant intensity of the ramjet baseline for long duration flight at Mach 2.5/sea level.

62. *(10 points). Chapter VI (Measures of Merit and Launch Platform Integration/System Engineering).* Using data from the example in the text, calculate the frontal IR detection range if the if the radiant intensity is reduced by 50%.

63. *(10 points). Chapter VI (Measures of Merit and Launch Platform Integration/System Engineering).* Using data from the text example for reduced frontal RCS, calculate detection range and exposure time for $+/-4$ dB, $1\ \sigma$ uncertainty in RCS.

64. *(10 points). Chapter VI (Measures of Merit and Launch Platform Integration/System Engineering).* Assuming a reliability of 98%, what is the missile circular error probable (CEP) that is required to provide a 95% probability of kill for a warhead lethal radius of 5 ft?

65. *(10 points). Chapter VI (Measures of Merit and Launch Platform Integration/System Engineering).* Calculate a typical system reliability of a missile that combines the autopilot, navigation sensors and computer as a single subsystem and has no seeker. Compare with the text example.

66. *(10 points). Chapter VI (Measures of Merit and Launch Platform Integration/System Engineering).* For a seven year development program of a 300 lb missile with a learning curve of 0.7, calculate the following for a total buy of 10,000 missiles:
- development cost
- total production cost
- average unit production cost
- unit production cost of missile number 10,000

67. *(20 points). Chapter VI (Measures of Merit and Launch Platform Integration/System Engineering).* Using the rocket baseline motor example of the text, what is the inner surface temperature of the motor if the initial temperature is 70°F and it is subjected to an ambient temperature of $-60°F$ for 1 h?

68. *(20 points). Chapter VI (Measures of Merit and Launch Platform Integration/System Engineering).* Using the rocket baseline motor example of the text, what is the maximum temperature of a titanium motor case?

69. *(10 points). Chapter VII (Sizing Examples and Sizing Tools).* What are the visual detection and recognition ranges of a small UCAV target that has a presented area $A_P = 10\ \text{ft}^2$ and a contrast $C_T = 0.1$?

70. *(30 points). Chapter VII (Sizing Examples and Sizing Tools).* Compare the rocket baseline motor case with a higher strength motor case made of 4130 heat treated steel with an ultimate tensile strength of 250,000 psi. Discuss design considerations such as brittleness, fracture sensitivity, material cost, motor case manufacturing cost

(e.g., machining, welding), required case thickness, and required case weight. Is a higher strength 4130 motor case a good idea?

71. *(60 points). Chapter VII (Sizing Examples and Sizing Tools).* Using the rocket baseline air-to-air standoff range example, compare the results based on the 1DOF analytical equations of motion of Chapter V with results from a numerical solution of the time marching equations of motion.

72. *(30 points). Chapter VII (Sizing Examples and Sizing Tools).* For the rocket baseline, what is the required wing area for 40 g maneuverability at Mach 3, burnout, and 20 kft altitude?

73. *(30 points). Chapter VII (Sizing Examples and Sizing Tools).* Conduct a Design of Experiment (DOE) to define the wind tunnel model configuration alternatives for the harmonized rocket baseline. Specify the nose, body, wing, and tail geometry options for a light weight/small miss distance missile.

74. *(40 points). Chapter VII (Sizing Examples and Sizing Tools).* For the ramjet baseline, compare the inlet mass flow rate at Mach 2.5, sea level altitude with the mass flow rate at Mach 4.0, 80 kft altitude.

75. *(10 points). Chapter VII (Sizing Examples and Sizing Tools).* Based on the ramjet baseline data in Chapter VII and the Breguet range equation, calculate the cruise range for Mach 4/80 kft altitude. Assume that all of the fuel is available for cruise.

76. *(80 points). Chapter VII (Sizing Examples and Sizing Tools).* Size an extended range ramjet that has 30% greater range than the ramjet baseline. Assume launch at Mach 0.8/sea level with cruise at Mach 2.3/sea level. Size the design by extending the missile length while maintaining constant missile diameter and static margin. Compare the new body length, tail area, launch weight, and the individual weights of fuel, fuel tank, boost propellant, booster case, and tails with the ramjet baseline.

77. *(20 points). Chapter VII (Sizing Examples and Sizing Tools).* Calculate the frontal radar cross section RCS of the turbojet baseline.

78. *(30 points). Chapter VII (Sizing Examples and Sizing Tools).* Calculate the Mach $M = 0.4$ zero-lift drag coefficient C_{D_0}, normal force coefficient C_N, and lift-to-drag ratio L/D of the turbojet baseline. Compare with the data of Chapter VII.

79. *(40 points). Chapter VII (Sizing Examples and Sizing Tools).* From the Request for Proposal given in Appendix B, develop a House of Quality Customer Requirements/Most Important Requirements (MIRs) and an Importance Rating of the MIRs. Expand the rows and columns of the House of Quality. Give rationale for your selections and values.

80. *(20 points). Chapter VII (Sizing Examples and Sizing Tools).* For the soda straw rocket baseline, specify a tail geometry and area that provides neutral static stability.

81. *(20 points). Chapter VII (Sizing Examples and Sizing Tools).* For the soda straw rocket baseline, calculate the range neglecting drag $(C_{D_0} = 0)$. Compare with the Chapter VII range that includes the effect of drag.

82. *(30 points). Chapter VII (Sizing Examples and Sizing Tools).* For the soda straw rocket baseline, what is the zero-lift drag coefficient C_{D_0} if we assume a laminar boundary layer?

83. *(80 points). Chapter VII (Sizing Examples and Sizing Tools).* Design, build, and fly a soda straw rocket that is optimized for maximum range at an assumed launch condition of 30 psi launch pressure. The rocket design must be compatible with a launch platform constraint of a "Super Jumbo" straw launcher of 0.25 in diameter and 6 in available launch length. You may base your rocket on the materials provided in class, or you may use your own materials as long as you satisfy the launch straw constraint (0.25 in diameter, 6 in available length). Provide the following information for your design:
    * Geometric, weight, center-of-gravity, aerodynamic, and thrust-time characteristics and the rationale for their values.
    * Dimensioned drawing.
    * Velocity during boost as a function of time and distance.
    * Post-boost flight trajectory height and horizontal range as a function of time.
    * Effect of $+/-10\%$ (1σ) prediction uncertainty of the drag coefficient on horizontal range.
    * Effect of $+/-10$ ft/s (1σ) horizontal head/tail wind velocity on horizontal range.
    * Comparison of predicted range with flight test.

84. *(10 points). Chapter VII (Sizing Examples and Sizing Tools).* For the soda straw rocket house of quality of the text example, what is relative ranking of engineering design parameters if the customer emphasis is changed to 70% emphasis on light weight/30% emphasis on long range?

85. *(40 points). Chapter VIII (Development Process).* For the ASALM PTV flight envelope boundaries, what are the values of the booster transition thrust − drag, high dynamic pressure, high aero heating, high L/D cruise, and low dynamic pressure.

86. *(20 points). Chapter VIII (Development Process).* For the ramjet baseline, compute the Mach number when thrust equals drag at an altitude $h = 40$ kft if the equivalence ratio $\phi = 1$. Compare with the ASALM PTV flight test result.

87. *(20 points). Chapter VIII (Development Process).* What is the 95% confidence interval of an operational test program with 45 kills out of 50 flights?

88. *(20 points). Chapter VIII (Development Process).* Give an example of the typical sequence of events for flight trajectory modeling development of a typical tactical missile system.

89. *(20 points). Chapter VIII (Development Process).* Give an example of the typical sequence of events for propulsion system development of a typical tactical missile system.

90. *(20 points). Chapter VIII (Development Process).* Give an example of the typical sequence of events for structure development of a typical tactical missile system.

91. *(30 points). Chapter VIII (Development Process).* Show a history of the events in state-of-the-art SOTA advancement in the reduction in weight of synthetic aperture radar (SAR).

92. *(30 points). Chapter VIII (Development Process).* Show a history of the events in state-of-the-art SOTA advancement in the size of missile infrared seeker focal plane array.

93. *(30 points). Chapter VIII (Development Process).* Show a history of the events in state-of-the-art SOTA advancements in energy per weight and power per weight of missile power supply.

94. *(60 points). Appendix B.* Develop a technology roadmap for the Request for Proposal given in Appendix B.

95. *(60 points). Design Case Studies.* Select one of the design case study presentations from the website in support of the textbook and conduct a review of the design case study. Provide a scoring/evaluation of the presentation, including rationale. The review should address the areas of technical content (35% weighting), organization and presentation (20% weighting), originality (20% weighting), and practical application and feasibility (25% weighting).

Example of Request for Proposal

American Institute of
Aeronautics and Astronautics

2003/2004 Graduate Student

Team Missile Design Competition

Multi-Mission Cruise Missile (MMCM) Design and Analysis Study

Sponsored by the
Missile Systems Technical Committee (MSTC)
Revised October 15, 2003

Table of Contents

B.1 Introduction

The Missile Systems Technical Committee (MSTC) of the American Institute of Aeronautics and Astronautics (AIAA) sponsors the graduate team missile design competition in order to further the understanding of the sciences associated with the design and development of missile systems. The competition is designed to allow a team of graduate level college engineering students to gain hands-on design and development experience in a real life competitive environment.

B.2 Statement of Work

Multi-Mission Cruise Missile (MMCM) Design and Analysis Study

B.2.1 Statement of Need

This study addresses the opportunity of an advanced cruise missile to counter time critical targets (TCTs) as well as long range surface targets of the year 2015 time frame. Threat TCTs include (1) mobile theater ballistic missile (TBM) launchers, (2) surface-to-air (SAM) missile systems, (3) major command, control and communication (C3) sites, (4) storage and support sites for weapons of mass destruction, and (5) other strategic targets such as bridges and transportation choke points. Mobile threat TBMs and SAMs are of particular interest because the stationary dwell time may be less than 10 minutes.

The Tomahawk subsonic cruise missile is a current baseline approach used by the U. S. Navy to counter long range surface threats. However, because the location of TCTs is often uncertain or their appearance is sudden, the response capability of a subsonic cruise missile is often insufficient. A multi-mission cruise missile (MMCM) system with the combined capabilities of 1) fast response against time critical targets, 2) subsonic cruise and extended range against other targets, and 3) loitering while waiting for retargeting would have operational and logistical advantages.

An enabling synergistic capability for MMCM is the anticipated advancement of the command, control, communication, computers, intelligence, surveillance, reconnaissance (C4ISR) network projected for the year 2015 time frame. It is anticipated that near real time, accurate targeting will be available from overhead tactical satellite and overhead unmanned air vehicle (UAV) sensors. Figure B.1 illustrates an example of a ground station, overhead satellite sensors and satellite relays, and overhead UAV sensor platform elements of the C4ISR architecture. The assumed C4ISR of the year 2015 is projected to have a capability for a target location error

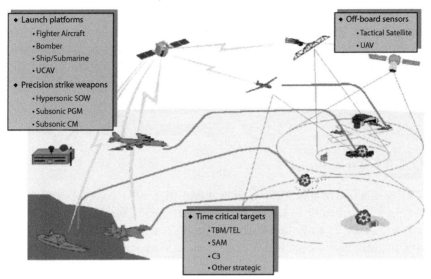

Note: C4ISR targeting state-of-the-art for year 2015 projected to provide sensor-to-shooter connectivity time less than 2 minutes and target location error (TLE) less than 1 meter.

Fig. B.1   Example of C4ISR Architecture for Hypersonic Standoff Missile Systems.

(TLE) of less than 1 meter (1 sigma) and an off-board sensor-to-shooter connectivity time of less than 2 minutes (1 sigma).

A second example of an enabling capability for MMCM is low cost precision guidance available from GPS/INS. The assumed GPS/INS of the year 2015 is projected to have a guidance navigation error of less than 3 meters circular error probable (CEP).

A third example of an enabling capability is the application of high bandwidth data link technology to a cruise missile, allowing target position updates, retargeting, and precision command guidance.

A fourth example of an enabling capability for MMCM is the recent cost reductions in standoff missiles, due in part to manufacturing processes such as castings that reduce parts count, the "spin on" application of commercial technologies (in areas such as electronics and materials) and the application of procurement reform. Examples include JDAM, JASSM and Tactical Tomahawk. Low cost, combined with high performance and operational flexibility, has the potential to allow MMCM to be used not only in TCT missions, but also other more traditional standoff missions. It could provide a neck-down benefit of a more simplified missile logistics system with fewer types of missiles.

Finally, a fifth example of an enabling capability for a multi-mission missile is the projected advances in turbine-based propulsion. It is anticipated that future turbine-based propulsion systems such as turbojet, turbo ramjet, and air turborocket will be capable of higher compressor pressure ratio and higher turbine temperature and will be capable of operating at higher Mach number. By the year 2015 it is anticipated a turbine-based propulsion system could be operational that could provide the required specific impulse and thrust necessary to operate across a Mach number range from subsonic to about Mach 3 to 5.

B.2.2 Objective

The objective of this study is to evaluate alternative concepts and technologies for a subsonic to hypersonic standoff missile system that would be used against TCTs and other surface targets. The baseline requirements in sizing the missile concept and the selection of subsystems/technologies are given below.

* Maximum Mach number of 3 (threshold), 4 (standard), and 5 (goal). An objective is a counterforce response capability against short dwell targets such as TBMs within the projected state-of-the-art of cost-effective technologies for the year 2010.
* Maximum subsonic cruise range against non-time-critical surface targets greater than 300 nm (threshold), 600 nm (standard), and 1000 nm (goal).
* Response time against TCTs less than 30 minutes (threshold), 15 minutes (standard), and 5 minutes (goal). This includes the command and control (C&C) decision time.
* Subsonic loiter time greater than 45 minutes (threshold), 60 minutes (standard), and 90 minutes (goal).
* Maximum post-loiter dash range after retargeting greater than 20 nm (threshold), 50 nm (standard), and 100 nm (goal).
* Weight less than 3400 lb. The basis is Vertical Launch System (VLS) carriage on cruisers and destroyers.
* Length less than 256 in for compatibility with VLS.
* Cross section less than 22 in by 22 in for compatibility with VLS.
* Electrical compatibility with VLS.
* Launch exhaust gas compatibility with VLS.
* Multipurpose (blast/frag/penetrator) warhead payload with a weight of 250 lb.
* Average unit production cost less than $1000K, based on 4000 units produced over a ten-year time frame.
* Wooden round with no shipboard maintenance and 15 year depot life.
* Satellite and UAV data link communication payload for retargeting and guidance.
* Guidance navigation error less than 3 meters CEP.

B.2.3 Tasks

A trade study will be conducted to evaluate alternative turbine-based missile concepts, their associated subsystems, and their associated technologies. The study will be based on projecting the current state-of-the-art (SOTA) to a technology readiness level (TRL) of 7 for Fiscal Year (FY) 2010. TRL 7 represents the Program Definition and Risk Reduction (PDRR) phase of a full-scale prototype in a full-scale flight environment. PDRR is comparable to demonstration/validation (demval). Following PDRR, a baseline assumption is that system development and demonstration (SDD) will begin in FY 2010. The desired initial operational capability (IOC) is FY 2015.

Tasks to be performed under this conceptual design study are as follows:

* Alternative Baseline Concepts and Subsystems Definition
* Alternative Baseline Concepts and Subsystems Evaluation
* Recommended Concept Refinement
* Mission Verification
* Technology Roadmap
* Documentation

Task 1. Alternative Baseline Concepts and Subsystems Definition

At least three alternative turbine-based concepts and their appropriate subsystems will be defined based on the requirements of Section 2.0. The characteristics of the alternative baseline concepts will be determined using the Tactical Missile Design (TMD) methods of Georgia Tech or similar conceptual design tools. A "house of quality" based on an integrated product and process development (IPPD) will be developed with Customer involvement for the relative weighting of the requirements. The turbine-based concepts will include at least the following:

* Turbojet
* Turbo ramjet
* Air turborocket

Task 2. Alternative Baseline Concepts and Subsystems Evaluation

The alternative baseline concepts and their subsystems will be evaluated against the requirements of Section 2.0, using the Georgia Tech TMD methods or similar conceptual design and analysis tools. Physics based models will developed that show the transparent prediction of specific impulse and thrust. The robustness of the design subsystems/technologies uncertainties and risks will be evaluated. Based on the capability against the requirements and the design robustness, a recommended MMCM and its subsystems will be selected.

Task 3. Recommended Concept Refinement

The MMCM recommended concept and subsystems will be refined based on considerations of alternative technologies. More sophisticated preliminary design and analysis tools will be used and results compared with the previous results from the conceptual design methods. Probabilistic/robust design, cost estimation, and optimization will be conducted. Design refinement will include:

- Turbine materials
- Compressor pressure ratio
- Inlet
- Fuels
- Insulation materials
- Airframe materials
- Aerodynamic configuration
- Forebody angles in front of the inlet
- Tail sizing
- Power supply
- Guidance, navigation, and control
- Data link
- Other subsystems and components
- Radar cross section and infrared signature

Task 4. Mission Verification

The MMCM concept will be evaluated in a three degree-of-freedom (3DOF) digital computer simulation. The flight trajectory and thrust profile will be optimized for maximum range, maximum loiter, and minimum time-to-target scenarios.

Task 5. Technology Roadmap

A technology roadmap will be developed for MMCM. The technology roadmap will address key enabling technologies that are driven by the requirements but will require additional development and demonstration to provide a required TRL of 7 to support a required SDD decision. The technology roadmap will include the major milestones, alternative approaches, risk mitigation plan, exit criteria for each TRL phase, and exit plan for failures. The technology development and demonstration activities will consider the following technology readiness levels (TRLs), leading to a TRL of 7 and an assumed SDD start in FY 2010:

* TRL 4 laboratory test demonstration of a component in a representative environment, but not full scale (6.2A exploratory development category funding).
* TRL 5 laboratory development or demonstration of a subsystem. The subsystem usually has full-scale components and is tested in a representative, but not full-scale environment. The category of funding is 6.2B exploratory development category.
* TRL 6 laboratory or flight Advanced Technology Demonstration (ATD) of a full-scale subsystem in a full-scale environment, with integration of some of the other subsystems and some of the other new technologies of a follow-on missile system. The category of funding is 6.3 advanced technology development.
* TRL 7 flight demonstration of either an ACTD or a PDRR full-scale prototype in a full-scale environment. The category of funding is 6.4 demonstration/validation (demval). All of the new critical technologies and subsystems are demonstrated. A driving consideration is to assure the system engineering and management confidence in the technologies. TRL 7 is normally performed where the technology and/or subsystem application is critical and high risk. The assumed Technology Availability Date (TAD) of year 2010 is based on successfully completing TRL 7.

Task 6. Documentation

The MMCM solution, rationale, and supporting technology will be documented. The documentation will be provided in a Kickoff Meeting, Midterm Review, Final Review, and Final Report.

* Kickoff Meeting. A presentation at the Kickoff Meeting will be given to the Sponsor and Customer representatives. It will be held in early December 2003. The Kickoff Meeting will address (1) "house of quality" weighting of the requirements, (2) clarification of requirements, (3) alternative concepts, and (4) the proposed plan for the study. A copy of the viewgraphs from the Kickoff Meeting will be provided.
* Midterm Review. A Midterm Review will be presented to the Sponsor and Customer at the completion of Task 2. It will be held in March 2004. Approval of the recommended concept will be required prior to the initiation of Task 3. A copy of the viewgraphs from the Midterm Review will be provided.
* Final Review. A Final Review will be presented to the Sponsor and Customer in late May 2004, after completing the study tasks. It will

address the final results of the study. A copy of the viewgraphs from the Final Review will be provided.

- Final Report. Six copies of the Final Report will be delivered to the Sponsor and Customer for review and scoring no later than June 1, 2004. The size of the Final Report will be no more than 100 pages. It will include the following information shown in Table B.1:

Table B.1 Final Report Information

• **Table of contents**, with sections consistent with the tasks of this statement of work (i.e., Tasks 1, 2, 3, 4, 5).
• Literature review **bibliography**.
• Tabulation of MMCM design **requirements**.
• **House of Quality** IPPD relative weighting of requirements.
• **Justification of MMCM concept,** including a comparison against the requirements, results of the design tradeoffs, robustness of the design and its technologies to uncertainties and risk, criteria used for selection, and advantages compared to alternative concepts.
• **Three-view drawing** of MMCM concept, with a layout showing the inboard profile of subsystems, including dimensions of the major subsystems. The center-of-gravity location at launch and burnout events will be shown on the drawing.
• Sketches of **alternative concepts.**
• Mission **flight profiles** of MMCM showing altitude, range, Mach number, weight, flight path angle, angle-of-attack, time, and major events such as booster ignition, surface deployments, booster burnout, booster separation, engine start, climb, cruise, descent, loiter, dash, dive, engine burnout, and impact.
• Operational **flight profiles** defining performance boundaries including altitude, speed, and maneuver g limits.
• **Aerodynamic, propulsion,** and **thermal characteristics** as a function of Mach number, angle of attack, angle of roll or sideslip, control surface deflection, and altitude.
• Airframe **structure** and **material** characteristics.
• **Sensitivity** of the system and subsystem parameters to requirements, with typical uncertainties.
• **Weight** and **balance** statement with subsystem weight, subsystem location (x,y,z), launch/burnout center-of-gravity locations, and launch/burnout moments-of-inertia.
• Discussion of **prediction methods** used to size the missile (e.g., aerodynamic configuration, propulsion system, guidance system, flight control system, structure, data link, power supply, other subsystems) and the methods used to predict the performance, cost, and constraint compliance. When practical, results will be verified as reasonable and consistent with other methods, available data, prior practice, and theory.
• Traceable **flow-down of system requirements** to subsystem and technology performance, cost, and constraints.
• Estimated **unit production cost** with units produced, production rate, learning curve, and basis for the learning curve.

(Continued)

Table B.1 Final Report Information (*Continued*)

- Estimated **SDD development cost** and schedule of SDD activities leading to production.
- Discussion of **VLS** integration.
- Discussion of the **year 2015 architecture** to support the areas of targeting, fire control, C4ISR, and GPS.
- **Technology roadmap** with a time phased schedule of exploratory development and advanced development programs and milestones required to demonstrate key enabling technologies by the year 2010.
- Discussion of other **life cycle** considerations with any operational, environmental, social, and technological issues that may affect the fitness of the concept over the system life cycle.
- Discussion of **manufacturing**, with considerations of reduced parts count, ease of manufacturing, life cycle cost, risk reduction, and compatibility with the logistics for the launch platforms.

B.3 Scoring/Evaluation

1. Technical Content (35 points)
   This addresses the correctness of theory, validity of reasoning used, apparent understanding and grasp of the subject, etc. Are all the major factors considered and a reasonably accurate evaluation of these factors presented?
2. Organization and Presentation (20 Points)
   The description of the design as an instrument of communication is a strong factor. Organization of written design, clarity, and inclusion of pertinent information are major factors.
3. Originality (20 points)
   The design proposal should avoid standard textbook information, and should show the independence of thinking or a fresh approach to the project. Does the method and treatment of the problem show imagination? Does the method show an adaptation or creation of automated design tools?
4. Practical Application and Feasibility (25 points)
   The proposal should present conclusions or recommendations that are feasible and practical and not merely lead the evaluators into further difficult or insolvable problems. Is the project realistic from the standpoints of cost, hazardous materials, and commonality with future systems?

B.4 Award

Based on a review and scoring of the final report, a trip and an award plaque may be provided by the Sponsor. The trip may consist of attending a missile launch, facility tour, or other aerospace related event. The Sponsor may award up to $5000 toward travel expenses.

B.5 Additional Information and Clarifications

Questions regarding this competition can be referred to the AIAA MSTC Sponsor members presented below.

Jacqueline Murdock	Eugene L. Fleeman
MSTC Chair	Georgia Institute of Technology
Atlantic Research Corporation (ARC)	School of Aerospace Engineering
5945 Wellington Rd	P.O. Box 150
Gainesville, VA	Atlanta, GA 30332-0150
Phone: (703) 754-5337	Phone: (703) 697-2187
E-mail: murdock@arceng.com	E-mail: Eugene.Fleeman@asdl.gatech.edu

Appendix C Nomenclature

The figures and tables in this text are designed as a stand-alone set of information. In most cases it is possible to use a figure or table without referring to the text or referring to other figures and tables. When practical, the symbols are defined in the figures and tables. As a complement, a list of symbols is provided in this section.

a	speed of sound
a_0	free stream speed of sound
A	target aspect angle, aspect ratio, or area
A_0	free stream air flow area
A_1	inlet throat area
A_2	diffuser exit area
A_3	combustor flame holder entrance area
A_4	combustor exit area
A_5	nozzle throat area
A_6	nozzle exit area
A_b	propellant burn area
A^*	cross sectional area of inlet or nozzle with Mach 1 flow
A_C	inlet capture area
A_d	detectors total area
A_{IT}	inlet throat area
Al	aluminum
a_M	acceleration of missile
A_o	optics aperture area
A_P	presented area of threat or target
A_{Ref}	reference area
A_t	throat area
A_V	target vulnerable area
b	span
B	bandwidth, Boron, body, bending, or billion
$(b_t)_{\mathrm{res}}$	target span resolution by seeker
c	specific heat or thermal capacitance, type of loading, or warhead charge weight

C	canard, contrast, explosive charge weight, coefficient, chord length, carbon, control, climb, or cost
C_1	cost of 1st unit
C_{1000th}	cost of 1000th missile
c^*	characteristic velocity
C_A	axial force coefficient
C/C_T	actual contrast-to-threshold contrast ratio
c_d	discharge coefficient
C_d	cadmium
C_D	drag coefficient
C_{D_0}	zero-lift drag coefficient
cg	center-of-gravity
cg_{BO}	center-of-gravity at burnout
cg_{Launch}	center-of-gravity at launch
C_i	initial contrast
Cl	chlorine
C_l	rolling moment coefficient
C_L	lift coefficient
C_{l_p}	rolling moment derivative from roll damping
C_{l_β}	rolling moment derivative from sideslip
$C_{l_{\delta a}}$	rolling moment derivative from roll control deflection
$C_{l_{\delta r}}$	rolling moment derivative from yaw control deflection
C_{l_ϕ}	rolling moment derivative from roll angle
C_m	pitching moment coefficient
c_{mac}	mean aerodynamic chord
C_{m_α}	pitching moment derivative from angle of attack
$C_{m\delta e}$	pitching moment derivative from pitch control deflection
C_n	yawing moment coefficient
C_N	normal force coefficient
C_{NC}	normal force coefficient from control deflection
$C_{N\alpha}$	normal force derivative from angle of attack
$C_{N\delta e}$	normal force derivative from pitch control deflection
C_{n_β}	yawing moment derivative from angle of sideslip
$C_{n_{\delta a}}$	yawing moment derivative from roll control deflection
$C_{n_{\delta r}}$	yawing moment derivative from yaw control deflection
C_{Nc}	normal force coefficient on control surface
$C_{N_{Trim}}$	normal force coefficient at trim
c_p	specific heat at constant pressure
cp	center-of-pressure
c_R	root chord
C_{SDD}	cost of system development and demonstration
c_{skin}	specific heat ratio of skin (airframe) material

c_T	tip chord or threshold contrast
C_x	cost of unit x
d	diameter
D	drag force, descent, or detection
D_0	zero-lift drag
dB	decibel
d_{BT}	diameter of boattail
d_{hemi}	diameter of hemisphere
d_o	optics diameter
d_p	pixel diameter
d_{Ref}	reference diameter
d_{spot}	spot diameter
dt	incremental time
D_t	target diameter
dz/dt	velocity in z-direction
d^2z/dt^2	acceleration in z-direction
D^*	specific detectivity
E	Young's modulus of elasticity, energy, or 10
E_c	energy per unit mass of charge
erfc	complementary error function
E_T	total energy
f	frequency or fragment
f/a	fuel-to-air ratio
F	force, flare, or noise factor
F_{CR}	critical force
f-number	aperture length/diameter
F-pole	standoff range at missile intercept
F_T	tensile force
F_{TU}	ultimate tensile force
g	acceleration of gravity (32.2 ft/s^2) or gram
g_c	gravitational constant ($32.2 \text{ ft lbm/lbf/s}^2$ or 32.2 lbm/slug)
GHz	10^{12} Hz
G_r	gain of receiver antenna
G_t	gain of transmitter antenna
h	altitude or inlet height
h	convection heat transfer coefficient
HCl	hydrogen chloride
H_f	heating value of fuel
h_i	initial altitude
h_f	final altitude
H_g	mercury
h_L	launch altitude

h_{mask}	mask altitude
h_{obstacle}	height of obstacle
I	moment-of-inertia
I_{SP}	specific impulse
I_t	total impulse
$(I_T)_{\Delta\lambda}$	Target radiant intensity between λ_1 and λ_2
I_y	yaw moment-of-inertia
j	integer
J	Joule
k	thermal conductivity, number of parameters
K	Boltzman's constant, thousands, or thickness constant
kg	kilogram
km	kilometer
l	length, number of levels
L	lift force, missile-target lead angle, learning curve, loss factor, or lifetime
$\dot{L}$	change in lead angle with time
l_b	length of body
lb	pound
lbf	pound force (unit of force)
lbm	pound mass (unit of mass)
l_c	inside chamber length
L_{CB}	missile-target lead angle for constant bearing flight trajectory
$(l_{\text{comb}})_{\text{min}}$	minimum efficient combustor length
l/d	length / diameter
L/D	lift / drag
l_N	length of nose
l_N/d	nose fineness ratio
l_{Ref}	reference length
L_λ	spectral radiance (Plank's Law)
m	meter
M	Mach number, moment, or warhead mass weight
$\dot{m}$	mass flow rate
M_0	free stream Mach number
$(M_3)_{TC}$	combustor entrance Mach number with thermal choking
$M_{\Lambda_{\text{LE}}}$	Mach number perpendicular to leading edge
M_∞	free stream Mach number
Max	maximum value
M_B	bending moment
M_C	mass of charge of warhead
M_g	magnesium
M_i	impact Mach number or initial Mach number

M_{IE}	inlet entrance Mach number
M_L	launch Mach number
M_m	mass of case liner of blast fragmentation warhead
M_{TC}	combustor entrance Mach number for thermal choking
M_{wh}	mass of warhead
n	number of pulses integrated, integer, type of warhead geometry, or burn rate exponent
N	normal force, noise, navigation ratio, Newton, or engine rotational speed
N'	effective navigation ratio
$n_{fragments}$	number of fragments
n_{hits}	number of hits
nm	nautical miles
n_M	missile maneuver acceleration g
N_{NU}	Nusselt number
n_T	target maneuver acceleration g
n_w	number of wings ($n_w=1$ is planar, $n_w=2$ is cruciform)
N_w	normal force on wing
n_x	acceleration g in longitudinal direction
n_z	acceleration g in vertical direction
O	oxygen
p	pressure, propellant, or pixel
P	penetration, load, or power
p_0	free stream static pressure
p_2	compressor entrance pressure
p_3	compressor exit pressure
p_{5_t}	turbine exit total pressure
P_a	Pascal
$P_{B,C}$	parameter of baseline, corrected (based on actual data)
$P_{B,U}$	parameter of baseline, uncorrected
p_{blast}	blast pressure
p_c	chamber pressure
$P_{CD,C}$	parameter of conceptual design, corrected
$P_{CD,U}$	parameter of conceptual design, uncorrected
p_e	exit pressure
p_{gauge}	gauge pressure
P_K	probability of kill
P_{KE}	penetration of kinetic energy warhead
P_r	power received
psf	pounds per square foot
psi	pounds per square inch
p_t	total pressure

P_t	power transmitted
p_{t0}	total pressure of free stream
p_{t2}	total pressure after normal shock
q	dynamic pressure $= \frac{1}{2}\rho V^2$
$\dot{q}$	heat transfer input flux
Q	heat transfer rate per unit area
r	radius, recovery factor, or propellant burn rate
R	range, radius, dome error slope, reliability, or gas constant
R_0	radar reference range
R_C	climb incremental range
R_D	detection range or descent incremental range
R_e	Reynolds number
R_F	flight range
R_{FCS}	fire control system range
$R_{F\text{-pole}}$	standoff range at missile intercept
R_L	launch range
R_{LOS}	line-of-sight range
R_{max}	maximum range
$R_{obstacle}$	range to obstacle
R_R	recognition range
R_T	turn radius
R.T.	room temperature
RT&A	research, technology and acquisition
R_{T_M}	radius of turn of missile
R_{T_T}	radius of turn of target
R_x	range in x-direction
R_y	range in y-direction
S	area or signal
S_{hemi}	cross sectional area of hemisphere
S/N	signal-to-noise ratio
$(S/N)_D$	signal-to-noise ratio for detection
S_P	presented area
S_{Ref}	reference area
S_T	tail area
S_W	wing area
S_{wet}	wetted area
t	time or thickness
T	thrust
T	temperature, torque, target, or tail
t_0	total time of flight
T_0	free stream temperature
$t_{90\%}$	time to achieve 90%

t_0/τ	number of time constants for intercept
T_1	inlet entrance temperature
T_2	compressor entrance temperature
T_3	compressor exit temperature
T_4	combustor exit temperature or turbine entrance temperature
T_{4_t}	combustion total temperature
T_5	turbine exit static temperature
T_{5_t}	turbine exit total temperature
t/t_0	fraction of time-to-go
t_B	rocket motor boost time
T_B	boost thrust
t_{Burst}	warhead burst time
t_C	coast time
t/c	thickness-to-chord ratio
t_{comb}	time required for combustion
T_e	telluride
t_{exp}	exposure time
t_f	time of flight
TH_z	10^{15} Hz
t_i	initial time
T_i	initial temperature
Ti	titanium
t_{mac}	maximum thickness of mean aerodynamic chord
t_{react}	reaction time
t_S	rocket motor sustain time
T_S	stall torque of single actuator
t_{SDD}	time duration of system development and demonstration
T_T	target temperature, total temperature
t_{wall}	thickness of wall material
T_Δ	temperature difference
u	velocity
V	velocity or vanadium
$\dot{V}$	time rate of change in velocity
V_{BC}	velocity at begin of coast
V_{BO}	velocity at burnout
V_C	velocity of climb or closing velocity
V_{comb}	combustion velocity
V_{CW}	velocity of cross wind
V_D	velocity of descent
V_e	exit velocity
V_{EB}	velocity at end of boost

V_{EC}	velocity at end of coast
V_f	fragment velocity
V_i	initial velocity
V_L	launch velocity
V_M	velocity of missile
V_T	velocity of target
V_x	velocity in x-direction
V_y	velocity in y-direction
V_∞	free stream velocity
w	load per unit length or wing
w_a	weight flow rate of air
W	weight, wing, glint noise spectral density, or Watt
W_{BC}	weight at begin of cruise
W_{BO}	weight at burnout
W_c	weight of warhead charge
W_E	weight per unit energy
W_f	weight of fuel
$\dot{W}_f$	fuel flow rate
W_i	initial weight
W_L	launch weight
W_m	weight of warhead metal case (fragments)
W_P	propellant weight or weight per unit power
$\dot{w}_p$	propellant weight flow rate
W_T	weight per unit torque
W_s	structure weight
x	longitudinal distance, independent variable
x_{AC}	aerodynamic center location
x_{cp}	center-of-pressure location
x_{CG}	center-of-gravity location
x_{HL}	hinge line location
y	lateral distance, dependent variable
Y_1	first year
y_{cp}	outboard center-of-pressure location
y_{offset}	lateral offset distance
z	warhead scaling parameter or vertical distance
z_{skin}	skin thickness
z_{max}	maximum value of z
α	angle of attack, thermal diffusivity, coefficient of thermal expansion, or atmospheric extinction coefficient
α'	local effective angle of attack
$\ddot{\alpha}$	angle of attack angular acceleration
α_{CW}	angle of attack of cross wind

α_{Trim}	trim angle of attack
α/δ	change in angle of attack with control deflection
$\alpha/\dot{\gamma}$	angle of attack sensitivity to turn rate
β	angle of sideslip or bi-static radar angle
δ	control deflection, body angle, or seeker angle
$\dot{\delta}$	control surface deflection rate
δ_{LE}	leading edge section angle
δ_{trim}	control deflection for trim
ϵ	nozzle expansion ratio (exit area/throat area), strain, dielectric constant, seeker angle error, or emissivity coefficient
ϕ	equivalence ratio (actual fuel-to-air compared to stochiometric) or missile roll angle
ζ	damping coefficient
γ	specific heat ratio (≈ 1.4 for ambient air, ≈ 1.2 for rocket motor) or flight path angle
γ_0	free stream specific heat ratio
γ_1	specific heat ratio at inlet entrance
γ_2	specific heat ratio at compressor entrance
γ_3	specific heat ratio at compressor exit or combustor entrance
γ_4	specific heat ratio at turbine entrance or combustor exit
γ_5	specific heat ratio at turbine exit
$\dot{\gamma}$	Rate of change in flight path angle
γ_C	Flight path climb angle
γ_D	Flight path dive or descent angle
γ_i	initial flight path angle
γ_M	Initial heading error of missile
η	efficiency ($\eta = 1$ is 100% efficient) or fraction of maximum solar radiation
η_a	atmospheric transmission
λ	taper ratio (tip chord/root chord), wavelength, or surface geometry coefficient
μ	Mach angle or aggregate thermal resistance coefficient
θ	missile pitch attitude, beam width, shock angle, radial angle, or surface angle
$\dot{\theta}$	pitch attitude angular acceleration
θ_{3dB}	1/2 power beam width
θ_a	angular resolution
θ_{BT}	boattail angle
θ_F	vision fovea angle of human eye that provides highest resolution
θ_i	incidence angle or initial angle

ρ	density
ρ_∞	free stream density
ρ_M	missile average density
ρ_p	density of penetrator warhead
ρ_T	density of target
ρ_{wall}	density of wall material
σ	radar cross section, stress, standard deviation, atmospheric attenuation coefficient or miss distance
σ_{Buckle}	buckling stress
σ_{glint}	miss distance from glint
σ_{HE}	miss distance from heading error
σ_{MAN}	miss distance from target maneuver acceleration
σ_{Max}	maximum stress
σ_t	tensile stress
σ_{TU}	target ultimate stress
σ_{TS}	thermal stress
σ_{yield}	yield stress
π	3.1418...
π_K	pressure sensitivity to temperature
τ	time constant or pulse duration
τ_δ	time constant from control effectiveness
$\dot{\tau}_\delta$	time constant from deflection rate limit
τ_{Dome}	time constant from radome error slope
ω	angular velocity
ω_1	first mode wing bending frequency
$\omega_{Actuator}$	actuator bandwidth
ω_{BB}	first mode body bending frequency
ω_{SP}	flight dynamics short period frequency
ψ	yaw angle
Δ	incremental
Δf_p	pixel detector bandwidth
Λ	sweep angle, solar absorbtivity
$\sum$	summation
$!$	factorial
$||$	absolute value
$\approx$	approximately equal to
$\sim$	similar to
$<$	less than
$>$	greater than
$\perp$	perpendicular to
$\#$	number
$2a$	major axis of ellipse
$2b$	minor axis of ellipse

Appendix D — Acronyms/Abbreviations

1D	one dimensional
1-DOF	one-degree-of-freedom
2D	two dimensional
2-DOF	two-degrees-of-freedom
3D	three dimensional
3-DOF	three-degrees-of-freedom
4-DOF	four-degrees-of-freedom
5-DOF	five-degrees-of-freedom
6-DOF	six-degrees-of-freedom
6.1	basic research
6.2	exploratory development
6.3	advanced development
6.4	demonstration & validation
6.5	engineering and manufacturing development
AAA	anti-aircraft artillery
AAM	air-to-air missile
AARGM	Advanced Anti-radiation Guided Missile
A/B	air-breathing
A/C	aircraft
ACM	Advanced Cruise Missile
ACTD	Advanced Concept Technology Demonstration
ADAM	Advanced Design of Aerodynamic Missiles
AEDC	Arnold Engineering Development Center
AGM	air-to-ground missile
AIM	air intercept missile
A/J	anti-jam
ALCM	Air Launched Cruise Missile
AMRAAM	Advanced Medium Range Air-to-Air Missile
ANS	Anti-Navire Supersonique
AoA	angle of attack or assessment of alternatives
AP	ammonium perchlorate
APKWS	Advanced Precision Kill Weapon System
ARH	anti-radiation homing

ARM	anti-radiation missile
ARO	all reflective optics
ARRMD	Affordable Rapid Response Missile Demonstrator
ASALM	Advanced Strategic Air Launched Missile
ASCM	anti-ship cruise missile
ASM	air-to-surface missile
ASMP	Air-Sol Moyenne Portée
ASP	advanced signal processing
ASRAAM	Advanced Short range Air-to-Air Missile
ATA	air-to-air or automatic target acquisition
ATACMS	Army Tactical Missile System
ATD	Advanced Technology Demonstration
ATM	atmosphere
ATR	automatic target recognition or air turbo rocket
ATS	air-to-surface
AUR	all up round
AVG	average
AWACS	Airborne Warning and Control System
B	billion
BAe	British Aerospace
BAT	Brilliant Anti-tank
BC	beginning of cruise
BDA	battle damage assessment
BDI	battle damage indication
BIT	built in test
BL	baseline or body line
BMD	ballistic missile defense
BMDO	Ballistic Missile Defense Organization
BO	burn out
BRU	bomb rack unit
BTT	bank-to-turn
BTU	British Thermal Unit
C2	command and control
C^3	command, control, and communication
C^3I	command, control, communication, intelligence
C4ISR	command, control, communication, computers, intelligence, surveillance, reconnaissance
CAD	computer aided design
CALCM	Conventional Air Launched Cruise Missile
CAS	close air support
CBU	cluster bomb unit
CCM	counter-countermeasures

CDR	critical design review
CEP	circular error probable
CFD	computational fluid dynamics
cg	center of gravity
CL	centerline
CLS	canister launch system
CL Tk	centerline tank carriage
CLU	command and launch unit
CM	cruise missile, countermeasure
cmW	centimeter wave
CONOPS	concept of operations
CONUS	continental United States
COTS	commercial off the shelf
cp	center of pressure
CPIA	Chemical Propulsion Information Agency
CPU	central processor unit
CTS	captive trajectory simulation
CW	continuous wave
DACS	divert and attitude control system
DAGR	Direct Attack Guided Rocket
DARPA	Defense Advanced Research Projects Agency
DATCOM	DATaCOMpendium
dB	decibel
DCR	Dual Combustor Ramjet-scramjet
DemVal	Demonstration and Validation
DoD	Department of Defense
DOE	design of experiment
DOF	degree of freedom
DOS	disk operating system
DT&E	development test & evaluation
ECCM	electronic counter-countermeasures
ECM	electronic countermeasures
EDPM	ethylene propylene diene monomer
EFP	explosively formed projectile
EKV	Exo-atmospheric Kill Vehicle
ELINT	electronic intelligence
EM	electro-mechanical or electro-magnetic
EMC	electro-magnetic compatibility
EMD	Engineering and Manufacturing Development
EMI	electro-magnetic interference
EMP	electro-magnetic pulse
EO	electro-optical

EOCM	electro-optical countermeasure
ESA	electronically steered antenna
ESSM	Evolved Sea Sparrow Missile
EW	electronic warfare
FCS	fire control system
FDTD	finite difference time domain
FEM	finite element model
FLIR	forward looking infrared
FM	frequency modulation
FMCW	frequency modulation continuous wave
FMRAAM	Future Medium Range Air-to-Air Missile
FOG	fiber optic gyro
FOR	field of regard
FOS	factor of safety
FOV	field of view
FPA	focal plane array
fps	feet per second
ft	foot
FW	fiscal year
g	gram
G&C	guidance & control
GBI	Ground Based Interceptor
GBU	guided bomb unit
GFE	government furnished equipment
GHz	Giga Hertz (10^9 Hertz)
GMD	Ground-Based Midcourse Defense
GMLRS	Guided Multiple Launch Rocket System
GPS	Global Positioning System
GTD	geometric theory of diffraction
HARM	High Speed Anti-Radiation Missile
HAWK	Homing-All-the-Way-Killer
HDBK	handbook
HE	high explosive or heading error
HELLFIRE	Heliborne Launched Fire and Forget
HIMARS	High Mobility Artillery Rocket System
HL	hinge line
HM	hypersonic missile or hinge moment
HMMWV	High Mobility Multipurpose Wheeled Vehicle
HMX	Her Majesty's Explosive
HOJ	home on jam
HOQ	house of quality
HOT	Haut subsonique Optiquement Téléguidé

HPM	high power microwave
HSAD	High-Speed Anti-radiation missile Demonstration
HTPB	hydroxyl-terminated polybutadiene binder
HUD	head up display
HWL	hardware-in-loop
Hz	Hertz (cycles per second)
IC	integrated circuit
ICBM	intercontinental ballistic missile
IE	inlet entrance
IF	intermediate frequency
IFOV	instantaneous field of view
IM	insensitive munition
IMU	inertial measurement unit
in	inch
INS	inertial navigation system
IOC	initial operational capability
IPPD	integrated product and process development
IR	infrared
IRBM	intermediate range ballistic missile
I^2R	imaging infrared
IIR	imaging infrared
IRR	integral rocket-ramjet
ISAR	inverse synthetic aperture radar
IT	inlet throat
ITCV	Inter-Tropical Convergence Zone
JAGM	Joint Air-to-Ground Missile
JASSM	Joint Air-to-Surface Standoff Missile
JDAM	Joint Direct Attack Munition
JHMCS	Joint Helmet Mounted Cueing System
JI	jet interaction
JSOW	Joint Standoff Weapon
JTIDS	Joint Tactical Information Distribution System
KE	kinetic energy
kg	kilogram
km	kilometer (1000 meter)
KV	kill vehicle
KW	kill weapon
LADAR	laser detection and ranging
LAR	launch acceptable range
LASER	light amplification by stimulated emission of radiation
LAU	launch adapter unit
LCC	life cycle cost

LCS	laser cross section
LE	leading edge
LO	low observable
LOAL	lock on after launch
LOBL	lock on before launch
LOCAAS	Low Cost Autonomous Attack System
LOGAR	Low-Cost Guided Imaging Rocket
LOS	line of sight
LOSAT	Line-of-Sight Anti-Tank
LPI	low probability of intercept
LRIP	low rate initial production
LWIR	long wave infrared
m	meter
M	million or molecular weight
mac	mean aerodynamic chord
MANPADS	man portable air defense system
MBB	Messerschmitt-Boelkow-Blohn
MCTR	Military Technology Control Regime
MEOP	maximum effective operating pressure
MD	miss distance
MDA	Missile Defense Agency
MEADS	Medium Extended Air Defense System
MEMS	micro-machined electro-mechanical systems
MIL STD	military standard
MIRs	most important requirements
MIRV	multiple independent reentry vehicle
Mk	Mark
MLRS	Multiple Launch Rocket System
mmW	millimeter wave
MOM	measure of merit, method of moments
MRAAM	medium range air-to-air missile
MRBM	medium range ballistic missile
MW	molecular weight
MWIR	medium wave infrared
N/A	not applicable
NASA	National Aeronautics and Space Administration
NATO	North Atlantic Treaty Organization
NCTID	non cooperative target identification
NEAR	Nielsen Engineering and Research
nm	nautical miles
NOAA	National Oceanic and Atmospheric Administration
NSWC	Naval Surface Warfare Center

NTW	Navy Theater Wide
NWC	Naval Weapons Center
OFAT	one factor at a time
OODA	observe-orient-decide-act
OP	operating pressure
OPS	operations
O&S	operations and support
OT&E	operational test & evaluation
P	parameter
PAC-3	Patriot Advanced Capability-3
P^3I	pre-planned product improvement
PBX	plastic bonded explosive
PC	personal computer
PDF	probability density function
PDRR	Program Definition and Risk Reduction
PGM	precision guided munition
PE	program element
PFR	preliminary flight rating
PK	probability of kill
PRF	pulse repitition frequency
PS	power supply
PTD	physical theory of diffraction
PTV	propulsion test validation
QWIP	quantum well infrared photodetector
RA	rolling airframe
rad	radian
RADAR	radio detection and ranging
RAM	Rolling Airframe Missile or radar absorbing material
RCS	radar cross section
R&D	research and development
RDT&E	research, development, test and evaluation
RDX	Royal Demolition Explosive
RES	radome error slope
RF	radio frequency
RFCM	radar frequency countermeasure
RFP	request for proposal
RJ	ramjet
RJ-4,-5,-6	ramjet fuel 4, 5, or 6
RJC	reaction jet control
RLG	ring laser gyro
RMS	root mean of squares
ROK	Republic of Korea

rpm	revolutions per minute
RSS	root sum of squares
RT&A	research, technology, and acquisition
RTM	resin transfer molding
RV	reentry vehicle
s	second
S&A	safe and arm
SADARM	Sense and Destroy Armor Munition
SAL	semi-active laser
SAM	surface-to-air missile
SAR	synthetic aperture radar
SATCOM	satellite communications
SDB	Small diameter Bomb
SDD	system development and demonstration
SEAD	suppression of enemy air defense
SED	scramjet engine demonstration
sfc	specific fuel consumption
SFW	Sensor Fuzed Weapon
SL	sea level
SLAM	Standoff Land Attack Missile
SLAM-ER	Standoff Land Attack Missile-Expanded Response
SLAMRAAM	Surface Launched AMRAAM
SM	static margin or Standard Missile
S/N	signal-to-noise ratio
SOTA	state of the art
SOW	statement of work
SRAM	Short Range Attack Missile
SRBM	short range ballistic missile
SRR	system requirements review
SSM	surface-to-surface missile
STA	station or surface-to-air
STANAG	standardization agreement
STD	standard
STS	surface-to-surface
STT	skid-to-turn
SW	Sidewinder
SWIR	short wave infrared
TALD	Tactical Air-launched Decoy
TBD	to be determined
TBM	theater ballistic missile
TC	thermal choking
TCT	time critical target

TD	target detection
TDACS	throttle-able divert and attitude control system
TDD	target detection device
TE	trailing edge or target error
TEL	transporter, erector, launcher
TERCOM	terrain correlation matching
THAAD	Theater High Altitude Area Defense
TK	tank
TLE	target location error
TM	telemetry
TMC	thrust magnitude control
TMD	Tactical Missile Design or theater missile defense
TNT	TriNitroToluene
TOW	Tube Launched, Optically Tracked, Wire command link Guided
TRD	technical requirements document
TRL	technology readiness level
TURB	turbulent
TV	television
TVC	thrust vector control
TVM	track via missile
UAV	unmanned air vehicle
UCAV	unmanned combat air vehicle
UHF	ultra high frequency
UK	United Kingdom
US	United States
USD	United States dollars
UV	ultraviolet
VARTM	vacuum assisted resin transfer molding
VLS	Vertical Launch System
V&V	verification and validation
w	with
WAN	wide area network
W/H	warhead
XLDB	cross-linked double base
w/o	without

Appendix E Conversion Factors

Table E.1 Conversion of English to Metric Units

Parameter	English unit	Metric unit	Multiply by
Acceleration	ft/s^2	m/s^2	0.3048
Area	ft^2	m^2	0.09294
Area	$in.^2$	m^2	6.452E−04
Density	$lbm/in.^3$	kg/m^3	2.767E+04
Density	$lbm/in.^3$	kg/l	27.67
Density	lbm/ft^3	kg/m^3	16.02
Density	$lbf\text{-}s^2/in.^4$	kg/m^3	1.069E+07
Density	$slug/ft^3$	kg/m^3	515.4
Energy	BTU	J or N-m	1055
Energy	ft-lbf	J or N-m	1.3557
Force	lbf	N	4.4484
Heat capacity	$BTU/lbm/^\circ F$	$J/kg/^\circ C$	4188
Heat transfer coefficient	$BTU/hr/ft^2/^\circ F$	$W/m^2/^\circ C$	5.6786
Heat transfer coefficient	$BTU/s/ft^2/^\circ F$	$W/m^2/^\circ C$	2.044E+04
Heat transfer rate	$BTU/ft^2/s$	W/m^2	1.135E+04
Length	ft	m	0.3048
Length	in.	m	0.0254
Length	mil (0.001 in.)	micron	25.4
Length	mile	m	1609
Length	nm	m	1852
Mass	lbm	kg	0.4535
Mass	$lbf\text{-}s^2/in.$	kg	1200
Mass	slug	kg	14.59
Mass flow rate	lbm/h	kg/s	1.260E−04
Mass flow rate	lbm/s	kg/s	0.4535
Mass flow rate	slug/s	kg/s	14.59
Moment-of-inertia	$ft\text{-}lbf\text{-}s^2$	$kg\text{-}m^2$	1.3557
Moment-of-inertia	$in.\text{-}lbf\text{-}s^2$	$kg\text{-}m^2$	0.113

(Continued)

Table E.1 Conversion of English to Metric Units (*Continued*)

Parameter	English unit	Metric unit	Multiply by
Power	BTU/h	W	0.2931
Power	hp	W	745.71
Pressure	lbf/ft^2	Pa or N/m^2	47.89
Pressure	$lbf/in.^2$	Pa or N/m^2	6895
Pressure	std atm	Pa or N/m^2	1.013E+05
Specific heat	BTU/lbm/°F	J/kg/°C	4186
Specific impulse	s	Ns/kg	9.81
Temperature	°F	°C	(°F - 32) 0.5556
Temperature	R	K	0.5556
Thermal conductivity	BTU/hr/ft/°F	W/m/°C	1.7307
Thermal conductivity	BTU/s/ft/°F	W/m/°C	6231
Thermal diffusivity	ft^2/s	m^2/s	0.09290
Torque	ft-lbf	N-m	1.3557
Torque	in-lbf	N-m	0.113
Torque	$slug-ft^2/s$	N-m	1.3557
Velocity	ft/s	m/s	0.3048
Velocity	knot or nm/h	km/h	1.852
Viscosity - absolute	$lbf-s/ft^2$	$N-s/m^2$	47.87
Viscosity - absolute	lbm-s/ft	$N-s/m^2$	1.4881
Viscosity - kinematic	ft^2/s	m^2/s	0.09294
Volume	ft^3	m^3	0.02831
Volume	$in.^3$	m^3	1.639E−05
Volume	US gallons	L	3.785
Volume	US gallons	m^3	0.003785

Appendix F   *Example Syllabus*

An example syllabus for a two-semester course on Missile Design and System Engineering is given below. This is a lecture-lab course that includes lectures, classroom team homework, individual homework problems, exams, student team design study/studies, customer reviews, and documentation. The first semester is 3 credit hours, consisting of 2 hours each week in the classroom plus design team participation outside the classroom. The second semester is 2 credit hours, consisting primarily of the design team study/studies, customer reviews, and documentation.

Summary: This is a self-contained course on the fundamentals of missile design and system engineering. It provides a system-level, integrated method for the missile aerodynamic configuration/propulsion system design and analysis. The course addresses the broad range of alternatives in meeting missile performance, cost and system measures of merit/constraint requirements. The methods presented are generally simple closed-form analytical expressions that are physics-based, to provide insight into the primary driving parameters. Configuration sizing examples are presented for rocket-powered, ramjet-powered, and turbojet-powered baseline missiles. Typical values of missile parameters and the characteristics of current operational missiles are presented. Also presented are the enabling subsystems and technologies for missiles and the current/projected state-of-the-art of missiles. During this course the students will size the configuration, size the propulsion system, estimate the weight, and estimate the flight performance for a conceptual missile design, in accordance with the requirements of a Request for Proposal (RFP). The students will also include first order system measures of merit/constraints (such as miss distance, lethality, cost, and launch platform integration) for the conceptual design and system engineering of a missile, in accordance with the requirements of the RFP. Computational methods used will progress from hand calculation to spreadsheet analysis to more sophisticated computer programs during the design maturation. Results will be presented to a customer review team at kickoff, midterm, and final reviews.

Textbook: *Missile Design and System Engineering* by Eugene L. Fleeman.

Prerequisites: Previous courses in flight vehicle aerodynamics, propulsion, structure, and performance.

Schedule:

Lectures: Weeks 1 – 15 of the first course, on Chapters 1 – 9 of the textbook.

Classroom Review of Textbook Problems: Upon completion of the lecture for each chapter of the textbook. The review will be conducted in the classroom. The problems are at the end of the chapter.

Classroom Homework Problems: A classroom homework assignment will be given each week, from Appendix A of the textbook. The following week, a selected two-student team will present their solution in the classroom.

Individual Homework Problems: Individual homework assignments will be given each week, from Appendix A of the textbook. Homework is due the following week after the assignment.

Midterm Exam: Upon completion of the Chapter 5 lecture (Flight Performance Considerations in Missile Design and System Engineering). It is anticipated that the midterm exam will be given during week 9 of the first course.

Final Exam: Upon completion of the Chapter 9 lecture (Summary and Lessons Learned). It is anticipated that the Final Exam will given during week 15 of the first course.

Request for Proposal: The RFP provides the statement of work and deliverable requirements for the missile design study. An example of an RFP is shown in Appendix B of the textbook. The RFP will be provided prior to week 10 of the first course.

Student Design Team(s): The student design team(s) will be formed prior to week 10 of the first course. Each student design team will consist of about ten students. One of the students will be the program manager and one of the students will be the systems engineer. The other students will be responsible for functional areas such as propulsion, aerodynamics, structure, flight control, guidance and navigation, weight and balance, design layout, warhead, flight performance, cost, and launch platform integration.

Customer Reviews: Three reviews are held with the customer—A Kickoff Meeting during week 15 of the first course, a Midterm Review upon completion of a down-select to a preferred concept(s) (about week 8 of the second course), and a Final Review (during week 13 of the second course). Dry runs will be held prior to the customer reviews.

Documentation: Documentation from the student design team(s) will include a final technical report of about 100 pages and slides from the customer reviews. The draft final report will provided 1 week following the Final Review. A paper may also be presented later at a technical conference. Drafts of the documentation will be reviewed prior to submittal to the customer(s).

Grading: Grades will be based on the exam scores, classroom team homework scores, individual homework scores, student team participation, classroom participation, presentation skills, the overall quality of the student team presentations, and the overall quality of the student team documentation.

Appendix G CEU Credit Quizzes

Date: _____

Name: _____

Organization: _____

E-mail: _____

Telephone: _____

Missile Design and System Engineering Short Course Quizzes

Continuing Education Unit (CEU) Credit

Quizzes are used to evaluate the student's understanding of the short course for CEU credit. More than 70 multiple choice questions are available for each of two quizzes (midterm, final). The student should select and answer *a minimum of 10 questions* for each quiz. Answering more than 10 questions for each quiz is encouraged but not required.

A grade of 80% correct answers is required for each quiz. The student may use "open notes."

Name: _____

Missile Design and System Engineering Short Course

CEU Midterm Quiz

Chapters 1 (Introduction), 2 (Aerodynamics), 3 (Propulsion), 4 (Weight), and 5 (Flight Performance)

1. Which missile is more maneuverable?
   a) ALCM
   b) Archer
   c) Storm Shadow
   d) Brimstone

2. Which has the least impact on aerodynamic configuration sizing?
   a) fuzing
   b) propulsion
   c) wing geometry
   d) length

3. Which design activity typically follows the others?
   a) mission/scenario/system definition
   b) weapon system requirements, trade studies and sensitivity analysis
   c) launch platform integration
   d) technology assessment and development roadmap

4. System integration includes
   a) environment extremes
   b) launch platform
   c) targeting
   d) all of the above

5. Which air-to-air missile has the longest range?
   a) Meteor
   b) AMRAAM
   c) IRIS_T
   d) Sparrow

6. Which air-to-surface missile has the highest speed?
   a) Hellfire
   b) HARM
   c) Storm Shadow
   d) Tomahawk

7. Which surface-to-surface missile is the lightest weight?
   a) Javelin
   b) MGM-140

Name: _____

c) BGM-109

d) MLRS

8. Which surface-to-air missile has the longest range?

a) FIM-92

b) PAC-3

c) GBI

d) SM-3

9. Campaign model results typically include

a) effectiveness of different mixes of weapons in the campaign

b) cost per target kill

c) C4ISR interface

d) all of the preceding

10. The rocket baseline missile flight range is least sensitive to which parameter?

a) Zero-lift drag coefficient

b) Static margin

c) Inert weight

d) Thrust

11. A typical value of tactical missile body fineness ratio is

a) $l/d = 5$

b) $l/d = 10$

c) $l/d = 25$

d) $l/d = 50$

12. Missile drag is proportional to

a) diameter

b) $\text{diameter}^{1.5}$

c) diameter^2

d) diameter^3

13. Radar seeker range is proportional to

a) diameter

b) $\text{diameter}^{1.5}$

c) diameter^2

d) diameter^3

14. The first mode body bending frequency should be

a) $> 0.1 \times$ flight control actuator bandwidth

b) $> 0.5 \times$ flight control actuator bandwidth

c) $\approx$ flight control actuator bandwidth

d) $> 2 \times$ flight control actuator bandwidth

Name: _____

15. Maximum effective boattail angle of a hypersonic missile is about
    a) 0 deg
    b) 2 deg
    c) 4 deg
    d) 8 deg

16. A disadvantage of a circular body cross section is
    a) higher RCS
    b) less efficient packaging of subsystems
    c) more difficult launch platform integration
    d) more complex aerodynamic/structural analysis

17. A disadvantage of a large wing is
    a) less range in subsonic flight
    b) larger seeker gimbal angle requirement
    c) less angle of attack requirement for maneuver
    d) none of the above

18. Which cruise missile has the smallest wing?
    a) JASSM
    b) Apache
    c) Taurus
    d) Harpoon

19. According to slender wing theory, wing normal force coefficient is independent of
    a) angle of attack
    b) aspect ratio
    c) Mach number
    d) none of the above

20. As Mach number increases from Mach 0 to 5, the wing aerodynamic center moves from about
    a) 25% to 35% of the mac
    b) 25% to 50% of the mac
    c) 35% to 50% of the mac
    d) 35% to 50% of the mac

21. A disadvantage of a delta wing is
    a) larger variation in aerodynamic center
    b) larger bending moment
    c) higher supersonic drag
    d) greater tendency for aeroelastic instability

22. The mean aerodynamic chord (mac) length of a delta wing is
    a) 1/3 root chord length
    b) 1/2 root chord length

Name: _____

c) 2/3 root chord length
d) 3/4 root chord length
23. Which missile has 8 control surfaces?
   a) Stunner
   b) Stinger
   c) JASSM
   d) Kitchen
24. A disadvantage of tail control for a statically stable missile is
   a) less efficient packaging of flight control actuators
   b) higher hinge moment/actuator torque
   c) less tail lift
   d) higher induced rolling moment
25. Which missile has tail control?
   a) Derby
   b) Mistral
   c) Mica
   d) U-Darter
26. Which missile has canard control?
   a) FSAS Aster
   b) Rapier 2000
   c) SD-10
   d) Python 5
27. An advantage of wing control is
   a) lower body rotation
   b) more efficient actuator packaging
   c) lower hinge moment/actuator torque
   d) lower induced rolling moment
28. Which missile has wing control?
   a) Sea Wolf
   b) Exocet
   c) Aspide
   d) Magic
29. The most popular type of TVC for tactical missiles is
   a) jet vane
   b) movable nozzle
   c) jet tab
   d) reaction jet
30. An advantage of a rolling airframe is
   a) higher maneuverability
   b) lower rate gyros

Name: _____

c) less sensitive to thrust misalignment
d) capability for two axis flight control

31. Which missile has a top inlet?
    a) Tomahawk
    b) CALCM
    c) RBS-15
    d) Storm Shadow

32. The lower limit for scramjet cruise is about
    a) Mach 5
    b) Mach 7
    c) Mach 8
    d) Mach 10

33. A turbojet compressor is powered by the
    a) combustor
    b) inlet
    c) nozzle
    d) turbine

34. A popular material for a subsonic tactical missile turbojet turbine is
    a) rhenium alloy
    b) single crystal nickel aluminide
    c) nickel super alloy
    d) ceramic matrix composite

35. Typical pressure ratio for a turbojet missile single stage axial compressor is about
    a) $p_3/p_2 \approx 1.6$
    b) $p_3/p_2 \approx 4$
    c) $p_3/p_2 \approx 8$
    d) $p_3/p_2 \approx 13$

36. Typical pressure ratio for a turbojet missile with a centrifugal $+2$ stage axial compressor is about
    a) $p_3/p_2 \approx 2$
    b) $p_3/p_2 \approx 3$
    c) $p_3/p_2 \approx 4$
    d) $p_3/p_2 \approx 8$

37. Which turbojet component typically has the highest efficiency?
    a) compressor
    b) nozzle
    c) inlet
    d) combustor

Name: _____

38. For which flight condition is the inlet free stream flow area A_0 approximately equal to the inlet capture area A_c?
    a) subsonic cruise
    b) transonic cruise
    c) supersonic cruise
    d) hypersonic cruise

39. A ramjet does not have the which component?
    a) inlet
    b) compressor
    c) combustor
    d) nozzle

40. Stoichiometric combustion of liquid hydrocarbon fuel occurs at a fuel-to-air ratio of about
    a) 6%
    b) 7%
    c) 8%
    d) 9%

41. For a supersonic ramjet with a combustor entrance Mach number $M = 0.1$, the ratio of the inlet throat area A_{IT} to the combustor entrance area A_3 should be equal to about
    a) 0.2
    b) 0.3
    c) 0.4
    d) 0.5

42. An example of a ramjet with higher cruise drag is
    a) integral rocket-ramjet
    b) aft drop-off booster ramjet
    c) podded ramjet
    d) forward booster ramjet

43. A country that does not have a supersonic air-breathing missile is
    a) United States
    b) United Kingdom
    c) France
    d) Russia

44. Which supersonic inlet typically has the best compromise of low drag, low pressure oscillation, and low start Mach number?
    a) external compression
    b) internal compression
    c) mixed compression
    d) none of the above

Name: _____

45. A ramjet inlet with an isentropic turning angle of 60 degrees is consistent with a flight Mach number of about
    a) Mach 1.2
    b) Mach 1.8
    c) Mach 3.6
    d) Mach 5.9

46. The fuel with the highest volumetric performance is
    a) JP-10
    b) boron
    c) HTPB
    d) aluminum

47. A typical value of solid propellant characteristic velocity is
    a) $c^* = 4200 \text{ ft/s}$
    b) $c^* = 5200 \text{ ft/s}$
    c) $c^* = 6200 \text{ ft/s}$
    d) $c^* = 7200 \text{ ft/s}$

48. A typical value of burn rate exponent is
    a) $n = 0.05$
    b) $n = 0.1$
    c) $n = 0.3$
    d) $n = 0.9$

49. A disadvantage of a bi-propellant gel motor compared to a solid propellant motor is
    a) higher toxicity
    b) lower specific impulse
    c) less available duty cycle
    d) less explosive safety

50. Which of the following is inconsistent with a minimum smoke propellant?
    a) ADN
    b) HMX
    c) RDX
    d) AP

51. A solid propellant rocket motor stored for 1 year at a temperature of 35 °Celsius will have a reduction on its lifetime of about
    a) 30%
    b) 40%
    c) 50%
    d) 60%

Name: _____

52. A disadvantage of a composite motor case is
    a) greater explosive sensitivity
    b) higher cost
    c) greater susceptibility to corrosion
    d) heavier weight

53. Which nozzle throat material would have the greatest erosion?
    a) silica/phenolic
    b) tungsten
    c) rhenium
    d) molybdenum

54. Weight density of missiles is about
    a) 0.02 lbm/in.^3
    b) 0.03 lbm/in.^3
    c) 0.04 lbm/in.^3
    d) 0.05 lbm/in.^3

55. Which typically requires the highest design factor of safety?
    a) captive carriage loads
    b) free flight loads
    c) pressure bottle
    d) thermal loads

56. Which is a machining manufacturing process?
    a) forge
    b) mill
    c) weld
    d) cast

57. A high parts count manufacturing process is
    a) filament wind
    b) pultrusion
    c) machine
    d) cast

58. A disadvantage of a steel motor case is
    a) greater susceptibility to buckling
    b) greater difficulty in joining to other materials
    c) higher cost
    d) lower maximum temperature

59. Which material has the highest modulus of elasticity?
    a) Kevlar fiber
    b) S-glass fiber
    c) carbon fiber
    d) steel

Name: _____

60. Which structural material has the highest allowable temperature?
    a) steel
    b) titanium
    c) graphite polyimide
    d) Inconel
61. Which material has the best insulation efficiency?
    a) silicone rubber
    b) teflon
    c) porous ceramic
    d) carbon/carbon
62. Thermal radiation is a function of
    a) temperature
    b) temperature^2
    c) temperature^3
    d) temperature^4
63. Which is least important in thermal stress?
    a) modulus of elasticity
    b) pressure load
    c) coefficient of thermal expansion
    d) temperature difference
64. Which has the lowest aerodynamic heating?
    a) nose tip
    b) surface leading edge
    c) upper body
    d) flare
65. Body structure weight fraction of tactical missile launch weight is about
    a) 4%
    b) 11%
    c) 22%
    d) 45%
66. A military standard procedure for captive loads calculation is
    a) MIL-A-8590
    b) MIL-A-8591
    c) MIL-A-8592
    d) MIL-A-8593
67. Solid propellant weight fraction of the total rocket motor weight is about
    a) 65%
    b) 83%

Name: _____

   c) 92%
   d) 96%

68. Compared to a composite motor case, a steel motor case is about
   a) 1.2 × heavier
   b) 1.5 × heavier
   c) 2 × heavier
   d) 6 × heavier

69. Infrared bandpass is best for which dome material?
   a) diamond
   b) zinc sulfide
   c) alon
   d) quartz

70. Which dome material has the lowest dielectric constant?
   a) pyroceram
   b) polyimide
   c) silicon nitride
   d) zinc sulfide

71. Compared to a thermal battery, advantages of a lithium battery include
   a) higher power density
   b) lower cost
   c) longer storage life
   d) higher energy density

72. Compared to an electromechanical actuator, a typical advantage of a cold gas pneumatic actuator is
   a) higher stall torque
   b) higher bandwidth
   c) higher reliability
   d) Lower cost

73. A point mass flight trajectory modeling has
   a) 3 degrees of freedom
   b) 4 degrees of freedom
   c) 5 degrees of freedom
   d) 6 degrees of freedom

74. For a 500 nm ramjet, the ratio of fuel weight to total missile weight at the beginning of cruise is about
   a) 30%
   b) 40%
   c) 50%
   d) 60%

Name: _____

75. In steady level flight
    a) thrust $\approx$ lift
    b) thrust $\approx$ weight
    c) drag $\approx$ weight
    d) none of the preceding

76. Which is false? A TVC missile has higher turn rate at
    a) higher thrust
    b) higher velocity
    c) lighter weight
    d) higher angle of attack

77. A ballistic flight trajectory has
    a) zero flight path angle
    b) zero acceleration
    c) zero angle of attack
    d) zero thrust

78. Proportional guidance divert distance is least sensitive to which parameter?
    a) seeker lock-on range
    b) effective navigation ratio
    c) missile velocity
    d) specific impulse

79. A constant bearing is easier for an intercept of a crossing target for
    a) a missile with high velocity
    b) a missile with high gimbal seeker
    c) a low speed target
    d) all of the above

Name: _____

Missile Design and System Engineering Short Course

CEU Final Quiz

Chapters 6 (Measures of Merit and Launch Platform Integration/ System Engineering), 7 (Sizing Examples), and 8 (Development Process)

1. The global annual average cloud cover is about
   a) 29%
   b) 43%
   c) 61%
   d) 69%
2. The atmospheric attenuation of a 10 GHz signal for clear weather is about
   a) 0.005 db/km
   b) 0.02 db/km
   c) 0.08 db/km
   d) 0.19 db/km
3. A "greenhouse" gas that attenuates an infrared signal through the atmosphere is
   a) H_2O
   b) O_3
   c) CO_2
   d) all of the above
4. A disadvantage of a synthetic aperture radar seeker compared to an infrared seeker is
   a) less capability in adverse weather
   b) shorter range
   c) limited Mach number
   d) lower technical maturity
5. A disadvantage of GPS/INS/data link guidance is
   a) less capability against moving target
   b) less capability in adverse weather
   c) heavier weight
   d) lower technical maturity
6. A typical advantage of a strapdown seeker compared to a gimbaled seeker is
   a) lower cost
   b) larger field of regard
   c) less susceptible to body bending error
   d) longer range

Name: _____

7. A scanning imaging infrared seeker has which advantage over a staring focal plane array seeker?
   a) field of view
   b) weight
   c) range
   d) performance in clutter

8. A subsonic airframe has maximum thermal emission at a wavelength of about
   a) 1 micron
   b) 4 micron
   c) 12 micron
   d) 29 micron

9. A disadvantage of a mmW seeker compared to a cmW seeker is
   a) resolution
   b) atmospheric attenuation
   c) performance in clutter
   d) bandwidth

10. Following midcourse guidance with seeker lock-on against a 10 m/s target, a target location error of 10 m requires a data link update rate of about
    a) 1 s
    b) 2 s
    c) 5 s
    d) 10 s

11. Optimum cruise altitude for a Mach 4 ramjet is about
    a) sea level
    b) 40,000 ft
    c) 80,000 ft
    d) 120,000 ft

12. Which has the least variation with altitude?
    a) temperature
    b) speed of sound
    c) pressure
    d) density

13. Typical EMD uncertainty in flight performance is about
    a) $+/-2\%$, 1σ
    b) $+/-5\%$, 1σ
    c) $+/-10\%$, 1σ
    d) $+/-20\%$, 1σ

14. A GPS guidance counter-countermeasure is
    a) pseudolite
    b) differential

Name: _____

   c) integrated GPS/INS
   d) all of the above
15. Which missile has an ARH-mmW seeker?
   a) AARGM
   b) HARM
   c) ARMAT
   d) Armiger
16. Which warhead is typically the least effective against a tank?
   a) shaped charge
   b) EFP
   c) blast frag
   d) KE
17. The warhead blast scaling parameter z is which function of distance from the center of explosion r and explosive charge weight c?
   a) $r/c^{1/4}$
   b) $r/c^{1/3}$
   c) $r/c^{1/2}$
   d) $r/c^{2/3}$
18. Which warhead is least representative of a cylindrical distribution of fragments?
   a) preformed fragments
   b) continuous rod
   c) smooth case
   d) multi-p charge
19. Maximum fragment total kinetic energy occurs for a charge-to-metal ratio of about
   a) 0.5
   b) 1
   c) 2
   d) 5
20. Compared to TNT, HMX explosive energy is greater by about
   a) 30%
   b) 40%
   c) 50%
   d) 60%
21. Kinetic energy is a function of
   a) Velocity
   b) Velocity^2
   c) Velocity^3
   d) Velocity^4
22. An approach to minimize collateral damage of a blast fragmentation warhead is
   a) high charge-to-metal ratio

Name: _____

b) light weight fragments
c) low density case
d) all of the above

23. An equation for proximity fuze angle is
   a) $\sin^{-1}[V_{fragment}/(V_{closing})_{max}]$
   b) $\tan^{-1}[V_{fragment}/(V_{closing})_{max}]$
   c) $\cos^{-1}[V_{fragment}/(V_{closing})_{max}]$
   d) $\cot^{-1}[V_{fragment}/(V_{closing})_{max}]$

24. An equation for proximity fuze time delay is
   a) $\sigma/(V_{closing}\cos\theta)$
   b) $\sigma/(V_{closing}\sin\theta)$
   c) $\sigma/(V_{closing}\cot\theta)$
   d) $\sigma/(V_{closing}\tan\theta)$

25. A disadvantage of command guidance is
   a) higher missile cost
   b) greater sensitivity to countermeasures
   c) lower launch platform survivability
   d) less capability for fire control system update

26. The probability of a 1σ miss distance is about
   a) 43%
   b) 50%
   c) 57%
   d) 68%

27. Which increases the effective navigation ratio of proportional guidance?
   a) higher missile velocity
   b) lower missile lead angle
   c) lower closing velocity
   d) all of the above

28. The missile time constant τ is the elapsed time to complete which fraction of the commanded maneuver acceleration?
   a) 63%
   b) 75%
   c) 95%
   d) 99%

29. Radome error slope is lowest for a nose fineness ratio of
   a) $l_N/d = 0.2$
   b) $l_N/d = 0.5$
   c) $l_N/d = 1$
   d) $l_N/d = 5$

Name: _____

30. Miss distance contribution due to initial heading error is typically lowest for a proportional guidance effective navigation ratio of
    a) $N' = 1$
    b) $N' = 2$
    c) $N' = 4$
    d) $N' = 6$

31. For a missile with proportional guidance effective navigation ratio $N' = 2.5$ intercepting a target that has a step maneuver acceleration n_T, the missile maneuver acceleration n_M must be at least
    a) $n_M > 2\, n_T$
    b) $n_M > 3\, n_T$
    c) $n_M > 5\, n_T$
    d) $n_M > 8\, n_T$

32. The adjoint miss distance equation for a weaving target is given by
    a) $\sigma_{\text{Weave}} = g n_T \tau^2 (\omega\tau)^{N'-1}/[1 + (\omega\tau)^2]^{N'/2}$
    b) $\sigma_{\text{Weave}} = g n_T \tau^2 (\omega\tau)^{N'-2}/[1 + (\omega\tau)^2]^{N'/2}$
    c) $\sigma_{\text{Weave}} = g n_T \tau^2 (\omega\tau)^{N'}/[1 + (\omega\tau)^2]^{N'/2}$
    d) $\sigma_{\text{Weave}} = g n_T \tau^2 (\omega\tau)^{N'+1}/[1 + (\omega\tau)^2]^{N'/2}$

33. Glint contribution to miss distance is typically lowest for a proportional guidance effective navigation ratio of
    a) $N' = 3$
    b) $N' = 4$
    c) $N' = 5$
    d) $N' = 6$

34. A solid rocket motor contrail (H_2O) occurs at an atmospheric temperature of about
    a) $-35°F$
    b) $-20°F$
    c) $0°F$
    d) $32°F$

35. Radar transmitter power required for target detection is which function of target radar cross section?
    a) σ^{-4}
    b) σ^{-3}
    c) σ^{-2}
    d) σ^{-1}

36. Which is usually not applicable for conceptual design prediction methods of RCS?
    a) target in free space (no ground effect)
    b) perfectly conducting target surfaces

Name: _____

c) target dimensions less than wavelength

d) target components add in random phase

37. The greatest contribution to the frontal RCS of the ramjet baseline missile is

   a) nose

   b) seeker

   c) inlet

   d) tails

38. Which is the characteristic rise time of a detonation?

   a) $\sim 2 \times 10^{-6}$ s

   b) $\sim 2 \times 10^{-5}$ s

   c) $\sim 2 \times 10^{-4}$ s

   d) $\sim 2 \times 10^{-3}$ s

39. Reliability is a function of

   a) parts count

   b) environment

   c) time of flight

   d) all of the above

40. Which is typically the lowest cost subsystem for a missile?

   a) seeker

   b) structure

   c) electronics

   d) propulsion

41. A typical duration of a moderate risk tactical missile EMD program is about

   a) 2 years

   b) 3 years

   c) 5 years

   d) 7 years

42. For production with an 80% learning curve ($L = 0.8$), doubling the number of units produced decreases the unit production cost by about

   a) 2%

   b) 5%

   c) 10%

   d) 20%

43. World-wide military/aerospace semiconductor sales are about which fraction of the total world-wide market?

   a) 1%

   b) 3%

   c) 8%

   d) 19%

Name: _____

44. A 50% reduction in parts count reduces production cost by about
    a) 8%
    b) 15%
    c) 21%
    d) 50%
45. The number of MEMS devices that are typically produced on a 5 in silicon wafer is about
    a) 30
    b) 300
    c) 3000
    d) 30000
46. Which launch platform has the greatest weight constraint for a guided weapon?
    a) tank
    b) helicopter
    c) submarine
    d) fighter aircraft
47. The rocket plume lateral boundary is which function of thrust T and free stream dynamic pressure q_∞?
    a) $(T/q_\infty)^{1/3}$
    b) $(T/q_\infty)^{1/2}$
    c) $(T/q_\infty)^{2/3}$
    d) (T/q_∞)
48. Which is an aircraft store compatibility wind tunnel test?
    a) flow field
    b) captive trajectory
    c) drop
    d) all of the above
49. An aircraft store suspension lug spacing of either 14 in or 30 in may be used for ejection launch of stores with weight between
    a) 101 to 250 lb
    b) 101 to 550 lb
    c) 101 to 1450 lb
    d) 101 to 2050 lb
50. Which missile uses the LAU-7 rail launcher?
    a) Maverick
    b) Sidewinder
    c) Hellfire
    d) Sparrow

Name: _____

51. Which launcher provides an adjustable pitch rate for AMRAAM?
    a) LAU-106/A
    b) LAU-142/A
    c) BRU-33/A
    d) BRU-69/A

52. The CBU-87/CEB Longshot kit provides compressed carriage through
    a) small span
    b) folded surfaces
    c) extended surfaces
    d) wrap around surfaces

53. Which is an aircraft carriage and fore control avionics interface?
    a) MIL-STD-1760
    b) MIL-STD-1553
    c) NATO STANAG 3837
    d) all of the above

54. Which missile uses laser command guidance?
    a) RBS-70
    b) Roland
    c) TOW
    d) BILL

55. Which missile does not use semi-active guidance?
    a) AMRAAM
    b) Sea Dart
    c) Laser Maverick
    d) Sparrow

56. How many VLS canister cells are there in a module?
    a) 4
    b) 8
    c) 12
    d) 16

57. A typical missile environmental maximum temperature specification is
    a) 120°F
    b) 130°F
    c) 160°F
    d) 180°F

58. A typical missile cold temperature specification is
    a) −30°F
    b) −40°F
    c) −50°F
    d) −60°F

Name: _____

59. Maximum solar radiation at "high noon" in a clear desert environment is about
    a) 155 BTU/ft^2/h
    b) 255 BTU/ft^2/h
    c) 355 BTU/ft^2/h
    d) 455 BTU/ft^2/h

60. The F-pole is the distance from the launch aircraft to the target when the
    a) missile impacts the target
    b) missile begins active guidance
    c) target begins evasive maneuvers
    d) target has turned 90 deg

61. Visual threshold contrast for detection is about
    a) 2%
    b) 3%
    c) 4%
    d) 5%

62. The rocket baseline missile radome is made of which material?
    a) silicon nitride
    b) slip cast silica
    c) pyroceram
    d) zinc sulfide

63. The rocket baseline missile body airframe is which material?
    a) titanium
    b) aluminum
    c) steel
    d) composite

64. The rocket baseline rocket motor case is which material?
    a) aluminum
    b) graphite composite
    c) steel
    d) inconel

65. Which typically provides the greatest sensitivity to the rocket baseline missile flight range?
    a) propellant weight
    b) specific impulse
    c) zero-lift drag coefficient
    d) static margin

66. The ramjet baseline missile airframe is which material?
    a) aluminum
    b) steel

Name: _____

c) titanium

d) composite

67. Maximum specific impulse of the ramjet baseline occurs at about

a) Mach 2

b) Mach 2.5

c) Mach 3

d) Mach 3.5

68. Which fuel provides the longest cruise range for the ramjet baseline?

a) RJ-5

b) JP-10

c) boron

d) JP-10/boron

69. The compressor for the turbojet baseline missile has

a) two stages

b) three stages

c) four stages

d) five stages

70. $(L/D)_{max}$ of the turbojet baseline missile occurs at an angle of attack of about

a) 8 deg

b) 10 deg

c) 12 deg

d) 14 deg

71. What is the maximum temperature of the turbojet baseline missile combustor?

a) 1800 R

b) 2000 R

c) 2200 R

d) 2400 R

72. The turbojet baseline missile flight range is most sensitive to which parameter?

a) fuel weight

b) specific impulse

c) inert weight

d) thrust

73. Compared to a preliminary design code, a conceptual design code typically has

a) faster turnaround time

b) physics-based methods

Name: _____

  c) more stable computation
  d) all of the preceding
74. The baseline soda straw rocket has a launch acceleration of about
  a) 8 g
  b) 56 g
  c) 221 g
  d) 318 g
75. The far left column of the House of Quality is
  a) customer importance rating
  b) customer requirements
  c) design characteristics
  d) design characteristics importance rating
76. The number of required designs for a DOE full factorial study with k parameters and l levels is
  a) $1 + k(l - 1)$
  b) $1 + k(l + 1)$
  c) $1 + kl$
  d) l^k
77. A DOE parametric study with k = 4 parameters and l = 2 levels requires how many designs?
  a) 3
  b) 4
  c) 5
  d) 6
78. EMD occurs before
  a) ACTD
  b) DemVal
  c) PDRR
  d) none of the preceding
79. US DoD RT&A expenditure on tactical missiles is what fraction of the US DoD total RT&A budget?
  a) 11%
  b) 16%
  c) 23%
  d) 28%
80. Which category is 6.4 funding?
  a) basic research
  b) exploratory development
  c) prototype demonstration
  d) advanced technology demonstration

Name: _____

81. The introduction of which missile led to the space race?
    a) R-7
    b) Atlas
    c) Polaris
    d) Titan

82. Which mission had the first application of laser guidance?
    a) air-to-air
    b) air-to-surface
    c) surface-to-air
    d) surface-to-surface

83. Which was the most important consideration in replacing AGM-130 with JASSM?
    a) higher reliability
    b) longer range
    c) better accuracy
    d) better capability in adverse weather

84. From the year 1985 to 1997, the number of US missile development contractors was reduced from 12 to
    a) 6
    b) 5
    c) 4
    d) 3

85. A flight test program with 10 kills for 10 shots has a P_K lower limit of the 95% confidence interval of
    a) $P_K = 0.7$
    b) $P_K = 0.8$
    c) $P_K = 0.9$
    d) $P_K = 0.95$

86. Which is not a preliminary design prediction method for missile aerodynamics?
    a) OTIS
    b) DATCOM
    c) SUPL
    d) AP09

Appendix H

Design Case Studies

The following seven missile design case studies were conducted by Georgia Tech aerospace engineering students during the years 1999–2005. These are available on the website in support of this textbook.

- Future Target Delivery System
- Boost Phase Interceptor
- High Speed Standoff Missile
- Multi-mission Cruise Missile
- Sea Based Missile Defense Interceptor
- Ship Launched Cruise Missile
- Ship Launched Ramjet Cruise Missile

Appendix I

Summary of Tactical Missile Design Spreadsheet

I.1 Help/User's/Installation Guide for the Tactical Missile Design Spreadsheet

Developed by:
Gene Fleeman
Andrew Frits
Jack Zentner
at the
Aerospace Systems Design Laboratory
School of Aerospace Engineering
Georgia Institute of Technology
Atlanta, GA 30332

Contact Information:
Eugene L. Fleeman
4472 Anne Arundel Court
Lilburn, GA 30047

Email: GeneFleeman@msn.com
Phone: (770) 925-4635

I.2 Installing/Opening

Note that the Tactical Missile Design Spreadsheet (TMD) is NOT a stand-alone program. It is a file that is designed to be run via Microsoft Excel 97, or any later versions of Excel. Microsoft Excel does not come with this software package, and must be purchased, licensed, and installed by the user.

To Operate the TMD Spreadsheet:

First, open Microsoft Excel 97 by clicking on the appropriate icon in the start menu or run the excel executable: Excel.exe

Second, go to the "file" pull-down menu, then "open," browse through your computer's file structure until you find the appropriate file named: TMDv1_0.xls (it should be on the CD-ROM drive if the TMD CD is inserted in your machine)

Double click on this file to open it.

A warning message may pop up, saying, "The workbook you are opening contains macros. Some macros contain viruses that may be harmful to your computer." You should click on "Enable Macros." The TMD spreadsheet will not run correctly if macros are not enabled.

When the spreadsheet opens, it should be at the "Master Input" page. Other pages can be viewed by simply clicking on the page tab at the bottom of the excel window. All input should be handled at the "Master Input" page.

Important Note: This spreadsheet uses circular cell references (i.e., a cell that calls itself) for some of its computations. In order for the circular reference to work properly, your Excel system must be set up so that it will iterate to solutions. Upon loading the file, this should be done automatically. However, opening other files while the TMD spreadsheet is open may actually turn iterations off. To check to see if Excel is set up to handle iterations appropriately to run the TMD spreadsheet, do the following steps:

1. Go to the "Tools" pull-down menu.
2. Select "Options."
3. A new window should appear. The window has tabs near the top, select the tab that is called: "Calculation."
4. See that "Iteration" is checked. If it is not checked, click on the white box to the left in order to activate it.
5. Set a "Maximum iterations." This should be set to at least 50.
6. Set the "Maximum change." 0.0001 is a good number for the maximum change.

These steps should ensure that the TMD spreadsheet will handle circular references correctly.

I.3   Using the Tactical Missile Design Spreadsheet

All inputs should be made to the "Master Input" sheet. Inputs are entered into the blue-colored fields, with the appropriate units specified. Some small menus are included so that the user may select discrete values, such as engine type, fuel type, etc. Note that some combinations of items will not work. For example, selecting a Ramjet with a Mach number of 0.5 will not work. Warnings to this effect will be printed, or, in some cases, the output will have errors such as: #value, #div/0.

Variable names listed in the "Master Input" sheet are not used in the spreadsheet (each individual analysis will often re-define the variable name in a text-form). The variable name on the "Master Input" page matches the text, and is used to help the user correlate the text-examples and equations with the TMD spreadsheet.

The values of two example systems are included, a baseline rocket and a baseline ramjet system. These numbers and results should match those given in Gene Fleeman's Text: "Tactical Missile Design". These numbers make a good starting point for any design.

Each analysis type is made on a separate Excel Sheet (structures, aerodynamics, etc). Each page is linked to the Master Input page, and is linked to output from other pages via the Master Output page. For example, the aerodynamics sheet uses the body minor diameter and major diameter (linked from the Master Input Page) to calculate the missile reference area. This reference area is then sent to the Master Output page, where it is used by the trajectory and propulsion pages for additional calculations.

The three analysis sheets that are intricately linked together are the aerodynamics, propulsion, and trajectory. These three sheets work together to take an initial aircraft geometry, propulsion system, and initial conditions to fly an appropriately sized missile. The system assumes that it is a co-altitude flight (i.e., the missile does not change altitude). Further, there are three stages to the flight:

Boost
Sustain
Coast

The boost stage uses a rocket engine (as specified by the propulsion inputs), with a specified boost fuel weight and burn time. The sustain phase can use a number of engines: rocket, ramjet, scramjet, etc. Note, however, that currently only a ramjet or a rocket type engine can be analyzed. Any other type of engine simply uses a look-up table for Isp. For rockets, only a constant thrust solid rocket system can be used, there is no adjustable grain geometry/variable thrust profiles. However, the user can have one thrust level for the boost motor and a different thrust level for the sustain motor, essentially creating a two-level constant thrust system (this is the thrust profile of the baseline rocket used in the Tactical Missile Design text). The coast stage has no thrust, it simply calculates the drag for a co-altitude coast, stopping when the Mach number reaches the "Terminal Mach Number" Criteria. This trajectory analysis allows the user to get a preliminary range and time-to-target for a given missile system.

The other sheets have output that is not linked to the trajectory module. These are stand-alone analyses that can be used to get estimates for motor case weights, temperature loads, warhead effectiveness, and other measures of merit. Again, the user should be aware that these outputs are not used by the integrated trajectory analysis. Important parameters for the trajectory analysis, including the empty weight (inputted as launch weight) must be input by the designer, though the designer may use some elements of the warhead/structural analysis to give him/her a better estimate of the empty weight.

Output may be viewed via three mechanisms:

First, the Master Output sheet has key output from many of the sheets. It also contains all of the values that are linked between sheets.

Second, the Summary sheet has a summary of the trajectory output. It gives the stage-by-stage range, weight, etc. It also has plots of Mach number and range versus time for each flight stage.

Third, individual analysis sheets have a lot of important data. They have numbers that are not included in the limited numbers on the Master Output sheet. The individual analysis sheets also have a lot of additional plots and charts.

The individual analyses are done, whenever possible, such that they closely follow the methodology illustrated in the "Tactical Missile Design" text. Example cases from the textbook should give results that are similar to those given in the text.

A Note on Printing: Most of the spreadsheets are wider than the width of paper. After printing the user will probably need to go to the computer screen as an aid in assembling the printout. The computer screen shows the edges of each page as a dashed line.

Warning: Often you will receive the following message: "Not enough system resources to display completely." This is a common error that excel has when it runs this spreadsheet. If you get this warning, simply hit "ok" and ignore it.

I.4   MAKING CHANGES

All of the sheets, with the exception of the Master Input sheets, are write- protected. This allows the user to change the input parameters and look at the results of the individual sheets, without the fear of accidentally altering the spreadsheet. The user is free to make changes wherever he/she feels is appropriate, and tailor the TMD spreadsheet to meet individual user needs. However, the responsibility of the results from any changes in the spreadsheet rests with the user. A sheet can be unprotected by selecting the "Tools" pull-down menu, selecting "Protection," and then selecting "Unprotect sheet."

When altering or adding analysis sheets, note the way that the current system is set-up. Each analysis only has links to the "Master Input" and "Master Output" sheets. This prevents a lot of invisible cross-linking by making all of the important numbers flow through the same choke points. Also note that each sheet, generally on the left hand side, has a listing of all the variables used in the analysis. These variables are often nothing more than links to the "Master Input" and "Master Output," however, by having a copy of all the important numbers on the analysis page, it further assists in cutting down on the number of cross-links between different analysis sheets of the TMD spreadsheet.

Here is an example of the way an analysis sheet is generally set up:

Inputs	Calculations
Linked to Master Input	Equations that use only the inputs on the left
Linked to Master Output	
Outputs	**Figures**
Output values are copies from results of the calculations	Figures are placed throughout the sheet
Linked to Master Output	

I.5   Question/Comments

Please direct any questions or comments regarding the Tactical Missile Sizing Spreadsheet and the text to Mr. Gene Fleeman. See his contact information above.

Sincerely,

Andrew P. Frits

Jack Zentner

– Spreadsheet implementers

I.6   Tactical Missile Design Spreadsheet Enhancement Proposal

I.6.1   Research Objective

The objective of the research proposed is to update a simple physics-based tool for rapid sizing of tactical missiles. The tool is based on the design methods from the AIAA textbook *Tactical Missile Design, 1st Edition.*

I.6.2   Proposed Work

An updated design tool based on verification and validation of the methods from the *Missile Design and System Engineering* textbook and short course. This tool provides an integrated sizing and synthesis environment for missile design that predicts missile aerodynamics, propulsion, weight, and flight performance. The environment will incorporate the analysis of the main disciplines involved with missile design through the use of physics-based formulations. The activity will extend the methods of the existing spreadsheet tool and also provide a MATLAB version of the tool. Extended prediction methods will include additional propulsion (turbojet), additional flight modes (climb, descent, ballistic, turn), additional measures of merit, and updated prediction methods. The verification process will include comparing the source code with the original algorithms and comparing results with other computer codes. The validation process will include comparing the results with test data. Test data will include wind tunnel data, propulsion test data, subsystem weight data, missile launch and burnout weight data, and missile flight performance data. Validation will be based on available unclassified data for existing missiles and launch systems. The deliverable will be an updated Microsoft Excel spreadsheet and a MATLAB computer code.

Soda Straw Rocket Science

Soda Straw Rocket Science is an aerospace program to demonstrate the physics of flight and development using a small air rocket. Up to eighteen projects introduce students and their teachers to the aerospace environment—including the design, build, and fly process; teamwork; and competition. Additional information is available in the presentation on the website in support of this textbook and the website http://genefleeman.home. mindspring.com/

The initial idea to design, build, and fly a small air rocket first came to me several years ago as an activity for my grandchildren, who at that time were ages 4 and 7. We built the rocket launcher from pipe fittings, an air pressure gauge, a gas valve, an air supply hose, and a water filter tank. The rockets were constructed from soda straws, ear plugs, and adhesive filing tabs. My grandchildren found that launching their rockets was not only fun, but also interesting to try different launch angles, launch pressures, and rocket designs. After that, word got around and I was asked to participate in local school classroom, Cub Scout, and science camp programs. Small air rockets are particularly suitable as aerospace outreach—the process of designing, building, and flying the air rockets is a good introduction to the aerospace environment.

As an aerospace outreach program for students and their teachers, the program introduces them to an aerospace environment. Attributes include:

- Introduces the design, build, and fly process, a fundamental process of aerospace systems development
- Incorporates teamwork, an essential part of aerospace systems development
- Illustrates the competitive nature of aerospace systems
- Is exciting and fun—capturing interest from kindergarten students to adults

Other potential alternatives to using small air rockets include Estes-type hot exhaust rockets and water rockets. The Estes-type rocket is more spectacular—with fire, smoke, noise, and higher performance. However, it can only be launched outside the classroom in a large space to be safe. Another disadvantage is the student has less insight into the physics of the rocket. A water rocket is also spectacular and is great fun to launch. However, it is messy and also has less insight into the physics of the rocket. The small air rocket of this program is safe, clean, and can be launched inside the classroom if necessary. The range can be directly controlled by the chamber pressure, launch angle, and rocket design. Students are introduced to the experimental and theoretical physics of thrust, total impulse, boost velocity, drag, vertical impact velocity, and flight trajectory. These are easily predicted with simple physics equations and can be easily confirmed with ground/flight test data. For these reasons, a soda straw air rocket was selected.

The aerospace outreach program for the soda straw rocket has been conducted with grades K-12+ students. As a pre-school student program, it is a one-hour activity that can be held either entirely in the classroom or partly inside/partly outside the classroom. It begins with a ten-minute presentation of six videos of rockets, ranging from the large Saturn V moon rocket to the small soda straw rocket, followed by questions. Next the students are shown how to build a soda straw rocket. It usually takes about twenty minutes for them to build their rockets. During the last twenty minutes they launch their rockets.

The elementary school program may be a slightly longer (e.g., $1\frac{1}{2}$ hour) activity, similar to the pre-school activity. The presentation includes the history of rockets, including rockets developed by the early Chinese, Dr. Goddard, Dr. von Braun, and Mr. Korolev.

For middle school science camp, the program may be expanded to three hours, with one hour each day. The first day may include a presentation and construction of launchers/test stands. The thirty-minute presentation addresses the history of rockets, videos, Galileo's gravity hypothesis, Newton's 2nd law, design parameters, the scientific method, how to build a soda straw rocket, how to build a launcher/test stand, and how to conduct tests. Following questions on the presentation the students may build launchers/test stands. The total cost of materials for a launcher, wind tunnel test stand, and a thrust test stand is about $100. Assembly of the launcher/test stands requires that the students pay attention to detail, to build equipment with minimal pressure leaks.

In the second day, the middle school students may build their soda straw rockets, conduct static thrust tests, and conduct wind tunnel tests. The students may conduct static thrust tests by measuring the force ($\sim$1 pound) in restraining a pressurized rocket. A pressure regulator is included in the static thrust tests to provide nearly constant thrust during blow down. Following static thrust tests, the students may conduct wind tunnel tests in a $\frac{3}{4}$ inch vertical exit pipe. Each soda straw rocket is suspended nose down into a vertical pipe and the gauge pressure is noted when the soda straw rocket first rises from the pipe (drag = weight). This provides an estimate of the flight dynamic pressure and drag coefficient. If funds are available, a low cost, kid-friendly, rugged digital movie camera is useful for data analysis.

The third day may begin with a demonstration of the flight trajectories of different types of rockets (e.g., rockets with canards, wings, different size tails). The students then conduct flight tests of their rockets to determine the maximum range. Again, a digital video camera is useful, but not required, for data analysis. Following flight tests and if additional time is available, the students may return to the classroom to perform calculations of predicted thrust, dynamic pressure, and drag coefficient. Students can also compare predicted results with the test data and present posters of their results. Prizes may be awarded to the students based on the quality of their presentations and the flight performance of their rockets.

In summary, a design, build, and fly program based on a small air rocket is a cost effective approach to aerospace outreach. As an aerospace outreach program to students and their teachers, it is educational, fun, safe, and low cost.

Georgia Tech Science Camp for Middle School Girls

Soda Straw Rocket Science Projects can be downloaded from
http://genefleeman.home.mindspring.com/

REFERENCES

[1] "Missile.index," http://missile.index.ne.jp/en/

[2] Nicholas, T. and Rossi, R., "US Missile Data Book, 1999," Data Search Associates, 1999.

[3] AIAA Aerospace Design Engineers Guide, American Institute of Aeronautics and Astronautics, 1993.

[4] Bonney, E. A. et al., *Aerodynamics, Propulsion, Structures, and Design Practice*, "Principles of Guided Missile Design", D. Van Nostrand Company, Inc., 1956.

[5] Jerger, J. J., *Systems Preliminary Design Principles of Guided Missile Design*, "Principles of Guided Missile Design", D. Van Nostrand Company, Inc., 1960.

[6] Chin, S. S., *Missile Configuration Design*, McGraw-Hill Book Company, 1961.

[7] Mason, L. A., Devan, L. and Moore, F. G., "Aerodynamic Design Manual for Tactical Weapons," NSWCTR 81–156, 1981.

[8] Pitts, W. C., Nielsen, J. N. and Kaattari, G. E., "Lift and Center of Pressure of Wing-Body-Tail Combinations at Subsonic, Transonic, and Supersonic Speeds," NACA Report 1307, 1957.

[9] Jorgensen, L. H., "Prediction of Static Aerodynamic Characteristics for Space-Shuttle-Like, and Other Bodies at Angles of Attack From $0°$ to $180°$," NASA TND 6996, January 1973.

[10] Hoak, D. E. et al., "USAF Stability and Control DATCOM," AFWAL TR-83-3048, Global Engineering, 1978.

[11] "Nielsen Engineering & Research (NEAR) Aerodynamic Software Products," http://www.nearinc.com/near/software.htm.

[12] Brebner, G. G., "The Control of Missiles," AGARD-LS-98, February 1979.

[13] Durham, F. P., *Aircraft Jet Powerplants*, Prentice-Hall, 1961.

[14] Ashley, H., *Engineering Analysis of Flight Vehicles*, Dover Publications, Inc., 1974.

[15] Anderson, J. D., Jr., *Modern Compressible Flow*, Second Edition, McGraw Hill, 1990.

[16] Kinroth, G. D. and Anderson, W. R., "Ramjet Design Handbook," CPIA Pub. 319 and AFWAL TR 80-2003, June 1980.

[17] "Technical Aerodynamics Manual," North American Rockwell Corporation, DTIC AD 723823, June 1970.

[18] Oswatitsch, K. L., "Pressure Recovery for Missiles with Reaction Propulsion at High Supersonic Speeds", NACA TM-1140, 1947.

[19] Bithell, R. A. and Stoner, R. C., "Rapid Approach for Missile Synthesis," AFWAL TR 81-3022, March 1982.

[20] Carslaw, H. S. and Jaeger, J. C., *Conduction of Heat in Solids*, Clarendon Press, 1988.

[21] Grover, J. H. and Holter, W. H., "Solution of the Transient Heat Conduction Equation for an Insulated, Infinite Metal Slab," *Journal of Jet Propulsion*, Number 27, 1957.

[22] Allen, J. and Eggers, A. J., "A Study of the Motion and Aerodynamic Heating of Ballistic Missiles Entering the Earth's Atmosphere at High Supersonic Speeds", NACA Report 1381, April 1953.

[23] Levens, A. S., *Nomography*, John Wiley & Sons, 1937.

[24] Klein, L. A., *Millimeter-Wave and Infrared Multisensor Design and Signal Processing*, Artech House, Boston, 1997.

[25] Schneider, S. H., *Encyclopedia of Climate and Weather*, Oxford University Press, 1996.

[26] Richardson, M. A. et al. *Surveillance & Target Acquisition Systems*, Brassey's, London, 2000.

[27] US Army Ordnance Pamphlet ORDP-20-290-Warheads, 1980.

[28] Taylor, G. I., "The Formation of a Blast Wave by a Very Intense Explosion, Part I. Theoretical Discussion", *Proceedings of the Royal Society of London*, Vol. 201, March 1950.

[29] Carleone, J., *Tactical Missile Warheads*, "AIAA Vol. 155 Progress in Astronautics and Aeronautics," American Institute of Aeronautics and Astronautics, 1993.

[30] Christman, D. R. and Gehring, J. W., "Analysis of High-Velocity Projectile Penetration Mechanics," *Journal of Applied Physics*, Vol. 37, 1966.

[31] Heaston, R. J. and Smoots, C. W., "Precision Guided Munitions," GACIAC Report HB-83-01, May 1983.

[32] Bennett, R. R. and Mathews, W. E., "Analytical Determination of Miss Distances for Linear Homing Navigation Systems," Hughes Tech Memo 260, 31 March 1952.

[33] Zarchan, P., *Tactical and Strategic Missile Guidance*, Vol. 5, American Institute of Aeronautics and Astronautics, 2007.

[34] Crispin, J. W., Jr., Goodrich, R. F. and Siegel, K. M., "A Theoretical Method for the Calculation of the Radar Cross Section of Aircraft and Missiles," University of Michigan Report 2591-1-H, July 1959.

[35] Cengel, Y. A., *Heat and Mass Transfer: A Practical Approach*, McGraw-Hill, 2006.

[36] Jarvinen, P. O. and Hill, J. A. F., "Universal Model for Underexpanded Rocket Plumes in Hypersonic Flow", *Proceedings of the 12th JANAF Liquid Propulsion Meeting*, Nov. 1970.

[37] Hyperphysics, Georgia State University, http://hyperphysics.phy-astr.gsu.edu/Hbase/hph.html

[38] Fleeman, E. L. and Donatelli, G. A., "Conceptual Design Procedure Applied to a Typical Air-Launched Missile," AIAA 81-1688, August 1981.

[39] Teledyne Turbine Engines Brochure, "Model 370, J402-CA-400 Performance," 2006.

[40] St. Peter, J., *The History of Aircraft Gas Turbine Engine Development in the United States: A Tradition of Excellence*, ASME International Gas Turbine Institute, 1999.

[41] Hindes, J. W., "Advanced Design of Aerodynamic Missiles (ADAM)," October 1993.

[42] Fleeman, E. L., *Tactical Missile Design*, 2nd Edition, American Institute of Aeronautics and Astronautics, 2006.

[43] Donatelli, G. A. and Fleeman, E. L., "Methodology for Predicting Miss Distance for Air Launched Missiles," AIAA Paper 82-0364, Jan. 1982.

[44] Frits, A. P. et al. "A Conceptual Sizing Tool for Tactical Missiles," AIAA Missile Sciences Conference, November 2002.

[45] Montgomery, D. G., *Design and Analysis of Experiments*, John Wiley & Sons, 2001.

[46] Dixon, W. J. and Massey, F. J., *Introduction to Statistical Analysis*, McGraw-Hill, 1969.

[47] Bruns, K. D., Moore, M. E., Stoy, S. L., Vukelich, S. R. and Blake, W. B., "Missile DATCOM," AFWAL-TR-91-3039, April 1991.

[48] Moore, F. G. and Moore, L. Y., "The 2009 Version of the Aeroprediction Code", *AIAA 2009-309, AIAA Aerospace Sciences Meeting*, January 2009.

[49] Nicolai, L. M., "Designing a Better Engineer," AIAA Aerospace America, April 1992

[50] Boyd and John, R., "The Essence of Winning and Losing," January 1996.

BIBLIOGRAPHY OF OTHER REPORTS AND WEB SITES

System Design

"DoD Index of Specifications and Standards," http://stinet.dtic.mil/str/dodiss.html

"Periscope," http://www.periscope1.com/

Defense Technical Information Center, http://www.dtic.mil/

NATO Research & Technology Organisation, http://www.rta.nato.int/

"Missile System Flight Mechanics," AGARD CP270, May 1979.

Hogan, J. C., et al., "Missile Automated Design (MAD) Computer Program," AFRPL TR 80-21, March 1980.

Rapp, G. H., "Performance Improvements with Sidewinder Missile Airframe," AIAA Paper 79-0091, January 1979.

Nicolai, L. M., *Fundamentals of Aircraft Design*, METS, Inc., 1984.

Lindsey, G. H. and Redman, D. R., "Tactical Missile Design," Naval Postgraduate School, 1986.

Lee, R. G., et al. *Guided Weapons, Third Edition*, Brassey's, 1998.

Giragosian, P. A., "Rapid Synthesis for Evaluating Missile Maneuverability Parameters," *AIAA Paper 1992-2615, 10th AIAA Applied Aerodynamics Conference*, June 1992.

Fleeman, E. L. "Aeromechanics Technologies for Tactical and Strategic Guided Missiles," *AGARD Paper presented at FMP Meeting in London*, England, May 1979.

Raymer, D. P., *Aircraft Design, A Conceptual Approach*, American Institute of Aeronautics and Astronautics, 1989.

Ball, R. E., *The Fundamentals of Aircraft Combat Survivability Analysis and Design*, American Institute of Aeronautics and Astronautics, 1985.

"National Defense Preparedness Association Conference Presentations," http://www.dtic.mil/ndia

Eichblatt, E. J., *Test and Evaluation of the Tactical Missile*, American Institute of Aeronautics and Astronautics, 1989.

"Aircraft Stores Interface Manual (ASIM)," http://akss.dau.mil/software/1.jsp

"Advanced Sidewinder Missile AIM-9X Cost Analysis Requirements Description (CARD)," http://deskbook.dau.mil/jsp/default.jsp

Wertz, J. R. and Larson, W. J., *Space Mission Analysis and Design*, Microprism Press and Kluwer Academic Publishers, 1999.

"Directory of U.S. Military Rockets and Missiles", http://www.designation-systems.net/

Fleeman, E. L., et al. "Technologies for Future Precision Strike Missile Systems," NATO RTO EN-018, July 2001.

"The Ordnance Shop", http://www.ordnance.org/portal/

"Conversion Factors by Sandelius Instruments", http://www.sandelius.com/reference/conversions.htm

"Defense Acquisition Guidebook", http://akss.dau.mil/dag/

"Weaponry", http://www.deagel.com/

Puckett, A. E. and Ramo, S., *Guided Missile Engineering*, McGraw-Hill book Company, 1959.

Aerodynamics

"A Digital Library for NACA," http://naca.larc.nasa.gov/

Briggs, M. M., *Systematic Tactical Missile Design, Tactical Missile Aerodynamics: General Topics*, "AIAA Vol. 141 Progress in Astronautics and Aeronautics," American Institute of Aeronautics, 1992.

Briggs, M. M. et al., "Aeromechanics Survey and Evaluation, Vol. 1–3," NSWC/DL TR-3772, October 1977.

"Missile Aerodynamics," NATO AGARD LS-98, February 1979.

"Missile Aerodynamics," NATO AGARD CP-336, February 1983.

"Missile Aerodynamics," NATO AGARD CP-493, April 1990.

"Missile Aerodynamics," NATO RTO-MP-5, November 1998.

Nielsen, J. N., *Missile Aerodynamics*, McGraw-Hill Book Company, 1960.

Mendenhall, M. R., et al. "Proceedings of NEAR Conference on Missile Aerodynamics," NEAR, 1989.

Nielsen, J. N., "Missile Aerodynamics – Past, Present, Future," AIAA Paper 79-1818, 1979.

Dillenius, M. F. E., et al. "Engineering-, Intermediate-, and High-Level Aerodynamic Prediction Methods and Applications," *Journal of Spacecraft and Rockets*, Vol. 36, No. 5, September–October, 1999.

Nielsen, J. N. and Pitts, W. C., "Wing-Body Interference at Supersonic Speeds with an Application to Combinations with Rectangular Wings," NACA Tech. Note 2677, 1952.

Spreiter, J. R., "The Aerodynamic Forces on Slender Plane-and-Cruciform-Wing and Body Combinations", NACA Report 962, 1950.

Simon, J. M., et al., "Missile DATCOM: High Angle of Attack Capabilities, AIAA-99-4258.

Burns, K. A., et al., "Viscous Effects on Complex Configurations," WL-TR-95-3060, 1995.

Lesieutre, D., et al., "Recent Applications and Improvements to the Engineering-Level Aerodynamic Prediction Software MISL3," AIAA-2002-0274.

Moore, F. G., *Approximate Methods for Weapon Aerodynamics*, American Institute of Aeronautics and Astronautics, 2000.

"1976 Standard Atmosphere Calculator," http://www.digitaldutch.com/atmoscalc/

"Compressible Aerodynamics Calculator," http://www.aoe.vt.edu/~devenpor/aoe3114/calc.html

Ashley, H. and Landahl, M., *Aerodynamics of Wings and Bodies*, Dover Publications, 1965.

John, J. E. A., *Gas Dynamics*, Second Edition, Prentice Hall, 1984.

Zucker, R. D., *Fundamentals of Gas Dynamics*, Matrix Publishers, 1977.

Fleeman, E. L. and Nelson, R. C., "Aerodynamic Forces and Moments on a Slender Body with a Jet Plume for Angles of Attack up to 180 Degrees," AIAA-1974-110, Aerospace Sciences Meeting, 1974.

Propulsion

Chemical Information Propulsion Agency, http://www.cpia.jhu.edu/

Mahoney, J. J., *Inlets for Supersonic Missiles*, American Institute of Aeronautics and Astronautics, 1990.

Sutton, G. P., *Rocket Propulsion Elements*, John Wiley & Sons, 1986.

"Tri-Service Rocket Motor Trade-off Study, Missile Designer's Rocket Motor handbook," CPIA 322, May 1980.

Humble, R. W., Henry, G. N. and Larson, W. J., *Space Propulsion Analysis and Design*, McGraw-Hill, 1995.

Jenson, G. E. and Netzer, D. W., *Tactical Missile Propulsion*, American Institute of Aeronautics and Astronautics, 1996.

Bathie, W. W., *Fundamentals of Gas Turbines*, John Wiley and Sons, 1996.

Hill, P. G. and Peterson, C. R., *Mechanics and Thermodynamics of Propulsion*, Addison-Wesley Publishing Company, 1970.

Mattingly, J. D., et al., *Aircraft Engine Design*, American Institute of Aeronautics and Astronautics, 1987.

Materials and Heat Transfer

Budinski, K. G. and Budinski, M. K., *Engineering Materials Properties and Selection*, Prentice Hall, 1999.

"Matweb's Material Properties Index Page," http://www.matweb.com

"NASA Ames Research Center Thermal Protection Systems Expert (TPSX) and Material Properties Database", http://tpsx.arc.nasa.gov/tpsxhome.shtml

Harris, D. C., *Materials for Infrared Windows and Domes*, SPIE Optical Engineering Press, 1999.

Kalpakjian, S., *Manufacturing Processes for Engineering Materials*, Addison Wesley, 1997.

MIL-HDBK-5J, "Metallic Materials and Elements for Aerospace Vehicle Structures", January 2003.

"Metallic Material Properties Development and Standardization (MMPDS)", http://www.mmpds.org

Mallick, P. K., *Fiber-Reinforced Composites: Materials, Manufacturing, and Design*, Second Edition, Maecel Dekker, 1993.

Chapman, A. J., *Heat Transfer*, Third Edition, Macmillan Publishing Company, 1974.

Incropera, F. P. and DeWitt, D. P., *Fundamentals of Heat and Mass Transfer*, Fourth Edition, John Wiley and Sons, 1996.

Guidance, Navigation, Control, and Sensors

"Proceedings of AGARD G&C Conference on Guidance & Control of Tactical Missiles," AGARD LS-52, May 1972.

Garnell, P., *Guided Weapon Control Systems*, Pergamon Press, 1980.

Locke, A. S., *Guidance, Principles of Guided Missile Design*, D. Van Nostrand, 1955.

Blakelock, J. H., *Automatic Control of Aircraft and Missiles*, John Wiley & Sons, 1965.

Lawrence, A. L., *Modern Inertial Technology*, Springer, 1998.

Siouris, G. M., *Aerospace Avionics Systems*, Academic Press, 1993.

Stimson, G. W., *Introduction to Airborne Radar*, SciTech Publishing, 1998.

Lecomme, P., Hardange, J. P., Marchais, J. C. and Normant, E., *Air and Spaceborne Radar Systems*, SciTech Publishing and William Andrew Publishing, 2001.

Wehner, D. R., *High-Resolution Radar*, Artech House, Norwood, MA, 1995.

Donati, S., *Photodetectors*, Prentice-Hall, 2000.

Jha, A. R., *Infrared Technology*, John Wiley and Sons, 2000.

Schlessinger, M., *Infrared Technology Fundamentals*, Marcel Decker, 1995.

Skolnik, M. I., *Introduction to Radar Systems*, McGraw-Hill, 1980.

Hovanessian, S. A., *Radar Detection and Ranging Systems*, Artech House, 1973.

Moir, I. and Seavridge, A., *Military Avionics Systems*, American Institute of Aeronautics and Astronautics, 2006.

Mahafza, B. A., *Radar Systems Analysis and Design Using MATLAB®*, 2nd Edition, Chapman & Hall/CRC, 2005.

Wolf, W. L. and Zissis, G. J., *Infrared Handbook*, Environmental Research Institute of Michigan, 1985.

Hudson, R. D., *Infrared System Engineering*, John Wiley & Sons, 1969.

Shneydor, N. A., *Missile Guidance and Pursuit – Kinematics, Dynamics and Control*, Horwood Publishing, 1998.

James, D. A., *Radar Homing Guidance for Tactical Missiles*, Macmillan Education LTD, 1986.

INDEX

Note: Page numbers with f represent figures. Page numbers with t represent tables

SUPPORTING MATERIALS

To access the materials that accompany this work, please go to http://www.aiaa.org/books and click on the "Supporting Materials" link. Select this work from the list provided and enter the password

conceptual

when prompted.

Many of the topics introduced in this book are discussed in more detail in other AIAA publications. For a complete listing of titles in the AIAA Education Series, as well as other AIAA publications, please visit www.aiaa.org.

AIAA is committed to devoting resources to the education of both practicing and future aerospace professionals. In 1996, the AIAA Foundation was founded. Its programs enhance scientific literacy and advance the arts and sciences of aerospace.

For more information, please visit www. aiaafoundation.org.